PEARSON
HEALTH

Pruitt, Allegrante, Prothrow-Stith

Master essential health skills with these new features!

Updated highlights include

- Information on school violence

- MyPlate Food Guide

- Current information on building healthy relationships, including dating and online friendships

- Health and Human Services: Healthy People 2020 Goals

- Digital Courseware, including eTexts and online resources

- Up-to-date statistics and data throughout the program

Teacher's Edition

Glenview, Illinois • Boston, Massachusetts • Chandler, Arizona • Upper Saddle River, New Jersey

ALWAYS LEARNING

PEARSON

PEARSON HEALTH »» TEACHER'S EDITION

Print Resources

- Student Edition
- Teacher's Edition
- Reading and Note Taking Guide
- Answer Key for Reading and Note Taking Guides
- Human Sexuality
- Human Sexuality, Teacher's Edition

Technology Resources

Media Resources

- Discovery Education™ Teens Talk Video Series DVDs
- ExamView® Test Generator CD-ROM

Digital Courseware on PearsonSuccessNet.com

- Student Edition and Teacher's Edition eTexts with bilingual audio glossary*
- Human Sexuality Student Edition and Teacher's Edition eTexts*

*Available for PC, Mac, iPad with iOS 5 or greater, and Android tablets with Android OS 3.1 or greater

Editable Resources

- Teaching Resources:
  - Lesson Plans
  - Letter to Parents
  - Practice and Enrichment Worksheets
  - Section Quizzes
  - Chapter Tests
  - Answer Keys
- Reading and Note Taking Guide

- Adapted Reading and Note Taking Guide
- Video Viewing Guide With Worksheets

Spanish Resources

- Spanish Reading and Note Taking Guide
- Video Viewing Guide With Spanish Worksheets
- Audio Section Summaries in Spanish

Presentation Materials

- Image Bank with Editable Worksheets
- Chapter PowerPoint® Presentations, including Warm-Ups and Building Health Skills

Audio and Video Resources

- Discovery Education™ Teens Talk Videos
- Audio Section Summaries

Online Activities

- Web Links
- Chapter Review Activities
- Skills for Physical Fitness Worksheets

Additional Material

- Teacher Online Access Pack

Acknowledgments appear on p. 780, which constitutes an extension of this copyright page.

ISBN-13: 978-0-13-327511-7

ISBN-10: 0-13-327511-6

6   16

PEARSON

Brief Contents

Teacher's Edition

Student Edition

GO ONLINE
PearsonSuccessNet.com
For: Online activities and content updates

A Health Program
Backed by Research

In developing **Pearson Health**, research studies were used as a central, guiding element. Research identified key elements of a health program that ensure students' success—high-quality, current videos to address important health topics; consistent opportunities for teaching health skills; and support for reading, writing, and math.

Exploratory Research: Needs Assessment

Along with periodic surveys concerning state and national standards as well as curriculum issues and challenges, Pearson conducted specific product development research, which included discussions with teachers and advisory panels, focus groups, and quantitative surveys. Pearson explored the specific needs of teachers, students, and other educators regarding each component of the *Pearson Health* program.

Formative Research: Development and Field-Testing

During this phase of research, Pearson worked to develop prototype materials, then field-tested the materials with students and teachers, and performed qualitative and quantitative surveys. Early prototype testing resulted in feedback about the lesson structure. Results were channeled back into the development of the program.

Summative Research: Validation

Finally, Pearson continues to conduct long-term research based on scientific, experimental designs under actual classroom conditions. This research identifies what works and what can be improved upon in the next revision of *Pearson Health*. Pearson also continues to monitor the program in the market through ongoing dialogue with users. This allows us to perpetually refine our products and provide the best support for today's and tomorrow's teachers and students.

Dear Health Educator:

We're pleased to introduce an exciting new Health program from Pearson, *Pearson Health*. Our primary goal in creating this program was simple: to help students make informed decisions, the right decisions for optimum health.

But how do you reach today's savvy teens?

With other teens. The *Teens Talk Video Series* complements the textbook; in these 15-minute videos, which accompany every chapter, real teens confront real issues. Your students will immediately make connections between classroom learning and the decisions they and their peers face in the real world. Additional features built into the text to engage your students include Building Health Skills, Media Wise, and Focus on Issues. With these tools, you'll soon open up a lively forum for classroom discussions.

Make it easy for all students to understand and succeed.

Pearson's proven formula for reading success makes perfect sense in this text as well. Students will find reading support before, during, and after every lesson, helping to ensure they understand the topic before moving on. We also maintain a conversational writing style to engage your students with the topic.

And yes, there's that test to consider.

Each chapter includes numerous opportunities for practicing reading, writing, and math using health content so that students can conquer high-stakes tests. Like you, we want every student to learn the content and skills that will lead them to a lifetime of health, and we also want them to be prepared for the rigors of standardized testing that they will face in other subject areas.

We are excited about the opportunity to reach out to today's teens in hopes of having a positive impact on their health and lives. It's a goal we set at the beginning of this project and one that we think defines *Pearson Health*. Have a wonderful school year.

Sincerely,
B. E. Pruitt
John Allegrante
Deborah Prothrow-Stith

B. E. Pruitt, Ed.D.
Professor of Health Education
at Texas A&M University

John Allegrante, Ph.D.
Professor of Health Education and
Deputy Provost at Columbia University
Teachers College

Deborah Prothrow-Stith, M.D.
Consultant with Spencer Stuart and
Adjunct Professor of Practice at Harvard
School of Public Health

5 Things Teachers Can Do to Promote Sexual Abstinence

B. E. Pruitt

The health risks for youth who engage in sexual activity are serious. Sexually active teens are at risk for infections, reduced fertility, unwanted pregnancy, and early parenthood. They are also at risk for the emotional problems that arise from early sexual involvement. As health educators, our goal is to promote the physical, social, and mental well-being of our students. In the area of sexuality, our role is to help students avoid the health risks associated with sexual activity. There is widespread agreement among public health officials, family planning organizations, and parents that sexual abstinence is the safest, healthiest, and most appropriate way for teens to avoid these risks.

You can help your students make the decision to abstain from sexual activity by conveying a strong, consistent abstinence message. At the same time, you need to teach students the skills they need to put that message into action. The following five guidelines can help you achieve this goal in your classroom.

1 Make the Abstinence Message Part of a High-Quality Health Education

When sexual abstinence is taught in the context of a health education class that also teaches decision-making, communication, and refusal skills, abstinence is more likely to become accepted as another component of a healthy regimen for teens. Having students practice the skills needed for abstinence, in a class in which the primary goal is positive health and well-being, helps students understand that good health is influenced by many factors—including their sexual behavior.

2 Avoid Fear Tactics

Using fear tactics in the hope of discouraging teens from engaging in sexual behavior can backfire. Adolescents may respond to fear tactics with denial rather than with rational behavior change. Such tactics may encourage "It can't happen to me" thinking. Or students may rebel against what they view as an attempt by adults to control their behavior.

How can you avoid fear tactics while still impressing upon students the importance of postponing sexual activity? Portray abstinence as a positive behavior, rather than solely as a way to avoid the negative risks associated with premature sexual involvement. Convey to students that abstinence is a choice that enhances health, communicates respect for oneself and others, and expands life options. Inviting role models, such as abstinent older students, to speak with your class can be a very effective way to promote the positive side of abstinence.[1]

3 Normalize Abstinent Behavior

Given that the vast majority of prime-time shows on television contain sexual content, it is not surprising that teens think being sexually active is the norm. However, the facts do not support this belief. Surveys reveal that the percentage of teens who have had sexual intercourse has declined since 1993.[2] Despite what is portrayed in the media and what many teens may think, abstinence is the norm among younger teenagers and it is common among older teens as well.

By emphasizing that the majority of teens are abstinent, you can normalize abstinence and help students make positive choices to postpone sexual activity. Abstinent peer role models and videos that portray abstinent teens can help communicate this message to your students.

> *"Despite what many teens think, abstinence is the norm."*

What about students who already have been sexually active? Unfortunately, the topic of abstinence is often presented in a way that implies that abstinence is no longer an option for these teens. Stress that teens who have had sexual experiences in the past can choose not to engage in those same behaviors in the future. Teens who have had sexual experiences do not forfeit their future rights to abstain.

4 Avoid Ageist and Sexist Attitudes

The goal of promoting abstinence cannot be achieved if students feel demeaned or belittled. So it is important to avoid conveying ageist or sexist attitudes. An ageist point of view would suggest that adolescents are too young to be sexual. In fact, teens become acutely aware of their own sexuality during adolescence. To successfully promote abstinence, educators must recognize students as sexual beings and respect their feelings. At the same time, teachers must fulfill their obligation to improve student's awareness of the responsibilities and risks of sexual activity.

Implying that abstinence is normal for girls but that "boys will be boys" is a sexist attitude that normalizes traditional male-female power relationships. This approach can appear to justify sexual exploitation and the kind of thinking that often underlies date or acquaintance rape. A better approach is to emphasize the mutual responsibility of both people in a relationship to avoid sexual risks. A good way to do this is to have male and female students work together in groups to develop "dating rules" that emphasize mutual respect and responsibility.

5 Invite Family Participation

For most teens, parents and other family members are their primary sexuality educators—their primary source of information, values, and attitudes. In one study, adolescents who reported feeling connected to parents and family were more likely than other teens to delay sexual involvement.[3] Thus, by encouraging parental involvement, you can enhance students' success in postponing sexual activity.

Parental involvement can occur at three levels—at the program level, at the instructional level, and in the home.

▶ At the program level, parents should be involved in all decisions related to school health, including not only classroom health education, but also food services, guidance counseling, and physical education.

▶ At the instructional level, parents should be involved in the curriculum development process, both as developers and as reviewers. Providing review copies of all books, videos, and other materials that will be used in your course is a good start in involving parents. In some states, this review process is formalized by the existence of Health Education Advisory Councils, made up of parents and community leaders.

▶ In the home, parents can influence their children through both verbal and nonverbal communication of their values, beliefs, and attitudes about sexuality. Parental involvement in the lives of their children can result in the direct and immediate promotion of abstinence. Clearly-stated expectations and support for abstinent behavior at home will reinforce the abstinence message that students receive in the classroom.

References

1 Goodson, P.; Suther, S.; Pruitt, B.E.; and Wilson, K. (2003). Defining Abstinence: Views of Directors, Instructors, and Participants in Abstinence-only-until-marriage Programs in Texas. *Journal of School Health*, 73(3), 91–96.

2 Centers for Disease Control and Prevention. (2003) Youth Risk Behavior Survey Surveillance summary—United States, 2003, Morbidity and Mortality Weekly Report, May 2004, 53(2).

3 Resnick, M.D. et. al. (1997) Protecting Adolescents from Harm: Findings from the National Longitudinal Study on Adolescent Health. *Journal of the American Medical Association* 278: 823–32.

How Can Teachers Help Stem the Overweight Epidemic?

John P. Allegrante

Overweight in our youth is now considered to be an epidemic of crisis proportions. The number of overweight children and adolescents in the United States has tripled since 1980. Approximately 15 percent of the nation's children and adolescents are overweight, and another 15 percent are in danger of becoming overweight.

Beyond the difficulties that overweight adolescents may face during their teen years, they are also at risk of becoming overweight or obese adults. Health educators can help students avoid the health problems associated with excess weight in adolescence and adulthood by teaching the importance of developing lifelong habits of healthy eating and regular exercise.

Causes of the Epidemic

The causes of the epidemic are complex, but it is clear that many of today's teens consume too many calories and devote little, if any, time to physical activity. Regular consumption of high-fat, super-sized fast-food meals and sugary soft drinks contributes to bulging waistlines. Few teens have an accurate sense of how many calories they consume in a day, or how different types of foods may influence their health.

Many teens consistently choose sedentary activities such as watching television and playing computer games rather than activities that involve movement and physical exertion. In addition, most communities were not designed with physical activity in mind.

Health Implications

The implications of the overweight epidemic for the future of the public's health are daunting. Excessive weight is responsible for the rapid surge of type 2 diabetes in young people. Just a decade ago, type 2 diabetes was so rare in children that it was also known as adult-onset diabetes. Today, at least eight percent of newly diagnosed patients with type 2 diabetes are children. The disease can result in long-term medical complications, including nerve damage, blindness, kidney failure, and amputations. The nation's financial burden due to diabetes in 2012 was $245 billion and is expected to continue to rise.[1]

> *"Poor health and fitness have a negative impact on learning, school performance, and academic achievement."*

Being overweight also puts youth at risk for developing cardiovascular diseases early in life, including hypertension and high cholesterol. In addition, excessive weight stresses the skeletal system, which increases the risk of osteoarthritis in joints such as the hip and knee.

Impact on Learning

Evidence suggests that poor health and fitness have a negative impact on learning, school performance, and academic achievement.[2] For example, overweight students who develop health problems may have difficulty concentrating in school.[3] Less physically fit youth have been shown to attain significantly lower scores on standardized tests and to achieve lesser gains in academic achievement than do youth who are more fit.[4]

Why do health and fitness influence learning and academic performance? There are a number of possible reasons. Engaging in regular physical activity may boost self-discipline, reduce stress, strengthen peer relationships, and improve self-confidence and self-esteem. These factors, in turn, are also likely to improve school performance. Aerobic activity, in particular, may increase mental alertness and improve mental functioning by increasing blood flow to the brain, thus facilitating transport of oxygen and removal of waste products.

What Teachers Can Do

To be sure, schools cannot solve America's epidemic of overweight young people without help. However, recent reports released by the American Academy of Pediatrics and the Institute of Medicine of the National Academies have offered educational and medical leaders a number of important recommendations about what schools, parents, and community leaders can do to help stem the epidemic. Implementing these recommendations could help ensure the future health and fitness of young people.

As a teacher, you can play a critical role in the lives of your students. Most teachers know that this means helping their students to achieve academic success. But it also means taking an active interest in their health and well-being and doing what you can do to help students attain optimal health through physical fitness and healthy eating habits. Here are some specific ways you can promote healthy habits in your students and help stem the overweight epidemic.

▶ **Participate in a health council or team in your school district or building.** Work to support comprehensive health instruction, nutritious cafeteria options, and physical education.

▶ **Work with students and others in the school to establish a healthy eating policy.** The policy should guide the foods available in the cafeteria, in vending machines, and at school-sponsored activities.

▶ **Implement a developmentally appropriate physical education program.** The program should provide a variety of enjoyable opportunities for students to get at least 60 minutes of moderate-to-vigorous physical activity during each school day or after school.

▶ **Encourage students to be more active outside the classroom.** Suggest that they participate in a wide variety of chores, sports, and recreational activities that help improve multiple fitness components (including cardiorespiratory endurance, muscular strength and endurance, and flexibility).

▶ **Educate students about how community design and architecture can influence physical activity.** Go for a walking tour of a neighborhood near your school and have students point out features of the neighborhood that may either facilitate or serve as barriers to physical activity.

▶ **Be a good role model for your students.** The more you can communicate your interest in healthy eating and being physically active, the more your students are likely to emulate these positive behaviors. For example, wear a pedometer to see how many steps you take in a week. Have students do the same, and compare results.

References

1 Yang W, Dall T, Halder P, Gallo P, Kowal S, Hogan P; American Diabetes Association. Economic costs of diabetes in the U.S. in 2012. *Diabetes Care* 2013; 36(4):1033-1046.

2 Taras H, Potts-Datema W. Obesity and student performance at school. *Journal of School Health* 2005; 75(8):291-295.

3 Allegrante J.P. Unfit to learn. *Education Week* 2004; 24(14):38.

4 *California Physical Fitness Test: A Study of the Relationship Between Physical Fitness and Academic Achievement in California Using 2004 Test Results.* Sacramento, CA: California Department of Education, April 2005.

A Public Health Approach to Violence Prevention

Deborah Prothrow-Stith

The need to better understand violence in the United States, dispel prevalent myths, and implement prevention strategies is acute. Fear of violence is shared by people of all races, ethnic origins, and socioeconomic levels. Violence also has no geographic boundaries, affecting urban, suburban, and rural areas alike.

In the past, violence was viewed mainly as a criminal justice problem. Criminal justice efforts to control violence have included increasing the number of law enforcement officers on the streets and handing down stiffer prison sentences. Today, violence is considered a public health problem as well.

Violence as a Public Health Problem

The public health approach to controlling violence focuses on prevention efforts. Many experts expect the same or greater success using prevention strategies to combat violence as has been seen with other public health problems. Public health officials have added violence to their list of problems for the following reasons.

The magnitude of the problem is tremendous. Youth homicide rates are higher in the United States than in most other industrialized nations. Nonfatal violence is also common. In a recent study, about one third of high school students reported being involved in a physical fight in the preceding year.

The majority of violent acts involve family members, friends, or acquaintances. Criminal justice approaches are likely to have little or no impact on these acts of violence. There are many successful public health prevention strategies that can be applied to violence prevention.

The Public Health Approach to Violence Prevention

Public health prevention strategies can be primary, secondary, or tertiary. With lung cancer for example, primary strategies focus on encouraging nonsmokers not to smoke, while secondary strategies target smokers. Tertiary strategies, which are intervention strategies, not prevention strategies, are used with people who have lung cancer.

For violence, primary prevention strategies focus on reducing the pressures and expectations to fight that many young people feel. Young people need to develop skills for managing conflict and confrontation effectively. These skills include anger management, assertive communication, and conflict resolution.

> *"Youth homicide rates are higher in the United States than in most other industrialized nations."*

High-risk youth need secondary prevention strategies. Young people who are chronically bullied, victims of violence, or who witnessed a lot of violence during their early years are at high risk for violence. Often they are in fights, end up in emergency rooms, skip school, or get suspended. Secondary strategies include individual counseling and group therapy to help teens replace unhealthy behaviors with healthy ones.

Tertiary strategies target youth who have already committed violent crimes. These strategies, which focus on rehabilitation, may be applied during incarceration or used as an alternative to prosecution and incarceration. Although rehabilitation strategies are usually applied after violent crimes have been committed, they can also be implemented before high-risk juveniles commit crimes.

Preparing to Teach Violence Prevention

As a health educator, you are using primary prevention strategies to address the problem of violence. You may be anxious about discussing violence and violence prevention with students. This is understandable. In teaching violence prevention, you are challenging some prevailing myths about violence, namely that violence is often justified, frequently necessary, and even enjoyable. There are some things you can do to improve your chances of success.

Be aware of your own attitudes. Before you begin, consider your own thoughts and feelings about violence. You must be convinced that violence is rarely the best solution to a problem if you hope to convince students that violence prevention is a worthwhile goal. You also must be convinced that violence not only should be avoided but that it actually *can* be avoided.

It is also important to question students about their attitudes and behaviors regarding violence. However, be careful to avoid making value judgments or laying blame. Remember, violence in the United States is everyone's problem, not just a teen problem.

Expand the definition of self-defense. Some students will insist that there are situations in which they have to fight, for example, when someone hits them. It may be best to agree that the use of violence in self-defense may sometimes be the only choice.

It is important to point out, however, that self-defense should begin well before a punch is thrown. All too often, students ignore the events that lead up to a fight. Self-defense should include choosing non-violent friends, abstaining from alcohol and other drugs, avoiding places where teens hang out unsupervised, and knowing when to walk away from a situation.

"In teaching violence prevention, you are challenging some prevailing myths about violence."

Build media literacy. Some students may be quick to justify, or even glorify, violence because of the influences of their peers, adults they know, and the media. Media violence is ubiquitous, and violence prevention goes against commonly held myths about violence. For example, the popular slogan, "Make my day," implies that using violence is a positive and even enjoyable experience. Make sure students know that most professionals who use violence on the job, such as military and law-enforcement personnel, do not enjoy using violence, even when it is justified and has a successful outcome.

Provide nonviolent role models. Because there are very few popular nonviolent role models, you must convince students of the merits of nonviolent alternatives. During class discussions, share actual examples of situations that provoked anger but were handled nonviolently. Encourage students to think of and share examples of their own. If popular students who know how to avoid trouble describe their strategies for avoiding fights, it will help make violence prevention seem achievable, even to the most skeptical students.

Teach violence-prevention skills. Students need to know how to express their emotions in positive ways, manage their anger, and communicate effectively. They also need to know how to use win-win negotiation and mediation. Students need opportunities to practice applying these skills in different situations. With practice, students can learn to anticipate, avoid, or change the circumstances that lead to violence.

Objectives
Before class begins, write the objectives on the board. Have students copy the objectives into their notebooks at the start of class.

1. Focus

Warm-Up **Quick Quiz**

Use the Warm-Up Presentation slide to survey student responses.

After students finish writing, read the first question in the quiz. Call on a volunteer to describe five adults who know the student by name, not counting adults at home. Also ask students to name community leaders and describe what each community leader does that influences health. Discuss why answering yes to these questions can be important to a person's overall health and well-being. Explain that in this section, students will learn how different kinds of communities affect personal health.

Presentation 25-1

Objectives
▶ **Identify** the different kinds of communities to which you belong.
▶ **Describe** how communities affect personal health.

Vocabulary
• social network
• community service organization
• mixed-use development
• urban sprawl

Warm-Up

Quick Quiz How connected are you to your community? See if you can answer "yes" to any of the following questions.

① Do at least five adults in your neighborhood know you by name?

② Can you name at least three of your community's leaders (e.g., the mayor, police chief, and the superintendent of schools)?

③ Can you describe what each of the community leaders do that influences health?

WRITING How is being connected to your community important to your overall health and well-being?

What Is Community?

If someone were to ask you, "To what community do you belong?," what would you answer? You might answer by giving the name of the city or town in which you live. However, the complete answer is more complex.

There are, in fact, many different kinds of communities to which you belong. **Besides being a resident of your city or town and your neighborhood, you are a member of a particular school, a cultural community, and probably one or more clubs or organizations.** Being a member of each of these communities is important to your sense of identity.

The people with whom you interact and look to for friendship, information, and social support in all of these different communities make up your **social network.** The extent and quality of your social network can play a major role in helping to keep you healthy.

WRITING and Health

L3 Magazine Article

Have students imagine that they have been hired by a travel magazine, and their first assignment is to write a description of the community in which they live. Tell students this article should be only a few paragraphs long, but they should include as much information as possible about their city, section of the city, or town. This information should include descriptions of various neighborhoods, cultural communities, schools, and prominent community organizations. Tell students to keep in mind that the readers of the magazine may live anywhere across the country, and therefore this article should not assume prior knowledge of their community.

Health and Community
Health at School
Health at Home

These activities ask students to apply health concepts learned in the classroom to their lives at home, at school, and in their communities.

Health and Community

Noise Pollution Does your community have any regulations related to noise? If so, do the regulations vary with time of day or location? Sources of noise that might be regulated are radios, car exhausts, power lawnmowers, and blasting for construction. Write a paragraph summarizing your findings. **WRITING**

Health at School

Resilience Interview a guidance counselor, school nurse, or social worker. Ask the person you interview to describe those factors that make it easier for a student to recover from an extremely stressful situation. Summarize what you learn in a paragraph. **WRITING**

Health at Home

Warning Signs of Stress Ask a few friends and trusted adults if they can tell when you are under stress. Ask them to describe the warning signs that you exhibit. Write a paragraph about what you find out. **WRITING**

Online Resources

 GO ONLINE PearsonSuccessNet.com

- **eText with bilingual audio glossary***
  *(Available for PC, Mac, iPad with iOS 5 or greater, and Android tablets with Android OS 3.1 or greater)

- **Teens Talk Videos**

- **Video Viewing Guides in English and Spanish**

- **Audio Section Summaries**

- **Chapter Review Activities**

- **Web Links and Activities on Current Health Topics**

- **Focus on Issues Resources**

- **Career Resources**

- **Skills for Physical Fitness Worksheets**

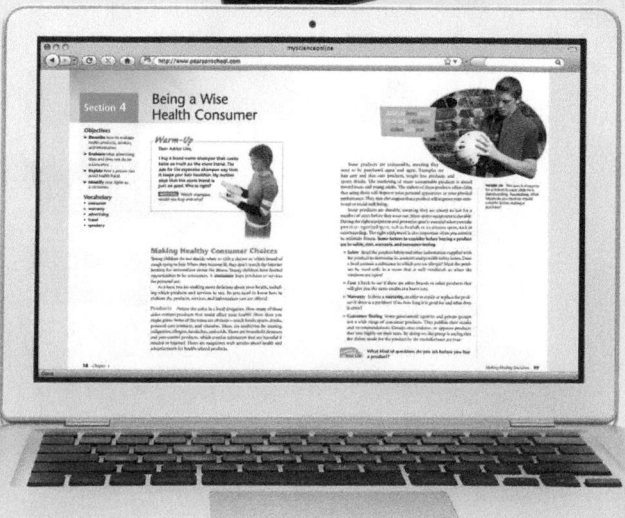

Differentiated Instruction

What's different about each of the students in your classroom? Just about everything. A typical classroom is comprised of students whose differences include culture, language, interest, motivation, and knowledge.

Differentiated Instruction in the *Health* Program

Differentiated instruction does not mean that the teacher offers each and every student in the class a "different" lesson. Rather, it means that multiple methods of instruction are used to maximize each student's likelihood of understanding the material. The *Pearson Health* program provides a variety of support and instructional materials to meet the learning needs of all students.

In the Student Edition

Considerate Text Structure

Built-in reading support with elements before, during, and after each section of the text, and the frequent use of analogies are all part of a considerate text. At the beginning of each section, the important learning objectives and vocabulary terms are introduced. The objectives are then highlighted as boldfaced sentences to encourage students to focus on the big ideas of health. Section Reviews reinforce the key concepts at the end of every section.

before

during

after

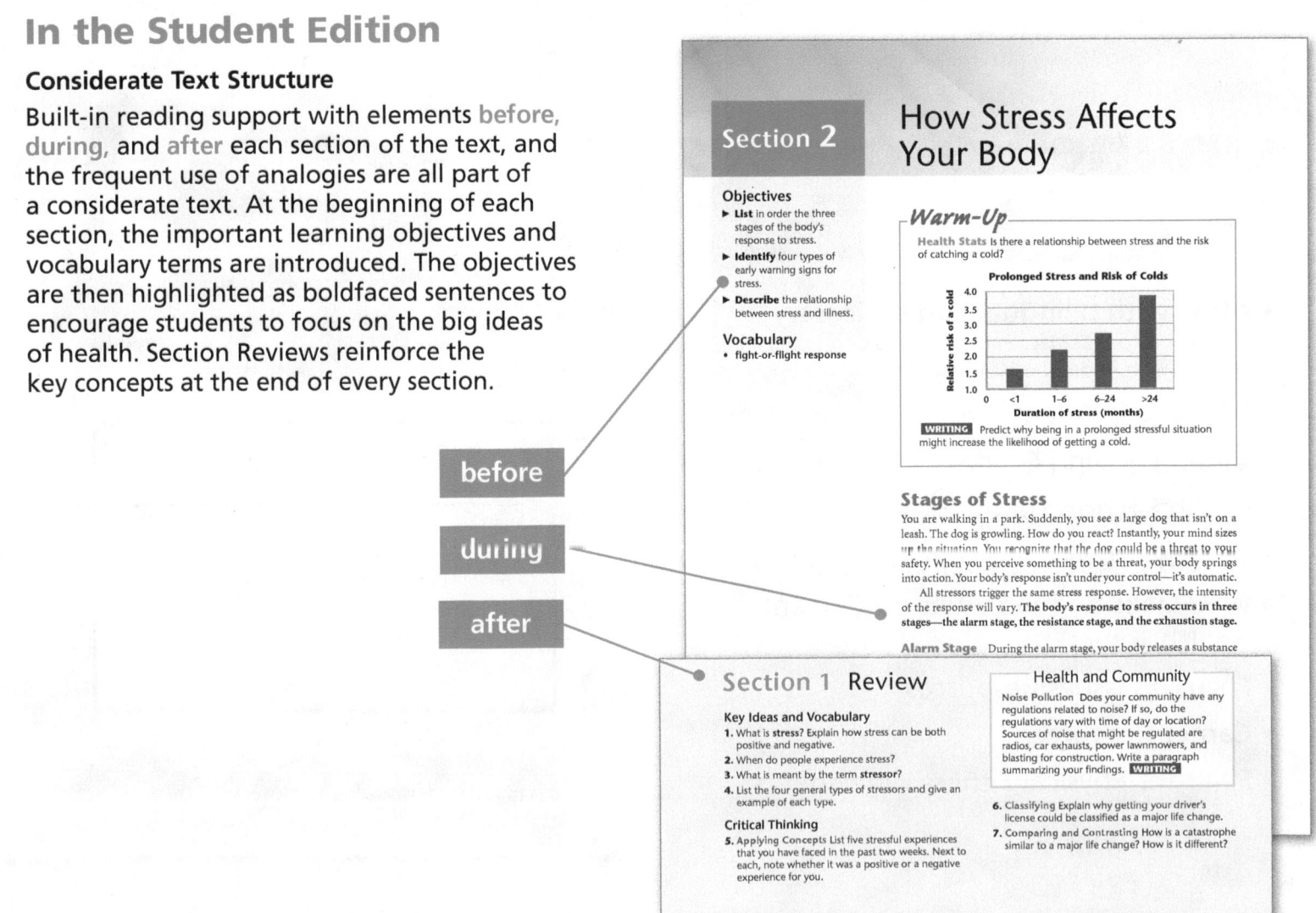

Section 2

How Stress Affects Your Body

Objectives
▸ **List** in order the three stages of the body's response to stress.
▸ **Identify** four types of early warning signs for stress.
▸ **Describe** the relationship between stress and illness.

Vocabulary
• fight-or-flight response

Warm-Up

Health Stats Is there a relationship between stress and the risk of catching a cold?

Prolonged Stress and Risk of Colds

Relative risk of a cold / Duration of stress (months): 0, <1, 1–6, 6–24, >24

WRITING Predict why being in a prolonged stressful situation might increase the likelihood of getting a cold.

Stages of Stress

You are walking in a park. Suddenly, you see a large dog that isn't on a leash. The dog is growling. How do you react? Instantly, your mind sizes up the situation. You recognize that the dog could be a threat to your safety. When you perceive something to be a threat, your body springs into action. Your body's response isn't under your control—it's automatic.

All stressors trigger the same stress response. However, the intensity of the response will vary. **The body's response to stress occurs in three stages—the alarm stage, the resistance stage, and the exhaustion stage.**

Alarm Stage During the alarm stage, your body releases a substance

Section 1 Review

Key Ideas and Vocabulary
1. What is **stress**? Explain how stress can be both positive and negative.
2. When do people experience stress?
3. What is meant by the term **stressor**?
4. List the four general types of stressors and give an example of each type.

Critical Thinking
5. Applying Concepts List five stressful experiences that you have faced in the past two weeks. Next to each, note whether it was a positive or a negative experience for you.

Health and Community

Noise Pollution Does your community have any regulations related to noise? If so, do the regulations vary with time of day or location? Sources of noise that might be regulated are radios, car exhausts, power lawnmowers, and blasting for construction. Write a paragraph summarizing your findings. **WRITING**

6. Classifying Explain why getting your driver's license could be classified as a major life change.
7. Comparing and Contrasting How is a catastrophe similar to a major life change? How is it different?

Visual Learning

Graphs, charts, illustrations, and photos work hand-in-hand with the text to clarify complex topics for students who think visually.

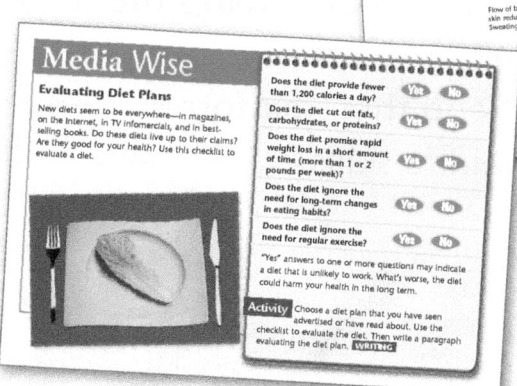

Active Learning

- Building Health Skills, Warm-Up activities, Media Wise, and Hands-On Activities in the Student Edition offer opportunities for active involvement and peer communication. These activities also help to build the skills that are necessary for critical thinking.

- Online activities bring timely, relevant, and appropriate health topics into the classroom.

In the Teacher's Edition

Chapter Planning Guides label activities by level of difficulty, to help you meet the needs of all students. Program resources are identified by level—for students with special needs, less proficient readers, all students, gifted and talented students, and English language learners.

The Teacher's Edition also includes many Differentiated Instruction teaching strategies. To facilitate use, these practical teaching tips appear at point-of-use.

Differentiated Instruction

EL English Language Learners

Use an analogy to explain the stages of stress. Say that stress is like swimming against a current. At first, you can swim faster than the current and move forward in the water (alarm stage). After awhile, you get tired and can only manage to stay in the same place (resistance). Eventually, you get too tired to swim and are carried backward by the current (exhaustion).

L2 Less Proficient Readers

Pair less proficient readers with advanced readers, and ask the pairs to create flow-charts of the stages of stress, including changes that occur at each stage. Post the flowcharts in the classroom where students can see them as they continue to learn about the effects of stress.

Online Resources

GO ONLINE PearsonSuccessNet.com

Support for differentiated instruction can easily be found online via the Student and Teacher's Edition eTexts*.

*(Available for PC, Mac, iPad with iOS 5 or greater, and Android tablets with Android OS 3.1 or greater)

Student Resources

- Reading and Note Taking Guides in English and Spanish

- Adapted Reading and Note Taking Guide

- Audio Section Summaries in English and Spanish

Teaching Resources

- Lesson Plans

- Enrich Worksheet

- Teacher Edition Reteach Strategy

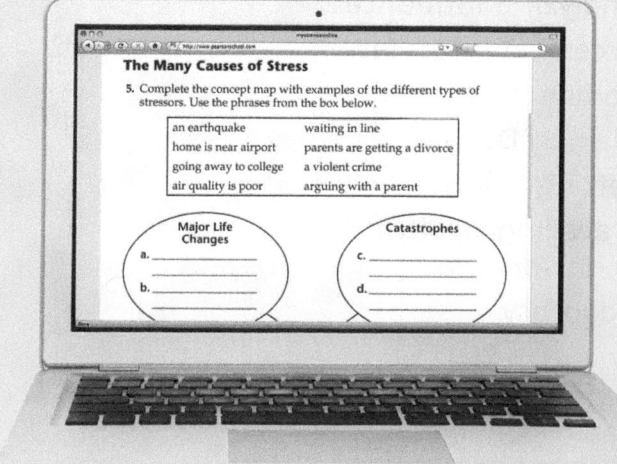

Health **Skills**

Pearson Health helps students develop the skills they need as they work to improve their personal and interpersonal health. Each health skill is taught and then reinforced, ensuring that students master these essential life skills.

Building Health Skills

appears once in every chapter.

Real-World Situations

set the scene for learning new health skills.

Step-by-step Procedures

make it easier for students to master essential health skills in the following areas:

- Analyzing Influences
- Accessing Information
- Communicating
- Making Decisions
- Setting Goals
- Practicing Healthful Behaviors
- Advocacy

 **Practicing Healthful Behaviors**

Managing Your Time

Last night, José stayed up late to write a report that was assigned two weeks ago. He planned to do his math homework in the morning, but then slept through his alarm. In his haste this morning, José left his gym clothes at home. Running toward the school as the bell rang, José felt anxious and tense.

José needs to manage his time better. A good time manager completes daily tasks and still finds time to relax. Follow these steps to better manage your time.

1 Track how you spend your time.

- ► Use a sheet from a daily planner that is divided into 15-minute blocks or make your own version on ruled paper. Prepare a sheet for each day of the week.

- ► Mark all your scheduled activities on the grid, beginning with your classes at school. Include other activities that you attend on a regular schedule, such as religious classes or team practice.

- ► Use the grids to track how you currently spend your "free" time.

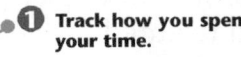

Monday	
8:00	Algebra I
9:00	English
10:00	American History
11:00	Earth Science
12:00	Lunch
1:00	Studio Art I
2:00	Basketball Practice

2 Make a daily "To Do" list.

- ► Before you go to bed, make a list of the tasks you need to do the next day.

- ► Include tasks that you know you have to do, such as homework and chores, along with tasks that you would like to do.

- ► Break long-range tasks, such as term papers and projects, into smaller, more manageable tasks. This makes it easier to fit these tasks into your schedule.

68

3 **Prioritize your tasks.**

Rate each task according to this scale.
A = very important
B = somewhat important
C = not very important

To Do List	
Do math homework	A
Do laundry	B
Outline history paper	A
Organize CDs	C
Call grandmother	B
Watch TV	C
Practice jump shots	B
Get permission slip signed	A

4 **Plan your day.**

► Assign an amount of time for each task. Make a practice of allowing more time for a task than you think it will require.

► Use copies of the grids you made in Step 1 to schedule your tasks.

► Do not schedule too many tasks each day. Allow some time for unplanned events.

► Try to do "A" tasks before you do "B" tasks, and "B" tasks before you do "C" tasks, even if a "C" task is easier.

5 **Monitor your progress.**

At different points during the day, ask yourself, "Is this the best use of my time?" If your answer is *no*, consider these questions:

► *Am I doing a "C" task because an "A" task seems overwhelming?* If so, break the "A" task into smaller steps that can be done in less than fifteen minutes.

► *Am I avoiding a task because I am afraid to fail or make a mistake?* You can waste a lot of time worrying about a task. If you just begin doing the task, you may realize that it is not as difficult as you thought.

► *Is this the right time to do this task?* For example, if your math homework is challenging, don't leave it until late at night when you are tired.

► *Am I being distracted by phone calls or instant messages?* Tell your friends when it is okay to contact you and when you need time to concentrate on homework or chores.

BUILDING HEALTH SKILLS

Practice the Skill

1. For one week, keep track of how you spend your time each day. Decide whether or not you are spending your time wisely. Are there tasks that you can eliminate? Are there tasks that you can do more quickly?

2. During the second week, make a "To Do" list each day. Break down complex activities into a set of simpler tasks. Assign a specific, realistic amount of time for each task.

3. Use the A-B-C scale to prioritize your tasks and then decide which tasks you will do in each of the available time periods. Do your "A" tasks first each day, followed by "B" and "C" tasks.

4. If you are having trouble finishing your tasks, ask yourself the questions from Step 5.

5. At the end of the week, report to your class on how helpful the time management process has been for you. What can you do to improve your time-management skills?

Managing Stress **69**

Illustrations and charts

model the processes that students can use as they apply the skill to their lives.

Practice the Skill

gives students an opportunity to practice and apply their newly learned skill.

Digital/Video Pathway

With *Pearson Health,* you can organize your teaching around the *Teens Talk Video Series.* These engaging videos will help students make connections between classroom learning and the decisions they face every day.

◑ TEENS Talk Video Series

One video for every chapter of the student edition—26 engaging videos in all!

- Videos feature real teens facing real issues in their daily lives
- Video Viewing Guide with teaching strategies plus worksheets in English and Spanish

Use the Digital/Video Pathway to organize your teaching around the video program.

The Video Pathway in the Teacher's Edition guides you in how to organize your teaching around the videos. The Video Pathway will help you

- **Organize** the key video, technology, and print resources to match your curriculum needs with ease.

- **Develop** lessons that differentiate the way you deliver health topics to your students and keep them engaged.

- **Save time** coordinating the program resources needed for each lesson.

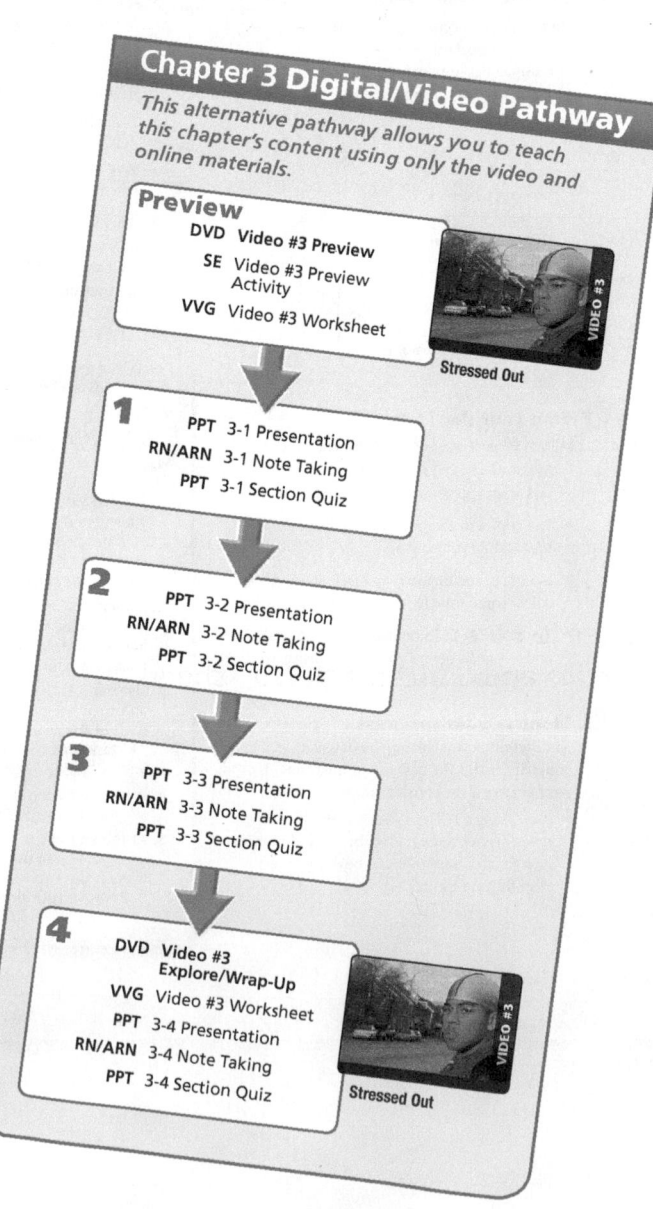

Chapter 3 Digital/Video Pathway

This alternative pathway allows you to teach this chapter's content using only the video and online materials.

Preview
- DVD Video #3 Preview
- SE Video #3 Preview Activity
- VVG Video #3 Worksheet

Stressed Out

1
- PPT 3-1 Presentation
- RN/ARN 3-1 Note Taking
- PPT 3-1 Section Quiz

2
- PPT 3-2 Presentation
- RN/ARN 3-2 Note Taking
- PPT 3-2 Section Quiz

3
- PPT 3-3 Presentation
- RN/ARN 3-3 Note Taking
- PPT 3-3 Section Quiz

4
- DVD Video #3 Explore/Wrap-Up
- VVG Video #3 Worksheet
- PPT 3-4 Presentation
- RN/ARN 3-4 Note Taking
- PPT 3-4 Section Quiz

Stressed Out

Digital Courseware at Your Fingertips

Easy navigation through eText

An array of teacher resources are accessible via the left navigation in the Teacher's Edition eText.

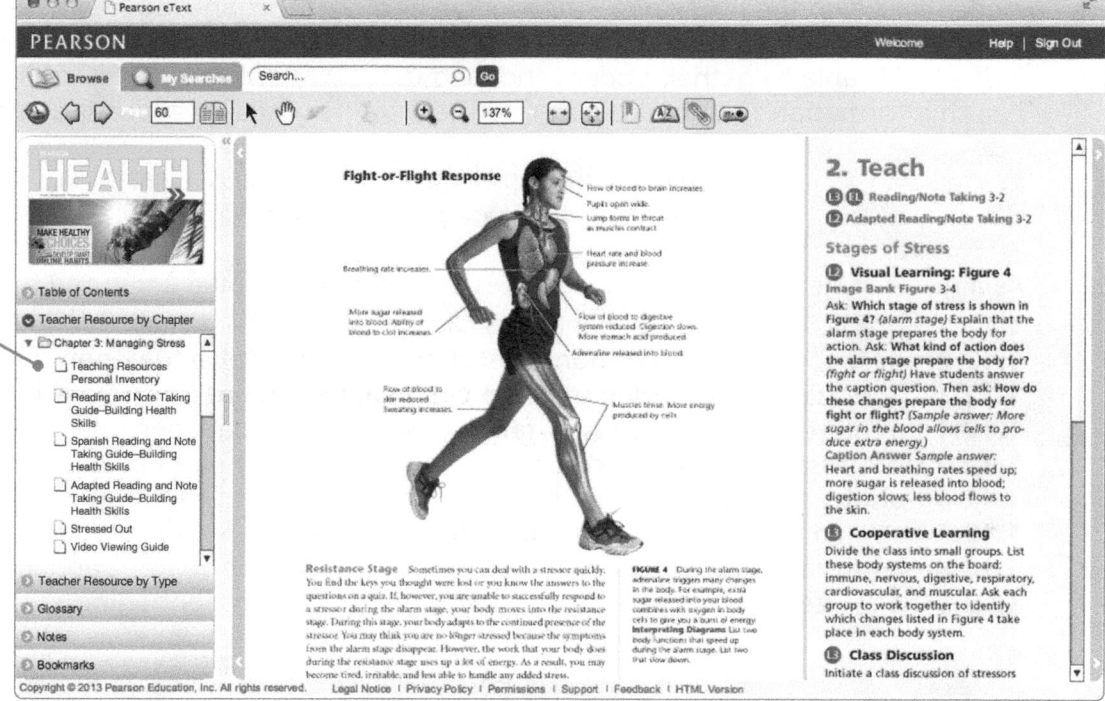

Online Resources

GO ONLINE PearsonSuccessNet.com

Editable Resources

- Teaching Resources:
  - Lesson Plans
  - Letter to Parents
  - Practice and Enrichment Worksheets
  - Section Quizzes
  - Chapter Tests
  - Answer Keys
- Reading and Note Taking Guide
- Adapted Reading and Note Taking Guide
- Video Viewing Guide With Worksheets

Spanish Resources

- Spanish Reading and Note Taking Guide
- Video Viewing Guide With Spanish Worksheets
- Audio Section Summaries in Spanish

Presentation Materials

- Image Bank with Editable Worksheets
- Chapter PowerPoint® Presentations, including Warm-Ups and Building Health Skills

Audio and Video Resources

- Discovery Education™ Teens Talk Videos
- Audio Section Summaries

Online Activities

- Web Links
- Chapter Review Activities
- Skills for Physical Fitness Worksheets

Additional Material

- Teacher Online Access Pack

The National Health Education Standards

These health standards were developed to enable students to gain the awareness, knowledge, and skills essential for health literacy. A health-literate individual is able to gather, understand, and use health information to enhance his or her health.

The health standards provide a framework for organizing health knowledge and skills into curricula, while allowing state and local school districts to determine the exact content of their health education programs.

Standard 1
Students will comprehend concepts related to health promotion and disease prevention to enhance health.

As a result of health instruction in Grades 9-12, students should know and be able to

1.12.1 predict how healthy behaviors can impact health status.
1.12.2 describe the interrelationships of emotional, intellectual, physical, and social health.
1.12.3 analyze how environment and personal health are interrelated.
1.12.4 analyze how genetics and family history can impact personal health.
1.12.5 propose ways to reduce or prevent injuries and health problems.
1.12.6 analyze the relationship between access to health care and health status.
1.12.7 compare and contrast the benefits of and barriers to practicing a variety of healthy behaviors.
1.12.8 analyze personal susceptibility to injury, illness or death if engaging in unhealthy behaviors.
1.12.9 analyze the potential severity of injury or illness if engaging in unhealthy behaviors.

Standard 2
Students will analyze the influence of family, peers, culture, media, technology and other factors on health behaviors.

As a result of health instruction in Grades 9-12, students should know and be able to

2.12.1 analyze how family influences the health of individuals.
2.12.2 analyze how culture supports and challenges health beliefs, practices and behaviors.
2.12.3 analyze how peers influence healthy and unhealthy behaviors.
2.12.4 evaluate how the school and community can impact personal health practice and behaviors.
2.12.5 evaluate the effect of media on personal and family health.
2.12.6 evaluate the impact of technology on personal, family and community health.
2.12.7 analyze how the perceptions of norms influence healthy and unhealthy behaviors.
2.12.8 analyze the influence of personal values and beliefs on individual health practices and behaviors.
2.12.9 analyze how some health risk behaviors can influence the likelihood of engaging in unhealthy behaviors.
2.12.10 analyze how public health policies and government regulations can influence health promotion and disease prevention.

Standard 3
Students will demonstrate the ability to access valid information and products and services to enhance health.

As a result of health instruction in Grades 9-12, students should know and be able to

3.12.1 evaluate the validity of health information, products and services.
3.12.2 utilize resources from home, school and community that provide valid health information.
3.12.3 determine the accessibility of products and services that enhance health.
3.12.4 determine when professional health services may be required.
3.12.5 access valid and reliable health products and services.

Standard 4

Students will demonstrate the ability to use interpersonal communication skills to enhance health and avoid or reduce health risks.

As a result of health instruction in Grades 9-12, students should know and be able to

4.12.1 utilize skills for communicating effectively with family, peers, and others to enhance health.
4.12.2 demonstrate refusal, negotiation, and collaboration skills to enhance health and avoid or reduce health risks.
4.12.3 demonstrate strategies to prevent, manage or resolve interpersonal conflicts without harming self or others.
4.12.4 demonstrate how to ask for and offer assistance to enhance the health of self and others

Standard 5

Students will demonstrate the ability to use decision-making skills to enhance health.

As a result of health instruction in Grades 9-12, students should know and be able to

5.12.1 examine barriers that can hinder healthy decision making.
5.12.2 determine the value of applying a thoughtful decision-making process in health related situations.
5.12.3 justify when individual or collaborative decision making is appropriate.
5.12.4 generate alternatives to health-related issues or problems.
5.12.5 predict the potential short and long-term impact of each alternative on self and others.
5.12.6 defend the healthy choice when making decisions.
5.12.7 evaluate the effectiveness of health-related decisions.

Standard 6

Students will demonstrate the ability to use goal-setting skills to enhance health.

As a result of health instruction in Grades 9-12, students should know and be able to

6.12.1 assess personal health practices and overall health status.
6.12.2 develop a plan to attain a personal health goal that addresses strengths, needs, and risks.
6.12.3 implement strategies and monitor progress in achieving a personal health goal.
6.12.4 formulate an effective long-term personal health plan.

Standard 7

Students will demonstrate the ability to practice health-enhancing behaviors and avoid or reduce health risks.

As a result of health instruction in Grades 9-12, students should know and be able to

7.12.1 analyze the role of individual responsibility for enhancing health.
7.12.2 demonstrate a variety of healthy practices and behaviors that will maintain or improve the health of self and others.
7.12.3 demonstrate a variety of behaviors to avoid or reduce health risks to self and others.

Standard 8

Students will demonstrate the ability to advocate for personal, family and community health.

As a result of health instruction in Grades 9-12, students should know and be able to

8.12.1 utilize accurate peer and societal norms to formulate a health-enhancing message.
8.12.2 demonstrate how to influence and support others to make positive health choices.
8.12.3 work cooperatively as an advocate for improving personal, family and community health.
8.12.4 adapt health messages and communication techniques to a specific target audience.

CORRELATION of the Student Edition to the Health Standards

Standard 1 Students will comprehend concepts related to health promotion and disease prevention to enhance health.

1.12.1 predict how healthy behaviors can impact health status.

1–1 What Is Health?, **p. 5**
8–1 Carbohydrates, Fats, and Proteins, **pp. 194–199**
8–2 Vitamins, Minerals, and Water, **pp. 202–209**
8–3 Guidelines for Healthful Eating, **pp. 210–214**
9–3 Nutrition for Individual Needs, **pp. 233–236**
10–2 Keeping Your Digestive System Healthy, **pp. 248–251**
10–3 Your Excretory System, **pp. 257–258**
11–1 Your Skeletal System, **pp. 270–271**
11–2 Your Muscular System, **pp. 274–275**
11–3 Your Nervous System, **pp. 284–286**
12–1 Your Cardiovascular System, **p. 296**
12–2 Cardiovascular Health, **pp. 299–303**
12–3 Respiratory Health, **pp. 309–310**
13–1 The Importance of Physical Activity, **pp. 316–321**
14–1 Your Teeth and Gums, **pp. 344–346**
14–2 Your Skin, Hair, and Nails, **pp. 349–353**
14–3 Your Eyes and Ears, **pp. 358–359, 362–363**
14–4 Sleep and Feeling Fit, **pp. 364–366**
18–4 Heredity, **p. 481**
19–2 A Healthy Pregnancy, **pp. 492–496**
19–3 Childbirth, **pp. 498, 502**
20–3 Adulthood and Marriage, **p. 530**
21–3 Common Infectious Diseases, **pp. 562–563**
22–4 Protecting Yourself From HIV and AIDS, **pp. 592–593**

1.12.2 describe the interrelationships of emotional, intellectual, physical, and social health.

1–1 What Is Health?, **p. 3**
3–2 How Stress Affects Your Body, **pp. 63–64**
3–3 Stress and Individuals, **pp. 66–67**
4–2 Eating Disorders, **pp. 90–93**
13–1 The Importance of Physical Activity, **pp. 316–317**
18–1 The Endocrine System, **pp. 460–463**
20–1 Adolescence: A Time of Change, **pp. 514–521**
Hands-On Activity, **p. 4**

1.12.3 analyze how environment and personal health are interrelated.

1–2 Identifying Health Risks, **p. 7**
3–1 What Causes Stress?, **p. 59**
12–3 Respiratory Health, **pp. 309–310**
16–3 Risks of Tobacco Use, **pp. 414–415**
18–4 Heredity, **p. 481**
19–2 A Healthy Pregnancy, **p. 494**
21–1 Understanding Infectious Diseases, **pp. 548–551**
21–4 Emerging Infectious Diseases, **pp. 566–568**
23–2 Cancer, **p. 610**
23–3 Other Chronic Diseases, **pp. 616–617**
24–4 Global Public Health, **p. 656**
25–1 Your Community, Your Health, **pp. 664–669**
25–2 Air Quality and Health, **pp. 672–676**
25–3 Protecting Land and Water, **pp. 677–683**

1.12.4 analyze how genetics and family history can impact personal health.

1–2 Identifying Health Risks, **p. 6**
4–1 Mental Disorders, **p. 83**
9–2 Safely Managing Your Weight, **pp. 226–227**
12–2 Cardiovascular Health, **p. 302**
15–3 Long-Term Risks of Alcohol, **p. 388**
18–4 Heredity, **pp. 478–482**
20–1 Adolescence: A Time of Change, **p. 517**
23–1 Cardiovascular Diseases, **p. 607**
23–2 Cancer, **p. 610**
Building Health Skills, **pp. 476–477**

1.12.5 propose ways to reduce or prevent injuries and health problems.

1–3 Taking Responsibility for Your Health, **pp. 12–15**
3–3 Stress and Individuals, **p. 67**
6–3 Responsible Relationships, **pp. 150–151**
7–4 Preventing Fights, **pp. 100–104**
9–3 Nutrition for Individual Needs, **pp. 233–236**
10–2 Keeping Your Digestive System Healthy, **pp. 248–251**
11–1 Your Skeletal System, **pp. 270–271**
11–2 Your Muscular System, **pp. 274–275**
11–3 Your Nervous System, **pp. 284–286**
12–2 Cardiovascular Health, **pp. 302–303**
13–3 Physical Activity and Safety, **pp. 331–336**
14–1 Your Teeth and Gums, **p. 344**
14–2 Your Skin, Hair, and Nails, **pp. 347–353**
18–2 The Male Reproductive System, **pp. 467–468**
18–3 The Female Reproductive System, **pp. 474–475**
21–1 Understanding Infectious Diseases, **pp. 550–551**
26–1 Safety at Home and in Your Community, **pp. 695–697, 701**
26–2 Safety at Work and Play, **pp. 703–709**
26–3 Motor Vehicle Safety, **pp. 713–715**
First Aid Appendix, **pp. 722–735**
Building Health Skills, **pp. 276–277**
Focus on Issues, **pp. 456–457**

1.12.6 analyze the relationship between access to health care and health status.

1–2 Identifying Health Risks, **p. 9**
4–3 Depression and Suicide, **pp. 97, 98**
4–4 Treating Mental Disorders, **pp. 102–104**
19–2 A Healthy Pregnancy, **pp. 494–496**
24–1 The Healthcare System, **pp. 634–640**
24–2 Participating in Your Healthcare, **pp. 641–647**
24–3 Public Health, **pp. 648–653**
24–4 Global Public Health, **pp. 656–658**
Focus on Issues, **pp. 630–631**

Standard **2**

Students will analyze the influence of family, peers, culture, media, technology and other factors on health behaviors.

CORRELATION *continued*

Standard **3** Students will demonstrate the ability to access valid information and products and services to enhance health.

Standard 4

Students will demonstrate the ability to use interpersonal communication skills to enhance health and avoid or reduce health risks.

CORRELATION *continued*

Standard **7**
Students will demonstrate the ability to practice health-enhancing behaviors and avoid or reduce health risks.

Standard **8**
Students will demonstrate the ability to advocate for personal, family and community health.

Course Pacing Guide

Chapter	Class Periods per Chapter					
	Full Courses		Short Courses			
	Year	Semester	Nutrition and Fitness	Mental and Social Health	Life Skills	Safety and First Aid
1 Making Healthy Decisions	7	3.5	3	3	4	3
Unit 1 Mental Health						
2 Personality, Self-Esteem, and Emotions	7	3.5		4	2	
3 Managing Stress	6	3		4	3	
4 Mental Disorders and Suicide	8	4		4	2	2
Unit 2 Social Health						
5 Family Relationships	6	3		4	3	
6 Building Healthy Peer Relationships	6	3		4	3	1
7 Preventing Violence	7	3.5		4	2	4
Unit 3 Nutrition						
8 Food and Nutrition	7	3.5	3			
9 Making Healthy Food Choices	6	3	4		2	
10 Digestion and Excretion	5	2.5	3			1
Unit 4 Physical Fitness						
11 Movement and Coordination	7	3.5	5			2
12 Cardiovascular and Respiratory Health	6	3	4			
13 Exercise and Lifelong Fitness	7	3.5	5	2	2	2
14 Personal Care	7	3.5	4		3	
Unit 5 Substance Abuse						
15 Alcohol	7	3.5		3	3	2
16 Tobacco	6	3		2	3	2
17 Preventing Drug Abuse	9	4.5		3	3	2
Unit 6 Human Development						
18 Reproduction and Heredity	6	3		1		
19 Pregnancy, Birth, and Childhood	7	3.5			2	
20 Adolescence and Adulthood	0	4		3	3	3
Unit 7 Preventing Disease						
21 Infectious Diseases	6	3	3			2
22 Sexually Transmitted Infections and AIDS	7	3.5	3	2	2	2
23 Chronic Diseases and Disabilities	8	4	3			3
Unit 8 Community Health and Safety						
24 Safeguarding the Public	7	3.5		2		4
25 A Healthy Community and Environment	7	3.5			2	3
26 Preventing Injuries	7	3.5	3			5
First Aid Appendix	3	1.5	2		1	5
Total	**180**	**90**	**45**	**45**	**45**	**45**

PEARSON

HEALTH »

Pruitt, Allegrante, Prothrow-Stith

Master essential health skills with these new features!

Updated highlights include

- Information on school violence

- MyPlate Food Guide

- Current information on building healthy relationships, including dating and online friendships

- Health and Human Services: Healthy People 2020 Goals

- Digital Courseware, including eTexts and online resources

- Up-to-date statistics and data throughout the program

Glenview, Illinois • Boston, Massachusetts • Chandler, Arizona • Upper Saddle River, New Jersey

ALWAYS LEARNING

PEARSON

PEARSON
HEALTH »

Print Resources
- Student Edition
- Teacher's Edition
- Reading and Note Taking Guide
- Answer Key for Reading and Note Taking Guides
- Human Sexuality
- Human Sexuality, Teacher's Edition

Technology Resources

Media Resources
- Discovery Education™ Teens Talk Video Series DVDs
- ExamView® Test Generator CD-ROM

Digital Courseware on PearsonSuccessNet.com
- Student Edition and Teacher's Edition eTexts*
- Human Sexuality Student Edition and Teacher's Edition eTexts*

*Available for PC, Mac, iPad with iOS 5 or greater, and Android tablets with Android OS 3.1 or greater

Editable Resources
- Teaching Resources:
  - Lesson Plans
  - Letter to Parents
  - Practice and Enrichment Worksheets
  - Section Quizzes
  - Chapter Tests
  - Answer Keys

- Reading and Note Taking Guide —English and Spanish
- Adapted Reading and Note Taking Guide
- Video Viewing Guide With Worksheets—English and Spanish

Presentation Materials
- Image Bank With Editable Worksheets
- Chapter PowerPoint® Presentations, including Warm-Ups and Building Health Skills

Audio and Video Resources
- Discovery Education™ Teens Talk Videos
- Audio Section Summaries—English and Spanish

Online Activities
- Web Links
- Chapter Review Activities
- Skills for Physical Fitness Worksheets

Additional Material
- Teacher Online Access Pack

Acknowledgments appear on p. 780, which constitutes an extension of this copyright page.

ISBN-13: 978-0-13-327030-3
ISBN-10: 0-13-327030-0

PEARSON

3 4 5 6 7 8 9 10   V0UD   18 17 16 15 14

B. E. Pruitt

B. E. Pruitt, Ed.D., is Professor of Health Education at Texas A&M University. He served as executive director of the American Association for Health Education, and was the editor of the *American Journal of Health Education.* He has received numerous professional honors, including two National Professional Service Awards and the "Scholar" Award from the American Association for Health Education.

John P. Allegrante

John P. Allegrante, Ph.D., is Professor of Health Education and Deputy Provost at Teachers College and Adjunct Professor of Public Health in Sociomedical Sciences at Columbia University. A past president and Distinguished Fellow of the Society for Public Health Education, he is editor-in-chief of *Health Education & Behavior.* He received the Distinguished Career Award in Public Health Education and Health Promotion from the American Public Health Association.

Deborah Prothrow-Stith

Deborah Prothrow-Stith, M.D., is a Consultant with Spencer Stuart and Adjunct Professor of Practice at Harvard School of Public Health. As former Massachusetts Public Health Commissioner, she expanded HIV and substance abuse services. She is nationally recognized for her leadership in addressing violence as a public health problem and for her books *Murder Is No Accident* and *Sugar and Spice and No Longer Nice.*

Content Reviewers

Amanda S. Birnbaum, Ph.D., M.P.H.
Weill Medical College
Cornell University
New York, New York

Marla R. Brassard, Ph.D.
Teachers College
Columbia University
New York, New York

Loretta Brewer, M.S.W., Ph.D.
Arkansas State University
Jonesboro, Arkansas

Elizabeth Coolidge-Stolz, M.D.
North Reading, Massachusetts

Jena Curtis, Ed.D.
State Unversity of New York
College at Cortland
Cortland, New York

Jean DeSaix, Ph.D.
Department of Biology
University of North Carolina
Chapel Hill, North Carolina

Ralph J. DiClemente, Ph.D.
Rollins School of Public Health
Emory University
Atlanta, Georgia

Joseph R. DiFranza, M.D.
Department of Family Medicine
University of Massachusetts Medical School
Worcester, Massachusetts

Theodore C. Dumas, Ph.D.
Institute of Neuroscience
University of Oregon
Eugene, Oregon

Timothy E. Fenlon, M.D.
Clemson University
Clemson, South Carolina

Carl I. Fertman, Ph.D., CHES
University of Pittsburgh
Pittsburgh, Pennsylvania

Elizabeth M. Ginexi, Ph.D.
National Institute on Drug Abuse
Bethesda, Maryland

Dawn Graff-Haight, Ph.D., CHES
Department of Health, Human
Performance and Athletics
Linfield College
McMinnville, Oregon

Molly Green, Kristen McCausland, Katherine Wunderink
American Legacy Foundation
Washington, D.C.

Mary Fran Hazinski, R.N., M.S.N.
Vanderbilt Children's Hospital
Nashville, Tennessee

Richard A. Jenkins, Ph.D.
Centers for Disease Control and
Prevention
Atlanta, Georgia

Jerome Kotecki, Ph.D.
Department of Physiology and
Health Science
Ball State University
Muncie, Indiana

Lori Lange, Ph.D.
Department of Psychology
University of North Florida
Jacksonville, Florida

Christopher M. Ledingham, M.P.H., CHES
Texas A&M University
College Station, Texas

Bruce Lubotsky Levin, Ph.D., M.P.H.
Louis de la Parte Institute
College of Public Health
University of South Florida
Tampa, Florida

Marylin Lisowski, Ph.D.
Eastern Illinois University
Charleston, Illinois

Kim MacInnis, Ph.D.
Department of Sociology
Bridgewater State College
Bridgewater, Massachusetts

James P. Marshall, Ph.D.
Utah State University
Logan, Utah

Jennifer McLean, M.S.P.H., CHES
Pennsylvania College of Technology
Williamsport, Pennsylvania

Angela D. Mickalide, Ph.D., CHES
Home Safety Council
Washington, D.C.

Linda Ponder, M.A.
Department of Health Policy and
Management
Texas A&M University
College Station, Texas

Janet F. Pope, Ph.D.
School of Human Ecology
Louisiana Tech University
Ruston, Louisiana

David L. Reid, Ph.D.
Blackburn College
Carlinville, Illinois

Glenn E. Richardson, Ph.D.
Department of Health Promotion and
Education
University of Utah
Salt Lake City, Utah

Richard W. Robins, Ph.D.
Department of Psychology
University of California, Davis
Davis, California

Rochelle D. Schwartz-Bloom, Ph.D.
Department of Pharmacology and
Cancer Biology
Duke University Medical Center
Durham, North Carolina

Arturo Sesma, Jr., Ph.D.
Search Institute
Minneapolis, Minnesota

David Shaffer, M.D.
Columbia University College of Physicians
and Surgeons
New York, New York

Edward J. Zalisko, Ph.D.
Department of Biology
Blackburn College
Carlinville, Illinois

Teacher Reviewers

Mike Code
Highlands High School
Fort Thomas, Kentucky

Elizabeth J. Godwin
Cape Coral High School
Cape Coral, Florida

Diane Henson
Conway High School East
Conway, Arkansas

Margo Jones
Taylorsville High School
Taylorsville, Utah

Charles Muller
Ida Baker High School
Cape Coral, Florida

Brenda Pasek
Melbourne High School
Melbourne, Florida

Jason A. Perch
Eisenhower High School
Blue Island, Illinois

Joanne Ray
G. Ray Bodley High School
Fulton, New York

Kathleen St. Laurent, R.N., M.S.N.
Coyle and Cassidy High School
Taunton, Massachusetts

Jerry D. Styrsky
Thornwood High School
South Holland, Illinois

Cristina Thyron
Prairie High School
Vancouver, Washington

Susan L. Tutko
Riverdale High School
Fort Myers, Florida

Coleen Walsh
Springfield School Department
Springfield, Massachusetts

Melissa Diane Williamson, D.P.M.
Titusville High School
Titusville, Florida

Contents

Unit 2   Social Health

Unit 4 Physical Fitness

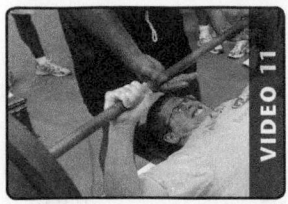

TEENS Talk

The Risks of Steroids

TEENS Talk

Living With Asthma

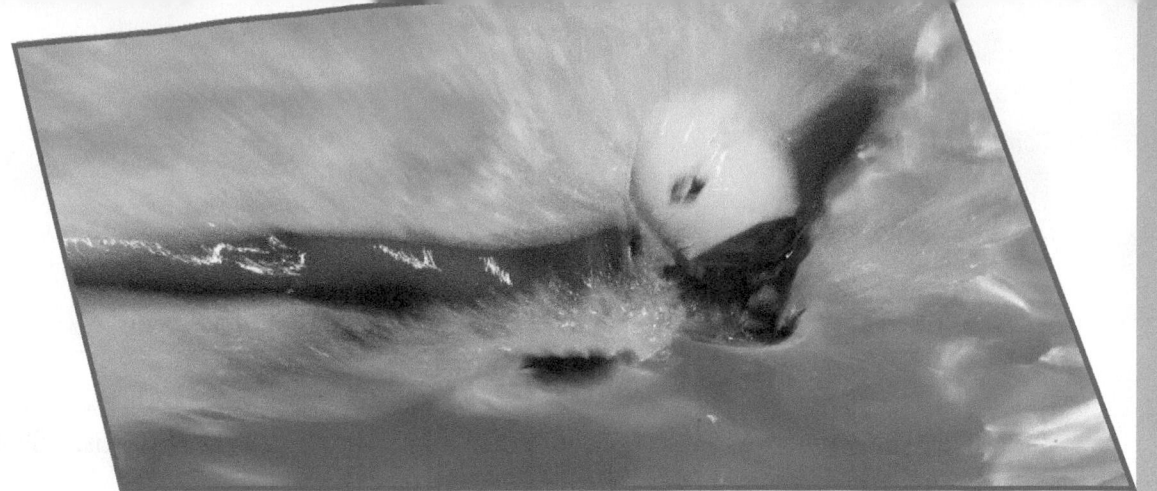

TEENS Talk

Fit for Life

CHAPTER 13

Exercise and Lifelong Fitness

TEENS Talk

Taking Care of You

CHAPTER 14

Personal Care

Unit 5   Substance Abuse

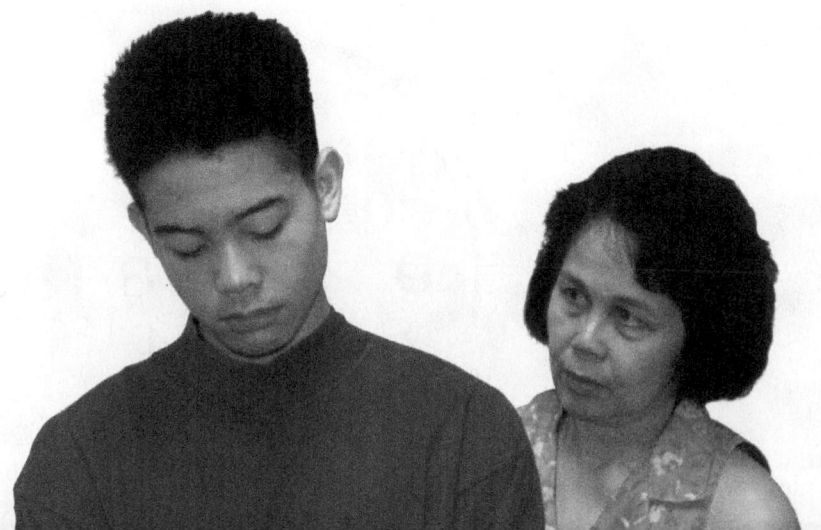

Unit 6 Human Development

Unit 7 Preventing Disease

TEENS Talk

Protection from Infection

TEENS Talk

Risks and STIs

TEENS Talk

Living With Disabilities

Unit 8   Community Health and Safety

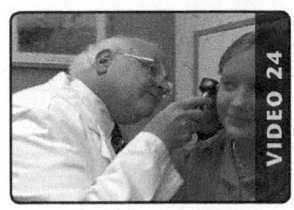

Building Health Skills

Master essential health skills by following simple step-by-step procedures.

VIDEO

TEENS Talk

▶ Watch and discuss how teens handle real-world issues.

Features

Media Wise

Analyze the influence of the media on the health decisions you face.

Hands-On *Activity*

Reinforce health concepts through hands-on experiences.

Technology & Health

Evaluate how technological advances affect personal, family, and community health.

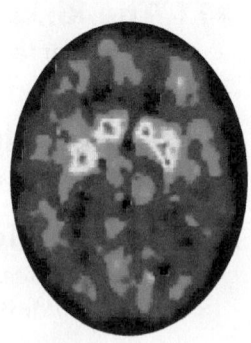

Focus on ISSUES

Communicate your opinions about some of today's important health issues.

CAREERS

Explore a variety of health-related careers.

Online Resources

 GO ONLINE PearsonSuccessNet.com

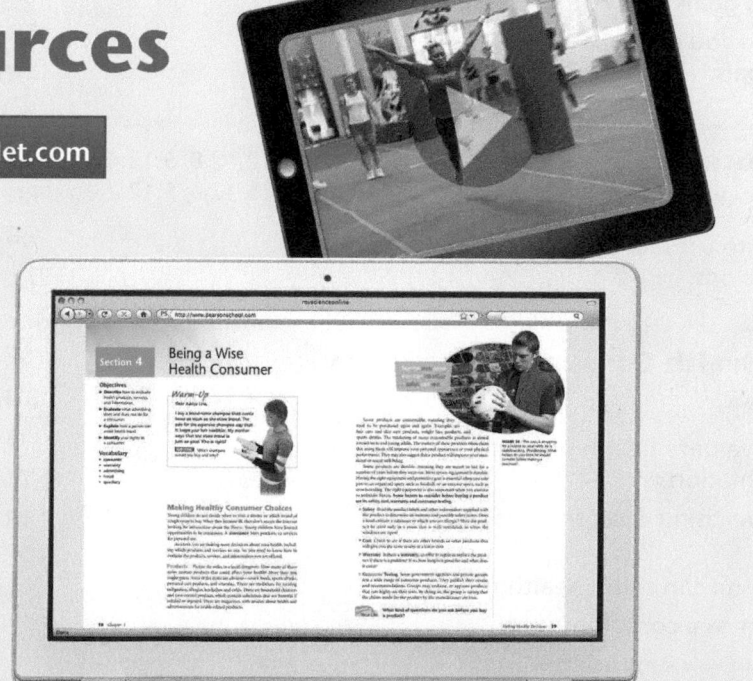

- eText*
  *(Available for PC, Mac, iPad with iOS 5 or greater, and Android tablets with Android OS 3.1 or greater)

- Teens Talk Videos

- Video Viewing Guides in English and Spanish

- Audio Section Summaries

- Chapter Review Activities

- Web Links and Activities on Current Health Topics

- Focus on Issues Resources

- Career Resources

- Skills for Physical Fitness Worksheets

CHAPTER 1 Making Healthy Decisions

Section Objectives	Standards Correlation	Instructional Resources	SE eTEXT	TE eTEXT	PRINT
1 What Is Health? ⏱ 1 period; 1/2 block	NHES: 1.12.1, 1.12.2, 5.12.2, 7.12.1	**SE** Warm-Up, p. 2	•	•	•
1.1.1 Describe two factors that can be used to evaluate overall health.		**SE** Hands-On Activity Health in the Balance, p. 4	•	•	•
1.1.2 List three aspects of overall health.		**RN** Note Taking Guide 1-1	•	•	•
1.1.3 Explain how the choices that people make can affect their positions on the health continuum.		**IB** Image Bank 1-1, 1-2		•	
		TR Practice 1-1		•	
		TR Section 1-1 Quiz		•	
2 Identifying Health Risks ⏱ 2 periods; 1 block	NHES: 1.12.3, 1.12.4, 1.12.6, 1.12.7, 2.12.2, 2.12.5, 2.12.6, 5.12.5, 7.12.1	**SE** Warm-Up, p. 6	•	•	•
1.2.1 Identify factors that can influence a person's health.		**RN** Note Taking Guide 1-2	•	•	•
1.2.2 Describe three strategies you can use to evaluate risk factors.		**TR** Practice 1-2		•	
		TR Section 1-2 Quiz		•	
3 Taking Responsibility for Your Health ⏱ 1 period; 1/2 block	NHES: 1.12.5, 2.12.1, 3.12.1, 6.12.4	**SE** Warm-Up, p. 12	•	•	•
		RN Note Taking Guide 1-3	•	•	•
1.3.1 Describe the broad goals of *Healthy People 2020*.		**IB** Image Bank 1-7		•	
1.3.2 Identify three steps you can take to meet your personal health goals.		**TR** Practice 1-3		•	
		TR Section 1-3 Quiz		•	
The DECIDE Process ⏱ 1 period; 1/2 block	NHES: 2.12.8, 5.12.4, 5.12.5, 5.12.7	**SE** Practice the Skill, p. 17	•	•	•
		RN Building Health Skills 1	•	•	•
BHS.1 Demonstrate how to use the DECIDE process to make healthy decisions.		**IB** Image Bank Page 16		•	
4 Being a Wise Health Consumer ⏱ 2 periods; 1 block	NHES: 2.12.5, 2.12.10, 3.12.1, 3.12.5	**SE** Warm-Up, p. 18	•	•	•
		RN Note Taking Guide 1-4	•	•	•
1.4.1 Describe how to evaluate health products, services, and information.		**IB** Image Bank 1-12		•	
1.4.2 Evaluate what advertising does and does not do for a consumer.		**TR** Practice 1-4		•	
1.4.3 Explain how a person can avoid health fraud.		**TR** Section 1-4 Quiz		•	
1.4.4 Identify your rights as a consumer.					

Chapter Review and Assessment

SE Chapter 1 Review, p. 26 L3
CTB Chapter 1 Test L2 L3 L4
SE Standardized Test Prep, p. 27 L3

PROGRAM COMPONENTS

SE Student Edition	**CTB** Computer Test Bank
TE Teacher Edition	**AUD** Audio Section Summaries
TR Teaching Resources	
RN Reading and Note Taking Guide	**DVD** Teens Talk Video Series
ARN Adapted Reading and Note Taking Guide	**VVG** Video Viewing Guide
	PPT Presentation
IB Image Bank	

Differentiated Instruction
L1 L2 L4 EL

		SE eTEXT	TE eTEXT	PRINT
ARN	Note Taking Guide 1-1 L2	•	•	
RN	Note Taking Guide 1-1 EL	•	•	•
AUD	Audio Summary 1-1 L1 L2 EL	•	•	
TE	Reteach Strategy, p. 5 L2		•	•
TR	Enrich 1-1 L4		•	
ARN	Note Taking Guide 1-2 L2	•	•	
RN	Note Taking Guide 1-2 EL	•	•	•
AUD	Audio Summary 1-2 L1 L2 EL	•	•	
TE	Reteach Strategy, p. 11 L2		•	•
TR	Enrich 1-2 L4		•	
ARN	Note Taking Guide 1-3 L2	•	•	
RN	Note Taking Guide 1-3 EL	•	•	•
AUD	Audio Summary 1-3 L1 L2 EL	•	•	
TE	Reteach Strategy, p. 15 L2		•	•
TR	Enrich 1-3 L4		•	
ARN	Building Health Skills 1 L2	•	•	
RN	Building Health Skills 1 EL	•	•	•
ARN	Note Taking Guide 1-4 L2	•	•	
RN	Note Taking Guide 1-4 EL	•	•	•
AUD	Audio Summary 1-4 L1 L2 EL	•	•	
TE	Reteach Strategy, p. 24 L2		•	•
TR	Enrich 1-4 L4		•	

ABILITY LEVELS

- **L1** For students with special needs
- **L2** For less proficient readers
- **L3** For all students
- **L4** For gifted and talented students
- **EL** For English language learners

Chapter 1 Digital/Video Pathway

This alternative pathway allows you to teach this chapter's content using only the video and online materials.

Preview

DVD	**Video #1 Preview**
SE	Video #1 Preview Activity
VVG	Video #1 Worksheet

Decisions, Decisions

1

PPT	1-1 Presentation
RN/ARN	1-1 Note Taking
PPT	1-1 Section Quiz

2

PPT	1-2 Presentation
RN/ARN	1-2 Note Taking
PPT	1-2 Section Quiz

3

DVD	**Video #1 Explore/Wrap-Up**
VVG	Video #1 Worksheet
PPT	1-3 Presentation
RN/ARN	1-3 Note Taking
PPT	1-3 Section Quiz

Decisions, Decisions

4

PPT	1-4 Presentation
RN/ARN	1-4 Note Taking
PPT	1-4 Section Quiz

Chapter Preview

Section 1 What Is Health?
Life expectancy and quality of life can be used to evaluate overall health, which consists of physical health, mental and emotional health, and social health. People's choices can affect their positions on a health continuum.

Section 2 Identifying Health Risks
Influences on health include heredity, environment, media, technology, healthcare, and behavior. People need to consider the short- and long-term consequences of their behavior. They need to analyze the possible benefits and risks of a decision.

Section 3 Taking Responsibility for Your Health
The broad goals of *Healthy People 2020* are to increase the quality and years of healthy life, to eliminate differences in health based on race, ethnic group, or income, to create environments that promote good health, and to promote healthy behaviors across all life stages. Steps to meet personal health goals include gaining awareness, gaining knowledge, and building health skills.

Making Decisions
The DECIDE Process
Students learn to use the DECIDE process to make healthy decisions.

Section 4 Being a Wise Health Consumer
Wise health consumers consider product safety, the qualifications of a service provider, and the source of health information. Ads rarely help a person make wise consumer choices. Evaluating claims about a treatment or product can help a person avoid fraud. Consumers have rights, such as the right to information.

GO ONLINE
PearsonSuccessNet.com
For resources and activities for this chapter.

Making Healthy Decisions

GO ONLINE PearsonSuccessNet.com

TEENS Talk

VIDEO 1

Decisions, Decisions

Preview **Activity**

How Many Decisions Do You Make?

Complete this activity before you watch the video.

1. Predict how many decisions you make in an hour during a typical day.
2. List all the decisions you made today from the time you woke up until the time you arrived at school.
3. Select one decision from your list and describe the process you used to make that decision. **WRITING**

xviii

🚩 **Sensitive Issues**

• Illness and causes of death may be sensitive issues for students who have close friends or family members with serious health problems or who have experienced the death of a loved one. Be attuned to the comfort level of students during discussions of these topics.

• Because this chapter stresses the effect of behavior on health, students with serious health problems may feel that they have failed in some way. In discussions on health-related behaviors, use the terms *healthy* and *unhealthy*. Avoid the value-laden terms *good* and *bad*.

Video Objectives

Use the video to help students

Apply the steps of the DECIDE process to decisions they face.

Evaluate the effect of peer pressure on teens' decisions.

Identify strategies that can be used to help them make good decisions.

Preview **Activity**

How Many Decisions Do You Make?

Assign the Preview Activity for homework a few days before you plan to show the video. After students complete the assignment, discuss the number of decisions that students made from the time they awoke to their arrival at school. Then ask for volunteers to describe the process they used to make a particular decision.

From the Authors

An important goal of Chapter 1 is to help students understand how their decisions affect their health. Healthy decisions move students away from illness and toward wellness. Once people make one healthy decision, it is easier to make a second one, and even easier to make a third one. This is something I call "health momentum."

You can keep students moving in the right direction along the health continuum by helping them develop good decision-making skills. Encourage students to apply the DECIDE model described on pages 16–17 to all their important decisions, especially those decisions that affect their health.

Objectives
Before class begins, write the objectives on the board. Have students copy the objectives into their notebooks at the start of class.

1. Focus

Warm-Up Health Stats

Ask students to study the graph and answer the writing questions. Call on students to share their reasons for the trend. *(Sample answer: more food and better medicines)* Explain that life span is an important indicator of the overall health of a community.

Presentation 1-1

2. Teach

L3 **EL** **Reading/Note Taking 1-1**

L2 **Adapted Reading/Note Taking 1-1**

Health Today

L3 **Addressing Misconceptions**

Life Expectancy Students may assume that life expectancy will continue to rise. In fact, some experts think the increasing trend in life expectancy may soon level off or reverse direction. They argue that the growing problem with obesity in the United States increases the risk of heart disease, diabetes, and other serious health problems that can shorten life.

Section 1 **What Is Health?**

Objectives
▶ **Describe** two factors that can be used to evaluate overall health.
▶ **List** three aspects of overall health.
▶ **Explain** how the choices that people make can affect their positions on the health continuum.

Vocabulary
• health
• life expectancy
• quality of life
• goal
• physical health
• mental health
• emotional health
• social health
• continuum
• wellness

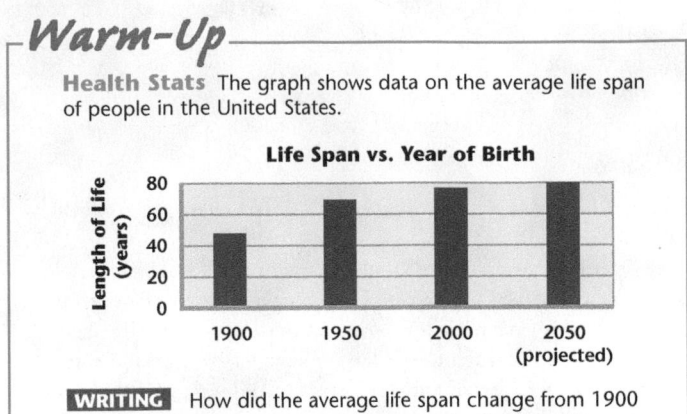

Warm-Up

Health Stats The graph shows data on the average life span of people in the United States.

Life Span vs. Year of Birth

WRITING How did the average life span change from 1900 to 2000? What are some possible reasons for this trend?

Health Today

In the past, if you didn't have an illness, you were considered healthy. Today, the term *health* no longer means just the absence of illness. Instead, **health** refers to the overall well-being of your body, your mind, and your relationships with other people. **Two factors that can be used to evaluate health are life expectancy and quality of life.**

Life Expectancy At the time when your great-grandparents lived, it was quite an accomplishment for a person to survive until age 50. Today, most people live well beyond age 50. The number of years a person can expect to live is called **life expectancy.** In the United States, life expectancy increased by 30 years between 1900 and 2000. Some reasons for this increase were better healthcare, nutrition, sanitation, and working conditions.

Quality of Life Two women are born in the same year. One woman is physically active and mentally alert throughout her life. She has close relationships with family and friends. The other woman has a series of health problems during her life that reduces her ability to enjoy life. Although the women have the same life expectancy, they have a different quality of life. **Quality of life** is the degree of overall satisfaction that a person gets from life. For many people, a high quality of life is one of their goals. A **goal** is a result that a person aims for and works hard to reach.

MATH and Health

L3 **Averages (Mean, Median, Mode)**

Point out in the Warm-Up graph that the average life span in the United States was about 48 years in 1900, 69 years in 1950, and 76 years in 2000. Ask: **By how many years, on average, did life span increase during each decade between 1900 and 1950?** *(69 years − 48 years = 21 years; 21 years ÷ 5 decades = 4.2 years/decade)*

What was the increase between 1950 and 2000? *(76 years − 69 years = 7 years; 7 years ÷ 5 decades =1.4 years/decade)* **How many times faster did life span increase per decade from 1900 to 1950 as compared with 1950 to 2000?** *(4.2 years/decade ÷ 1.4 years/decade = 3 times faster)*

Aspects of Health

To achieve a high quality of life, a person cannot concentrate on only one aspect of health. Instead, the person must work hard to improve all aspects of health. **The aspects of health that are important to overall well-being are physical health, mental and emotional health, and social health.**

Physical Health Do you have enough energy to go to school, enjoy your spare time, and take care of your responsibilities at home? If so, your physical health is probably good. **Physical health** refers to how well your body functions. When you are physically healthy, you are able to carry out everyday tasks without becoming overly tired. A healthy diet, regular exercise, adequate sleep, and proper medical and dental care are all important for physical health.

Mental and Emotional Health The state of being comfortable with yourself, with others, and with your surroundings is called **mental health.** When you are mentally healthy, your mind is alert, you can learn from your mistakes, and you recognize your achievements. **Emotional health** refers to how you react to events in your life. You are emotionally healthy when the feelings you experience are appropriate responses to events. To maintain your emotional health, you need to take the time to relax, and you need to share your feelings with others.

Social Health Being able to make and keep friends is one sign of social health. **Social health** refers to how well you get along with others. When you are socially healthy, you have loving relationships, respect the rights of others, and give and accept help. Building healthy relationships with family and friends is important for social health. So is communicating your needs to others. But good social health doesn't just happen. You have to work at it by getting involved with others at school and in your community, and perhaps most importantly, by building strong relationships with members of your family.

FIGURE 1 All aspects of health are equally important. They "fit" together like the pieces of a puzzle. A problem in one area can affect other areas. **Evaluating** How would you rate your overall physical, emotional, and social health?

Social Health

Physical Health

Mental and Emotional Health

Class Discussion

To help students better understand what is meant by *quality of life*, offer the example of older adults who are unable to renew a driver's license because they cannot pass the eye exam. Talk about how this change might affect these older adults. Point out that how people react to a change will vary depending on their circumstances. For example, someone who has access to public transportation is less dependent on a driver's license than someone who lives in a rural area.

Aspects of Health

Visual Learning: Figure 1
Image Bank Figure 1-1

Call on students to describe what each photo shows and how it illustrates an aspect of health. Then, ask: **Which aspect of health are you building if you work at getting along better with a brother or sister?** *(social health)* **If you try to learn from your mistakes?** *(mental and emotional health)* **If you get enough sleep?** *(physical health)* **Caption Answer** Allow students to keep their answer to this question private.

Differentiated Instruction

Special Needs

This section presents abstract concepts that may be difficult for some students to grasp. Use concrete examples to help students understand the concepts. For example, a student falls asleep in class (physical health); a person gets very angry over little things (emotional health); a teen volunteers at a hospital (social health).

Then, describe other examples and have students try to identify which aspect each example represents. For example, a teen is out of breath after climbing a flight of stairs (physical health); a student treats other people with respect (emotional health); a child has trouble making friends (social health).

Hands-On *Activity*

Health in the Balance

Ask students to bring in old magazines. Stress that the hole must be punched in the center of the triangle.

Think and Discuss Answers

1. Explanations should show that students understand how the activities contribute to the three aspects of health.

2. Have students focus on the analogy between an unbalanced mobile and a lack of balance among their aspects of health. Don't ask students to reveal information about their health.

3. Allow students to answer this question in their private journals.

A Continuum of Health

L2 Teacher Demo

Play a music CD, and gradually increase the volume from barely audible to loud. Explain that this gradual change in volume is an example of a continuum. Contrast the gradual change with what happens when a CD stops playing.

L2 Visual Learning: Figure 2

Image Bank Figure 1-2

Have students read the traits on the illness and wellness ends of the health continuum. Ask: **Where do you think most people are on the health continuum?** *(somewhere between the two ends)* **Why?** *(because most people can improve their health in some way)*
Caption Answer It will move you closer to the wellness end of the continuum.

 **Connect to Your Life** Allow students to answer this question in their private journals.

L3 Online Activity [GO ONLINE]

Visit Pearson SuccessNet to access an online activity about accessing your health. Have students complete the Web activity.

Hands-On *Activity*

Health in the Balance

In this activity you will create a mobile that balances the three aspects of health.

Materials
cardboard • scissors • pen or pencil
magazines • glue • string • tape

Try This

1. Cut out a cardboard triangle that is 8 inches on each side. Label the sides of the triangle "Physical Health," "Mental and Emotional Health," and "Social Health."

2. Carefully punch a small hole through the center of the triangle. Thread a piece of string through the hole, then tie a knot.

3. Cut pictures from magazines that show healthy activities.

4. Glue each picture onto cardboard. Use string and tape to attach each picture to the appropriate side of the triangle.

5. Hang the mobile from the center string to see how well it balances.

Think and Discuss

1. Describe each of the activities in your mobile and explain how it contributes to physical, social, or mental and emotional health.

2. How well did the mobile balance? In your life, are your physical, social, mental, and emotional health in balance? Explain.

3. Describe some things you could do to improve each aspect of your overall well-being.

 **GO ONLINE**
PearsonSuccessNet.com
For: More on assessing your health

A Continuum of Health

Suppose that someone asked you this question: "Would you say that you are in perfect health or in poor health?" How would you answer? You might not feel comfortable choosing either of these options. You might wish that you had been given some choices in between the two extremes.

Defining a Continuum Try to picture a solid line that is white at one end, then light gray, gray, dark gray, and finally black at the other end. What you have just pictured is one type of continuum. A **continuum** (kun TIN yoo um) is a gradual progression through many stages between one extreme and another. In the example of the line, the extremes are white and black and the stages are the many shades of gray in between.

A Health Continuum Figure 2 shows one model of a continuum for health. One end of the continuum represents poor health, which is often referred to as "illness." The other end represents perfect, or ideal, health, and is often referred to as "wellness." **Wellness** is a state of high-level health. Look at Figure 2 to see some characteristics that describe people at either end of the continuum. Because the continuum includes the full range of health, each person's health status would be marked by a point along the continuum.

Connect to Your Life Where do you think you are on the health continuum and why?

TEENS *Are Asking . . .*

Q: My father keeps nagging me to get more sleep. He acts as though losing a few hours of sleep will kill me. How can I get him to back off about my bedtime?

A: Your father understands how important getting enough sleep is for your health. You may think that you don't need more sleep, but depriving yourself of sleep can have negative consequences for your health.

Not getting enough sleep, especially if it happens night after night, increases your risk of developing an illness. It is harder to learn when you are tired. Lack of sleep also affects your ability to concentrate and your reaction time, putting you at risk of injuries, especially if you drive. If you fall asleep at the wheel, your lack of sleep could indeed kill you.

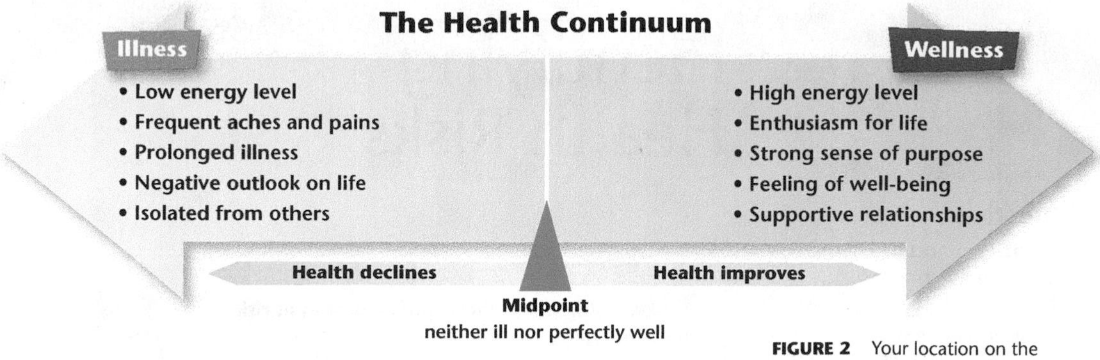

The Health Continuum

Illness
- Low energy level
- Frequent aches and pains
- Prolonged illness
- Negative outlook on life
- Isolated from others

Wellness
- High energy level
- Enthusiasm for life
- Strong sense of purpose
- Feeling of well-being
- Supportive relationships

Health declines ← → Health improves

Midpoint
neither ill nor perfectly well

FIGURE 2 Your location on the health continuum and the direction in which you are moving are both important. **Predicting** How might deciding not to smoke affect your position on the health continuum?

Movement Along the Continuum Your location on the health continuum is not constant throughout your life. You can move toward illness or you can move toward wellness.

At a point in the middle of the continuum, you are not sick, but you are not enjoying the full benefits of overall health either. At one time, many people were satisfied just to be in the middle of the continuum. They were more concerned about avoiding illness and death than about improving the quality of their lives. Today, however, achieving a higher level of health and a better quality of life is possible for most people.

Many of the choices you make on a daily basis affect your position on the health continuum. Some decisions move you closer to the illness end of the continuum. Suppose you choose to ride a bicycle without a helmet. If you are thrown from the bicycle in a crash, the result could be serious brain damage. Some decisions move you closer to the wellness end of the continuum. If you choose not to smoke, you will be less likely to develop lung cancer or heart disease later in life. You have more control over your health than you may think.

Section 1 Review

Key Ideas and Vocabulary

1. Why are both life expectancy and quality of life used to evaluate overall health?
2. What are the three aspects of overall health?
3. What is a **continuum?** Describe the extremes of the health continuum.
4. How are the choices people make related to their positions on the health continuum?

Critical Thinking

5. **Comparing and Contrasting** What is the difference between mental health and emotional health?

Health at School

Promoting Well-Being Think of two programs that a school could offer to help improve the overall health of students and teachers. Write a paragraph explaining your ideas. **WRITING**

6. **Relating Cause and Effect** What are two ways you could improve your physical health? Your emotional health? Your social health?
7. **Evaluating** Cody eats a lot of "junk" food and doesn't get much exercise. However, he doesn't have any obvious signs of illness. Where would you place Cody on the health continuum? Explain.

Evaluate

These assignments can help you assess students' mastery of the section content.

Section 1 Review

Answers appear below.

Teaching Resources

- Practice 1-1
- Section 1-1 Quiz

L2 Reteach

On the board, draw a horizontal line and a triangle. Have students copy the two drawings and label them correctly with the terms *social health, illness, physical health, health continuum, wellness,* and *mental/emotional health.*

L4 Enrich

Teaching Resources

- Enrich 1-1

Health at School

Promoting Well-Being If students are having trouble getting started with this activity, discuss a few programs that already exist at school, such as healthy food choices in vending machines. Also remind students to consider all three aspects of health.

Section 1 Review

1. Together these factors address length of life and degree of overall satisfaction.
2. physical health, mental and emotional health, and social health
3. a gradual progression through many stages between one extreme and another; illness (poor health) and wellness (ideal health)
4. Healthy choices, such as biking with a helmet, move people closer to wellness. Unhealthy choices, such as smoking, move people closer to illness.
5. Being comfortable with yourself, others, and your surroundings is a sign of mental health. Having feelings that are appropriate to events is a sign of emotional health.
6. Let students record their responses in their private journals. Ask volunteers to offer general suggestions for improving health in all three areas.
7. *Sample answer:* near the midpoint, because inadequate exercise and poor diet will affect his health in the future

1. Focus

Warm-Up Myth/Fact

Ask students to read the myth and respond to the writing prompt. Ask a few students to share their responses. Make a list of possible sources on the board. Briefly discuss the reliability of the sources students mention. Use the discussion to introduce factors that can influence health.

Presentation 1-2

Objectives

Before class begins, write the objectives on the board. Have students copy the objectives into their notebooks at the start of class.

Section 2

Identifying Health Risks

Objectives
▶ **Identify** factors that can influence a person's health.
▶ **Describe** three strategies you can use to evaluate risk factors.

Vocabulary
• heredity
• gender
• environment
• culture
• media
• habit
• risk factor

Warm-Up

Myth Using a cell phone puts a person at risk for developing cancer.

Fact Cell phone use does not increase the risk of developing cancer. However, cell phone use while driving does greatly increase the risk of a car crash.

WRITING Where do you think people get their information about health risks? How reliable are those sources of information?

Influences on Health

Two babies are born on the same day in the same city in the United States. Which baby will live longer? Which will have a higher quality of life? To answer these questions, you would need to consider the different factors that influence a person's health. **Factors that can influence health include heredity, environment, media, technology, healthcare, and behavior.**

Heredity To some extent, your level of health is already determined at the time you are born. This is because of your **heredity,** all the traits that are passed biologically from parent to child. Traits that you inherit can affect your health. Your skin color, for example, can affect your risk of developing skin cancer. With fair skin, you have a greater likelihood of developing skin cancer than if your skin is dark. Another example is breast cancer. Some women inherit a higher risk for this disease.

Even if you inherit a risk factor, you can lower your overall risk by avoiding other risk factors. If you have fair skin, you can be sure to use sunscreen. Women who inherit a risk factor for breast cancer can choose not to smoke because smoking is another risk factor for breast cancer.

Another part of your heredity is your **gender**—whether you are male or female. Gender can influence your health because risk factors may vary between males and females.

Sensitive Issues

For students with health problems, the role of personal behavior in health may be a sensitive issue. Make sure students understand that they cannot control all the factors that influence their health, but they can have considerable control over their behavior.

TEENS *Are Asking . . .*

Q: **My parents are overweight. Does that mean I will be overweight as an adult?**

A: Not necessarily. Even if heredity had an influence on how much your parents weigh, it was not the only influence. The foods people learn to like as children, how much they eat, and their level of physical activity all have an effect on their weight.

You cannot control your heredity, but you can control your behavior—what you eat, how much you eat, and how physically active you are. Use your concern about weight to make healthy decisions about those factors you can control. But do not overreact and starve yourself because you are afraid of gaining weight.

Physical Environment The **environment** is all of the physical and social conditions that surround a person and can influence that person's health. Your physical environment includes both your outdoor and indoor surroundings. The quality of the air you breathe and the water you drink are important to your health. So is your exposure to disease-causing organisms, to loud noise, and to radiation from the sun and other sources.

Being aware of potential risks in your physical environment can help you protect your health. If you know that breathing in the smoke exhaled by a smoker increases your risk of lung cancer, you can try to avoid second-hand smoke. If you know that loud noises damage your hearing, you may be more likely to keep your music at less-than-harmful levels.

Social Environment Your social environment includes the people you spend time with—your family, friends, classmates, and other people in your community. Most people learn their first basic health lessons from their family. Wash your hands before you eat. Brush your teeth before going to bed. Look both ways before crossing the street. Family members also can have a major influence on your mental and emotional health.

Your friends can influence your health in many ways. Friends who take too many risks can put a lot of pressure on you to do the same. Your social environment is healthier when you choose friends who show concern for their own health and yours.

Culture A person's culture is part of his or her social environment. **Culture** is the beliefs and patterns of behavior that are shared by a group of people and passed from generation to generation. The group may be a nation, a region of a country, or an ethnic group. Some aspects of culture can influence your health. One example is the foods you choose to eat. In some cultures people eat little or no meat; in others, meat is the main part of the diet. Another example is the way you show your emotions. In some cultures, public displays of emotion are typical; in others, people tend to keep their emotions private.

Connect to Your Life How do your friends affect your physical, emotional, and social health?

FIGURE 3 Your physical and social environments, including culture, influence your health.
Relating Cause and Effect Use the examples in the photographs to explain how the environment could affect a person's health.

Physical Environment

Social Environment

Culture

2. Teach

L3 EL **Reading/Note Taking** 1-2
L2 **Adapted Reading/Note Taking** 1-2

Influences on Health

L1 Visual Learning: Figure 3

Have students look at the photographs and read the caption. Before students try to answer the caption question, ask volunteers to describe the content of each photograph. Encourage students to think of other ways they could illustrate these influences on health.

Caption Answer *Sample answer:* A person who listens to loud music can damage his or her hearing. Spending time with friends and family members provides opportunities to share your thoughts and feelings with people who care about you.

EL Cultural Connection

Have students identify differences among cultures that they think can have an influence on health. For example, in some cultures people tend to eat whole-grain breads or include less red meat in their diet. Attitudes toward the expression of emotions or toward physical activity can vary among cultures.

Connect to Your Life Allow students to answer this question in their private journals.

Differentiated Instruction

L2 Less Proficient Readers

Pair less proficient with more proficient readers, and ask pairs to make graphic organizers of factors that influence health. They can use any type of graphic organizer (e.g., outline, concept map, spider diagram) that suits the material. Have students include examples of each factor that influences health.

Media   How much time each week do you spend watching television, listening to music, playing video games, or going to the movies? Do you read magazines or newspapers? What all these activities have in common is that they involve media. **Media** are forms of communication that provide news and entertainment. You may not realize that media can have a positive or negative influence on your health.

Think about television, for example. An average teen spends about 20 hours a week watching television. How can television have a positive influence on your health? You might receive useful information from a public service announcement or from a news report on a health topic. You might learn about a medical issue from a television series or talk show.

How can television have a negative influence on your health? The hours you spend in front of the television are hours that you are not exercising. You also are not relating to other family members or taking part in community projects. Some characters on television shows may be poor role models who indulge in risky behavior. Advertisers may present misleading claims about health products they want you to buy.

Technology   Advances in technology help doctors to detect health problems sooner and improve the quality of life for patients. Many people use sites on the Internet to learn about health topics that interest them. This approach requires caution and good judgment. Some Web sites provide accurate information about health. Others are filled with misleading or self-serving information. Be sure to consider the source of the information on a Web site and the purpose of the site. What is the goal of the people posting the information, and what are their qualifications?

Spending many hours on the computer also limits the time for other activities, such as exercise. If you use the computer to meet new people, there is the risk that you will connect with someone dangerous.

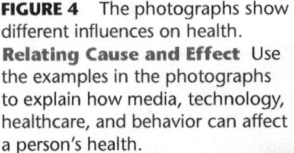

FIGURE 4   The photographs show different influences on health. **Relating Cause and Effect** Use the examples in the photographs to explain how media, technology, healthcare, and behavior can affect a person's health.

Media

Technology

Focus on **ISSUES**

Healthcare Your health is influenced by the healthcare that is available to you and your family. Healthcare includes the medical services provided by doctors, nurses, dentists, and therapists. Healthcare also includes the places these people work, such as clinics and hospitals.

Some factors increase the likelihood that a person will take advantage of available healthcare. The service must be in a location that is easy to get to. The service should be open on weekends or evenings for people who can't take time off from work. Finally, people need some form of health insurance so that they can afford the costs of necessary checkups and treatments, including medicines.

Behavior Suppose that a friend came up to you and said, "A group of us are going swimming tonight at the lake after dark. Be ready at eight— I'll pick you up." What would you do? Would you go along without giving things a second thought? Or would you stop and think about the risks involved? Of all the influences on your health, the decisions you make and the actions you take often have the greatest impact on your health.

Sometimes behaviors become habits. A **habit** is a behavior that is repeated so often that it becomes almost automatic. For example, you may have a habit of brushing your teeth after meals. That is a healthy habit because it helps prevent tooth decay and gum disease. You may also have a habit of staying up late watching television. That is not a healthy habit because it reduces the number of hours available for sleep. When you lose sleep, it is difficult to concentrate the next day. A repeated lack of sleep can make it hard for your body to fight off an illness or repair an injury.

Unhealthy habits can be broken. When you find that you keep repeating a behavior that may threaten your health, you can set a goal to change your behavior. Your goal should include a plan for changing your habit. Such a plan often works best when you involve friends or family members for support.

Connect to Your Life Why do you think that teenagers tend to take more risks than any other age group?

L1 Class Discussion
Invite the school nurse to class to discuss the role of a school nurse in providing healthcare to students. Provide a box for students to submit questions in advance in case there are questions they would not feel comfortable asking in class.

L3 Building Health Skills
Advocacy As a class, identify a few unhealthy habits (for example, eating "junk" food, not exercising, staying up late). Then split the class into small groups. Have each group pick one unhealthy habit and make a list of excuses a person might offer for not being able to break the habit. Then, ask the students to think of arguments they could use to counter each excuse.

Connect to Your Life *Sample answer:* because they do not expect bad things to happen to them or they do not think about the consequences of an action

Healthcare

Behavior

NO JUMPING, DIVING OR SWIMMING FROM DOCK

9

Differentiated Instruction

EL English Language Learners
Pair English learners with more proficient readers. Have them look at the sign in the Figure 4 photograph labeled "Behavior." After the proficient reader helps the English learner understand any unfamiliar words, they should discuss the reason for the sign. Then, ask the pairs to identify other types of warnings about risks, such as traffic signs or warning labels on products. Challenge students to design their own warning labels or signs for a particular health risk.

Evaluating Health Risks

Visual Learning: Figure 5

Caption Answer He can control how much sun exposure he receives. He cannot control the color of his skin or other hereditary risk factors for skin cancer.

(L1) Class Discussion

To make sure students understand the meaning of *short-term* versus *long-term*, use examples of behaviors that can have both short- and long-term consequences. For example, a short-term consequence of unprotected exposure to sunlight is a painful sunburn; a possible long-term consequence is skin cancer.

(L2) Cooperative Learning

Divide the class into small groups. Have each group brainstorm a list of risks and benefits for participating in a team sport at school. Remind students to consider all aspects of health: physical health, mental health, emotional health, and social health. As groups share their ideas with the class, compile a list of risks and benefits on the board.

(L3) Visual Learning: Figure 6

Ask students to read the benefits and risks and decide which are most important. Call on volunteers to answer the caption question. Challenge students to make risk-benefit charts for another health-related decision.
Caption Answer *Sample answer:* no, because the driver would be too inexperienced

Connect to Your Life Allow students to answer this question in their private journals.

(L3) Online Activity **GO ONLINE**

Visit Pearson SuccessNet to access an online activity about risk factors. Have students complete the Web activity.

FIGURE 5 Spending time outside on a sunny day could increase a person's risk of developing skin cancer. **Observing** Which risk factor for skin cancer can this person control? Which risk factor can't he control?

GO ONLINE
PearsonSuccessNet.com
For: More on risk factors

Evaluating Health Risks

Should you try the latest fad diet to lose weight? How do you decide? One way to think about the decision is in terms of its risk factors. A **risk factor** is any action or condition that increases the likelihood of injury, disease, or other negative outcome. For example, one risk factor of a fad diet is that it may not include all the foods that your body needs.

There are three ways you can evaluate a risk factor. **Consider both short- and long-term consequences. Decide whether you can control the risk factor. Analyze the possible benefits and risks of a decision.**

Short- and Long-Term Consequences Some behaviors can have an immediate effect on your health. You take a shortcut through an unfamiliar yard and end up with a nasty case of poison ivy. You don't buckle your seatbelt and get injured in a car crash.

With some risky behaviors, the consequences are not immediate. Suppose you eat a mainly fast-food diet, which is high in fats, sugar, and salt. People tell you that your diet increases your risk of developing heart disease and diabetes later in life. But you feel healthy and energetic. So why not wait until you are older to change your behavior? First, it can be very difficult to change habits that have existed for years and, even if you do change your eating habits later in life, you may not be able to repair the damage you have done to your body.

Connect to Your Life List three of your current habits that could have negative long-term consequences.

Risk Factors You Cannot Control A friend invites you to the beach. You are worried because you have fair skin. You can't control the color of your skin or other risk factors that are part of your heredity. Nor can you control all the risk factors in your environment. For example, you may have less emotional support if someone you are close to gets ill and dies.

For Your INFORMATION!

Absolute Risk and Relative Risk

Absolute risk describes the chance that an event will happen in a certain time period. For example, an American male has a 17 percent chance of developing prostate cancer during his lifetime. The absolute risk that he will develop this cancer within a year varies. It is lower in young men and higher in older men.

Relative risk is used to describe the impact of a risk factor on the risk of developing a disease. Relative risk is based on a comparison between a group (e.g., male smokers) and a control group (male nonsmokers). Men who smoke are about 23 times more likely to develop lung cancer than men who do not smoke.

Risk Factors You Can Control So what risk factors can you control? You can control risk factors that are related to your behavior. For example, you can control your exposure to ultraviolet radiation in sunlight and in tanning booths, which will reduce your risk of developing skin cancer. Or you can maintain close relationships with many people. That way, if one of your relationships ends, you will still have emotional support. These are other examples of risk factors over which you have control.

► Your level of physical activity

► Your intake of fat, sugar, or salt

► Your use of tobacco, alcohol, and other drugs

► Your use of protective gear, such as seat belts

► Your choice of friends

You may be able to control some risk factors in your environment. For example, you can join with others in your community to find solutions for problems such as pollution or lack of open spaces.

Analyzing Benefits and Risks There is no such thing as a risk-free life. Most of the things you do involve some degree of risk. Without taking risks and trying new things, it would be impossible to grow as a person. So how can you decide which risks are worth taking and which are not? You need to weigh the risks of an action against the possible benefits.

Suppose that a friend who only has a learner's permit offers to drive you home so you won't miss your curfew. What are the risks and benefits of accepting this offer of a ride? You can use a risk-benefit chart like the one in Figure 6 to help you decide if the benefits outweigh the risks.

Analyzing Benefits and Risks

Benefits	Risks
Home before curfew	Inexperienced driver crashes car
Avoid argument with parents	Parents are angry about decision
Show confidence in friend's skills	Friend loses permit or is arrested

FIGURE 6 A risk-benefit chart can help you decide whether to accept a ride from a friend who doesn't have a license.
Making Judgments Would you accept a ride with a driver who has only a learner's permit? Why or why not?

Section 2 Review

Key Ideas and Vocabulary

1. What does the term **heredity** mean?
2. List five factors other than heredity that can influence your health.
3. What is a **habit?** Describe one healthy habit and one unhealthy habit.
4. In relation to health, how is a **risk factor** defined?
5. List three ways to evaluate a risk factor?

Critical Thinking

6. **Applying Concepts** List the risks and benefits of swimming in a lake at night with friends.

Health at Home

Identifying Health Risks Identify three risk factors that affect the health of your family. Think about risks related to heredity, environment, and behavior. Then pick one of the risk factors and describe some ways that your family could reduce this health risk. **WRITING**

7. **Evaluating** Do you think that your physical environment or your social environment is a more important influence on your health? Explain.
8. **Predicting** How could spending a lot of time playing video games have a negative influence on someone's health?

3. Assess

Evaluate

These assignments can help you assess students' mastery of the section content.

Section 2 Review

Answers appear below.

Teaching Resources
• Practice 1-2
• Section 1-2 Quiz

L2 Reteach

Have students write paragraphs that address section objectives and correctly use all the vocabulary terms.

L4 Enrich

Teaching Resources
• Enrich 1-2

Health at Home

Identifying Health Risks Students should record their responses to this activity in their private journals. Suggest that students share their ideas with other family members.

Section 2 Review

1. all the traits that are passed biologically from parent to child

2. environment, media, technology, health-care, and behavior

3. *Sample answer:* a behavior that is repeated so often that it becomes almost automatic; brushing teeth after meals (healthy habit); eating "junk" food (unhealthy habit)

4. any action or condition that increases the likelihood of injury, disease, or other negative outcome

5. consider both short- and long-term consequences, decide whether you can control the risk factor, and analyze the possible benefits and risks of a decision

6. *Sample answer:* Risks are unseen hazards and no lifeguard; benefits are exercise and being with friends.

7. Answers should show that students understand how physical and social environments can influence health.

8. It is time not spent on exercise and family activities.

Section 3

Taking Responsibility for Your Health

Objectives
Before class begins, write the objectives on the board. Have students copy the objectives into their notebooks at the start of class.

1. Focus

Warm-Up **Quick Quiz**

Use the Warm-Up Presentation slide to survey student responses.

Remind students that behavior is a major influence on health. Tell them that they will learn some steps in this section that will help them take more responsibility for their own health.

Presentation 1-3

2. Teach

L3 **EL** **Reading/Note Taking** 1-3

L2 **Adapted Reading/Note Taking** 1-3

Healthy People 2020

EL **Building Vocabulary**

Help students understand the important concept of prevention by explaining that *prevention* comes from a Latin word meaning "to anticipate," or come before. When people anticipate the possible outcomes of behaviors, they can take action in advance to prevent those outcomes.

Section 3

Taking Responsibility for Your Health

Objectives
▶ **Describe** the broad goals of *Healthy People 2020*.
▶ **Identify** three steps you can take to meet your personal health goals.

Vocabulary
• prevention
• values
• action plan
• advocacy
• health literacy

Warm-Up

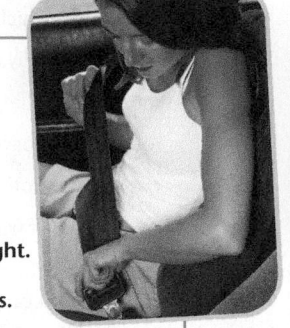

Quick Quiz How many of these statements accurately describe your behaviors?

① **I exercise at least three times a week.**

② **I set aside some time each day to relax.**

③ **I get about eight hours of sleep each night.**

④ **I avoid alcohol, tobacco, and other drugs.**

⑤ **I always wear a seat belt when riding in a car.**

WRITING Make a connection between the number of "Yes" answers and how responsible you are about your health.

Healthy People 2020

A nation wants its people to be as healthy as possible. Healthy people are more productive at school and at work. Plus, the cost of caring for people once they become ill can be a burden on families, employers, and the government. For decades, the Department of Health and Human Services has led a national effort to improve health in the United States. A major focus of this effort is on **prevention**—taking action to avoid disease, injury, and other negative health outcomes.

Healthy People 2020 has four broad goals:

▶ **Increase the quality and years of healthy life**

▶ **Eliminate differences in health based on race, ethnic group, or income**

▶ **Create social and physical environments that promote good health**

▶ **Promote healthy behaviors, health development, and quality of life across all life stages**

Healthy People 2020 includes a set of specific objectives aimed at reducing risky health behaviors. Look at the graph in Figure 7. Note that the leading causes of death for young people are related to behaviors. So, one goal of Healthy People 2020 is for 92.4% of the population to use seat belts by the year 2020, which would represent a 10 percent increase over current levels of seat belt use.

For Your **INFORMATION!**

Healthy People 2020

In *Healthy People 2020,* there are 42 focus areas and nearly 600 specific objectives—what this book refers to as "smaller goals." *Healthy People 2020* tracks progress toward the specific objectives by monitoring twelve different health measures called Leading Health Indicators. The indicators are access to health services, clinical preventive services, environmental quality, injury and violence, maternal, infant, and child health, mental health, nutrition, physical activity, and obesity, oral health, reproductive and sexual health, social determinants, substance abuse, and tobacco. Each of these twelve indicators is associated with one or more specific objectives.

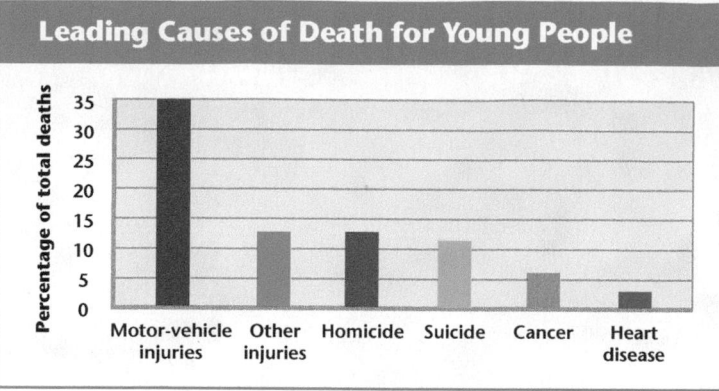

Leading Causes of Death for Young People

FIGURE 7 The graph shows causes of death for young people in the United States. **Interpreting Graphs** What percentage of the total deaths are due to injury or violence?

Visual Learning: Figure 7

Image Bank Figure 1-7

Ask: **Which causes of death in the graph are due to injury or violence?** *(motor-vehicle injuries, other injuries, homicide, and suicide)* Then, call on a volunteer to answer the caption question. Discuss why deaths due to injury and violence are largely preventable.
Caption Answer about 70 percent

A Healthy You

Building Media Literacy

Pick a health topic that is currently newsworthy. Display media reports about this topic from different print media including daily newspapers, news magazines, health magazines, and health journals. Give students a chance to examine these sources. Then compare and contrast the presentations.

 Connect to Your Life Allow students to answer this question in their private journals.

A Healthy You

You, too, can set goals to eliminate personal health risk factors. Some of your goals may match those in *Healthy People 2020*. Others may be unique to you. Some goals, such as wearing a seat belt, are easy to achieve. Others, such as cutting down on fat in your diet, may be more challenging. Whatever your target goals, your overall goal should be the same as the one set for the nation—a healthier you in 2020 and beyond. **There are three steps you can take to help you meet your personal health goals—gaining awareness, gaining knowledge, and building skills.**

Gaining Awareness You must first be able to recognize a health problem before you can do anything about it. Some problems are easy to recognize. You know, for example, when you twist your ankle or have a cold. However, other health problems, such as high blood pressure, don't have obvious signs. This is one reason why it is important to see a doctor for an annual checkup. Doctors are trained to recognize early signs of disease and to help you identify risk factors.

Gaining Knowledge Once you become aware of a health problem, the next step is to learn about the problem. This can mean learning about causes, warning signs, and possible outcomes. You also need to know how the problem can be prevented or treated. Most importantly, you need to learn about risk factors, especially those related to behavior.

Reports about new research results and health studies appear in the news all the time. Popular magazines, Web sites, and friends are some other sources of information about health. Some sources are more reliable than others. But even with reliable sources, you may see two reports on the same topic that have opposing conclusions. One goal of this book is to provide enough basic information about health so that you will be better able to evaluate new information.

 **Connect to Your Life** What is your most common source of health information? What is your most reliable source?

Differentiated Instruction

Gifted and Talented

If you don't have a copy of *Healthy People 2020*, you can find all of the target goals, objectives, and more at HealthyPeople.gov. Ask a group of interested students to identify target goals that are relevant for teens. Then, as you address a health topic, display any related *Healthy People 2020* objectives.

L3 Journal Writing

Have students record in their private journal one or two goals they would like to achieve in the next few months. Ask them to record why they chose these goals. Then ask them to make a list of specific steps they will take to achieve these goals. **WRITING**

L2 Visual Learning: Figure 8

Discuss what risks the woman may be facing by camping alone. (*Possible answers include injury from a fall, frostbite, a blizzard, or wild animals.*) Then, call on a few volunteers to answer the caption question.

Caption Answer *Sample answer:* She could access information about the area from expert campers and check a long-range weather forecast; this would help her decide what gear to pack and how to get help in an emergency.

L3 Cultural Connection

Explain that being aware of your values is key to making important decisions. Ask students to share the DECIDE process on pages 16–17 with adult family members. Suggest that they take the opportunity to have a family discussion about values.

L3 Content Update GO ONLINE

Visit Pearson SuccessNet to access more information about health skills. Have students complete the Web activity.

FIGURE 8 This woman is on a camping trip alone in winter. **Predicting** How could knowing how to access information and make decisions help to keep her safe during her trip?

 GO ONLINE
PearsonSuccessNet.com
For: More on health skills

Building Health Skills Knowledge isn't very useful if you do not have the skills to apply it. What would you think of a baseball player who knew the rules of baseball but never practiced hitting a curve ball or laying down a bunt? In the same way, just knowing which behaviors are healthy isn't a guarantee of good health. You need to master the skills listed below. You will get to practice these skills throughout the year, especially in the Building Health Skills section of each chapter.

▶ **Analyzing Influences** How do you decide what foods to eat? Do you select certain foods because they are familiar from your culture? Does advertising affect your choices? Do you try foods if your friends like them? An important skill for promoting health is recognizing the influence culture, media, and friends have on your health habits.

▶ **Accessing Information** Which sources of information about health-related products and services can you trust? How do you locate a doctor or mental-health counselor in your community? To answer such questions you need to know how to find and evaluate health information.

▶ **Communicating** Being able to communicate your thoughts and feelings effectively helps you to maintain close relationships. Good communication skills allow you to resolve conflicts. They also help you express your opinions and show caring and respect for others.

▶ **Making Decisions** Making wise decisions is key to protecting your health. The DECIDE process on pages 16–17 can help you make difficult decisions. This process teaches you to identify your alternatives, think about the possible outcomes of a decision, and consider your values. Your **values** are the standards and beliefs that are most important to you.

14 *Chapter 1*

WRITING and Health

L4 Proposal

Challenge students to identify a small, but important, change that could make their community a healthier place to live. The change could target physical, mental, emotional, or social health.

Ask students to write a brief proposal for implementing this change, including an action plan with specific steps. Ask students to identify obstacles they might need to overcome to make the change a reality.

► **Setting Goals** The goals you set help you translate knowledge into behavior. Once you set a goal, you can develop an **action plan**—a series of specific steps you can take to achieve the goal. The plan is like a roadmap that helps you get from where you are to where you want to go.

► **Practicing Healthful Behaviors** Do some of your current behaviors enhance your health? Do others place your health at risk? You need to develop strategies for maintaining healthy behaviors and reducing risky behaviors. Often, you will need to practice a new behavior repeatedly until it becomes a habit.

► **Advocacy** To *advocate* means to speak or write in support of a person or issue. The skill of **advocacy** involves using communication to influence and support others in making positive health decisions. For example, you can advocate for a friend who has frequent severe headaches by encouraging your friend to see a doctor. You can offer to go with your friend to the doctor's appointment. You can also advocate for changes that will make your community a healthier place to live.

Achieving Health Literacy The term *literacy* is used to describe the ability to read and write. But the term can be applied to many areas. For example, a person with computer literacy has the knowledge and skills to use a computer. A person with **health literacy** has the ability to gather, understand, and use health information to improve his or her health.

Awareness, knowledge, and skills all contribute to health literacy. If you become aware that the amount of fat in a diet is a health concern, you can learn which foods are high in fat. Then you can apply the skills of decision making and setting goals to lower your intake of high-fat foods.

FIGURE 9 Making your community a healthier place to live is one type of advocacy. These people are growing foods in a community garden that can provide a healthier diet for their neighbors.

Section 3 Review

Key Ideas and Vocabulary

1. What does the term **prevention** mean in relation to health?

2. List the four broad goals of *Healthy People 2020*.

3. What are three steps that can help people meet their personal health goals?

4. What is an **action plan**? What health skill are you applying when you develop an action plan?

Critical Thinking

5. Relating Cause and Effect Look at the causes of death in Figure 7. For which cause of death is diving into a shallow pool a risk factor? Explain.

Health at School

Preventing Injuries One *Healthy People 2020* goal is to reduce injuries during school-sponsored sports events. The specific goal is to increase the use of protective gear for the head, face, eye, and mouth. What are the rules about using such protective gear at your school? Do these rules support the *Healthy People 2020* goal? Write a paragraph summarizing your findings. **WRITING**

6. Classifying Each day on the way to band practice, Kelsey buys a large order of French fries. Her friend Ana encourages her to buy some fruit or a low-fat energy bar instead. What health skill is Ana using? Explain your answer.

🔊 **GO ONLINE** PearsonSuccessNet.com   Audio Summary Section 1.3   *Making Healthy Decisions* **15**

3. Assess

Evaluate

These assignments can help you assess students' mastery of the section content.

Section 3 Review
Answers appear below.

Teaching Resources
• Practice 1-3
• Section 1-3 Quiz

Ⓛ2 **Reteach**

Call on students to name the seven health skills. Call on other students to give examples of the skills.

Ⓛ4 **Enrich**

Teaching Resources
• Enrich 1-3

Health at School

Preventing Injuries If your school has a sports handbook, collect some copies for students to use. If students want to interview a coach, have the students work in small groups and prepare some questions in advance.

Section 3 Review

1. taking action to avoid disease, injury, and other negative health outcomes

2. increase the quality and years of healthy life, eliminate differences in health based on race, ethnic group, or income, create environments that promote good health, and promote healthy behaviors across all life stages

3. gaining awareness, gaining knowledge, and building health skills

4. An action plan is a series of specific steps you can take to achieve a goal. You are setting goals.

5. "Other injuries," because diving into a shallow pool may result in a fatal injury.

6. Ana is advocating for Kelsey to make a positive health decision.

The DECIDE Process

Objective

Demonstrate how to use the DECIDE process to make healthy decisions.

Teaching Strategies

Image Bank Page 16

- Before introducing the DECIDE process, have students think about a time when they had trouble making an important decision. Make a class list of obstacles to decision making. *(e.g., too many choices, afraid to make the wrong decision)* Then, ask students to think of a time when they were able to make an important decision. Make a list of factors that can help a person make effective decisions. *(e.g., one obvious good choice, input from trusted adults)* Leave the lists on the board as you teach the DECIDE process.

- Explain that the DECIDE process will help students make difficult decisions. In fact, it is most useful for important decisions involving multiple alternatives. As a class, apply the steps of the DECIDE process to a teen-relevant decision, such as whether to go to a party where alcohol will be served.

- You may want to give extra attention to the "Identify your values" step. Students may think of values as abstract concepts, such as "truth" and "justice," and have a hard time seeing the connection between values and decisions. The connection may be easier to understand if students think about a decision that involves a conflict between values. For example, being asked by a friend to lie to his parents about his whereabouts sets up a conflict between honesty and loyalty.

The **DECIDE** Process

You just found the perfect after-school job. It's near home, it will be fun, and it will pay for the bicycle you've wanted to buy. That same day, you find out that you finally made the basketball team. Unfortunately, team practices will occur during the hours you would need to be at work. How do you choose between the team and the job?

Many of your decisions are not this complicated, but some decisions are even more difficult. Such decisions require much thought and soul-searching because they can make an important difference in your life. Do you sometimes "hide from" tough choices because they make you feel anxious? Do you ever rush headlong into decisions without really thinking? There is a process, called DECIDE, that can help you think through decisions. This process is easy to remember because each letter in the word DECIDE stands for a step in the process.

Define the problem.

Consider the decision you are facing, and state the issue clearly. Is it important or complex enough to warrant using DECIDE? Some choices are so easy that you already know what to do. In other situations, your decision won't really make much difference—a flip of a coin would do.

Explore the alternatives.

Make a list of possible alternatives for solving your problem. Include "doing nothing" if it is appropriate. If you need more information to fully understand the problem or any of the alternatives, do the research now. You may find that some of the choices are unrealistic. If so, remove them from the list.

Consider the consequences.

One by one, think through what might happen if you were to choose each alternative on your list. Be sure to do the following.

▶ Include both positive and negative results.

▶ Consider what probably would happen, not what you hope would happen.

▶ Ask yourself: How risky is each alternative? What are its chances of success? How would it affect my future? Remember to consider the effects on other people as well.

Identify your values.

Sometimes your values influence your decisions even when you are not aware of the influence. At other times, you may overlook your values because you want something badly. When you do this, however, you may feel uncomfortable with your decision later.

▶ Consider your long-term goals as well as the beliefs of your family and culture.

▶ Consider your own and others' health and safety, and your self-respect.

▶ Identify those choices that are a good match for your values.

Decide and act.

▶ Use the information you have collected to compare the alternatives. Decide which one is best for you. Remember, sometimes there is more than one "right" choice.

▶ Make a plan to act on your decision. You may need to break the plan into smaller steps. Set realistic deadlines for each step. Then follow through with your plan.

Evaluate the results.

Sometime after you have put your decision into effect, take some time to review it.

▶ How did your decision work out?

▶ How has it affected your life?

▶ How has it affected others?

▶ What did you learn?

▶ If you could do it over again, what would you do differently? If you can still change some things for the better, do it now.

 **Practice the Skill**

1. Suppose you were facing the decision described in the introduction—to choose the job or the team. Follow the steps of DECIDE to determine what you would do in this situation. Be sure to consider all alternatives; there may be more than two. (For example, it may be possible to postpone a choice or to take another route to a goal.)

2. List some other important decisions for which DECIDE might be useful. Do they fall into categories? What categories of decisions might not be suitable for DECIDE?

3. Think about a tough decision that you have made in the past or that you are facing now. Use DECIDE to determine what you should do (or should have done).

4. Did using DECIDE help you focus on important values or choices you might otherwise have overlooked? Which ones? Did DECIDE make the decision-making process easier? Why or why not?

Making Healthy Decisions **17**

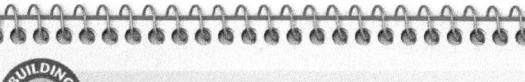 **Practice the Skill**

1. In addition to choosing the job or joining the team, alternatives might include trying to work different hours, looking for a different job, postponing taking a job, or waiting another year to play basketball.

2. Other possible important decisions are deciding what to do after high school, whether to date, and whether to smoke or drink. Decisions could be classified as short- and- long-term or simple and complicated. DECIDE is generally less appropriate for simple decisions and split-second decisions in emergency situations.

3. Students should record this answer in their private journals.

4. Answers will vary, but students may say that DECIDE made the decision-making process easier by providing a step-by-step process to follow.

Health and Community

Community Decisions

Ask interested students to attend a community meeting at which a decision is being discussed. Have students take notes on the discussion and identify any steps in the DECIDE process that are applied to make the decision. After the meeting, ask students to write a report describing the problem, how the decision was made, and whether the steps of the DECIDE process were followed. They also should identify any steps that were not followed and explain how this may have affected the decision. Ask students to share their reports with the class. **WRITING**

Objectives
Before class begins, write the objectives on the board. Have students copy the objectives into their notebooks at the start of class.

1. Focus

Warm-Up Advice Line

Call on a few students to share their written responses. Discuss how they might find out whether the more expensive shampoo is worth the extra cost without having to buy it. *(ask people who have tried it; look for a consumer report on shampoos)* Tell students that they will learn how to evaluate health-related products, services, and information.

Presentation 1-4

Section 4

Being a Wise Health Consumer

Objectives

▶ **Describe** how to evaluate health products, services, and information.
▶ **Evaluate** what advertising does and does not do for a consumer.
▶ **Explain** how a person can avoid health fraud.
▶ **Identify** your rights as a consumer.

Vocabulary
- consumer
- warranty
- advertising
- fraud
- quackery

Warm-Up

Dear Advice Line,

I buy a brand-name shampoo that costs twice as much as the store brand. The ads for the expensive shampoo say that it keeps your hair healthier. My mother says that the store brand is just as good. Who is right?

WRITING Which shampoo would you buy and why?

Making Healthy Consumer Choices

Young children do not decide when to visit a doctor or which brand of cough syrup to buy. When they become ill, they don't search the Internet looking for information about the illness. Young children have limited opportunities to be consumers. A **consumer** buys products or services for personal use.

As a teen, you are making more decisions about your health, including which products and services to use. So you need to know how to evaluate the products, services, and information you are offered.

Products Picture the aisles in a local drugstore. How many of those aisles contain products that could affect your health? More than you might guess. Some of the items are obvious—snack foods, sports drinks, personal care products, and vitamins. There are medicines for treating indigestion, allergies, headaches, and colds. There are household cleansers and pest-control products, which contain substances that are harmful if inhaled or ingested. There are magazines with articles about health and advertisements for health-related products.

18 *Chapter 1*

MATH and Health

L3 Proportions

Tell students that they have a choice of three brands of pain relievers. The three brands have the same strength, so they should choose the brand with the lowest unit price. Brand A costs $3.99 for 60 pills, brand B costs $2.49 for 35 pills, and brand C costs $4.59 for 75 pills.

Ask: **Which brand has the lowest unit price?** *(Brand C has the lowest unit price, or price per pill. The unit price of brand C is $4.59 ÷ 75 pills = $0.06 per pill. The unit prices of the other two brands are calculated the same way and equal $0.07 per pill.)*

American teens spend more than 150 billion dollars each year.

Some products are consumable, meaning they need to be purchased again and again. Examples are hair care and skin care products, weight loss products, and sports drinks. The marketing of many consumable products is aimed toward teens and young adults. The makers of these products often claim that using them will improve your personal appearance or your physical performance. They may also suggest that a product will improve your emotional or social well-being.

Some products are durable, meaning they are meant to last for a number of years before they wear out. Most sports equipment is durable. Having the right equipment and protective gear is essential when you take part in an organized sport, such as football, or an extreme sport, such as snowboarding. The right equipment is also important when you exercise to maintain fitness. **Some factors to consider before buying a product are its safety, cost, warranty, and consumer testing.**

▶ **Safety** Read the product labels and other information supplied with the product to determine its contents and possible safety issues. Does a food contain a substance to which you are allergic? Must the product be used only in a room that is well ventilated, as when the windows are open?

▶ **Cost** Check to see if there are other brands or other products that will give you the same results at a lower cost.

▶ **Warranty** Is there a **warranty,** an offer to repair or replace the product if there is a problem? If so, how long is it good for and what does it cover?

▶ **Consumer Testing** Some government agencies and private groups test a wide range of consumer products. They publish their results and recommendations. Groups may endorse, or approve products that rate highly on their tests. By doing so, the group is saying that the claims made for the product by the manufacturer are true.

 **What kind of questions do you ask before you buy a product?**

FIGURE 10 This teen is shopping for a helmet to wear while he is skateboarding. **Predicting** What factors do you think he should consider before making a purchase?

2. Teach

L3 **EL** Reading/Note Taking 1-4
L2 Adapted Reading/Note Taking 1-4

Making Healthy Consumer Choices

EL Cooperative Learning

Pair up students. Give each pair an advertising flyer from a store that sells both consumable and durable products. Have students classify the products to demonstrate their understanding of the terms *consumable* and *durable*.

L3 Building Health Skills

Practicing Healthful Behaviors Have students find two brands of a health-related product. Ask students to compare the two brands with regard to the factors listed in the text and select the brand they think is the better buy. Then, have students write a paragraph explaining their choice. Call on a few volunteers to read their paragraphs to the class. Discuss which factors most influenced students' decisions. **WRITING**

Visual Learning: Figure 10

Caption Answer *Sample answer:* type of helmet, safety features, cost, and warranty

Connect to Your Life Allow students to answer this question in their private journals.

Differentiated Instruction

L1 Special Needs

Show students empty product packages or package inserts that illustrate all the factors to consider before buying a product (safety, cost, warranty, and consumer testing). Ask students to find information relating to each factor by looking over the packaging materials. Explain how to use the information to decide whether to buy the products.

Visual Learning: Figure 11

Caption Answer I could find out if the classes offered are appropriate for my needs and if the instructors are attentive and knowledgeable.

(L2) Building Health Skills

Communicating If any students attend fitness and recreation programs offered by local non-profit organizations, ask if they would be willing to be interviewed about these programs. Challenge students to ask the kinds of questions wise consumers might ask when they contact a reference for a service.

(L3) Addressing Misconceptions

Infomercials Ask students if they know what an infomercial is *(a long commercial designed to look like an educational news program or talk show)*. By using this type of format, the producer hopes to convince viewers that the information being presented is reliable. Explain that few, if any, health-related products sold through infomercials will do everything the infomercial promises they will do.

FIGURE 11 A fitness center is an example of a health-related service. **Predicting** How could attending a class as a guest help you to decide whether to join a fitness center?

Services You probably don't get to choose your doctor or dentist. But you do get to choose some services that can affect your health. For example, if you choose the wrong nail salon, you might develop an infection. If you choose the wrong health club, you might end up with an injury because of poor advice from a trainer.

When you evaluate a service, you need to find out whether the person who will perform the service is qualified. Whether you choose a service on your own or use a service chosen for you, there are questions you should ask.

▶ What kind of education and experience does the person have? Does the person have the required educational degree, license, or certification?

▶ Does the person have references? Ask for the names and telephone numbers of people who have used the service.

▶ Have any complaints been filed with your state's Attorney General?

Information Before you purchase a product or service, you need to evaluate the information you receive about it. Is it accurate? Is it useful? You need to ask the same type of questions about any health information you receive. **To evaluate health information, you need to evaluate the source of the information.**

▶ Is the source qualified to speak on the topic?

▶ Does the source bring a bias, or slant, to the topic? For example, are they trying to sell a product or service?

▶ Are there other reliable sources that reach the same conclusion?

▶ Is the information current and up to date?

Government agencies, medical associations, and non-profit private health groups often provide reliable information. So do reporters who specialize in science and health topics.

20 *Chapter 1*

Focus on **ISSUES**

(L3) Debate: Advertising and Health

Including all media, the average teen sees between 20,000 and 40,000 advertisements each year. Have groups of students support and oppose the following premise: Viewing advertisements has a major influence on teen behavior and health.

You might want to have students narrow the focus of the debate to advertisements for particular types of products. For example, do advertisements for "junk" foods contribute to obesity? Does seeing advertisements for alcohol make drinking seem appealing?

The Effects of Advertising

Businesses spend millions of dollars each year on advertising because they want to attract customers. **Advertising** is the public promotion of a product or service. Ads appear on television and radio, in newspapers and magazines, on billboards, and in movie theaters. They also pop up on the Internet. Everyone is influenced to some extent by advertising. But as a consumer, you need to base your choices on facts, not on advertisements.

Ads can let you know what products and services are available, but they rarely provide the information you need to make wise choices. For example, an ad may say that a certain medicine contains an ingredient that most doctors recommend. The statement may be true. However, this ingredient is likely to be found in all similar medicines.

An ad may say that a certain store is selling a product at the lowest possible price. Unless you check to see what the price is at other stores, you will not know if this claim is true. An ad may mention scientific studies. But unless the ad explains how the studies were done or provides actual results, a claim based on these studies may be false or misleading. Figure 12 discusses six methods advertisers use to sell products and services. For more information on advertising, see the Building Health Skill on analyzing advertising appeal on pages 404–405.

 **Have you bought a product based on an ad? If so, how did the ad convince you to buy the product?**

FIGURE 12 Advertising can influence people to buy certain products. **Evaluating** Which of these advertising methods do you think is most effective? Why?

Advertising Methods

Method	Message	Example
Scientific studies	Scientific tests prove the product is effective.	"Tests prove that Brand X works fast."
Bandwagon approach	Everyone is using the product. You should, too.	"Don't be left behind—use Product X."
Testimonial	The product is effective because trustworthy people recommend it.	"The medicine recommended by doctors and their families"
Comparison to other products	The product is more effective than others.	"Brand X now has 20% more painkiller than Brand Y."
Emotional appeal	The product is safest for you and your family.	"Choose Brand X—your family's health depends on it."
Price appeal	The product gives you more for your money.	"Brand X—the most for the least"

The Effects of Advertising

 Journal Writing

To start students thinking about how advertising affects their consumer decisions, ask them to write a journal entry about a product they bought because of an ad. Students should describe the product and the ad, explain how the ad influenced them to buy the product, and note whether the product lived up to the ad's claims. They should also comment on what, if anything, they learned from the experience. **WRITING**

L2 Visual Learning: Figure 12

Image Bank Figure 1-12

Bring in examples of each advertising method. As you discuss each method, ask students to think of other examples. **Caption Answer** *Sample answers:* price appeal, because most people are on a budget; bandwagon approach, because people often do things just to fit in

L4 Building Media Literacy

Tell students that advertisers may target ads to specific cultural groups through their selection of actors or models and through the situations shown. Have students look for ads that appear to target certain cultures. Ask students to write a paragraph explaining why they think the advertiser believes the given product will be of interest to people in the targeted group.

 Connect to Your Life Allow students to answer this question in their private journals.

Differentiated Instruction

L2 Less Proficient Readers

Have students find and clip magazine ads that represent several of the following advertising methods: scientific studies, bandwagon approach, testimonial, comparison to other products, emotional appeal, and price appeal. Ask students to label the ads with the methods they represent and use them to make a chart of advertising methods. Students should highlight or circle any clues in the ads that show which type of advertising methods they use. Display the charts in the classroom.

Health Fraud

 **Visual Learning: Figure 13**

Tell students that medicine shows were popular between the Civil War and World War I. Between musical acts or contests, people hawked products such as Hamlin's Wizard Oil. The ingredients included alcohol or other drugs, such as opium. In response to the sale of such potions, Congress passed the Food and Drugs Act in 1906. Explain that health fraud is not a thing of the past. Ask students to suggest examples of current products that would qualify.

Caption Answer The poster claims that wizard oil cures all pain in "man or beast."

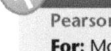 **Class Discussion**

Discuss reasons why people might be susceptible to health fraud (they are desperate for a cure, they cannot afford prescribed medications, they have a distrust of conventional medicine, or they see some evidence that the claims are true). Then ask why teens may be vulnerable to exaggerated claims about products targeted at their appearance.

Connect to Your Life *Sample answer:* I saw a health claim that a product could completely cure acne in 24 hours.

Content Update ⟶ **GO ONLINE**

Visit Pearson SuccessNet to access more information about fraud, quackery, and health. Have students complete the Web activity.

FIGURE 13 Promises of impossible cures are a sure sign of quackery. **Observing** What claim does this poster make about wizard oil?

Health Fraud

If a person tells lies to obtain money or property, the person is guilty of an illegal act called **fraud.** People who sell useless medical treatments or products are engaged in health fraud, or **quackery** (KWAK ur ee). These people are called quacks. Quacks promise that a treatment or product will bring about a miracle cure or at least greatly improve a person's health. One danger of quackery is that it can keep someone from receiving proper medical care. If a person believes that a quack remedy is working or might work, he or she might postpone seeing a doctor.

Recognizing Health Fraud Quacks depend on people's lack of knowledge and their desperate desire to find a cure. If a disease is life threatening, such as cancer, it is a likely target of quacks. So are conditions that are long lasting, such as arthritis or problems with weight control. **People can avoid health fraud by carefully evaluating the claims made about a treatment or product.** These are some warning signs of quackery.

► Someone claims that a product or treatment is the only possible cure for a health problem.

► The promised results seem too good to be true.

► A product or treatment is said to cure many different ailments.

► A product is said to contain "special" or "secret" ingredients.

Responding to Health Fraud If you have doubts about any product or treatment, ask a doctor or pharmacist. Notify your state's Office of the Attorney General about any health fraud you uncover in your state. If a local business is involved, let your local Better Business Bureau know as well. If you buy a fraudulent product that is shipped to you by mail, notify your local postmaster.

GO ONLINE
PearsonSuccessNet.com
For: More on fraud, quackery, and health

Connect to Your Life What health claim have you seen that was too good to be true?

TEENS *Are Asking . . .*

Q: I got a bad hair cut last week, but I didn't say anything because I don't like to complain. Is it too late to do something?

A: Most businesses want to know when their customers are not satisfied because they depend on repeat business and word-of-mouth advertising. If you do go back to the salon, be specific about what "bad" means.

Do a role-play with a friend to practice the dialogue you might have with the person who cut your hair. Also consider asking an adult to go back to the salon with you. If you don't feel comfortable pursuing the issue at this time, just thinking about what you could say might make it easier for you to speak up the next time you have a problem.

Your Rights as a Consumer

Kiana bought an exercise bike so she could stay fit all year round. A week later, a pedal broke off the bike. She went back to the store and was given a new pedal. Two months later, the speedometer stopped working. She went back to the store again, but the salesperson told her the exercise bike only had a 30-day warranty, and the store was no longer responsible. Kiana was upset but was not sure what her rights were as a consumer. **As a consumer, you have the right to information, the right to consumer protection by government agencies, and the right to complain.**

The Right to Information As a consumer, you need information in order to make wise choices. You need enough information to make an informed judgment about whether a product or service will be safe and effective.

Consumer Protection Figure 14 lists some government agencies that help to protect consumers. Some agencies test products before they can be sold to consumers. Other agencies take action against quackery. Some agencies remove unsafe products from the marketplace.

The Right to Complain If you have a problem with a product, complain to both the store that sold you the product and the manufacturer. Ask for a refund. Follow these steps to make your complaint effective. Use the same approach if you have a problem with a service.

- ▶ **Identify the Problem** Be as clear and specific as possible about what is wrong.

- ▶ **Decide on Your Goal** Decide on a fair way to resolve your complaint. Do you want a refund, replacement, repair, or credit?

- ▶ **Collect Documents** Gather sales receipts, warranties, canceled checks, contracts, or repair records to back up your complaint.

- ▶ **Identify the Person in Charge** Find out who has the power to deal with your problem. It may be a customer service representative or a manager.

Government Consumer Agencies

The Federal Trade Commission (FTC)
Prevents unfair or deceptive advertising and labeling

The Food and Drug Administration (FDA)
Protects public from sale of unsafe foods, drugs, and cosmetics

The Consumer Product Safety Commission (CPSC)
Establishes safety standards for consumer goods and takes dangerous products off the market

WARNING
CHILDREN CAN FALL INTO BUCKET AND DROWN.
KEEP CHILDREN AWAY FROM BUCKET WITH EVEN A SMALL AMOUNT OF LIQUID.

FIGURE 14 These agencies help protect consumers from unsafe products and from health fraud. **Classifying** Which agency would you notify to report false advertising?

L3 **Building Health Skills**

Communicating Ask students to write a paragraph explaining the three basic consumer rights in a way that is understandable to students in grades five or six. Students should use examples to demonstrate the rights, and the examples should be relevant to students in these grades. Arrange for students to share their paragraphs with younger students. **WRITING**

Visual Learning: Figure 14

Caption Answer the Federal Trade Commission

L2 **Building Health Skills**

Practicing Healthful Behaviors Discuss the steps for making an effective complaint (identify the problem, decide on your goal, collect documents, and identify the person in charge). Then, have students apply the steps to Kiana's problem with her exercise bike.

Differentiated Instruction

L4 **Gifted and Talented**

Have interested students locate the Web site for the office of the attorney general in your state. Ask students to find out what services or information are available related to health fraud or consumer complaints.

Have students prepare a graphic roadmap that indicates pathways from the home page to relevant information on the site itself or on linked sites. Give students an opportunity to explain their roadmaps.

3. Assess

Evaluate

These assignments can help you assess students' mastery of the section content.

Section 4 Review

Answers appear below.

Teaching Resources
- Practice 1-4
- Section 1-4 Quiz

 **Reteach**

Ask students to write fill-in-the-blank questions based on the information in the section. Then, have pairs of students exchange and answer each other's questions.

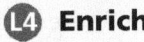 **Enrich**

Teaching Resources
- Enrich 1-4

Health and Community

Comparison Shopping Make sure students understand the meaning of *consumable*. Students are likely to find that smaller stores have higher prices. They may also find that prices vary depending on the neighborhood.

FIGURE 15 When you complain about a product, you will need documents, such as a sales receipt, to back up your claim. So you should store important documents in a place where you can easily find them.

Put Your Complaint in Writing Sometimes you will need to write a letter of complaint. It might be because you no longer live near the store where you bought a product or that you ordered from a catalog or a Web site. You might also need to write a letter if you do not get satisfactory results by complaining in person. A letter is especially important if the product has a time-limited warranty. Include the following information.

- ▶ the product's model and serial number
- ▶ the location and date of purchase
- ▶ your specific complaint and suggested resolution
- ▶ your name, address, and phone number and the best times to reach you
- ▶ a summary of any conversations you had in person
- ▶ a reasonable date by which you expect action to be taken

Be firm, calm, and respectful. Avoid writing an angry or threatening letter. Keep a copy of the letter and all the documents.

If you don't receive a response or are unhappy with the response, contact the national headquarters of the company. You can also write a letter to the Better Business Bureau or your local or state consumer protection agency. When all else fails, people may file a complaint in small claims court. These court proceedings usually do not require a lawyer and are relatively simple, quick, and inexpensive.

Section 4 Review

Key Ideas and Vocabulary

1. What is a **warranty?** What are three other factors to consider when buying a product?
2. In general what do you need to do when you evaluate a service or information?
3. What is **advertising?** What can you learn from advertising? What can't you learn?
4. How can you avoid health fraud?
5. What three rights do consumers have?

Critical Thinking

6. **Predicting** Why might a company president answer a letter from an unhappy customer?

Health and Community

Comparison Shopping Pick a consumable product that you use. Compare prices at as many stores in your area as possible. Write a paragraph discussing your results. Is there a noticeable pattern in the price differences? For example, does the size or the location of a store matter? **WRITING**

---

7. **Classifying** A company chooses a popular sports figure to advertise a product. Which advertising method is the company using?
8. **Making Judgments** A health club has inexpensive introductory memberships. List three questions you should ask before joining.

(( )) **GO ONLINE** PearsonSuccessNet.com   Audio Summary Section 1.4

Section 4 Review

1. an offer to repair or replace a product if there is a problem; safety, cost, and consumer testing
2. For a service, you need to find out whether the person who will perform the service is qualified. For information, you need to evaluate the source of the information.
3. Advertising is the public promotion of a product or service. You can learn what products and services are available from advertising, but you cannot learn all the information you need to make wise consumer choices.
4. by carefully evaluating the claims made about a treatment or product
5. the right to information, the right to consumer protection by government agencies, and the right to complain
6. *Sample answer:* to show the customer that the company takes the complaint seriously and values the customer's business
7. testimonial
8. *Sample answer:* What is the cost after the introductory period? What hours is the club open? Are staff members certified trainers?

Chapter 1
At a Glance

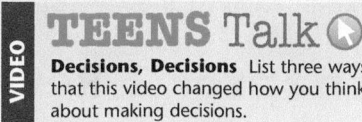 **TEENS** Talk

Decisions, Decisions List three ways that this video changed how you think about making decisions.

Section 1   What Is Health?

Key Ideas

▶ Two factors that can be used to evaluate health are life expectancy and quality of life.

▶ The aspects of health that are important for overall well-being are physical health, mental and emotional health, and social health.

▶ Many of the choices that you make on a daily basis affect your position on the health continuum.

Vocabulary

- health (2)
- life expectancy (2)
- quality of life (2)
- goal (2)
- physical health (3)
- mental health (3)
- emotional health (3)
- social health (3)
- continuum (4)
- wellness (4)

Section 2   Identifying Health Risks

Key Ideas

▶ Heredity, environment, media, technology, health-care, and behavior are factors that influence health.

▶ When you evaluate a risk factor, consider both the short-term and long-term consequences. Decide whether you can control the risk factor. Analyze the possible benefits and risks of a decision.

Vocabulary

- heredity (6)
- gender (6)
- environment (7)
- culture (7)
- media (8)
- habit (9)
- risk factor (10)

Section 3   Taking Responsibility for Your Health

Key Ideas

▶ The broad goals of *Healthy People 2020* are to increase the quality and years of healthy life, to eliminate differences in health based on race, ethnic group, or income, to create environments that promote good health, and to promote healthy behaviors across all life stages.

▶ There are three steps you can take to help you meet your personal health goals—gaining awareness, gaining knowledge, and building skills.

Vocabulary

- prevention (12) • values (14) • action plan (15)
- advocacy (15) • health literacy (15)

Section 4   Being a Wise Health Consumer

Key Ideas

▶ Before buying a product, consider safety, cost, the warranty, and consumer testing. Find out whether the person who will perform a service is qualified. To evaluate health information, you need to evaluate the source of the information.

▶ Ads can let you know what products and services are available, but they rarely provide the information you need to make wise choices.

▶ People can avoid health fraud by evaluating the claims made about a treatment or product.

▶ As a consumer, you have the right to information, the right to consumer protection by government agencies, and the right to complain.

Vocabulary

- consumer (18) • warranty (19) • advertising (21)
- fraud (22) • quackery (22)

Chapter 1
At a Glance

VIDEO **Decisions, Decisions** Ask for volunteers to share their answers. Use examples from the video to review ways that teens' decisions can affect their health.

Key Ideas Review

EL Have pairs of students use the illustrations in the chapter to review the key ideas. Ask students to let you know if they are having trouble connecting a figure to a key idea.

L2 Ask students to read the headings throughout the chapter. After they read each heading, they should pause to recall important facts about it. Tell students to reread the material under any headings for which they cannot recall important facts.

Vocabulary Review

L1 Read the definitions of the chapter vocabulary terms in random order, and call on students to identify the terms. For any terms students cannot identify, ask them to reread the definitions and use the terms in sentences.

L3 Have students make a crossword puzzle incorporating at least 12 of the chapter vocabulary terms. Ask pairs of students to exchange and solve each other's puzzles.

Chapter 1 Review

 GO ONLINE

PearsonSuccessNet.com

Students can go online for a review activity for Chapter 1.

Reviewing Key Ideas

Section 1

1. c

2. physical health: able to carry out everyday tasks without tiring; mental health: being mentally alert, being able to learn from your mistakes and recognize your achievements; emotional health: having feelings that are appropriate to events; social health: having loving relationships, respecting others' rights, giving and accepting help

3. Accept any reasonable examples including getting enough sleep and exercising regularly.

4. *Sample answer:* It could keep you from interacting with others.

5. *Sample answer:* physically active, mentally alert, close relationships, able to enjoy life

Section 2

6. b

7. Students will probably say that their environment is harder to control than their behavior.

8. In the short-term, weight gain; in the long-term, heart disease

9. Risks might include muscle strains and injuries from falls; benefits might include stronger muscles and stress reduction.

Section 3

10. c

11. Leading causes of death for young people are due to risky behaviors. Reducing these behaviors increases the years of healthy life, which is a broad goal of *Healthy People 2020.*

12. To gain awareness means to recognize a health problem. To gain knowledge means to learn how to prevent or treat a problem.

13. *Sample answer:* It requires more effort to cure a problem than to prevent a problem.

Chapter 1 Review

Reviewing Key Ideas

 GO ONLINE

PearsonSuccessNet.com

For: Chapter 1 review activity

Section 1

1. The number of years that a person can expect to live is called
  a. quality of life.
  b. quantity of life.
  c. life expectancy.
  d. life history.

2. Describe ways to recognize good physical health, mental health, emotional health, and social health.

3. List two behaviors that could move you toward wellness on the health continuum.

4. **Critical Thinking** How could having to deal with a physical, mental, or emotional problem affect a person's social health?

5. **Critical Thinking** What are four standards you would use to measure the quality of your life?

Section 2

6. Which of these factors is part of your social environment?
  a. heredity
  b. culture
  c. media
  d. technology

7. Do you think that you have more control over risk factors in your environment or behavioral risk factors? Explain.

8. What is one possible short-term consequence of eating a high-fat diet? What is a possible long-term consequence?

9. **Critical Thinking** Analyze the risks and benefits of going rock climbing.

Section 3

10. When you try to influence decisions others make about health, which skill are you using?
  a. setting goals
  b. making decisions
  c. advocacy
  d. analyzing influences

11. How does a focus on reducing risky health behaviors help the nation to achieve the broad goals of *Healthy People 2020*?

12. Explain what it means to gain awareness and to gain knowledge about a health problem.

13. **Critical Thinking** Use the saying "an ounce of prevention is worth a pound of cure" to explain the importance of prevention to your well-being.

Section 4

14. A flyer announcing the opening of a health food store is an example of
  a. advertising.
  b. quackery.
  c. advocacy.
  d. public service.

15. What questions could you ask to find out if a person who runs a gym is qualified?

16. List two reliable sources and one poor source of health information. Explain your choices.

17. Describe three ways that government agencies protect consumers.

18. **Critical Thinking** Which do you think makes people more vulnerable to fraud, a lack of knowledge or desperation? Explain.

Building Health Skills

19. **Advocacy** Why do you think many teens smoke despite the health risks? What argument against smoking would be most effective for teens?

20. **Analyzing Influences** Do ads for healthcare products appeal more to your emotions than to your ability to reason? Explain.

21. **Making Decisions** You are thinking about using a liquid diet supplement. What steps should you take before making this decision?

22. **Setting Goals** Choose a behavior that moves you closer to the wellness end of the health continuum. Make an action plan for making this behavior a habit. Put your plan into action for a week and monitor your progress. Then adjust your plan, if necessary. **WRITING**

Health and Community

Defining Health Ask ten people of different ages to define the term *health*. Record the responses. Then write a paragraph comparing and contrasting the responses. How were the definitions alike? How were they different? **WRITING**

Section 4

14. a

15. Ask about education, experience, and whether the person is certified.

16. Government agencies, medical associations, and non-profit private health groups are usually reliable. Sources that are trying to sell a product or service are less reliable.

17. prevent unfair or deceptive advertising; protect public from the sale of unsafe foods, drugs, and cosmetics; establish safety standards for consumer goods; take dangerous products off the market

18. a lack of knowledge because people are unable to detect false claims; desperation because people want to believe the false claims

Standardized Test Prep

Math Practice

The graph compares data on smoking for high school students from 2009 and adults from 2008. It also shows the Healthy People 2020 target goals for smoking. Use the graph to answer Questions 23–26.

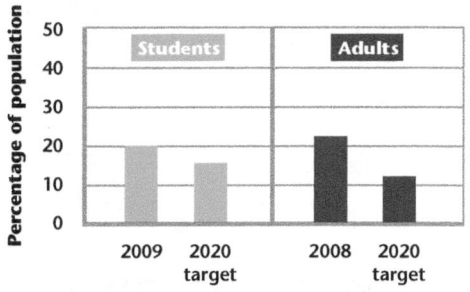

23. What percentage of high school students were cigarette smokers in 2009?
A 12%   B 16%
C 21%   D 20%

24. What was the difference in percentage of high school students who smoked and adults who smoked in the late 2000s?
F 1%   G 8%
H 12%   J 20%

25. What is the percentage decrease in high school smokers targeted by *Healthy People 2020?*
A 0%   B 4%
C 16%   D 20%

26. Assume the target goals for 2020 are met. Out of 500 high school students, how many would you predict would be smokers?
F 16   G 35
H 60   J 80

Test-Taking Tip

On test day, think positive thoughts. Tell yourself, "I will do well on this test. I am prepared."

Reading and Writing Practice

Read the passage. Then answer Questions 27–30.

People's perceptions of risk often don't match the facts. More people are afraid of flying than of car travel. Yet, the risk of a fatal car crash is much higher than the risk of a plane crash. A risk seems smaller than it actually is when you think you are in control or when you can benefit from taking the risk. New risks, especially those that are highlighted in the media, seem greater than risks that are familiar. The danger of inaccurate perception of risks is that people worry too much about low-level risks, such as shark attacks, and too little about significant risks, such as smoking.

27. What is the main idea of this passage?
A People should worry less about risks.
B People often misjudge the level of a given risk.
C Car travel is more risky than air travel.
D Your level of control affects how you view a risk.

28. Based on this passage, what does the word *perceptions* mean?
F feelings
G fears
H understandings
J observations

29. Which of the following statements is supported by this passage?
A People are usually less concerned about risks that are discussed in the media.
B The media only discusses risks that are new.
C The media decides which behaviors are risky.
D The media can affect your assessment of a risk.

Constructed Response
30. Why do you think it is dangerous for people to focus too much on low-level risks and not enough on more common risks?

Standardized Test Prep
Math Practice
23. D
24. F
25. B
26. J

Reading and Writing Practice
27. B
28. H
29. D
30. People are less likely to take steps to reduce the most common health risks.

Building Health Skills

19. *Sample answer:* Teens smoke due to peer pressure. Argue that bad breath and stained teeth are unattractive.

20. *Sample answer:* Most ads appeal to emotions because people often make hasty decisions based on emotions.

21. *Sample answer:* Gather information about the product from an unbiased source before making a decision.

22. Allow students to record their goal and action plan in their private journals.

Health and Community

Defining Health Some people may focus mainly on physical health. Some may focus on the absence of illness. Some may include quality of life.

CHAPTER 2 Personality, Self-Esteem, and Emotions

Section Objectives	Standards Correlation	Instructional Resources L3	SE eTEXT	TE eTEXT	PRINT
1 Personality ⏱ 2 periods; 1 block	NHES: 1.12.4, 2.12.1, 2.12.2, 2.12.3, 2.12.7	SE Warm-Up, p. 30	•	•	•
2.1.1 **Name** five traits that are used to define personality.		RN Guided Reading 2-1	•	•	•
2.1.2 **Identify** two factors that determine how your personality develops.s		TR Practice 2-1			•
2.1.3 **Describe** what happens to personality over a lifetime.		TR Section 2-1 Quiz			•
2 Self-Esteem ⏱ 2 periods; 1 block	NHES: 2.12.1, 2.12.4, 2.12.7, 2.12.8, 5.12.1, 5.12.2	SE Warm-Up, p. 36	•	•	•
2.2.1 **Compare** the effects of high and low self-esteem on health.		RN Note Taking Guide 2-2	•	•	•
2.2.2 **Describe** the changes in self-esteem that can occur as people age.		IB Image Bank 2-8			•
2.2.1 **Identify** ways to achieve and maintain high self-esteem.		TR Practice 2-2			•
2.2.2 **Summarize** Maslow's theory of self-actualization.		TR Section 2-2 Quiz			•
Expressing Anger in Healthy Ways ⏱ 1 period; 1/2 block	NHES: 4.12.1, 4.12.3, 6.12.1, 6.12.2, 6.12.3, 7.12.3	SE Practice the Skill, p. 43	•	•	•
BHS.2 **Implement** a plan to evaluate and improve personal strategies for expressing anger.		RN Building Health Skills 2	•	•	•
3 Expressing Your Emotions ⏱ 2 periods; 1 block	NHES: 2.12.2, 2.12.5, 2.12.7, 4.12.1	SE Warm-Up, p. 44	•	•	•
2.3.1 **Identify** four primary emotions and three learned emotions.		SE Media Wise News Content and Emotions, p. 47	•	•	•
2.3.2 **Explain** why it is important to recognize your emotions.		RN Note Taking Guide 2-3	•	•	•
2.3.3 **Distinguish** helpful from harmful coping strategies.		IB Image Bank 2-12		•	
		TR Practice 2-3		•	
		TR Section 2-3 Quiz		•	

Chapter Review and Assessment

SE   Chapter 2 Review, p. 51 L3
CTB Chapter 2 Test L2 L3 L4
SE   Standardized Test Prep, p. 53 L3

PROGRAM COMPONENTS

SE Student Edition	CTB Computer Test Bank
TE Teacher Edition	AUD Audio Section Summaries
TR Teaching Resources	
RN Reading and Note Taking Guide	DVD Teens Talk Video Series
	VVG Video Viewing Guide
ARN Adapted Reading and Note Taking Guide	PPT Presentation
IB Image Bank	

Differentiated Instruction
L1 **L2** **L4** **EL**

		SE eTEXT	TE eTEXT	PRINT
ARN	Note Taking Guide 2-1 **L2**	•	•	
RN	Note Taking Guide 2-1 **EL**	•	•	•
AUD	Audio Summary 2-1 **L1** **L2** **EL**	•	•	
TE	Reteach Strategy, p. 35 **L2**		•	•
TR	Enrich 2-1 **L4**		•	
ARN	Note Taking Guide 2-2 **L2**	•	•	
RN	Note Taking Guide 2-2 **EL**	•	•	•
AUD	Audio Summary 2-2 **L1** **L2** **EL**	•	•	
TE	Reteach Strategy, p. 41 **L2**		•	•
TR	Enrich 2-2 **L4**		•	
ARN	Building Health Skills 2 **L2**	•	•	
RN	Building Health Skills 2 **EL**	•	•	•
ARN	Note Taking Guide 2-3 **L2**	•	•	
RN	Note Taking Guide 2-3 **EL**	•	•	•
AUD	Audio Summary 2-3 **L1** **L2** **EL**	•	•	
TE	Reteach Strategy, p. 50 **L2**		•	•
TR	Enrich 2-3 **L4**		•	

ABILITY LEVELS
L1 For students with special needs
L2 For less proficient readers
L3 For all students
L4 For gifted and talented students
EL For English language learners

Chapter 2 Digital/Video Pathway

This alternative pathway allows you to teach this chapter's content using only the video and online materials.

Preview

DVD	Video #2 Preview
SE	Video #2 Preview Activity
VVG	Video #2 Worksheet

Being Yourself

1

PPT	2-1 Presentation
RN/ARN	2-1 Note Taking
PPT	2-1 Section Quiz

2

DVD	Video #2 Explore/Wrap-Up
VVG	Video #2 Worksheet
PPT	2-2 Presentation
RN/ARN	2-2 Note Taking
PPT	2-2 Section Quiz

Being Yourself

3

PPT	2-3 Presentation
RN/ARN	2-3 Note Taking
PPT	2-3 Section Quiz

Chapter Preview

Section 1 Personality
Personality consists of behaviors, thoughts, and attitudes. Heredity and environment both play a role in personality development. Personality continues to develop throughout an individual's lifetime.

Section 2 Self-Esteem
An individual's level of self-esteem may affect his or her health. The level of self-esteem is likely to change during an individual's lifetime. According to Maslow, a person's basic needs, including the need for esteem, must be met before the person can achieve self-actualization.

Communicating
Expressing Anger in Healthy Ways

By identifying their responses to anger, students learn to replace destructive behaviors with constructive ones.

Section 3 Expressing Your Emotions
Emotions can be classified as primary or learned. Recognizing emotions is the first step toward coping with emotions in healthy ways.

Personality, Self-Esteem, and Emotions

1 Personality

2 Self-Esteem

4 Building Health Skills
- **Communicating** Expressing Anger in Healthy Ways

3 Expressing Your Emotions
- **Media Wise** News Content and Emotions

GO ONLINE PearsonSuccessNet.com

VIDEO 2
TEENS Talk
Being Yourself

Preview **Activity**

Whose Opinion of You Matters Most?

Complete this activity before you watch the video.

1. Read the quote below.
No one can make you feel inferior without your consent.
Eleanor Roosevelt

2. Then write a short paragraph describing what the quote means to you. **WRITING**

3. Pair up with another student to share and discuss your paragraphs.

28

GO ONLINE

PearsonSuccessNet.com

For resources and activities for this chapter.

Sensitive Issues

Remind students that individuals have different personality traits, levels of self-esteem, and methods of expressing emotions. Throughout the chapter, use hypothetical discussions to help students explore these concepts.

- Never ask students to disclose information they would rather keep confidential.
- Always give students other options for activities in which they are asked to apply what they learn to their own lives.

29

VIDEO 2 TEENS Talk
Being Yourself

Video Objectives

Use this video to help students

Explain how factors such as a learning disability, a physical trait, or shyness can affect self-esteem.

Evaluate the effect of other people's opinions on their self-esteem.

Identify strategies they can use to boost their self-esteem.

Preview Activity

Whose Opinion of You Matters Most?

Assign the Preview Activity for homework a few days before you plan to show the video. After students complete the writing assignment, have students pair up and discuss what the quote means to them. Then ask some pairs to share their thoughts with the class.

From the Authors

As much as we might want to connect high self-esteem with good health, we cannot conclude that high self-esteem always equates with good health. In this chapter, we are talking about *global* self-esteem—a person's overall opinion of himself or herself. Research has not found a correlation between global self-esteem and low-risk behaviors. People who like themselves tend to take care of themselves. However, people who like themselves also can be involved in high-risk behaviors.

Research is beginning to show a connection between *situational* self-esteem and behavior. Situational self-esteem refers to a particular aspect of a person's life. A poor body image, for example, can have an effect on a person's willingness to exercise.

Personality

Objectives

Before class begins, write the objectives on the board. Have students copy the objectives into their notebooks at the start of class.

1. Focus

Warm-Up Quick Quiz

Use the Warm-Up Presentation slide to survey student responses.

Tell students that they will not have to share their responses to the Quick Quiz and Writing activity. After students complete the assignment, discuss examples of behaviors that would support different ratings. For example, what behaviors would indicate that a person is cautious? Then ask students to predict whether their responses would be likely to change if they took the same quiz in ten years. Have students offer reasons for their predictions.

Presentation 2-1

Sensitive Issues

- Students are likely to be sensitive about their personalities, especially if they perceive some traits as more desirable than others. Help students understand that it is normal to want to change some personality traits.
- Heredity and environment can be sensitive topics for students. For example, some students may not know their biological parents. Others may be experiencing major family problems.

Section 1

Personality

Objectives

▶ **Name** five traits that are used to define personality.

▶ **Identify** two factors that determine how your personality develops.

▶ **Describe** what happens to personality over a lifetime.

Vocabulary

- personality
- psychologist
- modeling
- peer group
- identity

Warm-Up

Quick Quiz For each pair of adjectives, rate yourself on a scale from 1 to 5. For example, if *cautious* describes you perfectly, pick 1. If *adventurous* is perfect, pick 5. Otherwise, pick 2, 3, or 4.

	1 2 3 4 5	
Cautious	① ② ③ ④ ⑤	Adventurous
Outgoing	① ② ③ ④ ⑤	Shy
Calm	① ② ③ ④ ⑤	Anxious
Suspicious	① ② ③ ④ ⑤	Trusting
Excitable	① ② ③ ④ ⑤	Even-tempered

WRITING Use an example from your life to support the rating you chose for one of the adjective pairs.

Describing Personality

Think about how people behave at a party. One person may be the "life of the party." Another person may sit quietly on the couch. Did you ever wonder why people act so differently in the same situation? It is because each person has a unique personality. Your **personality** consists of the behaviors, attitudes, feelings, and ways of thinking that make you an individual. For example, when you are introduced to new people, you may be characteristically outgoing or you may be shy.

Being outgoing or shy are examples of personality traits. So are being reliable, organized, and forgiving. A **psychologist** (sy KAHL uh jist) studies how people think, feel, and behave. Psychologists have described hundreds of personality traits. **Many researchers use five central traits to describe how people behave, relate to others, and react to change. These traits are extroversion, agreeableness, conscientiousness, emotional stability, and openness to experiences.**

Extroversion This trait describes how much you like being with other people. The labels extrovert (EK struh vurt) and introvert are often used to describe the extremes of this personality trait. An extrovert tends to be outgoing, talkative, and sociable. An introvert tends to be shy, quiet, and reserved. Extroverts tend to seek out other people. Introverts are more comfortable spending time on their own.

For Your INFORMATION!

Personality Traits

For centuries, people have been trying to explain differences in personality. Some ancient Greeks proposed a theory of personality based on mixtures of four bodily fluids, or humors—blood, phlegm, black bile, and yellow bile. The humors produced different traits. A person with excess yellow bile would be angry and irritable. A person with excess blood would be cheerful and optimistic. A proper balance of bodily fluids would result in a well-adjusted personality.

Agreeableness This trait describes your tendency to relate to other people in a friendly way. People who are agreeable tend to cooperate with others. They are usually forgiving and good-natured. They assume that other people are honest and trustworthy. People who are disagreeable tend to be suspicious or hostile. They assume that other people are unreliable or ready to take advantage of them.

Conscientiousness This trait describes how responsible and self-disciplined you are. Conscientious (kahn shee EN shus) people tend to be dependable and make good decisions. They approach tasks in an organized, deliberate, and thorough manner. On the other end of the scale are people who do not think through decisions, are careless, and easily distracted. They may give up on a task or lose interest in the task before the task is complete.

Emotional Stability People who are emotionally stable tend to be relaxed, secure, and calm, even during difficult situations. They tend to focus on the positive side of things. On the other end of the scale are people who are fearful, worried, and angry. They tend to focus on the negative and to expect the worst in most situations.

Openness to Experiences People who are open to new experiences tend to be curious, imaginative, and creative. They are likely to have a wide range of interests and may be less predictable. People who are less open tend to be more predictable and less independent. They are likely to do what everyone else is doing.

 How would you describe your personality, using the five central traits?

FIGURE 1 Keeping one's room clean and orderly takes self-discipline. **Evaluating** Based solely on these photographs, where would you rate these young women on the conscientiousness scale?

31

L3 **EL** Reading/Note Taking 2-1

L2 Adapted Reading/Note Taking 2-1

Describing Personality

L2 Building Vocabulary

Write the terms *introvert* and *extrovert* on the board. Underline the word parts *intro-* and *extro-*. Explain that *extro-* means outward and *intro-* means inward. Have students relate this information to the meanings of the terms *introvert* and *extrovert.*

EL Cooperative Learning

Have students work with a partner who is fluent in English to make a list of adjectives that can be used to describe personality. The list should emerge from a conversation about how people behave. As the partners talk about personality traits, the fluent partner can identify adjectives that match behaviors the English language learner describes.

L3 Visual Learning: Figure 1

Have students use the pictures to answer the caption question. Then ask: **Do you think most people exhibit the same degree of conscientiousness in all parts of their lives?** *(Sample answer: No, some people tend to be very conscientious about tasks that interest them, but not about those they find boring.)* **Caption Answer** Based solely on the photos, the young women appear to be at opposite ends of the conscientiousness scale.

 Allow students to answer this question in their private journals.

Differentiated Instruction

L2 Less Proficient Readers

Have students preview Section 1 to locate the boldface heads in the section. Explain that the boldface heads divide the text by topic and can be used to divide the reading into manageable sections. Have students use the following strategy when they complete a reading assignment: read the boldface head, predict what will be covered in that section of text, read the text, review their predictions, and then use the Section Review questions to check comprehension.

How Personality Forms

L3 Building Health Skills

Analyzing Influences Remind students that infants display inherited personality traits. Some infants are cheerful, and some tend to cry a lot. Ask students to consider how these traits could affect how adults respond to the infants. Then consider how those responses might reinforce or modify an infant's inherited personality.

L3 Addressing Misconceptions

Heredity and Personality Students may have the misconception that some traits are predetermined by heredity. Explain that inherited traits can be modified by an individual's experiences. For example, children who tend to resist new experiences can be encouraged to become more open as they mature.

L1 Class Discussion

Some students may be unclear about what it means to inherit traits. If there is a pair of identical twins at your school, arrange for them to visit your class to talk about what it is like to have a twin. This will give students a chance to observe both their physical traits and their personalities. Afterwards, discuss what the students observed.

How Personality Forms

Which has the greater influence on personality—"nature" or "nurture"? Nature refers to traits you are born with, ones you inherit from your parents. Nurture refers to the environment you are raised in and the experiences you have during your life. **Personality traits are influenced by a combination of heredity and environment.**

Heredity Why are some infants calm and cheerful while others tend to cry a lot? Why do some babies seem uncomfortable in new surroundings while others seem to thrive? These early differences are evidence that infants are born with distinct tendencies to act in certain ways. In fact, some differences are evident before birth. For example, some babies kick and move around a lot inside their mothers, while others are relatively quiet. There is evidence that traits such as cheerfulness and shyness are inherited. There is also evidence that talents, such as musical and artistic abilities, can be inherited.

One way that researchers study how heredity influences personality is by studying identical twins. Identical twins come from a single fertilized egg. Thus, they inherit the same traits. The identical twins in Figure 2 were separated as infants and raised by different families. When they met as adults they were surprised to discover how many behaviors and interests they shared. Identical twins who are raised separately often have similar careers and hobbies. They even like the same type of clothing and food.

FIGURE 2 These identical twins were raised by different families and reunited as adults. They were surprised how much they had in common, including their chosen careers as firefighters.

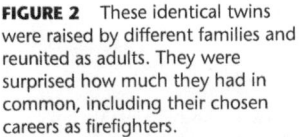

32

TEENS *Are Asking . . .*

Q: Other students at school enjoy talking and joking with friends. But I have a hard time talking to anyone. Why am I so shy?

A: Shyness is a personality trait that seems to be inherited. The trait can be recognized in infants. Studies show that infants who are shy react strongly to mild stress.

Inherited personality traits can be modified by experience. Join clubs or volunteer organizations in which you will meet people who share your interests. When you work with people on a project, it is easier to find things to say. Through these experiences, you can develop your communication skills.

FIGURE 3 Young people learn how to behave by observing older relatives. They can also learn skills, attitudes, and cultural traditions.

Environment Just because you inherit certain tendencies doesn't mean that your personality is set for life when you are born. Heredity is only half the picture. Environment plays an equally important role. Your family, your friends, and your cultural group are important parts of your environment. They all have an influence on your personality.

▶ **Family** Experiences you had as a child helped to shape your personality. Children learn about feelings, attitudes, and appropriate ways to behave from their families. As children develop, they copy the behavior of others. This is called **modeling.** For example, a child may learn to be respectful to older adults by observing a parent's behavior toward grandparents. Children also learn by being rewarded for desirable behaviors and punished for less desirable ones.

▶ **Friends** Starting in childhood and throughout the teenage years, friends become an increasingly important influence on personality. Most teens in the United States spend more time with other teens than with their families. These friends, who are about the same age and share similar interests, are called a **peer group.** If your peer group models healthy behaviors, such as cooperation, the group can have a positive influence on your personality.

▶ **Culture** Personality traits that are valued in one culture may not be as highly valued in another culture. Some cultures encourage people to be independent while others put a higher value on fitting in with the group. In some cultures, it is normal to show your feelings in public. In other cultures, people are expected to be more reserved. When people from different cultures meet, such differences can lead to misunderstandings.

 GO ONLINE
PearsonSuccessNet.com
For: More on personality

 In what ways have your friends influenced your personality?

Personality, Self-Esteem, and Emotions **33**

L2 Building Health Skills

Advocacy Having a peer group that models healthy behaviors can have a positive impact on students' personalities and behaviors. Challenge students to think of specific actions they could take to model agreeableness. Then, have students make posters that use words and images to encourage others to carry out these actions.

L3 Cultural Connection

Discuss the tendency for some people to assign personality traits to someone based on his or her cultural background. Ask if students think this tendency is justified. Also ask if it matters whether the trait being assigned is viewed as positive or negative. *(Even if a trait is seen as positive, individuals should not be prejudged based on their connection to a group.)*

 Sample answer: Because of my friends, I am more open to new experiences, such as trying different foods or different cultural activities.

L3 Online Activity

Visit Pearson SuccessNet to access an online activity about personality. Have students complete the Web activity.

Differentiated Instruction

L4 Gifted and Talented

Explain that the use of tests that assess personality has become common in the workplace. However, many experts question the validity, reliability, and usefulness of these tests. Have students use online or library resources to learn more about the use and misuse of personality tests.

Ask students to form teams to debate the question of whether or not personality tests are useful and appropriate. Remind students to find resources that will allow them to back up their statements with research results and expert opinions.

Stages of Personality Development

L1 Visual Learning: Figure 4

Have students describe the content of each photograph. Then help them connect the content to the challenge faced in each life stage.

Caption Answer *Sample answer:* An infant learns to trust when his or her need for food is met. A child who is toilet trained is less dependent. When children design their own play, they are taking initiative. Doing household chores helps children learn skills they need as adults. A teen chooses clothing to reflect her identity. Given their joy, the couple has probably developed close bonds. Teaching is a nurturing activity. Based on his expression, the older man appears to be content.

L3 Cooperative Learning

Have students work in small groups to share their experiences with children in Erikson's fourth stage (ages 6 to 12). What evidence is there that the children have developed trust, learned to be independent, and take initiative? What evidence is there that the children are developing skills?

L3 Cultural Connection

Discuss how a teen's search for identity might cause conflicts with family and cultural traditions. The conflict may be about appearance or about behavior. Ask if students think that teens who rebel are trying to assert their independence, conform to the standards of a peer group, or express their own sense of self.

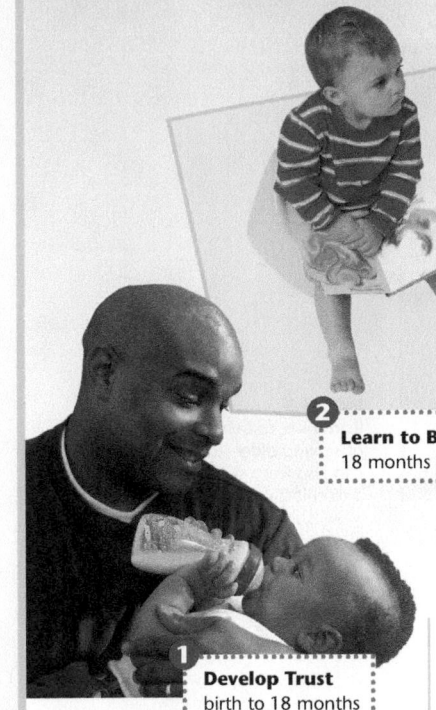

Take Initiative
3 to 6 years

Learn to Be Independent
18 months to 3 years

Develop Skills
6 to 12 years

Develop Trust
birth to 18 months

FIGURE 4 According to Erikson, in each stage of life people will confront a different challenge. **Interpreting Photographs** Look at the content of each photograph. How does the content illustrate the series of challenges a person will meet throughout life?

Stages of Personality Development

By age 25, your central personality traits will be well established. But, this does not mean that you will not continue to change. **According to the psychologist Erik Erikson, personality develops throughout life as people meet a series of challenges.** Erikson divided life into the eight stages shown in Figure 4. Each stage presents a different challenge to work on. When you successfully accomplish the challenge in one stage, you are better prepared to meet the challenge of the next stage.

❶ **Develop Trust**   An infant depends on other people to meet its need for food, a clean diaper, and affection. If these needs are met, the child learns to trust other people. If the needs are not met, the child learns mistrust and may withdraw from others.

❷ **Learn to Be Independent**   This is the stage when young children learn to do things on their own. They start to gain control over their own bodies. They learn to walk and use the toilet. If children fail to master these tasks, they develop self-doubt. If their efforts are ridiculed, they may feel ashamed.

❸ **Take Initiative**   During this stage, children start to plan their own activities. Through imitating others and through fantasy play, they begin to develop a sense of right and wrong. If children are harshly scolded for poor initiatives, they may feel unworthy, guilty, or resentful.

❹ **Develop Skills**   Children learn skills they will need as adults. They learn how to help around the home, how to succeed at school, and how to get along with others. These skills make children feel competent—capable of achieving their goals. Without skills, a child may feel like a failure.

34   *Chapter 2*

Differentiated Instruction

EL English Language Learners

Have English learners use a standard dictionary to find the meanings of unfamiliar words associated with Erickson's stages of personality development. Beginning English language learners can work with a partner to complete this activity. Intermediate

English language learners should try to complete this activity independently. However, you may need to review the organization of a dictionary and the use of guide words before they begin.

Create and Nurture
Middle Adulthood
(ages 40–65)

⑤ Search for Identity
12 to 20 years

⑥ Establish Intimacy
Young adulthood
(ages 20–40)

⑧ Look Back With Acceptance
Late Adulthood (age 65+)

⑤ Search for Identity According to Erikson, as a teenager, your main challenge is a search for **identity,** or a sense of self. You begin to question who you are and what you want to do with your life. This search leads some teens to try new experiences and to behave in ways that differ from family teachings. Other teens focus on shaping their identities to go along with standards set by their family or culture.

⑥ Establish Intimacy As a young adult, your challenge will be to establish close bonds with others. If you learn to make commitments to other people, you will have their support as you face other challenges.

⑦ Create and Nurture During middle adulthood, people need to stay productive and creative in all parts of their life. During this stage, adults get satisfaction from helping younger people to learn and grow.

⑧ Look Back With Acceptance During older adulthood, people reflect on their lives. Some accept the choices they made, while others may regret the opportunities they missed.

Section 1 Review

Key Ideas and Vocabulary

1. What five central traits can be used to define personality?

2. What two general factors combine to influence your personality?

3. What did Erickson say about how your personality develops throughout your life?

4. Define the term **identity.** At what life stage does the search for identity begin?

Health and Community

Role Models Think of a person you consider a role model. Why did you choose this person? Have you met this person or do you know the person through the media? Write a paragraph summarizing your answers. **WRITING**

Critical Thinking

5. Evaluating Do you choose friends whose personality traits are similar to or different from yours? Why do you think that is so?

---

3. Assess

Evaluate
These assignments can help you assess students' mastery of the section content.

Section 1 Review
Answers appear below.

Teaching Resources
• Practice 2-1
• Section 2-1 Quiz

ⓛ2 Reteach
Have students choose a character from a book, television program, or movie. Ask students to use the five central personality traits to describe the character. Have students share their responses with the class or a small group.

ⓛ4 Enrich
Teaching Resources
• Enrich 2-1

Health and Community

Role Models After students complete the assignment, ask volunteers to share their answers with the class. Ask students who don't want to share their reasons to indicate whether their role model is a family member, a coach, an athlete, and so on. Then discuss why certain types of people tend to be chosen as role models.

Section 1 Review

1. extroversion, agreeableness, conscientiousness, emotional stability, openness

2. Personality traits are influenced by a combination of heredity and environment.

3. According to Erikson, personality develops throughout life as people meet a series of challenges.

4. An identity is a sense of self. The search for identity begins in the teen years.

5. Students may choose friends with personality traits similar to their own, or maybe "opposites attract." The key is for students to think about why they choose friends with certain personality types.

Objectives
Before class begins, write the objectives on the board. Have students copy the objectives into their notebooks at the start of class.

1. Focus

Warm-Up Health Stats

After students have finished writing, ask volunteers to share one survey response that surprised them, and why it seemed surprising. Then use the survey results to introduce the concept of self-esteem.

Presentation 2-2

Section 2
Self-Esteem

Objectives
- ▶ **Compare** the effects of high and low self-esteem on health.
- ▶ **Describe** the changes in self-esteem that can occur as people age.
- ▶ **Identify** ways to achieve and maintain high self-esteem.
- ▶ **Summarize** Maslow's theory of self-actualization.

Vocabulary
- • self-esteem
- • self-actualization
- • hierarchy of needs

Warm-Up

Health Stats These data show the results of a survey that asked teens, "What would make you feel better about yourself?" They could choose more than one answer.

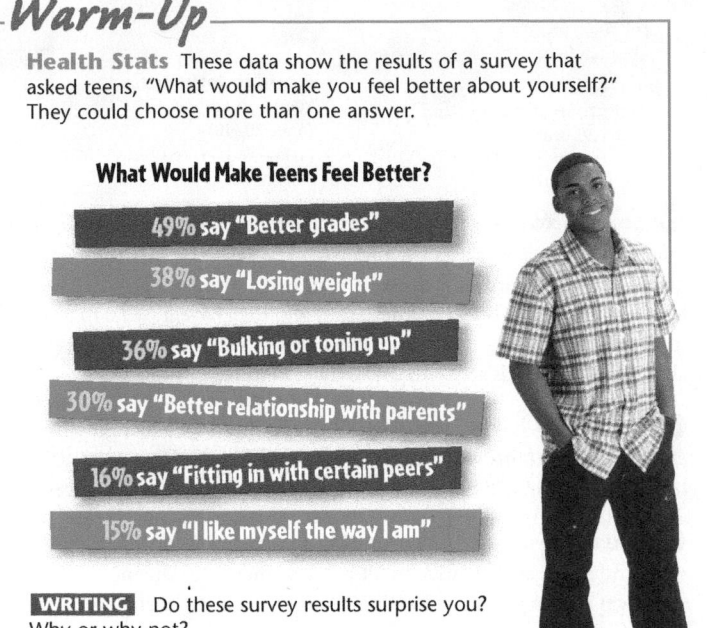

What Would Make Teens Feel Better?

49% say "Better grades"

38% say "Losing weight"

36% say "Bulking or toning up"

30% say "Better relationship with parents"

16% say "Fitting in with certain peers"

15% say "I like myself the way I am"

WRITING Do these survey results surprise you? Why or why not?

Self-Esteem and Your Health

How do you decide which movie to go to? Do you read or listen to a review of the movie? Do you notice what rating the movie has or how long the lines are at the box office? Perhaps you depend on the opinions of friends to help you decide. Everyone, including you, has opinions—about movies, music, clothing, food, and other people. You may not be aware of it, but you also have an opinion about yourself.

One term psychologists use to describe your opinion of yourself is self-esteem. **Self-esteem** refers to how much you respect yourself and like yourself. As with so many other concepts in mental health, you can think of self-esteem as a continuum, ranging from high self-esteem to low self-esteem. **Many psychologists think that high self-esteem has a positive effect on health, while low self-esteem has a negative effect on health.**

36 *Chapter 2*

MATH and Health

L3 Percentages

Use the statistics in the Warm-Up activity to review percentages. Explain that a percent is a ratio in which the second term is 100. For example, a result of 49% means that 49 out of 100 teens would feel better about themselves if they got better grades. Explain that results reported as percentages don't necessarily mean the sample size was 100. You can calculate percentages from any size sample. Ask: **According to this survey, if you asked 200 teens what would make them feel better about themselves, how many would say losing weight?** *(76)*

Benefits of High Self-Esteem People with high self-esteem accept themselves for who they are. They have a realistic view of their strengths and weaknesses and maintain a positive attitude even when they fail at a task. They form close relationships with people who respect and value them because they value themselves.

Some research shows that, if you feel good about yourself, you will be more likely to eat well, to exercise regularly, and to avoid risky behaviors. You will also be more likely to set goals for yourself, ask for help when you need it, and bounce back quickly from setbacks and disappointments.

Risks of Low Self-Esteem People with low self-esteem don't have much respect for themselves. They judge themselves harshly and worry too much about what others think of them. They may "put on an act" in public to impress others and hide their insecurities. Their fear of failure and looking bad may prevent them from trying new things. Negative thoughts such as "I can't do that" or "I'm not smart enough" make it difficult to succeed. So does thinking that success is a matter of luck rather than hard work.

Some studies show that teens with low self-esteem are more likely than their peers to use drugs, drop out of school, become pregnant, and suffer from eating disorders. They are also more likely to engage in violent or self-destructive behaviors.

 **Connect to Your Life** Do you have high or low self-esteem? How does your self-esteem affect the way you behave?

Boost Your Self-Esteem

- ▶ Maintain a positive attitude.
- ▶ Focus on your strengths.
- ▶ Form close relationships.
- ▶ Set goals for yourself.
- ▶ Avoid risky behaviors.
- ▶ Ask for help.
- ▶ Help others.

FIGURE 5 Identifying and developing your talents is one way to boost your self-esteem.

---

2. Teach

L3 EL Reading/Note Taking **2-2**

L2 Adapted Reading/Note Taking **2-2**

Self-Esteem and Your Health

L2 Building Health Skills

Practicing Healthful Behaviors Name several everyday challenges faced by students, for example, getting a lower-than-expected test score or failing to make a sports team. Explain that a person with low self-esteem might react to these challenges differently than a person with high self-esteem. They might react with negative thinking. Ask students to suggest negative thoughts a person might have in each situation. Then ask students to replace the negative thoughts with positive ones.

L3 Active Learning

Point out to students that focusing on their strengths is a great way to boost their self-esteem. Have students develop a class bulletin board that celebrates one strength or talent of each student in the class. Sometimes people fail to recognize their strengths because their definition of a strength is too limited. Challenge students to think beyond typical examples of talents (athletics, music, academics) to include a variety of strengths, such as kindness, compassion, and a sense of humor.

Connect to Your Life Allow students to answer this question in their private journals.

How Self-Esteem Develops

L3 Content Update  **GO ONLINE**

Visit Pearson SuccessNet to access more information on building self-esteem. Have students complete the Web activity.

L3 Building Health Skills

Analyzing Influences Have students examine magazine advertisements that are aimed at teens. Ask each student to choose one advertisement to analyze. Have students consider how the advertisement could impact the self-esteem of students their age. Call on students to share a short description of their analysis with the class. Follow up with a class discussion of the way media messages impact the self-esteem of teens as a group. Ask students to cite specific examples to support their opinions.

L2 Visual Learning: Figure 6

Have students examine the graph that shows how self-esteem changes with age. Ask: **What trends do you see in the data for both males and females?** *(Sample answer: Both males and females experience a decline in self-esteem in early adolescence.)* Ask: **Why does self-esteem tend to drop during elementary school?** *(Sample answer: Students begin to compare their accomplishments with the accomplishments of others.)*
Caption Answer At ages other than childhood and late adulthood, males have a higher self-esteem than females.

 **GO ONLINE**
PearsonSuccessNet.com
For: More on building healthy self-esteem

FIGURE 6 The graph shows how the self-esteem of females and males changes as they age.
Comparing and Contrasting How does the self-esteem of females and males compare?

How Self-Esteem Develops

Self-esteem is not a constant. It can increase or decrease as people interact with their family, their peers, and their community. Figure 6 shows the results of studies of self-esteem that were done with different age groups. **On average, self-esteem drops in early adolescence, increases gradually during adulthood, and decreases again toward the end of life.**

Childhood Young children need support and encouragement from family members. If they have the chance to succeed at small tasks and to build skills, they are likely to become confident individuals. Most children enter school with relatively high self-esteem, but there is often a gradual decline in self-esteem during elementary school. This may be because students begin to compare themselves with other children. Or the students may receive more negative feedback from teachers, parents, or peers.

Adolescence It is normal for teens to be critical of their appearance, their abilities, their interests, and their shortcomings. But some teens are overly self-conscious and judge themselves too harshly. They may compare themselves only to the best athletes or the most attractive celebrities. As a result, their self-esteem may suffer.

The larger world around you has an influence on your self-esteem. You receive messages about your appearance, your gender, your cultural group, and your values from the media. Messages like "only thin people have fun" or "the latest electronic gadget will make you popular" can make you feel that you are not as good as others.

Adulthood Self-esteem generally rises during adulthood. Adults begin to accomplish their goals and take control of their lives. Also, adults are better able to keep things in the proper perspective. Researchers are not sure why self-esteem tends to decrease in older adults. The drop may be caused by health problems or limited roles for older adults in society.

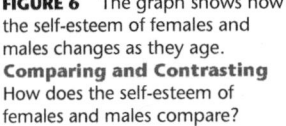
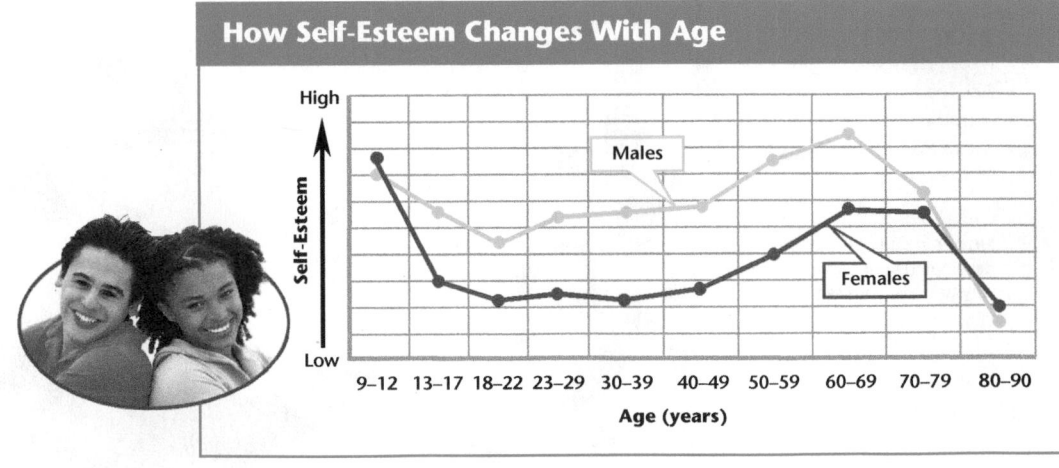

How Self-Esteem Changes With Age

High

Self-Esteem

Males

Females

Low

9–12 13–17 18–22 23–29 30–39 40–49 50–59 60–69 70–79 80–90

Age (years)

Focus on **ISSUES**

L3 Gender and Self-Esteem

Have students work in small groups to discuss one trend shown in Figure 6—the gap in self-esteem between males and females throughout most of life. Students may want to start by looking at How Self-Esteem Develops for possible explanations. If students are having trouble with this assignment, remind them to use their analyzing influences skill. Have groups prepare a brief presentation, which they can use to describe their proposed explanation to the class. The presentation should include evidence in support of the explanation.

Improving Your Self-Esteem

How can you achieve and maintain high self-esteem? **Don't base your self-esteem solely on other people's opinions of you. Focus on your accomplishments, your talents, and your contributions to your family and community.** If you do well in school, excel at a sport, or display other talents, your achievements and the encouragement you receive can boost your self-esteem. Below are some additional tips for boosting self-esteem. Try to incorporate some of these suggestions into your daily life. You will gain confidence in your abilities and feel better about yourself.

▶ **Make a list of your strengths and weaknesses.** Learn to focus on your strengths and build on the things you do well. Don't dwell on your weaknesses, but identify areas where you can make an effort to improve.

▶ **Set ambitious, but realistic goals for yourself.** Then develop a plan to achieve your goals. Take the time to appreciate and reward yourself when you accomplish a goal.

▶ **Do not be too hard on yourself.** When you make a mistake or experience a defeat, figure out what went wrong. Try to learn something positive from the experience and then move on.

▶ **Rely on your values.** You will feel better about yourself when you do things that match your values. Avoid doing things just to "go along with the crowd." Choose friends who share your values, support your goals, and encourage your efforts to do your best.

▶ **Learn to accept compliments.** However, try to distinguish genuine praise from insincere flattery.

▶ **Look beyond your own concerns.** Do something nice for others. Consider helping out more at home or doing volunteer work in your community.

▶ **Do not focus too much on appearance.** A focus on appearance can undermine self-esteem. Making sure that you are well groomed, however, can help build self-confidence.

 **Think about the last time you made a mistake. How did you respond? Was your response helpful?**

FIGURE 7 You can improve your self-esteem by doing something nice for others. This teen is removing a window from the second floor of a house she helped to renovate.

Improving Your Self-Esteem

L3 Building Health Skills

Setting Goals Discuss with students what it means to set ambitious, but realistic goals. Then have students set a goal related to one of the other strategies listed for improving self-esteem. Have students write an action plan in their private journal. The plan should contain the specific steps they will use to meet their goal. Ask students to monitor their progress toward their goal over the next several weeks.

EL Cooperative Learning

As a class, discuss strategies for giving genuine compliments to others and graciously receiving compliments from others. Remind students that compliments do not need to focus on physical appearance. Then pair English language learners with fluent English speakers. Have the students practice giving and receiving compliments.

L3 Journal Writing

Ask students to make a list of their strengths and weaknesses in their private journal. Have students reflect on ways that their strengths can boost their self-esteem. **WRITING**

 Allow students to answer this question in their private journals.

Differentiated Instruction

L2 Less Proficient Readers

Have students work in pairs with advanced readers to make an outline of the chapter. Provide a model outline for students to use as they work. Explain that the key ideas are printed in boldface type. Remind students to include the key ideas in their outlines. Have students use their outlines as a study aid when they prepare for the Chapter Review.

Achieving Your Potential

L2 Visual Learning: Figure 8
Image Bank Figure 2-8

Ask students to identify the content of the photographs. Then discuss how the photographs relate to levels in Maslow's pyramid.
Caption Answer physical needs and the need for safety

L1 Active Learning

Show students a three-dimensional pyramid, and explain how the material at the base of the pyramid supports the material at higher levels in the pyramid. If the math department has a hollow pyramid, you could use different colors of sand to build a 3D representation of Maslow's pyramid.

L3 Class Discussion

Remind students that Maslow identified two types of esteem, approval of others and self-esteem. Maslow thought self-esteem was more important than the approval of others. Ask students if they agree with Maslow. Have students support their responses with examples and logical reasoning.

L4 Building Media Literacy

Have students look for interviews that profile prominent people. Is it possible to determine whether the interviewee has some traits of a self-actualized person? Do the types of questions asked differ depending on where the interview appears—e.g., a newspaper, a sports or celebrity magazine, or a teen magazine?

FIGURE 8 The pyramid shows the hierarchy of human needs that Maslow proposed. Martin Luther King is an example of a self-actualized person.
Interpreting Diagrams Which needs did Maslow think must be satisfied before the need to belong can be met?

Achieving Your Potential

The psychologist Abraham Maslow thought that people have an inborn drive to be the best that they can be. The process by which people achieve their full potential is called **self-actualization.** In the 1950s, Maslow offered an explanation for why few people ever reach their full potential.

According to Maslow, before people can achieve self-actualization, their basic needs must be met. These needs are physical needs, the need to feel safe, the need to belong, and the need for esteem. Maslow arranged these needs in a pyramid, as shown in Figure 8. He called this arrangement the **hierarchy of needs** (HY ur ahr kee).

▶ **Physical Needs** A person's most basic needs are the physical needs of the body. Physical needs include the need for food, water, and sleep. If these basic needs are not met, a person has little or no energy to pursue higher needs.

▶ **Safety** The next level of need is for safety, or protection. A person needs shelter from the elements, such as heat, cold, and rain. A person needs to feel safe from violence in the home and in the community. In the modern world, safety needs also include a need for enough money to meet basic physical needs and other safety needs.

▶ **Belonging** The third level of needs is a need to connect with other people. Family, friends, and others in your community can provide the love and acceptance needed for your emotional health.

▶ **Esteem** Maslow's fourth level is a need for esteem. He divided esteem into the approval of others and self-esteem. The need for the approval of others includes the need for recognition, respect, appreciation, and attention. It can also include the need for fame, glory, and status—your position in life. Maslow regarded self-esteem as a more important need than the approval of others because, once achieved, it is more permanent.

WRITING and Health

L3 Letter to the Editor

Ask students to reflect on ways that the need for belonging can be met in the school community. Challenge students to think about how they as individuals can help others meet their need for belonging in the school environment. Then, have students write a letter to the editor of the school newspaper explaining the importance of a sense of belonging and identifying specific ways that students can help others meet this need.

Esteem

Self-Actualization

Personality Traits of Self-Actualized People

▶ Realistic and accepting
▶ Independent, self-sufficient
▶ Appreciative of life
▶ Concerned about humankind
▶ Capable of loving others
▶ Fair, unprejudiced
▶ Creative and hard-working
▶ Not afraid to be different

▶ **Self-Actualization** Once all of a person's other needs are met, he or she can go on to achieve the qualities of a self-actualized person. Maslow made a list of personality traits that people who had reached their potential share. Figure 8 lists these ideal traits.

Research has shown that Maslow correctly identified the set of human needs. However, psychologists now think that people don't have to progress through the hierarchy of needs in the way that Maslow described. It is possible to not meet some of your basic needs and still strive to meet higher needs. For example, Mozart was an extremely creative composer even though some of his basic needs were not met. Nevertheless, a well-fed person who has adequate shelter is more likely to be friendly and self-confident. This person is also more likely to perform tasks better than a person with low self-esteem.

Section 2 Review

Key Ideas and Vocabulary

1. Define **self-esteem**. Explain the effects that high and low self-esteem may have on health.
2. In general, what happens to self-esteem during adolescence? Explain why this change occurs.
3. Identify three things you should focus on if you want to improve your self-esteem.
4. Define the term **self-actualization**. What did Maslow claim must happen before a person can achieve self-actualization?

Health at School

Building Self-Esteem Make a list of events that happen in school that can increase a person's self-esteem. Make a second list of events that happen in school that can lower a person's self-esteem. Choose one event from each list and write a paragraph explaining how these events can affect self-esteem. **WRITING**

Critical Thinking

5. **Making Judgments** Describe something that you accomplished in the past year that made you feel proud and explain why. **WRITING**
6. **Classifying** Which personality traits in Figure 8 do you have?

3. Assess

Evaluate

These assignments can help you assess students' mastery of the section content.

Section 2 Review

Answers appear below.

Teaching Resources

• Practice 2-2
• Section 2-2 Quiz

L2 Reteach

Have students make a poster that uses words and pictures to show a variety of actions or activities that could be used to boost self-esteem. Have students explain why they chose each action or activity.

L4 Enrich

Teaching Resources

• Enrich 2-2

Health at School

Building Self-Esteem You may wish to have students work as a class to produce the lists of events that can increase or lower a person's self-esteem. After students complete the writing assignment, have volunteers share their responses with the class.

Section 2 Review

1. Self-esteem refers to how much you respect yourself and like yourself. Many psychologists think that high self-esteem has a positive effect on health, while low self-esteem has a negative effect.
2. Self-esteem usually drops during adolescence because teens are influenced by media messages and comparisons to others.
3. accomplishments, talents, and contributions to family and community
4. Self-actualization is the process by which people achieve their full potential. Maslow claimed that a person's basic needs must be met before he or she can achieve self-actualization.
5. *Sample answer:* I am proud that I volunteer in a nursing home, because I am able to help others.
6. The traits chosen will vary.

Expressing Anger in Healthy Ways

Objective

Implement a plan to evaluate and improve personal strategies for expressing anger.

Teaching Strategies

- Encourage students to express their opinions about how Matt and Toni handled their anger. Discuss the importance of expressing anger in ways that improve the situation or allow you to cope with a situation in a healthy way.

- Review each suggestion in Step 4 with the class. Have students suggest other constructive strategies for dealing with anger, and record their responses on the board. Remind students that knowing several constructive ways to deal with anger can help them to manage a variety of situations.

- Discuss the misconception that it is cathartic to "blow off steam." People think that direct aggression (yelling, hitting) or vicarious aggression (video games) can reduce anger. However, these behaviors can increase anger and the tendency toward aggression.

- Ask an English teacher to recommend a passage from a novel or play in which a person has to deal with his or her anger. Have students read the passage and evaluate the response.

Communicating

Expressing Anger in Healthy Ways

Matt and Toni had been going out for over a year. Matt thought that things were great between them. Toni felt differently. She wanted to stop seeing Matt. When she told Matt, he was stunned at first and couldn't speak. Then, he began to yell at Toni. Now Toni was angry too. She later told friends a secret about Matt that she had promised not to tell.

How would you react if you were in this situation? Yell? Cry? Act as if you didn't care? These behaviors are possible responses to anger. Some responses can improve the situation or at least make you feel better. Other responses can make a bad situation worse. The following guidelines will help you learn to express your anger in healthy ways.

1 **Accept your feelings.**

Anger is a normal emotion. Denying your anger will not make it go away, and ignoring your anger can lead to more destructive behaviors later on. Once you accept your anger, you can start to work on expressing your anger in healthy ways.

2 **Identify your triggers.**

Before you can deal with your anger, you need to know what makes you angry. You may be angry at a specific person or situation. Thinking about events in your past might make you angry. So might thinking about your future. One way to monitor your feelings is to record them in a journal.

⚑ **Sensitive Issues**

- Acknowledge that identifying and recording situations that trigger anger and personal responses to anger can be uncomfortable. Explain that these are important steps in learning to express anger in a healthy way.

- Assure students that they will not be required to share their specific responses to Steps 2 through 4 in Practice the Skill. They should record these responses in their private journals.

❸ Describe your response.

Record what you did in response to your anger and what happened after you responded. Circle those responses that led to a positive outcome.

> **Friday**
> 1. My sister wore my sweater. I yelled at her. She yelled back. Mom got mad.
> 2. Argued with Dad about the car. Went for a bike ride. Then talked to Dad.

❹ Seek constructive alternatives.

- ▶ **Address the Problem** After you calm down, try to discuss the problem. Make it clear how you feel without blaming the other person. Listen with respect to what the other person has to say. Even if talking doesn't fix the problem, you may feel ready to move on.

- ▶ **Release Excess Energy** Do some physical activity that you enjoy or do some activity that requires you to be creative. Something as simple as taking a walk can also help.

- ▶ **Avoid Certain Situations** If some situations act as triggers for your anger, you may be able to avoid them. Or you may decide to leave a situation if you start to feel angry.

- ▶ **Avoid Destructive Behaviors** Overeating or not eating, drinking, smoking, using drugs, or taking extreme physical risks may help you forget your problems for a short time. However, these behaviors can cause damage that lasts a lifetime.

- ▶ **Ask for Help** If you are having trouble controlling your anger, talk to a trusted adult. The adult can either help you figure out how to cope or can direct you to someone who can. There are counselors who specialize in helping people learn to manage their anger.

❺ Evaluate your progress.

Continue to keep track of your responses to anger in your journal. At first it may take a lot of self-control to change the way you respond to anger. But the more you practice constructive behaviors, the more automatic they will become.

Practice the Skill

1. Review what happened between Matt and Toni. List two positive ways they could have expressed their anger. Predict what the results might have been for each strategy.

2. Briefly describe three times in the past when you experienced anger. For each, describe what caused you to become angry, how you expressed your anger, and the result of your response. Which response worked best? Which was the least effective? Why?

3. For a week, keep a journal to record each time you felt angry. Include the cause, how you responded, and the result. Circle those responses that led to positive outcomes. At the end of the week, use your journal to evaluate your progress. Did your responses improve during the week?

4. If you are not happy with the progress you are making, set a specific goal for controlling your anger. Your goal could be walking away from certain situations or waiting to express your anger until you calm down. Write your goal in your journal and monitor your progress over the next few weeks.

Personality, Self-Esteem, and Emotions **43**

Practice the Skill

1. *Sample answer:* Matt could have walked away and waited to talk with Toni about her decision until after he had cooled down. He might not have been able to get Toni to change her mind, but he might have been able to end their relationship on a positive note. Instead of responding to her anger by breaking her promise to Matt, Toni could have talked with a trusted adult about her feelings. The adult might have helped Toni understand why Matt responded the way he did.

2. Students' private responses will vary.

3. Without asking for any specifics, you could ask if students think that the process helped them to improve their responses to anger.

4. Remind students to continue to monitor their progress over the next few weeks.

Health at Home

ⓛ₃ Managing Anger in a Family

Ask students to think about situations that occur at home that cause them to get angry. Ask them to also think about how they typically respond at home when they are angry. Have students record this information in their private journals. Then, have a class discussion about typical situations in a family that can cause a teen to be angry. Have students brainstorm constructive responses to these situations. **WRITING**

Objectives
Before class begins, write the objectives on the board. Have students copy the objectives into their notebooks at the start of class.

1. Focus

Warm-Up Myth/Fact

Assure students that they can keep their responses to the writing assignment confidential. After students have completed the activity, discuss the myth. Ask them to think of examples of situations in which it might not be healthy to "let your feelings out." Tell students that in this section they will learn some examples of constructive and destructive ways of expressing emotions.

Presentation 2-3

Section 3

Expressing Your Emotions

Objectives
▶ **Identify** four primary emotions and three learned emotions.
▶ **Explain** why it is important to recognize your emotions.
▶ **Distinguish** helpful from harmful coping strategies.

Vocabulary
- emotion
- primary emotion
- grief
- learned emotion
- coping strategy
- defense mechanism

Warm-Up

Myth It is always healthy to "let your feelings out."

Fact Some ways of expressing your emotions are positive and constructive. Other ways of expressing emotions are negative and destructive.

WRITING Think of a time when you felt afraid and a time when you felt guilty. Describe how you behaved in response to each feeling.

Primary Emotions

One important part of a healthy personality is being able to express emotions in appropriate ways. An **emotion** is a reaction to a situation that involves your mind, body, and behavior. Research shows that people are born with a few basic, or primary, emotions. **Primary emotions** are emotions that are expressed by people in all cultures. **Happiness, sadness, anger, and fear are examples of primary emotions.**

Happiness   People feel happy for many different reasons and sometimes for no particular reason at all. Happiness is a normal response to pleasant events in one's life. Feeling happy helps you feel good about yourself. Make a list of the things you enjoy. Then, try to make room in your daily life for these experiences. If you enjoy skating with friends, for example, make plans with your friends to go skating. If you like to read books, set aside some time each day for reading. The good feelings that result will stay with you for the rest of the day.

Sadness   Sadness is a normal response to disappointing events in your life. A day when nothing goes right, a poor grade in school, or family problems can all leave you feeling sad and empty. When you are sad, you may cry, eat more or less than normal, feel tired, or withdraw from those around you. If you are sad about the death of a loved one, you will likely experience a period of deep sorrow known as **grief.**

Sensitive Issues
Students who have problems expressing their feelings or who are currently dealing with a strong emotion, such as grief, may be particularly vulnerable when discussing ways in which people express and cope with emotions.

WRITING and Health

L3 Persuasive Speech
Have students think of an activity that makes them happy (one they can share with the class). Then ask students to write a brief persuasive speech about the activity. Explain that a persuasive speech is designed to change the attitude of a listener. In this case, students will be trying to convince a person who is unfamiliar with the activity or who has had no interest in the activity to try the activity. In other words, the student has to make the activity sound appealing.

What can you do to overcome feelings of sadness? You can share your feelings with a close relative or friend. If you are sad about a failure, it might help to make a list of your accomplishments or do something nice for yourself. It is important not to withdraw from other people or isolate yourself. If you do, your sadness can become overwhelming.

Anger Feelings of anger can range from mild resentment to intense rage. You probably have experienced the tense muscles, racing heart, and rapid breathing associated with anger. You may even have gotten red in the face and clenched your fists. Anger is a normal response to feeling frustrated or helpless.

Anger can be either a helpful or harmful emotion. Anger is helpful when it provides you with the energy necessary to try to change things. Clayton is angry because his parents often say, "Why can't you get good grades like your brother?" After thinking about the situation, Clayton realizes that his brother puts a lot of effort into his schoolwork. He decides to ask his brother to help him improve his approach to his studies.

Anger can also be destructive. What if Clayton decides to focus his anger on his brother? He might start avoiding his brother or find reasons to fight with him. People who tend to express anger in negative ways may hurt themselves and others. They are also at greater risk for developing illnesses such as heart disease. The Building Health Skills activity on pages 42–43 offers strategies for dealing with anger in healthy ways.

Connect to Your Life If a close friend insulted you, how would you feel? How might you react?

FIGURE 9 Primary emotions produce distinct facial expressions that are easy to recognize. **Observing** Which emotion is being expressed in each photo—happiness, anger, sadness, or fear?

45

Personality, Self-Esteem, and Emotions **45**

L3 Content Update GO ONLINE

Visit Pearson SuccessNet to access more information about emotions. Have students complete the Web activity.

Learned Emotions

L3 Cultural Connection

Because the expression of learned emotions can vary between cultures, people from different cultures may not correctly identify the emotion that is being expressed. Discuss strategies that can be used to avoid misunderstandings resulting from cultural differences in the expression of emotions. For example, you might need to carefully observe all the available verbal and nonverbal clues. Or, you might need to apply your active listening skills to make sure you understand the other person's feelings.

L2 Building Health Skills

Analyzing Influences Some students may be fans of graphic novels. If you are unfamiliar with these novels, check out Web sites that review graphic novels aimed at teens. Ask students to bring some of their favorites to class. Have them analyze how the drawings are used to express emotions. Then ask students what influence these novels might have on how teens express their emotions.

GO ONLINE
PearsonSuccessNet.com
For: More on emotions

Fear   Fear is the emotion you feel when you recognize a threat to your safety or security. You feel fear if the car you are riding in starts to skid, someone threatens to hit you, or the smoke alarm goes off in your home. As with anger, when you are afraid, your heart races and your breathing speeds up. You may also feel cold and sweaty.

Fear can be a helpful emotion because it can lead you to run from life-threatening situations. Fear can be a harmful emotion when it is not based on a real threat or when it is an overreaction to a perceived threat. Unrealistic fears can prevent people from living a normal life and doing the things they want to do. For example, a person who is afraid of elevators may be unable to live or work in a high-rise building.

Learned Emotions

Some emotions are not expressed in the same way by all people. These emotions are called social emotions, or **learned emotions.** The expression of learned emotions depends on the social environment in which a person grows up. **Love, guilt, and shame are examples of learned emotions.**

Love   What do love between family members, love between friends, and romantic love have in common? All are marked by deep feelings of affection and concern. These feelings can be expressed in many different ways—through caring words, loving touches, thoughtful actions, and more.

In many cultures, women tend to express love differently than men. Women are often more comfortable expressing their love in words. Many men are more comfortable expressing their love through actions such as shared activities. These different tendencies reflect what women and men learn about expressing emotions from their culture.

You can feel love toward places and things, as well as toward people. You may love your country. You may love a certain style of music. You may feel love and concern for your fellow humans. Love is one of the most positive emotions people are capable of feeling. The capacity to give and receive love is essential for mental health.

FIGURE 10   You can express love by showing affection and concern for others. You may also express love for your country.

For Your INFORMATION!

Emotions Are Contagious

Studies have shown that emotions are contagious, that is, they are spread from one person to another. Researchers have found that excitement, happiness, sadness, and anger are the most contagious emotions.

Although studies show that emotions are spread most easily among family members and close friends, even viewing facial expressions on a computer screen can have an impact on an individual's mood.

Media Wise

News Content and Emotions

What stories appear on the evening news and why? To attract viewers, news directors may select stories that are highly emotional. Can watching the news increase your level of fear or anxiety? Evaluate the evening news using this checklist.

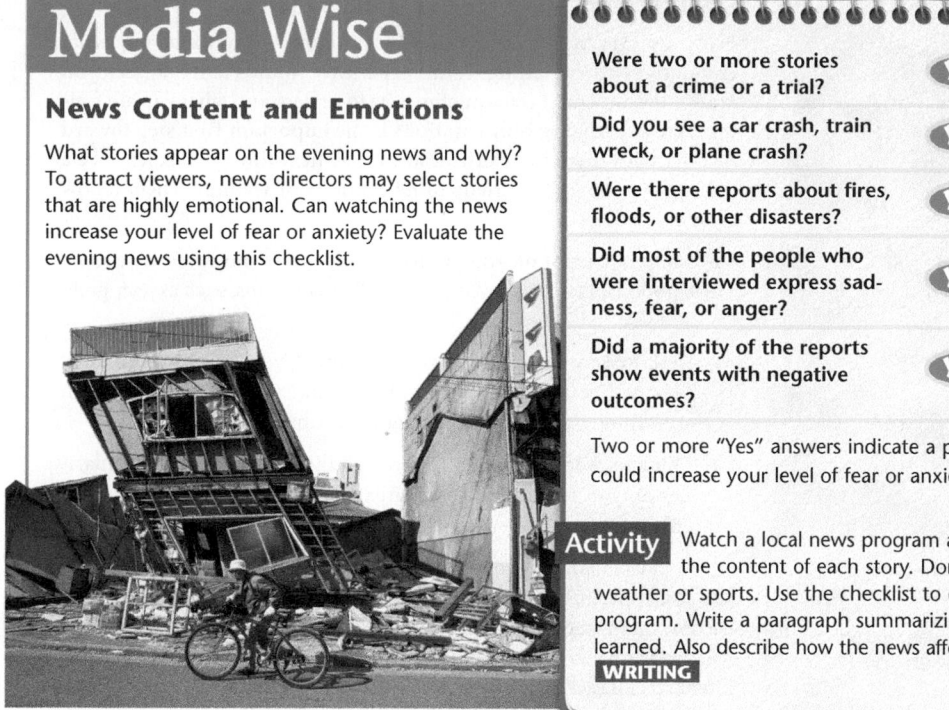

Were two or more stories about a crime or a trial?	Yes	No
Did you see a car crash, train wreck, or plane crash?	Yes	No
Were there reports about fires, floods, or other disasters?	Yes	No
Did most of the people who were interviewed express sadness, fear, or anger?	Yes	No
Did a majority of the reports show events with negative outcomes?	Yes	No

Two or more "Yes" answers indicate a program that could increase your level of fear or anxiety.

Activity Watch a local news program and record the content of each story. Don't include weather or sports. Use the checklist to evaluate the program. Write a paragraph summarizing what you learned. Also describe how the news affected you. **WRITING**

Guilt and Shame Leah's dad lost his job. Leah is angry because there isn't enough money and she can't find a part-time job to help out. Today she spotted a twenty-dollar bill in her friend Rosa's locker. When Rosa looked away, Leah grabbed the money and stuffed it into her pocket. Because Leah knows that what she did was wrong, she feels guilty.

Guilt can be a helpful emotion. Guilt can stop you from doing something you know is wrong, or it can make you take action to correct something you've done. The best way to deal with feelings of guilt is to correct the situation, if possible, and to talk about your feelings. Sometimes people feel guilty when they haven't done anything wrong. For example, when parents divorce, children often blame themselves.

Leah might also feel shame for stealing the money. Shame is different from guilt because it focuses on the person rather than the action. When you feel guilty you think, "I did a bad thing." When you feel ashamed, you think, "I am a bad person." Shame can be harmful because it lowers self-esteem. Shame also makes it less likely that a person will try to correct the bad situation.

 **What advice would you give Leah to help her correct the situation with Rosa?**

Media Wise

News Content and Emotions
Explain that the more people who watch a television news program, the higher the ratings, and the more the station can charge advertisers. Therefore, news directors highlight those stories they think will attract the viewers. Introduce students to the phrase "If it bleeds, it leads." Explain that this figure of speech refers to the practice of opening a news program with a story about a violent crime or other catastrophe.

Activity Have students complete the survey at home. Remind students to bring their results to class the next day. Ask students to work as a class to compare the news programs on various local stations in the same time slot. Also have students compare national and local news programs and news programs shown at different times of day.

L3 Cultural Connection
Introduce this activity by writing this saying by Benjamin Franklin on the board: "Whatever is begun in anger ends in shame." Ask students what they think the saying means. Then ask them to think of sayings from different cultures that refer to emotions. Group the sayings by emotion. Then see if the sayings reveal any cultural differences in people's attitudes about emotions.

 Sample answer: Leah could admit what she did, apologize, and agree on a plan for paying back the money.

L4 Gifted and Talented
Have students extend the Media Wise activity by analyzing the content of news stories in a daily newspaper, a newsmagazine, and an online news provider. Students should use the checklist from the Media Wise activity. Encourage students to use charts and graphs to summarize their findings. Also ask them to compare how they felt when they read the news stories to how they felt when they watched segments about similar stories on television. Have students share their reports with the class.

Recognizing Your Emotions

L3 Building Health Skills

Practicing Healthful Behaviors If students are uncomfortable exploring their own emotions, have them first practice recognizing other people's emotions. Have students record what they observe in their private journals. For each strong emotion they identify, ask students to record the verbal and nonverbal clues they used. (Remind students that nonverbal clues can be misleading. For example, crying can be a sign of sadness, anger, or joy.) After a few days, have students review the steps for identifying emotions that are listed in the text. Ask students to practice these steps the next time they experience a strong emotion. Have students record the results in their private journals.

Connect to Your Life *Sample answer:* Students may say that it is easier to identify an emotion than to pinpoint the source of the emotion because they cannot isolate the trigger from all the other events in their lives.

Coping With Your Emotions

L2 Addressing Misconceptions

Every Coping Strategy Is Positive
Common usage of the word *coping* can lead students to the misconception that coping strategies are always positive. For example, "I'm coping with the problem" simply means "I'm handling the problem," but people assume it means "I'm handling the problem in a positive way." Explain that some coping strategies are helpful, some are harmful, and some (defense mechanisms) can be harmful if they are overused.

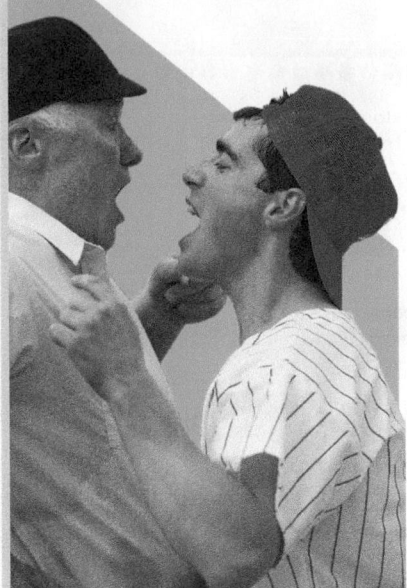

FIGURE 11 When a player is arguing with an umpire, you do not need to hear the words to recognize the emotion. You only need to look at the gestures and body language.

Recognizing Your Emotions

Have you ever been overwhelmed by emotion without knowing what emotions you were feeling? If this experience sounds familiar, then you know how difficult it can sometimes be to understand what you are feeling. **Yet, recognizing your emotions is the important first step toward dealing with them in healthful ways.** The next time you experience a strong emotion, pause briefly to reflect on your feelings. Then, follow these steps.

▶ Name the emotion you are feeling. Be aware, however, that some emotions, such as anger, can mask other emotions, such as fear, guilt, and shame.

▶ Determine what triggered the emotion. Try to pinpoint the exact source of your feeling. It may be difficult to isolate the cause from everything else that is happening at the time.

▶ Think back to past times that you felt the same way. What similarities do you notice about the situations? Are there any important differences?

By pausing to reflect on your feelings, you will learn a lot about yourself and your emotions. With practice, recognizing your emotions will become more automatic. Over time, you will begin to see patterns in your reactions and emotional responses. Still, there will always be times when intense feelings cloud your ability to sort things out. When this happens, use the steps listed above to make your feelings clearer. The end result will be a deeper understanding of the situation and of yourself.

 **Connect to Your Life** Which is more difficult to do, name the emotion you're feeling or pinpoint its source? Why?

Coping With Your Emotions

Sometimes emotions can become too much to handle. In such cases, you may use coping strategies. A **coping strategy** is a way of dealing with an uncomfortable or unbearable feeling or situation. **Coping strategies are helpful when they improve a situation or allow a person to handle a situation in a better way. Coping strategies are harmful when they make a situation worse or a person is less able to handle a situation.**

Defense Mechanisms You use some coping strategies without being aware that you are using them. **Defense mechanisms** are coping strategies that help you to protect yourself from difficult feelings. You may recognize some of the defense mechanisms described in Figure 12. Notice that they all involve a bit of mental juggling. By twisting the reality of a situation a bit in your mind, the situation becomes easier to accept. Fooling yourself in this way allows you to put off dealing with the problem and the emotions it causes.

48 *Chapter 2*

TEENS *Are Asking . . .*

Q: Sometimes I'm really irritable and angry, and an hour later I'm calm and happy. What's wrong with me?

A: What you describe is normal. The hormones that cause your body to grow and mature can cause rapid mood shifts. You also may be having trouble adjusting to all the changes in your life.

Try not to overreact to each mood swing. If you are experiencing a strong negative emotion, remember that your mood is likely to change again soon. Try to identify events or situations that trigger these moods. If your negative emotions persist for many weeks, it is important to turn to a trusted adult for help.

Common Defense Mechanisms

Denial	Refusing to recognize an emotion or problem	Your parents are getting divorced, but you act as though nothing is wrong. When friends express their concern, you laugh and tell them it does not bother you.
Compensation	Making up for weaknesses in one area by excelling in another area	You are failing two classes in school. You compensate by becoming the lead saxophone player in the school band.
Rationalization	Making excuses for actions or feelings	You work in a convenience store. When no one is watching, you take some magazines. You figure it's a large store and they can afford it.
Reaction Formation	Behaving in a way opposite to the way you feel	You feel guilty for bullying a kid at school. You cover up your feelings by bragging to friends about your actions.
Projection	Putting your own faults onto another person	At your after-school job you do not complete your tasks. When you get fired, you blame your boss, saying she did not take the time to explain the tasks to you.
Regression	Returning to immature behaviors to express emotions	You are angry at your brother for reading your diary. You scream at him and your parents, run into your room, and sulk.

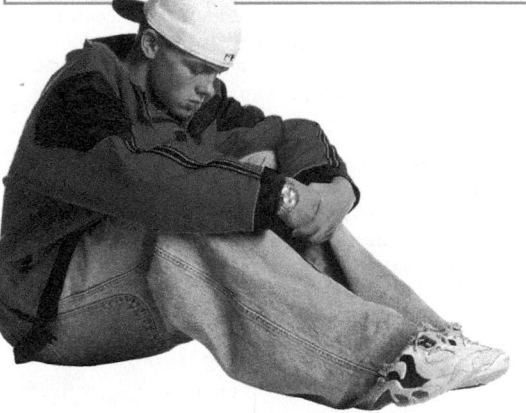

FIGURE 12 Defense mechanisms can be helpful if they are not overused. However, if you become too dependent on defense mechanisms, you may not learn to express your true feelings. You may not develop skills that are important for your mental and emotional health.

3. Assess

Evaluate

These assignments can help you assess students' mastery of the section content.

Section 3 Review

Answers appear below.

Teaching Resources

- Practice 2-3
- Section 2-3 Quiz

 **Reteach**

Challenge volunteers to pantomime each of the primary emotions described in the section. Have the remainder of the class identify the emotion being acted out. After each pantomime, take a minute to have students identify healthy ways to cope with and/or express that particular emotion.

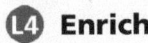 **Enrich**

Teaching Resources

- Enrich 2-3

Health at Home

Expressing Emotion Assure students that they will not be required to share their responses. However, after students complete their responses, ask if any students want to share what they learned. Finally, ask whether people sometimes try to hide their emotions. Why might a person who is angry or sad smile?

FIGURE 13 One helpful way of coping with your emotions is to write about them.

Helpful Ways of Coping Think back to the last time you experienced a strong emotion. How did you react? Internally, you may have used a defense mechanism, such as rationalization, to make the situation easier to accept. But how did you react outwardly? People react in many different ways to their own strong feelings. Some helpful ways of coping are listed below. What are some other helpful coping strategies that have worked for you?

- ► Confront the situation head-on. If possible, take action to improve the situation.

- ► Release your built-up energy by exercising, cleaning your room, or being active in some other way.

- ► Take a break by reading a book, listening to music, taking a walk, writing in your journal, or otherwise relaxing.

- ► Talk through your feelings with a family member, friend, counselor, or other trusted person. Sometimes, just talking about your feelings will help you see things more clearly.

Harmful Ways of Coping People may respond in unhealthy ways to intense emotions. They may use coping strategies that make their problems worse. Using alcohol or other drugs is an example of a harmful coping strategy. Withdrawing from friends and family is another.

Learning to express your emotions in positive ways is not an easy skill to master. Most people need help dealing with their emotions from time to time. If you find that you resort to harmful coping strategies, it may be time to ask for help.

Section 3 Review

Key Ideas and Vocabulary

1. Define the term **emotion**. What is the difference between primary emotions and learned emotions?
2. Explain the importance of being able to recognize your emotions.
3. How do healthful and harmful coping strategies differ? Give an example of each.
4. Define the term **defense mechanism**. When do defense mechanisms stop being helpful?

Critical Thinking

5. **Classifying** Students often pick on Tito, but he says that this behavior is a sign that the other students like him. What defense mechanism is Tito displaying? Explain.

Health at Home

Expressing Emotion Discuss with your family how you typically express emotions such as sadness or joy. Are there "rules" in your culture about when it is appropriate to express emotions and when it is not? Write a summary of what you learn. **WRITING**

6. **Predicting** People who design ad campaigns want you to react to their ads by buying their products. Think about ads you have seen for products. Based on these ads, do you think that advertisers are more likely to design ads that appeal to your mind or your emotions? Explain your answer.

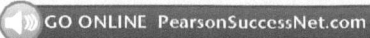 GO ONLINE PearsonSuccessNet.com   Audio Summary Section 2.3

Section 3 Review

1. An emotion is a reaction to a situation that involves your mind, body, and behavior. Primary emotions are expressed by people in all cultures. The expression of learned emotions depends on the social environment in which a person was raised.

2. Recognizing your emotions is the first step toward dealing with them in healthful ways.

3. *Sample answer:* Healthful ways of coping, such as talking through your feelings, improve a situation. Harmful coping strategies, such as using alcohol, tend to make a situation worse.

4. Defense mechanisms are coping strategies that help you protect yourself from difficult feelings. They can be harmful when overused.

5. Tito is in denial, because he is refusing to recognize the problem and his emotions.

6. *Sample answer:* Advertisements tend to appeal to emotions, which may triumph over rational decision making.

Chapter 2
At a Glance

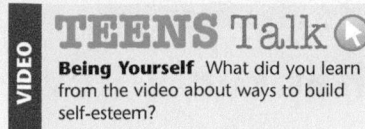 **TEENS Talk** VIDEO
Being Yourself What did you learn from the video about ways to build self-esteem?

Section 1   Personality

Key Ideas

▶ Many researchers use five central traits to describe how people behave, relate to others, and react to change. These traits are extroversion, agreeableness, conscientiousness, emotional stability, and openness to experiences.

▶ Personality traits are influenced by a combination of heredity and environment.

▶ According to the psychologist Erik Erikson, personality develops throughout life as people meet a series of challenges.

Vocabulary
- personality (30)
- psychologist (30)
- modeling (33)
- peer group (33)
- identity (35)

Section 2   Self-Esteem

Key Ideas

▶ Many psychologists think that high self-esteem has a positive effect on health, while low self-esteem has a negative effect on health.

▶ On average, self-esteem drops in early adolescence. It increases gradually during adulthood and decreases again toward the end of life.

▶ Don't base your self-esteem solely on other people's opinions of you. Focus on your accomplishments, your talents, and your contributions to your family and community.

▶ According to Maslow, before people can achieve self-actualization, their basic needs must be met. These needs are physical needs, the need to feel safe, the need to belong, and the need for esteem.

Vocabulary
- self-esteem (36)
- self-actualization (40)
- hierarchy of needs (40)

Section 3   Expressing Your Emotions

Key Ideas

▶ Happiness, sadness, anger, and fear are examples of primary emotions.

▶ Love, guilt, and shame are examples of learned emotions.

▶ Recognizing your emotions is the important first step toward dealing with them in healthful ways.

▶ Coping strategies are helpful when they improve a situation or allow a person to handle a situation in a better way. Coping strategies are harmful when they make a situation worse or a person is less able to handle a situation.

Vocabulary
- emotion (44)
- primary emotion (44)
- grief (44)
- learned emotion (46)
- coping strategy (48)
- defense mechanism (48)

Personality, Self-Esteem, and Emotions **51**

Chapter 2
At a Glance

VIDEO **Being Yourself** Ask for volunteers to share their answers. Use examples from the video to review strategies for building self-esteem.

Key Ideas Review

L1 Use the illustrations to review the key ideas. Help students connect the content of each figure to one of the key ideas.

L3 Ask students to prepare three quiz questions and answers for each of the three sections in the chapter. Have students work in small groups to ask and answer the quiz questions.

Vocabulary Review

EL Have students write four sentences. Each sentence should clearly explain the relationship between two different vocabulary terms.

L2 Have students make a graphic organizer that shows the relationship between all of the vocabulary terms in one of the sections.

Chapter 2 Review

Chapter 2 Review

GO ONLINE

PearsonSuccessNet.com

Students can go online for a review activity on Chapter 2.

Reviewing Key Ideas

Section 1

1. c   **2.** b

3. Children learn by example and copy, or model, the behavior of others.

4. Young children begin to gain independence as they learn to do things on their own and master tasks such as walking and using the toilet.

5. High degrees of extroversion and agreeableness would help a person effectively campaign for class president. The traits of conscientiousness and emotional stability would help a person do a good job as class president.

6. *Sample answer:* When I am with my friends, I behave differently than when I am with my family, so my friends and family may observe different personality traits.

Section 2

7. a   **8.** b

9. Helping others helps you to look beyond your own concerns and to gain confidence in your abilities.

10. Students' answers should indicate their knowledge of the traits of a self-actualized person.

Section 3

11. d   **12.** a

13. Anger can help a person change; if anger is expressed in negative ways, it is harmful. Fear can help a person avoid a life-threatening situation; when fear is an overreaction to a perceived threat, it is harmful.

14. Being able to give and receive love is essential for mental health.

15. Withdrawing from family and friends is a harmful coping strategy because family and friends can offer emotional support during difficult times.

Reviewing Key Ideas

Section 1

1. A person who is very talkative and sociable is demonstrating a high degree of
  a. conscientiousness.
  b. agreeableness.
  c. extroversion.
  d. emotional stability.

2. According to Erikson, the main challenge people face during adolescence is to
  a. develop competence.
  b. search for identity.
  c. develop trust.
  d. look back with acceptance.

3. Why is it important how adults behave in front of children?

4. Describe how young children begin to gain independence.

5. **Critical Thinking** Review the five central personality traits. Which traits would help elect someone as class president? Which traits would help the elected president do a good job?

6. **Critical Thinking** Would your friends and your family describe your personality in the same way? Explain your answer.

Section 2

7. Which of the following describes people with low self-esteem?
  a. They judge themselves harshly.
  b. They have a positive attitude.
  c. They accept themselves for who they are.
  d. They have a realistic view of their abilities.

8. Self-actualization is the process by which people can
  a. improve self-esteem.
  b. reach their full potential.
  c. establish an identity.
  d. develop trust.

9. How can helping others have a positive effect on your self-esteem?

10. **Critical Thinking** Describe a person who has achieved self-actualization. Use someone you know, someone you admire, or a character in a book you have read.

Building Health Skills

16. Evaluate the posters on how well they are able to communicate a concept to younger children.

17. Survey questions should reflect knowledge of factors that can affect teens' self-esteem. Remind students to respect the privacy of others.

Section 3

11. An example of a learned emotion is
  a. fear.   **b.** anger.
  c. sadness.   **d.** guilt.

12. A child who had been toilet-trained starts to wet the bed again when a new baby arrives. This behavior is an example of
  a. regression.   **b.** denial.
  c. projection.   **d.** compensation.

13. How can anger and fear be both helpful and harmful emotions?

14. Explain why love is such an important emotion.

15. **Critical Thinking** Why is withdrawing from family and friends a harmful way to cope with strong emotions?

Building Health Skills

16. **Advocacy** Design a poster to teach young children healthful ways to cope with anger.

17. **Analyzing Influences** Design a survey to help you determine the major influences on the self-esteem of teens. Include questions about factors such as parents, friends, teachers, religion, culture, and media.

18. **Setting Goals** Identify a defense mechanism from Figure 12 that you overuse. Then make an action plan to limit your overuse of the defense mechanism. Decide on a series of steps you can use to break this habit. Monitor your progress and adjust your action plan, if necessary. **WRITING**

Health and Community

Shared Emotions Sometimes an emotion is felt throughout a community in response to an event. Find two newspaper articles that include words such as *anger, grief, joy, fear, guilt,* or *pride.* For each article, write a paragraph explaining the source of the emotion and the response to the emotion. **WRITING**

GO ONLINE

PearsonSuccessNet.com

For: Chapter 2 review activity

18. Ask students to evaluate the success of their action plans.

Standardized Test Prep

Math Practice

The graph shows how two central personality traits—emotional stability and conscientiousness—change as people age. The scores are based on studies of thousands of people. Use the graph to answer Questions 19–22.

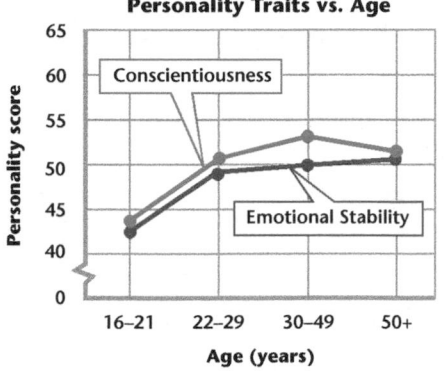

Personality Traits vs. Age

19. What was the score for emotional stability for people ages 16–21?
    A 40   B 43
    C 44   D 50

20. At what age are the scores for conscientiousness highest?
    F 16–21   G 22–29
    H 30–49   J 50+

21. At what ages are the conscientiousness and emotional stability scores most similar?
    A 16–21 and 22–29
    B 16–21 and 30–49
    C 16–21 and 50+
    D 30–49 and 50+

22. According to the graph, which of the following statements is true?
    F Adults are less conscientious and more emotionally stable than teenagers.
    G Adults are more conscientious and less emotionally stable than teenagers.
    H Adults are less conscientious and less emotionally stable than teenagers.
    J Adults are more conscientious and more emotionally stable than teenagers.

Reading and Writing Practice

Read the passage. Then answer Questions 23–26.

There is no scientific basis for personality profiles based on birth dates, palm readings, or handwriting analysis. However, people who read or hear these profiles often say, "That sounds just like me." People react this way because the descriptions are usually so general that they could apply to anyone. The statements also tend to use flattering words, such as *smart* or *honest* or *kind.* People usually pay attention to statements that they either think are true or want to be true and ignore the incorrect statements.

23. What is the main idea of this passage?
    A Personality profiles are never accurate.
    B Personality profiles have a scientific basis.
    C Everyone has the same general personality.
    D People believe personality profiles that have no scientific basis.

24. According to this passage, flattering descriptions are
    F accurate.   G used to please people.
    H often untrue.   J general and vague.

25. Which of the following statements is supported by this passage?
    A Handwriting can tell you a lot about your personality.
    B People tend to ignore statements they agree with.
    C People are likely to accept positive descriptions of themselves and reject negative ones.
    D People born on the same day have similar personalities.

Constructed Response

26. In a paragraph, write a personality profile that might appear in a magazine. Try to make it so general that it could apply to almost anyone.

Test-Taking Tip

When taking a test, have confidence in the first answer you choose. Change an answer only if you are sure your first choice is wrong.

Standardized Test Prep

Math Practice
21. B
22. H
23. C
24. J

Reading and Writing Practice
25. D
26. J
27. C
28. If students are unfamiliar with the type of personality profiles discussed in the passage, supply some examples.

Health and Community

Shared Emotions Provide students with newspapers. After they complete the assignment, make a list of events that are likely to produce shared emotions.

Section Objectives	Standards Correlation	Instructional Resources (L3)	SE eTEXT	TE eTEXT	PRINT
1 What Causes Stress? ⏱ 1 period; 1/2 block	NHES: 1.12.3, 2.12.4, 2.12.10, 6.12.1	**SE** Warm-Up, p. 56	•	•	•
3.1.1 **Describe** what causes a person to experience stress.		**RN** Note Taking Guide 3-1	•	•	•
3.1.2 **Identify** four general types of stressors.		**TR** Practice 3-1		•	
		TR Section 3-1 Quiz		•	
2 How Stress Affects Your Body ⏱ 1 period; 1/2 block	NHES: 1.12.2, 1.12.9	**SE** Warm-Up, p. 60	•	•	•
3.2.1 **List** in order the three stages of the body's response to stress.		**RN** Note Taking Guide 3-2	•	•	•
		IB Image Bank 3-4, 3-5		•	
3.2.2 **Identify** four types of early warning signs for stress.		**TR** Practice 3-2		•	
3.2.3 **Describe** the relationship between stress and illness.		**TR** Section 3-2 Quiz		•	
3 Stress and Individuals ⏱ 1 period; 1/2 block	NHES: 1.12.2, 1.12.5, 6.12.1	**SE** Warm-Up, p. 65	•	•	•
3.3.1 **Explain** how individuals can have different responses to the same stressor.		**RN** Note Taking Guide 3-3	•	•	•
		TR Practice 3-3		•	
3.3.2 **Describe** two ways that personality affects stress.		**TR** Section 3-3 Quiz		•	
3.3.3 **Identify** the key factor in resilience.					
Managing Your Time ⏱ 1 period; 1/2 block	NHES: 5.12.7, 6.12.2, 6.12.3	**SE** Practice the Skill, p. 69	•	•	•
BHS.3 **Develop** a plan to manage time efficiently.		**RN** Building Health Skills 3	•	•	•
4 Coping With Stress ⏱ 2 periods; 1 block	NHES: 3.12.4, 7.12.2, 7.12.3	**SE** Warm-Up, p. 70	•	•	•
		SE Hands-On Activity Progressive Relaxation, p. 73	•	•	•
3.4.1 **Identify** ways to control stress, reduce tension, and change the way you think about stressors.		**RN** Note Taking Guide 3-4	•	•	•
3.4.2 **Explain** why building resilience is important.		**TR** Practice 3-4		•	
3.4.3 **Describe** the value of seeking support from others when you are under stress.		**TR** Section 3-4 Quiz		•	

Chapter Review and Assessment

SE Chapter 3 Review, p. 78 (L3)
CTB Chapter 3 Test (L2)(L3)(L4)
SE Standardized Test Prep, p. 79 (L3)

PROGRAM COMPONENTS

SE Student Edition	**CTB** Computer Test Bank
TE Teacher Edition	**AUD** Audio Section Summaries
TR Teaching Resources	
RN Reading and Note Taking Guide	**DVD** Teens Talk Video Series
	VVG Video Viewing Guide
ARN Adapted Reading and Note Taking Guide	**PPT** Presentation
IB Image Bank	

Differentiated Instruction

(L1) (L2) (L4) (EL)

		SE eTEXT	TE eTEXT	PRINT
ARN	Note Taking Guide 3-1 (L2)	•	•	
RN	Note Taking Guide 3-1 (EL)	•	•	•
AUD	Audio Summary 3-1 (L1) (L2) (EL)	•	•	
TE	Reteach Strategy, p. 59 (L2)		•	•
TR	Enrich 3-1 (L4)		•	
ARN	Note Taking Guide 3-2 (L2)	•	•	
RN	Note Taking Guide 3-2 (EL)	•	•	•
AUD	Audio Summary 3-2 (L1) (L2) (EL)	•	•	
TE	Reteach Strategy, p. 64 (L2)		•	•
TR	Enrich 3-2 (L4)		•	
ARN	Note Taking Guide 3-3 (L2)	•	•	
RN	Note Taking Guide 3-3 (EL)	•	•	•
AUD	Audio Summary 3-3 (L1) (L2) (EL)	•	•	
TE	Reteach Strategy, p. 67 (L2)		•	•
TR	Enrich 3-3 (L4)		•	
ARN	Building Health Skills 3 (L2)	•	•	
RN	Building Health Skills 3 (EL)	•	•	•
ARN	Note Taking Guide 3-4 (L2)	•	•	
RN	Note Taking Guide 3-4 (EL)	•	•	•
AUD	Audio Summary 3-4 (L1) (L2) (EL)	•	•	
TE	Reteach Strategy, p. 76 (L2)		•	•
TR	Enrich 3-4 (L4)		•	

ABILITY LEVELS

- (L1) For students with special needs
- (L2) For less proficient readers
- (L3) For all students
- (L4) For gifted and talented students
- (EL) For English language learners

Chapter 3 Digital/Video Pathway

This alternative pathway allows you to teach this chapter's content using only the video and online materials.

Preview

DVD Video #3 Preview
SE Video #3 Preview Activity
VVG Video #3 Worksheet

Stressed Out

1
PPT 3-1 Presentation
RN/ARN 3-1 Note Taking
PPT 3-1 Section Quiz

2
PPT 3-2 Presentation
RN/ARN 3-2 Note Taking
PPT 3-2 Section Quiz

3
PPT 3-3 Presentation
RN/ARN 3-3 Note Taking
PPT 3-3 Section Quiz

4
DVD Video #3 Explore/Wrap-Up
VVG Video #3 Worksheet
PPT 3-4 Presentation
RN/ARN 3-4 Note Taking
PPT 3-4 Section Quiz

Stressed Out

Chapter Preview

Section 1 What Causes Stress?
Stress is how a person responds to a challenge or threat. Stress can be caused by four types of events or situations: major life changes, catastrophes, everyday problems, and environmental problems.

Section 2 How Stress Affects Your Body
The body responds to stress in three stages: alarm, resistance, and exhaustion. Severe or prolonged stress can trigger illness and reduce the body's ability to fight illness.

Section 3 Stress and Individuals
How individuals react to a stressor depends on how they assess the situation. People who are pessimists or perfectionists tend to assess situations more negatively and find them more stressful. Resilience, or the ability to bounce back from stress, depends on the support of family and friends.

 Practicing Healthful Behaviors

Managing Your Time
Mastering time-management skills can help reduce sources of stress in people's lives.

Section 4 Coping With Stress
Two ways to reduce stress are time management and mental rehearsal. Strategies to help relieve stress include physical activity, relaxation, positive thinking, and humor. Building resilience and reaching out to others for support can also help people cope with stress.

 GO ONLINE
PearsonSuccessNet.com
For resources and activities for this chapter.

Managing Stress

1 What Causes Stress?

2 How Stress Affects Your Body

3 Stress and Individuals

 Building Health Skills
• **Practicing Healthful Behaviors** Managing Your Time

4 Coping With Stress
• **Hands-On Activity** Progressive Relaxation

GO ONLINE PearsonSuccessNet.com

TEENS Talk
VIDEO 3
Stressed Out

Preview **Activity**

Have Sources of Stress Changed Over the Years?

Complete this activity before you watch the video.

1. Make a list of the top five everyday problems that cause stress in your daily life.

2. Interview one or two adults and ask them to recall the top five everyday problems they faced in high school.

3. Write a paragraph that compares the problems you listed with the problems the adults listed. Based on this comparison, would you say that sources of everyday stress have changed, or stayed the same? Explain. **WRITING**

54

Sensitive Issues

Stress can be a sensitive issue for students who are experiencing problems at home or school. Students may also be sensitive about how they react to stress.

• Never ask students to disclose information they would rather keep confidential.

• Always give students other options for activities in which they are asked to apply what they learn to their own lives.

VIDEO 3 TEENS Talk

Stressed Out

Video Objectives

Use this video to help students

Identify sources of stress for teens—from everyday problems to major life changes.

Compare how different individuals respond to stressful situations.

Evaluate the use of strategies to manage stress, including time management and building resilience.

Preview Activity

Have Sources of Stress Changed Over the Years?

Assign the Preview Activity for homework a few days before you plan to show the video. After students complete the assignment, compile a class list of the sources of stress that teens and adults identified. Discuss whether sources of everyday stress have changed or stayed the same, and the possible reasons why.

From the Authors

Stress can be a challenging topic for students because it is more abstract and requires higher order thinking than many of the topics in a health course. Everyone agrees that stress affects a person's overall health, but the mechanisms are not clearly understood.

In any class, there will be a wide variety of responses to the same stressor. Some students have a natural ability to manage stress.

Others are frequently "stressed out." So students bring different levels of interest, need, and capability to this topic.

The activities and questions in this chapter are designed to make the topic as concrete as possible and to help students make connections to their own lives. See, for example, the Health at Home activity on page 64 and the Quick Quiz on page 65.

Section 1
What Causes Stress?

Objectives
Before class begins, write the objectives on the board. Have students copy the objectives into their notebooks at the start of class.

1. Focus

Warm-Up Myth/Fact

After students complete the writing assignment, call on a few volunteers to read their ideas to the class. Most students will be able to think of something potentially stressful about the situation. Then ask students to reread the myth. Discuss the myth to find out what students think stress is and whether they think stress is always negative.

Presentation 3-1

Objectives
► **Describe** what causes a person to experience stress.
► **Identify** four general types of stressors.

Vocabulary
• stress
• eustress
• distress
• stressor
• catastrophe

Warm-Up

Myth People should try to avoid all situations that can lead to stress.

Fact Stress is a normal part of life that you cannot avoid. Sometimes stress can have a positive outcome.

WRITING You are invited to a friend's birthday party. What about this situation could cause you to experience stress?

What Is Stress?

It is early morning and you are fast asleep. Suddenly, your alarm clock sounds. You sit up quickly, open your eyes, and jump out of bed. As you react to the ringing alarm, you experience stress. **Stress** is the response of your body and mind to being challenged or threatened. **You experience stress when situations, events, or people make demands on your body and mind.** Most people think of stress as a negative experience, but stress can be positive as well. Stress is positive when it helps you escape from a dangerous situation, promotes your personal growth, or helps you accomplish your goals. Positive stress is sometimes called **eustress.** Negative stress is sometimes called **distress.**

Think about something you have accomplished lately—perhaps you did well on a test or your team defeated a tough opponent in soccer. You may remember the feelings you experienced before and during the event. Do you think you performed better as a result of the stress?

At moderate levels, stress can actually improve your ability to concentrate and perform at your best. Beyond that level, however, it begins to take a negative toll on performance. Suppose that you were scheduled to take your driver's test next week. Feelings of stress might assure that you practice during the week. On the day of the test, your nervousness might make you more alert behind the wheel. But what if you experience overwhelming stress during the test? You might find it difficult to concentrate and you might make mistakes that cause you to fail the test.

Sensitive Issues
Do not press students to give examples of stressors in their own lives. Instead, give them the choice of using hypothetical examples.

WRITING and Health

L3 Dialogue
Have students write a dialogue between two teens who are discussing a major life change, such as leaving home for college. The dialogue should show how the life change is both positive and stressful.

Invite a few students to share their dialogues with the class. Discuss why major life changes are stressful, even when they are positive. Through the dialogues and discussion, students should come to appreciate that change itself is stressful.

The Many Causes of Stress

An event or situation that causes stress is called a **stressor.** A ringing alarm clock is one example of a stressor. Other stressors in your life may be a difficult homework assignment or an argument with a friend. These events make demands on your body and mind. **Four general types of stressors are major life changes, catastrophes, everyday problems, and environmental problems.**

Major Life Changes Do you remember how you felt on your first day of high school? Were you excited? Were you nervous? Perhaps you experienced both emotions at the same time. You had to adjust to new surroundings, new people, and increased expectations. Starting high school is an example of a major life change. So is graduating from high school. Major life changes are stressful because it takes energy to adjust to a new situation. A major life change may also threaten your sense of security or your self-esteem. The more major life changes you experience in a year, the more stress you are likely to feel.

Figure 1 lists some major life changes. Notice that the list includes positive changes as well as negative ones. While being accepted to the college of your choice is indeed a positive event, it can be just as stressful as a negative event, such as having a parent lose a job. It is important to realize that change, both positive and negative, is in itself stressful.

 **Connect to Your Life** List three major life changes you experienced during the past five years.

Major Life Changes

- Graduating from high school
- Experiencing death of a parent
- Going through parents' divorce
- Experiencing remarriage of parent
- Having a newborn sister or brother
- Having a serious illness
- Moving to a new school district
- Failing a grade
- Being accepted to college
- Breaking up with boyfriend or girlfriend
- Having parent lose his or her job
- Learning you were adopted
- Not making the team
- Being elected to student government
- Being recognized for an achievement
- Leaving home for college or a job

FIGURE 1 A major life change may be related to health, family, employment, friendships, or education. **Classifying** Which of the life changes listed would you classify as positive?

Managing Stress **57**

---

2. Teach

L3 EL Reading/Note Taking 3-1

L2 Adapted Reading/Note Taking 3-1

What Is Stress?

L2 Building Vocabulary

Have students read the definition of *stress* on page 56. Then point out the terms *eustress* and *distress.* Explain that the prefix *eu-* means "good," and the prefix *dis-* means "bad." Ask: **What is eustress?** *(good stress).* **What is distress?** *(bad stress).* Describe an example of each kind of stress. Call on volunteers to give additional examples.

The Many Causes of Stress

L3 Cooperative Learning

Divide the class into groups. Ask each group to take a survey of other students in school about which events and situations cause them stress. Have each group rank the stressors identified in their survey by frequency and classify them as major life changes or everyday problems. Ask groups to make charts summarizing the results of their surveys. Display the charts in the classroom.

L3 Visual Learning: Figure 1

Have students look at the list of major life changes in the figure. Explain that major life changes are common events. For example, each year in the U.S., about 3 million people graduate from high school and more than 4 million marry. Call on volunteers to answer the caption question. Then, ask: **Which of the life changes would you classify as negative?** *(Sample answer: death of a parent, having a serious illness, failing a grade)* **Which of the life changes could be either positive or negative?** *(Sample answer: remarriage of a parent, moving to a new school district, leaving home for college or a job)*

Caption Answer *Sample answer:* graduating from high school, being accepted to college, being elected to student government, being recognized for an achievement

Connect to Your Life Allow students to answer this question in their private journals.

 **Content Update**  GO ONLINE

Visit Pearson SuccessNet to access more information about stress. Have students complete the Web activity.

EL Cultural Connection

Tell students that acculturation, or adapting to a new culture, is a major cause of stress for many people. Over a million people immigrate to the U.S. each year, and most of them go through some degree of acculturation. Ask: **What are some reasons acculturation can be stressful?** *(Possible reasons: new customs, new language, lack of familiar foods, the need to make new friends, lack of extended family)*

L3 Building Media Literacy

Ask students to find three different newspaper or magazine articles about the same catastrophe, such as a natural disaster, violent crime, terrorist attack, or war. Have students compare the coverage of the catastrophe in the different articles. For example, what aspects of the catastrophe did each article focus on? How did each article address the human effects of the catastrophe? Have students write a paragraph summarizing their analysis of the articles. Ask a few volunteers to read their paragraphs aloud. **WRITING**

L1 Teacher Demo

Help students appreciate how stressful environmental problems can be. Point out that noise is an environmental problem that causes stress. Then ask students to do a task that requires concentration, such as adding long columns of figures, while you play loud music (without lyrics). After the activity, have students brainstorm places that might be stressful because of loud noises. *(Places might include the cafeteria at lunchtime, a busy city street, and a crowded school bus.)*

Connect to Your Life Allow students to answer this question in their private journals.

 GO ONLINE
PearsonSuccessNet.com
For: More on stress

Catastrophes Major life changes are an expected part of life; other highly stressful events are unexpected. A **catastrophe** (kuh TAS truh fee) is an event that threatens lives and may destroy property. Natural disasters such as hurricanes, floods, and tornadoes are catastrophes. So are violent crimes, terrorism, and war. A person who experiences a catastrophe may deal with the psychological effects for years after the event. Reading about a catastrophe or seeing images on television can also cause stress.

Everyday Problems Some of the most common stressors are minor, but frequent, everyday events. These common stressors are sometimes called "hassles." Hassles include misplacing your keys, missing your bus, or having too many homework assignments on the same day. While such problems seem minor, they contribute greatly to your overall feeling of stress. This is because hassles occur day in and day out. Can you remember a day in the past month that was free of hassles?

Conflict—disagreements with family members, friends, or others—is another common source of stress. Some high school students experience more conflict than they did when they were younger or disagree over issues that are more serious. How you dress, what music you listen to, what friends you see—these are all possible sources of conflict and stress.

For many people, the pressure to succeed is a major source of stress. They don't want to fail and they don't want to disappoint their families, their friends, or themselves. You can feel this pressure any time there is competition—in class, at a swim meet, playing chess, or in a debate. Not knowing what you will do once you leave school can also be stressful.

Connect to Your Life What everyday problems did you experience today that were stressful for you?

FIGURE 2 For some people, waiting in line to buy a ticket can be stressful.

Avoid Waiting in Line
- **Purchase tickets in advance.**
- **Pick a different time of day.**
- **Wait a while to see a new release.**

TEENS *Are Asking . . .*

Q: I need to be involved in more extra-curricular activities so I'll have a better chance of getting into a good college. But I'm afraid I'll be too stressed out if I add more activities. What should I do?

A: Although many colleges consider extra-curricular activities in the admissions process, how involved you are in the activities is generally more important than the number of activities you take part in. Instead of adding more activities to your schedule, demonstrate long-term commitment and leadership in just a few activities that really interest you.

Environmental Problems Conditions in your immediate surroundings affect your level of stress each day. Suppose, for example, that you commute to school on an overcrowded subway or bus. Your level of stress might be quite high by the time you arrive at school. If you then have to hunt for a book in a messy locker, your level of stress will continue to rise.

A major stressor that occurs all around you but is often overlooked is noise. People who live near airports show signs of high stress levels due to the noise of airplanes taking off and landing. Living near an elevated commuter rail or a busy highway can have a similar effect.

Living in unsafe or crowded conditions also tends to increase feelings of stress. So does living where the air quality is poor or where litter collects on sidewalks. Weather conditions can also contribute to stress. During a heat wave or a long spell of freezing temperatures, people may feel increased stress. This may be because they feel cooped up indoors. Or they may be stressed because they cannot afford to keep the temperature indoors as cool or as warm as they might like it to be.

FIGURE 3 Adding something attractive to the neighborhood can help to reduce stress. These teens are painting a mural.

Section 1 Review

Key Ideas and Vocabulary

1. What is **stress**? Explain how stress can be both positive and negative.
2. When do people experience stress?
3. What is meant by the term **stressor**?
4. List the four general types of stressors and give an example of each type.

Critical Thinking

5. **Applying Concepts** List five stressful experiences that you have faced in the past two weeks. Next to each, note whether it was a positive or a negative experience for you.

Health and Community

Noise Pollution Does your community have any regulations related to noise? If so, do the regulations vary with time of day or location? Sources of noise that might be regulated are radios, car exhausts, power lawnmowers, and blasting for construction. Write a paragraph summarizing your findings. **WRITING**

6. **Classifying** Explain why getting your driver's license could be classified as a major life change.
7. **Comparing and Contrasting** How is a catastrophe similar to a major life change? How is it different?

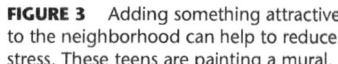

---

3. Assess

Evaluate

These assignments can help you assess students' mastery of the section content.

Section 1 Review

Answers appear below.

Teaching Resources
• Practice 3-1
• Section 3-1 Quiz

L2 Reteach

Using the board or an overhead transparency, work with students to make a concept map of major types of stressors. Then call on students to add several examples of each type of stressor to the concept map. Ask students to copy the completed concept map into their notebooks.

L4 Enrich

Teaching Resources
• Enrich 3-1

Health and Community

Noise Pollution Introduce the activity by describing some health problems associated with noise pollution, such as hearing damage and loss of sleep. Suggest that students contact their local police department, town or city hall, or representative for information on local noise regulations. Remind students of specific sources of noise in their community, such as trains or airports, that might be regulated. If their community does not have noise regulations, students can go online to find noise regulations for other communities.

Section 1 Review

1. Stress is the response of your body and mind to being challenged or threatened. Eustress helps people accomplish goals; distress takes a toll on performance.

2. when situations, events, or people make demands on their bodies and minds

3. an event or situation that causes stress

4. The four types of stressors are major life changes, catastrophes, everyday problems, and environmental problems. Check that students have given a suitable example of each type of stressor.

5. Lists of stressors will vary. The same stressors may be positive or negative to different students.

6. *Sample answer:* Getting your driver's license gives you the ability to be much more independent.

7. Both are highly stressful. Major life changes are usually expected; they can be positive or negative. A catastrophe is unexpected and almost always negative.

Section 2

How Stress Affects Your Body

Objectives

Before class begins, write the objectives on the board. Have students copy the objectives into their notebooks at the start of class.

1. Focus

Warm-Up Health Stats

After students finish writing, call on a few volunteers to share their predictions. They might predict, for example, that prolonged stress causes people to become "run down" or "worn out." Tell students to check whether their predictions were correct when they read about stress and illness. (Note: A risk of 1.0 represents the risk of developing a cold under a normal level of everyday stress.)

Presentation 3-2

Objectives

▶ **List** in order the three stages of the body's response to stress.

▶ **Identify** four types of early warning signs for stress.

▶ **Describe** the relationship between stress and illness.

Vocabulary

• fight-or-flight response

Warm-Up

Health Stats Is there a relationship between stress and the risk of catching a cold?

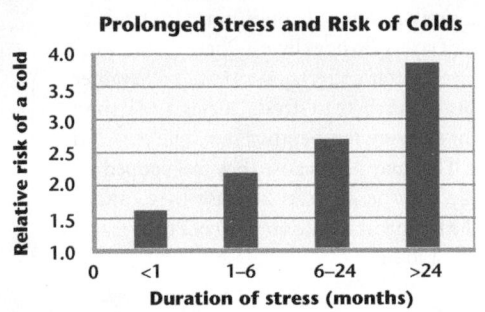

Prolonged Stress and Risk of Colds

Relative risk of a cold / Duration of stress (months)

WRITING Predict why being in a prolonged stressful situation might increase the likelihood of getting a cold.

Stages of Stress

You are walking in a park. Suddenly, you see a large dog that isn't on a leash. The dog is growling. How do you react? Instantly, your mind sizes up the situation. You recognize that the dog could be a threat to your safety. When you perceive something to be a threat, your body springs into action. Your body's response isn't under your control—it's automatic.

All stressors trigger the same stress response. However, the intensity of the response will vary. **The body's response to stress occurs in three stages—the alarm stage, the resistance stage, and the exhaustion stage.**

Alarm Stage   During the alarm stage, your body releases a substance called adrenaline (uh DREN uh lin) into your blood. Adrenaline causes many immediate changes in your body, as shown in Figure 4. Your heart beats faster, your breathing speeds up, and your muscles tense. Your attention narrows as you focus on the stressor.

These changes prepare you to either "fight" the stressor or "take flight" and escape. Thus, this initial reaction of the body to stress is called the **fight-or-flight response.** This response probably helped early humans survive. Today, your body still reacts to any stressor with the same set of changes even when fight-or-flight is not a useful response.

For Your **INFORMATION!**

Tend and Befriend

According to recent research, the fight-or-flight response is not the only biological response to stress. The "tend and befriend" response also may have helped early humans to survive. "Tend and befriend" describes the tendency to protect offspring and to reach out to others for support.

Some researchers think that this response is triggered by the release of the hormone oxytocin into the blood, and that the release of oxytocin increases during periods of acute stress. Both males and females produce oxytocin, but females produce greater amounts of this hormone. Estrogen tends to enhance the effect of oxytocin, while testosterone counteracts the effect of oxytocin.

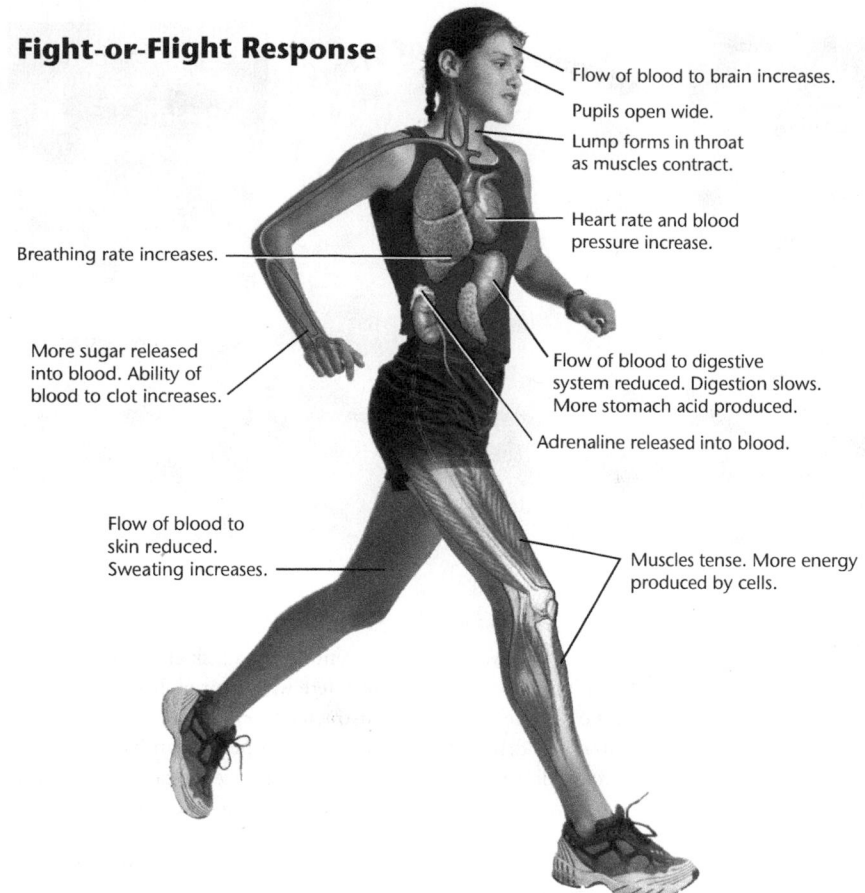

Fight-or-Flight Response

Flow of blood to brain increases.

Pupils open wide.

Lump forms in throat as muscles contract.

Heart rate and blood pressure increase.

Breathing rate increases.

More sugar released into blood. Ability of blood to clot increases.

Flow of blood to digestive system reduced. Digestion slows. More stomach acid produced.

Adrenaline released into blood.

Flow of blood to skin reduced. Sweating increases.

Muscles tense. More energy produced by cells.

Resistance Stage   Sometimes you can deal with a stressor quickly. You find the keys you thought were lost or you know the answers to the questions on a quiz. If, however, you are unable to successfully respond to a stressor during the alarm stage, your body moves into the resistance stage. During this stage, your body adapts to the continued presence of the stressor. You may think you are no longer stressed because the symptoms from the alarm stage disappear. However, the work that your body does during the resistance stage uses up a lot of energy. As a result, you may become tired, irritable, and less able to handle any added stress.

Exhaustion Stage   The third stage of the stress response is the exhaustion stage. Your body can no longer keep up with the demands placed on it. Your physical and emotional resources are depleted.

The exhaustion stage does not occur with each stress response. If it did, your body would wear out. Exhaustion occurs only if a stressor continues for a long time—usually weeks, months, or even years. People may reach the exhaustion stage when they experience extreme stress that is beyond their control—such as a death of a family member.

FIGURE 4   During the alarm stage, adrenaline triggers many changes in the body. For example, extra sugar released into your blood combines with oxygen in body cells to give you a burst of energy. **Interpreting Diagrams** List two body functions that speed up during the alarm stage. List two that slow down.

Managing Stress   **61**

Stages of Stress

L2 **Visual Learning: Figure 4**
Image Bank Figure 3-4

Ask: **Which stage of stress is shown in Figure 4?** *(alarm stage)* Explain that the alarm stage prepares the body for action. Ask: **What kind of action does the alarm stage prepare the body for?** *(fight or flight)* Have students answer the caption question. Then ask: **How do these changes prepare the body for fight or flight?** *(Sample answer: More sugar in the blood allows cells to produce extra energy.)*
Caption Answer *Sample answer:* Heart and breathing rates speed up; more sugar is released into blood; digestion slows; less blood flows to the skin.

L3 **Cooperative Learning**

Divide the class into small groups. List these body systems on the board: immune, nervous, digestive, respiratory, cardiovascular, and muscular. Ask each group to work together to identify which changes listed in Figure 4 take place in each body system.

L3 **Class Discussion**

Initiate a class discussion of stressors that might continue long enough for a person to reach the exhaustion stage of stress. Remind students that the stressors must last for weeks, months, or even years for this to occur. *(Possible stressors might include a prolonged serious illness of a family member and not being able to pass a standardized test required for graduation.)*

Differentiated Instruction

EL **English Language Learners**
Use an analogy to explain the stages of stress. Say that stress is like swimming against a current. At first, you can swim faster than the current and move forward in the water (alarm stage). After awhile, you get tired and can only manage to stay in the same place (resistance). Eventually, you get too tired to swim and are carried backward by the current (exhaustion).

L2 **Less Proficient Readers**
Pair less proficient readers with advanced readers, and ask the pairs to create flowcharts of the stages of stress, including changes that occur at each stage. Post the flowcharts in the classroom where students can see them as they continue to learn about the effects of stress.

Recognizing Signs of Stress

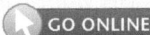 **Visual Learning: Figure 5**

Image Bank Figure 3-5

Have students read the warning signs of stress in the figure. Name a few specific warning signs, and ask students to identify the type of change each sign represents. Then challenge students to think of other specific warning signs of stress for each type of change. (e.g., *nail biting for behavioral change*) Ask: **Could increased sweating be caused by something other than stress?** (*Increased sweating could be a sign of an illness such as the flu.*) Point out that many of the signs in Figure 5 could have multiple causes. So it is important to use a set of warning signs as an indication of stress rather than a single sign.

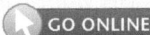 **Building Health Skills**

Practicing Healthful Behaviors Ask students to start keeping a private stress diary. In their diaries, they should make a list of warning signs of stress from Figure 5 that apply to them. Ask students to add other signs that they associate with stress. They should also write brief descriptions of events or situations that cause them to experience these signs of stress. Encourage students to keep their diaries long enough to identify the chief causes of stress in their daily lives. **WRITING**

Connect to Your Life Allow students to answer this question in their private journals.

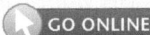 **Online Activity** **GO ONLINE**

Visit Pearson SuccessNet to access an online activity about how to recognize stress. Have students complete the Web activity.

Warning Signs of Stress

Behavorial Changes
- Overeating or hardly eating at all
- Sleep problems
- Hurrying; talking fast
- Withdrawing from relationships
- Reckless behavior

Physical Changes
- Muscle tension
- Headache
- Upset stomach
- Pounding heart
- Shortness of breath
- Increased sweating
- Skin rash

Changes in Thinking
- Unable to concentrate
- Negative thinking
- Excessive worrying
- Self-criticism
- Critical of others

Emotional Changes
- Irritable
- Angry
- Impatient
- Nervous
- Increased crying

FIGURE 5 These are some common warning signs of stress. They include physical changes, emotions, thoughts, and behaviors.

GO ONLINE
PearsonSuccessNet.com
For: More on how to recognize stress

Recognizing Signs of Stress

If you have ever tried to concentrate on a task after a stressful day, then you know that stress can interfere with your ability to focus and think clearly. When people are distracted, they risk injuring themselves and others. A driver may not notice that a pedestrian has stepped into the crosswalk. Or the pedestrian may not notice the car. Reducing the risk of injury is one reason to reduce your level of stress. Another reason is to prevent the effects of prolonged stress on your body.

Before you can deal with stress, you must recognize the warning signs. **The warning signs of stress include changes in how your body functions and changes in emotions, thoughts, and behaviors.** As you look over the list of warning signs in Figure 5, think about how you act and feel when under stress. Begin your own personal list of warning signs by selecting items from Figure 5 that apply to you. Add other changes you associate with being stressed. The next time you experience some of the warning signs on your list, you will know that you are under stress.

The next step is to try to identify the stressor you are facing. Sometimes this task is easy because the source of the stress is obvious; for example, a close friend is moving away. Noticing patterns can help you identify a stressor. Perhaps you always show signs of stress when you haven't had enough sleep. When it is difficult to pin down the source of your stress, try recording your activities and responses in a journal. Don't get discouraged. It may take time for a pattern to emerge. By recognizing the warning signs as early as possible and by identifying stressors, you may be able to prevent some of the more serious effects of stress.

Connect to Your Life What warning signs of stress do you routinely experience?

MATH **and Health**

 **Percentages**

Point out the statistics in Figure 6 on percentages of female teens and male teens who have reported having at least one headache each week. Then say that between 10 and 20 percent of teens have had at least one migraine headache and that migraines are three times as common in female teens as male teens. Ask: **What percentage of migraines in teens occurs in female teens and what percentage occurs in male teens?** (*75 percent in female teens and 25 percent in male teens*)

Stress and Illness

Severe or prolonged stress can affect your health. **Stress can trigger certain illnesses, reduce the body's ability to fight an illness, and make some diseases harder to control.**

Stomachaches A "stomachache" can occur in your stomach, small intestine, or large intestine. Stress disrupts the movement of food through the digestive system. The food may move too quickly or too slowly. You might experience gas, cramps, diarrhea (dy uh REE uh), or constipation.

Stress also increases the amount of stomach acid. Doctors used to think that excess acid attacked the lining of the stomach and caused open sores, called ulcers, to form. Then researchers found bacteria in the stomach that could cause ulcers. When medicine was used to kill the bacteria, the ulcer healed. Current thinking is that excess acid makes it more likely that an ulcer will form and makes it more difficult for an ulcer to heal.

Asthma Asthma (AZ muh) is another illness for which stress can be a trigger. An asthmatic attack happens when the air passages of the respiratory system narrow, making it difficult to breathe. During an attack, the person coughs, wheezes, and gasps for air. These symptoms usually can be controlled by medication that is inhaled. But it helps if people with asthma recognize which stressors can trigger an attack.

Headaches Stress can trigger headaches. Tension in the muscles around your scalp, face, and neck may produce an aching or pounding sensation in your head. A type of headache called a migraine (MY grayn) begins when blood vessels in the brain and scalp narrow, which limits the supply of oxygen to the brain. The blood vessels must then open wide to increase the flow of oxygen. This stretching of the blood vessels causes the painful throbbing of a migraine. If you suffer from frequent headaches, you may want to keep a diary to determine what factors trigger the onset of a headache. In addition to stress, certain foods, such as chocolate or large amounts of caffeine, can trigger headaches.

37.6% of female teens and 21.3% of male teens report having at least one headache each week.

FIGURE 6 This image illustrates the pain associated with a migraine headache.

Managing Stress **63**

Stress and Illness

(L3) Building Media Literacy

Help students recall what they learned in Chapter 1 about evaluating sources of information. Then have students find two reliable Web sites that provide information about stress and illness. For each Web site, they should write a brief explanation of why it is reliable. Make a list on the board of the criteria students used. Then have the class evaluate the criteria.

(L2) Addressing Misconceptions

Stress-Related Physical Symptoms
Students may think that stress-related physical symptoms are not as "real" as the same symptoms caused by viruses, bacteria, or injuries. Ask: **Did anyone ever tell you that stress-related symptoms were "all in your head"?** *(Students are likely to have heard this expression.)* Explain that stress-related symptoms are just as real as the symptoms of a cold. In both cases, the symptoms are due to underlying physical changes in the body.

Differentiated Instruction

(EL) English Language Learners

Students may not understand all the warning signs of stress listed in Figure 5 because some of the terms, such as *withdrawing, relationships,* and *irritable,* are unfamiliar. For these warning signs, describe or act out a simple example. For example, for "Withdrawing from Relationships," you might describe a student who starts eating lunch alone after eating with friends for months. For "Irritable," you might act out being very annoyed because you dropped some important papers in a puddle. Ask students if there are other warning signs they would like you to demonstrate.

3. Assess

Evaluate
These assignments can help you assess students' mastery of the section content.

Section 2 Review
Answers appear below.

Teaching Resources
• Practice 3-2
• Section 3-2 Quiz

 Reteach

Work with the class to create a bulletin board illustrating section content. Head the bulletin board with three labels corresponding to the main headings in the section: Stages of Stress, Signs of Stress, and Stress and Illness. Ask students to add relevant examples, in writing or pictures, under the appropriate labels. Review any topics for which students have trouble thinking of examples.

L4 Enrich

Teaching Resources
• Enrich 3-2

Health at Home

Warning Signs of Stress Avoid asking students to reveal their personal signs of stress. Instead focus on whether students learned anything new about themselves from the interviews. Discuss the value of getting other views of oneself.

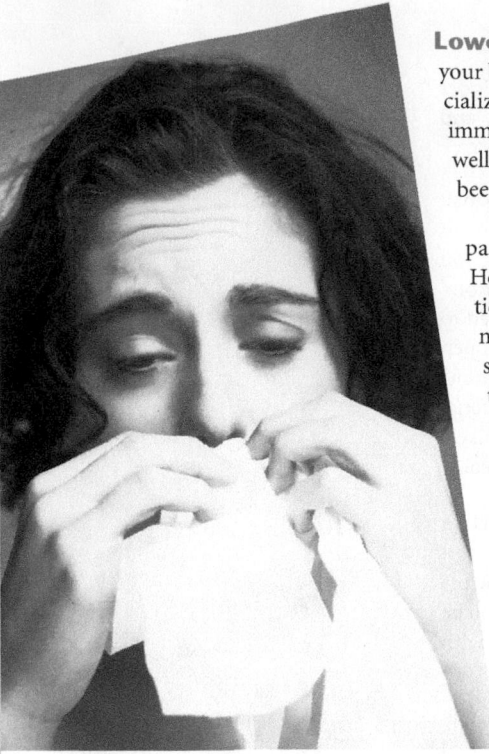

FIGURE 7 Prolonged stress can weaken your immune system, which makes it harder to fight off a cold or flu.

Lowered Resistance to Disease The immune system protects your body from disease through a complex process involving many specialized cells. When you speak of fighting off the flu or a cold, your immune system does the fighting. When your immune system functions well, you are better able to resist some of the illnesses to which you have been exposed.

Scientific research has shown that, during the alarm stage, some parts of your immune system may function better than usual. However, prolonged stress can prevent the immune system from functioning well. If your immune system is weakened, you may develop minor illnesses, such as colds, more often. For people with diseases such as cancer, a weakened immune system makes it harder to control the disease.

Heart Disease Some effects of frequent or prolonged stress don't show up until later in life. Remember that during the alarm stage, your heart beats faster. Your blood vessels narrow and your blood pressure rises. Your heart must work harder to keep blood flowing through your body. Stress that is frequent or prolonged can cause damage to the muscle fibers in the heart. Prolonged stress can also damage the linings of blood vessels, which are under increased pressure. Because high blood pressure has no obvious symptoms and often goes undetected, it is sometimes called the "silent killer." Reducing stress is one of the ways that people can lower their blood pressure and reduce the risk of heart disease and stroke.

Section 2 Review

Key Ideas and Vocabulary
1. What are the three stages of the stress response? In what order do they occur?
2. Why is the body's response during the first stage of stress called the **fight-or-flight response?**
3. Describe four ways that you can recognize when you are under stress.
4. What is the relationship between stress and illness?

Critical Thinking
5. **Relating Cause and Effect** Why is it important to identify signs of stress early?

Health at Home

Warning Signs of Stress Ask a few friends and trusted adults if they can tell when you are under stress. Ask them to describe the warning signs that you exhibit. Write a paragraph about what you find out. **WRITING**

---

6. **Applying Concepts** Explain how changes that occur during the alarm stage could help you escape from a threatening situation.
7. **Making Judgments** A doctor with a patient who complains about stomach pains is likely to do a series of tests to determine the cause. Why might the doctor also ask about the patient's mental and emotional health?

GO ONLINE PearsonSuccessNet.com   Audio Summary Section 3.2

Section 2 Review

1. alarm, resistance, and exhaustion
2. Changes occur that prepare the body to fight a threat or flee.
3. through physical changes and changes in thinking, emotions, and behavior
4. Stress can trigger certain illnesses, reduce the body's ability to fight an illness, and make some diseases harder to control.
5. so causes of stress can be identified and addressed before they cause serious health problems such as heart disease
6. *Sample answer:* It takes energy to run. An increased heart rate and breathing rate bring extra oxygen and sugar to cells, where these substances are used to produce a burst of energy.
7. because stomach pains can be a warning sign of stress

Stress and Individuals

Warm-Up

Quick Quiz How many of the following statements accurately describe how you think or behave?

1. I need to be the best at everything I do.

2. If something doesn't go as planned, I feel like a failure.

3. I tend to expect the worst in most situations.

4. I want to be liked by everyone.

5. I really enjoy competition.

WRITING Review your responses. Then explain why you might be more or less likely to be under stress than others.

Responses to Stress Vary

Your teacher walks into class and says, "Okay, everyone, put away your books. We are going to have a surprise quiz now." How would you react? Now look around the classroom and imagine your classmates' reactions. Would their reactions be the same as yours? Your teacher's announcement might bring on a wide range of reactions—mild stress, extreme stress, confidence, and indifference are just some reactions you could predict.

Why does one person remain calm when faced with a stressor while another becomes anxious and tense? The answer to this question points out an important fact about stress—it is a highly personal experience. **How you react to a stressor depends on how you assess the situation.** As you assess the situation, you are answering two important questions:

▶ Is this situation a threat to my well-being?

▶ Do I have the necessary resources to meet the challenge?

Time, energy, skills, and experience are resources. Situations that cause the most distress are those in which you answer *no* to the second question.

You might see a surprise quiz as a threat if you need to maintain a certain grade to be eligible to play on a team. If you did poorly on previous quizzes, you might not be confident of doing well on this one. Your past experiences have a lot to do with how you respond to new situations.

Differentiated Instruction

L1 Special Needs

Provide students with a concrete example of the key idea of the section: How you react to a stressor depends on how you assess the situation. Tell students that knowing that you are able to deal with a situation usually makes the situation less stressful. Describe a potentially stressful situation with which most students can identify, such as missing the bus after school. Discuss how having a plan for dealing with this situation (e.g., knowing who to talk to at school or how to contact a parent at work) would affect their response.

Section 3

Objectives

▶ **Explain** how individuals can have different responses to the same stressor.

▶ **Describe** two ways that personality affects stress.

▶ **Identify** the key factor in resilience.

Vocabulary

- optimism
- pessimism
- perfectionist
- resilience

Section 3

Stress and Individuals

Objectives

Before class begins, write the objectives on the board. Have students copy the objectives into their notebooks at the start of class.

1. Focus

Warm-Up Quick Quiz

Use the Warm-Up Presentation slide to survey student responses.

Give students a few minutes to do the quiz. Then point out that the statements reveal ways of thinking that are likely to increase stress. For example, no one can be the best at everything, so needing to be the best is likely to cause stress. Discuss how differences in ways of thinking might influence how much stress different people feel. You may want to revisit this quiz after students read about avoiding negative thinking.

Presentation 3-3

2. Teach

L3 EL Reading/Note Taking 3-3

L2 Adapted Reading/Note Taking 3-3

Responses to Stress Vary

L2 Teacher Demo

Announce a surprise quiz. Give students a few moments to react before telling them you are not serious. Then ask students to write what they thought or how they felt when you announced the quiz. Have them hand in (anonymously) what they wrote, and read aloud some of their responses. With the class, discuss how the responses vary.

Stress and Personality

 **Visual Learning: Figure 8**

Have students read the traits listed for the two football players in Figure 8. Ask: **Based on their traits, which player is optimistic and which player is pessimistic?** *(Player A is optimistic, and player B is pessimistic.)* **What might player A be thinking?** *(Accept any relevant optimistic responses, such as "I know we can beat these guys.")* **What might player B be thinking?** *(Accept any relevant pessimistic responses, such as "We'll never score against this team.")* **Caption Answer** *Sample answer: Player A's positive thoughts and feelings may help him perform better than player B.*

L3 Class Discussion

Explain that procrastination, or the delaying of tasks, is a common trait, characterizing one in five people most of the time, and the majority of people some of the time. Describe an example, such as not starting to work on a term paper until the night before it is due. Encourage students to describe other examples. Ask students to discuss how stressed out they would feel if they were in each situation. Explain that aiming for perfection is one cause of procrastination. Review the time-management skills of prioritizing tasks and breaking down large tasks into smaller ones. Discuss how the skills can help people deal with procrastination.

Connect to Your Life Allow students to answer this question in their private journals.

L3 Content Update GO ONLINE

Visit Pearson SuccessNet to access more information about stress and personality. Have students complete the Web activity.

Player A is...
• Confident
• Eager
• Calm
• Focused
• Optimistic

Player B is...
• Uncertain
• Hesitant
• Nervous
• Distracted
• Pessimistic

Figure 8 Personality can affect how two people respond to the same situation. **Predicting** How could these players' thoughts and feelings affect their ability to perform?

GO ONLINE
PearsonSuccessNet.com
For: More on stress and personality

Stress and Personality

Your personality also has a lot to do with how you respond to stressors. For example, a friend invites you to a party. The only person that you will know at the party is your friend. How you respond to the situation will depend on your personality. If you are outgoing and confident, you might look forward to the opportunity to meet new people. However, if you are shy, you might feel threatened by the thought of meeting so many strangers. **Your personality influences your assessment of a situation.**

Optimism and Pessimism Carla and Joan play on a softball team. Their team is about to face the best team in the league. Carla is looking forward to the challenge. She likes competing against the best opponents. Her response reflects her optimism. **Optimism** is the tendency to focus on the positive aspects of a situation. Joan is threatened by the situation. She assumes that she will play poorly and that the other team will win by a wide margin. Her response reflects her pessimism. **Pessimism** is the tendency to focus on the negative and expect the worst.

Aiming for Perfection A **perfectionist** is a person who accepts nothing less than excellence. If you are a perfectionist about your appearance, for example, you may spend hours getting ready to go to school. If you are a perfectionist about your work, you may spend hours agonizing over each sentence in a paper and still not be satisfied.

Because perfectionists set goals that are impossible to attain, they are never satisfied with what they have accomplished. This can lead to a vicious cycle of trying harder, not being satisfied, and trying harder still. There are ways to break the cycle and reduce your stress.

► Accept that you cannot be perfect.

► Take pride in the things you do well.

► Don't focus on your mistakes.

Connect to Your Life  Are the goals that you set for yourself easy to reach, difficult to reach, or impossible to reach?

TEENS *Are Asking . . .*

Q: I'm not happy unless I do everything just right. How can I stop being a perfectionist?

A: It may not be easy to change, but the rewards will be worth it. You will have more time to achieve and to relax if you spend less time worrying about mistakes. Accept the fact that nobody is perfect, including you. Make a list of activities that you do well. These are likely to be things that you also enjoy doing. Use the list to assess your strengths and set realistic goals. Focus on your achievements instead of on what you see as shortcomings. To overcome your fear of making mistakes, try making some mistakes that don't matter on purpose. Send an e-mail with a typo, or wear a pair of socks that don't match.

Resilience

Some people seem to tolerate high levels of stress. They tend to view stressful events as challenges rather than as threats. For example, they might view the loss of a job as an opportunity to pursue a new career. Also, they believe that they are in control—that they can influence the outcome of a stressful event.

Even stress-hardy people will face a catastrophe or major life change that they are unable to control. They need to find a way to adapt to an extremely distressful situation. The ability to recover, or "bounce back," from extreme or prolonged stress is called **resilience.** Many factors contribute to resilience. **The key factor in resilience is having the support of family and friends.** These relationships offer encouragement, reassurance, and love. People with resilience share other characteristics.

FIGURE 9 People may use a "group huddle" to encourage one member of the group or the group as a whole.

► They know their strengths and have confidence in their abilities.

► They make realistic plans and take the steps to carry out those plans.

► They have good communication and problem-solving skills.

► They are able to recognize and control their feelings.

► They recognize that change is a normal part of life. They are able to put life changes in perspective.

In the next section, as you study ways to cope with stress, you will learn how to build your resilience.

Section 3 Review

Key Ideas and Vocabulary

1. Why might two individuals have different responses to the same stressor?

2. How does personality affect a person's response to stress?

3. Define the term **resilience.**

4. What is the key factor in determining whether a person has resilience?

Critical Thinking

5. Applying Concepts The weather report says there is a 50 percent chance of rain. How might your optimism or pessimism affect how you interpret this report?

Health at School

Resilience Interview a guidance counselor, school nurse, or social worker. Ask the person you interview to describe those factors that make it easier for a student to recover from an extremely stressful situation. Summarize what you learn in a paragraph. **WRITING**

---

6. Predicting Impatience is a common personality trait. Predict how impatience could affect a person's level of stress.

7. Classifying After Kenny completes his math homework, he checks his answers to see if they make sense. Based solely on this behavior, do you think Kenny is a perfectionist? Explain.

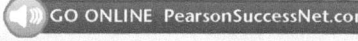 GO ONLINE PearsonSuccessNet.com Audio Summary Section 3.3

Managing Stress **67**

Managing Your Time

Objective

Develop a plan to manage time efficiently.

Teaching Strategies

- Explain that time management involves setting priorities, breaking down large tasks into smaller ones, making a realistic schedule, and saying *no* to requests that are not priorities.

- Show the class how to apply time-management techniques to a complex activity, such as writing a research paper. Have the class brainstorm all the steps required to complete the activity. Make sure the steps are listed in the correct order. Then ask students how much time they think each step will take. Set a hypothetical deadline for the research paper, and show students how to work backward from the deadline to schedule all the tasks so the paper will be finished on time.

- Help students learn to make realistic estimates of the time required for particular tasks. Ask them to estimate the time they think it will take to finish one of the tasks on their list. Then have them keep a log of the actual time it takes to complete the task.

- Point out that priorities may change through time as some tasks become more or less important. For example, the importance of completing a term paper increases as the deadline approaches. If an event is postponed, preparing for the event might have a lower priority. Explain that this is why it is important to reassess priorities on a regular basis.

Managing Your Time

Last night, José stayed up late to write a report that was assigned two weeks ago. He planned to do his math homework in the morning, but then slept through his alarm. In his haste this morning, José left his gym clothes at home. Running toward the school as the bell rang, José felt anxious and tense.

José needs to manage his time better. A good time manager completes daily tasks and still finds time to relax. Follow these steps to better manage your time.

❶ Track how you spend your time.

▶ Use a sheet from a daily planner that is divided into 15-minute blocks or make your own version on ruled paper. Prepare a sheet for each day of the week.

▶ Mark all your scheduled activities on the grid, beginning with your classes at school. Include other activities that you attend on a regular schedule, such as religious classes or team practice.

▶ Use the grids to track how you currently spend your "free" time.

Monday	
8:00	Algebra I
9:00	English
10:00	American History
11:00	Earth Science
12:00	Lunch
1:00	Studio Art I
2:00	Basketball Practice

❷ Make a daily "To Do" list.

▶ Before you go to bed, make a list of the tasks you need to do the next day.

▶ Include tasks that you know you have to do, such as homework and chores, along with tasks that you would like to do.

▶ Break long-range tasks, such as term papers and projects, into smaller, more manageable tasks. This makes it easier to fit these tasks into your schedule.

Sensitive Issues

Some students may need to do things that they would rather not reveal to others, such as seeing a psychologist about a mental health problem. Make sure students do not feel pressured to share their "To Do" lists with the class. They can report on how helpful the time-management process was without revealing how they actually spent their time.

❸ Prioritize your tasks.

Rate each task according to this scale.

A = very important
B = somewhat important
C = not very important

To Do List	
Do math homework	A
Do laundry	B
Outline history paper	A
Organize CDs	C
Call grandmother	B
Watch TV	C
Practice jump shots	B
Get permission slip signed	A

❹ Plan your day.

► Assign an amount of time for each task. Make a practice of allowing more time for a task than you think it will require.

► Use copies of the grids you made in Step 1 to schedule your tasks.

► Do not schedule too many tasks each day. Allow some time for unplanned events.

► Try to do "A" tasks before you do "B" tasks, and "B" tasks before you do "C" tasks, even if a "C" task is easier.

❺ Monitor your progress.

At different points during the day, ask yourself, "Is this the best use of my time?" If your answer is *no,* consider these questions:

► *Am I doing a "C" task because an "A" task seems overwhelming?* If so, break the "A" task into smaller steps that can be done in less than fifteen minutes.

► *Am I avoiding a task because I am afraid to fail or make a mistake?* You can waste a lot of time worrying about a task. If you just begin doing the task, you may realize that it is not as difficult as you thought.

► *Is this the right time to do this task?* For example, if your math homework is challenging, don't leave it until late at night when you are tired.

► *Am I being distracted by phone calls or instant messages?* Tell your friends when it is okay to contact you and when you need time to concentrate on homework or chores.

Practice the Skill

1. For one week, keep track of how you spend your time each day. Decide whether or not you are spending your time wisely. Are there tasks that you can eliminate? Are there tasks that you can do more quickly?

2. During the second week, make a "To Do" list each day. Break down complex activities into a set of simpler tasks. Assign a specific, realistic amount of time for each task.

3. Use the A-B-C scale to prioritize your tasks and then decide which tasks you will do in each of the available time periods. Do your "A" tasks first each day, followed by "B" and "C" tasks.

4. If you are having trouble finishing your tasks, ask yourself the questions from Step 5.

5. At the end of the week, report to your class on how helpful the time management process has been for you. What can you do to improve your time-management skills?

Managing Stress **69**

Practice the Skill

1. Students should keep a log of how they spend their time each day and decide whether they are spending their time wisely. They should also identify tasks they could eliminate (e.g., searching through a messy locker) or do more quickly (e.g., getting ready for school).

2. Remind students to include some leisure activities in their "To Do" lists, to include all the simpler tasks that make up complex activities, and to allow adequate time for each task.

3. If students have difficulty assigning priorities to their tasks, suggest that, for each task, they ask themselves, "What will happen if I do not complete this task today?" Weighing the consequences of not doing the tasks should help students assign priorities to them.

4. Encourage students to ask themselves the questions from Step 5. If this does not help them complete their tasks, they should consider whether they are trying to accomplish too much.

5. At the end of the week, allow class time for students to report on how helpful the time-management process was for them. Students might say that it helped them realize how much time they waste or how useful it is to prioritize tasks. They should identify at least one way they could apply what they learned to improve their time-management skills, such as always breaking down complex activities into smaller tasks to make them more manageable.

Health and Community

L3 Managing Time on the Job

Invite someone on the school staff to speak with the class about the importance of time management on the job. The speaker should have a job that requires multi-tasking or helping others schedule their time.

Possible speakers might include the food service manager, guidance counselor, or office administrator. Encourage students to ask questions after the talk.

Objectives

Before class begins, write the objectives on the board. Have students copy the objectives into their notebooks at the start of class.

1. Focus

Warm-Up Advice Line

After students finish writing, call on several volunteers to share their ideas with the class. Try to get a diversity of responses. Ideas might include making note cards and practicing in front of a mirror. Use the responses to make the point that there are many ways to cope with stress.

Presentation 3-4

Section 4
Coping With Stress

Objectives

▶ **Identify** ways to control stress, reduce tension, and change the way you think about stressors.

▶ **Explain** why building resilience is important.

▶ **Describe** the value of seeking support from others when you are under stress.

Vocabulary

• mental rehearsal

Warm-Up

Dear Advice Line,

When I have to speak in front of a group, I panic. I begin to sweat and my heart pounds. My mouth gets so dry that it's hard to speak. Is there anything I can do about this problem?

WRITING What advice would you offer to someone who is afraid of speaking in public?

Take Control of Stress

Many people tend to think that all stress is out of their control. This is not true. You can do many things to keep stress under control. In a sense, everything you do to maintain your health is a way to manage stress.

It is important to distinguish between stressors that you can control and those that you cannot. You cannot control natural disasters or major life changes such as the death of a grandparent. The adults in your family control your physical environment. They decide where you live and who lives with you.

There are, however, many stressors in your life that you can work to change. These stressors tend to be the everyday problems. For example, suppose you were in danger of failing math. What could you do? You could ignore the problem and pretend not to be worried or you could confront the problem and devise a plan to improve your grade. Your plan might include asking a friend for help, cutting down on other activities to focus more on math, and paying closer attention in class.

If you direct your energy toward those things that are within your power to change, you may be surprised to see what a difference you can make. **Two techniques that can help you keep stress under control are time management and mental rehearsal.**

Sensitive Issues

After reading about the adverse health effects of stress, students may worry about the health of over-stressed loved ones. It may help students to share with loved ones what they learn in this section about coping with stress.

TEENS *Are Asking . . .*

Q: When I have a problem, I try to ignore it so I won't feel so stressed out. Is this a good way to cope with stress?

A: Ignoring a problem might make you feel better for a while, but it will not solve the problem, and the problem may even get worse. It is better to face most problems head on. Decide whether the problem is something that you can control. If it is, take steps to resolve it. If necessary, ask a parent, teacher, or guidance counselor for advice. If the cause of the problem is not under your control, try to cope with the stress it causes in healthful ways, such as physical activity.

Time Management Do you often wish there were more hours in the day? Do you tend to put things off until the last minute? If you answered *yes* to these questions, you may not be managing your time effectively. Poor time management is one of the biggest contributors to stress. The Building Health Skills on pages 68–69 can help you learn to use time more productively. Not only will you get more done each day, but you will also feel more in control of your life. As a bonus, you might also end up with more time for fun and relaxation.

Mental Rehearsal Suppose you have a big event coming up, such as a solo in a concert. If you are worried about your performance, you might use a technique known as a mental rehearsal to help you prepare. In a **mental rehearsal,** you practice an event without actually doing the event. The event takes place in your mind as you imagine yourself performing at your best. You might rehearse every aspect of the event a few times over until you feel confident that you can perform it as imagined. Of course, a mental rehearsal doesn't replace the need to actually practice for an event.

Athletes often use mental rehearsal while preparing for a competition. This technique helps athletes stay focused on their performances during highly stressful times. You also can use mental rehearsal to prepare for a difficult conversation with a family member or a friend.

When you first try this technique, it may be difficult to keep your mind focused on your rehearsal. You might find that you are easily distracted by outside events. With practice, though, you will improve your ability to focus and put all distractions aside.

Connect to Your Life Have you used mental rehearsal before an event? If so, did it help your performance?

FIGURE 10 Time wasters keep you from making the best use of the time you have to study. **Evaluating** Which example do you think costs you the most time? What other examples would you add to the list?

Time Wasters

▶ Playing video games
▶ Talking on the phone
▶ Watching TV
▶ Listening to music
▶ Daydreaming
▶ Worrying
▶ Not having a plan
▶ Not following instructions
▶ Not being able to concentrate
▶ Agreeing to do too many things
▶ Using social media

Managing Stress **71**

---

2. Teach

L3 EL Reading/Note Taking 3-4
L2 Adapted Reading/Note Taking 3-4

Take Control of Stress

L3 Journal Writing

Have students write a journal entry in which they list several stressors in their lives. Then have students draw a line through any of the stressors over which they have no control. Ask students to write a sentence or two stating how they might reduce or eliminate each of the remaining stressors. **WRITING**

L2 Active Learning

Review how to do mental rehearsal: find a quiet place without distractions, focus only on the task, and imagine yourself successfully completing each step of the task. Ask students to select a task that causes them stress, such as shooting a foul shot or giving a class presentation. Tell students to mentally rehearse the task at least once a day for a week. When they actually perform the task, they should assess whether mental rehearsal decreased their stress.

L3 Visual Learning: Figure 10

Have students read the list of time wasters in the figure. Call on a few volunteers to answer the caption question. Discuss how wasting time contributes to stress. Point out that some of the time wasters in the figure can also be stress relievers when done in moderation. As a transition to the discussion of reducing tension, ask: **Which activities do you think might be good for relieving stress?** *(Students might state any of the first four examples.)*

Caption Answer Answers will vary but should be one of the examples in the list. Other examples might include hanging out at the mall and trying to do everything perfectly.

Connect to Your Life Students who have used mental rehearsal are likely to say that it helped their performance.

Reduce Tension

L3 Building Health Skills

Advocacy Have students create short infomercials for teens in which they advocate the use of physical activity to reduce tension. Help students recall infomercials on television or radio for the appropriate style of writing. Tell students their infomercials should describe how physical activity reduces tension and suggest ways to increase physical activity, such as trying out for a team sport, walking short distances instead of driving, or taking stairs instead of elevators and escalators. Give students a chance to present their infomercials to the class. Urge students to apply the information to their own lives. **WRITING**

L2 Cooperative Learning

Divide the class into pairs, and ask each pair to practice deep breathing. While one member of the pair reads the instructions in the text, the other member can follow them. Then have partners change roles. After all the students have had a chance to practice the technique, take a class vote to see how many students feel more relaxed.

L3 Cultural Connection

The physical activities that people use to reduce tension can vary from one culture to another. So can relaxation methods. Ask students to describe relaxation strategies that they are familiar with from their cultural traditions.

Reduce Tension

Even when a stressor isn't under your control, there are things you can do to reduce the stress. When you recognize warning signs of stress, such as muscle tension or restlessness, you need to find a way to relieve the tension. **Two strategies that can help you relieve tension are physical activity and relaxation.** These methods work by altering the physical state of your body.

Physical Activity   Bicycling, taking a walk, playing the drums—these are some ways to release tension when you are under stress. By doing something physically active, you provide your body with a healthy outlet for built-up energy. At the same time, you shift your focus from your problems to the task at hand. This gives your mind a chance to relax, too.

You do not have to be an athlete to use physical activity to manage stress. The activities you choose don't have to be competitive sports, and you don't have to be the best at them. Instead, select activities that you enjoy. If you enjoy an activity, you are more likely to do it on a regular basis. Try to incorporate physical activity into your daily routine. That way, you will always have a way to work off the day's tension.

Relaxation   The goal of relaxation techniques is to give your mind and body a rest. When you are relaxed, you may be awake and alert, but you are not responding actively to stressors. You may relax your mind by reading a book, taking a nap, listening to music, or doing something creative, such as playing the guitar. You can relax tense muscles by taking a hot shower or bath, stretching, or having someone massage your neck.

Deep breathing is a relaxation method that offers quick relief from stress. Take a few deep breaths in a row. Slowly breathe in as much air as you can through your nose. Hold the air in for a few seconds and then slowly exhale through your mouth. Place one hand on your chest and one on your abdomen as you inhale. Your abdomen should expand more than your chest. When you breathe deeply, you take in more oxygen, which helps your body to function better.

FIGURE 11 Being physically active improves physical fitness, provides an outlet for excess energy, and takes your mind off your problems.

72 *Chapter 3*

Hands-On *Activity*

Progressive Relaxation

You can use progressive relaxation to release the tension that builds up in your muscles.

Try This

❶ Sit quietly in a comfortable chair or lie down and close your eyes. Make sure that your arms and legs are uncrossed.

❷ Tighten each muscle group in your body, hold for 10 seconds, and relax. Follow the order in the bulleted lists.

❸ Finally, tense all the muscles in your whole body. Hold for 10 seconds and relax.

Think and Discuss

❶ Compare how you felt before doing this activity to how you felt after doing the progressive relaxation.

❷ Think back to what you learned about the alarm stage of your body's response to stress. Why do you think progressive relaxation is an effective stress-reduction technique?

❸ List some times during a typical week when it would be helpful to use progressive relaxation.

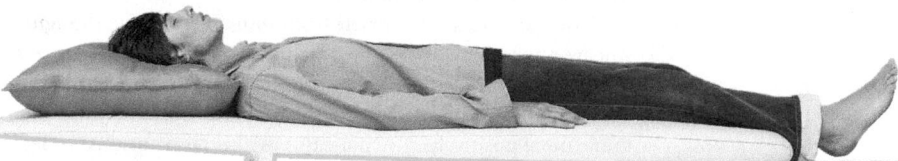

- Wrinkle your forehead. Try to make your eyebrows touch your hairline.
- Close your eyes as tightly as you can.
- Form a frown with the corners of your mouth.

- Raise your shoulders up to your ears.
- Bend your elbows and tense your upper arms.
- Tightly clench your fists.
- Gently arch your back.

- Tighten your stomach muscles.
- Tighten your hip and buttock muscles.
- Squeeze your legs together.
- Curl your toes under as tightly as you can.

The Importance of Happiness Recall that happiness is one of the primary emotions that are expressed by people in all cultures. Yet happiness is more than just a pleasant universal emotion—it may be one of the keys to a healthy life. What is happiness? It is the perception of your own well-being and the belief that your own life is worthwhile. There is growing scientific evidence that happiness can actually make you healthier and may even help you live longer.

If happiness can make you healthier, you need to know what makes you happy. Scientists have shown that a positive attitude and being involved with activities that you find rewarding can result in happiness. What probably won't make you happy, according to current studies, are money and material things.

Sometimes happiness results from activities you do by yourself, such as going for a walk or volunteering for a good cause, or from activities you do with other people, such as dancing, singing, or playing games.

Connect to Your Life What makes you happy? Did you identify things that you do by yourself or with other people?

Hands-On *Activity*

Progressive Relaxation

If students do the activity at home, they should lie on a comfortable surface and ask a friend or family member to read the steps aloud while they do the activity. If students do the activity in class, they should sit comfortably in their seats and you should read the steps aloud.

Think and Discuss Answers

1. Students are likely to feel more relaxed after doing progressive relaxation. For example, their muscles may not feel as tight.

2. In the alarm stage, stress speeds up the heart and breathing and causes muscles to tighten, among other changes. Progressive relaxation helps to control these physical changes.

3. *Sample answer:* Progressive relaxation would be helpful to relieve stress before a big test or important competition.

🔵 Active Learning

Have students design a small display or give a brief, informal presentation about the importance of happiness in their culture. Encourage students to interview family members about what makes them happy and how they show it.

Connect to Your Life Students can identify any physical activity they enjoy, such as hiking, playing basketball, swimming, or skiing.

Differentiated Instruction

🔵 Gifted and Talented

Encourage students to learn more about the importance of happiness by conducting a survey. Direct groups of students to construct a list of activities that may make someone happy (e.g., playing sports, reading, volunteering in the community). Then, have students survey their peers to determine which activity most often results in happiness. Encourage students to give their survey to a variety of people in the school community. Ask students to summarize their findings in a written or oral report.

Change Your Thinking

Ⓛ Online Activity

Visit Pearson SuccessNet to access an online activity about coping with stress. Have students complete the Web activity.

Ⓛ Building Health Skills

Practicing Healthful Behaviors Describe stressful events teens might experience, such as taking a final exam or trying out for a play. For each event, state a negative way of thinking, and then call on a student to respond with a positive way of thinking. For example, you might say, "I know I'm going to fail this test," and a student might respond, "I did my best to prepare for this test." Conclude by asking: **How would the two different ways of thinking make you feel, and how might they affect your performance?** *(Students are likely to say that positive ways of thinking would make them feel and perform better than negative ways of thinking.)*

Ⓛ Cultural Connection

A culture's sayings often reflect positive or negative thinking. For example, the saying, "Every cloud has a silver lining," reflects positive thinking, and the saying, "When it rains, it pours," reflects negative thinking. Many cultures have similar sayings. Ask students to think of examples and identify whether they reflect positive or negative thinking.

Ⓛ Cooperative Learning

Divide the class into groups, and ask each group to create a cartoon or comic strip that treats a common stressor with humor. Stressors might include being too busy, being annoyed by a younger sibling, or having to speak in public. Make sure groups do not select stressors that are violent, sensitive, or in bad taste. Post their cartoons and comic strips in the classroom, and use them to start a class discussion of the role of humor in stress reduction.

GO ONLINE
PearsonSuccessNet.com
For: More on coping with stress

Change Your Thinking

Do you tend to overreact to unexpected events or worry a lot about the future? Sometimes you can reduce your level of stress by changing the way you think about stressors. **One way to change your thinking is to replace negative thoughts with positive ones. You can also use humor in some stressful situations.**

Avoiding Negative Thinking Think back to the last time you were in a stressful situation. What thoughts were going through your mind? Were you thinking things like "I'll never be able to do this," or "Everyone will think I'm stupid," or "I'm not as good as the others"? For many people, negative thoughts like these accompany stressful situations. Of course, such negative thinking only increases a person's stress level. With negative messages running through the person's mind, it becomes almost impossible to succeed.

How can you stop yourself from thinking negative thoughts when you are under stress? One way is to monitor your internal conversations closely and substitute positive or realistic thoughts for negative thoughts. For example, instead of thinking "I'll never be able to do this," you might think, more positively, "I've done things like this before." Another way to eliminate negative thinking is to act as a "coach" while you think about an upcoming stressful event. As you do a mental rehearsal of the event, give yourself positive messages such as "You can do it." This will boost your self-confidence, which will help you during the actual event.

Humor Finding humor in a situation can be an effective way to deal with stress. Have you ever laughed at yourself after doing something that was not really funny, such as slipping on a wet floor or saying something embarrassing in front of a group of people? If so, you probably realized that your laughter helped to relieve your feelings of stress.

If you use humor carefully, it can be an effective tool for managing stress. Humor allows you to deal quickly with a stressor and keep it in the proper perspective. But don't use humor to cover up your true feelings. Also avoid laughing at serious situations. Remember that making fun of yourself is different than making fun of other people's problems.

FIGURE 12 Humor can be an effective way to ease tension and provide relief from stress.

74 *Chapter 3*

For Your INFORMATION!

Positive Thinking and Longevity

A study of 660 people aged 50 and older showed that positive thinking can affect the length and quality of life. Participants were surveyed about their attitudes toward aging. When the researchers followed up more than 20 years later, they found participants with positive attitudes toward aging lived an average of 7.5 years longer and had better health than those with negative attitudes. The researchers think positive thinking prolongs life by reducing stress.

Build Resilience

The strategies discussed so far for coping with stress may not be sufficient for dealing with all types of stressors. **You need to build your resilience to help you deal with extreme or prolonged stress.** The strategies listed below can help you increase your resilience. Pick the approaches that you think will work best for you.

Even the most resilient person in the world will be unhappy or worried some of the time. However, knowing these strategies can help you "bounce back" from setbacks in your life.

▶ **Take Care of Yourself** Exercise, eat well, and get enough sleep. Find time for activities you enjoy. When your general health is good, you are better able to deal with stressful situations.

▶ **Build a Support System** Develop good relationships with family, friends, and other people who will care for and listen to you.

▶ **Take Action** Decide what needs to be done and act on your decision. Set short-term goals that you know you can accomplish.

▶ **Help Somebody** Volunteer to work on a project in your community or help a friend with a problem.

▶ **Confide in Yourself** Sometimes it is too difficult to talk with others about your feelings. You can confide in yourself by writing about stressful events in a journal.

▶ **Go Easy on Yourself** When something bad happens, your response to other stressors may be more intense. So cut yourself a little slack.

▶ **Put Things in Perspective** Look beyond a difficult situation to a time when things will be better. When you talk about bad times, remember to talk about the good times in your life, too.

▶ **Find a Hassle-Free Zone** Find someplace where you can feel free from stress—your home, a relative's house, a community center, or the library.

▶ **Stick to Your Routines** During a major life change, keep to daily routines, such as a nightly conversation with a friend.

Where are some places you can go to feel free from stress?

FIGURE 13 A library can provide a quiet place to get away from the everyday hassles of school and home.

Build Resilience

L2 **Active Learning**

Ask students to make posters illustrating several of the strategies for building resilience. Students can use pictures from newspapers and magazines or their own drawings to illustrate the strategies. For example, for the strategy "Take Care of Yourself," they might use a food pyramid and a picture of someone exercising. Posters should include a brief explanation of how each strategy helps build resilience. Display the posters in the classroom.

L3 **Building Health Skills**

Setting Goals Have students select one of the resilience-building strategies they think would work best for them and make an action plan for adopting the strategy. For example, if students select the strategy "Confide in Yourself," they might plan to start a stress diary, write in it at least three times a week, and reread their entries after a month to assess their progress. Urge students to adopt their action plans and work toward their goals.

L4 **Active Learning**

Ask interested students to interview a person, such as a firefighter, who has a highly stressful job. Ask the students to find out if the person uses any of the strategies for building resilience, and if these strategies help the person cope with stress at work. Have students write a short report summarizing what they learn. Give students a chance to share their reports with the class. **WRITING**

Allow students to answer this question in their private journals.

Differentiated Instruction

EL **English Language Learners**

Select one or two of the bulleted items on this page that may contain unfamiliar words, such as "Find a Hassle-Free Zone." Ask students to try to rephrase the items, using simpler, more familiar words. Provide them with a dictionary so they can look up any words they do not know. You may want to work through an example with them first, such as "Find a place where you will not be bothered" for "Find a Hassle-Free Zone." Make sure students' rephrasings have the same meanings as the original items.

Reach Out for Support

L2 Teacher Demo

Demonstrate how to reach out for support. Role-play a teen calling a friend to talk about a problem. Ask students to think of people they could confide in.

3. Assess

Evaluate

These assignments can help you assess students' mastery of the section content.

Section 4 Review

Answers appear below.

Teaching Resources

- Practice 3-4
- Section 3-4 Quiz

L2 Reteach

Call on students to identify the methods of coping, and list the methods on the board. Then, call on volunteers to demonstrate their understanding of the methods by describing, demonstrating, or giving an example of each method. Review any methods with which students appear to have difficulty.

L4 Enrich

Teaching Resources

- Enrich 3-4

Health at Home

Building Resilience *Sample answer:* For "Go Easy on Yourself," think more about your accomplishments than your setbacks.

FIGURE 14 Sharing a problem with someone you trust can help you to better understand the problem. Just talking about your problems can often help reduce your stress.

Section 4 Review

Key Ideas and Vocabulary

1. List seven techniques you can use to cope with stress:
   a. two techniques that help you take control
   b. three strategies to help relieve tension
   c. two ways to change your thinking
2. What are some ways you can relax?
3. Why is it important to build resilience?
4. How can seeking the support of others help when you are under stress?

Critical Thinking

5. **Relating Cause and Effect** Explain how relaxation techniques help to reduce stress.

GO ONLINE PearsonSuccessNet.com   Audio Summary Section 3.4

Reach Out for Support

What if you try many of the stress-management techniques described in this chapter and nothing seems to work? Sometimes the stress in your life becomes too overwhelming for you to handle on your own. At those times, you may want to ask someone to help you with your problems. Sometimes all you need is someone to talk to. **Sharing your problems can help you see them more clearly. Just describing your concerns to someone else often helps you to understand the problem better.** Many people are willing to listen and lend support if you ask.

- ▶ a parent or other adult relative
- ▶ a teacher or a coach or a religious leader
- ▶ a school counselor or nurse
- ▶ a sibling or friend

The person you choose to talk to may not be able to help you with your specific concerns. But he or she may be able to refer you to someone who can.

At some time in your life, you may want or need some kind of counseling. Many specialists are available to work with people who need help coping with stress. Some specialists are trained to help you identify the stressors in your life and learn constructive strategies for coping with them.

Health at Home

Building Resilience Look at the list of strategies for building resilience on page 75. Describe specific ways that you could use four of the strategies to help manage your stress. **WRITING**

6. **Making Judgments** Do you think the saying "Don't sweat the small stuff" is good advice for coping with stress? Why or why not?

7. **Applying Concepts** Your best friend's father just lost his job. Your friend is worried that his family might have to move to a different city. How could you help your friend through this stressful time?

Section 4 Review

1. **a.** time management and mental rehearsal **b.** physical activity, relaxation, and doing something that makes you happy **c.** avoiding negative thinking and using humor

2. reading a book; playing guitar; taking a hot shower

3. Resilience helps you deal with extreme or prolonged stress.

4. Sharing your problems can help you see them more clearly.

5. provide outlet for energy; give mind a rest by shifting focus from problems

6. *Sample answer:* When you "don't sweat the small stuff," you avoid worrying about little things and reduce your stress.

7. Students might write that they could listen to the friend's concerns and offer support.

Chapter 3
At a Glance

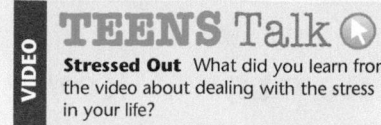

 **TEENS** Talk ⊙
Stressed Out What did you learn from the video about dealing with the stress in your life?

Section 1   What Causes Stress?

Key Ideas

▶ You experience stress when situations, events, or people make demands on your body and mind.

▶ Four general types of stressors are major life changes, catastrophes, everyday problems, and environmental problems.

Vocabulary
- stress (56)
- eustress (56)
- distress (56)
- stressor (57)
- catastrophe (58)

Section 2   How Stress Affects Your Body

Key Ideas

▶ The body's response to stress occurs in three stages—the alarm stage, the resistance stage, and the exhaustion stage.

▶ The warning signs of stress include changes in how your body functions and changes in emotions, thoughts, and behaviors.

▶ Stress can trigger certain illnesses, reduce the body's ability to fight an illness, and make some diseases harder to control.

Vocabulary
- fight-or-flight response (60)

Section 3   Stress and Individuals

Key Ideas

▶ How you react to a stressor depends on your assessment of the situation.

▶ Your personality influences your assessment of a situation.

▶ The key factor in resilience is having the support of family and friends.

Vocabulary
- optimism (66)
- pessimism (66)
- perfectionist (66)
- resilience (67)

Section 4   Coping With Stress

Key Ideas

▶ Two techniques that can help you keep stress under control are time management and mental rehearsal.

▶ Two strategies that can help you relieve tension when you are stressed are physical activity and relaxation.

▶ One way to change your thinking is to replace negative thoughts with positive ones. You can also use humor in some stressful situations.

▶ You need to build your resilience to deal with extreme or prolonged stress.

▶ Sharing your problems can help you see them more clearly. Just describing your concerns to someone often helps you to understand the problem better.

Vocabulary
- mental rehearsal (71)

Managing Stress **77**

Chapter 3
At a Glance

VIDEO **Stressed Out** Ask for volunteers to share their answers. Use examples from the video to review strategies for dealing with stress.

Key Ideas Review

L2 Have students reword the section objectives as questions and then try to answer them. Students should find answers in the text for any questions they cannot answer.

L3 Ask students to write a concise paragraph in which they summarize what causes stress, how stress affects the body, why individuals can have different responses to the same stressor, and how to cope with stress. Students should try to limit what they write to just one or two sentences per question while still providing a complete answer.

Vocabulary Review

EL Have students make flashcards to review chapter vocabulary. They should write each term on one side of an index card, and on the other side they should write the definition and an example of the term. Ask students to choose partners and quiz each other using the flashcards.

L1 Ask: **What is stress?** *(the response of your body and mind to being challenged or threatened)* Call on students to explain how each of the remaining vocabulary terms in the chapter is related to stress.

Chapter 3 Review

GO ONLINE

PearsonSuccessNet.com

Students can go online for a review activity on Chapter 3.

Reviewing Key Ideas

Section 1

1. b

2. Stress can be positive if it helps you escape from danger, promotes personal growth, or helps accomplish goals.

3. because it takes energy to adjust to new situations and they may threaten your sense of security or self-esteem

4. *Sample answer:* yes, because teens often experience more conflict and greater pressure to succeed.

Section 2

5. b

6. any six changes from Figure 4

7. Stress can trigger an asthmatic attack.

8. It can weaken your immune system and prevent it from functioning well.

9. *Sample answer:* Sleep problems are easier to recognize than many other warning signs of stress.

Section 3

10. b

11. Is this situation a threat to my well-being? Do I have the necessary resources to meet the challenge?

12. These relationships offer love, encouragement, and reassurance.

13. *Sample answer:* Individual sports put all the responsibility for doing well on the individual athlete, and there are no team members to offer support.

Section 4

14. c

15. It can help you stay focused when you perform in stressful situations and increase your self-confidence.

16. when the person feels too overwhelmed by stress to handle it alone

17. *Sample answer:* Lying is stressful; stress causes the heart and breathing rates to increase.

Chapter 3 Review

Reviewing Key Ideas

GO ONLINE

PearsonSuccessNet.com

For: Chapter 3 review activity

Section 1

1. A good friend is in the hospital with a serious illness. This stressor can be classified as
   a. an everyday problem.
   b. a major life change.
   c. a catastrophe.
   d. an environmental problem.

2. Explain how stress can be a positive experience.

3. Why are major life changes stressful?

4. **Critical Thinking** Do you think that adolescence is an especially stressful time? Explain.

Section 2

5. The stage when your body adapts to the continued presence of a stressor is the
   a. alarm stage.   b. resistance stage.
   c. exhaustion stage.   d. adaptation stage.

6. List six things that happen to your body during the fight-or-flight response.

7. Explain the relationship between stress and the onset of an asthmatic attack.

8. What effect can prolonged stress have on your immune system?

9. **Critical Thinking** Why do you think that sleep problems are a useful warning sign of stress?

Section 3

10. What is the statement "I'll never be able to do this" an example of?
    a. aiming for perfection
    b. negative thinking
    c. optimism
    d. resilience

11. As you assess a stressful situation, what two general questions are you answering?

12. How does having the support of family and friends contribute to resilience?

13. **Critical Thinking** Researchers have compared the level of stress in different sports. They found that individual sports, such as gymnastics, can cause more stress than team sports, such as basketball. Why do you think this difference exists?

Section 4

14. Stressors that you can control tend to be
    a. catastrophes.
    b. major life changes.
    c. everyday hassles.
    d. environmental problems.

15. Explain how the process of mental rehearsal can help you manage stress.

16. When is it important for a person who is stressed to reach out for support?

17. **Critical Thinking** A lie detector measures changes in a person's heart rate and breathing rate. How might changes in these body functions indicate that a person is lying?

Building Health Skills

18. **Advocacy** You have a friend who is involved in so many activities that he no longer has time for you. Lately, he complains that he "can't think straight anymore." Use an e-mail to offer some advice to your friend. **WRITING**

19. **Making Decisions** A product called "Stress Vitamins" claims to "replace essential vitamins that are lost during times of stress." How would you decide whether or not to buy the vitamins?

20. **Setting Goals** Make an action plan to help you reduce the stress of test-taking. Apply strategies you learned for coping with stress. Put your plan into action a week before your next test and monitor your progress. After the test, adjust your action plan, if necessary. **WRITING**

Health and Community

Volunteering Helping others is one way to build resilience. Describe something you could do for one hour each week to help younger students learn to deal with stress. **WRITING**

Building Health Skills

18. Students might advise dropping some activities and learning how to manage time.

19. *Sample answer:* I could ask my doctor whether I need the vitamins.

20. Students should make specific, step-by-step plans, evaluate their progress, and modify their plans, if necessary.

Health and Community

Volunteering *Sample answers:* I could baby-sit younger siblings and show them how to relax for naps. I could volunteer at my school's latch-key program and show younger students how to relieve tension with physical activity. I could tutor younger students and explain ways to reduce stress when they take exams.

Standardized Test Prep

Math Practice

The graph shows how listening to music affects the heart rates of surgery patients. Group A listened to the music of their choice during and after surgery. Group B did not. Use the graph to answer Questions 21–24.

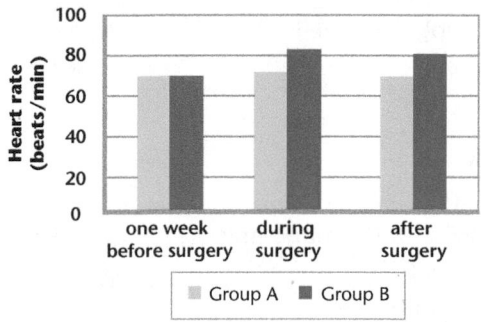

21. What was the average heart rate for both groups a week before surgery?
A 65 beats per minute
B 70 beats per minute
C 75 beats per minute
D 80 beats per minute

22. What happened to the average heart rate of Group B during surgery?
F The heart rate increased.
G The heart rate decreased.
H The heart rate stayed the same.
J The heart rate was equal to the average heart rate of Group A.

23. What happened to the average heart rate of Group A during surgery?
A The heart rate increased.
B The heart rate decreased.
C The heart rate stayed the same.
D The heart rate increased and then decreased.

24. Based on the graph, which of the following statements is true?
F Listening to music has no effect on stress.
G Listening to music can increase stress.
H Listening to music can decrease stress.
J Average heart rate is not a good measure of stress.

Reading and Writing Practice

Read the passage. Then answer Questions 25–28.

When people rely heavily on technology, they may become victims of *technostress*. With cell phones and instant messaging, people expect to be able to reach someone at any time and at any place—at work, in the car, at home. This constant stimulation and interruption can be stressful. So can having a computer crash when you are facing a deadline. This situation is ironic. Technology is designed to make people more productive—able to accomplish more in the same amount of time. But technostress can make people less productive because they become forgetful or cannot concentrate.

25. What is the main idea of the passage?
A People should not use technology.
B Technology makes people less productive.
C Relying on technology can cause stress.
D Stress makes it harder to concentrate.

26. Based on this passage, the word *ironic* means
F stressful.
G predictable.
H unexpected.
J funny.

27. Technology is designed to
A reduce the time a person spends at work.
B increase the time a person spends at work.
C increase the time needed to do a given task.
D decrease the time needed to do a given task.

Constructed Response
28. In a paragraph, explain how technology can cause stress. Give at least two examples of technostress.

> **Test-Taking Tip**
>
> When taking a test, be aware of how much time you have and the total number of questions. Wear a watch to keep track of your progress.

Standardized Test Prep

Math Practice
21. B
22. F
23. C
24. H

Reading and Writing Practice
25. C
26. H
27. D
28. *Sample answer:* With technology, people experience more interruptions. Technology that you rely on may not be available when you need to do a task.

Section Objectives	Standards Correlation	Instructional Resources L3	SE eTEXT	TE eTEXT	PRINT
1 Mental Disorders ⏱ 3 periods; 1 1/2 blocks 4.1.1 **Explain** how mental disorders are recognized. 4.1.2 **Identify** four causes of mental disorders. 4.1.3 **Describe** five types of anxiety disorders and four other types of mental disorders.	NHES: 1.12.4, 2.12.6, 3.12.2	SE Warm-Up, p. 82	•	•	•
		SE Technology & Health Virtual Reality and Phobias, p. 89	•	•	•
		RN Note Taking Guide 4-1	•	•	•
		TR Practice 4-1		•	
		TR Section 4-1 Quiz		•	
2 Eating Disorders ⏱ 1 period; 1/2 block 4.2.1 **Identify** health risks associated with anorexia. 4.2.2 **Explain** the relationship between bulimia and dieting. 4.2.3 **List** the main health risks of binge eating disorder.	NHES: 1.12.2, 2.12.5, 2.12.7, 3.12.2, 3.12.4	SE Warm-Up, p. 90	•	•	•
		SE Media Wise Body Image and Magazines, p. 91	•	•	•
		RN Note Taking Guide 4-2	•	•	•
		TR Practice 4-2		•	
		TR Section 4-2 Quiz		•	
3 Depression and Suicide ⏱ 2 periods; 1 block 4.3.1 **Explain** why it is important to identify and treat clinical depression. 4.3.2 **Explain** why individuals might deliberately injure themselves. 4.3.3 **Describe** one major risk factor for suicide.	NHES: 1.12.6, 2.12.3, 2.12.4, 3.12.3, 3.12.4, 4.12.4, 7.12.1	SE Warm-Up, p. 94	•	•	•
		RN Note Taking Guide 4-3	•	•	•
		IB Image Bank 4-10, 4-13		•	
		TR Practice 4-3		•	
		TR Section 4-3 Quiz		•	
🔺 Dealing With Setbacks ⏱ 1 period; 1/2 block BHS.4 **Develop** a plan for dealing with setbacks.	NHES: 5.12.4, 6.12.2, 6.12.3, 7.12.2	SE Practice the Skill, p. 101	•	•	•
		RN Building Health Skills 4	•	•	•
4 Treating Mental Disorders ⏱ 1 period; 1/2 block 4.4.1 **List** reasons that might prevent a person from seeking help for a mental disorder. 4.4.2 **Identify** four types of mental health professionals. 4.4.3 **Describe** some general types of treatment for mental disorders.	NHES: 1.12.6, 1.12.7, 2.12.7, 2.12.8, 3.12.4	SE Warm-Up, p. 102	•	•	•
		RN Note Taking Guide 4-4	•	•	•
		TR Practice 4-4		•	
		TR Section 4-4 Quiz		•	

Chapter Review and Assessment

SE Chapter 4 Review, p. 106 L3
CTB Chapter 4 Test L2 L3 L4
SE Standardized Test Prep, p. 107 L3

PROGRAM COMPONENTS

SE Student Edition	**CTB** Computer Test Bank
TE Teacher Edition	**AUD** Audio Section Summaries
TR Teaching Resources	
RN Reading and Note Taking Guide	**DVD** Teens Talk Video Series
	VVG Video Viewing Guide
ARN Adapted Reading and Note Taking Guide	**PPT** Presentation
IB Image Bank	

Differentiated Instruction
(L1) (L2) (L4) (EL)

		SE eTEXT	TE eTEXT	PRINT
ARN	Note Taking Guide 4-1 (L2)	•	•	
RN	Note Taking Guide 4-1 (EL)	•	•	•
AUD	Audio Summary 4-1 (L1)(L2)(EL)	•	•	
TE	Reteach Strategy, p. 88 (L2)		•	•
TR	Enrich 4-1 (L4)		•	
ARN	Note Taking Guide 4-2 (L2)	•	•	
RN	Note Taking Guide 4-2 (EL)	•	•	•
AUD	Audio Summary 4-2 (L1)(L2)(EL)	•	•	
TE	Reteach Strategy, p. 93 (L2)		•	•
TR	Enrich 4-2 (L4)		•	
ARN	Note Taking Guide 4-3 (L2)	•	•	
RN	Note Taking Guide 4-3 (EL)	•	•	•
AUD	Audio Summary 4-3 (L1)(L2)(EL)	•	•	
TE	Reteach Strategy, p. 99 (L2)		•	•
TR	Enrich 4-3 (L4)		•	
ARN	Building Health Skills 4 (L2)	•	•	
RN	Building Health Skills 4 (EL)	•	•	•
ARN	Note Taking Guide 4-4 (L2)	•	•	
RN	Note Taking Guide 4-4 (EL)	•	•	•
AUD	Audio Summary 4-4 (L1)(L2)(EL)	•	•	
TE	Reteach Strategy, p. 104 (L2)		•	•
TR	Enrich 4-4 (L4)		•	

ABILITY LEVELS

- (L1) For students with special needs
- (L2) For less proficient readers
- (L3) For all students
- (L4) For gifted and talented students
- (EL) For English language learners

Chapter 4 Digital/Video Pathway

This alternative pathway allows you to teach this chapter's content using only the video and online materials.

Preview

- **DVD** Video #4 Preview
- **SE** Video #4 Preview Activity
- **VVG** Video #4 Worksheet

Starving for Control

1
- **PPT** 4-1 Presentation
- **RN/ARN** 4-1 Note Taking
- **PPT** 4-1 Section Quiz

2
- **DVD** Video #4 Explore/Wrap-Up
- **VVG** Video #4 Worksheet
- **PPT** 4-2 Presentation
- **RN/ARN** 4-2 Note Taking
- **PPT** 4-2 Section Quiz

Starving for Control

3
- **PPT** 4-3 Presentation
- **RN/ARN** 4-3 Note Taking
- **PPT** 4-3 Section Quiz

4
- **PPT** 4-4 Presentation
- **RN/ARN** 4-4 Note Taking
- **PPT** 4-4 Section Quiz

Chapter Preview

Section 1 Mental Disorders
Mental disorders are illnesses that affect the mind and reduce a person's ability to function. Mental disorders have a variety of causes and symptoms, and they vary widely in severity.

Section 2 Eating Disorders
Eating disorders, such as anorexia, bulimia, and binge eating disorder, are characterized by abnormal behaviors related to food. Eating disorders can have a negative impact on physical and emotional health, and can be fatal.

Section 3 Depression and Suicide
Feelings of sadness and hopelessness that persist are symptoms of clinical depression. Untreated depression is a major risk factor for suicide. If people understand the risk factors and protective factors for suicide, they can help to reduce the suicide rate.

Setting Goals
Dealing With Setbacks
When dealing with everyday setbacks, people need to keep these events in perspective. People who experience setbacks need to avoid negative self-talk and focus energy in positive ways.

Section 4 Treating Mental Disorders
Individuals with mental disorders do not always get professional help because they may not understand their symptoms or may not know where to get help. Mental health professionals use a variety of treatments for mental disorders.

GO ONLINE
PearsonSuccessNet.com
For resources and activities for this chapter.

Mental Disorders and Suicide

1 Mental Disorders
 • **Technology & Health** Virtual Reality and Phobias

2 Eating Disorders
 • **Media Wise** Body Image and Magazines

3 Depression and Suicide

 Building Health Skills
 • **Setting Goals** Dealing With Setbacks

4 Treating Mental Disorders

GO ONLINE PearsonSuccessNet.com

TEENS Talk

VIDEO 4

Starving for Control

Preview **Activity**

How Do You Relate to Food?

Complete this activity before you watch the video.

1. How many of the following statements describe ways you behave or think about food?
 a. I keep eating even when I no longer feel hungry.
 b. Feeling sad or angry affects the amount of food I eat.
 c. I prefer to eat when I am alone rather than with others.
 d. I often feel guilty after I eat.
2. Review your responses. Would you say that your eating habits and thoughts about food are healthy or unhealthy? Write a paragraph explaining your answer. **WRITING**

80

Sensitive Issues

• The subject of mental disorders can be frightening for teens, who may recognize some symptoms in themselves. Reassure students that symptoms of a disorder can occur in a person who does not have the disorder. Mental health experts look at the intensity and duration of symptoms and the effect on a person's ability to function.

• Students who are in therapy or have family members with mental disorders may feel uncomfortable during class discussions. Other students may be eager to learn more about mental disorders. Use hypothetical situations and discourage students from revealing personal information about themselves, family members, or friends.

TEENS Talk

Starving for Control

Video Objectives

Use the video to help students

Describe health risks associated with eating disorders.

Recognize when they or someone they know has an eating disorder.

Identify possible causes of eating disorders and ways to help a person recover from an eating disorder.

Preview Activity

How Do You Relate to Food?

Assign the Preview Activity for homework a few days before you plan to show the video. Tell students to record their responses in their private journals. After students complete the assignment, compile two class lists on the board—one of eating habits students think are healthy and another of eating habits they think are unhealthy. Ask students to provide reasons for their choices.

81

From the Authors

Sol Gordon refers to suicide as "a permanent solution to a temporary problem." What a clear statement about a problem that is far too prevalent among teens! Prevention of suicide would be much easier if there were a checklist of reliable warning signs. Unfortunately, our expert reviewers warned us against relying on an absolute list of warning signs for suicide.

Suicide can occur at unexpected times or to unexpected people. Someone who attempts suicide may exhibit none of the traditional signs. Someone who exhibits these signs may never attempt suicide. As you discuss this subject, keep in mind that one of your students may be thinking of (or has thought of) suicide and is searching for evidence that his or her problems are only temporary.

Section 1
Mental Disorders

Objectives

Before class begins, write the objectives on the board. Have students copy the objectives into their notebooks at the start of class.

1. Focus

Warm-Up **Quick Quiz**

Use the Warm-Up Presentation slide to survey student responses.

Give students several minutes to read the choices and select their responses. Then ask students to prepare their written explanations for each answer. Call on volunteers to share their responses with the class.

Presentation 4-1

Objectives

▶ **Explain** how mental disorders are recognized.

▶ **Identify** four causes of mental disorders.

▶ **Describe** five types of anxiety disorders and four other types of mental disorders.

Vocabulary

• mental disorder
• anxiety
• anxiety disorder
• phobia
• obsession
• compulsion
• mood disorder
• depression
• schizophrenia
• personality disorder

Warm-Up

Quick Quiz Which of the following statements are always true? Which are sometimes true? Which are always false?

① It is easy to identify a person with a mental disorder.

② Mental disorders are caused by emotional problems.

③ Mental disorders affect a person's ability to function.

④ People who have a mental disorder are dangerous.

WRITING For each of your responses, explain why you gave the answer you did.

What Are Mental Disorders?

A **mental disorder** is an illness that affects the mind and reduces a person's ability to function, to adjust to change, or to get along with others. For example, a mental disorder could affect a person's ability to study, keep a job, or make friends.

Recognizing Mental Disorders Some behaviors fall outside the broad range of normal behaviors. For example, it is normal to wash your hands before eating. But it isn't normal to keep washing your hands when they are already clean. If behaviors, feelings, or thoughts are highly unusual and not appropriate to a situation, they are considered abnormal. **Mental health experts see abnormal thoughts, feelings, or behaviors as signs, or symptoms, of a mental disorder.** The distress that people who have mental disorders experience affects their ability to function.

Figure 1 lists symptoms of attention-deficit/hyperactivity disorder or ADHD. ADHD usually appears in childhood. A person with ADHD often has difficulty in school, at home, and in social settings. When ADHD is treated with medication, the results may be immediate and dramatic.

Remember, just because someone has trouble sitting still or paying attention from time to time, it doesn't mean that person has ADHD. The symptoms must be frequent and affect the person's ability to function.

82 *Chapter 4*

⚑ **Sensitive Issues**

It is likely that some of your students are being treated for mental disorders. Avoid using labels such as *schizophrenic*. Use "a person with schizophrenia" or "a person who has schizophrenia" instead.

Focus on **ISSUES**

L3 **Overdiagnosis of ADHD**

Mental health professionals disagree on the reason for the rapid increase in ADHD diagnoses. Some think the diagnosis is overused, especially for boys, who make up 80–90 percent of ADHD cases. They argue that many of these children are just normal, active children. Others argue that the rapid growth in diagnosed cases is due to increased recognition of the disorder by parents, educators, and psychologists. Still others argue that ADHD is an under-diagnosed disorder.

Signs of Attention Deficit
• Doesn't pay attention to details
• Makes careless mistakes
• Does not seem to listen
• Is disorganized
• Forgets to do daily activities
• Is easily distracted
• Has difficulty following instructions

Signs of Hyperactivity
• Fidgets or squirms while seated
• Has trouble staying in seat
• Frequently runs about or climbs
• Has trouble working quietly
• Talks excessively
• Has trouble waiting or taking turns
• Interrupts others

FIGURE 1 Some people with ADHD display the entire range of symptoms. Others mainly show signs of attention deficit or hyperactivity.

Causes of Mental Disorders Researchers have made progress on figuring out what causes mental disorders, but there is still much to learn. Sometimes a mental disorder has a single cause. But more often a combination of factors are involved. **Physical factors, heredity, early experiences, and recent experiences can cause mental disorders.**

▶ **Physical Factors** Damage to the brain may cause a mental disorder. The damage could be caused by a growth, or tumor, in the brain; an injury to the brain; or an infection that destroys brain cells. Exposure to a poison such as lead, or prolonged use of alcohol or other drugs can also damage the brain.

▶ **Heredity** A person may inherit a tendency toward a mental disorder. This doesn't mean the person will necessarily have the disorder. It only means that the person is at greater risk if events in his or her life act as a trigger for the disorder.

▶ **Early Experiences** Extremely negative experiences that occur early in life can lead to mental illness. For example, a child who is neglected or a child who is abused may develop a mental disorder.

▶ **Recent Experiences** Some mental health experts think that recent experiences are more likely than early experiences to trigger a mental disorder. An example would be the death of a loved one.

 **Connect to Your Life** How would having ADHD affect someone's ability to study?

What Are Mental Disorders?

L2 **Visual Learning: Figure 1**

As a class, make a list on the board of expectations teachers have for student behavior in a classroom. Explain that those expectations could be considered a norm, or standard, against which any given student's behavior is measured. Then, ask students to look at the signs for hyperactivity in Figure 1. Discuss how these behaviors would make it difficult for a student to function in most classrooms and how they might affect a student's ability to get along with others.

L3 **Addressing Misconceptions**

Causes of Mental Disorders Students may think that having a mental disorder is a sign of weakness or bad character. Review the causes of mental disorders listed in the text. Then ask students how much control they think a person has over those causes. Explain that, given the causes, one could argue that people have less control over the development of most mental disorders than they have over the development of most physical disorders, for which there are often risk factors related to behavior.

L2 **Cooperative Learning**

Have students work with a partner to make a concept map that organizes the information about the four listed causes of mental disorders. Make sure students understand that mental disorders can be caused by a combination of factors.

Connect to Your Life *Sample answer:* ADHD would make it difficult for a person to focus on studying, especially for long periods of time.

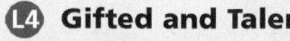

Differentiated Instruction

L4 **Gifted and Talented**

Researchers continue to explore the effect of neurotransmitters—the molecules that transmit messages between neurons—on mental disorders. Some examples include serotonin, GABA, and dopamine. Because neurotransmitters have multiple functions in the body, it is difficult to pinpoint their role in mental disorders.

Many drugs used to treat mental disorders act by decreasing or increasing the level of neurotransmitters, or inhibiting their effect on specific neurons. Have students collect and annotate articles from newspapers or online news sites about the latest research on neurotransmitters and mental disorders. Display the annotated articles in class.

Anxiety Disorders

L3 Class Discussion

Remind students that fear is a helpful emotion when it encourages people to practice healthful behaviors such as wearing a seat belt. Fear is a harmful emotion when it is an overreaction to a threat, whether real or imagined.

L1 Visual Learning: Figure 2

Pronounce the name of each phobia in Figure 2. Explain that the suffix *–phobia* means "fear of." Make sure students understand the difference between a dislike and a phobia. (Phobias affect a person's ability to function.) Call on students to answer the caption question.
Caption Answer: *Sample answer:* The phobias most likely to interfere with everyday activities are agoraphobia and claustrophobia.

EL Building Vocabulary

If students are having trouble with the term *panic attack*, you might want to discuss the term *panic button*. People say "Don't push the panic button" when they think someone might overreact to a situation and do something foolish.

Connect to Your Life Allow students to answer this question in their private journals.

FIGURE 2 About 19 million Americans are affected by phobias at some point in their lives. **Predicting** Which of these phobias might interfere with normal, everyday activities?

Common Phobias	
Arachnophobia	fear of spiders
Aviophobia	fear of flying
Acrophobia	fear of high places
Agoraphobia	fear of open or public places
Claustrophobia	fear of small, closed-in places
Ophidiophobia	fear of snakes

Anxiety Disorders

Have you ever been extremely afraid in a situation even though you knew the actual threat did not justify such an intense response? Have you ever been fearful without knowing why? If so, you have experienced anxiety. **Anxiety** (ang ZY ih tee) is fear caused by a source you cannot identify or a source that doesn't pose as much threat as you think.

Everyone experiences anxiety now and then. For example, you may feel anxious before a final exam, a school dance, or tryouts for the wrestling team. These feelings are normal and usually short-lived. When the anxiety persists for a long time and interferes with daily living, this is a sign of an **anxiety disorder.** About 13 percent of children and teens age 9 to 17 will have an anxiety disorder. **Examples of these disorders are generalized anxiety disorder, phobias, panic attacks, obsessive-compulsive disorders, and post-traumatic stress disorder.**

Generalized Anxiety Disorder A person with this disorder displays intense worry, fears, or anxiety most days for at least six months. These thoughts and emotions do not have a single specific source. They occur in many different situations. Many of the warning signs of stress can also be signs of this disorder, including irritability, muscle tension, trouble falling asleep, and trouble concentrating.

Phobias Martin was on his way to visit his grandparents. As he walked toward the elevator in their building, he began to feel dizzy and nauseous. His heart began to pound, and he had trouble catching his breath. He knew he could not face getting into the elevator, so he climbed three flights of stairs instead. Martin has a fear of small, closed-in places, such as an elevator. Anxiety that is related to a specific situation or object is called a **phobia** (FOH bee uh). Martin's phobia is called claustrophobia. Figure 2 lists some common phobias.

 **Do you have a phobia that you are aware of? If so, how do you deal with your phobia?**

TEENS *Are Asking . . .*

Q: I worry about getting into college, making the team, and having time to work at my job. Do I have an anxiety disorder?

A: Typical teens have a lot to worry about. In fact, a bit of worry or anxiety can help you to get motivated to perform tasks such as studying. Short-term anxiety brought on by a particular situation is perfectly normal.

However, anxiety that interferes with daily life and lasts for a long time period is a sign of an anxiety disorder. If you are concerned, you should discuss your anxiety with a parent, guardian, or other trusted adult. The school counselor or nurse can also help you to deal with your anxiety.

Panic Attacks   Brianna was standing in line at the movies. Suddenly, for no apparent reason, she felt intense fear and a strong desire to leave the theater. Brianna was having a panic attack. During a panic attack, a person will experience some of the following symptoms.

- fast heart rate
- rapid breathing
- fear of suffocation
- believes he or she is dying
- sweating
- trembling or shaking

- choking sensation
- chest discomfort or pain
- nausea or stomach distress
- dizziness or lightheadedness
- fear of losing control
- an "out of body" sensation

People who have repeated panic attacks tend to worry about having another. To avoid another attack, they may change their behavior. If, for example, they have attacks in restaurants, they may stop going out to eat.

Obsessive-Compulsive Disorder   An unwanted thought or image that takes control of the mind is an **obsession** (ub SESH un). An obsession may lead to a **compulsion** (kum PUHL shun), an unreasonable need to behave in a certain way to prevent a feared outcome. Repeatedly checking that the stove isn't on or that a door is locked is a compulsion. A person who thinks and acts in such ways has an obsessive-compulsive disorder (OCD).

Post-Traumatic Stress Disorder   People who survive a life-threatening event may develop post-traumatic stress disorder. They may have flashbacks or nightmares that produce intense fear or horror. They may be unable to sleep or to concentrate. Because situations that remind them of the event can produce intense anxiety, they begin to avoid those situations. They may feel guilty because they survived and others did not.

FIGURE 3   People who witness traumatic events as part of their jobs are at risk for post-traumatic stress disorder. This firefighter witnessed the September 11th attacks in New York City.

85

Other Mental Disorders

L3 Online Activity 🔵 GO ONLINE

Visit Pearson SuccessNet to access an online activity about bipolar disorder. Have students complete the Web activity.

L2 Class Discussion

After students have read the description of manic-depressive disorder, ask them to distinguish between normal mood shifts and mood shifts that would signify a disorder. *(Normal mood shifts occur based on events or situations in a person's life. The shifts experienced by a person with manic-depressive disorder occur for no apparent reason.)* Explain that teens often experience rapid, extreme mood shifts. Remind students that this is a normal part of adolescence.

L3 Addressing Misconceptions

Schizophrenia Students may think that schizophrenia results in split, or multiple, personalities. This is a misconception that is reinforced by the frequent misuse of the term *schizophrenia* in books and movies. Point out that, although the term *schizophrenia* does mean "split mind," this refers to a split from reality, not a split personality.

L4 Building Media Literacy

Challenge students to find examples of works of literature or movies that focus on characters with mental disorders. Have students analyze the type of disorder depicted as well as any stereotypes about individuals with mental disorders that are present in the book or movie. Ask students to share their findings with the class.

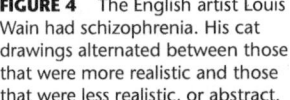

GO ONLINE
PearsonSuccessNet.com
For: More on bipolar disorder

FIGURE 4 The English artist Louis Wain had schizophrenia. His cat drawings alternated between those that were more realistic and those that were less realistic, or abstract.

Other Mental Disorders

Young people can have mental disorders other than anxiety disorders. **Some teens and young adults have mood disorders or schizophrenia. Others have impulse-control disorders or personality disorders.**

Mood Disorders People who have a **mood disorder** experience extreme emotions that make it difficult to function well in their daily lives. Bipolar disorder is an example of a mood disorder. Normally, people have moods that shift from happy to sad, based on what is happening in their lives. People who suffer from bipolar disorder shift from one emotional extreme to another for no apparent reason.

Bipolar disorder is also called manic-depressive disorder. During a manic episode, people are usually overly excited and restless. They may talk so rapidly that it is impossible to follow what they are trying to say. They may have difficulty concentrating for long on any one thing. They often show poor judgment. Manic episodes alternate with periods of deep depression. **Depression** is an emotional state in which a person feels extremely sad and hopeless. In between manic episodes and periods of depression, a person with bipolar disorder may behave normally.

Schizophrenia One of the most serious mental disorders is called **schizophrenia** (skit suh FREE nee uh). It can be identified by severe disturbances in thinking, mood, awareness, and behavior. *Schizophrenia* means "split mind." People with this disorder have minds that are "split off" or separated from reality.

People who have schizophrenia are rarely harmful to others. At times they may even appear normal. At other times, they may talk to themselves, display inappropriate emotional responses, dress and act strangely, and withdraw from others. Sometimes they develop fears that are not supported by reality. They may believe that someone or something controls their thoughts or wants to harm them.

86 *Chapter 4*

For Your INFORMATION!

Development of Schizophrenia

There is an explanation for why the onset of schizophrenia occurs in late adolescence or early adulthood. Researchers have identified abnormalities in the brain structure of people who develop schizophrenia. Not everyone who has these abnormalities will develop schizophrenia. Brain damage that occurs during fetal development or at birth increases the risk. The final trigger occurs during adolescence when there is a natural pruning of synapses in the brain to make the brain more efficient. In the brains of people who will develop schizophrenia, too many synapses are pruned.

Impulse-Control Disorders   People with an impulse-control disorder cannot resist the impulse, or drive, to act in a way that is harmful to themselves or to others. You may have heard of people who cannot resist the impulse to take items that they don't need or want. These people have an impulse-control disorder called kleptomania.

About 4% of people in the United States cannot control the urge to gamble. Their need to gamble is so great that they will go into debt or even steal in order to continue to gamble. This impulse-control disorder is most common among males. Being able to place a bet on the Internet has contributed to the problem. Plus, poker tournaments on television have made poker more popular among younger people. Uncontrolled gambling among male teens is on the rise. One teen became so addicted to playing poker online that he lost $5000 of his parents' money. He then stole another $3500 from a friend's house.

Mental health experts may add uncontrolled shopping to the list of impulse-control disorders. For shopping to be classified as uncontrolled, the shoppers must buy many things that they do not need and must know that they don't need these things. The shopping must also interfere with work, school, or family obligations, or cause financial problems. About 85 percent of uncontrolled shoppers are female.

 **Connect to Your Life**   **Do you know someone with an impulse-control disorder? How does this affect his or her life?**

FIGURE 5   Some teens spend hours playing poker online or with their friends. A person who cannot resist the urge to gamble has an impulse-control disorder.

L2 **Building Health Skills**

Communicating Ask students to assume they have a friend who has a problem with gambling on the Internet. Have students form small groups to discuss strategies they could use to communicate their concern. Have each group write a role-play that demonstrates one strategy. Ask groups to perform their role-plays for the class. **WRITING**

L3 **Building Health Skills**

Accessing Information Have students research various support groups and other resources available for those with impulse-control disorders. Then, as a class, discuss which resources seem most helpful.

Connect to Your Life Allow students to answer this question in their private journals.

Mental Disorders and Suicide   **87**

Differentiated Instruction

L1 **Special Needs**

Allow students with special needs to focus on a general definition of the term *mental disorder* rather than the definitions of specific disorders. Emphasize the effect of mental disorders on a person's ability to function.

Ask students to fold a stack of three pieces of notebook paper in half to form a small booklet. Have the students work alone or with a partner to record facts about mental disorders in their booklets.

3. Assess

Evaluate

These assignments can help you assess students' mastery of the section content.

Section 1 Review

Answers appear below.

Teaching Resources
- Practice 4-1
- Section 4-1 Quiz

L2 Reteach

Have students use the heads and sub-heads to review the information about mental disorders presented in this section. Call on students to verbally summarize the characteristics of each disorder.

L4 Enrich

Teaching Resources
- Enrich 4-1

Health at School

Dealing With ADHD Introduce the activity by having students review the symptoms of ADHD that are listed in this section. If you have students in your class with ADHD, consider how they might respond to this assignment. Some may prefer to avoid the topic. Some may want to act as expert witnesses.

FIGURE 6 Just looking at a crowd of people usually won't tell you who has a personality disorder.

Personality Disorders Recall that your personality determines how you tend to relate to other people. Most people can get along with a variety of people in different situations. Other people are not as flexible. People who have a **personality disorder** display rigid patterns of behavior that make it difficult for them to get along with others. The many different types of personality disorders fall into three broad groups.

▶ **Group A:** People with personality disorders in this group tend to be cold and distant. They cannot form close relationships. Some may be so absorbed in their own thoughts that they withdraw from reality. Paranoid personality disorder is a Group A disorder. The term *paranoid* is used to describe someone who is overly suspicious of other people.

▶ **Group B:** People with personality disorders in this group are often overly emotional or unstable. They can be selfish and demanding. They may place a high value on themselves and no value on others. Antisocial personality disorder is a Group B disorder. A person with this disorder may commit violent acts without any sense of guilt.

▶ **Group C:** People with personality disorders in this group often cannot make decisions. They may have a strong need for the approval of others. They may avoid people for fear of rejection. Dependent personality disorder is a Group C disorder. People with this disorder often need help from others to properly care for themselves.

Section 1 Review

Key Ideas and Vocabulary

1. What is a **mental disorder**? How are mental disorders recognized?
2. List four possible causes of mental disorders.
3. What is an **anxiety disorder**? What is the key difference between a phobia and generalized anxiety disorder?
4. What is a **compulsion**? How does a compulsion differ from an **obsession**?
5. What are some symptoms of a **mood disorder**?

Critical Thinking

6. **Relating Cause and Effect** Explain how someone who has frequent unexpected panic attacks might develop a phobia.

Health at School

Dealing With ADHD Interview a teacher or guidance counselor at your school. Ask what strategies can help a student with ADHD to succeed in school. How can students help a classmate with ADHD? Write a paragraph summarizing your findings. **WRITING**

7. **Classifying** Eric spends about six hours a day playing video games. He resents being called away from the computer for supper. He has lost interest in most other activities and his grades are dropping. What type of mental disorder might Eric have? Explain.

🔊 GO ONLINE PearsonSuccessNet.com   Audio Summary Section 4.1

Section 1 Review

1. an illness that affects the mind and reduces a person's ability to function; abnormal thoughts, feelings, or behaviors
2. physical factors, heredity, early experiences, recent experiences
3. anxiety that persists and interferes with daily living; a phobia is related to a specific object or situation, generalized anxiety disorder has no specific source
4. an unreasonable need to behave in a certain way; a compulsion involves an action, while an obsession is a thought or image
5. extreme emotions that make it difficult to function
6. They fear situations that trigger attacks.
7. Eric may have an impulse-control disorder; he cannot resist the impulse to play.

Technology & Health

Virtual Reality and Phobias

Today, virtual reality technology can help people overcome their phobias. Typically, therapists treat people with phobias by having them slowly confront the actual object or situation they fear. With virtual reality, a similar process can occur without leaving the therapist's office. A person who is afraid of heights, for example, might be placed in a series of "virtual situations" with increasing heights. At each stage, the person learns to relax and control the anxiety.

WRITING Pick another phobia from Figure 2 on page 84. Describe the images you would include in a virtual reality program to help a person deal with this phobia.

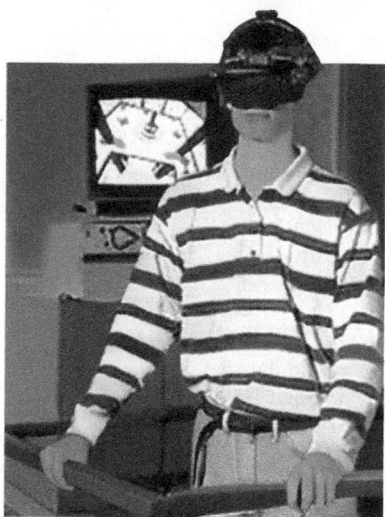

▲ A Virtual Reality Session

With the visor, a person can see 3D computer-generated images. The images change when the person moves his or her head or uses a joystick.

▲ Riding a Virtual Elevator

This is a virtual view from a glass elevator in a 46-story hotel. When a person feels comfortable at this height, he or she can move the elevator to a higher floor.

◄ A Real-World Test

If the therapy is successful, the person will be able to do actual activities that involve height. For example, the person could travel in an airplane.

89

Technology & Health
Virtual Reality and Phobias

Teaching Strategies

- Review the definition of *phobia*. Tell students that phobias are often treated with behavior modification. The person is gradually exposed to the object or situation that is the source of the fear. Discuss possible advantages and disadvantages of using virtual reality. After students complete the writing assignment, discuss their suggestions.

- Encourage creative thinking by having students describe ways that virtual reality might be applied to help those with mental disorders other than phobias. Have volunteers share their responses with the class.

- Have interested students do research to learn more about the technology used to produce a virtual reality experience. Students can work in pairs or small groups to complete this project. Ask these students to prepare a presentation to explain the technology to the class.

WRITING Responses should reveal both an understanding of phobias and of how virtual reality can be used to modify behavior. For objects, students may suggest showing the object at a distance and working toward an extreme close up of the object. For a situation, the virtual elevator provides a model. The images should reflect the person's view of the situation. For fear of flying, this could include the ticket counter, the boarding ramp, and so on.

For Your INFORMATION!

Virtual Reality

With virtual reality, the therapy takes place in the privacy of an office at a convenient time. In addition, it is easier to control the exposure the patient has to the source of the phobia. However, the technology may not be available in all communities.

Virtual reality is being applied by mental health professionals for several purposes. Managing or eliminating phobias is just one example. Studies have shown that virtual reality can also be useful in treating post-traumatic stress disorder.

Objectives

Before class begins, write the objectives on the board. Have students copy the objectives into their notebooks at the start of class.

1. Focus

Warm-Up Myth/Fact

Ask students why they think this myth about eating disorders exists. *(Media attention has been focused on eating disorders in females.)* Have students share their responses to the writing assignment. List the suggested factors on the board and refer to the list as you discuss each eating disorder.

Presentation 4-2

2. Teach

L3 **EL** Reading/Note Taking 4-2

L2 Adapted Reading/Note Taking 4-2

Anorexia Nervosa

L3 **Addressing Misconceptions**

Anorexia Nervosa Students may think of anorexia nervosa as a physical problem. Point out that anorexia involves changes in brain chemistry that are similar to those that occur in individuals who have anxiety disorders. Although many symptoms of anorexia are physical, the underlying problem is not.

Objectives

▶ **Identify** health risks associated with anorexia.

▶ **Explain** the relationship between bulimia and dieting.

▶ **List** the main health risks of binge eating disorder.

Vocabulary

- eating disorder
- anorexia nervosa
- bulimia
- binge eating disorder

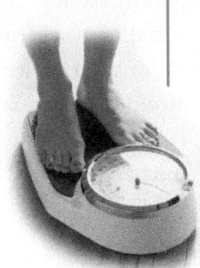

Warm-Up

Myth Eating disorders affect only females.

Fact Eating disorders affect females more than males, but males do develop eating disorders. Because of this myth males are even less likely than females to seek help for an eating disorder.

WRITING What factors other than gender might keep someone from seeking help for an eating disorder?

Anorexia Nervosa

What image comes to mind when you hear the word *Thanksgiving*? Do you think of a turkey dinner with all the trimmings? In most cultures, people celebrate holidays and other important occasions by preparing traditional foods. But for some people food can be a source of anxiety.

An **eating disorder** is a mental disorder that reveals itself through abnormal behaviors related to food. Eating disorders are about more than just food. They are about emotions, thoughts, and attitudes. A person with **anorexia nervosa** (an uh REK see uh nur VOH suh) doesn't eat enough food to maintain a healthy body weight. The main symptom is extreme weight loss. Other symptoms include slowed heart and breathing rates, dry skin, lowered body temperature, and growth of fine body hair. In females, another symptom is loss of menstrual periods.

FIGURE 7 People with anorexia think they are fat even when they are thin. Anorexia affects about one out of every one hundred teenaged girls

---

TEENS *Are Asking . . .*

Q: **How can I tell if my friend Kim has anorexia or is just dieting?**

A: There are several behaviors you can look for when trying to distinguish anorexia from ordinary dieting. Is Kim willing to discuss her diet with close friends or is she secretive about her eating habits? Is she excited to share news about her weight loss or does she try to hide her weight loss by wearing bulky clothing? Does she have a specific goal (for example, losing five pounds) or does she not mention a specific goal or stopping point? These indicators are not foolproof, so it is always wise to talk with a trusted adult if you are worried that a friend may have an eating disorder.

Media Wise

Body Image and Magazines

Many teens are not satisfied with the size or shape of their bodies. This dissatisfaction can sometimes lead to an eating disorder. Images in magazines can contribute to the problem. Use this checklist to evaluate the messages that teen magazines send about your body and appearance.

Do the images show a narrow range of body shapes and sizes?	Yes No
Are the females in the images taller and thinner than typical teenage girls?	Yes No
Are the males in the images taller and more muscular than typical teenage boys?	Yes No
Are there stories about people who are dieting, bulking up, or getting a makeover?	Yes No
Does the magazine make you feel dissatisfied with your body?	Yes No

Two or more "Yes" answers reveal how magazines influence readers' feelings about their own bodies.

Activity Look at a magazine that is aimed at teens. Use the checklist to evaluate the images in the magazine. Then write a paragraph summarizing what you learned. Also describe how looking at the images affected you. **WRITING**

Health Risks Even when they are extremely thin, people with anorexia see themselves as fat and work hard to lose more weight. They may use exercise or diet pills to help lose weight. **A person with anorexia can starve to death. In some cases, a lack of essential minerals causes the heart to stop suddenly, leading to death.**

Possible Causes The lack of a chemical that regulates mood is one possible cause of anorexia. Other possible causes are low self-esteem and a strong desire to please others. A person with anorexia may have a history of troubled relationships. By controlling what they eat, or more accurately what they don't eat, people with anorexia may be attempting to take control of their lives. Instead, the disorder begins to control them.

Treatment People with anorexia usually deny that there is a problem. They need to be encouraged to get help. Because of their extreme weight loss, they are often first treated in a hospital. Doctors, nurses, and dietitians work together to stop the weight loss and change a person's eating habits. At the same time, mental health experts work with the patient and family members to address the underlying emotional problems.

Connect to Your Life What factors might influence a person's decision to gain or lose weight?

Media Wise

Body Image and Magazines

Have students bring in magazines to analyze. Provide additional magazines for students to use.

Activity Allow students to work in pairs or small groups to analyze the images, but have them do the writing assignment by themselves. Allow students to record in their private journals how looking at the images made them feel.

L2 Building Vocabulary

Explain that the word *anorexia* literally means "lack of appetite." Ask: **Why is this an inaccurate description of anorexia nervosa?** *(Individuals with anorexia nervosa have a normal appetite and do experience hunger.)*

L3 Building Health Skills

Advocacy Ask students to make a pamphlet or poster that describes the possible causes, symptoms, treatments, and health risks of anorexia nervosa. Encourage students to use powerful words and images to capture teens' attention. Arrange for students to display their completed posters or pamphlets throughout the school.

Connect to Your Life *Sample answer:* Students may refer to media images, peer pressure, or the inability to participate in activities.

Differentiated Instruction

L2 Less Proficient Readers

Have students work in three groups. Each group should use the text to learn about one of the eating disorders described in this section. Ask the students in each group to find a creative way to share their information with the other groups. After each group has presented its information, ask students to preview the Section 2 Review questions on page 93. If students cannot answer the questions, have them review the information in the text to find the answers.

Bulimia

L3 Online Activity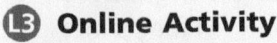

Visit Pearson SuccessNet to access an online activity about eating disorders. Have students complete the Web activity.

L1 Visual Learning: Figure 8

Ask students why it can be harder to recognize that a person has bulimia as compared to anorexia. *(There isn't usually an obvious weight loss with bulimia.)* Emphasize the health risks associated with bulimia.

L2 Active Learning

Have students use a Venn diagram to compare and contrast bulimia and anorexia nervosa. Ask students to include information about the possible causes, treatments, symptoms, and health risks of each disorder. After students complete their diagrams, have them make a large Venn diagram on the board or on an overhead with information from their individual diagrams.

Connect to Your Life Allow students to answer this question in their private journals.

GO ONLINE

PearsonSuccessNet.com

For: More on eating disorders

Bulimia

Another eating disorder that is seen mainly in young women is bulimia. People who have **bulimia** (byoo LIM ee uh) go on uncontrolled eating binges followed by purging, or removing, the food from their bodies. They purge the food by making themselves vomit or by using laxatives.

Health Risks Most people with bulimia maintain a weight within their normal range. However, the cycle of bingeing and purging has a negative effect on their health. They may suffer from dehydration, kidney damage, and a lack of necessary vitamins and minerals. The stomach acid in vomit irritates the throat and erodes the enamel from teeth. People with bulimia often become depressed and may even think about suicide.

Possible Causes Many of the causes listed for anorexia also apply to bulimia. In addition, people who binge may use food as a way to feel better emotionally. Then they purge because they are concerned about gaining weight. **Bulimia may begin in connection with a diet, but the person soon becomes unable to stop the cycle of bingeing and purging.**

Treatment People who have bulimia are aware of what they are doing, but they are unable to control their behavior. They often are too ashamed of their behavior to seek help. If you know someone with the signs listed in Figure 8, offer your support in private. Then gently encourage the person to seek the help of a mental-health professional. There are many effective treatments for bulimia.

Connect to Your Life If you suspected that a friend was bingeing and purging, what would you say to your friend?

FIGURE 8 Some athletes are at risk for an eating disorder because their sport has rules about weight. For example, a wrestler must be within a set weight range to qualify for a given weight class.

Possible Signs of Bulimia
- Unable to control eating binges
- Eating too much food too quickly
- Eating in private
- Cycles of weight gain and loss
- Bathroom visits right after eating
- Hoarding or storing food

92

WRITING and Health

L3 Public Service Announcement

Have students write a brief announcement about bulimia that is aimed at parents. The announcement should describe the eating disorder, explain the health risks, and provide some possible warning signs.

Challenge students to consider other aspects of an announcement designed to appear on television. For example, would they use a spokesperson or a voice over? What kind of images or music would they use?

Binge Eating Disorder

Have you ever eaten so much at a holiday dinner that you couldn't eat dessert? Or perhaps you ate all of your Halloween candy in a single evening. Everyone overeats once in awhile. But some people cannot control their compulsion to overeat. People with **binge eating disorder** regularly have an uncontrollable urge to eat large amounts of food. They usually do not purge after a binge. People with binge eating disorder cannot stop eating even when they are full. They may intend to eat two slices of bread and end up eating the entire loaf.

Health Risks   Someone with binge eating disorder isn't going to starve to death or suffer the consequences of repeated purging. But there are health risks with binge eating. **The main physical risks of binge eating disorder are excess weight gain and unhealthy dieting.** When people gain an unhealthy amount of weight, they are at greater risk for illnesses such as diabetes, and physical disorders such as high blood pressure. To deal with the weight gain from binges, some people try extreme diets that promise rapid weight loss. The hunger caused by such diets can trigger more binges, which can trigger more dieting—a yo-yo effect.

Possible Causes   Some people use binge eating to avoid dealing with difficult emotions, such as anger, or with stressful situations. The food may provide some temporary relief, but it can lead to other difficult emotions, such as guilt or depression.

Treatment   People with binge eating disorder need help in learning how to control their eating. They may need to eat more slowly and deliberately. They often need to address underlying emotional problems.

FIGURE 9   Someone with a binge eating disorder eats a large amount of food in a short amount of time. **Evaluating** Based on the containers, do you think the amount of food eaten qualifies as a binge? Explain.

Section 2 Review

Key Ideas and Vocabulary

1. What is an **eating disorder**?

2. What health risks are associated with anorexia? Why are people with anorexia unlikely to ask for help?

3. What is **bulimia**? Explain the connection between bulimia and dieting.

4. What health risks are possible for someone with binge eating disorder?

Critical Thinking

5. Comparing and Contrasting How are bulimia and anorexia alike? How are they different?

Health at School

Eating Disorders and Athletes Interview a coach or trainer about the role athletics may play in some eating disorders. Ask in which sports eating disorders are most often seen. Ask what a coach or trainer can do to help prevent eating disorders. Write a paragraph summarizing what you find out. **WRITING**

6. Evaluating When Brittany visits her aunt, her aunt insists that she take second helpings at dinner. To please her aunt, Brittany eats beyond the point that she feels full. Is this a sign that Brittany has an eating disorder? Explain your answer.

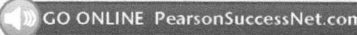 GO ONLINE PearsonSuccessNet.com   Audio Summary Section 4.2

Mental Disorders and Suicide   **93**

Binge Eating Disorder

Visual Learning: Figure 9

Caption Answer *Sample answer:* Based on the size and number of containers, if all this food were consumed by a single person, it would qualify as a binge.

L3 **Building Health Skills**

Advocacy Have students discuss the physical risks of binge eating, anorexia, and bulimia. Ask students to describe strategies they would use to advocate for a friend who has an eating disorder.

3. Assess

Evaluate

These assignments can help you assess students' mastery of the section content.

Section 2 Review

Answers appear below.

Teaching Resources
• Practice 4-2
• Section 4-2 Quiz

L2 **Reteach**

For each eating disorder described in the section, ask students to complete the following sentence: I would suspect that a friend had anorexia (bulimia, binge eating disorder) if I observed the following three symptoms: . . .

L4 **Enrich**

Teaching Resources
• Enrich 4-2

Health at School

Eating Disorders and Athletics Ask students to prepare their interview questions in advance. After students complete the activity, have a class discussion about what students learned from their interviews.

Section 2 Review

1. mental disorder that reveals itself through abnormal behaviors related to food

2. Risks include starvation and cardiac arrest. They usually deny there is a problem.

3. Bulimia is characterized by uncontrolled eating followed by purging. Purging is used to lose or maintain weight.

4. excess weight gain and unhealthy dieting

5. Both mental disorders include abnormal behaviors related to food. With anorexia, a person avoids eating; with bulimia, a person binges and purges.

6. *Sample answer:* No, because Brittany does not overeat on a regular basis

Mental Disorders and Suicide   **93**

Objectives
Before class begins, write the objectives on the board. Have students copy the objectives into their notebooks at the start of class.

1. Focus

Warm-Up **Health Stats**

Call on someone to summarize the information in the table. Then have volunteers share their responses to the writing activity. Talk about the role that students can play in making other students feel connected.

Presentation 4-3

Sensitive Issues

- Students who are dealing with depression or who self-injure may feel uncomfortable during these discussions. Be certain that information about resources for teens dealing with these issues is available to all students in the class.
- If there have been recent suicide attempts among students at your school, this may make discussing suicide more difficult. On the other hand, such unfortunate events may help motivate students to focus on ways to prevent suicide.

Objectives
▶ **Explain** why it is important to identify and treat clinical depression.
▶ **Explain** why individuals might deliberately injure themselves.
▶ **Describe** one major risk factor for suicide.

Vocabulary
- clinical depression
- cutting
- suicide
- cluster suicides

Warm-Up

Health Stats What relationship is there between risk of depression and how connected teens feel to their school?

Connection to School	Risk of Depression
Very connected	Very low
Quite a bit	Low
Somewhat	Low to moderate
Very little	Moderate
Not at all connected	High

WRITING What could make someone feel very connected to school? What could make someone feel disconnected?

Clinical Depression

Everyone feels depressed now and then. It is normal to feel depressed if you experience a significant loss or failure. For example, you would expect to feel depressed if someone you loved moved away or if you didn't make a team you tried out for. Usually, however, the feeling of depression lifts after a few days or weeks, and you get on with your life. Sometimes, however, feelings of depression linger.

Defining Depression Maria used to be energetic and happy. She had good grades and loved playing in the school band. But recently her grades have dropped and she quit the band. She cannot sleep and feels tired all the time. Feelings of despair have taken over Maria's life.

Maria has a mood disorder known as clinical depression. People with **clinical depression** may feel sad and hopeless for months. They are unable to enjoy activities that were once a source of pleasure. As the depression deepens, people often are unable to accomplish their daily tasks. **Depression can cause problems at school, at home, and in one's social life. If untreated, depression can also lead to substance abuse, serious behavior problems, and even suicide.**

For Your INFORMATION!

School Connectedness

The degree of school connectedness a student feels depends on the individual character of the school and the student. Students who are assured socially and have the skills required to learn usually feel comfortable at school. They tend to have positive experiences that reinforce their connectedness.

Students with learning difficulties or poor social skills can feel disconnected. Those with anxiety or mood disorders will feel the need to avoid others. Students who are bullied might start to feel disconnected. When the school culture is controlled, fair, and engaging, it is possible to win over even the most disconnected students.

Recognizing Depression For a teen to be moody, irritable, or tired at times is not unusual. So how do mental health experts distinguish the signs of depression from typical teenage moods and behaviors? Mental health experts use the symptoms listed in Figure 10 to diagnose depression. A person who has clinical depression will experience four or more of the symptoms nearly every day for at least two weeks.

About one out of 10 teens will experience clinical depression before they are 18. After age 15, females are twice as likely as males to suffer from depression. Some teens may have a single episode of clinical depression; others experience more than one episode of depression.

Risk Factors Depression sometimes seems to arrive "out of the blue," but there are often explanations. The following risk factors have been identified for depression. It is important to know that having one or more risk factors doesn't mean that you will become depressed.

▶ A parent or other close biological relative with a mood disorder

▶ A major life change or a prolonged stressful situation

▶ Being the victim of a violent crime or witnessing violence

▶ A previous bout of depression

▶ A sense of hopelessness

Treatment for Depression Medication is an effective treatment for clinical depression. Normally, chemicals in the brain control how signals pass from one nerve cell to another. When someone is depressed, the brain does not use these chemicals properly. Medication helps to restore normal brain function. Mental health experts can also help people who are depressed to learn new strategies for coping with their problems.

Connect to Your Life Do you have any of the signs of depression? Do you have any of the risk factors for depression?

GO ONLINE
PearsonSuccessNet.com
For: More on depression

FIGURE 10 People who are depressed often avoid being with others. However, doing things you enjoy on your own is not a sign of depression.

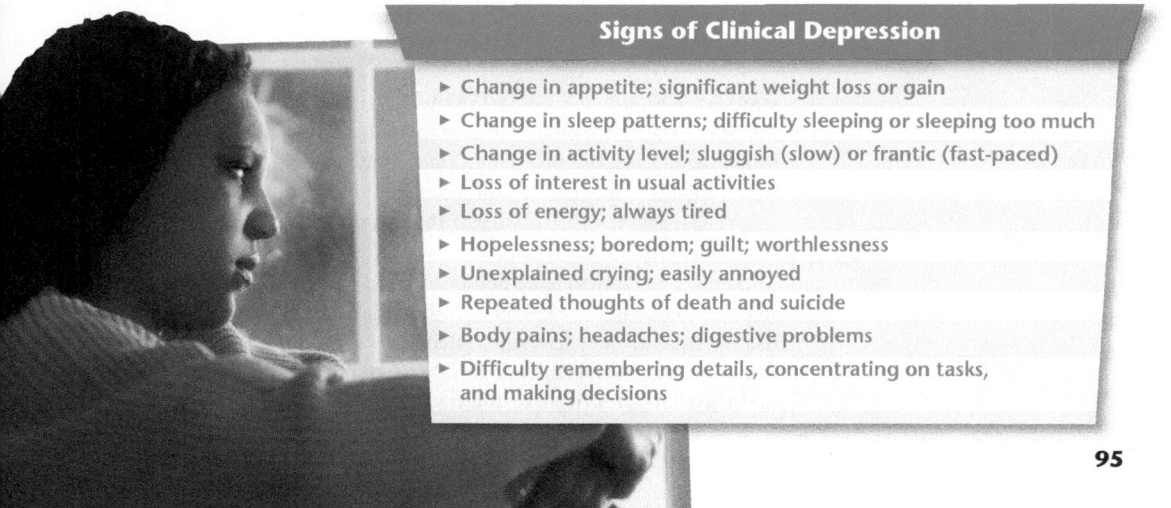

Signs of Clinical Depression

▶ Change in appetite; significant weight loss or gain
▶ Change in sleep patterns; difficulty sleeping or sleeping too much
▶ Change in activity level; sluggish (slow) or frantic (fast-paced)
▶ Loss of interest in usual activities
▶ Loss of energy; always tired
▶ Hopelessness; boredom; guilt; worthlessness
▶ Unexplained crying; easily annoyed
▶ Repeated thoughts of death and suicide
▶ Body pains; headaches; digestive problems
▶ Difficulty remembering details, concentrating on tasks, and making decisions

95

2. Teach

L3 EL Reading/Note Taking 4-3
L2 Adapted Reading/Note Taking 4-3

Clinical Depression

L3 Content Update  **GO ONLINE**

Visit Pearson SuccessNet to access more information about depression. Have students complete the Web activity.

L3 Cooperative Learning

Have students work in small groups to write a summary about ways that depression could cause problems for an individual at school, at home, and in the community. Have students share their responses with the class. Use these summaries to help students understand the importance of treatment for those experiencing depression. **WRITING**

L2 Visual Learning: Figure 10
Image Bank Figure 4-10

Caution students that some of the signs of clinical depression listed in the figure are behaviors and feelings that most people experience on occassion. Ask: **How do mental health professionals distinguish everyday feelings of sadness from clinical depression?** *(They determine if an individual exhibits four or more of these symptoms almost daily for two weeks or longer.)*

Connect to Your Life Allow students to answer this question in their private journals.

Differentiated Instruction

EL English Language Learners

The everyday usage of the term *depressed* may confuse English language learners. Point out that the term *clinical depression* describes a disorder that is diagnosed and treated by mental health professionals.

Contrast this usage to everyday usage with which students may be familiar. (e.g., I'm so depressed—I got a D on the test.) Have students explain how these two usages differ.

Self-Injury

L2 Visual Learning: Figure 11

Ask: **What do most of the alternatives to cutting listed in the figure have in common?** *(Sample answer: They provide a way to relieve stress.)*

L3 Building Health Skills

Accessing Information Have students use the Internet, a phone directory, or other sources to find information about resources for teens who self-injure. The school nurse or guidance counselor may also have suggestions. Have students work as a class to assemble a list of resources that can be posted in the school nurse's office.

Suicide Prevention

L3 Building Media Literacy

Ask students to suggest examples of teen suicide in television programs, movies, or books. Explain that, in some cases, the media glamorizes suicide—that is, makes it seem like an attractive alternative to dealing with life's problems. Have students analyze a few portrayals of teen suicide. Ask students whether they think these portrayals would encourage or discourage teen suicide.

If You Have the Urge to Cut
- Rub an ice cube on your skin.
- Take a shower.
- Write in your journal.
- Call a friend.
- Go for a walk or run.
- Listen to music that shifts your mood.
- Play with a pet.

FIGURE 11 Some people with a mental disorder use cutting to cope with their emotions or anxiety.

Self-Injury

When Nicole's mother asked about the cuts on Nicole's arms, Nicole said that her friend's cat scratched her. But the truth is that Nicole cut her arms with a razor blade. **Cutting** is the use of a sharp object to intentionally cut or scratch one's body deep enough to bleed. Cutting is one example of self-injury. Burning the skin on purpose with a lighted match or cigarette is another. Although cutting and burning leave scars, people often hide these signs of their behavior. For example, they may wear long-sleeved shirts even in warm weather. Self-injury occurs most often in young women, but it can occur in young men, too.

Self-injury is an unhealthy way to cope with emotions, stress, or traumatic events. People who self-injure are not usually trying to kill themselves. They are trying to feel better. They say that the behavior provides temporary relief from painful feelings. But self-injury doesn't address any of their underlying problems. Self-injury can be a symptom of a mood disorder, anxiety disorder, or eating disorder.

Self-injury isn't common, but it is a serious problem. The behavior may begin as an unplanned impulsive act, but it often turns into a compulsion. Someone who relies on cutting or burning to cope with emotions should tell a trusted adult. With the help of a mental health professional, they can learn better ways to cope with their problems.

Suicide Prevention

Suicide is the intentional killing of oneself. Suicide affects all kinds of people: young, old, bright, average, rich, poor, female, male. In the United States, suicide is the tenth-leading cause of death among young people ages 15–24. Between 1950 and 1990, the teen suicide rate quadrupled. But since 1990, the rate has declined.

Is there any way to tell whether or not someone is going to attempt suicide? Mental health experts have identified factors that put people at risk for suicide. They have identified other factors that protect people from suicide. If people understand these risk factors and protective factors, they can take steps to further reduce the suicide rate.

96 *Chapter 4*

 **and Health**

L4 Proposal

Have students develop a written proposal for an educational program that could be used to teach teens about the dangers of self-injury. Explain that their proposals should include a detailed plan for conveying this information to teens. Have students share their completed proposals with the class.

Risk Factors Is there a connection between depression and suicide? **Mood disorders, such as depression, are a major risk factor for suicide.** Other factors that may put a person at risk for suicidal behavior include:

► A previous suicide attempt or a family history of suicide

► Having both a mental disorder and a substance abuse disorder

► Feelings of hopelessness or isolation

► Lack of access to mental health treatment

► Being influenced by the suicide of family members, peers, or celebrities

Protective Factors If a person is at risk for suicide, there are some factors that can help reduce the risk. The first is treating a person's mental disorders, especially depression. Getting treatment for the abuse of alcohol or other drugs is important. So is feeling connected to school and having close relationships with family, friends, and others in the community.

Another protective factor is having personal beliefs that discourage suicide. Knowing how to resolve conflicts in non-violent ways also lowers a person's risk for suicide.

Cluster Suicides Sometimes a suicide or an attempted suicide triggers other suicides, especially among teens. **Cluster suicides** are a series of suicides that occur within a short period of time in the same peer group or community. Some cluster suicides involve a pact between friends. Others occur in response to an initial suicide. Immediate counseling of peers after a suicide or a suicide attempt can help to prevent cluster suicides.

 Connect to Your Life What other factors do you think are protective factors for suicide?

FIGURE 12 Feeling connected to school helps protect teens from suicide.

97

L3 Class Discussion

Stress that alcohol abuse is a major risk factor for suicide, especially for males. Alcohol affects the availability of the neurotransmitter serotonin. One function of serotonin is to help calm people when they are stressed. Ask students to think about how a person who uses alcohol to relieve stress is actually producing the opposite effect.

L3 Building Health Skills

Setting Goals After students read about protective factors for suicide, have them make an entry in their private journals. Ask students to identify a protective factor that they would like to strengthen. Remind students to make a specific action plan to meet this goal.

L2 Active Learning

Have students work together to develop a list of questions about suicide prevention that they could ask the school guidance counselor. After students develop the list, invite the counselor to class to discuss the questions. If the counselor is unable to visit class, he or she may be able to provide written answers to students' questions.

Connect to Your Life *Sample answer:* I think having a hobby you enjoy could be a protective factor for suicide.

Differentiated Instruction

L2 Less Proficient Readers

Make a list of risk factors for suicide on the board. Make a second list of protective factors for suicide. Then, have students work in small groups to discuss the connections between these factors. Ask them to consider which protective factors can help to reduce which risk factors. For example, mood orders, such as depression, are a major risk factor for suicide, so it is important to get treatment for these mental disorders.

L3 Visual Learning: Figure 13

Image Bank Figure 4-13

Make sure students understand why it is important to do items in the "Do" list and avoid doing items in the "Do Not" list. Have students consider how a person might respond if he or she did just the opposite of what is recommended. **Caption Answer** *Sample answer:* I think that I would be able to listen carefully and to trust my feelings.

L2 Cooperative Learning

Have students work in small groups to brainstorm a list of stressors that teens might face. Ask students to consider how these stressors might contribute to the suicide rate among teens. Also ask them to consider other factors, such as a lack of experience in dealing with setbacks or the normal mood swings associated with adolescence.

L3 Journal Writing

Explain that having an action plan prepared in advance is useful in any crisis. Challenge students to develop an action plan that they could use if a friend mentioned that he or she is thinking about suicide. Have them record their plans in their journals. **WRITING**

Connect to Your Life *Sample answer:* I would listen and show concern. I would also notify a trusted adult.

When a Friend Is Thinking About Suicide

Do . . .

- trust your feelings.
- take the threats seriously.
- say how concerned you are.
- listen carefully.
- talk calmly.
- involve a trusted adult.
- stay until help arrives.

Do Not . . .

- dare the person to go ahead with the suicide attempt.
- judge the person.
- analyze the person's motives.
- argue or offer reasons not to attempt suicide.
- leave the person alone.

FIGURE 13 These lists identify things you can do and things you should avoid doing when a person is thinking about suicide. **Evaluating** Which of the items on the list of things to do would you feel most able to do and why?

Warning Signs It would be very helpful if someone who was about to attempt suicide showed unmistakable warning signs. Unfortunately, most suicides occur without warning. Teens who attempt suicide usually don't talk about it in advance, write about it in school essays, or give away their possessions. A sudden drop in grades or an increase in drug abuse are warning signs of a problem, but that problem isn't always suicide.

So should you ignore radical changes in behavior that you observe in a friend? No, but you should proceed with caution. Don't assume you know what problem the person is dealing with. Offer your support and encourage the friend to talk to a trusted adult.

Helping Others A friend makes comments like "They'll be sorry when I'm gone" or "I have nothing to live for." What would you do? If you know that your friend has tried suicide before or if your friend describes a detailed plan of action, this is cause for serious concern. Your friend may make you promise not to tell anyone about his or her plan. Whether or not your friend realizes it, by confiding in you, your friend is asking you for help. To help your friend, you must break the promise and notify an adult that your friend is in danger. You should also notify an adult if you become aware of a suicide pact among a group of teens.

An important thing to remember is that suicidal behavior is a cry for help in dealing with problems that seem overwhelming. Suicidal people often feel that they have looked to others for support and have received no response. It is important that you show care and concern for the person. You can help by listening to and providing support for friends or family members who are feeling depressed, hopeless, or overwhelmed by stress. When the support you offer is backed by professional intervention, a life may be saved. Figure 13 offers suggestions about what to do and what not to do if you are faced with this situation.

 **Connect to Your Life** What would you do if someone told you about a plan to commit suicide?

TEENS *Are Asking . . .*

Q: I've been feeling hopeless for weeks. I envy people who have the courage to commit suicide. Why shouldn't I choose suicide to end my suffering?

A: Please do not make a hasty decision. The truly courageous act is being willing to ask for help. Share your feelings with a trusted adult such as a parent, guardian, school nurse, or guidance counselor. If you don't feel comfortable with this choice, call a crisis center or hotline. The National Suicide Prevention Lifeline provides free help 24 hours a day, 7 days a week, including services using TTY for hearing impaired callers and interpretation for those who do not speak English. Discussing your problems can help you deal with your feelings and find ways to cope with life's challenges.

Helping Yourself If you have been feeling depressed, remember that no matter how overwhelming the problems in your life may seem, suicide is never a solution. It is vital that you talk about your feelings with a trusted adult or mental health professional. Together, you will be able to find solutions that you may not have thought of on your own. No matter how isolated you may feel, you do not have to deal with your problems alone. No matter how hopeless you feel your situation is, there are positive steps that you can take.

Perhaps you are unable or unwilling to talk with an adult you live with. If so, consider talking with a family member who lives nearby, an adult friend of the family, or an adult in your faith community. There are also resources at your school that you can turn to—a school nurse, a social worker, a counselor, or a psychologist. These people are trained to screen for depression and suicide. If you are asked whether you have thought about or attempted suicide, tell the truth. That way, the person you are talking with will be able to get you the help you need.

Crisis centers and suicide-prevention hotlines are other resources you can use. These resources are staffed 24 hours a day. Look in the front of your local telephone directory or online for a listing of these hotlines. You can also get telephone numbers for crisis centers and hotlines in your area from the information operator, or directory assistance.

FIGURE 14 People have jumped from the Golden Gate Bridge in San Francisco. So the city placed a phone on the bridge that connects people to a crisis center.

Section 3 Review

Key Ideas and Vocabulary

1. How do mental health experts diagnose **clinical depression**?

2. Why is it important to identify and treat clinical depression?

3. Describe the self-injury behavior known as **cutting**. Explain why individuals might injure themselves on purpose.

4. What is a major risk factor for suicide? What protective factor can help to reduce the effect of this risk factor?

5. What are **cluster suicides**? What can be done to prevent them?

Health and Community

Suicide Hotlines Find out whether there are suicide hotlines in your community. Are the people who answer the phones employees or volunteers? What kind of training do people have before they are allowed to answer the phone? Are teens allowed to be volunteers? If so, what kind of role can they play? Write a paragraph summarizing what you find out. **WRITING**

Critical Thinking

6. **Evaluating** Why do you think cluster suicides occur most frequently among teenagers?

7. **Applying Concepts** Your friend Bryan has shown some signs of clinical depression for a month. You are very worried about Bryan, but he refuses to talk to you about his feelings. What could you do to help Bryan?

3. Assess

Evaluate

These assignments can help you assess students' mastery of the section content.

Section 3 Review

Answers appear below.

Teaching Resources

• Practice 4-3
• Section 4-3 Quiz

L2 Reteach

Have students discuss in small groups the relationship between depression and suicide. Ask each group to summarize and share its response with the class.

L4 Enrich

Teaching Resources

• Enrich 4-3

Health and Community

Suicide Hotlines Help students locate suicide hotlines in their community. After students have completed their research, have volunteers share their written responses with the class. Ask interested students to follow up by learning more about volunteer work with the hotline.

Section 3 Review

1. If individuals experience four or more symptoms of depression almost daily for two weeks, they are clinically depressed.

2. Untreated depression can lead to substance abuse, behavior problems, and suicide.

3. the use of a sharp object to cut or scratch deep enough to draw blood; temporary relief from painful feelings

4. depression; getting treatment for mental disorders, especially depression

5. suicides that occur within a brief time period in a peer group or community; counseling after the initial suicide

6. Teens are influenced by actions of peers.

7. Students are likely to recommend "Do" items from Figure 13.

Dealing With Setbacks

Objective

Develop a plan for dealing with setbacks.

Teaching Strategies

- Ask students to identify and discuss the emotions Sarah may have experienced when she learned that she was no longer a starter on the soccer team. Challenge students to think of positive and negative ways Sarah could have handled these emotions.

- Have students identify a character on a fictional television program or in a book who has handled a setback in a positive way. Ask students to share and discuss their examples with the class.

- Have students work as a class to make a bulletin board that describes strategies for dealing with setbacks. Ask students to create drawings, written slogans, and tips to add to the bulletin board.

Setting Goals

Dealing With Setbacks

Sarah stared at her coach with disbelief—she was no longer a starter on her soccer team! All of the friends she's played soccer with for years would be on the field at the start of the game, but not her. "I'm such a failure. I can't do anything right," Sarah said to herself. "Why do bad things always happen to me?"

Like Sarah, everyone experiences setbacks in their lives. And, like Sarah, most people are discouraged by a setback, at least at first. But, what do you do next? Do you think of yourself as a failure or a victim? Or are you able to bounce back and move on? Here are some tips that can help you handle setbacks in positive ways.

100

Sensitive Issues

- Students who have recently suffered a significant setback may feel they are failures, especially if they don't like how they dealt with the setback. Remind students that everyone experiences setbacks in life, and no one handles every setback equally well.

- When discussing setbacks, call only on students who volunteer. Remind students that they should not reveal personal information about their family members or friends during discussions of setbacks.

1 Think of a setback as an isolated event.

If you experience a setback, remind yourself of its limits. In other words, don't think of a setback as evidence that you're a failure overall. Instead, tell yourself that you did not succeed at one thing at one particular time. By thinking this way, you keep the setback in the proper perspective. Otherwise, the setback can begin to affect other things you do.

2 Recognize that a setback is temporary.

Some setbacks have long-term effects, but many setbacks do not. Although a setback will probably alter your immediate plans and goals, you can view a setback as an opportunity. For example, Sarah could ask her coach for advice on how she could work toward becoming a starter again.

Also, remember that a setback doesn't mean that you need to abandon your original goal. Ask yourself these questions, which may help you discover a new path to pursue.

▶ Is there a different path I can take to reach my goal?

▶ Can I arrange for a second opportunity to try and reach my goal, either now or in the near future?

▶ Can I modify my goal somewhat?

3 Become aware of your "self-talk."

Pay attention to what you are thinking and saying to yourself about the setback. One way to monitor your thoughts is by jotting them down. Then, dispute each negative thought ("I can't do anything right") with a response ("I play guitar really well."). This will help you turn off the negative thinking.

4 Take action.

One key to bouncing back from a setback is to focus your energy in productive ways. For example, do you now have time to pursue a new interest? Can you view the setback as a challenge to work even harder at improving your skills? By looking ahead and focusing your efforts toward a new goal, you can put the setback behind you.

Practice the Skill

1. Your friend, Sarah, just told you that she is no longer a starter on her soccer team. What could you say to help her view the setback as an isolated and temporary event?

2. For each of the negative thoughts below, write a response to yourself that disputes it.
   a. "I never do anything right."
   b. "Nobody likes me."
   c. "I'm the stupidest person in the class."

3. Recall a setback you experienced recently. In a paragraph, describe how you handled the setback. Include details about what you were feeling and thinking, and what actions you took. In a second paragraph, describe other, more positive steps you could have taken to deal with the setback.

Practice the Skill

1. *Sample answer:* I might suggest that Sarah talk with her coach about what would be required for her to be a starter again, or ask Sarah if she has other goals she wants to pursue.

2. a. *Sample answer:* I improved my grades and learned to play the flute this year.

   b. *Sample answer:* I'll make some friends at this school once people get to know me.

   c. *Sample answer:* I did poorly on this test, but if I study more, I know I can do better.

3. Allow students to answer this question in their private journals.

Health at Home

L3 Handling Setbacks as a Family

Although many setbacks that teens face happen at school, it is also important to be able to handle setbacks at home. Have students discuss a variety of setbacks that are common in families. Then, have students discuss ways in which family members can work together to deal with these setbacks. Ask students to write a paragraph summarizing these discussions. **WRITING**

Objectives

Before class begins, write the objectives on the board. Have students copy the objectives into their notebooks at the start of class.

1. Focus

Warm-Up Advice Line

Ask students to reflect on this letter and write a thoughtful response. Then have volunteers share their responses with the class. Use students' responses to start a class discussion about attitudes toward mental disorders and how these attitudes can be a barrier that prevents people from seeking treatment.

Presentation 4-4

2. Teach

L3 **EL** Reading/Note Taking 4-4

L2 Adapted Reading/Note Taking 4-4

Locating Community Resources

L2 **Class Discussion**

On the board, write three reasons that keep people from seeking help for a mental disorder (*not recognizing the signs of a mental disorder; being told to use willpower to overcome the problem; not knowing where to get help.*) Ask students to work as a class to develop strategies for addressing each barrier.

Section 4	Treating Mental Disorders

Objectives

▶ **List** reasons that might prevent a person from seeking help for a mental disorder.

▶ **Identify** four types of mental health professionals.

▶ **Describe** some general types of treatment for mental disorders.

Vocabulary

• psychiatrist
• neurologist
• clinical psychologist
• psychiatric social worker
• therapy

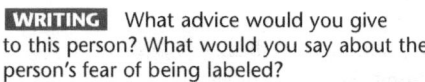 

Warm-Up

Dear Advice Line,

Lately, I spend a lot of time just staring at the ceiling or crying for no reason at all. I haven't told anyone about my problems. I don't want to be labeled as "a mental case."

WRITING What advice would you give to this person? What would you say about the person's fear of being labeled?

Locating Community Resources

Each year, about 20 percent of Americans experience the symptoms of a mental disorder. However, the majority of these people do not seek help. What could keep a person with a mental disorder from getting the help he or she needs? **Sometimes people don't recognize the signs of a mental disorder. Or they may have been told that, with willpower alone, they can overcome the problem. Or they may not know where to go for help.**

The first step toward recovery is recognizing the need for help. Do not ignore the warning signs of mental disorders. But don't rely too much on your own diagnosis. Treat a mental disorder the same way you would treat a physical illness. If you have a physical illness, you should see a doctor to receive appropriate treatment. If you have a mental disorder, you should see a mental health professional for treatment.

Although it may be difficult, try to share your problems with an adult that you trust. This could be a parent, guardian, teacher, counselor, doctor, or religious leader. The adult can help you find mental health services in your community. A local hospital may have a mental health center. Some communities have mental health clinics or counseling centers. Others have drop-in centers for teens, where counselors provide help and guidance. For some types of treatment, you will need the consent of a parent or guardian. See the Building Health Skill on locating community resources in Chapter 25 for additional information.

For Your **INFORMATION!**

Preventing Mental Disorders

Most people understand the need for prevention in physical health, but they are less aware of the need for prevention in mental health. For example, when a person with a family history of depression faces a significant setback, counseling may prevent the onset of clinical depression.

In a study that compared teens at risk for depression who received therapy to those who did not, therapy reduced the incidence of depression in at-risk teens. Identifying at-risk individuals can be difficult, as is getting authorization for costly treatments based on the possibility of a disorder developing.

Types of Mental Health Professionals

Mental health professionals are trained to recognize mental disorders and to treat them. The type of treatment they offer depends upon their training. **Psychiatrists, clinical psychologists, social workers, and mental health counselors are four types of mental health professionals.**

Psychiatrists   After medical school, doctors may get advanced training in the treatment of mental disorders. Their goal is to become a **psychiatrist** (sy KY uh trist), a physician who can diagnose and treat mental disorders. A psychiatrist will do a medical exam to rule out physical causes. Then, he or she will talk with a patient to find out what symptoms the patient has.

Psychiatrists use a variety of treatment methods. As physicians, they are able to prescribe medications. If they suspect that a patient's symptoms may have a physical cause, they may ask the patient to see a neurologist (noo RAHL uh jist). A **neurologist** is a physician who treats physical disorders of the nervous system.

Clinical Psychologists   A **clinical psychologist** is trained to recognize and treat behavior that is not normal. Clinical psychologists have a doctoral degree in psychology and at least two years of practical training in clinics or hospitals. A psychologist may help a psychiatrist to diagnose a patient's disorder. The psychologist may interview the patient or use a diagnostic test. In some states, clinical psychologists can prescribe medications.

Social Workers   Social workers listen to and advise people. Often, they act as a link between people who need help and community resources that provide help. A **psychiatric social worker** helps people with mental disorders and their families to accept and adjust to an illness.

Mental Health Counselors   Some mental health counselors focus on specific problems or work with specific groups of people. Substance abuse counselors, for example, work with people who have problems with alcohol or other drugs. School counselors work with students. Youth counselors work with teenagers. Members of faith communities often have practical training as counselors.

 **Connect to Your Life**   Are there mental health counselors at your school? If so, what type of problems do they deal with?

FIGURE 15   Talking about a problem can help a person identify the source of the problem. **Predicting** What kinds of questions might a mental health professional ask?

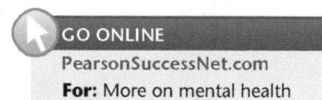 **GO ONLINE**
PearsonSuccessNet.com
For: More on mental health

Types of Mental Health Professionals

Visual Learning: Figure 15

Caption Answer *Sample answer:* He or she might ask about symptoms an individual is experiencing, as well as questions that can help establish how well the individual is functioning in everyday life.

L2 Active Learning

Ask students to make a table or other graphic organizer that summarizes the information about mental health professionals presented in the text. Have several students share with the class the methods they used to organize the information.

L3 Building Health Skills

Analyzing Influences Ask students to recall movies they have seen in which a main character is a psychiatrist or other mental health professional. Did these movies tend to present the mental health professionals as heroes or villains? Do students think these portrayals would encourage a person to seek help from a mental health professional?

Connect to Your Life Answers should reflect the actual services offered at your school.

L3 Content Update  **GO ONLINE**

Visit Pearson SuccessNet to access more information about mental health. Have students complete the Web activity.

 **Differentiated Instruction**

EL English Language Learners

Write the terms *psychiatrist* and *psychologist* on the board. Explain that *psych-* means "mind or brain." Point out that the letter *p* at the beginning of these words is silent. Explain that the letter *p* is often silent at the beginning of words when it is followed by an *s, t,* or *n.* Show students examples of other words that start with a silent *p.* (psalm, psychic, pneumonia)

Kinds of Treatment

L4 Cooperative Learning

Have students work in groups to create a multimedia presentation about the methods of treating mental disorders described in the text. Encourage students to do research to find additional information to add to their presentations.

3. Assess

Evaluate

These assignments can help you assess students' mastery of the section content.

Section 4 Review

Answers appear below.

Teaching Resources
• Practice 4-4
• Section 4-4 Quiz

L2 Reteach

Have students work in pairs, with one student quizzing the other about the mental health professionals described in the text. Then, have students reverse roles to review the information about treatments for mental disorders.

L4 Enrich

Teaching Resources
• Enrich 4-4

Health at Home

Views on Mental Illness Remind students to keep specific responses from family members confidential. After students finish the assignment, discuss attitudes toward mental illness. Ask students if, based on their interviews, they think these attitudes have changed and, if so, why.

FIGURE 16 One type of therapy is group therapy. The counselor works with a group of people who have similar mental disorders.

Kinds of Treatments

How does a mental health professional decide which treatment method, or therapy, to use? Some disorders and some patients respond better to some treatments than to others. **Psychotherapy, drug therapy, and hospitalization are three methods used to treat mental disorders.**

Psychotherapy During psychotherapy (sy koh THEHR uh pee), a person talks with a therapist. These talks help people understand and overcome their mental disorders. Three types of psychotherapy are:

▶ **Insight Therapy** This type of therapy helps people better understand the reasons for their behavior. The hope is that, with this insight, they will be able to change some of their behaviors.

▶ **Cognitive and Behavioral Therapy** This type of therapy helps a person to identify situations, objects, or thoughts that trigger abnormal behaviors. The goal is for the patient to learn new ways to behave.

▶ **Group Therapy** In group therapy, people meet with other people who have similar disorders. A mental health professional leads the group. Group members work together to develop coping skills.

Drug Therapy Doctors prescribe drugs to treat many mental disorders. The drugs can relieve symptoms and allow patients to function normally. Drug therapy and psychotherapy may be used together.

Hospitalization Sometimes people with mental disorders need constant attention or are in danger of harming themselves or others. These people may have to be treated in a hospital. In the hospital, patients receive therapy. The staff helps patients prepare to leave the hospital. When patients return home, social workers often help them adjust to the change.

Section 4 Review

Key Ideas and Vocabulary

1. State three reasons why someone might not seek help for a mental disorder.
2. Briefly describe four types of mental health professionals.
3. What three general methods are used to treat mental disorders?

Critical Thinking

4. Relating Cause and Effect Why might a person with a mental disorder end up in a hospital?

Health at Home

Views on Mental Illness Talk with some adults in your family about their attitudes toward mental illness. Do they think of mental disorders in the same way that they think of other illnesses? Have their attitudes about mental illness changed over the years? Write a paragraph summarizing what you find out. **WRITING**

5. Classifying In what type of therapy are people most likely to discuss their childhood experiences? Explain.

GO ONLINE PearsonSuccessNet.com   Audio Summary Section 4.4

Section 4 Review

1. not recognizing symptoms, believing that mental disorders can be overcome using willpower, not knowing how to get help
2. psychiatrist: a physician who treats mental disorders; clinical psychologist: trained to treat abnormal behavior; social worker: an advisor and link to community resources; mental health counselor: works with specific problems or specific groups of people
3. psychotherapy, drug therapy, hospitalization
4. needs constant attention or is in danger of harming himself or herself and others
5. *Sample answer:* Childhood experiences are most likely to be discussed in insight therapy, because this therapy helps people understand the reasons for their behavior.

Chapter 4
At a Glance

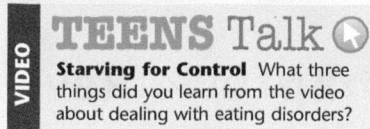
TEENS Talk
VIDEO
Starving for Control What three things did you learn from the video about dealing with eating disorders?

Chapter 4
At a Glance

VIDEO
Starving for Control Ask for volunteers to share their answers. Then, use examples from the video to review eating disorders.

Section 1   Mental Disorders

Key Ideas

▶ Mental health experts see abnormal thoughts, feelings, or behaviors as signs of a mental disorder.

▶ Physical factors, heredity, early experiences, and recent experiences can cause mental disorders.

▶ Anxiety disorders include generalized anxiety disorder, phobias, panic attacks, obsessive-compulsive disorders, and post-traumatic stress disorder.

▶ Some teens have mood disorders, schizophrenia, impulse-control disorders, or personality disorders.

Vocabulary

• mental disorder (82)
• anxiety (84)
• anxiety disorder (84)
• phobia (84)
• obsession (85)
• compulsion (85)
• mood disorder (86)
• depression (86)
• schizophrenia (86)
• personality disorder (88)

Section 2   Eating Disorders

Key Ideas

▶ A person with anorexia can starve to death or die from a lack of essential minerals.

▶ Bulimia may begin in connection to a diet, but the person soon becomes unable to stop the cycle of bingeing and purging.

▶ The main physical risks of binge eating disorder are excess weight gain and unhealthy dieting.

Vocabulary

• eating disorder (90) • anorexia nervosa (90)
• bulimia (92) • binge eating disorder (93)

Section 3   Depression and Suicide

Key Ideas

▶ Depression can cause problems at school, at home, and with one's social life. If untreated, depression can also lead to substance abuse, serious behavior problems, and even suicide.

▶ Self-injury is an unhealthy way to cope with emotions, stress, or traumatic events.

▶ Mood disorders are a major risk factor for suicide.

Vocabulary

• clinical depression (94)
• cutting (96) • suicide (96)
• cluster suicides (97)

Section 4   Treating Mental Disorders

Key Ideas

▶ Sometimes people don't recognize the signs of a mental disorder. Or they may not know where to go for help.

▶ Psychiatrists, clinical psychologists, social workers, and mental health counselors are four types of mental health professionals.

▶ Psychotherapy, drug therapy, and hospitalization are three methods used to treat mental disorders.

Vocabulary

• psychiatrist (103) • neurologist (103)
• clinical psychologist (103)
• psychiatric social worker (103) • therapy (104)

Key Ideas Review

L2 Have students fold a piece of notebook paper in quarters. Then have them open the paper. In the four sections of the paper, ask students to summarize each section of the chapter with a bulleted list of main ideas.

L1 Ask students to work in small groups to verbally review the main ideas of the chapter. Allow students to skim their texts for ideas as they review.

Vocabulary Review

EL Have students use a word processing program to make a glossary containing chapter vocabulary terms and their definitions. Allow students to work with a partner to complete this activity.

L2 Ask students to use the vocabulary terms to write four sentences. Each sentence should clearly explain the relationship between two different vocabulary terms.

Chapter 4 Review

GO ONLINE

PearsonSuccessNet.com

Students can go online for a review activity on Chapter 4.

Reviewing Key Ideas

Section 1

1. b   **2.** c

3. *Sample answer:* Experiencing or witnessing a disaster could trigger post-traumatic stress disorder.

4. All personality disorders involve rigid behavior patterns that make it difficult for an individual to get along with others.

5. *Sample answer:* The break from reality that is associated with schizophrenia severely affects a person's ability to function, a key characteristic of a mental disorder.

Section 2

6. c

7. Some possible causes of anorexia include a lack of a chemical that regulates mood, low self-esteem, a strong desire to please others, and a history of troubled relationships.

8. Bulimia and binge eating disorder both involve uncontrolled eating binges. With bulimia, the binges are followed by purging.

9. *Sample answer:* People with an eating disorder display behaviors that cause them distress and affect their ability to function.

Section 3

10. c

11. Untreated depression is a major factor for suicide.

12. *Sample answer:* Having close relationships provides a support system that can help you deal with difficult times. It also provides people who will help you recognize when to seek professional help for a problem.

13. No, it is normal for people to feel depressed for short periods of time.

Chapter 4 Review

Reviewing Key Ideas

GO ONLINE

PearsonSuccessNet.com

For: Chapter 4 review activity

Section 1

1. Claustrophobia is an example of a(n)
  a. mood disorder.   **b.** anxiety disorder.
  c. personality disorder.   **d.** impulse-control disorder.

2. An unreasonable need to behave in a certain way is called a(n)
  a. obsession.   **b.** phobia.
  c. compulsion.   **d.** panic attack.

3. Give an example of how an experience in a person's life could trigger a mental disorder.

4. What is the common factor in all personality disorders?

5. Critical Thinking Use the definition of a mental disorder to explain why schizophrenia is a serious mental disorder.

Section 2

6. An eating disorder marked by bingeing and purging is
  a. anorexia nervosa.   **b.** binge eating disorder.
  c. bulimia.   **d.** yo-yo dieting.

7. What are some possible causes of anorexia?

8. How are bulimia and binge eating disorder similar? How are they different?

9. Critical Thinking Why do you think that eating disorders are classified as mental disorders? Do you agree with this classification? Explain.

Section 3

10. A person with clinical depression
  a. feels sad now and then.
  b. feels extremely sad for a week.
  c. feels sad or hopeless for months.
  d. still tends to find enjoyment in life.

11. What is the link between depression and suicide?

12. How can having close relationships help you stay mentally healthy?

13. Critical Thinking You feel depressed at times, but always snap out of it quickly. Should you seek help? Why or why not?

Section 4

14. Which mental health professional acts as a link between a patient and community resources?
  a. psychologist   **b.** psychiatrist
  c. social worker   **d.** neurologist

15. How are mental and physical disorders similar?

16. How are psychotherapy and drug therapy similar? How are they different?

17. Critical Thinking Families of people with mental disorders often need support and counseling. Why do you think this is so?

Building Health Skills

18. Analyzing Influences Many works of fiction focus on characters with mental disorders. What positive or negative effects could reading about these characters have on readers?

19. Communicating People who are hospitalized for mental disorders may be released to "halfway houses." At the halfway house, they learn to readjust to life in the community. What would you say if someone objected to having a halfway house in your neighborhood?

20. Setting Goals Make a list of qualities that are important in someone you could confide in. Then use the list to evaluate yourself. Make an action plan to be a better confidant. Decide on steps you can take to improve your communication and listening skills. Monitor your progress and adjust your action plan, if necessary. **WRITING**

Health and Community

Suicide and Older Adults The suicide rate is high among adults over age 65. One of the risk factors for older adults is a sense of isolation. What does your community do to reduce feelings of isolation among older adults? Are there ways you can help? Write a paragraph summarizing what you find out. **WRITING**

Building Health Skills

18. *Sample answer:* Positive effect: the readers learn about mental disorders. Negative effect: depiction of mental disorders is inaccurate or negative.

19. *Sample answer:* People in a half-way house are supervised, not released directly into the community.

20. Students' plans should include a realistic goal for improving skills.

Section 4

14. c

15. They both require treatment by medical professionals.

16. Both are used to treat mental disorders. Psychotherapy helps people understand and overcome their disorders; drug therapy relieves symptoms.

17. *Sample answer:* Coping with a family member who has a mental disorder is stressful for other family members.

Standardized Test Prep

Math Practice

The risk of developing schizophrenia changes when different family members have the disorder. Use the graph to answer Questions 21–23.

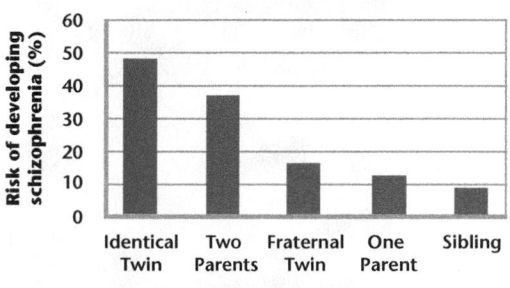

Heredity as a Risk Factor for Schizophrenia

21. What is the risk of developing schizophrenia if one parent has the disorder?
    A 9%   B 12%
    C 16%   D 45%

22. When is a person at greatest risk for developing schizophrenia?
    F when one parent has the disorder
    G when two parents have the disorder
    H when any sibling has the disorder
    J when an identical twin has the disorder

23. How does the risk of having an identical twin with schizophrenia compare to the risk of having a fraternal twin with schizophrenia?
    A The risk is the same.
    B The risk is twice as great.
    C The risk is three times as great.
    D The risk is four times as great.

Test-Taking Tip

When taking a test, answer the easy questions first. This approach can boost your confidence.

Reading and Writing Practice

Read the passage. Then answer Questions 24–27.

A lack of natural light can cause seasonal affective disorder (SAD). As the supply of natural light decreases in winter, people with SAD become depressed. Unlike some depressed people, who have trouble eating and sleeping, SAD patients may sleep up to 18 hours a day, crave starchy foods, and gain weight. Treatment for SAD involves phototherapy, exposure to a full range of bright lights, for 10–30 minutes a day. For up to 70 percent of SAD sufferers, the treatment restores the balance of chemicals in the body, which relieves the symptoms of SAD.

24. What is the main idea of this passage?
    A Depression is caused by a lack of natural light.
    B A lack of natural light causes one kind of depression.
    C Phototherapy can cure all types of depression.
    D Phototherapy can cure all cases of SAD.

25. From this passage, you can infer that a lack of natural light
    F decreases certain chemicals in the body.
    G increases certain chemicals in the body.
    H restores the balance of chemicals in the body.
    J upsets the balance of chemicals in the body.

26. Which statement is supported by this passage?
    A Some symptoms of SAD are not typical of depression.
    B Most depressed people crave starchy foods.
    C Sleeping for 18 hours is a typical sign of depression.
    D SAD and clinical depression are similar disorders.

Constructed Response

27. There is a type of SAD that occurs in the summer when the hours of daylight increase. Write a paragraph predicting what the symptoms of summer SAD might be.

Mental Disorders and Suicide **107**

Standardized Test Prep

Math Practice
21. B
22. J
23. C

Reading and Writing Practice
24. B
25. J
26. A
27. *Sample answer:* The symptoms of summer SAD are insomnia, weight loss, and decreased appetite, essentially the opposite of the symptoms of winter SAD. Accept any well-supported prediction.

Health and Community

Suicide and Older Adults If students cannot locate programs in their community that clearly address this issue, ask students to propose a program they think would be helpful. Also remind students to suggest ways that they can help seniors.

Mental Health

Teaching Strategies

- Elicit from students a list of personal traits that they think are important for careers in mental health. Ask: **What adjectives describe someone you would prefer to speak with about a personal problem?** *(Sample answers: kind, caring, sympathetic, thoughtful, understanding)* Discuss why these traits are important for careers in mental health.

- Have students read the feature, and then challenge the class to brainstorm other careers in mental health. *(Possible careers might include psychiatric nurse, child psychologist, and substance abuse counselor.)* Call on volunteers to share anything they know about these other mental health careers.

- If students find a career in mental health that interests them, have them research the required qualifications for this career. Suggest that students set a short-term goal that would help them meet this long-term career goal, and write an action plan.

CAREERS

Mental Health

Some mental health workers help treat people with mental disorders. Others help people deal with stress and anxiety.

Recreational Therapist

Recreational therapists use activities as therapy. Activities can include art, dance, music, or sports. The goal may be to reduce anxiety, build confidence, and develop social skills. Recreational therapists help patients express themselves. For example, they may teach people to communicate their feelings through dance movements. This career usually requires a bachelor's degree, but some jobs require only an associate degree.

Social Worker

Some social workers assist people with mental disorders by providing counseling for patients and their families. They may help people who have been in a hospital adjust to life back in the community. For example, a social worker may help a person find a job or enroll in school. Many social workers have a master's degree in social work and are licensed and certified by their states.

Psychiatric Aide

A psychiatric aide helps care for people who have mental disorders. The aide helps patients with basic functions such as eating, dressing, and personal grooming. An important part of the job is to socialize with patients during activities and to observe their behavior. Entry into this career requires a high school degree.

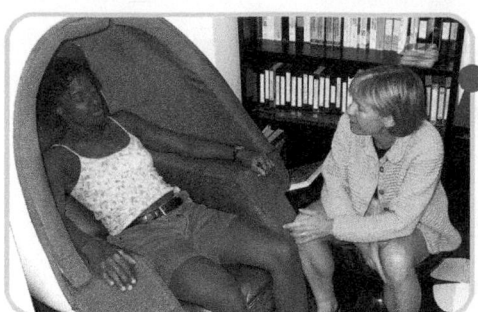

Sport Psychologist

Sport psychologists work with athletes to improve their performance. They teach athletes to use relaxation and mental rehearsal to cope with the stress of competition. They help athletes increase their motivation, confidence, and focus. A sport psychologist must know about both the mind and the body. This career requires at least a master's degree. Certification by the Association for the Advancement of Applied Sport Psychology (AAASP) is recommended.

Career Focus

Kirsten Peterson, Sport Psychologist for the U.S. Olympic Committee

How did you get interested in sport psychology?
"In high school I was a softball pitcher. In college, I suddenly could not throw a strike. It was a very difficult experience and there was no one available to help me. I was studying psychology then when I learned about the field of sport psychology. I realized this was a way for me to help athletes deal with difficult sport experiences like mine."

Where do you work and which athletes do you work with?
"I work for the U.S. Olympic Training Committee in Colorado Springs. In the summer, I work with the wrestling teams. In the winter, I work with the bobsled and skeleton teams. I attend my teams' practices and I travel with the teams quite a lot."

What do you do as a sport psychologist?
"I help Olympic athletes develop their mental skills so they can perform at a higher level. I help them to recognize and manage their anxiety in competition. I teach athletes how to quickly refocus when difficult situations happen; this can save critical time in a competition. I also counsel them on their regular life issues so that they can focus and do their job."

Health and Careers

Careers in Mental Health Research other careers in mental health. Choose a career that interests you and explain why your personality would be a good match for this career. **WRITING**

Health and Careers

Careers in Mental Health A good source of information about careers is the *Occupational Outlook Handbook* (OOH). This resource is published by the Bureau of Labor Statistics and is available online. Share the resource with students, and suggest that they use it for careers mentioned throughout the book. After students choose a career that interests them, they should identify personality traits that would suit a person for that career. Suggest that students use specific examples to show that they have the requisite personality traits for the careers they choose.

109

Section Objectives	Standards Correlation	Instructional Resources L3	SE eTEXT	TE eTEXT	PRINT
1 Families Today ⏲ 2 periods; 1 block 5.1.1 **Explain** why healthy family relationships are important. 5.1.2 **Identify** three main factors that have changed the form of families. 5.1.3 **Describe** some family forms that exist today. 5.1.4 **Summarize** the division of responsibilities within a family.	NHES: 2.12.1, 2.12.2, 2.12.6, 2.12.7	SE Warm-Up, p. 112	•	•	•
		SE Technology & Health How's Your Driving?, p. 118	•	•	•
		RN Note Taking Guide 5-1	•	•	•
		TR Practice 5-1		•	
		TR Section 5-1 Quiz		•	
2 Family Problems ⏲ 1 period; 1/2 block 5.2.1 **List** some causes of stress in families. 5.2.2 **Describe** three types of abuse that can happen in families. 5.2.3 **Explain** what problems runaways are likely to have.	NHES: 2.12.1, 3.12.2, 3.12.4, 7.12.1, 8.12.4	SE Warm-Up, p. 119	•	•	•
		RN Note Taking Guide 5-2	•	•	•
		IB Image Bank 5-5		•	
		TR Practice 5-2		•	
		TR Section 5-2 Quiz		•	
Using Win-Win Negotiation ⏲ 1 period; 1/2 block BHS.5 **Demonstrate** how win-win negotiation can be used to resolve conflicts in families.	NHES: 4.12.1, 4.12.2, 4.12.3	SE Practice the Skill, p. 125	•	•	•
		RN Building Health Skills 5	•	•	•
3 Keeping the Family Healthy ⏲ 2 periods; 1 block 5.3.1 **List** some characteristics of healthy families. 5.3.2 **Describe** four skills families need to stay healthy. 5.3.3 **Identify** places where families can go for help with their problems.	NHES: 2.12.1, 3.12.3, 3.12.4, 4.12.1, 4.12.3, 5.12.3, 8.12.3	SE Warm-Up, p. 126	•	•	•
		SE Hands-On Activity Group Juggling, p. 129	•	•	•
		RN Note Taking Guide 5-3	•	•	•
		TR Practice 5-3		•	
		TR Section 5-3 Quiz		•	

Chapter Review and Assessment

SE Chapter 5 Review, p. 132 L3

CTB Chapter 5 Test L2 L3 L4

SE Standardized Test Prep, p. 133 L3

Program Components

SE Student Edition	**CTB** Computer Test Bank
TE Teacher Edition	**AUD** Audio Section Summaries
TR Teaching Resources	
RN Reading and Note Taking Guide	**DVD** Teens Talk Video Series
ARN Adapted Reading and Note Taking Guide	**VVG** Video Viewing Guide
	PPT Presentation
IB Image Bank	

Differentiated Instruction

L1 L2 L4 EL

		SE eTEXT	TE eTEXT	PRINT
ARN	Note Taking Guide 5-1 L2	•	•	
RN	Note Taking Guide 5-1 EL	•	•	•
AUD	Audio Summary 5-1 L1 L2 EL	•	•	
TE	Reteach Strategy, p. 117 L2		•	•
TR	Enrich 5-1 L4		•	
ARN	Note Taking Guide 5-2 L2	•	•	
RN	Note Taking Guide 5-2 EL	•	•	•
AUD	Audio Summary 5-2 L1 L2 EL	•	•	
TE	Reteach Strategy, p. 123 L2		•	•
TR	Enrich 5-2 L4		•	
ARN	Building Health Skills 5 L2	•	•	
RN	Building Health Skills 5 EL	•	•	•
ARN	Note Taking Guide 5-3 L2	•	•	
RN	Note Taking Guide 5-3 EL	•	•	•
AUD	Audio Summary 5-3 L1 L2 EL	•	•	
TE	Reteach Strategy, p. 130 L2		•	•
TR	Enrich 5-3 L4		•	

ABILITY LEVELS

L1 **For students with special needs**

L2 **For less proficient readers**

L3 **For all students**

L4 **For gifted and talented students**

EL **For English language learners**

Chapter 5 Digital/Video Pathway

This alternative pathway allows you to teach this chapter's content using only the video and online materials.

Preview

DVD	**Video #5 Preview**
SE	Video #5 Preview Activity
VVG	Video #5 Worksheet

Family Matters

1

PPT	5-1 Presentation
RN/ARN	5-1 Note Taking
PPT	5-1 Section Quiz

2

DVD	**Video #5 Explore/Wrap-Up**
VVG	Video #5 Worksheet
PPT	5-2 Presentation
RN/ARN	5-2 Note Taking
PPT	5-2 Section Quiz

Family Matters

3

PPT	5-3 Presentation
RN/ARN	5-3 Note Taking
PPT	5-3 Section Quiz

Chapter Preview

Section 1 Families Today
The family is the basic unit of society, in which children first learn to relate to others. An increased number of women in the workforce, a high divorce rate, and the postponement of marriage have caused changes in the American family. Although their forms vary, all families share some important qualities. Within a family, both adults and children have responsibilities.

Section 2 Family Problems
Financial problems, illness, divorce, and drug abuse are all sources of stress in families. Violence in the family may take the form of physical, sexual, or emotional abuse. Children who leave home without permission for a period of time face serious risks.

 Communicating
Using Win-Win Negotiation
Win-win negotiation can be used to resolve family conflicts.

Section 3 Keeping the Family Healthy
Characteristics of healthy families include commitment, respect, empathy, communication, and cooperation. Skills used by healthy families include resolving conflicts, expressing emotions, making decisions, and managing time. When families face problems that seem overwhelming, they can get help from family agencies, family therapists, and support groups.

GO ONLINE
PearsonSuccessNet.com
For resources and activities for this chapter.

Family Relationships

1 Families Today
 • **Technology & Health** *How's Your Driving?*

2 Family Problems
 • **Building Health Skills**
  • **Communicating** Using Win-Win Negotiation

3 Keeping the Family Healthy
 • **Hands-On Activity** Group Juggling

GO ONLINE PearsonSuccessNet.com

TEENS Talk

VIDEO 5

Family Matters

Preview **Activity**

What Causes Tension in a Family?

Complete this activity before you watch the video.

1. Parents and teens may disagree about a number of things. Rank the following areas of possible disagreement from 1 (most likely) to 8 (least likely) to be a source of tension between parents and teens.
   ___ privacy   ___ appearance
   ___ chores   ___ friends
   ___ grades   ___ music
   ___ money   ___ curfew
2. Are there other areas of disagreement that should be added to the list? If so, what are they and where would you rank them?
3. Are you sometimes the cause of tension in your family? If so, how? **WRITING**

110

Sensitive Issues
 • Topics such as divorce, abuse, and financial problems can be difficult for students to discuss, even when the scenarios are hypothetical. Before you discuss these topics, you might want to caution students to avoid revealing sensitive, personal information during class discussions.

 • Students may want to discuss their family problems with you. In some cases, you might need to consult with the guidance counselor, school nurse, principal, or other school officials to avoid legal problems. In all states, teachers are mandated reporters of suspected abuse and neglect.

111

VIDEO 5

TEENS Talk

Family Matters

Video Objectives

Use this video to help students

Recognize that change is a part of family life.

Analyze the short-term and long-term effects of changes within the family.

Identify the skills they need in order to cope with changes in their families.

Preview **Activity**

What Causes Tension in a Family?

Assign the Preview Activity for homework a few days before you plan to show the video. After students complete the assignment, list the possible areas of disagreement on the board. Tally students' responses by determining how many number 1 ratings each area received. Ask what other possible areas of disagreement students identified. Have volunteers explain why they think a particular area is a likely source of tension in families.

From the Authors

About one-half of the students in most public school classrooms in the United States are not living with both biological parents. This means that those of us who teach health must be sensitive to the varied family structures in which our students live.

Most topics in this chapter—for example, responsibilities within the family, causes of family stress, characteristics of a healthy family, and useful skills for families—are presented in ways that are applicable to all families. See, for example, the Hands-On activity on page 129.

Objectives
Before class begins, write the objectives on the board. Have students copy the objectives into their notebooks at the start of class.

1. Focus

Warm-Up Health Stats

Ask a volunteer to describe the trend shown in the graph. Then have students complete the writing assignment. Call on volunteers to share their writing with the class. Keep a list on the board of factors students identify as causes for the trend in the graph. Point out that the family is still the basic unit of society, even when there are changes in family structure.

Presentation 5-1

2. Teach

L3 **EL** Reading/Note Taking 5-1

L2 Adapted Reading/Note Taking 5-1

The Family and Social Health

L2 **Cooperative Learning**
Have students work in small groups to develop a list of at least ten words that could be used to describe families or aspects of family life. Then, have each group share its list with the class. Ask students to identify words found on more than one groups' list. Challenge students to explain why these words were chosen by more than one group.

Connect to Your Life *Sample answer:* Yes, I agree, because the family is where children learn the basic skills of social health.

Section 1
Families Today

Objectives
► **Explain** why healthy family relationships are important.
► **Identify** three main factors that have changed the form of families.
► **Describe** some family forms that exist today.
► **Summarize** the division of responsibilities within a family.

Vocabulary
- divorce
- nuclear family
- adoption
- single-parent family
- extended family
- blended family
- foster family
- socialization

Warm-Up

Health Stats How have the number of households with a married couple and their children changed over time?

Married Couples With Children

(bar graph: Percentage of total households vs. year)
- 1970: 40
- 1980: 31
- 1990: 26
- 2000: 23
- 2010: 20

y-axis: 0, 20, 25, 30, 35, 40

WRITING What might have caused the trend you identified?

The Family and Social Health

The family is often called the "basic unit of society." It is the structure within which children are raised, and values and customs are passed from generation to generation. The family is also the basic unit of social health because it is where a person first learns to relate to other people. **If the relationships with family members are healthy, a child learns to love, respect, and get along with others, and to function as part of a group.**

In a family, a child can see that each person depends on the others in the group. One person's actions can affect everyone else in the family. Ideally, the child learns that lasting relationships must be based on mutual caring, trust, and support. People often use the relationships they observe and participate in at home as a model for relationships outside the home.

Families are part of larger social units that influence what happens within families. For example, a family often shares many of the traditions, values, and views on relationships of its cultural group. The neighborhood a family lives in can affect how much freedom children are given to explore the area beyond their home. Where a parent works can affect how much time the parent has to spend with his or her children.

 **Connect to Your Life** Do you agree that the family is the basic unit of society? Why or why not?

For Your INFORMATION!

Divorce Rates

In the United States, the divorce rate is high, but not 50 percent—a figure calculated by comparing the number of marriages in a given year to the number of divorces. Social scientists look at how many people who were ever married eventually got a divorce. By this method, the rate has never been higher than 41 percent.

After more than a century of rising divorce rates, the rates stopped rising around 1980. The overall divorce rate does not reveal the trends in different populations. Since 1980, for example, the divorce rate among women with college degrees has declined sharply, but the rate among women who do not have college degrees has held steady.

FIGURE 1 As families change, both men and women have different options. Some men choose to stay at home to care for their children.

Today, fathers account for over 3% of all stay-at-home parents.

The Changing Family

Until the mid-1800s, parents both stayed home, farming or working at trades, and both shared in raising the children. The Industrial Revolution changed things—men went to work in factories and offices while most women stayed home. Today, fewer than 10 percent of families in the United States fit this model. **Three main factors account for changes in the American family: more women in the work force, a high divorce rate, and an increase in the age at which people marry.**

More Women in the Work Force   Today, more than half of all mothers with preschool children are in the work force. Women work outside the home for different reasons. Some are single parents, others want to continue a career, or the family needs two incomes to pay the bills. When parents work outside the home, families spend less time together. The parents have to trust other people to care for their children.

High Divorce Rate   Each year, many children experience their parents' divorce. A **divorce** is a legal agreement to end a marriage. In most states, it is easier to get a divorce now than in the past because of "no-fault" divorce. With this type of divorce, neither person is blamed for the divorce. There is some positive news. Since 1990, the divorce rate has gradually decreased.

   Divorce affects a family's structure, finances, and health—emotional and physical. Family members have to adjust to new roles, relationships, and living arrangements. If a parent remarries, the adjustments continue.

Postponing Marriage   Today many young people delay marriage and parenthood until later in life. As a result, families tend to be smaller. Most women have two children, and a growing number have none. In contrast, in the 1950s women had three or four children, on average.

Family Relationships **113**

Family Forms

Visual Learning: Figure 2

Caption Answer Each family consists of children and at least one adult. The number of adults and their relationship to the children varies among families.

L1 Active Learning

Provide students with discarded magazines, and ask them to find and cut out pictures that show different family forms. Have students use the pictures to create a collage. Ask students to add vocabulary terms from the textbook to label the families in their collages. Then have each student describe his or her collage to a partner or to the class. Challenge students to explain why they chose the labels that they used.

L3 Cooperative Learning

Ask students to work in small groups to identify various forms of families found in books with which they are familiar. Challenge students to find an example of each type of family described in the text. Have each group share its examples with the class. Ask students if it was difficult to find examples of some forms.

Nuclear Family

Single-Parent Family

FIGURE 2 Families come in many forms and sizes.
Comparing and Contrasting
How are these four families similar? How are they different?

Family Forms

The word that best describes families today is *diversity*. Families reflect the diverse circumstances, needs, values, and cultures of the people in them. **Children can live in nuclear, single-parent, extended, blended, or foster families.** As you read about these family forms, think about the important qualities that all families share.

Nuclear Family   A **nuclear family** consists of a couple and their child or children living together in one household. The children may be the parents' biological children, or they may have been adopted. **Adoption** is the legal process by which parents take another person's child into their family to be raised as their own.

Single-Parent Family   About half of all children today will live, at least for a time, in single-parent families. A **single-parent family** is a family in which only one parent lives with the child or children. Some single-parent families are the result of divorce. Other single-parent families form when one parent dies, when parents never marry, or when a single person adopts a child.

Mothers head about 85 percent of single-parent families. However, a growing number of fathers are raising children on their own. Caring for the family alone can be difficult for single parents. They must earn a living, care for children, and perform all the other tasks needed to keep the family functioning. Financial worries are often a major problem in single-parent families.

Extended Family   A nuclear or single-parent family may be part of a larger family unit. An **extended family** is a group of close relatives living together or near each other. The extended family often includes grandparents, aunts, uncles, or cousins.

114   *Chapter 5*

TEENS *Are Asking . . .*

Q: I live with my mother, stepfather, and a younger stepbrother. My stepfather is harder on me than he is on his own son. How can I get some fair treatment and positive attention from my stepfather?

A: Your stepfather may expect more of you because you are older. Also, he may not be aware that he treats you differently.

Try to find ways to spend time alone with your stepfather doing something that you both enjoy doing. As he begins to know you better, he may learn to trust you more, and you may be able to share your feelings in a respectful way. Also share your concerns with your mother so she can help you solve this problem. If things do not improve, you may want to talk with a counselor.

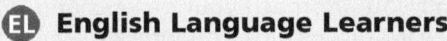
Extended Family

Blended Family

In extended families, family responsibilities are shared among all members. Children might be raised by their grandparents, aunts, and uncles as well as by their parents. Extended families provide a strong system of support for family members. For single parents, especially, this extra support helps strengthen the family.

Blended Family   When parents remarry, they form a blended family. A **blended family** consists of a biological parent, a stepparent, and the children of one or both parents. A stepparent is a parent related by marriage. Today, at least five million children under the age of 18 live in blended families.

In blended families, the usual problems of families may become more complex. Children may feel that a stepparent is an intruder and not really part of the family. Children may have trouble getting along with stepbrothers and stepsisters. Successful blended families say that it is important to be flexible. Parents need to spend time with their biological children, their stepchildren, and the entire family group.

Foster Family   In a **foster family,** an adult or couple cares for children whose biological parents are unable to care for them. The foster family provides a temporary home for the children. Some children remain in a foster family for an extended time. Sometimes foster parents are able to adopt the children in their care.

Other Families   Other groups of people also are considered families. One example is a married couple without any children. Another is a group of unrelated people who choose to live together and support and care for one another.

 Which family forms most closely match your family and those of your friends?

> **GO ONLINE**
> PearsonSuccessNet.com
> **For:** More on families

L3 Journal Writing

Have students write an entry in their private journals that identifies and describes challenges of the particular family structure in which they live. Remind students that a *challenge* is not always a *problem*, but it does require extra effort. Then have students reflect on and record one way they could help the family manage the identified challenge. **WRITING**

L4 Active Learning

Ask students to work in small groups to prepare a multimedia project that shows various types of families. Challenge students to convey the factual information found in the text in a creative and accurate way. Encourage students to use presentation software to prepare their project. Ask each group to share its presentation with the class.

Connect to Your Life   Allow students to answer this question in their private journals.

L3 Online Activity

Visit Pearson SuccessNet to access an online activity about families. Have students complete the Web activity.

Differentiated Instruction

EL English Language Learners

Provide each student with six index cards. Have students use the index cards to organize the information about various family forms. On each index card, students should write the term that describes a particular type of family.

Then, ask students to draw a picture on the card to help them remember each type of family. Students can use stick figures, other symbols, or graphic organizers. Have students review the information on their index cards with a partner.

Responsibilities Within the Family

L3 **Visual Learning: Figure 3**

Begin to discuss responsibilities by asking volunteers to share their answers to the caption question. Point out that the rules that work for one family might not be right for another family. Family and cultural traditions can affect the rules in a given family. Ask students to suggest other factors that could affect the rules.

Caption Answer Students may say the rules are fair because they set reasonable expectations for a teenager, or the rules are not fair because they are too rigid.

EL **Building Vocabulary**

To help students understand and recall the meaning of *socialization*, use related terms that may be more familiar, such as *society* or *sociable*.

L3 **Active Learning**

Ask students to make a poster that could be used to teach younger children about the benefits of shared responsibilities in a family. If possible, arrange for the posters to be displayed in a hallway or other public area.

Connect to Your Life Allow students to answer this question in their private journals.

Typical Household Rules
- No watching television or playing video games before homework is done or after bedtime.
- Be home by 10 P.M. on weekdays and by midnight on weekends.
- Keep your room clean, take out the trash, and do other chores.
- Only use the internet for school work before homework is done.
- No friends over when an adult isn't home, without permission.

FIGURE 3 In a family, children are often responsible for assigned chores. One of the responsibilities of adults is to set rules for children. **Evaluating** Do you think the rules in this list are fair? Why or why not?

Responsibilities Within the Family

For a family to function effectively, each member of the family must do his or her part. Each family divides up responsibilities in its own way. **Often there are some responsibilities that clearly belong to the adults, some that clearly belong to the children, and some that can be shared.**

Adults' Responsibilities The heads of families are expected to provide for their children's basic needs. These needs include food, clothing, shelter, education, health care, security, and love. When children's basic needs are met, they feel loved and secure, and they gain self-esteem.

Adult family members are also responsible for teaching children to behave in a way that is acceptable to the family and to society. This process is called **socialization** (soh shuh lih ZAY shun). Through this process, children develop into responsible adults. They learn to respect the rights of others and to give and receive love. They also absorb the values, beliefs, and customs that are important to their families.

Adult family members set rules to protect their children's safety and to maintain order within the family. Figure 3 lists some typical rules that parents may set for teenage children.

 **Connect to Your Life** What kinds of tasks are the adults in your family responsible for doing?

TEENS *Are Asking . . .*

Q: I think I'm old enough to set my own rules, but my parents don't agree. How can I get them to change their minds?

A: Your parents still have the responsibility to set rules that will help protect your safety. But it is reasonable for you to want to be involved in developing some of these rules.

Why don't you approach your parents and ask if they would include you when they discuss and establish rules? If your parents agree to include you in the discussion, be sure to demonstrate maturity, honesty, and open-mindedness. Then, follow the agreed-upon rules so that you establish and build your parents' trust in you.

Children's Responsibilities   As a young child, you may have been responsible for dressing yourself, tidying up your room, and doing your homework. Today, you may have to do household chores or care for younger brothers and sisters. You may even add to the family income with earnings from a part-time job. You are also responsible for following family rules and for showing respect for all family members.

At times, young people may disagree with some of the rules set by their parents. For example, teens may want to stay out later on weeknights or weekends. Disagreements may also arise between brothers and sisters. They may argue about items that must be shared, such as a computer.

When such conflicts arise, family members need to discuss their problems in a calm, respectful manner. If each member recognizes the need for rules and limits that are satisfactory to all, it will be easier to work together to resolve the conflict. The Building Health Skills on pages 124–125 teaches a method for resolving conflicts.

Shared Responsibilities   In most families, there never seems to be enough time for chores. Many families divide up the responsibilities. For example, each person may prepare dinner one night a week. Children may take turns doing the laundry or grocery shopping. All family members may help care for elderly or disabled family members.

There are other benefits to sharing household chores. Children can master skills such as cooking that will be vital to them as adults. Children who are trusted with important tasks develop a sense of responsibility and higher self-esteem. Most importantly, family members learn that the family is stronger when they work as a team and depend on each other.

FIGURE 4   When family members share chores they learn to depend on one another and work as a team.

Section 1 Review

Key Ideas and Vocabulary

1. Explain why the family is called the basic unit of social health.
2. What are the three main factors that account for changes in the American family? Give an example of the impact of each factor.
3. What is a **blended family?** What other types of families exist?
4. What is **socialization?** Which family members are responsible for this process?

Critical Thinking

5. **Evaluating** List three tasks that you are responsible for in your family. How do these tasks help prepare you for adulthood?

Health at School

Responsibilities In some ways, a school is like a family. The responsibilities are divided between students and teachers. Make a list of things you think teachers are responsible for at school. Make a second list of things that students are responsible for. Do students and teachers have any shared responsibilities? **WRITING**

6. **Predicting** Sankong lives with his father, who is divorced. The father is about to marry a woman with two teenage sons. They will all live in Sankong's apartment. List the possible advantages and disadvantages of this change for Sankong. How could focusing on the advantages help Sankong cope with the change? **WRITING**

3. Assess

Evaluate

These assignments can help you assess students' mastery of the section content.

Section 1 Review

Answers appear below.

Teaching Resources

• Practice 5-1
• Section 5-1 Quiz

L2 Reteach

Ask students to prepare a Venn diagram that organizes the information about responsibilities within the family. Have students label one side of the diagram Adults' Responsibilities and the other side Children's Responsibilities. The intersecting region should be labeled Shared Responsibilities.

L4 Enrich

Teaching Resources

• Enrich 5-1

Health at School

Responsibilities Introduce the activity by providing one obvious choice for each list. Then, ask students to prepare their lists as described. After students have completed their writing, ask volunteers to share their responses with the class. Make a combined list of the responses on the board. To extend the activity, ask students to write a humorous paragraph about what might happen in a school if students and teachers exchanged responsibilities.

Section 1 Review

1. because it is the structure in which children are raised and values are taught
2. *Sample answer:* With more women in the workforce, parents must trust others to care for children. Divorce can affect a family's finances and emotional health. Postponing marriage has resulted in smaller families.
3. a family formed when parents remarry; foster, nuclear, single-parent, extended
4. teaching children to behave in an acceptable way; the responsibility of adults
5. *Sample answer:* Students may say that the tasks they do help them learn skills they will need as adults.
6. *Sample answer:* Some advantages are other teens to do things with and a happy father; some disadvantages are having to share time with his father and not getting along with new family members. If Sankong focuses on the advantages, it will help him maintain a positive outlook.

Technology & Health

How's Your Driving?

Teaching Strategies

- Begin by focusing on why a parent might want to monitor a teen's driving behavior. Ask: **Why are drivers between the ages of 15 and 24 involved in more motor vehicle crashes than any other age group?** *(lack of experience and a willingness to take risks)* Then talk about how students would feel if a parent or guardian installed a monitoring device on the car. Would it matter if they knew in advance that the device were being installed? Would it help if the adult's driving behavior were also being monitored?

- Have students work in small groups to brainstorm a list of situations when having a monitoring device in the car could make it easier for a teen to avoid an unhealthy behavior. Ask students to explain how having the device would help. *(If, for example, a teen is asked to drag race, he or she could use the device as an excuse for refusing to take part in this risky behavior.)*

- Invite a driving instructor to join the class to discuss other ways drivers can improve their driving skills. They may use simulations or take advanced driving courses that let them practice techniques such as skid control.

WRITING *Sample answer:* If the device shows that a teen consistently drives safely, the parents' trust will increase. Then the teen is likely to be given more freedom.

Technology & Health

How's Your Driving?

The leading cause of death for teens is car crashes. So when teens begin to drive without adult supervision, parents worry. A new device can reassure parents and help teens improve their driving skills. The device is installed in the car to monitor speed and aggressive behaviors, such as tailgating. Some devices even provide feedback on the use of direction signals and seat belts.

WRITING How could using a monitoring device help a family to build trust? How could it lead to more freedom for a teen driver?

Vehicle Trip Report

Report Date	
Ending Odometer	08-21
Total Miles	7215
Overforce Count	23
Overspeed count	20
Highest Overspeed (mph)	5
Unsafe reverses	80
Seatbelt violations	0
	2

▲ **The Monitoring Device**
The device monitors and captures driving behavior. It collects data and video. Parents can see a report that lists all the violations.

▼ **Location of Vehicle**
Some devices can record the route taken by a driver and any stops made along the way. Some systems can notify a parent if a driver leaves an agreed-upon area.

Seat Belts ▶
When the device detects an unsafe behavior, such as an unbuckled seat belt, it beeps or a light goes on.

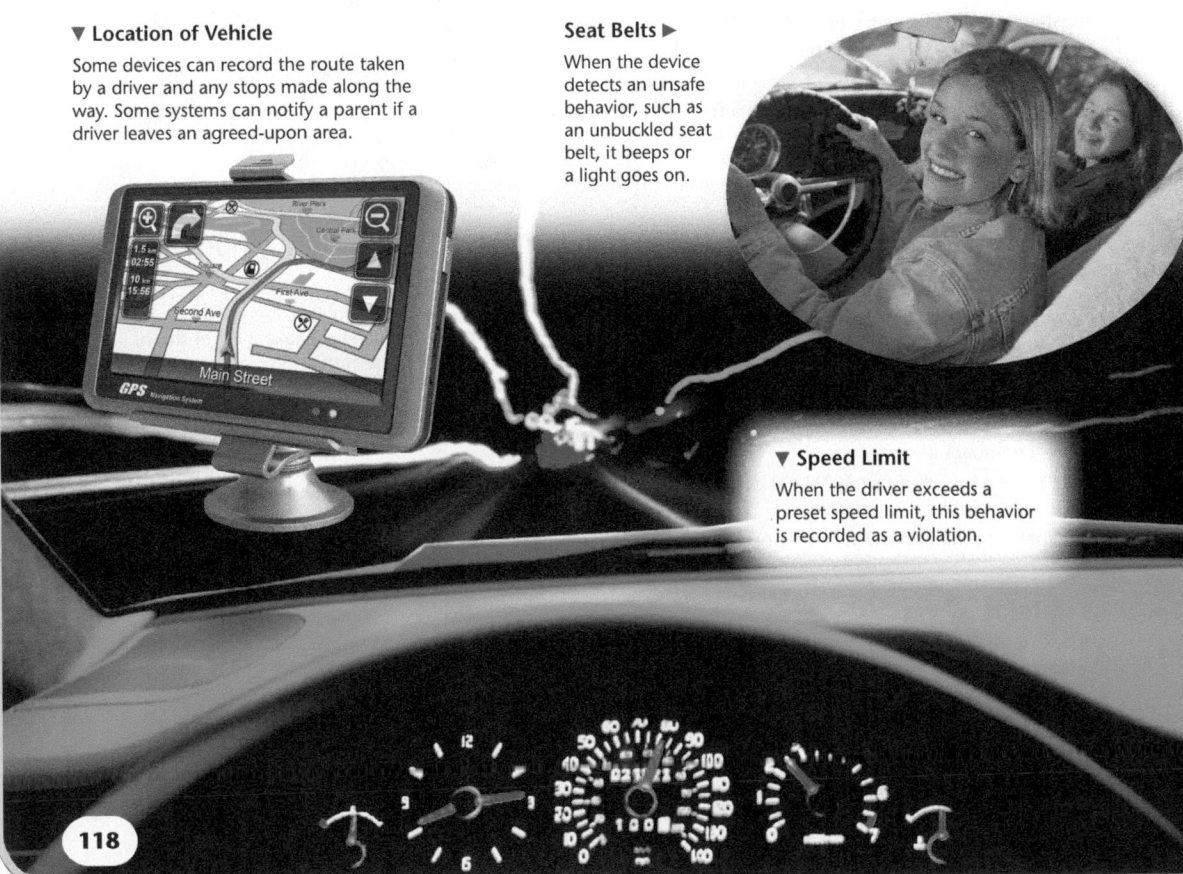

▼ **Speed Limit**
When the driver exceeds a preset speed limit, this behavior is recorded as a violation.

For Your INFORMATION!

Monitoring Devices

Vehicle monitoring devices were made initially for businesses, such as trucking companies, who wanted to keep track of how their vehicles were being driven. Some driving schools use the devices. Insurance companies may start to offer discounts to drivers who allow monitoring devices to be installed in their cars.

The most basic, least costly devices need to be removed from the car and hooked up to a computer for data retrieval. More expensive versions remain in the car; data is reported by e-mail or instant messaging, or on a Web site. Monthly fees are quite high for options that use GPS technology or allow adults to get "real-time" alerts of driving behavior.

Family Problems

Section 2
Family Problems

Warm-Up

Dear Advice Line,

My parents are getting a divorce. My father complains to me about my mother and my mother does the same about my father. It feels like they want me to pick a side.

WRITING What advice would you give to someone whose parents are getting a divorce?

Causes of Family Stress

The families shown in television shows seem to solve their problems quickly and easily. In real families, however, problems are not resolved so easily. **Some sources of family stress are illness, financial problems, divorce, and drug abuse.**

Illness When one family member has a serious illness, it affects everyone in the family. Everyone worries about the outcome of the illness. Will the person recover? Will the family change? The family's focus is on the person who is sick. Other family members may feel ignored, and then they may feel guilty for thinking about themselves.

Financial Problems A serious illness can lead to financial problems in the family. So can a divorce or the loss of a job. Financial problems can have serious emotional effects on all family members. Adults may feel guilty that they are unable to provide for their families. Children may feel angry that they must go without things that friends have. Both adults and children may worry about the future.

Financial problems can be less stressful if family members work together to improve the situation. Teenagers can try to find part-time work to help out. Younger children can find ways to cut back on their spending. Other relatives may offer help as well.

Family Relationships **119**

Objectives

► **List** some causes of stress in families.

► **Describe** three types of abuse that can happen in families.

► **Explain** what problems runaways are likely to have.

Vocabulary

- separation
- domestic abuse
- physical abuse
- sexual abuse
- emotional abuse
- neglect
- runaway

Objectives
Before class begins, write the objectives on the board. Have students copy the objectives into their notebooks at the start of class.

1. Focus

Warm-Up Advice Line

After students have completed the writing assignment, ask volunteers to share their responses with the class. Point out that it is normal for families to have problems, but some problems are more stressful than others. After students look at Figure 5, you may want to have students evaluate their responses to the Warm-Up.

Presentation 5-2

2. Teach

L3 **EL** Reading/Note Taking 5-2

L2 Adapted Reading/Note Taking 5-2

Causes of Family Stress

L2 **Class Discussion**

Ask students what movies about families they have seen recently. Have students identify some of the problems faced by these fictional families. Record their responses on the board. Then ask students to compare and contrast the problems portrayed in the movies to those faced by actual families.

Differentiated Instruction

EL **English Language Learners**

Ask students to work with a partner to make a concept map that shows the four sources of family stress that are described in the text. Then have each student work with his or her partner to write one or two sentences that describe these sources of family stress.

As an alternative, pair beginning English language learners with more fluent classmates. Have each pair identify terms in the subsection on causes of family stress that are unfamiliar to the beginning English language learner. Then, ask the pairs to discuss and define each term.

L2 Visual Learning: Figure 5

Image Bank Figure 5-5

Have students review the advice for dealing with divorce shown in Figure 5. Then discuss each individual point. For example, ask how concentrating on things you enjoy could be helpful. *(keeps the person from dwelling on the divorce)* In conclusion, ask volunteers to identify points they think would be most helpful. Ask them to explain their choices.

L3 Building Health Skills

Advocacy Discuss the resources that are available at school and in the community for a teen who is dealing with the stress of divorce. Show students where to look for appropriate resources in a telephone directory. Make a list of resources on the board. Then, have each student use the information to make an informative poster that can be displayed in the school. Challenge students to create posters that capture the attention of others and clearly convey information.

Connect to Your Life Allow students to answer this question in their private journals.

L3 Content Update

Visit Pearson SuccessNet to access more information about family stress. Have students complete the Web activity.

FIGURE 5 When parents divorce, children need to deal with their anger and sadness. Talking with other teens who are in a similar situation may help.

Advice for Dealing With Divorce

What to Do	What Not to Do
► Concentrate on things you enjoy.	► Don't feel responsible for the divorce.
► Read a book or articles about divorce.	► Don't get drawn into arguments between your parents or act as a messenger.
► Talk with relatives about your feelings.	► Don't feel forced to choose sides.
► Meet with other teens who are dealing with divorce.	► Don't feel guilty about being angry. You can feel anger and love at the same time.
► Talk with a mental health counselor, especially if you are depressed.	► Don't isolate yourself from your friends.

Separation and Divorce It is normal for couples to experience conflict and tension. But sometimes the conflicts are so serious or frequent that a couple may try a separation. A **separation** is an arrangement in which spouses live apart and try to work out their problems. If a couple is not able to work out their differences, a separation may lead to divorce. For many, divorce is a devastating experience. People who divorce sometimes think of themselves as failures, and suffer from grief and loss.

A separation or divorce is often painful for children in the family. They may feel helpless because they are unable to solve their parents' problems. They may feel a range of emotions—resentment, guilt, sadness, anger, or embarrassment. Children may think that the separation or divorce is their fault. They need to be reassured that they are not to blame for their parents' problems. Figure 5 lists things that you should do and things you should avoid doing if your parents are getting a divorce.

Drug Abuse When a family member has a problem with alcohol or another drug, the whole family is affected. Some effects are subtle. Family members may be embarrassed or worried about their loved one. Some effects are serious. Family members may be afraid to go home or to bring friends home for fear that the person who is abusing drugs will be violent.

There are groups that can help families deal with a drug or alcohol problem. Al-Anon, for example, helps people cope with a family member who has an alcohol problem. Alateen provides help for teenagers who have an alcoholic in the family. These groups hold meetings that are open to anyone who wants to share experiences about living with an alcoholic. To find groups in your area that help family members of drug abusers, look under "Drug Abuse" in your telephone book or search online.

Connect to Your Life Who can you turn to for help if you are experiencing a family problem?

GO ONLINE
PearsonSuccessNet.com
For: More on family stress

WRITING and Health

L3 News Report

Ask students to rewrite the information provided on drug abuse in the style of a news report. Provide examples of news reports for students to use as models as they write. Help students identify the characteristics of a news report and encourage students to begin their reports with a hypothetical human interest story about drug abuse. After students have completed their writing, ask volunteers to share their news reports with the class.

Family Violence

Violence in families may be the most destructive problem that a society must deal with. Violence can occur in all kinds of families—rich or poor, urban or rural, uneducated or educated. The heart of the problem is one person's desire to have power or control over others. **The violence, or abuse, may be physical, sexual, or emotional.** Any family member can be a victim of abuse—a spouse, a child, or an elderly parent. The abuse of one spouse by the other is sometimes called **domestic abuse.** This discussion of abuse will focus on the abuse of children by adults.

Physical Abuse   When an adult punishes a child and leaves a mark that can be seen the next day, this act is considered physical abuse. **Physical abuse** is intentionally causing physical harm to another person. A child who is physically abused may avoid going home. Some victims start to think that they are responsible for the beatings. They think, that if they could figure out the right way to behave, the abuse would stop. But victims are not responsible for the abuse. Only the abuser is responsible.

Children who are physically abused often hide the signs of abuse. They may be ashamed or they may be afraid that, if they tell, their family will be destroyed. They may also be afraid that the abuser might retaliate for revealing the secret.

It is far more damaging, however, for a child to keep silent than to seek help. Web sites and phone books list toll-free numbers for child abuse hotlines. If children cannot find an appropriate group to call, they should talk with a trusted adult. Speaking up is the first step toward putting an end to a dangerous situation.

FIGURE 6   Posters like this one are used to advocate against physical abuse of children. **Predicting** What people do you think this poster is aimed at? Explain.

Family Violence

(L3) Building Health Skills

Making Decisions Ask students to decide what they would do if a friend confided that he or she was a victim of family violence. Have students define the problem, consider the alternatives, identify their values, and decide. Ask students to make an entry in their private journals describing the steps in the decision-making process. Encourage volunteers to share their decisions with the class. **WRITING**

(L2) Visual Learning: Figure 6

Have students look at the poster in Figure 6. Ask: **How is this poster an example of advocacy?** *(The poster draws attention to the problem of child abuse and encourages people to report cases of abuse.)* Discuss how an image often can be more powerful than words when you want to convey a message. **Caption Answer** *Sample answer:* The poster may be aimed at adults because it uses an image of an adult male's fist.

(L3) Class Discussion

Remind students that child abuse is never the child's fault. Emphasize that abuse should not be kept a secret, but should be reported to a trusted adult. Explain that abuse can also be reported to the National Child Abuse hotline (1-800-422-4453 or 1-800-4-A-CHILD). Tell students this is a free telephone call, and the hotline is available 24 hours a day, 7 days a week.

L3 Class Discussion

Challenge students to complete the phrase "Sticks and stones can break my bones..." *(but names will never hurt me)*. Ask students if they think this saying is true or false. Encourage students to revise this phrase to accurately reflect the damage that can be inflicted by emotional abuse. Have volunteers share their revised saying with the class.

EL Building Vocabulary

Write the words *neglect* and *abuse* on the board. Ask students to give a brief verbal definition of each word. Then, ask students to identify ways that abuse and neglect are similar and ways that they are different.

L4 Active Learning

Have a group of interested students arrange to interview a police officer about what role law enforcement plays in dealing with family violence. Ask students to prepare questions in advance, and to share their findings with the class.

Connect to Your Life Allow students to answer this question in their private journals.

FIGURE 7 A volunteer removes shoes from the steps of the statehouse in Boston, Massachusetts. Hundreds of pairs of shoes were used as symbols of child abuse and neglect cases in the state. The display was organized as part of a news conference to proclaim April as Child Abuse Prevention Month.

Sexual Abuse When an adult uses a child or adolescent for sexual purposes, he or she commits a criminal offense known as **sexual abuse**. Both boys and girls can be victims of sexual abuse. Typically, the adult is someone the child knows well. The adult may be a parent, stepparent, older brother or sister, other relative, or a family friend.

Even a single instance of sexual abuse can have a devastating effect. The child often feels guilty and ashamed. In the victim's mind, he or she assumes all the responsibility or blame for the event. Later in life, it may be difficult for the child to trust others and develop caring relationships.

Victims of sexual abuse should talk with a trusted adult or call the Child Abuse Hotline. Deciding to seek help may be difficult. Victims risk angering, hurting, or betraying the abuser. Sometimes other relatives don't want to believe what is going on and may accuse the victim of lying. The abuser may threaten the child to keep the child from telling. But it is more dangerous to believe the abuser's threats than to report the abuse. Remember, no one has the right to touch you without your consent.

Emotional Abuse "You rotten, no-good punk, you never do anything right." "I wish you had never been born." A child who constantly hears negative statements like these is likely to suffer from emotional abuse. **Emotional abuse** is the nonphysical mistreatment of a person. Emotional abuse doesn't leave visible scars. But it does leave victims feeling helpless, inadequate, or worthless. Children who are emotionally abused need help just as much as children who are physically or sexually abused.

Neglect When adults fail to provide for the basic needs of children, it is called **neglect**. These needs include food, security, socialization, and love. When parents fail to give their children love and emotional support, the children can feel that they do not belong. Victims of emotional neglect often have trouble developing a healthy personality. The state may remove children from a home if they suffer from neglect.

Connect to Your Life What would you do if you knew that a friend was being abused?

TEENS *Are Asking . . .*

Q: My friend Paul is planning to run away from home. I think this is a bad decision, but he won't listen to me. What can I do to change his mind?

A: What you say to Paul depends on why he is planning to run away. If Paul wants to run away because he thinks his parents are too strict, stress the dangers that many runaways face. Also help him think of strategies he can use to convince his parents to allow him to have more freedom. If Paul is being abused, encourage him to talk with a trusted adult who can help arrange for a safe place to live. Another option is to call an abuse hotline.

Runaways

A **runaway** is a child who leaves home without permission and stays away for at least one night, or two nights for teens 15 or older. Some leave home because of violence in their families. Others run away because of emotional problems or school failure. Some are angry about family rules that they think are too strict.

Some runaways go to safe locations such as the home of a relative or friend. But many runaways end up with no place to live and no means of support. **They may become ill or turn to crime. They become easy targets for people who are involved with prostitution, pornography, and drugs.**

Many communities have shelters for homeless youth. Some hotlines for runaways, such as the National Runaway Switchboard, arrange for free bus rides home. They supply more than a free ticket. They arrange a call with the family and negotiate a course of action before the runaway returns home. They help the family find resources in the community to help rebuild the family relationships.

If you are thinking of running away, you owe it to yourself to call your local runaway hotline. Call directory assistance, look in the self-help pages at the front of your telephone book, or search online. The counselors can advise you about where to get help for family or other problems.

FIGURE 8 Running away might seem to be a solution to problems. In reality, most runaways encounter serious problems while on their own.

Section 2 Review

Key Ideas and Vocabulary

1. List four general types of problems that can cause stress in families.
2. How is a **separation** different from a divorce?
3. Briefly describe physical abuse, sexual abuse, and emotional abuse.
4. What is **neglect**?
5. What kinds of problems might running away from home lead to?

Critical Thinking

6. **Relating Cause and Effect** Explain why a serious illness affects all members of a family.

Health and Community

Managing Money Some financial problems in families are caused by major life crises such as a serious illness or job loss. But sometimes, people just don't know how to manage money wisely. Ask someone at a local bank or credit union about programs in your community that help teens to learn about managing money. Write a paragraph summarizing what you learn. **WRITING**

7. **Predicting** How might meeting with other teens whose parents are getting divorced help a teen cope with a family breakup?
8. **Relating Cause and Effect** More children run away in summer than in winter. What factors could help explain this difference?

Runaways

L3 Cooperative Learning

Have students work in small groups to make a list of alternatives to running away. Then, compile a list of alternatives on the board. Ask students to suggest reasons why teens might run away from home. For each reason, identify one or two appropriate alternatives.

3. Assess

Evaluate

These assignments can help you assess students' mastery of the section content.

Section 2 Review

Answers appear below.

Teaching Resources

- Practice 5-2
- Section 5-2 Quiz

L2 Reteach

Ask students to record the boldface heads from the section on a piece of paper. For each head, have students write one sentence that summarizes the main ideas of that subsection of text.

L4 Enrich

Teaching Resources

- Enrich 5-2

Health and Community

Managing Money For background on this topic, visit the Web site for the National Endowment for Financial Education. Have interested students extend the activity by developing a pamphlet that contains money management tips for teens.

Section 2 Review

1. illness, financial problems, separation and divorce, drug abuse
2. A separation may be temporary.
3. Physical: causing intentional physical harm to another person; sexual: an adult uses a child for sexual purposes; emotional: non-physical mistreatment.
4. when adults fail to meet the basic needs of a child
5. illness; involvement in crime, drugs, pornography, or prostitution
6. Possible answers include loss of income, stress on caregivers, and other family members who feel ignored.
7. *Sample answer:* It would give teens an opportunity to discuss their feelings with understanding peers.
8. *Sample answer:* Children may think they can survive outdoors; family problems may increase when children are not in school.

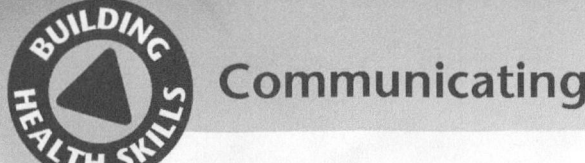
Using Win-Win Negotiation

Objective

Demonstrate how win-win negotiation can be used to resolve conflicts in families.

Teaching Strategies

- Use the opening dialogue between Rosa and her father to remind students that conflicts are a normal part of life. Ask students how teens tend to deal with curfews. Then, ask if these responses tend to improve the situation or make things worse.

- Explain that communication is the key to resolving most conflicts. Have students read the steps for win-win negotiation. Then describe another typical family conflict. Have students work in small groups to discuss how win-win negotiation could be applied to this conflict. Ask volunteers to use role-plays to demonstrate how win-win negotiation could be used to resolve the conflict.

- Ask students to write an entry in their private journals that identifies several ongoing conflicts in their family and ways that win-win negations could be applied to those situations.

Using Win-Win Negotiation

"Dad, there's no good reason why I shouldn't be able to stay out late on weekends. I'm tired of being treated like a baby!"

"You're only fifteen, Rosa. You can't just come and go as you please. Midnight is late enough."

Rosa and her father have been having this "discussion" for weeks. They just go around and around, getting more and more annoyed and stubborn. Often at the heart of a disagreement is a breakdown in communication.

When communication is poor, conflict can tear a relationship apart. But with good communication, conflict can lead to a solution and to greater understanding and growth as well.

The key to resolving conflicts is to find common goals that both people share. By using "win-win" negotiation, you can turn a no-win situation into one where everyone comes out a winner.

❶ **Describe the problem.**

When you have a conflict, take the time to really understand the problem. Write out answers to the following questions.

▶ What do you think the problem is?

▶ How does it make you feel?

▶ What don't you like about the situation?

▶ What do you want out of the situation?

Dad makes me come in so early. It makes me angry that he doesn't trust me, but I hate fighting with him. I'd like to have more freedom and to get along with him.

Rosa's not old enough to stay out late. I worry about her safety. I don't want to fight with her, but I don't want her to get hurt.

124　*Chapter 5*

🚩 **Sensitive Issues**

- During class discussion, do not ask students to relate conflicts that are specific to their family. Instead, discuss conflicts that are common to most families.

- Remind students that some negotiations about limits will not result in a change. After the negotiation, a teen will need to follow the existing rule.

2 See the other point of view.
Now describe the problem as you think the other person sees it. What do you think are the other person's thoughts, feelings, and goals?

Dad thinks he's protecting me. He worries when I'm out late, but he wants to get along with me and keep me out of trouble.

Rosa thinks I don't trust her. She's angry because she can't spend enough time with her friends. She wants me to trust her.

3 Involve the other person.
Explain the "win-win" process and ask the other person to try Steps 1 and 2. If the person isn't willing to try the process, ask another adult to play the role of the other person. Even if you don't have a partner, go through the steps yourself. Your willingness to see the other person's point of view may help the situation.

4 Share and discuss.
Discuss the situation with the other person.

► Listen closely and don't interrupt while the other person is talking.

► Say something that shows that you understand the other person's point of view. Understanding isn't the same as agreeing.

► Talk about and acknowledge each other's feelings. Unexpressed feelings often get in the way of resolving conflicts.

► Attack the problem, not the person. Seek solutions, and do not blame.

► Look for shared goals. Avoid taking specific positions at first.

► Focus on what you want to happen in the future. Look forward, not back.

Dad, I understand that you worry when. . . .

Rosa, I realize that time with your friends is important. . . .

5 Invent solutions.
Make a list of solutions that meet at least some of the needs that both of you have expressed. Invent solutions first; judge them later.

Dad, what if I call you if I'm out after 11 and have late hours twice a month?

Why don't you invite your friends over to our house sometimes, Rosa?

6 Agree on a solution.
Select the solution that best meets the most important goals that you both expressed. The two of you must agree on the solution.

So, Dad, I'll call you at 11 to let you know where I am and when I will be home.

OK, Rosa. That way I won't have to worry as much about where you are and whether you're all right.

 **Practice the Skill**

1. Omar and Ty are having a disagreement. In writing, describe their problem and use win-win negotiation to find a solution.

Omar: "How could you go to a baseball game tonight, Ty? You promised to help me study for tomorrow's math test!"

Ty: "How could you expect me to turn down free tickets to the most important game of the season?"

2. List five conflicts people your age may have with friends, family members, or teachers.

3. Think of a conflict you are now (or recently have been) involved in. Ask the other person to work through the win-win method with you. Then evaluate how successful the process was in resolving the conflict.

Family Relationships **125**

1. *Sample answer:* Ty needs to admit that Omar has a right to be angry because Omar was counting on Ty's help. Omar needs to see that it is reasonable for Ty to want to attend such an important game. Ty could work with Omar in the afternoon or help Omar find another tutor. Omar could study on his own and meet briefly with Ty the next morning to review a few of the more difficult concepts.

2. *Sample answer:* Students may argue with friends about being on time or keeping in touch. They may argue with family members about doing chores or privacy. They may argue with teachers about grades on papers or having too much homework.

3. Allow students to keep the content of the conflicts private. Ask volunteers to discuss how much success they had with the win-win negotiation strategy.

Health at Home

L3 **Negotiation Strategies**
Have students write a paragraph that compares and contrasts how they would apply the strategy of win-win negotiation to solve a conflict with a younger sibling or cousin, and a grandparent or other older relative. In what ways would they need to modify the strategy for each situation? What parts of the strategy could be applied in both situations? Have volunteers share their responses with the class. **WRITING**

Keeping the Family Healthy

Objectives

Before class begins, write the objectives on the board. Have students copy the objectives into their notebooks at the start of class.

1. Focus

Warm-Up Quick Quiz

Use the Warm-Up Presentation slide to survey student responses.

Students' quiz responses should be kept private. After students complete the writing assignment, ask volunteers to share their responses. Then discuss the characteristics of healthy families described in the text.

Presentation 5-3

2. Teach

L3 **EL** Reading/Note Taking 5-3

L2 Adapted Reading/Note Taking 5-3

Healthy Families

L2 **Cooperative Learning**

Divide the class into five groups, and assign each group one of the bulleted characteristics of healthy families. Have each group develop a list of specific actions that family members could take to demonstrate the assigned characteristic. Ask each group to share its list with the class. Encourage students to make a goal of carrying out one or more of the listed actions within the next week.

Objectives

▶ **List** some characteristics of healthy families.

▶ **Describe** four skills families need to stay healthy.

▶ **Identify** places where families can go for help with their problems.

Vocabulary

• empathy
• sibling
• support group

Warm-Up

Quick Quiz Which of the following statements accurately describe your family relationships?

1 I enjoy spending time with my family.

2 We find it easy to say "I love you."

3 When I have a problem, I can confide in a parent or guardian.

4 My parents support my goals.

WRITING Using these statements as a starting point, describe the qualities of a healthy family.

Healthy Families

Most people in the United States are satisfied with the way their families function—even teenagers. **Healthy families share certain characteristics: caring, commitment, respect, appreciation, empathy, communication, and cooperation.**

▶ **Caring and Commitment** People in healthy families really care about each other. They are committed to staying together through good times and bad times. When one family member makes a mistake, the others offer their support, even if they are angry or disappointed.

▶ **Respect and Appreciation** Family members make each other feel important. They show that they appreciate what other family members do by thanking them and praising them.

▶ **Empathy** The ability to understand another person's thoughts or feelings is called **empathy** (EM puh thee). Empathy allows family members to look at situations from the other person's viewpoint.

▶ **Communication** Family members can tell each other what they honestly think and feel. They listen with respect to what others have to say.

▶ **Cooperation** Responsibilities are divided fairly among family members. Each person does what he or she has promised to do.

WRITING and Health

L3 **Dialogue**

Have students write a dialogue between two fictional family members that demonstrates one or more of the characteristics of healthy families described in the text. Then ask volunteers to work with a partner to read their dialogues to the class.

After each dialogue is read, challenge the class to identify the characteristics demonstrated in the dialogue. Use the dialogues to spark a class discussion on the importance of communication skills for maintaining healthy families.

Reducing Sibling Rivalry
- Don't compare yourself to a sibling.
- Focus on your own achievements.
- Try to spend time alone with a parent.
- Try to resolve conflicts fairly.

Useful Skills for Families

Even healthy families have problems from time to time. For a family to remain healthy, family members must develop skills to work through their problems. **Healthy families know how to resolve conflicts, express emotions, make decisions, and manage their time.**

Resolving Conflicts   Have you ever argued with your parent over household chores? What do you do if your parent dislikes your friends? Does your sister complain about the time you spend on the computer?

These conflict situations often involve a struggle for power. Teens want control over their lives, while parents want family life to function in ways they believe are best. **Siblings,** or brothers and sisters, compete for their parent's attention, for possessions, and for recognition.

When trying to resolve conflicts, family members need to talk openly, honestly, and lovingly. The goal is to learn from one another. Good communication skills are key to conflict resolution. Saying what you mean, listening to others, and voicing disagreement respectfully are important.

Expressing Emotions   When you are trying to resolve a conflict, it is important to express your emotions in constructive ways. Suppose you attack the other person in an angry outburst such as "All you ever do is criticize me!" The other person is likely to attack you in return or to stop talking to you. Either way, the outburst will make the problem worse. It is better to focus on your own feelings by saying things like "I get upset when people criticize me." Then listen to the other person's concerns.

Being able to say "I'm sorry," "I love you," and "Thank you" also helps. If family members feel loved and appreciated, they are often more willing to help solve problems. The problem-solving process should not be seen as an opportunity to judge or place blame. If the process is a loving one, it can be easier and quicker to reach a solution.

 **Connect to Your Life** When you have an argument, how does the other person's actions affect how you respond?

FIGURE 9   Even when siblings are close, they can sometimes have conflicts. There are steps you can take to reduce sibling rivalry. **Evaluating** Which of the steps listed do you think is most important and why?

 GO ONLINE
PearsonSuccessNet.com
For: More on useful skills

Useful Skills for Families

 Visual Learning: Figure 9
Ask volunteers to read aloud the steps for reducing sibling rivalry. Encourage students to think of creative ways to incorporate these steps into their daily lives. After students have discussed ways to apply each step, have them make a poster that illustrates one of the steps and ways it can be applied. Display the completed posters in the classroom.
Caption Answer A student with many siblings might choose "try to spend time alone with a parent." A student with siblings who are close in age might choose "don't compare yourself with a sibling."

 Building Health Skills

Analyzing Influences Ask students to select a television program about a fictional family. Have them evaluate the problems chosen by the writers and the way that the family resolves conflicts. Ask students if they think the problems shown are realistic. Ask what strategies the family used to resolve conflicts. Is the portrayal realistic? How does having to fit the resolution into a half-hour or hour program affect the portrayal? Have students summarize their findings in one or two paragraphs. **WRITING**

 Connect to Your Life Allow students to answer this question in their private journals.

 **Content Update** **GO ONLINE**
Visit Pearson SuccessNet to access more information about useful skills. Have students complete the Web activity.

Differentiated Instruction

 Special Needs
Students with certain mental disorders may have trouble applying the skills of resolving conflicts, expressing emotions, making decisions, and managing time. These skills are impaired in varying degrees in oppositional defiant disorder, attention deficit/hyperactivity disorder, autism, bipolar disorder, and depression.

When one family member struggles with these skills, it can impact the health of the family. If students in your class need extra practice with these skills, have them use scripted role-plays for practice. The school counselor may have additional suggestions for activities that can be used to reinforce these important skills.

L3 Journal Writing

Ask students to consider the four skills for healthy families described in the text. Point out that every family, no matter how healthy, can improve on one or more of these skills. Challenge students to identify the one skill they feel their family most needs to work on. In their private journals, have students describe several ways they could help their family improve the identified skill. **WRITING**

L2 Building Health Skills

Making Decisions Have students review the DECIDE process, which is described on pages 16–17. Then challenge them to make a list of several common family conflicts that could be resolved by applying the steps of the DECIDE process. Divide the class into small groups. Have each group write a role-play that demonstrates the resolution of one of the identified conflicts. Ask each group to perform its role-play for the class.

L3 Cultural Connection

After students read the suggestions in Figure 10, have volunteers describe some family traditions from different cultures. Then, ask students to suggest why having traditions can help keep a family healthy.

 **Connect to Your Life** Allow students to answer this question in their private journals.

Making Decisions Suppose that a friend asks you to go to the movies on Saturday night. However, you promised your mother weeks ago that you would baby-sit your younger brother. What would you do? You could keep your promise to your mother and tell your friend that you are busy. But what if you haven't seen this friend in a long time?

Families often use decision-making skills to resolve conflicts. These skills involve choosing between two or more alternatives. If you and your mother discuss the problem, you may be able to think of alternatives and reach a solution that works for both of you. Perhaps you can find another baby sitter, or maybe you can take your brother to the movies with you. By using decision-making skills, you can avoid an argument. Plus you can show your mother that you are a mature and responsible person.

Making decisions as a family can be difficult. Each person has different needs or opinions. Some may find it difficult to communicate their opinions in a respectful way. A family member may disrupt the process or people outside of the family may try to influence the decision. In these cases, families may seek outside help to solve their problems.

Managing Time Between work, school, and chores, most families don't have much time to spend together. So the time that families do spend together is valuable. Figure 10 lists a few simple ways that families can spend their time together wisely and improve their relationships.

Healthy families tend to have strong ties with other relatives. These relatives often join the family for holidays and other important events. These events provide a sense of belonging and security. If problems arise, members of the extended family can offer their advice and support.

 **Connect to Your Life** When you spend time with your family, what kinds of things do you do?

FIGURE 10 The time this family spends together can help to strengthen the ties between family members.

Making the Most of Family Time
- Develop family traditions. Celebrate occasions in special ways.
- Make mealtimes special. Try to eat together and share the day's events.
- Hold family meetings. Discuss important issues or problems; make plans to do things together.
- Show that you care. Do an unassigned chore; give a sincere compliment.

128 *Chapter 5*

Focus on **ISSUES**

L3 Overscheduled Families

Point out that the term *overscheduled* is being used with increasing frequency to describe American families. Families are overscheduled when family members are involved in many outside activities. With so many activities, there is little time left for families to spend together.

Have students discuss the positive and negative aspects of a busy family schedule. *(Overscheduled family members have a chance to participate in activities, learn skills, and meet new people. In overscheduled families, people have less time to communicate.)*

Hands-On *Activity*

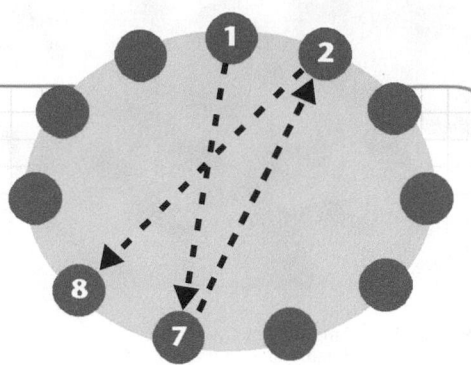

Group Juggling

In this activity you will work with others to accomplish a difficult task.

Materials (per group)
3 lightweight balls, volleyball size

Try This

❶ Form a large circle with 10 other people.

❷ Starting with one person and going clockwise, count off from 1 to 11. Then decide how you will pass the ball around the circle. It is best to pass the ball across the circle to the opposite side (for example, from 1 to 7, 7 to 2, 2 to 8, and so on).

❸ Person 1 throws the ball across the circle to the next person according to the decided order. That person throws the ball to the next person, and so on across the circle.

❹ Continue passing the ball until it has gone around the circle five times. If the ball drops, just pick it up and continue passing it around.

❺ Repeat Steps 3 and 4, but with two balls instead of one. Start one ball with person 1 and the other with person 3.

❻ When you have mastered "juggling" the two balls, add a third ball, starting it with person 5.

Think and Discuss

❶ How were cooperation and teamwork important in this activity? How are those same skills important for living in a family?

❷ How is group juggling easier than juggling alone? How is it more difficult? Relate this to living in a family.

❸ Suppose that, while juggling three balls, the group suddenly decided to reverse the direction of one ball. What do you think would happen? How is this similar to what happens when unexpected problems arise in families?

Getting Help for the Family

Even when a family is healthy, there may be times when the family is faced with a problem that seems overwhelming. The problem may be too difficult for the family to solve by itself. In this situation, asking for help is a sign of strength rather than a sign of weakness.

Where can families go for help in solving problems? Many families depend on relatives or trusted friends for help and support. Relatives and friends may offer useful advice because they know the family well. But they will not be qualified to deal with every problem. Some families may turn to members of the clergy or mental health professionals for advice.

When faced with a problem that needs immediate attention, a family may use a crisis hotline or contact a crisis center. People who work in crisis centers can serve as sympathetic listeners. They also can refer people to other sources of help. **Some sources of help for families are family agencies, family therapists, and support groups.**

Hands-On *Activity*

Group Juggling

Modify the activity for students with physical disabilities by having students work individually and then with a group to solve a mathematical problem. Ask students to compare working alone and working with a group.

Think and Discuss Answers

1. *Sample answer:* The group juggling worked best when the team was able to cooperate and communicate. Families also function best when family members use these skills.

2. *Sample answer:* Group juggling is easier than juggling alone because you can count on others for help. It can be more difficult than juggling alone if the team members don't cooperate. Living in a family can be easier than living alone because you can share responsibilities. It can be more difficult than living alone because it requires cooperation and compromise.

3. *Sample answer:* Reversing the direction of one of the balls is likely to cause confusion and may result in the balls being dropped. A family faced with an unexpected situation may also function poorly until it has adjusted to the change.

Getting Help for the Family

🔼 **Building Health Skills**

Advocacy Have students investigate whether support groups or other services for students who are experiencing family problems are available in the school. If none exists, have students write a letter to the school administrators explaining how these groups can benefit students. If support groups are available through the school, have students make posters or brochures that can be distributed to make other students aware of the services that are offered.

Differentiated Instruction

🔵 **English Language Learners**

Cultural and language barriers may prevent some families from seeking help from family agencies, family therapists, or support groups. When discussing sources of help for families, be sure to mention that many agencies have interpreters to help those who are not fluent in English.

Have English language learners work with a partner to create a chart that gives a short description of family agencies, family therapists, and support groups. Help students collect information about local agencies that use interpreters.

3. Assess

Evaluate
These assignments can help you assess students' mastery of the section content.

Section 3 Review
Answers appear below.

Teaching Resources
• Practice 5-3
• Section 5-3 Quiz

 **Reteach**

Have students work in pairs, with one student rephrasing the section objectives into questions and the other student locating the answers in the section.

 **Enrich**

Teaching Resources
• Enrich 5-3

Health at Home

Family Rules Introduce the activity by having students review the information in the section about expressing emotions and resolving conflicts. After students complete the assignment with their families, ask volunteers to share some of the rules their families developed.

FIGURE 11 Sometimes volunteer groups join with family agencies to help people with their problems. These young women are helping to build a home for a family.

Family Agencies Public and private agencies offer help to families in most communities. Some agencies offer counseling for families. Others may offer parenting classes. Mental-health agencies help meet the needs of people with mental disorders. Child-welfare agencies offer services for the protection of children. These services include arranging for foster care or dealing with child abuse. Other agencies help families with financial aid, food, housing, employment, healthcare, and other basic needs.

Family Therapy Some family agencies provide therapy for families with problems. If not, they can refer families to a therapist. Therapists work with family members to find better ways to solve problems. In most cases, family therapists encourage all family members to take part in the process. This helps the family learn how to resolve conflicts and improve family relationships.

Support Groups A **support group** is a network of people who help each other cope with a particular problem. Group members learn from one another rather than from a group leader. They share information about the problem and discuss their experiences. This process helps members of the group learn to deal effectively with their problems.

One well-known support group is Alcoholics Anonymous (AA). There are AA meetings in communities across the country for those who abuse alcohol. Some support groups help people cope with serious illness or death. Other groups deal with relationship problems in families related to divorce, family violence, gambling, or teens who commit crimes.

Section 3 Review

Key Ideas and Vocabulary
1. What characteristics do healthy families share?
2. What is **empathy**? How can empathy contribute to healthy family relationships?
3. Identify four skills that families need to stay healthy.
4. Define the term **siblings**. How can siblings cause conflicts in families?
5. What type of help is available for families from outside the family?

Critical Thinking
6. **Evaluating** Is this statement a constructive way to express your emotions? "You never listen when I talk." Why or why not?

Health at Home

Family Rules Ask other family members to work with you to develop rules for family discussions. The goal is to develop a set of rules that make it easier to resolve conflicts and communicate effectively. Also discuss some polite ways to deal with someone who breaks the rules. **WRITING**

7. **Predicting** If you were the parent of a teenager, how would you handle conflicts about curfews?
8. **Applying Concepts** Your sister borrowed your bike without asking again. Now you have no way to get to your friend's house to work on a project. How could you handle this situation in a positive manner? **WRITING**

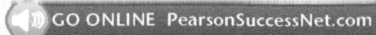 GO ONLINE PearsonSuccessNet.com   Audio Summary Section 5.3

Section 3 Review

1. caring and commitment, respect and appreciation, empathy, communication, cooperation
2. the ability to understand another person's thoughts and feelings; allows family members to look at situations from a different viewpoint
3. resolving conflicts, expressing emotions, making decisions, managing time
4. Siblings are brothers and sisters. When siblings compete for their parents' attention, this competition can lead to conflicts.
5. family agencies, family therapists, support groups
6. No, it puts the listener on the defensive.
7. *Sample answer:* I would set clear boundaries after discussing the teen's concerns; I would adjust the boundaries as the teen matures.
8. *Sample answer:* I would resolve the problem with my sister by working out a schedule of times when she can use my bicycle.

Chapter 5
At a Glance

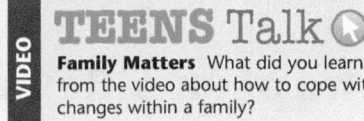
Section 1   Families Today

Key Ideas

▶ If the relationships with family members are healthy, a child learns to love, respect, and get along with others, and to function as part of a group.

▶ Three main factors account for changes in the American family: more women in the work force, a high divorce rate, and an increase in the age at which people marry.

▶ Children can live in nuclear, single-parent, extended, blended, or foster families.

▶ In families some responsibilities clearly belong to the adults, some clearly belong to the children, and some can be shared.

Vocabulary

- divorce (113)
- nuclear family (114)
- adoption (114)
- single-parent family (114)
- extended family (114)
- blended family (115)
- foster family (115)
- socialization (116)

Section 2   Family Problems

Key Ideas

▶ Some sources of family stress are illness, financial problems, divorce, and drug abuse.

▶ The violence, or abuse, that occurs in families may be physical, sexual, or emotional.

▶ Runaways may become ill or turn to crime. They become easy targets for people who are involved with prostitution, pornography, and drugs.

Vocabulary

- separation (120)
- domestic abuse (121)
- physical abuse (121)
- sexual abuse (122)
- emotional abuse (122)
- neglect (122)
- runaway (123)

Section 3   Keeping the Family Healthy

Key Ideas

▶ Healthy families share certain characteristics: caring, commitment, respect, admiration, empathy, communication, and cooperation.

▶ Healthy families know how to resolve conflicts, express emotions, make decisions, and manage their time.

▶ Family agencies, family therapists, and support groups offer help to families.

Vocabulary

- empathy (126)
- siblings (127)
- support group (130)

Family Relationships **131**

Chapter 5
At a Glance

VIDEO **Family Matters** Ask volunteers to share their answers. Use examples from the video to review how to cope with changes within a family.

Key Ideas Review

L1 Ask students to select one of the figures from the chapter and explain the major idea illustrated in the figure.

L2 Have students work with a partner to review and discuss the Warm-Up activities. Have each pair of students write a one-sentence summary of each Warm-Up that explains how the activity relates to a section objective. Call on several pairs of students to share their sentences.

Vocabulary Review

EL Have students make glossaries in which they can record unfamiliar terms they encountered in the chapter. Allow students to work with a partner to find the definitions of these terms in a dictionary. Ask students to record a definition in their glossaries for each term.

L3 Ask students to make a word search or crossword puzzle using the chapter vocabulary terms. Have students exchange their word puzzle with a partner.

Chapter 5 Review

 GO ONLINE

PearsonSuccessNet.com

Students can go online for a review activity on Chapter 5.

Reviewing Key Ideas

Section 1
1. b
2. a
3. The child can learn to love, respect, and get along with others, and to function as a part of a group.
4. Responsibilities are shared among all members, and a strong system of support is provided for family members.
5. In both cases a child joins a family. Foster placement is temporary; adoption is permanent.
6. *Sample answer:* It will take time for family members to get to know one another. Parents may have different rules, cook different foods, or have different expectations of children.

Section 2
7. b
8. c
9. Emotional abuse leaves victims feeling helpless or worthless.
10. Sometimes children run away to escape an abusive situation.
11. *Sample answer:* An adult may be unable to work because he or she is too ill or must care for a sick child. With a divorce, the money that was used to support one household must support two households. Money that is spent on drugs is not available for other family expenses.
12. *Sample answer:* If an adult tells a child that his or her behavior has caused the abuse, the child is likely to believe the adult.

Section 3
13. b
14. a
15. *Sample answer:* Family members can use good communication skills to resolve conflicts. When members express their love and respect for one another, they are more willing to help solve problems.

Chapter 5 Review

Reviewing Key Ideas

 GO ONLINE

PearsonSuccessNet.com

For: Chapter 5 review activity

Section 1
1. A group of close relatives living together or near each other is called a(an)
   a. nuclear family.
   b. extended family.
   c. blended family.
   d. foster family.
2. When a couple adopts a child, the unit that results is a(an)
   a. nuclear family.
   b. blended family.
   c. foster family.
   d. extended family.
3. Explain why it is important that children observe healthy relationships in the family.
4. What are some benefits of living in an extended family?
5. **Critical Thinking** How are the adoption of a child and the addition of a child to a foster family similar? How are they different?
6. **Critical Thinking** Which kinds of adjustments might the formation of a blended family require? Explain your answer.

Section 2
7. Domestic abuse is the abuse of
   a. a child by an adult.
   b. one spouse by the other.
   c. an elderly parent by a child.
   d. one family member by another.
8. The nonphysical mistreatment of a person is
   a. physical abuse.
   b. sexual abuse.
   c. emotional abuse.
   d. neglect.
9. Why is it as important to address emotional abuse as it is to deal with physical abuse?
10. Explain the possible relationship between family violence and runaways.
11. **Critical Thinking** Explain how a serious illness, divorce, and drug abuse can all lead to financial problems.
12. **Critical Thinking** Why do you think that a child who is abused by an adult might feel responsible for the abuse?

16. Family agencies offer counseling for families, mental-health services, protection for neglected or abused children, and help with basic needs, such as food, housing, and healthcare.
17. *Sample answer:* A smaller family might have fewer financial problems. A larger family has more members to share the responsibilities and support each other during difficult times.

Section 3
13. The ability to understand another person's thoughts or feelings is called
    a. appreciation.
    b. empathy.
    c. respect.
    d. caring.
14. A network of people who help each other deal with a particular problem is called a(an)
    a. support group.
    b. family agency.
    c. crisis center.
    d. crisis hotline.
15. How can good communication skills and expressing emotions in constructive ways help families resolve conflicts?
16. Describe four types of services that a family agency might provide.
17. **Critical Thinking** Describe one advantage that a small family might have over a larger family in keeping the family healthy. Describe one advantage the larger family might have.

Building Health Skills

18. **Advocacy** Should companies be required to give parents a leave of absence upon the birth of a child? Should this benefit apply to fathers as well as mothers? Explain your answers. **WRITING**
19. **Setting Goals** Make an action plan to spend more time with a busy parent or other family member. Are there things this person must do that you can do together? Are there things you can do for this person so he or she has more free time? Put your plan into action for a week and monitor your progress. Then adjust your action plan, if necessary. **WRITING**

Health and Community

Help for Families Work with your classmates to produce a booklet listing resources in your community for families. Use Web sites, brochures, or telephone interviews to find out what services each resource provides. Include a summary of these services for each agency. **WRITING**

 ## Building Health Skills

18. *Sample answer:* Businesses should offer both mothers and fathers a leave of absence. This promotes the emotional health of the family and can help attract and retain good employees.
19. Do not require students to reveal their action plans. Ask volunteers to share their plans.

Standardized Test Prep

Math Practice

The graph shows how household size changed in the United States from 1970 to 2011. Use the graph to answer Questions 20–23.

Households by Size

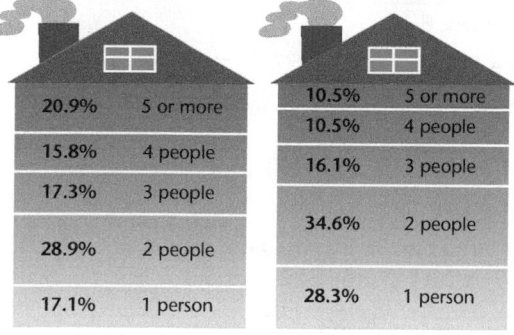

1970	
20.9%	5 or more
15.8%	4 people
17.3%	3 people
28.9%	2 people
17.1%	1 person

2011	
10.5%	5 or more
10.5%	4 people
16.1%	3 people
34.6%	2 people
28.3%	1 person

20. What percentage of households had 4 or more people in 1970?
- A 14.6%
- B 15.8%
- C 25.0%
- D 36.7%

21. What was the change in percent for households with one person between 1970 and 2011?
- F an increase of 17.1%
- G an increase of 28.3%
- H an increase of 11.2%
- J a decrease of 11.2%

22. In which of these households was there the greatest change between 1970 and 2011?
- A households with 1 person
- B households with 2 people
- C households with 4 people
- D households with 5 or more people

23. Based on the graph, which of the following statements is true?
- F The total number of families increased from 1970 to 2011.
- G Household size was constant from 1970 to 2011.
- H Household size decreased from 1970 to 2011.
- J Household size increased from 1970 to 2011.

Reading and Writing Practice

Read these first two stanzas from a poem by Edgar Guest. Then answer Questions 24–26.

Gettin' together to smile an' rejoice,
An' eatin an' laughter with folks of your choice.
An' kissin' the girls an' declaring that they
Are growing more beautiful day after day;
Chattin' an' braggin' a bit with the men,
Buildin' the old family circle again;
Livin' the wholesome an' old-fashioned cheer,
Just for awhile at the end of the year.

Greetings fly fast as we crowd through the door
And under the old roof we gather once more
Just as we did when the youngsters were small;
Mother's a bit grayer, that's all.
Father's a little bit older, but still
Ready to romp an' to laugh with a will.
Here we are back at the table again
Tellin' our stories as women an' men.

24. What is the main emotion that the author is expressing in this poem?
- A empathy
- B guilt
- C joy
- D jealousy

25. Based on the poem, which of the following statements is true about the author?
- F He has always lived with his parents.
- G He has not seen his parents for a while.
- H He has come home to live with his parents.
- J He is making a visit to his childhood home.

Constructed Response

26. Choose an appropriate title for this poem. Then, in a paragraph, give reasons for your choice.

Test-Taking Tip

Try not to argue with family members the night before an important test. You might not be able to concentrate on the test.

Family Relationships **133**

Standardized Test Prep

Math Practice
20. D
21. H
22. A
23. H

Reading and Writing Practice
24. C
25. J
26. Answers will vary, but should reflect the content of the poem. Students should offer logical reasons to support their choice of title.

Health and Community

Help for Families Help students divide the work among their classmates. Then, have students work together to produce their booklet. Have students share their completed booklet with the school nurse and guidance counselor.

Section Objectives	Standards Correlation	Instructional Resources L3	SE eTEXT	TE eTEXT	PRINT
1 Skills for Healthy Relationships ⏱ 1 period; 1/2 block 6.1.1 **Describe** four skills that contribute to effective communication. 6.1.2 **Explain** how cooperation and compromise help build healthy relationships.	NHES: 4.12.1, 4.12.2, 4.12.3, 8.12.2	SE Warm-Up, p. 136	•	•	•
		RN Note Taking Guide 6-1	•	•	•
		IB Image Bank 6-2		•	
		TR Practice 6-1		•	
		TR Section 6-1 Quiz		•	
2 Friendships ⏱ 2 periods; 1 block 6.2.1 **Explain** the importance of having friends. 6.2.2 **Distinguish** different types of friendships. 6.2.3 **Describe** some problems that occur in friendships.	NHES: 2.12.2, 2.12.3, 2.12.5, 8.12.2, 8.12.3	SE Warm-Up, p. 141	•	•	•
		SE Media Wise Gender Roles and Movies, p. 143	•	•	•
		RN Note Taking Guide 6-2	•	•	•
		TR Practice 6-2		•	
		TR Section 6-2 Quiz		•	
Supporting a Friend ⏱ 1 period; 1/2 block BHS.6 **Develop** strategies for providing support to friends.	NHES: 4.12.2, 4.12.4, 7.12.1, 8.12.2	SE Practice the Skill, p. 147	•	•	•
		RN Building Health Skills 6	•	•	•
3 Responsible Relationships ⏱ 1 period; 1/2 block 6.3.1 **List** some things you can learn about a person by dating. 6.3.2 **Describe** the cycle of violence.	NHES: 1.12.5, 2.12.7, 2.12.9, 7.12.1	SE Warm-Up, p. 148	•	•	•
		RN Note Taking Guide 6-3	•	•	•
		IB Image Bank 6-9		•	
		TR Practice 6-3		•	
		TR Section 6-3 Quiz		•	
4 Choosing Abstinence ⏱ 1 period; 1/2 block 6.4.1 **Identify** some risks of sexual intimacy. 6.4.2 **Explain** why emotional intimacy is important in close relationships. 6.4.3 **List** some skills that can help you choose abstinence.	NHES: 2.12.9, 4.12.1, 4.12.2, 5.12.1, 5.12.6, 6.12.2, 7.12.3	SE Warm-Up, p. 152	•	•	•
		RN Note Taking Guide 6-4	•	•	•
		TR Practice 6-4		•	
		TR Section 6-4 Quiz		•	

Chapter Review and Assessment

SE Chapter 6 Review, p. 158 L3
CTB Chapter 6 Test L2 L3 L4
SE Standardized Test Prep, p. 159 L3

PROGRAM COMPONENTS

SE	Student Edition	CTB	Computer Test Bank
TE	Teacher Edition	AUD	Audio Section Summaries
TR	Teaching Resources		
RN	Reading and Note Taking Guide	DVD	Teens Talk Video Series
		VVG	Video Viewing Guide
ARN	Adapted Reading and Note Taking Guide	PPT	Presentation
IB	Image Bank		

Differentiated Instruction
L1 L2 L4 EL

		SE eTEXT	TE eTEXT	PRINT
ARN	Note Taking Guide 6-1 L2	•	•	
RN	Note Taking Guide 6-1 EL	•	•	•
AUD	Audio Summary 6-1 L1 L2 EL	•	•	
TE	Reteach Strategy, p. 140 L2		•	•
TR	Enrich 6-1 L4		•	
ARN	Note Taking Guide 6-2 L2	•	•	
RN	Note Taking Guide 6-2 EL	•	•	•
AUD	Audio Summary 6-2 L1 L2 EL	•	•	
TE	Reteach Strategy, p. 145 L2		•	•
TR	Enrich 6-2 L4		•	
ARN	Building Health Skills 6 L2	•	•	
RN	Building Health Skills 6 EL	•	•	•
ARN	Note Taking Guide 6-3 L2	•	•	
RN	Note Taking Guide 6-3 EL	•	•	•
AUD	Audio Summary 6-3 L1 L2 EL	•	•	
TE	Reteach Strategy, p. 151 L2		•	•
TR	Enrich 6-3 L4		•	
ARN	Note Taking Guide 6-4 L2	•	•	
RN	Note Taking Guide 6-4 EL	•	•	•
AUD	Audio Summary 6-4 L1 L2 EL	•	•	
TE	Reteach Strategy, p. 156 L2		•	•
TR	Enrich 6-4 L4		•	

ABILITY LEVELS
- **L1** For students with special needs
- **L2** For less proficient readers
- **L3** For all students
- **L4** For gifted and talented students
- **EL** For English language learners

Chapter 6 Digital/Video Pathway

This alternative pathway allows you to teach this chapter's content using only the video and online materials.

Preview
DVD	**Video #6 Preview**
SE	Video #6 Preview Activity
VVG	Video #6 Worksheet

Choosing Abstinence

1
PPT	6-1 Presentation
RN/ARN	6-1 Note Taking
PPT	6-1 Section Quiz

2
PPT	6-2 Presentation
RN/ARN	6-2 Note Taking
PPT	6-2 Section Quiz

3
PPT	6-3 Presentation
RN/ARN	6-3 Note Taking
PPT	6-3 Section Quiz

4
DVD	**Video #6 Explore/Wrap-Up**
VVG	Video #6 Worksheet
PPT	6-4 Presentation
RN/ARN	6-4 Note Taking
PPT	6-4 Section Quiz

Choosing Abstinence

Chapter Preview

Section 1 Skills for Healthy Relationships
Skills that help a person communicate effectively include active listening, using "I" messages, being assertive, and using appropriate body language. Cooperation builds strong relationships based on trust, caring, and responsibility. Compromise is an important skill for resolving the conflicts that arise in relationships.

Section 2 Friendships
Friendships are relationships that offer a sense of belonging. Friends can offer honesty, encouragement, and understanding. Problems that can occur in friendships include envy, jealousy, and cruelty.

 Advocacy
Supporting a Friend
Developing strategies for supporting friends can strengthen relationships.

Section 3 Responsible Relationships
Dating, either in a group or as a couple, provides an opportunity to learn about another person's personality, interests, abilities, and values. Violence in dating relationships can include emotional, physical, or sexual abuse.

Section 4 Choosing Abstinence
The risks of sexual intimacy include the risk of pregnancy and the risk of sexually transmitted infections. Teens who choose abstinence need to set clear limits, communicate those limits, avoid high-pressure situations, and assert themselves.

GO ONLINE
PearsonSuccessNet.com
For resources and activities for this chapter.

Building Healthy Peer Relationships

1 Skills for Healthy Relationships

2 Friendships
  • **Media Wise** Gender Roles and Movies

Building Health Skills
  • **Advocacy** Supporting a Friend

3 Responsible Relationships

4 Choosing Abstinence

GO ONLINE PearsonSuccessNet.com

TEENS Talk

VIDEO 6

Choosing Abstinence

Preview **Activity**

What Do Your Choices Say About You?

Complete this activity before you watch the video

1. Think about this quote.
   It is our choices that show what we truly are, far more than our abilities.
2. Then write a short paragraph describing what the quote means to you. **WRITING**
3. Pair up with another student to share and discuss your paragraphs.

134

 Sensitive Issues

• Friendships can be a sensitive topic for those who struggle to make friends or who are facing a problem in a friendship.

• Those who are dating may be reluctant to discuss problems in dating relationships. Those who are not dating may feel left out of the discussions.

• Abstinence can be a difficult topic for students, especially if they are already sexually active. Don't require students to participate in a discussion if they are uncomfortable with the topic.

• Never ask students to disclose information they would rather keep confidential.

Video Objectives

Use this video to help students

Recognize the risks of sexual intimacy and the benefits of choosing abstinence.

Develop the decision-making and communication skills they need to resist the pressure to have sex.

Identify ways to avoid high-pressure situations.

Preview **Activity**

What Do Your Choices Say About You?

Assign the Preview Activity for homework a few days before you plan to show the video. Just before you show the video, have pairs of students discuss their responses. Then, as a class, review the role that values play in decision making.

135

From the Authors

As a teacher, you have an opportunity to reinforce the message of abstinence that teens hear from parents and clergy by stressing the value of abstinence to health. For teens, sexual abstinence is a behavior that makes good sense from a public health standpoint because it is a protective factor against unwanted pregnancy and sexually transmitted infections.

Because national data suggest that you will be teaching many students who have already become sexually involved, you can also stress the value of a return to abstinence. The Health at Home activity on page 156 is designed to encourage dialogue between students and adult family members about sexual decisions.

Objectives
Before class begins, write the objectives on the board. Have students copy the objectives into their notebooks at the start of class.

1. Focus

Warm-Up **Advice Line**

After students finish writing, ask volunteers to share their responses with the class. Then ask students what they think the phrase "stand up for himself" means. Tell students that one of the skills they will learn in this section is assertiveness, which is an effective way to stand up for yourself without being threatening or disrespectful to others.

Presentation 6-1

Objectives
▶ **Describe** four skills that contribute to effective communication.
▶ **Explain** how cooperation and compromise help build healthy relationships.

Vocabulary
• communication
• "I" message
• active listening
• passive
• aggressive
• assertive
• body language
• eye contact
• cooperation
• compromise

Warm-Up

Dear Advice Line,

A friend of mine makes plans for the two of us without checking with me first. He assumes that I will want to do whatever he wants, and I don't speak up to avoid problems. How can I get my friend to see that my opinion matters?

WRITING What advice would you give this person? How can he stand up for himself?

Effective Communication

When you laugh at a joke, hug a parent, or ask a friend for advice, you are communicating. **Communication** is the process of sharing information, thoughts, or feelings. Learning to communicate effectively takes practice, like learning to ride a bicycle. The more you practice, the less you have to think about what you are doing. With practice, you can master the skills of effective communication. **These skills include using "I" messages, active listening, assertiveness, and using appropriate body language.**

"I" Messages   To express your feelings accurately, it helps to use "I" messages. An **"I" message** is a statement that expresses your feelings, but does not blame or judge the other person.

Suppose you are upset with a friend who forgot to call you. When you speak to your friend the next day, you shout, "Can't you remember anything?" This approach could put your friend on the defensive and cause a serious disagreement. Instead of yelling at your friend, it would be better to focus on how the situation made *you* feel. By saying something like, "I am upset because we didn't talk last night," you open the lines of communication between you and your friend.

WRITING and Health

 Essay

Tell students that observing how others communicate can help them improve their own communication skills. Ask students to find a situation in a book, movie, or television program that shows two people arguing about a personal issue. Have students set the scene by briefly describing the relationship between the characters and why they are arguing. Then ask students to write an evaluation of the characters' communication styles and skills. Remind students to use specific examples to support their conclusions.

Active Listening   Many people think of communication as nothing more than talking. But for communication to be effective, it must be a two-way process. There must be a listener as well as a speaker. The listener must do more than simply hear what is said—he or she must be actively involved in the conversation.

Active listening is focusing your full attention on what the other person is saying and letting that person know you understand and care. An active listener responds to what is being said. The listener makes the speaker feel comfortable about opening up and expressing personal feelings. To become an active listener, try the following.

▶ Show your interest by looking at the person, nodding your head, and showing concern on your face.

▶ Encourage the speaker to begin speaking by saying "Do you want to talk about …" or "You seem upset about…."

▶ When the speaker pauses, show your interest by offering comments such as "Then what happened?" or "What did you do then?"

▶ Avoid passing judgment on what the speaker says.

▶ Show you have been listening by summarizing the speaker's ideas with phrases such as "It sounds like you were angry when…" or "I heard you say…."

▶ Help the speaker explore things further with phrases such as "Tell me more about…" or "I guess you felt…."

▶ Do not steer the conversation away from the speaker's problem and onto a problem of your own.

 **Connect to Your Life**   **How would you rate yourself as an active listener? In what ways could you improve?**

FIGURE 1   Using active listening in the classroom can help you to learn. **Evaluating** How do the questions that a teacher asks students contribute to the process of active listening?

137

2. Teach

L3 **EL** Reading/Note Taking 6-1

L2 Adapted Reading/Note Taking 6-1

Effective Communication

L3 **Building Health Skills**

Practicing Healthful Behaviors After you discuss the bulleted list of suggestions for becoming an active listener, ask students to rephrase each suggestion as one or more statements that can be included in a checklist. (For example, the first suggestion could be rephrased as "I look at the speaker" and "I nod or use facial expressions to show my concern.") Have students use the checklist to monitor and evaluate their own active listening skills. After one week, ask volunteers to share their observations with the class.

L2 **Cooperative Learning**

Divide the class into small groups. Ask the members of each group to discuss and select one everyday situation in which a teen could use active listening skills. Within the group, have students act out two versions of the same situation. The first version should not include active listening skills. The second version should demonstrate how active listening skills contribute to a positive outcome in the selected situation.

L3 **Visual Learning: Figure 1**

Discuss different ways that information can be shared in a classroom, including lectures, dialogues, and activities. Ask students to consider how active listening could be applied in each situation. **Caption Answer** *Sample answer:* The questions allow students to demonstrate that they have been paying attention. Plus the teacher can find out if students understand what has been said.

Connect to Your Life Allow students to answer this question in their private journals.

Differentiated Instruction

EL **English Language Learners**

Write the following statements on the board: (1) You always borrow my books without asking. (2) You're always late when we agree to meet somewhere. (3) All of my friends can stay out later than I can. Ask students to verbally rephrase each statement as an "I" message.

L1 **Special Needs**

Encourage students with visual or hearing impairments to discuss the skills they use to communicate. First consider skills that can be universally applied, such as the use of "I" messages. Then talk about how communication is affected when a person cannot see other people's facial expressions or hear their tone of voice.

⑫ Visual Learning: Figure 2
Image Bank Figure 6-2

After students read the examples of passive, aggressive, and assertive behaviors, have them apply what they read to some everyday scenarios. For example, a student cuts in front of them in the lunch line. Ask: **What are some possible passive, aggressive, and assertive responses?** *(saying nothing; yelling; using an "I" message to express displeasure)* **Why is an assertive response most likely to resolve a situation in a positive way?** *(You can express your feelings without being threatening or disrespectful to others.)*
Caption Answer A person who mumbles and fidgets has a passive communication style.

⑬ Building Media Literacy

Ask students to take note of the communication styles used in a television program they ordinarily watch. Have them record instances of passive, aggressive, and assertive communication that occur in the program. Encourage students to share their observations with the class. Then ask students to consider how communication styles used on television influence communication styles used by teens. Have students identify examples of ways that television programs positively and negatively influence teens' communications skills.

Passive, Aggressive, and Assertive Communication

Passive Behaviors	Aggressive Behaviors	Assertive Behaviors
► Hoping the other person will guess your feelings	► Using "you" messages to blame the other person	► Using "I" messages to explain your feelings
► Always listening; rarely talking	► Interrupting; being sarcastic	► Actively listening to the other person
► Denying your own feelings; making excuses	► Making fun of the other person's feelings	► Trying to understand the other person's feelings
► Criticizing yourself; always apologizing	► Criticizing the other person; never giving a compliment	► Expressing appreciation; being respectful
► Always giving in to the other person	► Always wanting your own way	► Seeking a compromise that does not go against either person's values
► Mumbling; looking away; fidgeting nervously	► Yelling; refusing to talk; finger pointing; glaring; using physical force	► Speaking confidently and clearly; making eye contact; showing interest

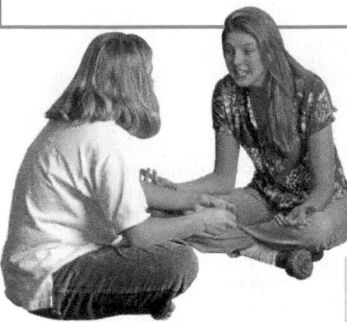

FIGURE 2 People provide both verbal clues and nonverbal clues when they communicate. **Classifying** Suppose a person mumbles and fidgets during a conversation. How would you describe that person's communication style?

Assertiveness How do you express your opinions and feelings when they differ from those of another person?

► Are you **passive,** holding back your true feelings and going along with the other person?

► Are you **aggressive?** Do you communicate opinions and feelings in a way that may seem threatening or disrespectful to other people?

► Are you assertive? When you are **assertive** (uh SUR tiv), you are able to stand up for yourself while expressing your feelings in a way that does not threaten the other person.

Figure 2 compares passive, aggressive, and assertive behaviors.

Assertiveness involves more than just what you say. How you say something, or the tone of your voice, also communicates your message. To understand how your tone of voice affects a message, try saying "Open your book to page 70" three different ways. First use a loud, demanding voice, then whisper the sentence, and then say it in a direct, assertive tone. The message changes with your tone of voice. The loud, demanding tone carries the implied threat "or else." The whisper suggests that you aren't sure the direction will be followed. The assertive tone shows that you expect the direction to be followed, without any implied threat.

People who are assertive tend to have healthier relationships than those who are passive or aggressive. Assertive behavior communicates respect both for yourself and for others. Passive behavior shows lack of respect for yourself. Aggressive behavior shows lack of respect for others.

138 *Chapter 6*

TEENS *Are Asking . . .*

Q: My dad always says "the squeaky wheel gets the grease." He encourages me to be aggressive to make sure I get what I want. Other people say being aggressive is bad. Who's right?

A: Your dad is right that there are times when it is important to speak up. But you don't need to be aggressive to be heard.

Being assertive doesn't mean being weak or unclear. It simply means acting in a way that shows respect for yourself and the person you are communicating with. Talk with your dad about the characteristics of aggressive and assertive behavior. He may be willing to change his advice from "be aggressive" to "be assertive."

Body Language You can also communicate information or feelings through body language. **Body language** includes posture, gestures, facial expressions, and body movements. People are often unaware of the silent messages sent by their body language. For example, if you slouch in your chair during class, the teacher may think you are bored or unprepared.

Sometimes a person's body language matches their spoken words, as when a person gestures to emphasize a point. Other times, the messages you send with your body language may contradict what you are saying. People may smile while saying something cruel or show little warmth with their face while saying something nice. In fact, people who lie sometimes give themselves away through their body language.

Like spoken language, body language varies from culture to culture. For example, most Americans expect you to make **eye contact,** or meet their gaze, when you talk with them. They may interpret a failure to make eye contact as shyness, indifference, embarrassment, or even sneakiness. But in Japanese and Native American cultures, making eye contact in some situations is a sign of disrespect.

GO ONLINE
PearsonSuccessNet.com
For: More on being assertive

 **Connect to Your Life** Which term describes your communication style, passive, aggressive, or assertive? Explain why.

Cooperation

Have you ever worked with classmates to complete a project? If so, then you know the importance of **cooperation,** or working together toward a common goal. To successfully meet the goal, people must work together as a team. Everybody on the team must meet their responsibilities and trust others to meet theirs.

Cooperation is important in all relationships. Suppose your aunt is coming to visit and your family needs to clean the house. If everyone works together to complete this chore, things will get done more easily than if one person has to do it alone. When friends study together, each can help the others master difficult material. **Cooperation builds strong relationships that are based on mutual trust, caring, and responsibility.**

FIGURE 3 These teens were asked to find a way to rise from a seated position while keeping their arms linked. This task demonstrates the need to cooperate to achieve a goal.

L3 Online Activity  GO ONLINE

Visit Pearson SuccessNet to access an online activity about being assertive. Have students complete the Web activity.

L3 Building Health Skills

Communicating Have students work in small groups to practice using appropriate body language to improve communication. Have the groups brainstorm a list of ten situations in which body language could make a difference. Provide some examples to get them started—being interviewed for a job, apologizing to a friend, testifying in court. After they complete their lists, students should take turns demonstrating body language that is appropriate and inappropriate for each situation. Ask each group to pick one situation to present to the whole class.

Connect to Your Life Allow students to answer this question in their private journals.

Cooperation

L1 Active Learning

Discuss with students the importance of body language in communication. Point out that most people use body language without even thinking about it. Explain that photographs provide an opportunity to examine people's use of body language. Provide students with magazines, and ask them to find pictures of people who are engaged in conversation. Have students analyze the body language in each picture. Then help students make a poster using the pictures and short descriptions of the body language shown in each picture.

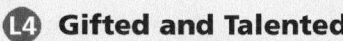

Differentiated Instruction

L4 Gifted and Talented

Explain that being able to cooperate is an essential skill in most workplaces. Then ask each student to choose an adult to interview about the importance of cooperation in the workplace. Remind students to prepare their questions in advance. Ask students to take notes, but explain that they will be able to keep their interview notes private. After students have completed their interviews, have them use their notes to write a report summarizing what they learned. Ask volunteers to share their reports with the class. **WRITING**

Compromise

L3 Journal Writing

Ask students to write in their private journals about a time when their ability to compromise helped strengthen a relationship. **WRITING**

3. Assess

Evaluate

These assignments can help you assess students' mastery of the section content.

Section 1 Review

Answers appear below.

Teaching Resources
• Practice 6-1
• Section 6-1 Quiz

L2 Reteach

Ask each student to choose one of the communication skills. Have them work with a partner to demonstrate the skill.

L4 Enrich

Teaching Resources
• Enrich 6-1

Health at School

Working in Groups The summary paragraph should focus on the group's ability to cooperate. Ask volunteers to share their responses. Then discuss what can make it easier or harder for a group to cooperate effectively.

FIGURE 4 For a compromise to work, both people must be satisfied with the solution

Compromise

Imagine that you and a friend are having a disagreement. You would like to go to the mall tonight, but your friend would rather go to the movies. How would you handle this problem? Because disagreements arise from time to time in all close relationships, it is important to be willing to compromise. **Compromise** (KAHM pruh myz) is the willingness of each person to give up something in order to reach agreement. Compromising is a skill of give-and-take. Both people must be willing to sacrifice something to get something in return. Both people also must feel comfortable with the solution reached.

Possible Solutions You and your friend could compromise in a number of ways. You could agree to go to the mall tonight and to a movie tomorrow. Or you could go to the mall first and then to a movie. Or you could even decide to do a totally different activity. Whatever agreement you arrive at, the ability to compromise will strengthen your relationship. **When you are willing to compromise, you let the other person know how important the relationship is to you.**

When Not to Compromise Of course, there are some situations in which it is important not to compromise. A friend might ask you to do something that is dangerous or that goes against your values. Instead of compromising with your friend, you need to use assertive communication. Let your friend know how you feel, and make it clear that there is no room for compromise on the issue.

Section 1 Review

Key Ideas and Vocabulary

1. What are four important communication skills?
2. Give an example of an "I" message.
3. How does **active listening** differ from just listening?
4. How can a willingness to cooperate or compromise strengthen a relationship?

Critical Thinking

5. **Evaluating** Can a person's body language affect a listener more than his or her words? Give an example to support your answer.

Health at School

Working in Groups With four of your classmates, write a short skit that illustrates the importance of good communication. After you have completed the skit, discuss how well the members of your group worked together to get the task done. Write a paragraph summarizing your discussion. **WRITING**

6. **Comparing and Contrasting** How does being aggressive differ from being assertive?
7. **Predicting** Which communication skills would be most helpful when you use e-mail or instant messaging? Which would be more difficult to apply? Use examples to support your answer.

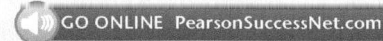
GO ONLINE PearsonSuccessNet.com   Audio Summary Section 6.1

Section 1 Review

1. using "I" messages, active listening, assertiveness, and using appropriate body language
2. *Sample answer:* I feel angry when you arrive later than promised.
3. Active listeners pay attention, show interest, and respond to the speaker.
4. Strong relationships are based on trust, caring, and responsibility. Cooperation shows that a relationship is important.
5. *Sample answer:* Yes. If a person with clenched fists says he or she is not angry, a listener is unlikely to believe the words.
6. Aggressive behaviors can be threatening or disrespectful; with assertive behaviors, you show respect for yourself and the listener.
7. You can use "I" messages and some active listening skills. Tone of voice and body language wouldn't be available.

Friendships

Warm-Up

Quick Quiz Which of these do you value most in a friend?

1. Someone who offers to help when you have a problem

2. Someone who makes you laugh even when you are sad

3. Someone who expresses emotions without hurting others

4. Someone who is honest and reliable

5. Someone who is a good listener

WRITING Explain why you selected the answer that you did.

Objectives

▶ **Explain** the importance of having friends.

▶ **Distinguish** different types of friendships.

▶ **Describe** some problems that occur in friendships.

Vocabulary

- friendship
- gender roles
- clique
- peer pressure

The Importance of Friendships

Do you have a close friend whom you have known since early childhood? Perhaps, as preschoolers, you spent hours together building whole cities with wooden blocks. Later, you may have discussed sports or favorite television programs. Now, as teenagers, you may talk about problems you face at home and school and give each other advice and encouragement.

The bond that you two have established is one kind of friendship. **Friendship** is a relationship based on mutual trust, acceptance, and common interests or values. **People look to their friends for honest reactions, encouragement during bad times, and understanding when they make mistakes.** Friends offer a sense of belonging. They are a handy reminder that there are other people who understand and care about you.

Most teens think that it is important to be part of one or more groups of friends. Interacting with others helps you to build self-esteem and to learn about yourself. You can experiment with different roles: leader, helper, advice-seeker, or supporter. Also, activities such as exercising, washing a car, or studying for a test can be more enjoyable when you do them with friends. Something that may seem silly to do alone, like dressing up in a costume, can be fun to do with friends.

Building Healthy Peer Relationships **141**

Objectives

Before class begins, write the objectives on the board. Have students copy the objectives into their notebooks at the start of class.

1. Focus

Warm-Up Quick Quiz

Use the Warm-Up Presentation slide to survey student responses.

Give students several minutes to read the choices and select a response. Then have students complete the writing assignment. For each possible quiz response, ask a volunteer who selected that response to share his or her writing with the class. Remind students that there are no right or wrong responses to this quiz.

Presentation 6-2

2. Teach

L3 EL Reading/Note Taking 6-2

L2 Adapted Reading/Note Taking 6-2

The Importance of Friendships

L2 Class Discussion

Write on the board the following headings: Honest Reactions, Encouragement, and Understanding. Point out that people often look to their friends for these three types of support. Have students identify and discuss examples of when it would be important for friends to offer each type of support.

Differentiated Instruction

L1 Special Needs

Discuss the qualities students feel are important in a friend. Then ask students to describe activities they enjoy doing with friends. Have students use words and drawings or magazine pictures to make a poster entitled "Friendship." After students finish their posters, ask them to explain why they chose certain words, pictures, or drawings. Encourage students to share any questions they have about friendships. Help students record their questions. After you complete the section, follow up to see if their questions were answered.

Types of Friendships

L3 Online Activity GO ONLINE

Visit Pearson SuccessNet to access an online activity about friendships. Have students complete the Web activity.

EL Cooperative Learning

Have students work with a partner to practice asking questions that require more than just a *yes* or *no* answer. Ask students to take turns. If one student asks a question that could be answered *yes* or *no*, the students should work together to rephrase the question.

L3 Journal Writing

Challenge students to think about a time when a close friend helped them through a difficult situation. Have students write an entry in their private journals that describes what the friend did to show support. After students have completed their writing, suggest they thank their friends, either verbally or in writing, for their support during the difficult time. **WRITING**

L4 Building Health Skills

Analyzing Influences Challenge students to find two passages from fiction in which characters demonstrate one or more qualities of a close friend. Ask students to explain in writing how each passage illustrates these qualities. Have students share their passages and explanations with the class. Then discuss how reading such passages might influence how people behave. **WRITING**

GO ONLINE
PearsonSuccessNet.com
For: More on friendships

FIGURE 5 Close friendships provide some security, while allowing you the chance to act independently.

Tips for Making Friends

▸ Be yourself; don't put on an act.
▸ Join groups that share your values or offer activities you like.
▸ Treat everyone with respect.
▸ Take a little time to talk with people you know casually.
▸ Ask questions that require more than just a *yes* or *no* answer.

142

Types of Friendships

Friendships range from the casual acquaintances you find through social media, to the friends you greet in the halls at school, to the friends who share your most personal thoughts. **Some friendships are casual, and some are close. Some are with friends of the opposite sex.** Each type of friend is valuable for different reasons.

Casual Friends Casual friendships can occur because people go to the same school, live in the same neighborhood, or have interests in common. Many casual friendships do not actually meet the definition of friendship. They are the so-called "friends" you make through social media. These electronic acquaintances provide an avenue to chat about food, or movies, or sports, but rarely involve communicating about highly personal or private matters. These "friends," however, provide a comforting sense of fitting in during this electronic age.

Short-term, casual friendships offer the chance to have fun, to try new things, and to learn to get along with a variety of people. Casual friends enjoy each other's company, and enjoy communicating through texts or telephone conversations. These friendships may remain casual, or they may develop into deeper, long-lasting friendships over time. Figure 5 offers some tips on making new friends.

Close Friends People tend to form close friendships with others who share similar goals, values, or interests. Sometimes people are drawn to each other because their personalities just seem to match.

No matter how a friendship forms, most people agree on four qualities that are important in a close friend.

▸ **Loyalty** A close friend sticks by you in both good times and bad.

▸ **Honesty** You can trust a close friend to be truthful, even when the truth is painful. You know that your friend isn't trying to hurt you.

▸ **Empathy** A close friend is caring and sensitive to your feelings.

▸ **Reliability** A close friend can always be counted on. You know your friend will try hard not to let you down.

For Your INFORMATION!

Independence and Conformity

Close friendships provide teens with a sense of belonging and security at a time when most adolescents are trying to gain some independence from their families. During adolescence, emotional needs that were met by the family begin to be met by friends.

Often friendships that ease the transition toward independence from the family depend on conformity to a particular peer group. So teen friendships both promote and discourage a teen's growing sense of independence and individuality.

Media Wise

Gender Roles and Movies

People learn about gender roles by observing how other people behave. Family members, friends, and other adults may serve as roles models. People also receive messages about gender roles from movies. Use this checklist to evaluate how gender roles are shown in a movie.

Do the females tend to be less assertive than the males?	Yes No
Are the male roles more action-oriented than the female roles?	Yes No
Do the females share their feelings more easily than the males?	Yes No
When there is a problem to solve, is the problem solver usually male?	Yes No
Do the men tend to work outside the home and the women inside the home?	Yes No

Two or more "Yes" answers indicate a movie that supports traditional gender roles.

Activity Use the checklist to evaluate gender roles in two movies. Then write a paragraph about what you observed. How do you think these movies affect people's opinions about gender roles? **WRITING**

Friends of the Opposite Sex When you were in elementary school, boys may have formed friendships with other boys with whom they had common interests. Girls may have formed close friendships with other girls. Today, you probably have both male and female friends.

Opposite-sex friendships may develop more easily now than in earlier generations because of changes in gender roles. **Gender roles** are the behaviors and attitudes that are socially accepted as either masculine or feminine. Gender roles vary from culture to culture. In the United States, gender roles are less rigid today than they have been in the past. Many people now choose activities and behave in ways that traditionally were reserved for members of the other gender. Both males and females learn to express various emotions, including tenderness and assertiveness. They let the event or situation dictate which emotion is appropriate.

In choosing friends today, most people look for males and females with interests and goals similar to their own. Friendships between males and females can be satisfying and close, but not involve romance. These friendships help you to feel comfortable with members of the opposite sex and allow you to develop fully as a person. A friendship with the opposite sex may develop into a romantic relationship. Often, it does not.

 **Are you comfortable having close friendships with both males and females? Why or why not?**

Media Wise

Gender Roles and Movies

Although gender roles in the United States are less clearly defined now than they were in the past, students will probably be able to identify examples of traditional gender roles in current movies. Interested students may want to extend the activity by analyzing and comparing the way that gender roles are portrayed in movies from different eras.

Activity Ask volunteers to share their summaries with the class. Then have students indicate by a show of hands if they feel that movies influence people's opinions about gender roles. Have students provide examples to support their opinions.

L3 Cultural Connection

Ask students what they think the saying "boys will be boys" means. Use their responses to introduce the topic of gender roles. Encourage students to discuss how gender roles vary among cultures. Ask students to identify ways that people learn about traditional masculine or feminine roles.

Connect to Your Life Allow students to answer this question in their private journals.

EL English Language Learners

Write the terms *loyalty, honesty, empathy,* and *reliability* on the board. Tell students that these terms describe four qualities of a good friend. Have students work with a partner to determine the meaning of each term. (Provide dictionaries, if needed.)

Ask students to record each word and its definition on an index card. Encourage students to state the definitions in their own words and to give an example of each quality. Call on student pairs to share their definitions with the class.

Problems in Friendships

L2 Visual Learning: Figure 6

Make sure students understand all the words used in the cartoon. Then ask them to answer the caption question. Explain that, given the way the cartoon is drawn, the cruelty was unintentional. Ask what Jeremy could have said to his friend instead. Then draw two large squares on the board, and challenge students to suggest how these two frames could be filled to show a positive way Jeremy and his friend could resolve this situation.

Caption Answer It was cruel to comment on her complexion.

L3 Cooperative Learning

Ask students to work in small groups to brainstorm a list of typical situations in which feelings of envy or jealousy might arise in a friendship. The group should choose one situation to discuss in detail. How might the envious or jealous friend behave? Will the reason for the behavior be clear to the other friend? What could each friend do to improve the situation? Ask one person from each group to summarize the discussion for the class.

L3 Class Discussion

Review the definition of *clique*. Then ask students if there are cliques at your school and, if so, what do the people in each clique have in common. Also ask how people in a clique typically treat people who are not in the clique. Finally, ask students if they think that having cliques at a school is a problem.

Connect to Your Life Allow students to answer this question in their private journals.

FIGURE 6 A cartoon often uses humor to make a serious point. **Interpreting Illustrations** How would you classify the problem illustrated in this cartoon? Explain.

Problems in Friendships

In all friendships, even close ones, problems arise from time to time. For a friendship to be a lasting one, it is important that friends face problems that arise and work together to resolve them. **Some possible problems in friendships are envy and jealousy, cruelty and manipulation, and cliques.**

Envy and Jealousy Envy can occur in a friendship when one person has something that the other person desires. The source of the envy can be appearance, talent, possessions, or popularity. Jealousy can occur when a "best" friend wants to develop other close friendships and the first friend feels left out.

It is normal at times to feel envy or jealousy, but if these feelings linger they can cause problems in a friendship. If you feel envy or jealousy, use your communication skills to discuss the problem. First, use "I" messages to get your feelings out in the open. It is best to do this in person, but if this is too difficult, write to your friend explaining your feelings. Be sure to listen to your friend's point of view and try to understand his or her feelings. Through active listening, you can gain a better understanding of your friendship and of ways to work things out.

Cruelty and Manipulation Sometimes a friend may be cruel or try to manipulate you even though you have done nothing to deserve such treatment. Your friend's behavior may have nothing to do with you. Your friend may be facing problems at home, at school, or elsewhere. Your friend may believe that controlling you, or being mean to you, will result in a stronger friendship. But cruelty and manipulation only lead to problems in a friendship. Unfortunately, people sometimes transfer the pain or anxiety they are feeling onto their close friends.

If a friend is cruel or tries to manipulate you, confront your friend to find out what the real problem is. Communicate that you are not willing to be mistreated. Also show your concern and desire to help your friend work things out.

Connect to Your Life Have you ever felt envy or jealousy toward a friend? If so, how did you deal with the feeling?

TEENS *Are Asking . . .*

Q: Why do guys spend so much time teasing each other? Even when the remarks are harsh, the guys just laugh them off.

A: Many guys find it easier to joke around than to have a serious conversation about feelings. The teasing can be a way of showing affection for friends. But put-downs or sarcasm may be used to express feelings of envy or jealousy. For example, if you envy a friend's success, you may try to belittle the achievement. Psychologists describe this behavior as devaluing or ridiculing what you cannot have.

Cliques Do you know a small, closed circle of friends that does not accept people who are different? If so, then you know a **clique** (klik), a narrow, exclusive group of people with similar backgrounds or interests.

Being a member of a clique can give a person a sense of belonging, but it also can deprive a person of forming friendships with a variety of people. A clique often discourages its members from thinking and acting independently. Clique members may experience **peer pressure,** a need to conform to the expectations of the tight circle of friends. Peer pressure can be a positive force when friends encourage each other to study hard, avoid drugs, or work hard toward a goal. It can be a negative force when friends feel pressured to do things that go against their values.

Peer pressure doesn't magically go away when you become an adult. Peer pressure is an issue that people deal with throughout their lives. However, peer pressure is an important issue during adolescence because this is the stage of life where you are searching for your identity. Health skills that you learn—making good decisions, refusing bad behaviors, setting goals, being assertive—will help you resist negative peer pressure. You will be less likely to encounter negative peer pressure if you choose your friends wisely. Choose people who care about you, share your values, and support your goals.

FIGURE 7 Members of a clique may feel pressured to dress and act in certain ways to go along with the group.

Section 2 Review

Key Ideas and Vocabulary

1. What is **friendship?** Why are friendships important?

2. Briefly describe three different types of friendships.

3. What are **gender roles?** How have changes in gender roles affected friendship patterns?

4. What kinds of problems can arise in friendships?

5. Explain how **peer pressure** can be both positive and negative.

Critical Thinking

6. **Comparing and Contrasting** How are casual friendships and close friendships similar? How are they different?

Health at School

Welcoming New Classmates Work in small groups to figure out ways to make teens who move to your school feel welcome. Make a list of possible things you could do. Then evaluate your list and decide which idea you think would work best. Finally, draft a proposal explaining how your idea would work. **WRITING**

7. **Applying Concepts** You and Cal have been friends for years, but recently he has been avoiding you. You're angry and hurt. What can you do to address the situation?

8. **Evaluating** What do you see as the most important problem that can arise within a social media friendship? Use an example to support your answer. How would you handle the problem?

Supporting a Friend

Objective

Develop strategies for providing support to friends.

Teaching Strategies

- Remind students that giving and receiving support is an important part of all friendships. Practicing effective strategies for giving support to others can enhance existing friendships and open the door to new friendships.

- Make sure students are clear on what it means to offer support that is empowering. Present examples of situations where a friend might need support (the friend is having trouble completing a term paper). Ask students to suggest ways to help and classify the responses as empowering (offer to read a draft and provide some feedback) or not empowering (offer to write the paper).

- Explain that an individual's need for support and ability to offer support to others varies over time. For example, an individual who is overwhelmed by problems at home might need a great deal of support from friends. When this individual's family situation has improved, he or she may be able to offer more support to others.

 Advocacy

Supporting a Friend

Ricardo has a part-time job after school working in a hardware store. He just heard of an opening at work and immediately called his friend Luis to tell him about it. Ricardo told Luis the questions he was asked in his interview so that Luis could be prepared when he met the manager. Ricardo also put in a good word for Luis with his boss. Ricardo knows that Luis really needs a job to help support his family because Luis' father just lost his job.

What are ways you can support a friend? The guidelines that follow offer helpful suggestions.

1 Identify ways you already support your friends.

There are many different kinds of support—a phone call, a visit, a hug, a ride to school, help with a project, advice, a sympathetic ear.

- ▶ Think of the important friends in your life. List the ways you think you support each of them.

- ▶ Ask yourself what else you could do to support them.

2 Offer support that empowers.

Make sure that the kind of support you offer doesn't take power or responsibility away from your friend. You don't want to make your friend feel helpless or incompetent. Support that empowers helps a friend to develop his or her own strengths and self-confidence.

- ▶ Help your friend improve at a skill you may be good at. But also let your friend teach or help you with something in return. Empowering support is a two-way street.

- ▶ Encourage your friend when he or she tries something new. Compliment your friend on doing well.

Sensitive Issues

- Most students will be reluctant to discuss problems they are having that might require support or problems that their friends are having. Assure students that their journal entries will remain private.

- Use hypothetical examples for class discussions, and ask questions such as "What kind of support could a teen offer in this situation?" rather than "What would you do in this situation?"

❸ Be an active listener.

▶ Show that you understand and care about your friend's problems. Be empathetic, not judgmental.

▶ Don't offer advice unless your friend asks for feedback. Then be constructive by helping your friend look beyond his or her current feelings or situation for possible solutions.

▶ If your friend is going through a difficult time, be especially sensitive. Make time to talk or do things with your friend. Sometimes just being there is helpful when a friend feels sad or angry.

▶ If your friend is doing something you think is dangerous or destructive, express your concern using "I" messages: "I feel … when you do.…" Offer to go with your friend if you think he or she needs professional help.

❹ Ask your friends for support.

Friends are not mind readers. If you need or want support, ask for it. Asking for support will make it easier for your friends to ask you for support when they need it.

▶ Make a list of the ways you would like to be supported by your friends.

▶ Be specific about what kind of support you would like.

▶ Show your appreciation when a friend does something nice for you.

❺ Encourage friends to ask you for support.

▶ Ask your friends if you can help them. Offer suggestions for how you might help.

▶ Follow through on what you say you will do.

Practice the Skill

1. For a few days, do what you normally would do, but keep a "support" journal. Record each time you offer support to a friend and each time a friend offers support to you. Write a brief description of the situation, the type of support offered, and the outcome.

Support Journal

Incident 1	Incident 2
Description	Description
I noticed that Marcus seemed dejected.	Olivia realized that I was having trouble keeping up in Social Studies.
Type of support	Type of support
When we had a moment alone, I told him what I had noticed and asked if he wanted to talk.	She offered to show me her system for taking notes in class.
Outcome	Outcome
Marcus told me about a problem he was having with his parents and I actively listened.	We reviewed my notes and Olivia showed me ways to improve them.

2. Review your journal entries. How often did you offer support to a friend? How often did a friend offer support to you? Were there any kinds of support offered that took away power? If so, how could these offers of support have been more empowering?

3. During the next week, look for at least three opportunities to support a friend. Also ask for support from one friend.

Practice the Skill

1. Have students prepare their support journals in advance, using the model shown in the text. Remind students that their support journals will remain confidential.

2. Ask for volunteers to talk in general about what they learned. For example, did they offer support more often than support was offered to them, or vice versa? If so, can they think of an explanation for this difference?

3. Encourage students to follow up on their experiences of giving and receiving support by writing a brief summary of their experiences in their private journal.

Health at Home

❸ Supporting Family Members

Remind students that the strategies used to support friends can also be used to support family members. Ask students to keep a support journal at home for several days. Have students record each time they offer support to a family member and each time a family member offers support to them. They should write a brief description of each situation, the type of support offered, and the outcome. After they review their entries, encourage students to share what they learned with their family. **WRITING**

Objectives

Before class begins, write the objectives on the board. Have students copy the objectives into their notebooks at the start of class.

1. Focus

Warm-Up Myth/Fact

Have a class discussion of the myth about rape before students begin their writing. Challenge students to identify specific precautions. Ask volunteers to share their responses with the class.

Presentation 6-3

🚩 **Sensitive Issues**

- If the norm at your school is for students to date, students who are not dating may be uncomfortable with discussions on dating.
- Be respectful of the variety of cultural and family practices regarding dating.
- Discuss hypothetical situations that might occur in dating relationships rather than asking students to relate personal experiences.

Section 3

Responsible Relationships

Objectives

- ▶ **List** some things you can learn about a person by dating.
- ▶ **Describe** the cycle of violence.

Vocabulary

- infatuation
- dating violence
- date rape

Warm-Up

Myth A person who is raped is usually attacked by a stranger.

Fact Most victims of rape know their attackers.

WRITING What precautions could someone take to reduce the risk of being raped by a friend or acquaintance?

Physical Attraction and Dating

The teenage years are a time when most young people begin to experience feelings of physical attraction. Have you ever had a "crush" on a movie star, athlete, teacher, or other person you admire? Most teenagers have. Another name for these feelings of intense attraction to another person is **infatuation.** Although these feelings can sometimes be overwhelming, they are normal and healthy for teenagers. From these feelings, you develop the ability to form close attachments later in your adult life.

When you are attracted to someone, you want to spend time with that person. Some people use the term *dating* to describe the time you spend together. **By dating someone, you can learn about his or her interests, personality, abilities, and values.** You can also learn how the other person views the gender roles that he or she learned as a child. You may even discover what qualities you want in a future marriage partner.

Dating practices vary with individuals, families, and cultures. Some teens don't date at all during high school because they don't want to or because dating is not permitted in their culture. When teens do date, some stick to traditional practices. For example, females may wait for males to ask them out, or expect the males to pay for the date. Today, however, many dating arrangements are more informal than in the past.

TEENS *Are Asking . . .*

Q: I am 14 years old. My parents say I'm too young to date. What can I do to convince them that they are wrong?

A: Ask your parents to set aside time to talk about this issue. Encourage them to state their specific concerns, and work together to find ways to address these concerns. Be respectful and mature—no yelling, sarcasm, or whining. Watch your body language. Here are some ways to address your parents' concerns. Arrange for your parents to meet the person you want to date. Invite him or her to share a meal with your family or to go on a family outing. Be honest and follow family rules, especially curfews. These actions will help you earn your parents' trust. Be willing to compromise. Offer to go out with a group, rather than as a couple.

Hanging Out and Talking People who are physically attracted to each other often begin to recognize that attraction when they hang out together for lengthy periods of time. Talking (and listening) can be a great way to get to know someone. Hanging out and talking can also occur in groups. There are advantages to hanging out as a group. It gives you an opportunity to see how people behave when they are with others. In return, the person you are attracted to can get to know more about you.

Going Out as Couples You may discover that you especially enjoy being with a certain friend. The person may be someone who shares your interests or has a similar sense of humor. You also may be physically attracted to this person. It is natural and healthy to feel physical attraction and to want to get to know the person better. This may lead to dating, either on your own or with other couples.

Dating After a few dates, a couple may decide not to go out with other people and to see each other on a regular basis. Dating a person exclusively can be a form of security—partners are assured of having someone to hang out with.

Exclusive dating has some drawbacks. You limit your chances of meeting other people you might like. You may feel pressured to make decisions about sexual intimacy before you are ready. If conflicts arise, it may be difficult to break off the relationship.

For some couples, exclusive dating leads to marriage. For couples who marry as teens, there are challenges beyond those faced by most married couples. These challenges may include a lack of emotional maturity, loss of freedom, and loss of shared activities with friends.

FIGURE 8 If you go out as a group or as couples, you get to know many different people. You also get to observe how a person you are attracted to interacts with others.

Connect to Your Life Do you think exclusive dating during high school is a good idea? Why or why not?

2. Teach

L3 EL Reading/Note Taking 6-3
L2 Adapted Reading/Note Taking 6-3

Physical Attraction and Dating

L2 Active Learning

Explain that dating is a way to learn about another person's personality, interests, abilities, and values. Distribute four index cards to each student. Tell students that their responses will be kept confidential. Ask students to write the word *personality* on the front of one card. On the back of the card, have students identify and record three personality traits they would find attractive in a person they might date. Have students complete similar cards titled *interests, abilities,* and *values.* Have a class discussion on the importance of thinking in advance about what qualities you might want in a date.

L3 Addressing Misconceptions

Teens and Dating Students may have the misconception that all teens date. Point out that many teens do not date, either by choice or due to cultural or family expectations. Some studies have found 38 percent of tenth graders and 34 percent of twelfth graders don't date.

EL Active Learning

Have students do brief, informal presentations about dating customs in their cultures. Encourage students to bring photographs or other objects to help them explain the customs.

Connect to Your Life *Sample answer:* I think exclusive dating during high school is not a good idea because it often leads to pressure for sexual intimacy.

Differentiated Instruction

L2 Less Proficient Readers

Have less proficient readers work as partners with advanced readers to prepare an outline of the material in this section. Have students use the boldface heads in the section as the main headings in their outlines. Under each heading, have students record key ideas, supporting details, and relevant vocabulary terms. Encourage students to review their outlines after they have completed the section and add information under each heading that will enhance their understanding of the content.

Violence in Dating Relationships

(L3) Visual Learning: Figure 9

Image Bank Figure 6-9

Have students read the description of each stage in the cycle of violence. Ask: **How is a victim likely to respond during the tension-building stage?** *(The victim may adjust his or her behavior in an attempt to please the abuser and avoid a violent episode.)* **What explanation can you offer for the abuser's actions during the calm stage?** *(Sample answer: The abuser is trying to maintain control, make the victim feel responsible, or keep the victim from seeking help.)* **Caption Answer** *Sample answer:* Victims may think they can control the cycle through their behavior, but abusers are always responsible for the violence.

(L1) Cooperative learning

Have students work together to make posters about the warning signs of abuse. If students are unclear about a warning sign, provide one or two examples. Encourage students to use drawings as well as words.

(L3) Building Health Skills

Advocacy Divide the class into small groups. Have each group develop a plan for advocating for a friend who is in a violent relationship. Then ask the groups to share their plans with the class. Challenge students to identify strategies that they feel would be most effective, and to provide reasons for their choices. Emphasize that notifying a trusted adult is important in all situations involving violence.

(L3) Content Update 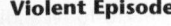 GO ONLINE

Visit Pearson SuccessNet to access more information about violence in dating relationships. Have students complete the Web activity.

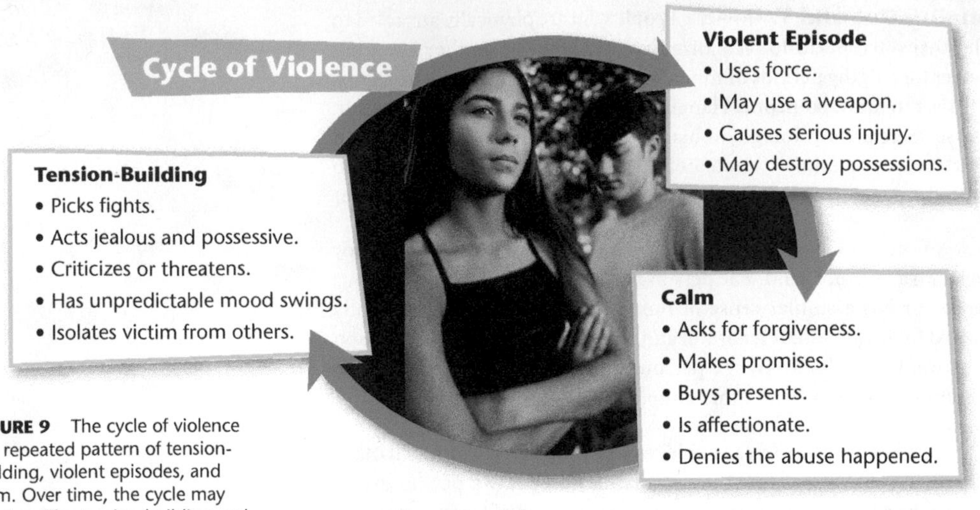

Cycle of Violence

Tension-Building
- Picks fights.
- Acts jealous and possessive.
- Criticizes or threatens.
- Has unpredictable mood swings.
- Isolates victim from others.

Violent Episode
- Uses force.
- May use a weapon.
- Causes serious injury.
- May destroy possessions.

Calm
- Asks for forgiveness.
- Makes promises.
- Buys presents.
- Is affectionate.
- Denies the abuse happened.

FIGURE 9 The cycle of violence is a repeated pattern of tension-building, violent episodes, and calm. Over time, the cycle may shorten. The tension-building and calm stages may disappear, leaving only a series of violent episodes. **Predicting** What control does the victim have over the cycle of violence?

GO ONLINE
PearsonSuccessNet.com
For: More on violence in dating relationships

Violence in Dating Relationships

Unfortunately, some teen relationships turn violent. One partner may slap the other when he or she is angry. Or make fun of the other's looks or abilities. Or constantly check up to find out what the person is doing. These are examples of dating violence. **Dating violence** is a pattern of emotional, physical, or sexual abuse that occurs in a dating relationship. One partner uses the abuse to gain control of the other partner.

The Cycle of Violence Often abuse occurs as part of the three-stage cycle in Figure 9. **The cycle of violence consists of a tension-building stage, a violent episode, and a calm or "honeymoon" stage.** During the tension-building stage, the victim may try to please the abuser or reason with the abuser in order to prevent violence. Sometimes victims describe this stage as "walking on eggshells." The tension is broken by a violent episode. During the calm stage, the abuser may apologize and promise to never abuse the victim again. The abuser may also blame the victim for the abuse. The calm is followed by another tension-building stage.

Warning Signs of Abuse A good way to avoid the cycle of violence is to recognize the warning signs that can lead to abuse.

- ► Your date is jealous when you talk to others. Your date makes fun of you in front of others.
- ► Your date makes all the decisions and tries to control what you do.
- ► Your date has a history of bad relationships.
- ► You feel isolated from your friends and family.
- ► You feel less self-confident. You worry about doing or saying the right thing. You change how you behave to avoid an argument.

 **and Health**

(L3) Dialogue

Have students consider the situation when a teen notices signs that a friend is in a violent dating relationship. Have students write a dialogue that the concerned friend might have with the abused friend. Ask students to consider how to best approach the topic. Have them consider how the abused friend might respond. Will the friend deny that the relationship is violent, or say that he or she is responsible for the behavior?

Date Rape More than half of young women who are raped know the person who raped them. The person may have been a steady date, a casual date, or an acquaintance. When the rape occurs during a date, the abuse is often referred to as **date rape.**

The rapist may have used a "date rape drug." These fast-acting drugs are hard to detect in food or a drink because they are colorless, tasteless, and odorless. Later, the victim will feel "hung over" and be unable to recall the rape. Friends will say that the victim acted drunk.

Rape and other forms of abuse are not just a problem for women. Men can be victims too. The emotional effects of rape can be long lasting. Thus, it is important to do what you can to decrease your chances of being attacked. Figure 10 lists some tips to reduce the possibility of date rape.

Tips for Dating Safely

- Go out as a group.
- Let someone know where you are going.
- Avoid alcohol or other drugs.
- Have money to get home.
- In an emergency, call 911.

FIGURE 10 These tips can help decrease the chances of date rape.

Ending the Abuse Why would a teen remain in an abusive relationship or hide the abuse from others? Some teens may view a possessive or jealous partner as romantic. Or they may think the behavior is normal because friends are in similar relationships. Females may think that males are supposed to act in a controlling manner or that physical aggression is a sign of masculinity. Males may be ashamed to admit that they are being abused for fear of being seen as weak. Sadly, some teens may think that they deserve to be abused. Others may fear being alone.

The first step to ending an abusive relationship is to admit that the abuse exists. The second step is to realize that you are not to blame for the abuse and that you cannot change how your abuser behaves. Finally, you don't have to deal with the problem on your own. Seek the support of friends and family. Call an abuse hotline if you want anonymous advice. Talk to a counselor, teacher, doctor, or social worker, but be aware that these adults are legally required to report abuse.

Section 3 Review

Key Ideas and Vocabulary

1. What does the term **infatuation** mean?
2. List three things people can learn by dating.
3. What is **dating violence?**
4. Describe the cycle of violence that can occur in a relationship.

Critical Thinking

5. **Comparing and Contrasting** What are some differences between infatuation and dating?
6. **Applying Concepts** Jordan has been your steady date for six months. You like Jordan, but want to start seeing others. What would be a caring way to tell Jordan how you feel?

Health and Community

Help Combat Dating Violence Find out about volunteer organizations in your community that deal with dating violence. For example, you could baby-sit for children at a local women's shelter. Or invite a police officer to talk about dating violence at a school assembly. Then write a paragraph summarizing what you learned. WRITING

7. **Evaluating** When Tamara's friends complain about how Dillon treats Tamara, she usually makes excuses for him. She says that he is under a lot of pressure and that her behavior often angers him. What advice would you give Tamara about her relationship with Dillon? WRITING

GO ONLINE PearsonSuccessNet.com Audio Summary Section 6.3

Section 3 Review

1. a feeling of intense attraction to another person
2. You can learn about someone's personality, interests, abilities, and values.
3. a pattern of emotional, physical, or sexual abuse that occurs in a dating relationship
4. There is a period of tension building, a violent episode, and a period of calm.
5. Infatuation is a one-sided, often unrealistic, relationship. A dating relationship is two-sided, with a realistic chance for growth.
6. Answers should include the use of "I" messages and active listening skills.
7. Answers should note that Tamara isn't responsible for Dillon's behavior.

3. Assess

Evaluate

These assignments can help you assess students' mastery of the section content.

Section 3 Review

Answers appear below.

Teaching Resources

- Practice 6-3
- Section 6-3 Quiz

L2 Reteach

Have students work in pairs to review the boldface headings in the section. For each heading, ask students to discuss the main ideas and vocabulary.

L4 Enrich

Teaching Resources

- Enrich 6-3

Health and Community

Help Combat Dating Violence Help the class brainstorm a list of activities that students could do to help combat dating violence. After students complete their writing, discuss what they learned. Ask students to identify any new or surprising facts that they learned about dating violence.

Objectives
Before class begins, write the objectives on the board. Have students copy the objectives into their notebooks at the start of class.

1. Focus

Warm-Up Health Stats

After students complete the writing assignment, ask if any of the results of the survey surprised them. Then, ask volunteers to share their responses to the writing assignment with the class.

Presentation 6-4

Objectives
▶ **Identify** some risks of sexual intimacy.
▶ **Explain** why emotional intimacy is important in close relationships.
▶ **List** some skills that can help you choose abstinence.

Vocabulary
• emotional intimacy
• abstinence

Warm-Up

Health Stats Who has the most influence on a teen's decisions about sex? The graph shows how some teens responded to this question.

WRITING Which influences do you think would help teens to make healthy decisions about sex?

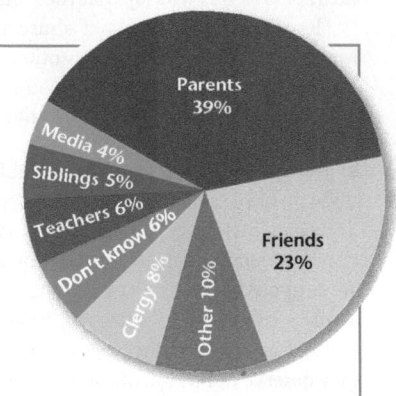

Parents 39%
Media 4%
Siblings 5%
Teachers 6%
Don't know 6%
Clergy 8%
Other 10%
Friends 23%

Risks of Sexual Intimacy

As teenagers become aware of their sexuality, some tough questions arise: How can I show affection without things going too far? Are my partner and I emotionally ready for a sexual relationship? There are no easy answers for such questions. It is important, however, to think about these questions before you have to make decisions that can affect the rest of your life.

As you think about sexual intimacy, there are some important issues for you to consider. **Sexual intimacy is not risk free. The risks include the effect on your emotional health, the effect on your relationship, the risk of pregnancy, and the risk of sexually transmitted infections.**

Effect on Your Emotional Health Decisions about sexual intimacy should be based on the values that you hold. Your family, friends, religion, culture, experiences, and the media help shape your values. Often the messages you receive from different sources will be contradictory. This makes it more difficult to sort out how you truly feel.

A decision to become sexually involved may go against a person's values. If the person makes the decision anyway, the person may feel guilty or ashamed. The person may feel that he or she has let down parents, friends, and others as well as himself or herself. The result of making snap decisions about sex is often a loss of self-respect. Using sex to prove something to oneself and others can also lower self-esteem.

152 *Chapter 6*

Sensitive Issues

Even a general discussion on issues related to sexual decision making may be uncomfortable for some students. Keep the discussion focused on what typical teens might be likely to do in certain situations.

MATH and Health

L3 Graphing

Ask students to convert the information from the Warm-Up into a bar graph. The *x*-axis label should be "Influences on a Teen's Decisions About Sex"; the *y*-axis label should be "Percentage of Teens." Discuss how changing the format in which information is displayed can change the impact information has on a viewer. Ask students if they think the circle graph or the bar graph has more impact. Then ask how the impact might change if the data were presented in a paragraph.

Effect on Your Relationship   A decision to become sexually intimate alters the way couples spend their time together. It also changes the way a couple relates to friends. Sexual intimacy can affect each person's expectations. One person may expect to have sex whenever the couple is together, while the other person may not. One person may become more possessive and put more demands on the other's time. One person may decide to end the relationship.

Often couples are not prepared for the complications that sexual intimacy adds to their relationship. Most couples find that these changes to their relationship are permanent. Although they may try, it is almost impossible to go back to the way things were before they had sex.

Risk of Pregnancy   A teenage pregnancy can pose serious health problems for the baby and the mother. Babies born to young mothers are often smaller and less healthy than those born to older women. Teenage mothers are more likely to have health problems during pregnancy than women in their twenties. This is because pregnant teens do not always eat well or get adequate medical care during pregnancy, especially in the early months.

Besides health problems, what effect does a baby have on a teenage couple? Parents are legally responsible to care for their children. Teenage parents often report feeling overwhelmed and trapped. Many teenage mothers drop out of school. Some fathers don't help support or care for the child; others drop out of school and work at low-paying jobs.

Young people are aware of the problems teenage parents face, but they often don't think that pregnancy can happen to them. Few teens want to become pregnant. But almost one third of young women become pregnant before age 20. Sexual intimacy is a high-risk behavior for anyone who isn't ready to accept the responsibility of children.

 **Connect to Your Life**   What effect might a pregnancy have on a teenage couple's relationship?

FIGURE 11   After caring for a baby, a teenage mother may not have enough energy left for school. **Predicting** How could dropping out of school affect the mother? How could it affect the baby?

About 25% of teen mothers have a second baby before age 20.

153

---

2. Teach

L3 EL **Reading/Note Taking 6-4**

L2 **Adapted Reading/Note Taking 6-4**

Risks of Sexual Intimacy

L1 Visual Learning: Figure 11

Ask students to describe the photograph in Figure 11. Then, discuss what a mother has to do to take care of a baby and how these tasks could interfere with her ability to stay in school. Encourage students to suggest other typical teen activities that the mother might no longer be able to do.

Caption Answer *Sample answer:* If the mother drops out of school, she limits her job opportunities, her future income, and her ability to provide for her child.

L3 Cooperative Learning

Have students work in small groups to prepare a 60-second radio public service announcement aimed at teens. The goal is to encourage teens to think about the risks of sexual intimacy. If possible, have students record their announcements so they can play them for the class. **WRITING**

L4 Active Learning

Have students research the lifelong financial impact of becoming a teen parent. Students should find information that relates to both teen mothers and teen fathers. Ask students to use the results of their research to prepare a short lesson to share with the class.

Connect to Your Life   *Sample answer:* A pregnancy could cause one or both partners to feel overwhelmed or trapped. These feelings would have a negative impact on the couple's relationship.

Emotional Intimacy

L1 Class Discussion

Explain that one way you can tell that a couple has a close, emotionally intimate relationship is to observe how they behave. Write a few examples on the board—finishing each other's sentences, doing unexpected kind things, or sharing "inside" jokes. Challenge students to add additional items to the list. Then discuss how these behaviors can strengthen a relationship.

Abstinence Skills

L3 Building Health Skills

Analyzing Influences Have students make a list of their ten favorite songs about relationships. Then ask students to analyze the content of the songs. Do the words describe or encourage sexual activity? Is any of the language used demeaning to females? Are there any references to emotional intimacy? After students complete the activity, ask volunteers to share their findings. Then discuss what influence music might have on a teen's sexual behavior.

EL Building Vocabulary

Write the term *abstinence* on the board. Explain that the broad meaning of the term is the act of voluntarily doing without something a person views as pleasurable—sex, alcohol, cigarettes.

L3 Building Media Literacy

Ask students to compare how attitudes toward sexual intimacy among teens are portrayed in television programs. Have students work as a class to create a graphic organizer or chart that displays the answers to the following questions: "Is sexual activity between teens a part of this program?" "Is abstinence from sexual activity mentioned?" "Are the risks of sexual intimacy between teens discussed?" Follow up with a class discussion on realistic and unrealistic portrayals of teen sexual intimacy that students have observed on television.

Risk of Sexually Transmitted Infections Some infections can be passed, or transmitted, from one person to another during sexual activity. These are called sexually transmitted infections, or STIs. If left untreated, many STIs cause serious health problems. For example, some STIs can cause infertility, or the inability to have children. Others shorten a person's life or require medical treatment throughout a person's life.

Emotional Intimacy

Contrary to what you may think, every teen is not sexually experienced. Millions of young people today choose to postpone sexual activity. On a television show, a young man spoke of his relationship with his girlfriend. "We're not ready for sex, but we share lots of other intimate experiences."

How can two people be intimate without being sexually involved? They can trust each other with personal feelings or dreams that they haven't told anyone else. They can exchange "inside" jokes. They can do kind things for each other and be best friends.

Emotional intimacy refers to the openness, sharing, affection, and trust that can develop in a close relationship. Two things can help a couple develop emotional intimacy. They must be honest with one another. They must be accepting and supportive of each other. **A couple can have a close relationship without being sexually intimate. But it is hard for them to keep a relationship close if there is no emotional intimacy.**

Abstinence Skills

Sergio and Selena met in class and became good friends. Soon, they started to date. As they spent more time together, they began to express their feelings of affection by hugging, kissing, and holding hands. Over time, the pressure to become more physically intimate grew stronger. But Sergio and Selena felt that abstinence was the best choice at this point in their lives.

Abstinence is the act of refraining from, or not having, sex. There are skills you can learn to help you choose abstinence when you are faced with the pressure to become more physically intimate. **These abstinence skills include setting clear limits, communicating your limits, avoiding high-pressure situations, and asserting yourself.**

FIGURE 12 Sharing and affection are two signs of strong emotional bonds. These bonds form when couples are honest and supportive of one another.

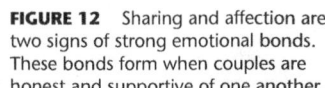

WRITING and Health

L3 Persuasive E-mail

Ask students to write a persuasive e-mail to a fictional friend that uses information from the section to encourage the friend to choose abstinence. Remind students that the term *persuasive* means having the power to convince someone to believe or do something. Post students' completed letters in the classroom. Allow students to circulate and read the letters. Then ask students to point out characteristics of particularly effective letters.

FIGURE 13 It is important to discuss your limits on sexual intimacy as early as possible in a relationship. **Evaluating** Which communication skills are most important when you want to clearly state your limits?

Set Clear Limits   It is natural to feel sexual attraction to someone you are dating. It is also natural to be unsure of how to handle these feelings. Most teenagers try to think ahead and set limits for expressing their sexual feelings. If you set limits before a situation arises, it will be easier to stick to the standards you set. Take some time now to set limits that you feel comfortable with. It is important to know your limits before you go out so you can avoid having to make a hasty decision.

To help yourself set limits, be sure to consider the important values that you hold and the possible consequences of your actions. Use the DECIDE process on pages 16–17 to help you make decisions with which you feel comfortable. Do not allow the expectations of friends, the media, and others to influence you to make decisions that may not be right for you.

Communicate Your Limits   Once you have decided on your limits, it is important to communicate your feelings to your partner. Of course, it is best to discuss things as early as possible in a relationship. Do not wait until a situation arises in which your partner's expectations may be different from yours. It may be difficult to have an open, constructive discussion if you wait until that point to talk.

Try to talk honestly to your partner about your feelings and values. You may be surprised at how relieved your partner may be to hear how you feel. He or she may have been anxious about your expectations.

If you have been sexually involved, it doesn't mean that you have to continue to be sexually involved. You may decide that a relationship built around emotional intimacy makes more sense and choose abstinence. If your partner tries to make you feel guilty, you may need to rethink your relationship. Do you really want to be with a person who does not respect your feelings or who does not value emotional intimacy?

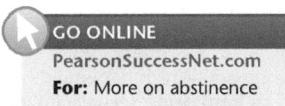
GO ONLINE
PearsonSuccessNet.com
For: More on abstinence

 Are you comfortable talking with friends about your values? Why or why not?

Building Healthy Peer Relationships   **155**

Visual Learning: Figure 13

Caption Answer *Sample answer:* Using "I" messages and assertiveness are most important when you want to clearly state your limits.

L3 Journal Writing

Remind students to consider their values when they make important decisions, such as setting limits for expression of sexual feelings. Ask students to write an entry in their private journals. In the entry, they should identify the personal values they can use to help them set limits for sexual activity. **WRITING**

L2 Cooperative Learning

Have pairs of students work together to make a list of "high-pressure" situations and "low-pressure" alternatives. For example, watching a rented movie as a couple when no one else is home versus going to a movie theater. Ask each group to share some responses with the class.

L3 Building Health Skills

Practicing Healthful Behaviors Have students work in small groups to practice refusal skills. Ask each group to make a list of ten things one person might say to convince another person to have sex. Then have the groups brainstorm a list of possible responses to each statement. Ask volunteers from each group to act out one statement and response. Remind students that tone of voice is key to the effective use of refusal skills.

Connect to Your Life Allow students to answer this question in their private journals.

L3 Content Update    GO ONLINE

Visit Pearson SuccessNet to access more information about abstinence. Have students complete the Web activity.

Differentiated Instruction

L2 Less Proficient Readers

Have students work in small groups to develop an idea for a television public service announcement about how a person's intended message about limits might get misunderstood. Encourage students to use humor to make their point.

Ask groups to present their ideas to the class. At minimum, the presentation should include a description of the situation and some dialogue. Some groups may want to use a storyboard with drawings to show the announcement frame by frame.

3. Assess

Evaluate
These assignments can help you assess students' mastery of the section content.

Section 4 Review
Answers appear below.

Teaching Resources
- Practice 6-4
- Section 6-4 Quiz

L2 Reteach
Ask students to make a bulleted list of the risks that are associated with sexual intimacy. Then, have students write a one-sentence description of each abstinence skill.

L4 Enrich

Teaching Resources
- Enrich 6-4

Health at Home

Comparing Viewpoints If local papers don't have an advice column for teens, have students access teen advice columns online. After students complete the activity, ask them what they learned from doing the activity. For example, were their responses to the letters and those of the adults similar or different? Do they think the activity will make it possible for them to talk more openly in the future with an adult about sexual choices?

FIGURE 14 One way for couples to avoid high-pressure situations is to go out as a group.

Avoid High-Pressure Situations Sticking to the limits you set can be difficult. You can make it easier for yourself by avoiding certain situations. For example, if you are at an unsupervised party, you might feel pressured to have sex. But if you are in a public place, the temptation to engage in sexual activities is not as great. It is also important to avoid alcohol and other drugs, as they can blur your ability to think clearly.

Spend time with friends that share your values. You might want to include your date in family outings. Not only will you not be tempted to have sex, you will see how your date interacts with different people.

Assert Yourself If you find yourself in a situation where you are not comfortable with the level of physical intimacy, don't feel guilty about saying no. State clearly and directly that you want to stop. You may want to offer a reason, such as "I'm just not ready," so that the other person won't feel hurt or rejected.

At times, however, simply saying no once may not be effective. You may need to be firm and say something like "No! I said I don't want to do that." You may need to repeat yourself a few times before your partner realizes that you are serious. If necessary, get up and walk away.

One person may try to pressure another by saying that, at some levels of intimacy, it is impossible to stop without causing physical harm. This isn't true. The person might also say things like "If you loved me, you would do it," or "Everybody does it." Remember that you will respect yourself more for sticking to your limits than for giving in to pressure.

If your partner does not respect the limits you set, the relationship may not be worth continuing. Try to meet people who understand the importance of dealing responsibly with sexual feelings. Look for people who value emotional intimacy.

Section 4 Review

Key Ideas and Vocabulary
1. What are four possible risks of sexual intimacy?
2. Define **emotional intimacy**.
3. How can emotional intimacy help a relationship to grow?
4. What is **abstinence**? What skills can help you to choose abstinence?

Critical Thinking
5. **Making Judgments** Review the risks of sexual intimacy. Which risk would be most likely to keep you from being sexually intimate? Give a reason for your choice.

Health at Home

Comparing Viewpoints Work with a parent or another trusted adult. Select two letters about teenage sexual choices from an advice column in a newspaper. Separately, the two of you should write responses to the letters. Then compare your responses to each other's and to the actual advice offered in the newspaper. **WRITING**

6. **Applying Concepts** How could a person who doesn't want to be sexually involved respond to each of these "pressure" lines?
   a. "If you loved me, you would have sex with me."
   b. "Everyone else is having sex. What's wrong with you?"
   c. "You know you want to. Everyone wants to."

156 Chapter 6

GO ONLINE PearsonSuccessNet.com Audio Summary Section 6.4

Section 4 Review

1. the effects on your emotional health and relationship, the risks of pregnancy and STIs
2. the openness, sharing, affection, and trust that can develop in a close relationship
3. It helps keep a relationship close.
4. the act of refraining from sexual intimacy; setting clear limits, communicating your limits, avoiding high-pressure situations, and asserting yourself
5. *Sample answer:* the risk of pregnancy, because becoming a parent would prevent me from focusing on my education
6. a. *Sample answer:* If you loved me, you would respect my values.

   b. *Sample answer:* There's nothing wrong with me. Many teens choose not to have sex.

   c. *Sample answer:* I don't have to do everything I may want to do.

Chapter 6
At a Glance

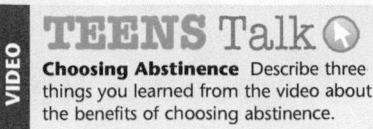
TEENS Talk

VIDEO

Choosing Abstinence Describe three things you learned from the video about the benefits of choosing abstinence.

Section 1   Skills for Healthy Relationships

Key Ideas

▶ Skills for effective communication include using "I messages," active listening, assertiveness, and using appropriate body language.

▶ Cooperation builds strong relationships that are based on mutual trust, caring, and responsibility.

▶ Being willing to compromise tells the other person how important the relationship is to you.

Vocabulary
- communication (136)
- "I" message (136)
- active listening (137)
- passive (138)
- aggressive (138)
- assertive (138)
- body language (139)
- eye contact (139)
- cooperation (139)
- compromise (140)

Section 2   Friendships

Key Ideas

▶ People look to their friends for honest reactions, encouragement, and understanding.

▶ Some friendships are casual and some are close. Some are with friends of the opposite sex.

▶ Some possible problems in friendships are envy, jealousy, cruelty, and cliques.

Vocabulary
- friendship (141)
- gender roles (143)
- clique (145)
- peer pressure (145)

Section 3   Dating Relationships

Key Ideas

▶ By dating someone, you can learn about his or her personality, interests, abilities, and values.

▶ The cycle of violence consists of a tension-building stage, a violent episode, and a calm stage.

Vocabulary
- infatuation (148)
- dating violence (150)
- date rape (151)

Section 4   Choosing Abstinence

Key Ideas

▶ The risks of sexual intimacy include the effect on your emotional health and your relationship; and the risk of pregnancy and sexually-transmitted infections.

▶ A relationship can be close without being sexually intimate. But it is hard to keep a relationship close without emotional intimacy.

▶ Abstinence skills include setting clear limits, communicating your limits, avoiding high-pressure situations, and asserting yourself.

Vocabulary
- emotional intimacy (154)
- abstinence (154)

Chapter 6
At a Glance

Choosing Abstinence Ask volunteers to share their answers. Use examples from the video to review the benefits of choosing abstinence.

VIDEO

Key Ideas Review

L3 Ask students to write three review questions for each section in the chapter. Have pairs of students use the questions to test each other's understanding.

L2 Ask students to select one section from the chapter and write a paragraph that summarizes the key ideas in that section. Ask volunteers to share their summaries with the class.

Vocabulary Review

L2 Have students write five game-show style questions pertaining to the chapter vocabulary terms. Have students working in small groups take turns asking and answering questions.

EL Have students make flash cards with a vocabulary term on one side and a definition on the other. Have pairs of students use the cards to review the chapter vocabulary.

Chapter 6 Review

 GO ONLINE

PearsonSuccessNet.com

Students can go online for a review activity on Chapter 6.

Reviewing Key Ideas

Section 1
1. b

2. The same body language can send different messages in different cultures, causing misunderstandings.

3. If a friend asks you to do something dangerous or against your values, it is not a good idea to compromise.

4. Person A used an "I" message to state personal feelings. Person B used an active listening skill—ask a question to encourage further conversation.

Section 2
5. b

6. loyalty, honesty, empathy, and reliability

7. These feelings can keep friends from supporting or encouraging each other.

8. *Sample answer:* Some people are shy or overly aggressive. Others may not be reliable, loyal, or empathetic.

Section 3
9. a

10. Benefits: security and getting to know one person well; drawbacks: limits chance of meeting others, increased pressure to take part in sexual activity

11. view the abuse as romantic, think abuse is normal, fear being alone, or think the abuse is deserved

12. *Sample answer:* a sense of humor, optimism, intelligence, empathy

Section 4
13. c

14. Parents feel trapped and overwhelmed.

15. *Sample answer:* do kind things for each other and share feelings

16. Setting limits in advance helps you avoid making a hasty decision later.

17. *Sample answer:* Jada may not be able to clearly communicate her limits.

Chapter 6 Review

 GO ONLINE

PearsonSuccessNet.com

For: Chapter 6 review activity

Reviewing Key Ideas

Section 1

1. A person who communicates feelings in a way that is disrespectful to another person is being
   a. passive.
   b. aggressive.
   c. assertive.
   d. an active listener.

2. If you use body language to communicate in another culture, what problem might arise?

3. When is it not a good idea to compromise?

4. **Critical Thinking** Person A says, "I'm angry because you are late." Person B says, "Did you think that I was being rude?" Which communication skill does each statement represent? Explain your answer.

Section 2

5. A clique is a small group of people
   a. who are part of an extended family.
   b. with similar backgrounds and interests.
   c. who value each other's differences.
   d. who are all the same age.

6. What qualities are important in a close friend?

7. Explain how envy or jealousy can cause problems in a friendship.

8. **Critical Thinking** Why do you think some people have trouble making or keeping friends?

Section 3

9. An infatuation is characterized by
   a. intense physical attraction.
   b. loyalty and empathy.
   c. shared interests and values.
   d. mutual trust and acceptance.

10. What are some benefits of steady dating? What are some drawbacks?

11. List at least four reasons why a teen might remain in an abusive relationship.

12. **Critical Thinking** Often people are first attracted to other people based on looks and personality. What other qualities might attract you to a person as you get to know him or her?

Section 4

13. The act of refraining from sex is called
    a. sexual intimacy.
    b. emotional intimacy.
    c. abstinence.
    d. sexual involvement.

14. In what ways does having a baby change the lives of teenage parents?

15. Describe two things a couple could do to increase their emotional intimacy.

16. Explain why it is important to think about your limits before you are faced with a decision about sexual intimacy.

17. **Critical Thinking** Jada's communication style is passive. How could this style lead to misunderstandings about sexual intimacy?

 Building Health Skills

18. **Communicating** You sit next to a teen you don't know at a club meeting. What would you say about yourself? What would you ask in return?

19. **Making Decisions** Develop a list of rules to follow in a dating relationship. Make sure your rules emphasize respect for yourself and others.

20. **Setting Goals** Choose one of the abstinence skills you studied in Section 4. Make an action plan to apply this skill to situations other than choosing abstinence. For example, you could set clear limits not to be interrupted when you are doing your homework. Monitor your progress and adjust your action plan, if necessary. **WRITING**

Health and Community

Community Guide for Teens Design a guide for teens who are new to your community. Describe things they can do to meet people. Include all the necessary details such as times, dress codes, and costs for activities. You may want to include a map with locations marked. **WRITING**

Building Health Skills

18. *Sample answer:* I might talk about why I like the club. If the person responds, I might ask about their other interests.

19. The rules should show an understanding of the meaning of *respect*, and an awareness of the warning signs of abuse.

20. Let students keep their plans private.

Health and Community

Community Guide for Teens Have students work in groups to make a list of things to do. Group members could cooperate to research the necessary details, write the copy, and produce the guide. Alternatively, interested students could work together to produce a guide that the school could give to new students.

Standardized Test Prep

Math Practice

The graph compares yes responses from teens in four countries to the following question: Do you often feel lonely? Use the graph to answer Questions 21–24.

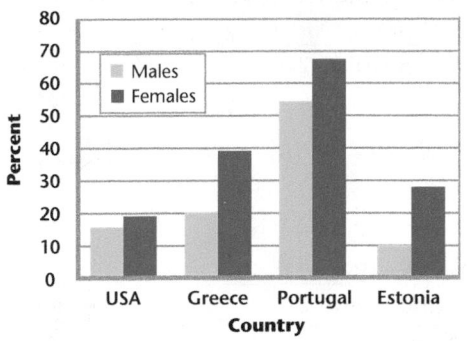

21. What percentage of male teens in the United States often feel lonely?
  A 10%   B 15%
  C 20%   D 25%

22. In which country are 19 percent of female teens often lonely?
  F United States   G Greece
  H Portugal   J Estonia

23. In which country is the difference between males and females greatest?
  A United States   B Greece
  C Portugal   D Estonia

24. In which country is the percent of lonely females almost double that of males?
  F United States
  G Greece
  H Portugal
  J Estonia

Test-Taking Tip

It may help to work with a friend while studying for a test. You can ask each other questions to see what you remember.

Reading and Writing Practice

Read the passage. Then answer Questions 25–28.

A communication device can give people who cannot speak the ability to communicate. A speech synthesizer in the device produces a voice. Some devices have a typical keyboard. The computer simply speaks the words typed in. Other keyboards have pictures instead of letters. This makes typing easier because each picture stands for an entire word. These systems are for people who have limited use of their hands. Many devices are small enough to be portable so that users are never without their "speech."

25. What is the main idea of this passage?
  A Communication devices are designed for people with limited use of their hands.
  B Some computer keyboards have pictures.
  C Computers can synthesize speech.
  D People who cannot speak can use technology to communicate.

26. Based on this passage, what does the word portable mean?
  F battery-operated
  G easily carried or moved
  H extremely small
  J easy to use

27. Which of the following statements is supported by this passage?
  A A speech synthesizer is used to speak words that are typed.
  B A speech synthesizer is used to translate typed words into pictures.
  C A speech synthesizer is used to increase the volume of spoken words.
  D A speech synthesizer is used to translate one language into another.

Constructed Response
28. A company asks you to design a machine that will improve people's ability to communicate. What kind of machine would you design? What would its purpose be and what features would it have?

Standardized Test Prep
Math Practice
21. B
22. F
23. B
24. G

Reading and Writing Practice
25. D
26. G
27. A
28. Answers will vary, but should reflect an understanding of communication skills. For example, a machine might analyze and interpret a speaker's facial expressions and convey this information through an earpiece to a listener who is visually impaired. A machine might analyze and describe tone of voice for a person who is hearing impaired.

CHAPTER 7   Preventing Violence

Section Objectives	Standards Correlation	Instructional Resources (L3)	SE eTEXT	TE eTEXT	PRINT
1 What Is Violence? ⏱ 2 periods; 1 block **7.1.1 Describe** all of the costs related to violence. **7.1.2 Identify** five risk factors for violence.	NHES: 1.12.9, 2.12.1, 2.12.3, 2.12.5, 2.12.9	SE Warm-Up, p. 162	•	•	•
		SE Media Wise Violence in Video Games, p. 165	•	•	•
		RN Note Taking Guide 7-1	•	•	•
		TR Practice 7-1		•	
		TR Section 7-1 Quiz		•	
2 Violence in Schools ⏱ 2 periods; 1 block **7.2.1 Explain** the relationship between harassment and the use of weapons at school. **7.2.2 Describe** effective ways to reduce bullying, hazing, sexual harassment, and hate violence in schools.	NHES: 2.12.3, 2.12.4, 2.12.6, 5.12.6	SE Warm-Up, p. 168	•	•	•
		RN Note Taking Guide 7-2	•	•	•
		IB Image Bank 7-5		•	
		TR Practice 7-2		•	
		TR Section 7-2 Quiz		•	
3 How Fights Start ⏱ 1 period; 1/2 block **7.3.1 Explain** how anger and a desire for revenge can lead to fights. **7.3.2 Describe** the role that friends and bystanders play in fights. **7.3.3 Explain** the relationship between a need for control and violence.	NHES: 1.12.8, 1.12.9, 2.12.3, 2.12.7	SE Warm-Up, p. 174	•	•	•
		RN Note Taking Guide 7-3	•	•	•
		TR Practice 7-3		•	
		TR Section 7-3 Quiz		•	
Mediating a Conflict ⏱ 1 period; 1/2 block **BHS.7 Develop** the ability to use mediation to help resolve a conflict peacefully.	NHES: 4.12.3, 4.12.4, 5.12.4, 8.12.2	SE Practice the Skill, p. 179	•	•	•
		RN Building Health Skills 7	•	•	•
4 Preventing Fights ⏱ 1 period; 1/2 block **7.4.1 Describe** two general approaches for resolving conflicts. **7.4.2 Explain** why safety should be a person's first concern in any conflict.	NHES: 1.12.5, 4.12.3, 4.12.4, 6.12.1, 8.12.2	SE Warm-Up, p. 180	•	•	•
		RN Note Taking Guide 7-4	•	•	•
		TR Practice 7-4		•	
		TR Section 7-4 Quiz		•	

Chapter Review and Assessment

SE Chapter 7 Review, p. 186 (L3)
CTB Chapter 7 Test (L2) (L3) (L4)
SE Standardized Test Prep, p. 187 (L3)

PROGRAM COMPONENTS

SE	Student Edition	CTB	Computer Test Bank
TE	Teacher Edition	AUD	Audio Section Summaries
TR	Teaching Resources		
RN	Reading and Note Taking Guide	DVD	Teens Talk Video Series
		VVG	Video Viewing Guide
ARN	Adapted Reading and Note Taking Guide	PPT	Presentation
IB	Image Bank		

Differentiated Instruction
(L1) (L2) (L4) (EL)

		SE eTEXT	TE eTEXT	PRINT
ARN	Note Taking Guide 7-1 (L2)	•	•	
RN	Note Taking Guide 7-1 (EL)	•	•	•
AUD	Audio Summary 7-1 (L1) (L2) (EL)	•	•	
TE	Reteach Strategy, p. 167 (L2)		•	•
TR	Enrich 7-1 (L4)		•	
ARN	Note Taking Guide 7-2 (L2)	•	•	
RN	Note Taking Guide 7-2 (EL)	•	•	•
AUD	Audio Summary 7-2 (L1) (L2) (EL)	•	•	
TE	Reteach Strategy, p. 173 (L2)		•	•
TR	Enrich 7-2 (L4)		•	
ARN	Note Taking Guide 7-3 (L2)	•	•	
RN	Note Taking Guide 7-3 (EL)	•	•	•
AUD	Audio Summary 7-3 (L1) (L2) (EL)	•	•	
TE	Reteach Strategy, p. 177 (L2)		•	•
TR	Enrich 7-3 (L4)		•	
ARN	Building Health Skills 7 (L2)	•	•	
RN	Building Health Skills 7 (EL)	•	•	•
ARN	Note Taking Guide 7-4 (L2)	•	•	
RN	Note Taking Guide 7-4 (EL)	•	•	•
AUD	Audio Summary 7-4 (L1) (L2) (EL)	•	•	
TE	Reteach Strategy, p. 184 (L2)		•	•
TR	Enrich 7-4 (L4)		•	

ABILITY LEVELS
- (L1) For students with special needs
- (L2) For less proficient readers
- (L3) For all students
- (L4) For gifted and talented students
- (EL) For English language learners

Chapter 7 Digital/Video Pathway

This alternative pathway allows you to teach this chapter's content using only the video and online materials.

Preview
DVD	Video #7 Preview
SE	Video #7 Preview Activity
VVG	Video #7 Worksheet

Bully-Proof

1
PPT	7-1 Presentation
RN/ARN	7-1 Note Taking
PPT	7-1 Section Quiz

2
DVD	Video #7 Explore/Wrap-Up
VVG	Video #7 Worksheet
PPT	7-2 Presentation
RN/ARN	7-2 Note Taking
PPT	7-2 Section Quiz

Bully-Proof

3
PPT	7-3 Presentation
RN/ARN	7-3 Note Taking
PPT	7-3 Section Quiz

4
PPT	7-4 Presentation
RN/ARN	7-4 Note Taking
PPT	7-4 Section Quiz

Chapter Preview

GO ONLINE
PearsonSuccessNet.com
For resources and activities for this chapter.

Preventing Violence

GO ONLINE PearsonSuccessNet.com

TEENS Talk

VIDEO 7

Bully-Proof

Preview **Activity**

What Do You Think About People Who Are Bullies?

Complete this activity before you watch the video.

1. Think about people you know who are bullies. Make a list of 5–10 words that describe a typical bully. For example, do you think a typical bully is strong or weak?
2. Do you think that bullying is a choice? If so, why would someone choose to be a bully? **WRITING**

 **Sensitive Issues**

The subject of this chapter may be difficult for many students to discuss. Many students have participated in or observed fights, and some students have been victims of violence at home, at school, or in the neighborhood. Students might be hesitant to talk about violence out of embarrassment, shame, guilt, or fear. Observe students closely for signs of discomfort during discussions. Encourage students to share with their friends and family members the methods of nonviolent conflict resolution discussed in this chapter.

TEENS Talk

Bully-Proof

Video Objectives

Use the video to help students

Describe the effect that bullying has on victims.

Explain why some people become bullies.

Identify effective strategies for dealing with bullies.

Preview **Activity**

What Do You Think About People Who Are Bullies?

Assign the Preview Activity for homework a few days before you plan to show the video. After students complete the assignment, use the individual lists to compile a class list of adjectives to describe bullies. Note which adjectives were used most frequently. Then ask volunteers to share their opinions on whether bullying is a choice and, if so, why someone would choose to be a bully.

161

From the Authors

Almost everyone will agree that if violence can be avoided, it should be. However, many people don't think that violence can be avoided. Instead, they consider it an inevitable part of life. Although stranger violence is a major focus for our society, students need to understand that violence among acquaintances, friends, and families is a large part of the problem.

By teaching violence prevention as a part of health education, you can help students become happier, healthier adults who are skilled at anger management and conflict resolution. Help students understand that conflict is a normal part of life. Students need to learn non-violent strategies for resolving conflicts, including when to ignore a conflict, when to negotiate, and when to seek help.

Objectives
Before class begins, write the objectives on the board. Have students copy the objectives into their notebooks at the start of class.

1. Focus

Warm-Up Myth/Fact

After students complete the writing assignment, ask volunteers to share their responses. *(One possible answer is that stranger-on-stranger crime is more likely to be reported to police and be covered by the media.)* Discuss how knowing this fact might affect how a society addresses violence.

Presentation 7-1

⚑ Sensitive Issues
- Family violence may be a sensitive issue for students who have experienced or observed violence at home.
- If there is gang activity in the areas where students live, avoid questions that would require individual students to discuss their involvement in gangs or to denounce gang activity. Such actions could put students at risk.

Objectives
▶ **Describe** all of the costs related to violence.
▶ **Identify** five risk factors for violence.

Vocabulary
- violence
- homicide
- victim
- assailant
- territorial gang

Warm-Up

Myth Most acts of violence are committed by strangers, often as part of robberies or other crimes.

Fact In the United States, most acts of violence are done by people who know their victims.

WRITING Why do you think that many people believe strangers commit most violent acts?

Violence and Health

What does the word *violence* mean to you? **Violence** is the threat of or actual use of physical force against oneself or another person. Violence often results in injury or death. Homicide is a type of violence that gets a lot of attention from the media. **Homicide** (HAHM ih syd) is the intentional killing of one person by another. It is the second leading cause of death for people age 15 to 24. Other examples of violence are suicide and rape. So is threatening to harm another person.

Violence is a huge problem in the United States. Consider this data from one recent year.

▶ There were 16,259 deaths by homicide—one every 32.5 minutes.

▶ There were 38,364 deaths by suicide—one every 13.5 minutes.

▶ There were 81,280 reported rapes of women—one every 6.5 minutes.

Figure 1 compares the homicide rates for selected countries.

Violence is of major concern to health professionals. Doctors and nurses treat people who are injured by violence. Mental health counselors deal with the emotional harm. People who work in the area of public health look for ways to reduce the level of violence. These health professionals are aware of the costs of violence. **With violence, there are costs to the victim, costs to the assailant, and costs to society as a whole.**

MATH and Health

L3 Calculating

Have students confirm the rates cited on page 162. First, have students calculate how many minutes there are in a year. *(60 minutes × 24 hours × 365 days = 525,600 minutes)* Then, have students divide the number of minutes in a year by the number of deaths by homicide in a year to determine the homicide rate. *(525,600 ÷ 16,259 = 32.3, rounded to 32.5)* Have them do a similar calculation for suicides and for reported rapes of women. *(525,600 ÷ 38,364 = 13.7, rounded to 13.5; 525,600 ÷ 81,280 = 6.5)*

Costs to the Victim   The **victim** is the person who is attacked. Death is the most serious outcome of a violent act, but it is not the only possible result. Victims who survive may suffer serious permanent injuries. Injuries to the head can lead to the loss of brain function. Other injuries can cause a permanent loss of feeling and movement in some part of the body. But even when injuries are less serious, they still may cause pain, require medical treatment, take time to heal, and leave scars.

There may also be emotional scars. Victims often experience anger, fear, and depression. It is also common for victims to replay the event over and over in their minds. This may make it difficult for them to focus on the future instead of the past. Family members and friends have to deal with feelings of loss or the burden of caring for an injured person.

Costs to the Assailant   Another person who pays a price for violence is the assailant. An **assailant** (uh SAY lunt) is a person who attacks another person. The assailant may be seriously injured in a fight. The assailant may feel guilt or shame, and live in fear of an act of revenge.

The assailant also may face criminal charges, court costs, lawyer's fees, and possible jail time. Having a criminal record can seriously affect a person for the rest of his or her life. For example, it can limit a person's chances of finding a job or prevent a person from voting in some states.

Costs to Society   There are financial costs associated with violence. It costs the healthcare system over 2 trillion dollars a year to treat injuries that result from violence. Taxpayers also must pay for law enforcement, courts, and prisons. If schools spend money for metal detectors or guards, there may not be money left in the budget to pay for music, art, or sports.

There are emotional costs to society as well. Violent acts affect people even when they don't know the victims or assailants. In communities where violent acts are common, a fear of violence controls many day-to-day decisions. People avoid certain neighborhoods or are afraid to go out at night. They install security locks or alarms, and are suspicious of strangers.

 **Do you know a survivor of a violent attack? If so, how did the attack affect the person?**

Homicide Rates by Country		
	Country	**Rate**
	Australia	1.2
	Brazil	22.7
	Costa Rica	11.3
	Denmark	0.9
	Japan	0.5
	Philippines	5.4
	Portugal	1.2
	Spain	0.9
	Thailand	5.3
	United Kingdom	1.2
	United States	5.0

FIGURE 1   The United Nations collected this data. The rates are given as deaths per every 100,000 people.
Reading Tables Which country listed has the highest homicide rate? Which countries have the lowest?

2. Teach

L3 EL Reading/Note Taking 7-1
L2 Adapted Reading/Note Taking 7-1

Violence and Health

L3 Building Media Literacy

Select a newspaper or magazine article about a non-fatal violent act such as a physical fight between neighbors over a parking spot. Avoid events in your own community to minimize the chance that your students know the participants. Have students analyze the coverage of the event. From the article, can they tell what the costs are to the victim, to the assailant, and to the community? Have students write a paragraph describing the costs, using their imaginations to fill in missing information. **WRITING**

L2 Visual Learning: Figure 1

After students have examined the table, ask: **What is the homicide rate in the United States?** *(5.0 homicides per 100,000 people)* Point out the rate is an average for the entire country, so the rate will be higher than the average in some communities and lower in others. Discuss the differences in rates among countries. After students offer their thoughts about why the rates differ, introduce the concept of risk factors for violence.

Caption Answer Brazil has the highest rate; Japan has the lowest.

L1 Class Discussion

Describe this situation for students: Jerry hits Dwayne, and the two begin to fight. After a teacher separates the boys, he notices that Jerry has a bloody nose that may be broken and an eye that is swollen shut. Because Jerry is injured, the teacher might assume that he is the victim. But because Jerry started the fight, he is the assailant. Point out that both participants in a fight can be seriously hurt.

Connect to Your Life Allow students to answer this question in their private journals.

Differentiated Instruction

L2 Less Proficient Readers

Ask students to make a table of the costs of violence to victims, assailants, and society. Summarizing information in a table or other graphic organizer can help students see the main points without distracting details. Use the following column heads to organize the material in the text: Physical Costs, Financial Costs, and Emotional Costs.

Risk Factors for Violence

L3 Online Activity  GO ONLINE

Visit Pearson SuccessNet to access more information about media violence. Have students complete the Web activity.

L2 Class Discussion

Before students read about risk factors for violence, ask them to brainstorm a list of factors in a person's life that might make him or her more likely to become involved in violence. Write students' responses on the board. Then have a volunteer read aloud the bold-face sentence on page 164, and note how many of the risk factors are the same or similar to those on the board.

L3 Cooperative Learning

Divide the class into small groups, and explain that each group represents a task force studying how to reduce violence in poor neighborhoods. Ask groups to develop a proposal for how best to achieve this goal. Have groups present their proposals to the class.

Connect to Your Life *Sample answer:* toy guns and action figures that promote violence

GO ONLINE
PearsonSuccessNet.com
For: More on media violence

Risk Factors for Violence

Researchers have identified some risk factors for violence. **These risk factors are poverty, family violence, exposure to media violence, availability of weapons, drug abuse, and membership in gangs.**

Poverty Most people who are poor are not violent. But when people don't have jobs, adequate food, healthcare, or respect from others, they may feel hopeless. They also may have a high level of frustration and anger because they are unable to improve their lives. A minor event may cause people who are already frustrated and angry to react more violently than normal. This helps to explain why the rate of violence is highest in poor urban communities where unemployment rates are high.

Movies and television shows can leave the impression that certain racial groups are more violent than others. Some racial groups are represented in higher numbers in violence statistics. But the reason is that some racial groups are poorer, on average, than others. When poor communities with different racial groups are compared, the homicide rates are similar.

Family Violence Children who grow up in violent homes—who witness violence or are victims of violence—are more apt to use violence to solve their own problems. Violence may be the only strategy they have been taught for solving problems. Children who are neglected are also more likely than other children to respond to conflict with violence.

Children can learn to avoid violence if adults don't use violence to solve their own problems or to discipline children. Parents reveal their values about violence by the toys they buy and the television shows they allow their children to watch. They also pass along their values by sharing how they feel about violence.

Connect to Your Life What kinds of children's toys do you think might promote violence?

FIGURE 2 In poor communities, the buildings and streets are often in need of repair. These conditions can add to a person's frustration and anger.

TEENS *Are Asking . . .*

Q: For years, I have watched arguments between my parents end with a violent act. Does this mean I will be violent?

A: Violence in the home is a risk factor for violence, but not everyone who observes or experiences violence in the home grows up to be violent. There are some actions you can take to reduce the risk. Look for adult role models who use non-violent methods to resolve conflicts. Learn to communicate your thoughts and feelings in an assertive, non-aggressive manner. Ask a trusted adult to help you find an appropriate counselor.

Media Wise

Violence in Video Games

People who play violent video games often take on the role of assailant. What effect might identifying with an assailant have on a player or group of players? Studies have linked violent video games to an increase in a player's level of aggression. Use this checklist to evaluate the content of a video game.

Is performing violent acts necessary to win the game?	Yes No
Is the effect of the violence on the victim ignored?	Yes No
Are women depicted as sexual objects?	Yes No
Does the video game package use violence to make the game look exciting?	Yes No
Does the video game have a *mature* or *adults only* rating?	Yes No

Two or more "Yes" answers may indicate a video game with a high level of violent content.

Activity Look at the packaging for a few video games that have a *mature* rating. Is violence used to sell these games? Provide some examples to support your answer. Do the text and visuals make you want to play the game? **WRITING**

Media Violence In the first cartoons you watched, the characters may have attacked each other and lived to fight another day. These cartoons were likely your first example of media violence. The media uses the excitement provided by violence to keep you glued to the screen. An action hero may use violence to kill or capture a villain. Or an expert in self-defense may take on 10 villains and beat them all. Viewers may be left with the impression that violence is a reasonable response to many situations. But violence in the world beyond television and the movies creates more problems than it solves.

People's attitudes and behavior can be shaped by the violence they see in the media. This is especially true of young children because their actual life experience is limited. Children may think what they see on television or in the movies is really happening. Children who witness a lot of media violence may grow up with an exaggerated sense of the amount of violence in the world. They also may tend to react with violence when they face a threatening situation in their own lives.

The way women are portrayed and treated in the media is also an issue. Some types of music and music videos can make people think that violence toward women is acceptable. There may be a link between these media portrayals and the rise in dating violence, rape, and other forms of violence toward women.

Media Wise

Violence in Video Games

Display a video game that will be familiar to many students, and then read the first question. Ask students who are familiar with the game to answer *yes* or *no* and explain their reasoning. Continue this process for the remaining questions. Discuss why *yes* answers may indicate that the game has a high level of violent content.

Activity Assign the activity for homework. Students should write a paragraph that responds to the questions. In class, call on volunteers to share their paragraphs. Discuss why video game companies might use violence in their products.

L3 Building Health Skills

Analyzing Influences Have students do an analysis of music videos similar to the one they did for video games. As a class, modify the checklist to work for music videos. Then, have students apply the checklist to a few music videos. Ask students to write a paragraph describing the results of their analysis. Have a few volunteers present their findings to the class. **WRITING**

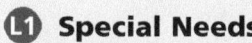

Differentiated Instruction

L1 Special Needs

Some gaming companies have developed audio games that are designed to mimic the experience of playing traditional video games. Ask your visually-impaired students if they are familiar with these audio games.

If so, ask students to bring some examples to class. Starting with the checklist from the Media Wise activity, develop a list of questions students can use to evaluate the content of a few audio games.

L3 **Active Learning**

Ask students to look in Chapters 15 and 17 for information about the effects of alcohol and drugs on the body. Then, have students use this information to explain why drug abuse is a risk factor for violence.

L2 **Cooperative Learning**

Have groups of students discuss why young people join gangs, with a focus on what needs gangs might meet in people's lives. *(e.g., a sense of belonging or pride; a need for protection)* Have groups brainstorm some positive ways to meet these needs without joining a gang. *(e.g., joining a club or team; gaining self-confidence and pride through volunteering; spending time at a supervised after-school program)*

L3 **Journal Writing**

Ask students to write an entry in their private journals that evaluates which of the six risk factors for violence influence their own lives. **WRITING**

Connect to Your Life Although the specific changes will vary, all answers should describe some change in behavior.

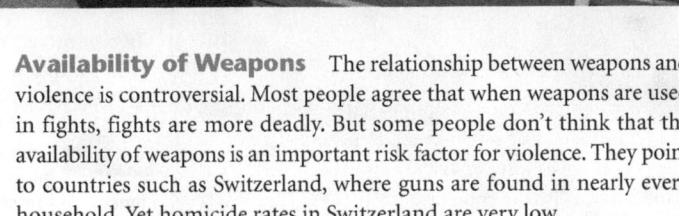

A gun kept in the home is more likely to kill a family member or friend than an intruder.

FIGURE 3 When people buy handguns for protection, they may take a course to learn how to handle the gun safely. Too often, however, handguns kept in a home are used to harm family members and friends.

Availability of Weapons The relationship between weapons and violence is controversial. Most people agree that when weapons are used in fights, fights are more deadly. But some people don't think that the availability of weapons is an important risk factor for violence. They point to countries such as Switzerland, where guns are found in nearly every household. Yet homicide rates in Switzerland are very low.

In the United States, handguns are used in the majority of homicides and suicides. Every 18 minutes someone in the United States dies from a gunshot wound. If firearms were not available, could these deaths be prevented? Experts do not know the answer.

The cycle of violence related to firearms seems difficult to break. When the homicide rate rises, fear of violence increases. More people purchase handguns for protection. But having a gun in the home can be more dangerous than not having one. The risk is even greater when the gun and the ammunition are not stored in separate locked locations.

Drug Abuse Would it surprise you to learn that at least 30 percent of homicide victims have alcohol in their blood? Would you expect the percentage to be the same or higher for assailants?

The reasons why alcohol use increases the risk of violence are not entirely clear. Researchers do know that alcohol affects the brain, clouding a person's judgment. This lack of judgment may lead people to say or do things that they ordinarily would not. This behavior may lead to a fight. In some cases, however, alcohol is used as an excuse or "to get up the nerve" to carry out preplanned acts of violence.

Drugs other than alcohol are also linked to violence. Like alcohol, illegal drugs, such as crack cocaine, can affect a person's judgment. In addition, people who are addicted to drugs may resort to robbery or other crimes to get money for drugs. Also, because many illegal drugs are sold for a large profit, the people who sell drugs often carry weapons.

 **Connect to Your Life** From what you have observed, how does alcohol or other drugs affect a person's behavior?

For Your INFORMATION!

Gun Ownership in Switzerland

Students' interest may be piqued when they read that guns are found in nearly every household in Switzerland. Widespread gun ownership is part of the country's national defense system, which consists of a militia. Citizens do an annual two- or three-week service. Soldiers are allowed to store their military weapons at home. Remind students that the availability of weapons is not the only risk factor for violence. Encourage interested students to research other risk factors, such as poverty and drug abuse, as they relate to Switzerland.

Membership in Gangs The term *gang* is used to describe a variety of groups, from loose bands of rowdy teens to criminal organizations. You can think of a gang as a type of clique. Gang members have similar backgrounds or interests. They are often subject to significant peer pressure. Because gangs don't readily associate with people who are perceived as different, their members are often isolated from the rest of the community.

Territorial gangs are groups that are organized to control a specific neighborhood or "turf." They are also referred to as "fighting" gangs because they will fight those who intrude on their turf. Most territorial gangs sell drugs and many are involved in other criminal behaviors. About two-thirds of territorial gang members are adults. They recruit students from poor or troubled families. The recruits may know of no way, other than gang membership, to gain a sense of belonging and protection.

Members of a gang may wear certain colors and jewelry, and use "secret" hand signs to identify themselves as gang members. A gang may hold elaborate initiation ceremonies. To join a gang, new members may undergo a beating. Or gang leaders may order them to commit a crime, such as robbery, kidnapping, rape, or murder. Quitting a gang can be much harder than joining one.

In many communities gang violence is a serious and growing problem. This is true for communities in urban, suburban, and rural areas.

FIGURE 4 One way to reduce violence is to offer choices for gang members. This bakery in Los Angeles was part of a community-based effort to provide jobs for former gang members.

Section 1 Review

Key Ideas and Vocabulary
1. How are **victim** and **assailant** defined?
2. List two possible costs of violence for a victim, an assailant, and society as a whole.
3. What are six risk factors for violence?
4. What is a **territorial gang**?

Critical Thinking
5. **Predicting** What is the possible cost to a victim of repeated threats of violence?

Health and Community

Survivors of Violence Sometimes survivors of violent acts or the families of victims who did not survive find positive ways to deal with their pain and grief. They may form groups to advocate against violence. Find out what anti-violence groups there are in your community. Then write a paragraph summarizing your findings. **WRITING**

6. **Evaluating** Which of the risk factors for violence do you think is most important? Give a reason for your answer.

🔊 **GO ONLINE** PearsonSuccessNet.com   Audio Summary Section 7.1

Preventing Violence **167**

Preventing Violence **167**

Objectives
Before class begins, write the objectives on the board. Have students copy the objectives into their notebooks at the start of class.

1. Focus

Warm-Up Health Stats

After students finish writing, call on a few volunteers to share their ideas about how to reduce school violence. Students might suggest physical changes such as adding metal detectors or policy changes such as zero-tolerance for bullying. Tell students that school violence can take many forms and each form may require a different approach.

Presentation 7-2

2. Teach

L3 **EL** Reading/Note Taking 7-2

L2 Adapted Reading/Note Taking 7-2

Weapons in School

L3 **Active Learning**

Have a group of volunteers interview a school administrator about the school's policy on weapons brought to school by students. Ask the group to prepare appropriate questions in advance and report their findings to the class.

Sensitive Issues

Students who have been the victim of bullying, hazing, sexual harassment, or hate violence are likely to be sensitive about these topics. Allow students to keep personal experiences private.

Section 2 | Violence in Schools

Objectives

▶ **Explain** the relationship between harassment and the use of weapons at school.

▶ **Describe** effective ways to reduce bullying, hazing, sexual harassment, and hate violence in schools.

Vocabulary

- harassment
- bullying
- cyber bullying
- hazing
- sexual harassment
- hate violence
- prejudice
- stereotype
- intolerance
- discrimination
- vandalism

Warm-Up

Health Stats These data show the results of a recent survey of teens.

In one year...

20.1% reported being bullied on school property

12% of teens reported being in a physical fight on school property

7.4% reported being threatened or injured with a weapon on school property

WRITING Do these numbers surprise you? What do you think could be done to decrease school violence?

Weapons in School

On December 14, 2012, a 20-year-old man carried three guns into Sandy Hook Elementary School in Newtown, Connecticut. The man killed 20 students and 6 adults before killing himself.

Despite tragic events such as the murders at Sandy Hook, schools remain a safe place when compared to other places in society. In terms of weapons, most schools are safer now than they were 30 years ago. Between 1983 and 2011, the number of males who reported carrying a weapon to school dropped from 18 percent to 8 percent. The number of females carrying weapons dropped from 5 percent to about 2 percent.

Even though most school violence does not end in murder, schools still need to worry about violence. Tragic episodes, such as the one at Sandy Hook, are called random acts of violence because the assailant doesn't target specific people. But the episodes themselves often are predictable. Many are a result of harassment. **Harassment** is unwanted remarks or actions that cause a person emotional or physical harm. **Students who use weapons at school often are acting on the rage they feel as victims of harassment.**

WRITING and Health

L2 **Comparison**

Ask students to compare traditional forms of bullying (the bully and the victim have face-to-face encounters) and cyber bullying (the bully uses electronic communication to harass the victim). Remind students to describe both similarities and differences. Also, ask them to include examples of each type of bullying. After students finish their writing, discuss the effect that bullying can have on the person being bullied.

Bullying

Robert hates going to school because almost every day, Amber and her friends pick on him. They call him names like "pimple boy" and "tiny." They make fun of the way he stutters. Sometimes their jock friends join in and literally toss him around or stuff him in his locker. He hates himself for not being able to stop them.

Bullying is the use of threats or physical force to intimidate and control another person. The bully chooses a victim who is less powerful in terms of physical strength or social connections. The bully may use name-calling and put-downs. He or she may shove or trip the victim. The bully may pressure friends to exclude or isolate the victim. The goal may be to steal money or other property from the victim. But sometimes the bully simply takes pleasure from the victim's embarrassment or humiliation.

Cyber Bullying Bullying that takes place by e-mail, instant messaging, text messaging, or at Web sites is called **cyber bullying** (SY bur). This form of bullying is especially cruel because the bullies can harass their victims at home at all hours of the day. The cyber bullies make threats or spread rumors about the victim. A bully may even enter a chat room, pretend to be the victim, and post messages that make the victim appear silly or offensive to others. This leaves the victim open to ridicule and may place the victim in danger.

Causes and Effects As a child, a bully may have learned to feel good at the expense of others. Bullies take out their frustrations and insecurities on others. A bully may seem extremely confident. But displays of bravado often hide a lack of self-confidence.

Bullying produces a climate of fear and disrespect at schools. The victims have increased levels of anxiety and depression. They may think about suicide. Most victims suffer in silence, but a few strike back. **The most effective way to stop bullying is to get bystanders involved.** Figure 5 lists some specific ways you can help stop bullying.

GO ONLINE
PearsonSuccessNet.com
For: More on bullying

FIGURE 5 Bullies often look to bystanders for approval. So bystanders can play a key role in stopping bullying.
Predicting Which strategy listed do you think would be most effective for stopping bullying?

Connect to Your Life Were you ever a target of bullying? How did you feel? How did you respond?

Ways to Help Stop Bullying

▶ Don't make jokes at others' expense or single out a person for exclusion.
▶ Don't reward a bully with laughter or other positive attention.
▶ Speak up. Silence is seen as approval.
▶ Don't believe rumors and don't spread rumors.
▶ Reach out to students who seem isolated.

169

Bullying

 Content Update  GO ONLINE

Visit Pearson SuccessNet to access more information about bullying. Have students complete the Web activity.

L2 Visual Learning: Figure 5
Image Bank Figure 7-5

Have students read the list of ways to stop bullying. Then ask volunteers to describe incidents of bullying they have witnessed. Caution students to avoid using names in these descriptions. After a student describes an incident, ask how the bullying was stopped, if it was. For each incident described, call on volunteers to propose ways the bullying might have been stopped.
Caption Answer *Sample answer:* Speak up—don't suffer bullying in silence.

Connect to Your Life Allow students to answer this question in their private journals.

Differentiated Instruction

L4 Gifted and Talented

Most schools have programs that focus on bullying, including education for staff and students as well as policies that call for intervention when bullying occurs and punishment and counseling for bullies.

Encourage interested students to find out about your school's bullying prevention program by talking to the appropriate school administrator. Ask students to share their findings with the class.

Hazing

L2 Class Discussion

Lead a class discussion on the dangers of hazing. To begin, call on volunteers to describe any hazing incidents they have witnessed or heard about. Ask students to withhold the names of people involved. After a few incidents have been described, ask students to consider how the victim in each case could have been harmed by the hazing. Make sure students consider all aspects of health, not just physical health.

L3 Building Health Skills

Analyzing Influences Point out that hazing can occur year after year, with those who were the victims of hazing becoming the ones who haze as they get older. Have students meet in small groups to discuss why hazing persists in teams and other organizations and what can be done to stop hazing.

 **Connect to Your Life** Allow students to answer this question in their private journals.

FIGURE 6 Students who join the cheerleading squad or other teams expect to work hard. They shouldn't have to worry about possible hazing from older members of the team.

Hazing

When Zoe auditioned for the cheerleading squad, she was excited to make the cut. Then she heard disturbing news. There would be a member-led initiation for new members. She was concerned about what might happen, but she didn't tell her parents. She was afraid they would make her quit cheerleading.

Hazing is requiring a person to do degrading, risky, or illegal acts in order to join a group. Sadly, hazing is a fairly common practice in school clubs and athletic teams. A person may be yelled at, forced to do personal chores, or asked to wear a ridiculous costume in public. Physical abuse and sexual abuse are part of some initiations.

Gender and Hazing Almost half of all high school students on school teams or clubs report being hazed. Male teens are more likely to report being beaten, being required to steal, or being forced to destroy property. Males also report being tied up and confined to small places.

Female teens report less physical abuse than do males, although the number of female athletes who report being beaten is surprisingly large. Females are more likely to report emotional abuse. This can take the form of put downs or being required to perform demeaning acts in public.

Preventing Hazing Hazing isn't an issue that students can easily deal with as individuals. Some students are confident and assertive enough to refuse to haze or be hazed. But most feel uncomfortable challenging older students. They also fear being rejected or being called a wimp.

In most states, hazing is illegal at both high schools and colleges. A school could also be sued if a student is injured during hazing. **School administrators and teachers need to take the lead in the prevention of hazing.** They must establish strict rules against hazing and make sure that students understand the rules. Coaches and other adults should be alert for signs of hazing. When a student reports an incident, the school should support the student and address the issue quickly and fairly.

Connect to Your Life Do you agree that all types of hazing should be banned at school? Why or why not?

WRITING and Health

L3 Persuasive Letter

Have students assume that a friend who attends another school is planning to take part in an initiation for a sports team that will involve hazing. Ask students to write a letter to persuade the friend not to take part in hazing and to try to prevent others from doing so. Explain that the letter should contain strong arguments for why the hazing should not occur. Students might want to mention the effects of hazing on the victims as well as the possible consequences for those who do the hazing.

Sexual Harassment

Mariah's friend, Eduardo, told her that there were some explicit sexual comments about her in the boy's bathroom. She didn't pay much attention until a student she didn't know asked her for a sexual favor. Humiliated and angry, Mariah talked with a teacher and then with the principal. She was told not to let the remarks get to her. The guys were just fooling around.

Sexual harassment is any uninvited and unwelcome sexual remark or sexual advance. Making comments about a person's body parts is an example. So is unwanted touching or spreading rumors about someone's sexual behavior. Telling crude jokes in study hall is also an example. The jokes may make some students uncomfortable and distract them from their studies. Sometimes sexual harassment is a part of hazing. A group may make sexual demands in exchange for admission into the group.

Sadly, sometimes the person doing the harassing is an adult. The difference in power between the adult and the student makes the behavior even less acceptable. **If school administrations, teachers, and students work together, they can stop sexual harassment.**

What Schools Must Do Sexual harassment in schools is illegal. The administration at a school is required by law to respond quickly and forcefully when students complain about sexual harassment. If the school doesn't act, and the harassment continues, the victim has grounds to sue the assailant and the school.

What You Can Do Here are ways you can stop sexual harassment.

▶ Speak up assertively when you feel disrespected.

▶ Use your refusal skills to reject unwanted sexual advances.

▶ Avoid having to be alone with someone you don't trust.

▶ Report behavior that you think is sexual harassment to an adult.

FIGURE 7 These young men are admiring two young women who are passing by. **Classifying** Do you think staring at a person's body is an example of sexual harassment? Why or why not?

Preventing Violence **171**

Sexual Harassment

L1 Visual Learning: Figure 7

Explain that it can be difficult for people to agree on what actions to classify as sexual harassment because you need to know how the potential "victim" feels. For example, one young woman might be flattered to have a group of young men stare at her while another might be uncomfortable. The action is the same, but the response is different. Discuss ways that people can respond if words or actions make them uncomfortable.

Caption Answer *Sample answer:* Staring at someone's body can be sexual harassment if the person being stared at feels uncomfortable with this attention.

L3 Building Health Skills

Communicating Describe this scenario to students: Each day, a female student takes the bus to school. An older male student rides the same bus. Almost every day, the male student makes some remark about the female's body. Sometimes he "accidentally" brushes against the female student as she walks down the aisle. Have students work in pairs to write a role-play that shows how the female student could communicate her displeasure to the male student or to school authorities. Call on pairs to perform their role-play for the class. Discuss which strategies might be most effective. **WRITING**

Differentiated Instruction

EL English Language Learners

Students learning English may have difficulty with the pronunciation of *harassment* as well as the verb *harass*. Explain that there are two common pronunciations of *harass*—a pronunciation with the emphasis on the first syllable and a pronunciation with the emphasis on the second syllable. Point out that the pronunciation with the emphasis on the second syllable is more common in the United States.

Hate Violence

ⓛ Building Health Skills

Practicing Healthful Behaviors Tell students that you want them to learn to speak up against hate speech, but you don't want them to use hate speech in class. Have small groups of students brainstorm ways to respond when a person makes hateful remarks. Ask each group to decide which responses would be most effective and why.

ⓔⓛ Building Vocabulary

Explain that the word *prejudice* comes from two Latin roots meaning "before" and "judge." Ask students to explain how a person who is prejudiced against a group is prejudging individuals in that group. *(A prejudiced person jumps to conclusions about people based on group stereotypes before he or she gets to know the people as individuals.)*

ⓛ Building Health Skills

Advocacy Have students work in small groups to develop a creative way to address intolerance at school. Encourage students to use different approaches. For example, they might use artwork, write a public service announcement, develop a skit, or write a rap song. After students have had time to develop their plans, ask groups to make presentations in class.

Connect to Your Life Allow students to answer this question in their private journals.

Hate Violence

After a basketball game at a rival school, 16-year-old Troy was badly beaten by three youths. The violent act seemed to be racially motivated. According to Troy, the youths shouted racial slurs as they repeatedly kicked and punched him.

Hate violence is speech or behavior that is aimed at a person or group based on personal characteristics. Behaviors range from gestures to physical attacks. Hate speech may be spoken or written. A person might be targeted because of race, ethnicity, gender, or religion. If the violence that takes place is against the law, the action is classified as a hate crime.

Prejudice and Intolerance   Hate violence often stems from prejudice and intolerance. **Prejudice** is negative feelings about a group based on stereotypes. A **stereotype** is an exaggerated belief or overgeneralization about an entire group of people. A person who is prejudiced will prejudge people based solely on their connection to a group. He or she fails to see people as individuals.

Prejudice can lead to intolerance. **Intolerance** is a lack of acceptance of another person's opinions, beliefs, or actions. Too often, people who are intolerant are looking for an excuse to attack someone. They may try to justify their actions by saying things like, "She was asking for it," or "It was him or me," or "I wasn't the only one."

Discrimination   Frequently, intolerance leads to discrimination. **Discrimination** is the unfair treatment of a person or group based on prejudice. People who are discriminated against may be unable to find jobs that fit their talents and education. They often cannot rent an apartment or buy a house in certain areas. They may receive poor service in restaurants or stores.

Psychologists use the term *microinsults* to describe a series of small but frequent acts of discrimination. For example, a person may be made to feel like an outsider or be treated impolitely. Or a person may have his or her talents underestimated. The anger brought on by microinsults can build over time and may eventually lead to violence.

FIGURE 8   When people have a wide variety of friends, they often are more tolerant of differences.

 **Connect to Your Life**   **Have you ever experienced prejudice? If so, how did you feel?**

TEENS *Are Asking . . .*

Q: At family gatherings, my aunt often tells racist jokes, which make me cringe. How should I handle this problem?

A: Your aunt may be trying to get a laugh without realizing the effect her words are having, or she may believe the stereotypes being expressed in the jokes. Either way, you don't want your silence to be seen as agreement with what is being said. Before the next family gathering, talk with an adult family member who shares your values and concerns. Perhaps the adult will volunteer to speak with your aunt privately. If not, you could ask to speak with your aunt one on one. Be respectful and use "I" messages to explain how the jokes make you feel.

Reducing Intolerance Many people believe that prejudice and intolerance are rooted in a fear of the unknown. When people see behaviors that are unfamiliar, they may think, "That's strange." They may even feel threatened and afraid. When people understand unfamiliar behaviors, they are less likely to be fearful. **The most effective way to deal with violence based on hate is through education.** When people learn about different cultures and get to know individuals from other groups, they are often more tolerant of differences.

Vandalism Sometimes hate is expressed through acts of vandalism. **Vandalism** is intentionally damaging or destroying another person's property. Not all acts of vandalism are motivated by hate. When teens break windows at school, they are not targeting a specific group. But when teens damage gravestones at a cemetery or scrawl offensive words on a school wall, they are usually targeting a group. Their intention is to humiliate and degrade.

Research shows that students who feel a strong positive connection to school are less likely to take part in vandalism of school property. How can schools strengthen students' feelings of connection to school? They can foster a climate in which students feel supported and better able to achieve their goals. Students feel supported when they have positive interactions with teachers and other school staff. They also feel supported when the school encourages teamwork among students.

36% of high school students report seeing hate-filled graffiti at school.

FIGURE 9 These students are painting over hate-filled graffiti at their school. This action helps remove the graffiti and shows that the students disapprove of hate violence.

Section 2 Review

Key Ideas and Vocabulary

1. What does the term **harassment** mean?
2. What is the connection between harassment and the use of weapons at school?
3. What is **cyber bullying?** What is the most effective way to stop bullying?
4. How can school administrators help prevent hazing and sexual harassment?
5. What is **hate violence?** What is the most effective way to deal with hate violence?

Critical Thinking

6. **Comparing and Contrasting** How are bullying and sexual harassment alike? How are they different?

Health at School

Role Playing Work with a group of students to prepare a skit about bullying. Include roles for a bully, a victim, and bystanders. Write a few different endings to show how the way that the bystanders respond can affect the outcome. **WRITING**

7. **Evaluating** Older students often feel that hazing is justified because they were hazed when they were freshman or sophomores. Do you think that these older students are right? Give reasons for your answer. **WRITING**
8. **Predicting** Yasmeen is the only person at her school who practices a particular religion. How might this fact affect her experiences at school?

GO ONLINE PearsonSuccessNet.com   Audio Summary Section 7.2   *Preventing Violence* **173**

Section 2 Review

1. unwanted remarks or actions that cause a person emotional or physical harm
2. Students who use weapons at school often are victims of harassment.
3. bullying that takes place by e-mail, IM, text messaging, or at Web sites; to get bystanders involved
4. Administrators should establish anti-hazing rules and address incidents quickly and fairly. They should respond quickly and forcefully to reports of sexual harassment.
5. speech or behavior aimed at a person or group based on personal characteristics; through education

3. Assess

Evaluate

These assignments can help you assess students' mastery of the section content.

Section 2 Review

Answers appear below.

Teaching Resources
• Practice 7-2
• Section 7-2 Quiz

L2 Reteach

Ask students to rewrite the section objectives as questions and then write answers to the questions. They can check their answers by rereading relevant passages in the text.

L4 Enrich

Teaching Resources
• Enrich 7-2

— Health at School —

Role Playing Explain that the role-plays should be based on what students have learned in the section as well as their own experiences, but should not depict specific students or actual incidents. Have groups perform their role-plays for the class. Then lead a class discussion on which role-plays were the most realistic or instructive for dealing with a bully.

6. *Sample answer:* With both bullying and sexual harassment, the victim suffers unwanted physical or verbal abuse. With sexual harassment, the remarks and advances are sexual.
7. *Sample answer:* No, the older students are wrong, because hazing is degrading and often dangerous.
8. *Sample answer:* She may experience prejudice and intolerance because of her religious beliefs.

Preventing Violence **173**

1. Focus

Warm-Up Advice Line

After students finish writing, use a show of hands to find out how many students agree with the student's response to the whispered insult. Ask students to provide reasons for their agreement or disagreement. Also ask if they would have the same response to a shouted insult. Emphasize that there is no "right" response; every situation is different. Explain that insults can lead to fights.

Presentation 7-3

Section 3

How Fights Start

Objectives
▶ **Explain** how anger and a desire for revenge can lead to fights.
▶ **Describe** the role that friends and bystanders play in fights.
▶ **Explain** the relationship between a need for control and violence.

Vocabulary
• escalate
• instigator

Warm-Up

Dear Advice Line,

There's a guy at school who whispers "loser" every time he sees me in the hall. I know this guy is a jerk, so I ignore him. My friends think I should insult him back.

WRITING Do you agree with this student's response? Why or why not? What if the insults were shouted, not whispered?

Arguments

Hey, what did you call me?
You heard what I said. What are you going to do about it?

Too often, a simple exchange like this one—on the basketball court, in a school hallway, on the streets—leads to tragic results. What starts as a disagreement may end up as a fight, leading to injury or even death. In fact, about 40 percent of all homicides stem directly from arguments. **Anger is at the root of most arguments and of many fights.**

Anger   The body reacts to anger the same way it does to stress. Recall the fight-or-flight response from Chapter 3. The physical changes that occur in this first stage of the stress response include tensed muscles, and increased heart and breathing rates. These changes prepare the body to fight or run.

Fighting or running away are not your only options for dealing with anger. Although the body's reaction to anger is automatic, you can control your overall reaction to anger. If you resort to fighting when someone makes you angry, you give the other person control over you. The person knows that, by provoking you, he or she can force you to fight. This means that the person can cause you to be kicked out of a game, suspended from school, or suffer other negative consequences of fighting. By choosing not to fight, you do not let the other person control you.

⚑ Sensitive Issues
Some students may feel strongly that fighting is the only way to handle situations like those described in this section. Be sure students understand that when people are provoked into fighting, they are letting another person control their lives. Also stress that even when a person "wins" a fight, that person may face serious consequences for fighting.

WRITING and Health
ⓛ₃ Newspaper Article
Ask students to imagine that a fight has taken place in their community and they are newspaper reporters. The city editor needs an article about the fight. (If some students want to use an actual fight as a model, remind them to change the names and other revealing details.)

Explain that the goal of a newspaper article is to answer who, what, when, where, and why questions. Also remind students that a columnist or editorial writer is allowed to express a personal opinion about an event, but a reporter should present only facts.

11% of high school students report having a physical fight at school.

FIGURE 10 A fight may start because of verbal insults or aggressive body language. **Observing** What aspects of this teen's body language might help to provoke a fight?

Hurt Pride and Embarrassment Think of a time when your pride was hurt or someone embarrassed you in public. Perhaps a classmate made negative remarks about your family or culture. Or students from a rival school chanted insults as your football team suffered a bad defeat. Maybe a friend revealed a secret that you had shared in confidence. Or you walked into a room and heard someone doing an unflattering imitation of you.

You may have been surprised at just how angry you felt when your pride was hurt or you were embarrassed. It is not surprising that hurt pride and embarrassment often lead to fighting.

Revenge

There's the guy who beat up your brother. What are you going to do?

He's going to pay for what he did. But this time I'll choose the time and place. He'll never know what hit him.

Some people mistakenly believe that fighting can settle an argument. But more often than not, this approach does not work. The person who loses the fight is usually left feeling angry and embarrassed. He or she may enlist the help of friends or family members to get revenge, or "even the score." **The desire for revenge leads to a dangerous cycle of fighting.**

In cases where revenge is the motive for a fight, the fighting can quickly **escalate,** or grow more intense. Where the first fight may have been a fistfight, the second fight may involve knives or guns. Where the first fight may have involved only two people, the second fight may involve many more. Plus, chances are good that the second fight will not settle the argument, which will only lead to more fights.

Revenge is a common motive in fights between territorial gangs. Gang members feel responsible for protecting one another and defending their turf. When one gang member is wronged, other members come to his or her aid. A cycle of revenge between gangs may last for years.

 **Connect to Your Life** Have you ever had a fight to settle an argument? If so, did the fight settle things? Why or why not?

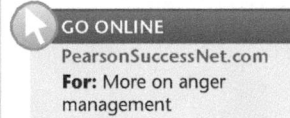
GO ONLINE
PearsonSuccessNet.com
For: More on anger management

Preventing Violence **175**

---

2. Teach

L3 **EL** Reading/Note Taking 7-3
L2 Adapted Reading/Note Taking 7-3

Arguments

L1 **Visual Learning: Figure 10**

Ask what emotion the student with the blond hair is expressing. *(anger)* Then, ask: **What do you think the other student is feeling?** *(She may be angry, too, or embarrassed or scared.)* Then help students recall some changes that occur in the body during the first stage of the stress response. *(tensed muscles; rapid heart rate and breathing rate)* Explain that similar changes occur when a person is angry. Ask students to recall some strategies for dealing with stress that could be applied to dealing with anger. *(relaxation, physical activity, humor)*

Caption Answer She has an angry facial expression and is leaning forward aggressively.

Revenge

L2 **Cooperative Learning**

Have pairs of students role-play a conversation between a person who is planning to seek revenge for an insult and a friend who is trying to talk him or her out of carrying out the plan for revenge. Call on some pairs to present their role-plays to the class. Discuss which reasons for avoiding revenge were most persuasive.

L3 **Cultural Connection**

Ask students if they are familiar with the sayings "an eye for an eye and a tooth for a tooth" or Gandhi's quote "an eye for an eye would make the whole world blind." Discuss how these and other sayings could influence a person's attitude toward violence.

Connect to Your Life Allow students to answer this question in their private journals.

L3 **Content Update**  **GO ONLINE**

Use the Web Code to access up-to-date information about anger management. Have students complete the Web activity.

Differentiated Instruction

L2 **Less Proficient Readers**

As students read, ask them to look for information related to the section objectives. For each objective, students should list relevant information. For example, for the first objective, they should look for details about how anger and revenge can lead to fights. For the second objective, they should list details about the role of friends and bystanders in fights. For the third objective, they should look for a description of the relationship between a need for control and violence.

Peer Pressure

L3 Cooperative Learning

Have students read the italicized copy under the heading Peer Pressure. Then divide the class into groups of four to role-play a conversation that begins with these comments. In the role-play, the three friends should continue to pressure the fourth friend, who does not want to fight. Have groups perform their role-plays, and discuss how difficult it is to resist such pressure from friends.

L2 Visual Learning: Figure 11

As students look at the photo, ask them to focus on the two bystanders. Ask: **Are they doing anything to stop the fight?** *(It doesn't look like they are.)* **Do you think the young man on the right will walk away from this fight? Why or why not?** *(probably not while the bystanders are watching because he would appear scared)*
Caption Answer They are observing an argument, and they may hope to see a fight. It will be difficult to settle the dispute with bystanders watching.

Control

L3 Building Health Skills

Advocacy Ask students to imagine they have a friend who is being abused. Have them think of things they might do to help the friend. Then ask them to consider the consequences of each action. Finally, students should choose the alternative they think is most likely to be effective and write a paragraph explaining their choice. **WRITING**

Visual Learning: Figure 12

Caption Answer *Sample answer:* She may be ashamed to admit that she is in an abusive relationship.

 Allow students to answer this question in their private journals.

Peer Pressure

You're not going to let her get away with that, are you?
Girl, I wouldn't take that from anyone.
Why do you carry a knife if you're afraid to use it?

One aspect of fights that is often overlooked is the role of friends and bystanders. When you hear the term *peer pressure* in relation to violence, you may immediately think of the influence that gang members have on each other to fight. But peer pressure can be an important factor in non-gang violence as well. **It is often more difficult for a person to avoid a fight when friends or bystanders are present.**

The Role of Friends You just had a loud disagreement with someone and your friends make comments like those above. How might these comments affect you? Chances are they would increase your feelings of anger and embarrassment, and add to the pressure you might already feel to fight. You might feel trapped—you don't want to fight but you may worry that your friends would lose respect for you if you walk away.

Friends who urge you to fight are acting as instigators. **Instigators** are people who encourage fighting between others while staying out of the fight themselves. Sometimes an instigator acts directly. He or she may exaggerate a conflict or embarrass a person into fighting. At other times, instigators act indirectly. For example, they may spread rumors about one person to another to create a conflict between them.

The Role of Bystanders Another form of instigation occurs when a crowd gathers at the scene of a potential fight. The people who gather do so hoping to see a fight. They may yell things or in other ways urge the people to fight. It can be very difficult to settle a dispute peacefully once a crowd has gathered. If a fight does break out, the person who loses may face an additional problem—dealing with the embarrassment of having had so many people witness the defeat.

Connect to Your Life Have you ever been an instigator in a fight? If so, why did you encourage the other person to fight?

FIGURE 11 When a fight is about to occur, bystanders can make a difference. **Observing** What role are the bystanders playing in the situation shown?

For Your INFORMATION!

Abusive Relationships

Unfortunately, some students in your class are probably all too familiar with the use of violence to gain and maintain control in a relationship. The following data are from a Bureau of Justice special report.

- About one in three high school students have been in an abusive relationship.
- Forty percent of young women ages 14 to 17 report knowing someone who has been hit or beaten by a boyfriend.

Control

Did you see her black eye and bruises?

Yes, and all because another guy gave her a ride home. How can a guy beat up on his girlfriend like that?

Girlfriend? He treats her more like a piece of property.

Domestic violence and dating violence are a growing problem in this country. **One person's desire to have control over another is the main reason for domestic violence and dating violence.** Although the victims can be men, they are most often women.

Men generally have greater physical strength than women. So a fight between a man and a woman is often quite one-sided. Plus the woman may not fight back for fear that the violence will escalate. Or she may begin to believe that she deserves to be hit. She is caught in a trap—too afraid to stay and challenge the abuser and too afraid to leave. The victim learns to follow the abuser's orders and to even anticipate his wishes to avoid further attacks.

There are laws that protect women in abusive relationships. The police can arrest the abuser or a judge can issue a restraining order telling the man to keep away from the woman. But a restraining order won't help unless the woman has a safe place to go. Doctors, counselors, or members of the clergy can help women find the support they need. In most areas, there are shelters for abused women where they can also get help for their legal, financial, and emotional needs. There are also groups that try to help abusers learn to control their violent behavior.

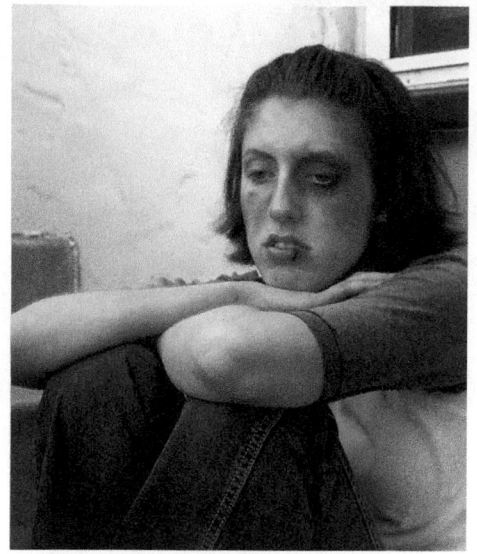

FIGURE 12 Often victims of violence try to hide their bruises. They might use makeup, dark glasses, or long-sleeved shirts. **Predicting** Why might a victim of violence try to hide her bruises?

Section 3 Review

Key Ideas and Vocabulary

1. How can anger and revenge lead to fights?
2. What does it mean to **escalate** a fight?
3. What effect can friends and bystanders have on fights?
4. What does the term **instigator** mean?
5. How does a desire for control contribute to violence toward women?

Critical Thinking

6. **Evaluating** Fighting between teenage girls has increased greatly in recent years. What reasons can you think of to explain this trend?

Health at Home

Attitudes Toward Fighting Interview three adults that you know well. Ask them how they feel about fighting as a way to resolve conflicts. Do all the adults have the same attitude? How do their attitudes compare with yours? Write a paragraph summarizing what you find out. **WRITING**

7. **Predicting** Do think that an insult based on characteristics such as race or religion is more likely to lead to a fight than an insult based on behavior? Why or why not? **WRITING**

8. **Comparing and Contrasting** Why would some of the strategies used for reducing stress also help a person control anger?

3. Assess

Evaluate

These assignments can help you assess students' mastery of the section content.

Section 3 Review

Answers appear below.

Teaching Resources
- Practice 7-3
- Section 7-3 Quiz

L2 Reteach

Pose the following question: What would you tell your 10-year-old brother or sister about how fights start? Then ask students to make a bulleted list of points they would share with their sibling. Call on volunteers to each read one point from their list. Make a list on the board, and have students copy the final list in their notebooks.

L4 Enrich

Teaching Resources
- Enrich 7-3

Health at Home

Attitudes Toward Fighting Before students begin their interviews, have the class brainstorm some questions that will elicit thoughtful responses about fighting. After students have completed the interviews and written the paragraph, call on volunteers to summarize their findings for the class.

Section 3 Review

1. Anger is at the root of most arguments and many fights. The desire for revenge can lead to a dangerous cycle of fighting.

2. The fight grows more intense.

3. It is often more difficult for a person to avoid a fight when friends or bystanders are present.

4. An instigator is a person who encourages fighting while staying out of the fight.

5. One person's desire to have control over another is a main reason for domestic violence and dating violence.

6. One possible reason is changes in gender roles, which make it more acceptable for women to fight.

7. Students are likely to choose race or religion because race and religion evoke emotions such as pride.

8. The body reacts to anger the same way it does to stress, so strategies for reducing stress should be effective at controlling anger.

Mediating a Conflict

Objective

Develop the ability to use mediation to help resolve a conflict peacefully.

Teaching Strategies

- Emphasize that students should not use mediation to resolve a potentially violent dispute because they would be jeopardizing their safety.

- Ask students why it is important for a mediator to establish neutrality. *(Both sides must have confidence that the mediator will not be biased or take sides.)* Discuss ways that a mediator can demonstrate neutrality throughout the mediation process. *(The mediator could offer solutions that require both sides to make concessions.)*

- Discuss why each guideline listed in Step 2 is important to the mediation process. *(For example, if people know that what is said will be kept confidential, they will be more likely to share their thoughts and feelings.)* Ask volunteers to explain why each of the other guidelines is important. Also ask students to suggest any additional guidelines they think would be important.

- Discuss ways in which a mediator can keep the participants involved in the process. *(The mediator can suggest new directions in which the participants can explore possible solutions. The mediator can compliment the participants on the progress made so far and encourage them to continue. The mediator can offer possible solutions for both sides to respond to.)*

Advocacy

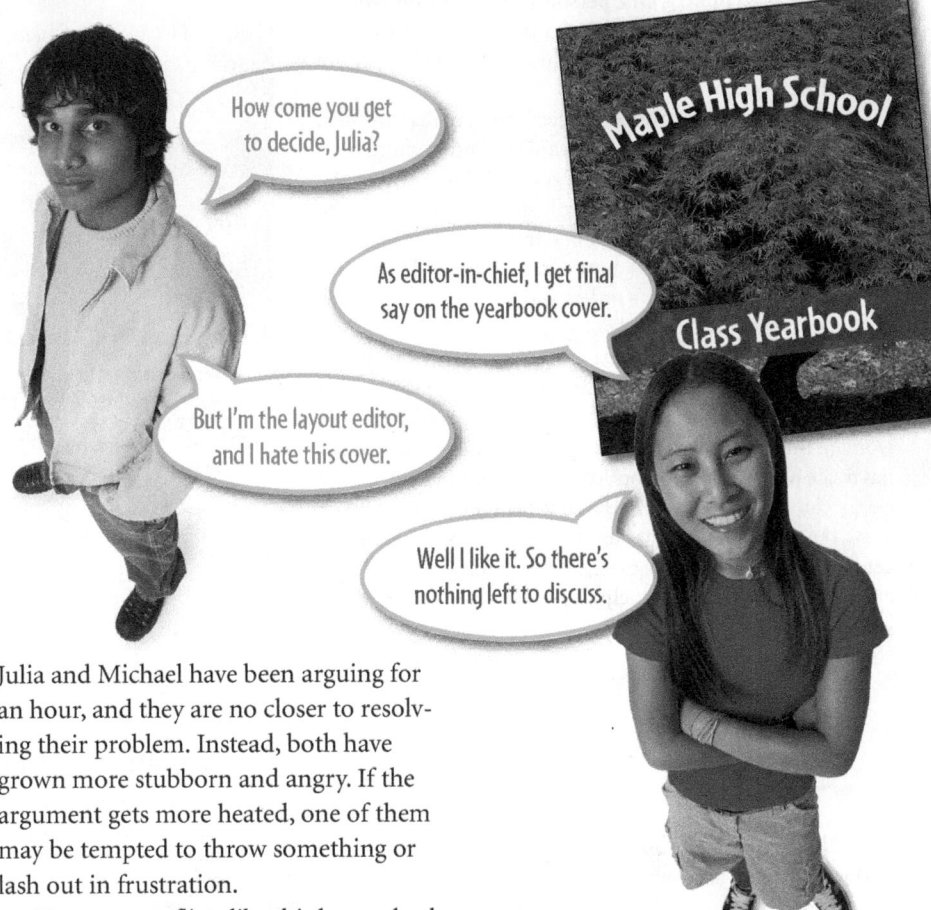

How come you get to decide, Julia?

As editor-in-chief, I get final say on the yearbook cover.

But I'm the layout editor, and I hate this cover.

Well I like it. So there's nothing left to discuss.

Maple High School

Class Yearbook

Julia and Michael have been arguing for an hour, and they are no closer to resolving their problem. Instead, both have grown more stubborn and angry. If the argument gets more heated, one of them may be tempted to throw something or lash out in frustration.

How can conflicts like this be resolved peacefully? One effective method, known as mediation, involves a third party in the negotiation process. The mediator explores the problem with the people to help them find a "win-win" solution—a solution that meets some of the important needs of both people. These steps outline the mediation process.

178

❶ Emphasize your neutrality.
Begin the mediation session by making it clear to both parties that you do not have a personal interest in the outcome. Explain that you will not take sides or decide who is right or wrong. Your role is to help find a solution that is acceptable to both parties.

> You both need to agree on some rules before we begin.

② Establish guidelines.

Ask the parties to agree upon the following rules before you begin.

▶ Keep everything that is said confidential.

▶ Be as honest as possible.

▶ Don't name-call or swear.

▶ Don't interrupt the other person.

▶ Take an active part in finding a solution.

▶ Follow through on any agreed-upon solution.

③ Ask each person to state his or her view.

▶ Allow each person to speak without interruption.

▶ Listen actively. If something that is said isn't clear, ask a question. Or restate the point and ask, "Is that what you mean?"

▶ Don't go on to the next person until you really understand the first person's position.

④ Identify each person's goal.

Try to figure out what principle, or goal, is driving each person's position. What a person truly cares about may not be what that person *says* he or she cares about.

⑤ Explore possible solutions.

If the participants seem relaxed, ask them to work together to brainstorm a list of possible solutions. During brainstorming, they should not judge any proposed solutions. Encourage the participants to use each other's suggestions to spark their own ideas.

If the participants are tense or hostile, help them explore solutions one at a time. Start by asking one person to propose a solution. Then, get the other person's reaction and ask for a counterproposal. Continue until you find a solution that satisfies both people.

⑥ Don't give up.

It isn't easy to find a win-win solution for every conflict, but it can be done.

▶ Focus on what the parties agree on. Use that common ground to help them bridge their different positions.

▶ Keep the participants involved in the process. The more involved they are, the more interest they will have in resolving the conflict.

▶ If you are unable to find an agreeable solution, ask for help from an adult who has the respect and trust of both participants.

 Practice the Skill

1. Review the disagreement described in the introduction. What questions would you ask Julia and Michael to get at the principle behind each person's position?

2. With two of your classmates, role-play the mediation session. Take turns playing the roles of mediator, Julia, and Michael. What solution, if any, did you reach in each role-play session? What difficulties did you encounter in mediating the conflict?

3. Think about a recent conflict that you had with a friend or family member. Would a mediator have been able to help you resolve the conflict? Why or why not?

4. Make a list of the types of conflicts that occur among teens. Which of the conflicts on your list would be appropriate for mediation? Which would not? Explain.

Preventing Violence **179**

Practice the Skill

1. *Sample answer:* For Julia: Why do you feel that you alone must make the decision? What exactly do you like about the cover? Are there any other designs that you like as much? For Michael: Why do you hate this cover? What cover design would you prefer? For both: What should a yearbook cover accomplish? Is there another design that would serve these purposes just as well?

2. Make sure that students use the mediation process as outlined. Have groups share their proposed solutions with the class and discuss the difficulties they encountered.

3. Allow students to answer this question in their private journals. Ask students if they think that mediation would be a useful strategy for resolving conflicts between family members.

4. Conflicts that are appropriate for mediation are situations in which both sides have valid, but contradictory, viewpoints. There must be some basis for agreement between the parties, such as shared values or goals.

Health and Community

Community Mediation Services

Ask volunteers to find out what mediation services or classes are available in their community. Sources of information might include local religious or youth groups, legal associations, or peer mediation groups at community colleges. Some cities and towns have mediation services that are available for residents as an alternative to a court process. Have students make a report of their findings to the class.

Objectives

Before class begins, write the objectives on the board. Have students copy the objectives into their notebooks at the start of class.

1. Focus

Warm-Up Quick Quiz

Use the Warm-Up Presentation slide to survey student responses.

After students have taken the quiz and completed the writing assignment, read the questions aloud and ask students to explain how *yes* responses are indicative of a peacemaker. Then ask students to describe the qualities of a peacemaker.

Presentation 7-4

2. Teach

L3 **EL** Reading/Note Taking 7-4

L2 Adapted Reading/Note Taking 7-4

Choosing Not to Fight

L2 **Class Discussion**

Discuss the types of behaviors that are warning signs that a fight is brewing. *(name calling; trading insults or threats; spreading rumors; pushing, tripping, or similar physical behaviors; playing a cruel joke on a person)* Discuss how being aware of these warning signs can help a person deal with a situation before it turns violent.

Objectives

▶ **Describe** two general approaches for resolving conflicts.

▶ **Explain** why safety should be a person's first concern in any conflict.

▶ **Summarize** how to confront a person wisely.

▶ **Identify** ways to help others avoid fighting.

Vocabulary

• mediation

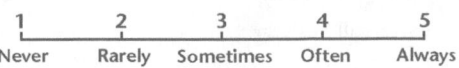

Warm-Up

Quick Quiz For each statement, rate yourself on this scale.

1	2	3	4	5
Never	Rarely	Sometimes	Often	Always

① When I am upset with someone, I talk to the person in private where we cannot be overheard.

② When I am angry, I avoid using insults or name-calling.

③ I apologize when I do or say something hurtful.

④ When I know a fight is brewing, I don't go to watch.

⑤ I avoid spreading rumors.

WRITING The higher your total score, the better your skills as a peacemaker. In which area would you most want to improve? Explain.

Choosing Not to Fight

It isn't always easy to avoid a fight, but it can be done. You need to learn peaceful alternatives to fighting, and how to pursue those alternatives even when the other person really wants to fight. As you read, think of ways you can adapt these strategies to situations in your life. You may come up with strategies of your own that you can share with friends, siblings, and others that you care about.

When people who know each other fight, there is usually a history of events leading up to the fight. For example, the spreading of rumors or name-calling may go on for days or weeks before a fight breaks out. If a conflict grows to the point where others know about it, friends may put pressure on one or both of the participants to do something. By the time a crowd has gathered for the showdown, it's almost too late.

It is best to deal with a conflict early on when people are less angry. Also, it is more difficult to resolve a problem after someone has been embarrassed in public or when instigators start to play a role. **Once you recognize that a conflict exists, there are two general approaches you can take. You can ignore the conflict or you can confront the person.**

180   *Chapter 7*

For Your INFORMATION!

Levels of Violence Prevention

Public health experts describe three levels of violence prevention. Primary prevention is aimed at changing attitudes and social norms through education and public awareness. Secondary prevention focuses on those who are at a greater risk for violence, such as children who are victims or witnesses of violence. Secondary prevention includes counseling, mentoring, and strategies for building resilience. Bullies would be candidates for secondary level strategies. Tertiary prevention is the intervention that comes after a violent episode, including arrest, prosecution, and incarceration.

Ignoring a Conflict

▶ A stranger bumps into you as you pass on the sidewalk.

▶ You are angry that some friends didn't ask you to go with them to the movies, even though you really didn't want to go.

▶ According to a friend of a friend of a friend, your boyfriend was flirting with a bridesmaid at his brother's wedding.

None of these situations seem worth fighting over. In some situations it may be smartest to walk away and do nothing at all. Figure 13 lists some tips to help you decide when it is best to ignore a situation.

Some people think that ignoring a conflict is a sign of cowardice. It is actually a sign of maturity and self-control. The act of cowardice may be to fight out of pride, or to "save face," or to impress your friends. But when you decide to ignore a conflict rather than fight, you may need to be flexible and you will need to control your own anger.

Be Flexible When you ignore a conflict, you need to proceed carefully. It is important to trust your judgment and be prepared to try a new tactic if your first choice doesn't defuse the situation. Suppose, for example, that you suspect the other person will become angrier if you ignore the situation. Then it may be better *not* to ignore the situation, even if you want to. **In deciding how to deal with any conflict, your safety should always be your first concern.**

Learn to Control Your Anger Learning to control your anger is an important skill to master if you want to avoid conflicts. If you cannot control your anger, you may overreact to a situation. You also leave yourself vulnerable to people who want to provoke you into a fight.

If you are not satisfied with the way you now deal with anger, many people can help you. Parents, teachers, coaches, school counselors, and members of the clergy are just some of the people you can turn to for help. If these people cannot help you themselves, they may be able to refer you to trained counselors who can. By asking for help, you take an important first step toward gaining control over your behavior and your future.

 **Connect to Your Life** Which conflicts are easiest to ignore—conflicts with strangers or conflicts with friends? Explain.

FIGURE 13 Rumors are not a reliable source of information. So it is often wise to ignore conflicts based on rumors.

Ignore a Situation If...

▶ you will probably never see the person again.

▶ the person or issue isn't very important to you.

▶ the conflict is based on rumors that can be overlooked.

▶ the conflict is about something trivial or silly.

▶ a person tries to get you in trouble by provoking a fight.

Ignoring a Conflict

L2 Visual Learning: Figure 13

After students have read the list of criteria for when to ignore a conflict, ask volunteers to describe an example of each situation. For each example, ask other students if they agree that it would be wise to ignore the conflict.

L3 Cooperative Learning

Pair up students to role-play a conflict between two teens. One should try to ignore the conflict and walk away. The other should remain angry and want to fight. Have pairs perform their role-plays for the class. Then discuss which strategies might work best when you want to ignore a conflict.

Connect to Your Life *Sample answer:* It is easier to ignore conflicts with strangers because you don't have to see them again; you are reminded of conflicts with friends whenever you get together.

 **Differentiated Instruction**

L1 Special Needs

Have students use the situations in the bulleted list under the heading Ignoring a Conflict to do role-plays, or substitute similar situations that are more relevant to your students. For each example, read the description aloud. Then have volunteers act out the situation. Discuss how each situation might be handled. Call on students to describe how they could be flexible and control their anger.

Confronting a Person Wisely

L1 Visual Learning: Figure 14

Use the photographs to help present the information about confronting a person wisely. For example, ask why it is wise for the young women in the first photograph to speak privately, but not in an isolated location.

Caption Answer If you cannot stay calm, you may not be able to remain in control of the situation.

L3 Journal Writing

Ask students to write an entry in their private journals describing ways they could stay calm if they decide that they need to confront a person. Suggest that students think about times in the past when they were able to stay calm in difficult situations. **WRITING**

L3 Online Activity GO ONLINE

Visit Pearson SuccessNet to access an online activity about handling conflicts. Have students complete the Web activity.

Choose a Safe Place • Stay Calm

FIGURE 14 Three general steps for confronting a person wisely are choosing the correct time and place, staying calm, and negotiating a solution. **Predicting** How could being unable to stay calm affect your ability to negotiate a solution?

GO ONLINE
PearsonSuccessNet.com
For: More on handling conflicts

Confronting a Person Wisely

Sometimes it may not be possible to ignore a conflict. The person may be someone with whom you are in frequent contact, or the issue may be too important to ignore. In these cases, you may decide to confront the person. The way in which you handle the confrontation, however, is critical to its success. **To confront a person wisely, you need to choose the right time and place, stay calm, and negotiate a solution.**

Choose the Time and Place Carefully When you need to confront a person, pick a time when you can talk face-to-face. Make sure that you don't have an audience. If people you know, especially friends, are around, the person may think that you want to embarrass him or her in front of the friends. The person may feel pressured to start a fight to avoid embarrassment.

It is best to meet in a public area, such as the food court in a mall or on a bench in a public park. Don't choose an isolated spot where there are no other people within shouting distance. That way you can get help if things don't go as you planned.

It is also important to avoid a confrontation when a person has been using alcohol or other drugs. Recall that alcohol and other drugs impair judgment and are a risk factor for violence. If you suspect the other person is under the influence of drugs, postpone your discussion.

Stay Calm It can be difficult to remain calm when you are upset, but it is important to try. Focus on keeping your voice low. By avoiding screaming or name-calling, you can remain in control of the situation.

People have different techniques for keeping calm under pressure. Some people find it helpful to rehearse the confrontation beforehand with an uninvolved person. Other people use deep breathing or count to 20 when they feel their temper begin to rise. Despite all your efforts, however, you may find yourself unable to stay calm and control your temper. If that happens, you may have to postpone your discussion.

TEENS *Are Asking . . .*

Q: When I need to confront someone, I have trouble staying calm. How can I keep from getting upset and angry?

A: Keeping calm can be difficult. Here are a few techniques that may help.

• Rehearse the conversation with a friend. Ask your friend to respond in ways that are likely to make you angry.

• When you feel angry or tense during a confrontation, pause and take a few slow, deep breaths.

• Think before you speak. Consider how the other person might respond to what you are about to say.

• If you cannot control your feelings, ask the other person if it would be okay to reschedule the conversation.

Why did you let me take all the blame for the cartoon on the board?

I was afraid of what my mom would say if I got another detention.

Negotiate a Solution

Negotiate a Solution   When you want to resolve a conflict peacefully, your communication style can affect the outcome. It is important to use skills such as "I" messages, assertiveness, and seeing the other person's point of view. When you say things like "I know this issue is important to both of us…," the other person is likely to be less defensive. Here are other strategies that may be useful during a negotiation.

▶ **Do the Unexpected** If, instead of being hostile, you are friendly, confident, and caring, the other person may relax his or her guard. Try to make the situation seem as if it is not serious enough to fight about.

▶ **Provide a Way Out** Sometimes fighting breaks out simply because people see no other way to resolve things without losing pride. To avoid fighting, present the other person with compromise solutions that you both can live with. By saying something like, "Let's try this for a week and see how it goes," you give the person an easy way out.

▶ **Be Willing to Apologize** In some situations, be willing to say "I'm sorry" or "I didn't mean to embarrass you." Sometimes a sincere apology can be the quickest way to defuse the situation.

Helping Others to Avoid Fights

When you are not personally involved in a conflict, you can still play an important role. **You can help prevent fighting through mediation, through your role as a bystander, and by involving an adult.**

Mediation   A process for resolving conflicts that involves a neutral third party is called **mediation** (mee dee AY shun). The Building Health Skills activity on pages 178–179 describes this process. As with all conflicts, mediators need to think about their own safety first. They should never get involved in heated conflicts that could turn violent at any moment.

 **What strategies do you use to help others avoid fights?**

L3 **Building Health Skills**

Communicating Have the class brainstorm a list of possible opening lines to use when confronting a person wisely. Emphasize the importance of using "I" messages and showing an understanding of the other person's feelings. Discuss how a person's tone of voice and body language may be as important to the message as the actual words spoken. Have volunteers practice delivering each of the opening lines.

Helping Others to Avoid Fights

EL **Building Vocabulary**

Explain that the word *mediation* comes from a Latin word that means "to be in the middle." (The word *medium* comes from the same Latin word.) Ask: **How is a mediator "in the middle" of a conflict?** *(The mediator stays neutral, taking a middle position between the two parties in a conflict.)*

 Allow students to answer this question in their private journals.

Differentiated Instruction

L4 **Gifted and Talented**

Encourage interested students to find out how the process of arbitration differs from the process of mediation. *(In arbitration, the parties agree in advance to abide by the arbitrator's decision.)* Also ask students to find out the types of disputes for which arbitration is effective. Have students share their findings with the class.

L2 Visual Learning: Figure 15

Have students explain why each of the tips listed for peacemakers might help prevent a fight. Start by asking: **How might the young men benefit from having the young woman listen to their concerns?** *(They would have the opportunity to express their feelings, which might help them calm down. Each might also hear the viewpoint of the other person in the conflict.)*

3. Assess

Evaluate

These assignments can help you assess students' mastery of the section content.

Section 4 Review
Answers appear below.

Teaching Resources
• Practice 7-4
• Section 7-4 Quiz

L2 Reteach

Ask students how they would respond to a friend who says, "I'm left with no choice but to fight that jerk." Call on students to describe a method they could use to prevent the fight from occurring.

L4 Enrich

Teaching Resources
• Enrich 7-4

Health at School

Peer Mediation Help students identify students at the school who have taken mediation training. If your school does not have a peer mediation process, check with a school counselor, who might know of students involved in a community mediation program.

FIGURE 15 Discouraging others from fighting is an important part of preventing violence.

Tips for Peacemakers
• Listen to people who are hurt.
• Help to correct unfair situations.
• Praise helps.
• Put-downs don't help.

Your Role as a Bystander You learned how friends and acquaintances often put pressure on people to fight. These same people, however, can play a key role in preventing fights. As a bystander, you can use the following strategies to show your disapproval of fighting as a way to resolve conflicts.

▶ Ignore those people who make negative remarks about other people.

▶ Refuse to spread rumors.

▶ Do not relay a threat or insult from one person to another.

▶ Stay away from any area where you expect a fight could take place.

As a friend, you can use your influence to support positive behaviors. You can show respect for people who apologize to others, ignore insults, and otherwise avoid fights. If you advise your friends to ignore someone's insults or not to hold grudges, you do them a very important service. You help keep them safe from the potential of deadly violence.

When to Involve an Adult If a friend reveals plans of violence to you, it is important to ask for help. Such plans should always be taken seriously, especially if your friend talks about using a weapon. Although it is never easy to break a friend's confidence, it is critical for you to share your friend's plans with a trusted adult. Doing so is a true act of caring. It shows that you care too much to let your friend be lost to violence.

Section 4 Review

Key Ideas and Vocabulary

1. What are two possible approaches when you are faced with a conflict?
2. What should your first concern be in any conflict?
3. Describe three steps you should take when you confront a person.
4. What does the term **mediation** mean?
5. How can you help others avoid a fight?

Critical Thinking

6. **Comparing and Contrasting** Why should you use "I" messages when you negotiate a solution for yourself? Why should a mediator not use "I" messages?

Health at School

Peer Mediation Interview a few students who have taken mediation training. Ask them what they learned and how they have used what they learned to resolve conflicts. Then write a paragraph discussing why you would or would not want to be trained as a mediator. **WRITING**

7. **Making Judgments** You hear that a fight is brewing between two students. A friend tells you that one of the students has a knife and intends to use it. What would you do? Why?

8. **Evaluating** Why do you think that it is difficult for some people to apologize even when they know they are wrong?

 GO ONLINE PearsonSuccessNet.com Audio Summary Section 7.4

Section 4 Review

1. ignore the conflict or confront the person
2. your own safety
3. Students should describe choosing the right place, staying calm, and negotiating a solution.
4. a process for resolving conflicts that involves a neutral third party
5. through mediation, through your role as a bystander, and by involving an adult

6. The other person in the negotiation will be less defensive. Mediators shouldn't share their own thoughts or feelings.
7. *Sample answer:* I would tell a trusted adult because the situation is too dangerous for me to handle on my own.
8. *Sample answer:* They may be too proud or be embarrassed to admit they are wrong.

Chapter 7
At a Glance

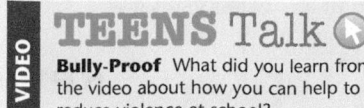

TEENS Talk
Bully-Proof What did you learn from the video about how you can help to reduce violence at school?

Section 1 What Is Violence?

Key Ideas

▶ With violence, there are costs to the victim, costs to the assailant, and costs to society as a whole.

▶ Risk factors for violence include poverty, family violence, exposure to media violence, availability of weapons, drug abuse, and membership in gangs.

Vocabulary
- violence (162)
- homicide (162)
- victim (163)
- assailant (163)
- territorial gang (167)

Section 2 Violence in Schools

Key Ideas

▶ Students who use weapons at school often are acting on the rage they feel as victims of harassment.

▶ The most effective way to stop bullying is to get bystanders involved.

▶ School administrators and teachers need to take the lead in the prevention of hazing. If school administrations, teachers, and students work together, they can stop sexual harassment.

▶ The most effective way to deal with violence based on hate is through education.

Vocabulary
- harassment (168)
- bullying (169)
- cyber bullying (169)
- hazing (170)
- sexual harassment (171)
- hate violence (172)
- prejudice (172)
- stereotype (172)
- intolerance (172)
- discrimination (172)
- vandalism (173)

Section 3 How Fights Start

Key Ideas

▶ Anger is at the root of most arguments and of many fights. The desire for revenge leads to a dangerous cycle of fighting.

▶ It is often more difficult for a person to avoid a fight when friends or bystanders are present.

▶ One person's desire to have control over another is the main reason for domestic violence and dating violence.

Vocabulary
- escalate (175)
- instigator (176)

Section 4 Preventing Fights

Key Ideas

▶ Once you recognize that a conflict exists, you can ignore the conflict or confront the person. In deciding how to deal with any conflict, your safety should always be your first concern.

▶ To confront a person wisely, choose the right time and place, stay calm, and negotiate a solution.

▶ You can help prevent fighting through mediation, through your role as a bystander, and by involving an adult.

Vocabulary
- mediation (183)

Preventing Violence **185**

Chapter 7
At a Glance

Bully-Proof Ask for volunteers to share their answers. Use examples from the video to review strategies for dealing with bullying.

Key Ideas Review

L2 Have students reword the section objectives as questions and then try to answer them. Students should find answers in the text for any questions they cannot answer.

L3 Divide the class into small groups, and ask each group to brainstorm a list of challenging questions that cover each of the sections' objectives. Then, have members of each group work together to answer the questions devised by another group.

Vocabulary Review

EL Pair English language learners with English proficient students, and ask each pair to make a crossword puzzle using at least ten terms from the chapter. Have pairs of students exchange and solve one another's puzzles.

L2 Ask each student to write two multiple choice questions for each section in the chapter. Tell students the questions should focus on vocabulary. Then pair up students, and have partners answer each other's questions.

Chapter 7 Review

Chapter 7 Review

GO ONLINE

PearsonSuccessNet.com

Students can go online for a review activity on Chapter 7.

Reviewing Key Ideas

Section 1
1. d

2. victims: emotional scars, including anger, fear, and depression; assailants: guilt or shame; society: fear of violence and suspicion of strangers

3. High levels of anger and frustration cause people to react more violently than normal. Children from violent homes are more apt to use violence to solve their own problems.

4. Students may cite media violence and availability of guns. Possible solutions are reducing media violence and stricter gun regulations.

Section 2
5. c

6. Students who use weapons at school are often acting on the rage they feel as victims of harassment, including bullying.

7. Speak up assertively, use refusal skills to reject sexual advances, avoid being alone with the person, and report the behavior to an adult.

8. An anger-management course can help students learn strategies for controlling anger. (Some students may need counseling to deal with the underlying reasons for their anger.)

Section 3
9. b

10. You might worry that your friends would lose respect for you if you walk away from a fight.

11. The main cause is one person's desire to have control over another. The woman may be afraid to stay and challenge the abuser, but also too afraid to leave.

12. Students should use the phrase to explain how revenge leads to a dangerous cycle of fighting.

Chapter 7 Review

Reviewing Key Ideas

GO ONLINE

PearsonSuccessNet.com

For: Chapter 7 review activity

Section 1
1. For an action to be classified as violence, the action must
   a. result in death.
   b. result in physical injury.
   c. involve physical force.
   d. involve a threat or actual use of physical force.

2. Describe the emotional costs of violence to victims, assailants, and society as a whole.

3. Explain why poverty and family violence are risk factors for violence.

4. **Critical Thinking** Why do you think that the homicide rate in the United States is so high? What could be done to lower the rate?

Section 2
5. A lack of acceptance of another person's opinions, beliefs, or actions is
   a. prejudice.   b. stereotyping.
   c. intolerance.   d. discrimination.

6. Explain how bullying might lead to the use of weapons at school.

7. What should a student do when faced with sexual harassment at school?

8. **Critical Thinking** Do you think that school courses in managing anger could help students learn to handle anger better? Why or why not?

Section 3
9. People who encourage fighting between others are called
   a. bystanders.   b. instigators.
   c. assailants.   d. peers.

10. How can the presence of acquaintances and friends make it more difficult to avoid a fight?

11. What is the main cause of domestic violence and dating violence? Explain how a woman may get trapped in an abusive relationship.

12. **Critical Thinking** Use the saying "an eye for an eye and a tooth for a tooth" to explain the role that revenge can play in fighting.

Section 4
13. Ignoring a conflict is
    a. never a good approach.
    b. an act of cowardice.
    c. one approach to handling conflicts.
    d. the best approach to all conflicts.

14. Explain how your safety could be at risk when you ignore a conflict, when you confront a person, and when you mediate a conflict.

15. What can bystanders do to help prevent fights?

16. **Critical Thinking** A person sitting next to you on a crowded subway is smoking, despite the *No Smoking* sign. Make a list of the potential risks and benefits of confronting this person. Then state what you would do. **WRITING**

Building Health Skills

17. **Advocacy** Your friend has been spreading untrue rumors about a new student at school. The new student is very angry. How could you prevent this situation from becoming violent?

18. **Analyzing Influences** Why do you think a teen might videotape an act of violence by other teens instead of trying to stop the violence?

19. **Setting Goals** Make an action plan to reduce the number of times you say negative things about other people. Put your plan into action for a week and monitor your progress. Then adjust your plan, if necessary. **WRITING**

Health and Community

Teens in the News Look through your local newspaper each day for a week. Record a brief summary of each story about teens. What percentage of the stories are about violence? What impression do you think an adult reading this newspaper would have of today's youth? **WRITING**

Section 4
13. c

14. If you ignore a conflict, the other person may become angrier. With friends around, a person may fight to avoid embarrassment. Don't mediate a conflict that could turn violent.

15. *Sample answer:* Ignore people who make negative remarks about others; refuse to spread rumors.

16. Benefit: person stops smoking; risk: person reacts with anger.

Building Health Skills

17. *Sample answer:* I could refuse to spread the rumor, advise the person spreading the rumor to stop, and include the new student in group activities.

18. *Sample answer:* The teen might be acting as an instigator.

19. Students should write a detailed plan, moniter their progress, and write about the process and results.

Standardized Test Prep

Math Practice

The table compares the number of homicides in eight states in 2011. Use the table to answer Questions 20–23.

State	Population	Homicides	Rate*
California	37,254,000	1,790	4.8
Florida	18,801,000	984	5.2
Iowa	3,046,000	44	1.5
Missouri	5,989,000	364	6.1
Nevada	2,701,000	129	5.2
New Jersey	8,792,000	379	4.3
Rhode Island	1,053,000	14	1.3
Utah	2,764,000	51	1.9

* Homicides per 100,000 people

20. Of the states listed, which state had the most homicides?
    A Florida
    B California
    C Nevada
    D Missouri

21. Of the states listed, which state had the largest population?
    F Florida
    G California
    H Nevada
    J Missouri

22. Of the states listed, which state had the highest homicide rate?
    A Florida
    B California
    C Missouri
    D Nevada

23. Based on the data, which of the following statements is true?
    F The smaller the population of a state, the lower its homicide rate.
    G There is no relationship between population and number of homicides.
    H States with larger populations have higher homicide rates.
    J When comparing homicide data for states, you should compare rates, not number of homicides.

Test-Taking Tip

If you are frustrated by the questions on a test, don't disturb others. Try to calm down so you can think clearly.

Reading and Writing Practice

Read the passage. Then answer Questions 24–27.

Police and health professionals have different roles when they deal with violence. Police respond to a violent event to find out what happened. Their goal is to gather enough evidence to make an arrest and help convict the person who committed the violent act. Police are charged with assigning blame and punishment after an episode of violence. Health professionals use what is known about violent events to try to understand what causes violence. Health professionals are charged with identifying the risk factors that can lead to violence.

24. What is the main idea of this passage?
    A Police are not interested in preventing violence.
    B Police and health professionals have different approaches to violence.
    C Health professionals are not concerned about placing blame for violent acts.
    D Health professionals try to identify risk factors for violence.

25. Based on this passage, what does the phrase "charged with" mean?
    F in favor of
    G trained to
    H responsible for
    J obsessed with

26. Which statement is implied—not said, but understood—by the passage?
    A The causes of violence are easy to understand.
    B All violent acts have the same cause.
    C Police and health professionals don't agree on how to prevent violence.
    D Identifying risk factors can help prevent violence.

Constructed Response

27. Which approach to reducing violence do you think is more effective, the one used by police or the one used by health professionals? Give some specific reasons for your answer.

Standardized Test Prep

Math Practice
20. B
21. G
22. C
23. J

Reading and Writing Practice
24. B
25. H
26. D
27. Students might identify either approach as more effective. The reasons for identifying one or the other should be thoughtful and logical.

Health and Community

Teens in the News Remind students that their summaries of content can be very brief, just enough information so that they can recall the article. Also remind students how to calculate a percentage. After students complete the activity, discuss their results and conclusions about the effect on adults.

Focus on ISSUES

How Has Technology Affected Teens' Communication Skills?

Teaching Strategies

- Invite students to describe which communication devices they depend on and for what types of communication.

- Ask volunteers to describe how their lives would be different if they did not have access to electronic communication. What other forms of communication would they use? How would using those other forms affect what they communicate and to whom?

- Have students read the cases for and against electronic communication, and answer the questions on page 189. Then, call on volunteers to go to the board and list pros and cons of using electronic communication. Challenge the class to think of other pros and cons not mentioned in the text.

Focus on ISSUES

How Has Technology Affected Teens' Communication Skills?

Every day, teens use e-mail, cell phones, instant messaging, and text messaging to communicate with family and friends. In fact, over 90 percent of teens in the United States have Internet access and at least 75 percent have cell phones.

Can you communicate as well electronically as you can when you are face to face? Does electronic communication have an effect on your communication skills and other social skills? Is the effect positive or negative?

188

For Your INFORMATION!

Electronic Communication and Writing

Do you know what LOL and IDK mean? Your students do. LOL means "laughing out loud" and IDK means "I don't know." LOL and IDK are two examples of the many shortcuts commonly used by teens in instant messaging and text messaging. Some experts worry about the effects of these forms of electronic communication on students' writing abilities. They argue that students will develop sloppy writing habits and a writing style that is too informal for many purposes. Other experts disagree. They argue that the new ways of communicating encourage students to express themselves concisely and to write more than they otherwise would.

The Case for Electronic Communication

Electronic communication has broadened teens' communication skills. The wide range of communication options allows teens to choose the best method for a particular situation. Also, teens can now stay in close touch with a larger circle of people—even friends and relatives around the world. With electronic communication, teens have mastered the communication skills they will need for careers in a "wired" world.

66 I used to be nervous about going up to someone at school that I didn't know that well. But if you send the person an instant message and chat that way, then you know you can go up to them in person. So now I feel much more comfortable talking to people and I've made a lot of new friends. 99

The Case Against Electronic Communication

When teens rely on electronic communication, their face-to-face communication skills suffer. They don't develop the ability to interpret clues such as body language and tone of voice. They also might favor e-mail and other less personal forms of communication when problems need to be resolved. In doing so, teens might not learn how to confront people directly—an important communication skill that people need throughout their lives.

66 I have friends who spend all their time on their cell phones, even when we're out together. They don't know how rude it is when they ignore you and keep talking really loudly. I go to a summer camp where no electronic stuff is allowed, and I love it. I think my communication skills are much better than those of kids who are wired all the time. 99

What do **YOU** think?

1. Possible positive effects might include getting more practice in writing and feeling freer to express thoughts and feelings that are difficult to share face to face. Possible negative effects might include developing a style of writing that is too informal and getting less practice in nonverbal communication skills.
2. Students' choices should be consistent with their values. For example, being able to communicate at all times with people in different locations might be important to someone who places a high value on friendships.
3. Students might make a case for electronic communication by citing the ability to stay in touch with friends who move away. They might argue a case against electronic communication by citing the possibility of miscommunication without the benefit of body language and other nonverbal clues.

GO ONLINE

PearsonSuccessNet.com

Visit Pearson SuccessNet to access more information about electronic communication.

What do **YOU** think?

Use these steps to analyze and express your opinion about technology and communication skills.

1. Analyze the Issue Carefully consider both sides of the issue. Make a table listing the positive and negative effects of electronic communication on teens' communication skills.

2. Consider Your Values Look at your list of pros and cons. Which items are most important to you? Which are least important? Explain how these choices reflect your values.

3. Take a Stand Write a paragraph expressing your opinion on the effect of electronic communication on teens. State your opinion clearly and give several reasons to support your opinion. **WRITING**

189

Section Objectives	Standards Correlation	Instructional Resources (L3)	SE eTEXT	TE eTEXT	PRINT
1 **Carbohydrates, Fats, and Proteins** ⏱ 3 periods; 1 1/2 blocks	NHES: 1.12.1, 2.12.4, 6.12.1, 7.12.2	SE Warm-Up, p. 192	•	•	•
8.1.1 **Name** the three classes of nutrients that supply your body with energy.		SE Hands-On Activity Which Foods Contain Fats?, p. 197	•	•	•
8.1.2 **Explain** how the body obtains energy from foods.		RN Note Taking Guide 8-1	•	•	•
		IB Image Bank 8-4		•	
8.1.3 **Describe** the roles that carbohydrates, fats, and proteins play in your body.		TR Practice 8-1		•	
		TR Section 8-1 Quiz		•	
Breaking a Bad Habit ⏱ 1 period; 1/2 block	NHES: 6.12.1, 6.12.2, 6.12.3, 6.12.4	SE Practice the Skill, p. 201	•	•	•
		RN Building Health Skills 8	•	•	•
BHS.8 **Implement** a plan for replacing an unwanted habit with a new, positive behavior.					
2 **Vitamins, Minerals, and Water** ⏱ 2 periods; 1 block	NHES: 1.12.1, 3.12.1, 3.12.2	SE Warm-Up, p. 202	•	•	•
		RN Note Taking Guide 8-2	•	•	•
8.2.1 **Identify** the two main classes of vitamins.		TR Practice 8-2		•	
8.2.2 **List** seven minerals your body needs in significant amounts.		TR Section 8-2 Quiz		•	
8.2.3 **Explain** why water is so important to your body.					
3 **Guidelines for Healthful Eating** ⏱ 1 period; 1/2 block	NHES: 1.12.1, 2.12.1, 2.12.7, 3.12.5, 6.12.1	SE Warm-Up, p. 210	•	•	•
		RN Note Taking Guide 8-3	•	•	•
		IB Image Bank 8-15		•	
8.3.1 **Explain** how the *Dietary Guidelines for Americans* can help you plan a healthful diet.		TR Practice 8-3		•	
8.3.2 **Summarize** the recommendations in the MyPlate plan.		TR Section 8-3 Quiz		•	

Chapter Review and Assessment

SE Chapter 8 Review, p. 216 L3
CTB Chapter 8 Test L2 L3 L4
SE Standardized Test Prep, p. 217 L3

PROGRAM COMPONENTS

SE	Student Edition	CTB	Computer Test Bank
TE	Teacher Edition	AUD	Audio Section Summaries
TR	Teaching Resources		
RN	Reading and Note Taking Guide	DVD	Teens Talk Video Series
		VVG	Video Viewing Guide
ARN	Adapted Reading and Note Taking Guide	PPT	Presentation
IB	Image Bank		

Differentiated Instruction

(L1) (L2) (L4) (EL)

		SE eTEXT	TE eTEXT	PRINT
ARN	Note Taking Guide 8-1 (L2)	•	•	
RN	Note Taking Guide 8-1 (EL)	•	•	•
AUD	Audio Summary 8-1 (L1) (L2) (EL)	•	•	
TE	Reteach Strategy, p. 199 (L2)		•	•
TR	Enrich 8-1 (L4)		•	
ARN	Building Health Skills 8 (L2)	•	•	
RN	Building Health Skills 8 (EL)	•	•	•
ARN	Note Taking Guide 8-2 (L2)	•	•	
RN	Note Taking Guide 8-2 (EL)	•	•	•
AUD	Audio Summary 8-2 (L1) (L2) (EL)	•	•	
TE	Reteach Strategy, p. 209 (L2)		•	•
TR	Enrich 8-2 (L4)		•	
ARN	Note Taking Guide 8-3 (L2)	•	•	
RN	Note Taking Guide 8-3 (EL)	•	•	•
AUD	Audio Summary 8-3 (L1) (L2) (EL)	•	•	
TE	Reteach Strategy, p. 214 (L2)		•	•
TR	Enrich 8-3 (L4)		•	

ABILITY LEVELS

(L1) **For students with special needs**
(L2) **For less proficient readers**
(L3) **For all students**
(L4) **For gifted and talented students**
(EL) **For English language learners**

Chapter 8 Digital/Video Pathway

This alternative pathway allows you to teach this chapter's content using only the video and online materials.

Preview

DVD	Video #8 Preview
SE	Video #8 Preview Activity
VVG	Video #8 Worksheet

Food for Thought

1

PPT	8-1 Presentation
RN/ARN	8-1 Note Taking
PPT	8-1 Section Quiz

2

PPT	8-2 Presentation
RN/ARN	8-2 Note Taking
PPT	8-2 Section Quiz

3

DVD	Video #8 Explore/Wrap-Up
VVG	Video #8 Worksheet
PPT	8-3 Presentation
RN/ARN	8-3 Note Taking
PPT	8-3 Section Quiz

Food for Thought

Chapter Preview

Section 1 Carbohydrates, Fats, and Proteins

Carbohydrates, fats, and proteins are three classes of nutrients that supply the body with energy. The energy from these nutrients is released during chemical reactions inside body cells.

 Setting Goals

Breaking a Bad Habit
The key to changing an unhealthful habit is to replace it with a new, positive habit.

Section 2 Vitamins, Minerals, and Water

Vitamins, minerals, and water are three nutrients that do not supply the body with energy. Vitamins are made by living things and required in small amounts to help body processes. Minerals occur naturally in soil and rock and are also needed in small amounts. Water is essential for all life processes, including the production of energy.

Section 3 Guidelines for Healthful Eating

The *Dietary Guidelines for Americans* gives information about how to make smart food choices, balance food and physical activity, get the most nutrition out of your calories, and handle food safely. The "MyPlate plan" helps people plan balanced meals based on their age, sex, and activity level.

GO ONLINE

PearsonSuccessNet.com

For resources and activities for this chapter.

Food and Nutrition

1 Carbohydrates, Fats, and Proteins
  • **Hands-On Activity** Which Foods Contain Fats?

Building Health Skills
  • **Setting Goals** Breaking a Bad Habit

2 Vitamins, Minerals, and Water

3 Guidelines for Healthful Eating

GO ONLINE PearsonSuccessNet.com

TEENS Talk

VIDEO 8

Food for Thought

Preview **Activity**

How Do Food Ads Influence You?

Complete this activity before you watch the video.

1. Predict how many food ads you are exposed to in a typical day.
2. Keep a log for a day. For each food ad you see, note the type of ad, where you saw it, and its message.
3. Did the actual number of food ads you saw surprise you? Was the number higher than you predicted?
4. In a paragraph, discuss some of the ways that food ads influence the food choices that you and other teens make. **WRITING**

 Sensitive Issues

• Some students may be hesitant to share information about their dietary habits because of ethnic, religious, or socioeconomic differences. Others may have medical problems that affect their food choices and nutritional needs.

• Students who are significantly overweight or underweight may also be uncomfortable with any topic related to food and diet.

TEENS Talk

Food for Thought

Video Objectives

Use this video to help students

Identify the factors that influence their food choices.

Analyze the techniques that food advertisers use to influence teens.

Make wiser consumer decisions when choosing foods.

Preview **Activity**

How Do Food Ads Influence You?

Assign the Preview Activity for homework a few days before you plan to show the video. Encourage students to write down their prediction in Step 1 before they begin keeping their logs. After students complete the assignment, discuss the number and types of food ads that students were exposed to. Most students will be surprised at how pervasive food ads are in their lives. Students may also not realize how much the ads influence both their food choices and their overall attitudes toward foods.

191

From the Authors

I once worked next door to a nutritionist. She was a wise woman who understood when I said, "Nutrition is far too complicated to teach." She clued me in to one simple key to nutrition: "Simply look at your plate of food. What do you see? If you see a variety of colors—green, yellow, orange, and so on—you have a fairly nutritious meal. If, on the other hand, you see foods that are all the same color—brown meat, brown gravy, brown fried potatoes—you are likely to have a less nutritious meal."

Sounds simple…but it's hard to argue with. If you can teach your students only one practical tip regarding nutrition, teach them to think about the colors of the foods they eat.

Objectives
Before class begins, write the objectives on the board. Have students copy the objectives into their notebooks at the start of class.

1. Focus

Warm-Up Quick Quiz

Use the Warm-Up Presentation slide to survey student responses.

Give students a few minutes to write their responses. Then tally the responses on the board. Reveal that each of the five statements is "sometimes true." Take note of those statements that students thought were "always true" or "always false." Be sure to address these statements while teaching this section.

Presentation 8-1

2. Teach

L3 **EL** Reading/Note Taking 8-1
L2 Adapted Reading/Note Taking 8-1

Food Supply Nutrients

L2 **Class Discussion**

List the six classes of nutrients on the board. Ask: **How does the body get these nutrients?** *(from food)* **Which of these nutrients supply the body with energy?** *(carbohydrates, fats, and proteins)* Explain that the body also uses fats and proteins in other ways. Point out that students will learn about vitamins, minerals, and water in the next section.

Objectives
▶ **Name** the three classes of nutrients that supply your body with energy.
▶ **Explain** how the body obtains energy from foods.
▶ **Describe** the roles that carbohydrates, fats, and proteins play in your body.

Vocabulary
- nutrient
- metabolism
- calorie
- carbohydrate
- fiber
- fat
- unsaturated fat
- saturated fat
- cholesterol
- trans fat
- protein
- amino acid

Carbohydrates, Fats, and Proteins

Warm-Up

Quick Quiz Which of these statements are always true? Which are sometimes true? Which are always false?

1. Foods that are high in calories are unhealthy.
2. You should avoid foods with sugars in them.
3. You should avoid fats in your diet.
4. Vegetarian diets are low in protein.
5. Snacking is bad for you.

WRITING For each of your responses, explain why you gave the answer you did.

Foods Supply Nutrients

What do you think of when you hear the word *food?* You probably recall your favorite foods. Maybe you imagine the smell of fresh-baked bread or the spicy taste of curry. You might also think of occasions when food is especially important, such as family celebrations and meals with friends. Food is more than something that satisfies your hunger. It is a source of enjoyment, and it is an important aspect of your social life as well.

Your body needs food, and the food that you eat affects your health in many ways—how you look and feel, how well you resist disease, and even how well you perform mentally and physically. It does all those things by providing your body with **nutrients** (NOO tree unts), substances that the body needs to regulate bodily functions, promote growth, repair body tissues, and obtain energy. Your body requires more than 40 different nutrients for these tasks. The process by which the body takes in and uses these nutrients is called nutrition.

There are six classes of nutrients: carbohydrates, fats, proteins, vitamins, minerals, and water. Each class of nutrient is necessary for good health. **Carbohydrates, fats, and proteins can all be used by the body as sources of energy.** Vitamins, minerals, and water perform other essential functions that will be discussed in the next section.

192 *Chapter 8*

WRITING and Health

L4 **Speech**
Have students write a speech about why food is important to them. Encourage students to describe all the sensory delights of food, as well as the social enjoyment they associate with sharing meals with friends and family members. Instruct students to also include the physiological reasons for eating food—obtaining nutrients and energy. Ask for volunteers to deliver their speeches to the class.

Foods Supply Energy

The foods you eat are your body's energy source. You rely on the energy from food for everything you do—running, playing a musical instrument, and even sleeping. You need energy to maintain your body temperature, keep your heart beating, and enable you to understand what you read.

Fuel for Your Body When your body uses the nutrients in foods, a series of chemical reactions occurs inside your cells. As a result, energy is released. **Metabolism** (muh TAB uh liz um) is the chemical process by which your body breaks down food to release this energy. Metabolism also involves the use of this energy for the growth and repair of body tissues.

What Are Calories? The amount of energy released when nutrients are broken down is measured in units called **calories.** The more calories a food has, the more energy it contains. You can see in Figure 1 that the calorie content of different foods varies greatly. Contrast the energy that you get from a slice of pizza with the energy that you get from an apple, an orange, or a salad.

For good health, the number of calories in the food that you eat should match the calorie needs of your body. But when planning what to eat, you need to think about more than just the calorie content of foods. You also need to consider whether or not the foods you choose contain all the nutrients your body needs.

 **Connect to Your Life** How many calories are in a serving of your favorite snack food?

FIGURE 1 These two meals contain the same amount of energy but different nutrients. **Calculating** About how many salads would it take to equal the calories found in one slice of pizza? **MATH**

Which Lunch Would You Eat?

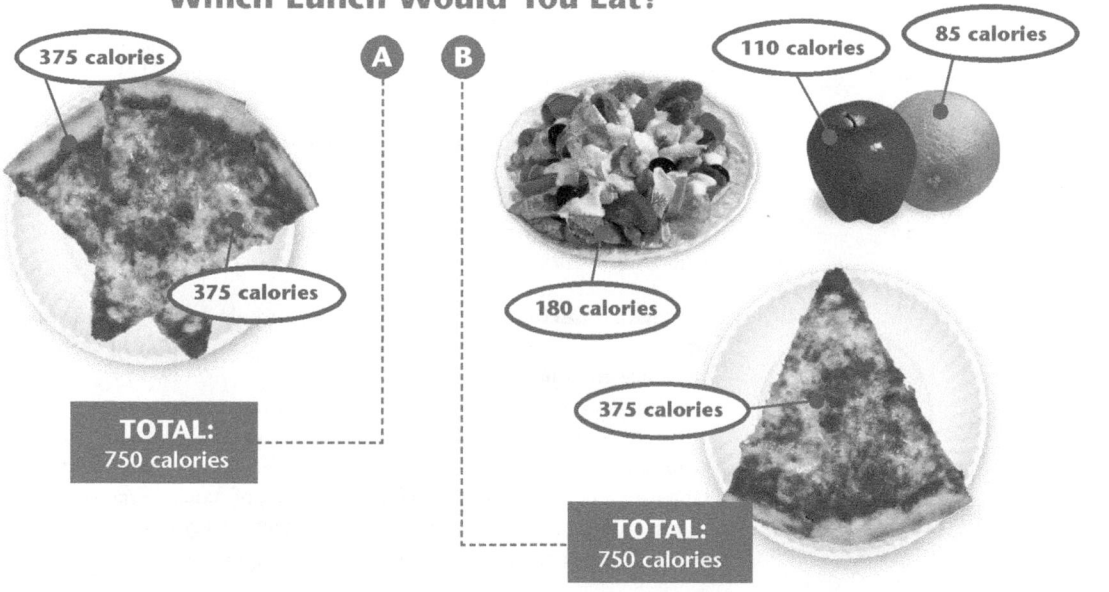

A

375 calories

375 calories

TOTAL:
750 calories

B

180 calories

375 calories

TOTAL:
750 calories

110 calories   85 calories

Foods Supply Energy

EL Building Vocabulary

As you discuss the meaning of the term *metabolism*, point out that the word contains the suffix *-ism*. Tell students that this suffix is added to many words to mean "the act of" or "the state of." Provide examples, such as *alcoholism* and *terrorism*, and challenge students to define these terms. What other words with this suffix can they think of? *(Sample answer: patriotism, symbolism, heroism)*

L3 Teacher Demo

To demonstrate how calories are a measure of energy, burn two potato chips with different calorie contents. You will need one regular potato chip and one low-fat baked potato chip. Both chips should be about the same size. Without revealing which chip is which, burn each (one at a time) in a shallow metal container. Have a student time how long each chip burns. Then ask: **Which is the higher-calorie chip? How can you tell?** *(Students should identify the regular chip as the high-calorie chip because it burned longer due to its higher energy content.)* Share with students the calorie content of each chip from the food labels.

L2 Visual Learning: Figure 1

Refer students to Figure 1. Ask for a show of hands for which lunch—A or B—students would prefer. Ask: **Which lunch provides more energy?** *(Both provide the same amount of energy.)* **Which lunch has more nutrients?** Explain. *(lunch B because it has a larger variety of foods)*

Caption Answer about two salads

Connect to Your Life *Sample answer:* An average serving of potato chips has 160 calories.

Differentiated Instruction

L1 Special Needs

Instruct students to move very slowly in place for one minute. Then have them move in place quickly for a minute. Ask: **Which movements do you think required more energy?** *(moving quickly)* **Where does the energy for moving come from?** *(food)*

What might happen if you did not eat enough food? *(You would not have enough energy to move.)* Also point out that their body would not have enough energy to grow.

Carbohydrates

L2 Visual Learning: Figure 2

Point out the foods in the photos. Ask: **What nutrient do these foods provide the body?** *(carbohydrates)* **Why are carbohydrates important for the body?** *(Carbohydrates supply energy for body functions.)* Then have students predict which types of carbohydrates are found in the following foods: apples *(sugars, fiber)*; potatoes *(starch, fiber)*; broccoli *(fiber)*; and milk *(sugars)*.

L1 Active Learning

Have students create a bulletin board display of carbohydrates. Students can use drawings, pictures from magazines, or clean boxes or labels from food products. Divide the bulletin board in half, and instruct students to label one side "Simple Carbohydrates" and the other side "Complex Carbohydrates." Students should put the pictures or labels on the appropriate side of the bulletin board.

L3 Cultural Connection

Explain that different cultures rely on different food sources for carbohydrates because of their customs and environment. For example, corn tortillas are traditional Mexican foods, while rice and noodles are traditional Asian fare. Rye bread and potato pancakes are traditional German foods. Have students choose an ethnic group and learn about a food that is a traditional source of carbohydrates. Have students find a recipe that uses this food, prepare it, and share the food with the class.

Watermelon (1 slice)
Total Carbs 22 g

Sugars	18 g
Starches	3 g
Fiber	1 g

Wheat Bread (1 slice)
Total Carbs 15 g

Sugars	1.5 g
Starches	12.0 g
Fiber	1.5 g

Pasta (1 cup)
Total Carbs 40 g

Sugars	1 g
Starches	37 g
Fiber	2 g

FIGURE 2 Whole-grain breads, fruits, and pasta are good sources of carbohydrates.

Carbohydrates

Carbohydrates (kahr boh HY drayts) are nutrients made of carbon, hydrogen, and oxygen. **Carbohydrates supply energy for your body's functions.** There are two general types of carbohydrates—simple carbohydrates and complex carbohydrates.

Simple Carbohydrates   Simple carbohydrates are also known as sugars. Sugars occur naturally in fruits, vegetables, and milk. They are added to many manufactured foods, such as cookies, candies, and soft drinks. There are several types of sugars, but glucose (GLOO kohs) is the most important because it is the major provider of energy for your body's cells. All other types of sugar are converted to glucose once they are inside your body.

Complex Carbohydrates   Complex carbohydrates are made up of sugars that are linked together chemically to form long chains, something like beads in a necklace.

Starches are one of the main types of complex carbohydrates. They are found in many plant foods, including potatoes and grains. Rice, oats, corn, and wheat are grains. Foods such as tortillas, whole-wheat rolls, and Chinese moo shu pancakes are excellent sources of starch. When you eat foods containing starch, your digestive system breaks the starch into simple sugars that can be absorbed into your bloodstream.

194   *Chapter 8*

TEENS *Are Asking . . .*

Q: **I have heard a lot of talk about "low-carb" diets. Should I avoid eating carbohydrates?**

A: Definitely not. In fact, about half of the calories you eat each day should come from carbohydrates. Carbohydrates are an important source of energy for the body. But not all carbohydrates are the same. You should eat more complex carbohydrates than simple carbohydrates. Simple carbohydrates, especially those found in foods with added sugar, should be avoided or eaten only in small amounts. These foods often have little nutritional value for the number of calories they contain. Complex carbohydrates, on the other hand, are a good long-term energy source for the body. Choose whole-grain carbohydrates, which are also a good source of fiber, vitamins, and minerals.

Fiber Fiber is a type of complex carbohydrate that is found in plants. Strictly speaking, fiber is not really a nutrient because it cannot be broken down and then absorbed into your bloodstream. Instead, fiber passes out of your body without being digested. However, it is still necessary for the proper functioning of your digestive system. A high-fiber diet

► helps prevent constipation

► may reduce the risk of colon cancer

► may help prevent heart disease

Whole-grain breads and cereals, vegetables, fruits, nuts, beans, and seeds provide fiber in your diet.

Your Body's Energy Reserves At a meal, you usually eat more carbohydrates than your body can immediately use. The extra glucose is converted into a type of starch called glycogen (GLY kuh jun), which is stored in your body. When your body needs more glucose, the glycogen is converted back to glucose. If you eat so many carbohydrates that the body's glycogen stores are full, then the excess carbohydrates are stored as fat instead.

Daily Carbohydrate Intake Nutritionists recommend that 45 to 65 percent of a person's daily calorie intake come from carbohydrates. It is better to eat foods rich in complex carbohydrates rather than simple carbohydrates. One reason is that while simple carbohydrates give quick bursts of energy, complex carbohydrates provide better long-term, sustained energy.

When you choose foods containing complex carbohydrates, try to choose whole grains. Whole grains are better than processed grains because they contain more fiber and nutrients. Whole-wheat breads and pastas and brown rice are examples of whole-grain foods. In contrast, foods high in sugars, such as candy and soft drinks, may have few valuable nutrients. If you have a craving for sweets, eat naturally sweet foods, such as fruits. Those foods provide vitamins and trace amounts of some minerals, too.

 **Connect to Your Life** List some carbohydrates you typically eat. Are they sugars or starches?

FIGURE 3 Beans and vegetables with edible skins and seeds are good sources of fiber.

Fats

EL Building Vocabulary

Clarify for students that there are two different uses for the term *fat*. Students are probably more familiar with the use of the term *fat* to mean "overweight." Explain that it is not necessarily true that fats in the diet will make a person fat. Emphasize that foods containing fats, expecially unsaturated fats, should be part of a healthy diet.

L2 Addressing Misconceptions

Fats in the Diet Poll the class to see how many students think that fats are "bad" for them. It is very common for students to think that fats are "bad" because of all the talk about low-fat diets. Then ask students what roles fats play in the body. *(supply energy, form cells, maintain body temperature, protect nerves)* List these roles on the board. Emphasize that restricting fats completely from their diet will actually harm the body. Point out that fats should make up about 20 to 35 percent of a person's daily calories, but most fats should be unsaturated fats.

L3 Journal Writing

In their private journals, have students list foods they typically eat that are high in saturated fats. *(Lists may include meats, cheeses, butter.)* Have students make another list of foods that are high in trans fats. *(Lists may include margarine, chips, baked goods.)* Then challenge students to list some changes they could make to their diet to lower their intake of these fats. **WRITING**

L3 Visual Learning: Figure 4

Image Bank Figure 8-4

Have students examine the graph in Figure 4 and ask: **Which food is highest in unsaturated fat?** *(olive oil)* **Which food is highest in saturated fat?** *(butter)* Make sure students know how saturated fat, unsaturated fat, and trans fat differ. Ask: **Which of these fats are more healthful?** *(unsaturated fats)* **Which of the foods shown in the graph would be the best source of fat? Why?** *(Olive oil; it has the most unsaturated fat and the least trans fat.)*

Caption Answer tub margarine

Fats

Like carbohydrates, **fats** are made of carbon, hydrogen, and oxygen, but in different proportions. **Fats supply your body with energy, form your cells, maintain body temperature, and protect your nerves.** Ounce for ounce, fat has twice as many calories as carbohydrates.

Unsaturated Fats Fats come in different forms. **Unsaturated fats** have at least one unsaturated bond in a place where hydrogen can be added to the molecule. Unsaturated fats are usually liquid at room temperature. These fats are found in vegetable oils, nuts, and seeds.

Unsaturated fats are classified as either monounsaturated fats or polyunsaturated fats. Foods that contain monounsaturated fats include olive oil, peanuts, and canola oil. Foods that contain polyunsaturated fats include safflower, corn, and soybean oil, as well as seafood. A balance between monounsaturated and polyunsaturated fats in the diet is important for cardiovascular health. Unsaturated fats can actually help fight heart disease.

Saturated Fats Fats that have all the hydrogen the carbon atoms can hold are called **saturated fats.** Saturated fats are usually solid at room temperature. Animal fats, such as lard, and dairy products contain saturated fats. Too much saturated fat in your diet can lead to heart disease.

Daily Fat Intake Nutritionists recommend that 20 to 35 percent of your calories come from fat, primarily unsaturated fat. To reduce your intake of saturated fat, you can substitute low-fat foods for the meats and dairy products that are high in saturated fats.

FIGURE 4 Eating foods containing unsaturated fats, such as olive oil, is more healthful than eating foods containing saturated fats.
Reading Graphs Which of the fat sources in the graph is lowest in saturated fat?

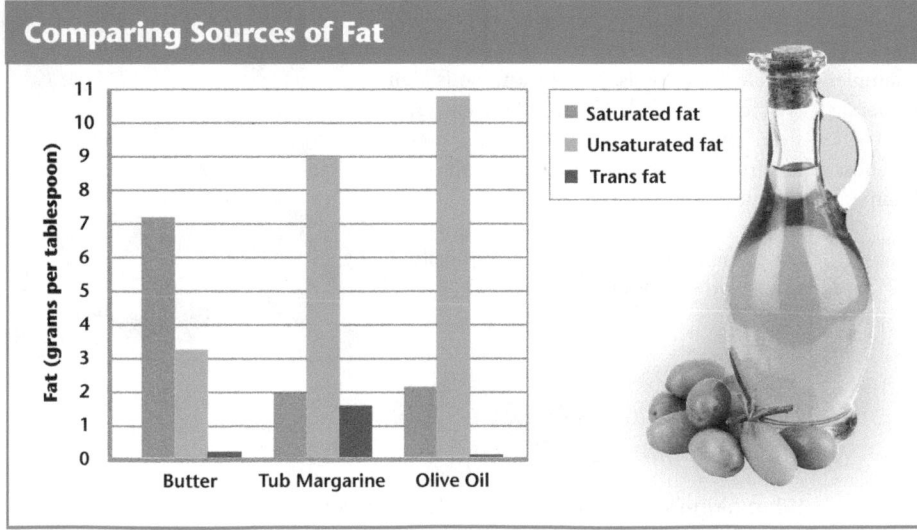

Comparing Sources of Fat

Fat (grams per tablespoon)

Butter   Tub Margarine   Olive Oil

■ Saturated fat
■ Unsaturated fat
■ Trans fat

MATH and Health

L3 Proportions

Tell students that one gram of fat has 9 calories, whereas one gram of carbohydrates has 4 calories. Ask: **If one serving of peanuts has 13 grams of fat, how many calories does it contain?** *(1 g/9 cal = 13 g/x cal; x = 117 calories.)* Then ask:

How many grams of carbohydrates would you need to eat to get the same number of calories as in one serving of peanuts? *(1 g/4 cal = x g/117 cal; x = 29.25 grams).* Point out that a person needs to eat more than twice the amount of carbohydrates than fats to obtain the same number of calories.

Hands-On *Activity*

Which Foods Contain Fats?

Materials
brown paper bag
scissors
marker
dropper
potato chip
milk chocolate
carrot
whole milk
skim milk
apple juice
ground beef

Try This
1. Cut a brown paper bag into squares about 3 inches on each side. Write the name of each food on a square.
2. Rub each food on the square with its name. If the food is a liquid, place a few drops on the square.
3. Let the squares dry. Then hold each square up to a light.

Think and Discuss
1. Which squares had a spot when you held them up to the light? Those foods contain fat. Which squares did not have a spot?
2. Does your daily diet include many foods that are high in fat? (To be sure, try testing some foods that you commonly eat.) How could you reduce the amount of fat that you consume each day?

Cholesterol   Cholesterol (kuh LES tuh rawl) is a waxy, fatlike substance that is found only in animal products. Your body needs a certain amount of cholesterol to make cell membranes and nerve tissue, certain hormones, and substances that aid in the digestion of fat. Your liver can make all of the cholesterol your body needs. Therefore, cholesterol is not a necessary part of the diet.

A diet high in fat and cholesterol can increase the amount of cholesterol in the blood. When the level of cholesterol circulating in the blood gets too high, deposits called plaque form on the walls of blood vessels. Heavy plaque buildup may block blood flow to the heart, depriving the heart of oxygen and leading to a heart attack.

Some research suggests that high blood cholesterol is hereditary. Cholesterol levels also tend to rise as a person ages. These are risk factors you can't change, but there is one you can control: your diet. You can reduce your risk of heart disease by reducing the amount of meat and dairy fat in your diet.

Trans Fats   You may have heard about trans fats. **Trans fats** are made when manufacturers add hydrogen to the fat molecules in vegetable oils. Foods that contain trans fats stay fresh longer than foods that contain unsaturated fats. But, trans fat seems to have few of the benefits of unsaturated fat and many of the risks of saturated fat. Trans fats are found in margarine, chips, and commercially baked goods. The stick forms of margarine tend to contain more trans fats than the softer, tub margarines.

 **Connect to Your Life**   What high-fat foods do you eat? How can you cut down on these foods?

 GO ONLINE
PearsonSuccessNet.com
For: More on healthy eating

Food and Nutrition **197**

Hands-On *Activity*
Which Foods Contain Fats?

Provide students with the foods to be tested. Supply cooked ground beef so that students do not have to handle raw meat. Emphasize that students should not eat any of the foods. If students wish to test additional foods, suggest they do so at home and then bring the labeled brown-paper squares to class.

Think and Discuss Answers
1. Squares with spots should include potato chip, milk chocolate, whole milk, and ground beef. The carrot, skim milk, and apple juice should not leave spots.
2. Answers will vary, but most students will have other sources of high-fat foods in their diets. If they are not sure, they should test them. To reduce fat intake, students can eat smaller portions of fatty foods or replace fatty foods with low-fat or fat-free foods, such as grains and vegetables.

L2 **Building Media Literacy**

Have students cut out ads from magazines for foods that are high in fats. Students should identify which type(s) of fat each food product is highest in and the target audience for each ad. Students should also assess whether the foods being advertised are healthful or not and explain their reasoning. Then have students make a recommendation about eating the advertised foods.

 Connect to Your Life   Allow students to answer this question in their private journals.

L3 **Online Activity**  **GO ONLINE**

Visit Pearson SuccessNet to access an online activity about healthy eating. Have students complete the Web activity.

Differentiated Instruction

EL **English Language Learners**

Have students create a booklet for the six classes of nutrients. They should allow a two-page spread for each nutrient. For each nutrient, students should write the name of the nutrient as the title of the spread. They can include a phonetic spelling of the nutrient as well. Have students cut out pictures of foods, including foods from their ethnic heritage, that are good sources of the nutrient. Students should also write the role of the nutrient in the body and the recommended daily intake of that nutrient.

Proteins

L2 **Visual Learning: Figure 5**

Refer students to the list of foods in Figure 5. Ask: **Which foods did you not expect to be sources of protein?** *(Answers will vary. Students might mention corn or orange juice.)* Point out that many plant products—tofu, refried beans, peanut butter, orange juice, and corn—supply the body with protein as do meat, fish, eggs, and dairy products. Ask: **Why are most proteins from plants said to be incomplete?** *(Most plant proteins lack one or more essential amino acids.)* **How can a vegetarian get all the essential amino acids?** *(by eating a combination of two or more plant protein sources)*
Caption Answer Beefsteak has more protein per ounce. (49.9 ÷ 6 = 8.3 in steak vs. 7.1 in cheese)

L1 **Cooperative Learning**

Divide the class into small groups, and provide each group with construction paper, scissors, tape, and other supplies. The groups should create a model of a protein that shows how it is made up of amino acids. Students can create paper chains, interlocking puzzle pieces, or another model. Have them label which parts of the model are amino acids and which is the protein.

L3 **Cultural Connection**

Supply students with a variety of ethnic and vegetarian cookbooks. Challenge them to find recipes for vegetarian dishes that form complementary protein combinations. Point out that many traditional dishes are based on complementary proteins. (Examples include combinations of legumes and grains such as refried beans on a tortilla, falafel on pita bread, and peanut butter on wheat bread; combinations of seeds and legumes such as hummus—ground sesame seeds and cooked chickpeas.) Encourage students to share their recipes with the class.

 *Sample answer:* meats, eggs, and milk

How Much **Protein** Is in Your Refrigerator?	
Broiled beefsteak (6 oz)	49.9 grams
Cheddar cheese (1 oz)	7.1 grams
Corn (1 ear)	2.0 grams
Egg (1 large)	6.3 grams
Fried chicken (1 drumstick)	13.2 grams
Orange juice (1 cup)	2.0 grams
Peanut butter (2 tbsp)	8.0 grams
Refried beans (1/2 cup)	6.9 grams
Salmon (6 oz)	37.6 grams
Tofu (1/2 cup)	10.3 grams
Whole milk (1 cup)	7.9 grams

FIGURE 5 Meats, fish, eggs, and dairy products are excellent sources of protein. **Calculating** Which has more protein per ounce: beefsteak or cheddar cheese? **MATH**

Proteins

Nutrients that contain nitrogen as well as carbon, hydrogen, and oxygen are called **proteins.** Like carbohydrates and fats, proteins can serve as a source of energy. **The most important function of proteins, however, is their role in the growth and repair of your body's tissues.** A good portion of your body is made up of protein. High-protein foods include meats, eggs, poultry, milk, and milk products. Nuts, dried beans, dried peas, and lentils also contain a lot of protein.

Amino Acids Like carbohydrates, proteins are long chains of smaller "links" that are bound together chemically. These smaller substances are known as **amino acids** (uh MEE noh). When you eat protein, your digestive system breaks it down into individual amino acids. These amino acids are then absorbed into your bloodstream and reassembled by cells to form the kinds of proteins you need.

Essential Amino Acids The proteins in your body are made up of 20 different amino acids. Your diet has to supply nine of these amino acids; your body can manufacture the rest. The nine amino acids that the body cannot manufacture are called essential amino acids. You can remember this by thinking of them as an essential part of your diet.

 **What are the main sources of protein in your diet?**

Focus on **ISSUES**

L3 **Vending Machines at School**

Have students survey the food and beverage choices in the school's vending machines. They should classify the foods according to which nutrients they are highest in—sugars, starches, unsaturated fats, saturated fats, trans fats, or protein. Students should also find the number of calories per serving.

With this information, discuss with the class how healthful and varied the snack and drink choices in the vending machines are. Challenge students to suggest healthier alternatives that could be offered in the vending machines. Encourage students to share their suggestions with the administration or food-service director.

Complete and Incomplete Proteins Protein from animal sources—meats, fish, and so forth—is said to be complete protein because it contains all nine essential amino acids in the proportions needed by your body. In contrast, most protein from plant sources, such as beans, is incomplete, because it lacks one or more essential amino acids.

Daily Protein Intake Nutritionists recommend that 10 to 35 percent of your calories come from proteins. A diet that contains both plant and animals foods can easily supply all of the essential amino acids you need. Simply eat a wide variety of foods, such as red and white meats, fish, dairy products, legumes, nuts, and grains.

Proteins for Vegetarians People who don't eat meat can combine two or more plant protein sources that, taken together, provide all the essential amino acids. Suppose, for example, you prepare a casserole that contains both rice and beans. The protein found individually in the rice and beans is incomplete. When the rice and beans are combined, however, they supply all the essential amino acids needed by your body. When you combine incomplete protein foods in such a way that you obtain all nine of the essential amino acids, you form a complementary protein combination.

FIGURE 6 Together, rice and beans form a complementary protein combination that contains all of the essential amino acids.

Section 1 Review

Key Ideas and Vocabulary

1. Which three classes of nutrients supply the body with energy?

2. Define the term **metabolism.** How is metabolism related to the nutrients in food?

3. What roles do the following nutrients play in the body?
   a. carbohydrates   **b.** fats   **c.** proteins

4. What is **cholesterol?** How does diet affect cholesterol levels in the blood?

Critical Thinking

5. Predicting Name some circumstances during which you might use your body's stores of glycogen.

Health at School

Promoting Well-Being Evaluate your school's lunch menu over a three-day period. To do this, list each lunch item and the classes of nutrients it provides. Then, write a paragraph about the influence of school lunches on health. **WRITING**

---

6. Comparing and Contrasting How do saturated fats differ from unsaturated fats? Name two sources of each type of fat.

7. Calculating Suppose that you ate 2,500 calories in a day. Of those calories, 1,200 calories were from carbohydrates, 875 from fats, and the rest from protein. What percentage of your total day's calories came from carbohydrates? From fats? From protein? **MATH**

Evaluate
These assignments can help you assess students' mastery of the section content.

Section 1 Review
Answers appear below.

Teaching Resources
- Practice 8-1
- Section 8-1 Quiz

L2 Reteach
List the vocabulary terms from this section on the board one at a time. For each term, ask students to give facts about the term. List all correct facts on the board. Do not move to the next term until all important information about the term has been given. Suggest that students copy this information into their notebooks.

L4 Enrich
Teaching Resources
- Enrich 8-1

Health at School

School Lunches Assess students' paragraphs based on how well they support their suggestions with information gathered from their evaluation of school lunches. Also look for a clear topic sentence, well-written supporting details, and a logical conclusion.

Section 1 Review

1. carbohydrates, fats, proteins

2. Metabolism is the chemical process by which the body breaks down food to release energy. The nutrients in food are metabolized to release energy.

3. **a.** supply energy for body functions
   b. supply energy, form cells, maintain body temperature, and protect nerves **c.** supply energy, aid in growth and repair of tissues

4. Cholesterol is a waxy, fatlike substance found only in animal products. Eating foods that are high in fat and cholesterol can increase the amount of cholesterol in the blood.

5. Glycogen can be used up during very long or intense exercise or if a person doesn't get enough calories.

6. Saturated fats have all the hydrogen atoms that carbon atoms can hold, while unsaturated fats do not. Saturated fats are solid at room temperature, while unsaturated fats are liquid. Saturated fats are found in animal fats and dairy products, while unsaturated fats are found in vegetable oils, nuts, and seeds.

7. 48% from carbohydrates; 35% from fats; 17% from protein

Breaking a Bad Habit

Objective

Implement a plan for replacing an unwanted habit with a new, positive behavior.

Teaching Strategies

- Although the example used here is a nutritional habit, students can apply this process to any habit they want to change. Suggest that the habit they choose should be something they feel is both possible and important to change.

- The four-step process for breaking a habit described here extends over a four-week period. Students should spend the first week collecting information about the habit they want to change, and then spend the following three weeks carrying out their action plan. During this four-week period, set aside the first five or ten minutes of each class period to discuss the behavior-change experience. This will give students an opportunity to share their questions, concerns, successes, and failures, if they volunteer to do so.

- During the first week, have students keep a record of the habit they want to change, using a chart like the Habit Record shown. Encourage students to include as much detail as possible in their records to help them detect any patterns of behavior. Be sure students incorporate their findings into their action plans. Students should also write a behavior contract for themselves.

- At the start of the second week, students should begin to keep a behavior log. They should record their behaviors over the next three weeks. Students will need lots of encouragement during this period if they are to succeed. Try grouping students together to form support groups. Also encourage students to involve their parents and friends in supporting them.

Breaking a Bad Habit

Sam has developed a poor nutritional habit—snacking on high-fat foods, such as potato chips. Although he wants to cut down on the amount of fatty foods he eats each day, he thinks that he doesn't have the willpower to do it.

The key to changing a habit you don't like is to replace it with a new, positive habit. The process works best in small steps and by putting everything in writing in a behavior contract. The steps given here will help you change almost any habit.

❶ Define the habit you want to change.
Describe your habit in a specific way. For example, instead of saying, "I don't eat very well," you might say, "I eat too many potato chips."

❷ Set your goal.
A goal describes the behavior you would like to substitute for the habit.

- ▶ Your goal should be specific. If a goal is too broad, break it into sub-goals.

- ▶ The goal should emphasize what you will do, not what you won't do—"For snacks, I will choose foods low in fat, such as fruits and low-fat cheeses."

- ▶ Set a realistic deadline.

- ▶ Write a behavior contract like the one shown, and fill in your goal.

Behavior Contract

Habit: *eating too many chips*

I _Sam Brown_ plan to _substitute fruit or low-fat cheese_ by _May 4th._

I will reach this goal by doing the following target behavior: _substituting fruit/cheese once a day at first and gradually increasing to three times a day_

To create a supportive change environment, I will get help from the following role models: _Mom and Loretta_, reward myself by _going to the movies with friends after successful weeks_ along the way, and by _buying myself a new baseball glove_ when I reach my goal.

Signed _Sam Brown_   Date _March 6th_

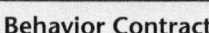

Sensitive Issues

Some students may not feel comfortable sharing information about the habit they have chosen to change. Do not ask students to discuss their habits or to share their logs. Use discretion even if students volunteer to share information with the class.

❸ Design an action plan.

▶ Monitor your habit. Spend a week carefully observing and recording your habit. Use a chart like the one shown. This will help you understand what triggers and reinforces the habit.

Habit Record

Beforehand		Behavior	Afterward
Scene	Feelings	Details	Results
Monday lunch at school	tired and bored	1 oz. bag of potato chips	less energetic

▶ Write your plan. Describe in detail the day-to-day changes you will make to reach your goal. Your plan should be a gradual, step-by-step process.

▶ Keep a log. Log your new behavior daily, including any setbacks.

Behavior Log

Action Plan	M	T	W	Th	F	Sa	Su
	← substitute fruit or cheese for chips →						
Behavior	✓	ate potato chips	✓	ate corn chips	✓	✓	✓

❹ Build a supportive environment.

▶ Reward yourself for accomplishments along the way. Ask family and friends to keep an eye on your progress.

▶ Keep a list handy of the benefits of your new behavior.

▶ Structure your surroundings to support your efforts. If you are trying to break a potato-chip habit, try not to keep any potato chips in your house.

 Practice the Skill

1. List three habits you would like to break.

2. Of the three habits, choose the one you would most like to change. Clearly define what the habit is. Set a specific goal for eliminating the habit. Write the goal on a behavior contract like the one shown.

3. Monitor your habit for one week. Every time you exhibit the habit, record where and when it occurred. Record your thoughts and feelings before and after. Can you detect any patterns in your behavior?

4. Use your behavior patterns to devise a detailed plan for breaking the habit. Record the plan on your contract. Also, fill in ways you can build a supportive environment.

5. Log your behavior for three weeks.

6. After three weeks, evaluate your performance. What made it hard for you to stick to the plan? What aspects of your plan worked for you? **WRITING**

Food and Nutrition **201**

1. Students can list any three habits they would like to change. These habits do not have to be nutritional habits.

2. Students should clearly state the habit they want to change (e.g., not handing in homework on time) and a specific goal (e.g., to turn in all assignments on time for the next month). Students should also complete a behavior contract using the one shown as a model.

3. Students should record their behaviors, feelings, and thoughts in a Habit Record like the one shown. Encourage them to focus on events and feelings that occur before the habit occurs. Students might observe a pattern to their behavior, such as not starting homework until 9 PM because of watching television beforehand.

4. Students should devise a plan for breaking the habit that involves a new, positive behavior. They should also identify who can help support them or how they should change their environment to make it easier for them to perform the new behavior. An example of an action plan might be to study in the library after school with a friend two days a week and gradually increase the time and frequency. Students should add this information to their behavior contract.

5. Students can record their behavior in a chart similar to the Behavior Log shown, or devise their own log.

6. At the end of the three weeks, allow class time for volunteers to share the results of their plans to break a habit. The most common problems students might experience include getting discouraged at minor setbacks, not logging their behavior, and not following through on the rewards system. Students should write a paragraph describing their experience, including whether they were successful at changing their habit, what was difficult to do, and what worked well.

Health and Community

ⓛ₃ Behavior Change Programs

Invite the school psychologist to talk about community programs that are available to help people change unhealthy behaviors. Some of these community groups might include Alcoholics Anonymous, weight-loss programs, or other support groups. Ask the school psychologist to discuss how the processes that these groups use to change behavior compare with the steps students have learned in this activity. Have students prepare questions to ask the psychologist about successful behavior change. Encourage students to base their questions on their own experiences.

Vitamins, Minerals, and Water

Objectives
Before class begins, write the objectives on the board. Have students copy the objectives into their notebooks at the start of class.

1. Focus

Warm-Up **Myth/Fact**

After students complete the writing assignment, invite volunteers to reveal where they get their information about nutrition. List their responses on the board. Circle those sources that students think provide accurate information, such as health-care professionals, and cross out those sources that they think do not, such as ads promoting a product. Discuss why some sources of nutritional information may actually create or perpetrate myths about nutritional requirements.
Ask: **Who might benefit from having people believe that dietary supplements are necessary for a healthy diet?** *(people or companies who sell supplements)*

Presentation 8-2

Section 2

Vitamins, Minerals, and Water

Objectives
▶ **Identify** the two main classes of vitamins.
▶ **List** seven minerals your body needs in significant amounts.
▶ **Explain** why water is so important to your body.

Vocabulary
• vitamin
• antioxidant
• mineral
• anemia
• homeostasis
• electrolyte
• dehydration

Warm-Up

Myth As part of a healthy diet, people need to take dietary supplements.

Fact A diet that contains a variety of healthful foods usually supplies all the vitamins and minerals that your body needs.

WRITING Where do you think most teens get their information about nutrition? How factual do you think their information is?

Vitamins

You're probably aware that vitamins are important for your body and health, but where do they come from? What do they do? And how many different kinds do you need?

One of the first discoveries of the importance of vitamins came in the 1700s. Sailors on long voyages survived on hard, dry biscuits, salted meat, and not much else. Because of their limited diet, many sailors developed a serious disease called scurvy. People with scurvy suffer from bleeding gums, stiff joints, and sores that do not heal.

A Scottish doctor, James Lind, discovered that sailors who were fed citrus fruits recovered from scurvy. Today, health scientists know that scurvy is caused by a lack of vitamin C, which is found in abundance in citrus fruits. After Lind made his discovery, sailors were provided with oranges, lemons, and limes. The word *limey*, a British slang term for sailor, comes from the limes that sailors ate to ward off scurvy.

WRITING and Health

L3 Persuasive Speech

Tell students to suppose that they were alive when Dr. Lind made his discovery about scurvy and vitamins in the diet. Have students write a persuasive speech directed at sailors about to embark on a long voyage. The speech should educate sailors about scurvy and convince them of the role of vitamins in preventing the disease. Encourage students to include catchy slogans, humor, and other creative techniques to help get their message across. Ask for volunteers to deliver their speeches to the class.

What Are Vitamins? Nutrients that are made by living things, are required only in small amounts, and that assist many chemical reactions in the body are **vitamins.** Unlike carbohydrates, fats, and proteins, vitamins do not directly provide you with energy or the raw materials of which your cells are made. Instead, vitamins help the body with various processes, including the use of other nutrients. Vitamins also play roles in various chemical reactions in the body. For example, vitamin K helps your blood clot when you get a cut or a scrape.

Your body is able to make some vitamins. For example, your skin manufactures vitamin D when it is exposed to sunlight. However, most vitamins must be supplied in the food you eat. **There are two classes of vitamins: fat-soluble vitamins, which dissolve in fatty materials, and water-soluble vitamins, which dissolve in water.**

Fat-Soluble Vitamins Fat-soluble vitamins—vitamins A, D, E, and K—occur in vegetable oils, liver, eggs, and certain vegetables. Figure 7 outlines the food sources and functions of each fat-soluble vitamin.

Fat-soluble vitamins can be stored by the body. The absorption of fat-soluble vitamins by the digestive system is enhanced by dietary fat. Some indigestible fat substitutes that are used in low-fat or low-calorie products can prevent absorption of these vitamins. To prevent this from happening, extra vitamins, particularly vitamins A and D, are often added to foods prepared with fat substitutes.

 **Connect to Your Life** **Name three foods you eat regularly that supply vitamin A.**

GO ONLINE
PearsonSuccessNet.com
For: More on nutrients

FIGURE 7 Fat-soluble vitamins are found in many dietary sources and have important functions.

Fat-Soluble Vitamins

Vitamin	Good Sources	Main Functions
A	Liver; eggs; cheese; milk; yellow, orange, and dark green vegetables and fruit	Maintains healthy skin, bones, teeth, and hair; aids vision in dim light
D	Milk; eggs; liver; exposure of skin to sunlight	Maintains bones and teeth; helps in the use of calcium and phosphorus
E	Margarine; vegetable oils; wheat germ; whole grains; legumes; green, leafy vegetables	Aids in maintenance of red blood cells, vitamin A, and fats
K	Green, leafy vegetables; potatoes; liver; made by intestinal bacteria	Aids in blood clotting

---

2. Teach

L3 **EL** Reading/Note Taking 8-2
L2 Adapted Reading/Note Taking 8-2

Vitamins

L3 **Content Update**  GO ONLINE

Visit Pearson SuccessNet to access more information about nutrients. Have students complete the Web activity.

L3 **Cooperative Learning**

Divide the class into small groups. Have each group list the main functions of vitamins in the body. Instruct students to use their list to write a "job description" for vitamins. Show students examples of job descriptions in classified ads to help them get started. In their job descriptions, students should describe the general functions of vitamins in the body and make reference to the two different classes of vitamins.

L1 **Active Learning**

Bring in empty packages from a variety of foods that are enriched with vitamins. Include packages of breakfast cereals, snack foods, bread, and milk. Have students identify which vitamins are added to the foods and in what amounts. Discuss why food manufacturers might add vitamins to foods. (*Vitamins may have been removed during processing or adding vitamins may increase sales.*)

L2 **Visual Learning: Figure 7**

Refer students to the chart of fat-soluble vitamins in Figure 7. Ask: **Which vitamins can be made by the body?** (*vitamins D and K*) **What are good sources of vitamin E?** (*margarine; vegetable oils; wheat germ; whole grains; legumes; green, leafy vegetables*) **Which vitamin helps vision in dim light?** (*vitamin A*)

 **Connect to Your Life** *Sample answer:* cheese, milk, carrots

---

Differentiated Instruction

L2 **Less Proficient Readers**

Have students create a table to compare and contrast fat-soluble and water-soluble vitamins. Some column headings students might use include *Vitamin, Dissolves In, Stored in Body?, Excess Amounts Harmful?,* and *Sources in My Diet.* As students read this section, encourage them to fill in the table. Below the table, have students write a sentence identifying those vitamins that their diet may be deficient in.

L2 Cooperative Learning

Have students work in small groups to prepare a menu for one day that includes foods containing all of the water-soluble vitamins. Consider having one student in each group be responsible for one meal or snack. Encourage students to choose foods that would be appetizing if served together. Students should list the vitamin(s) found in each of their menu items. Invite groups to share their menus with the class.

L3 Addressing Misconceptions

Vitamin C and Colds Some students might think that taking large amounts of vitamin C can help prevent colds. Explain that recent studies have shown high daily doses of vitamin C do not prevent colds, but might have a minimal effect on reducing the severity of colds. Point out that because vitamin C is water soluble, extra amounts of it are excreted from the body, which means it is wasted. Therefore, taking Vitamin C supplements will not help prevent colds.

L3 Building Health Skills

Making Decisions Present students with this scenario: You are thinking of becoming a vegan (a vegetarian who does not eat food from any animal source), but you are concerned about how to include enough water-soluble vitamins in your diet. Ask: **Which water-soluble vitamin might be most difficult to obtain from your diet?** (vitamin B12) **Where would you go for trustworthy information about the safety of vegan diets?** (doctors, nutritionists, nutrition books, or scientific articles) **What foods would be important to include in your diet?** (whole grain foods, legumes, green, leafy vegetables, fresh fruits)

L1 Visual Learning: Figure 8

Have students create an illustrated version of the chart in Figure 8. For each vitamin listed in the chart, students can create a collage of photos showing foods that are good sources of that vitamin. Provide students with magazines and other sources for photos.
Caption Answer Vitamin B2, vitamin B3, vitamin B6, pantothenic acid, and biotin

Water-Soluble Vitamins Water-soluble vitamins—including vitamin C and all of the B vitamins—are found in fruits, vegetables, and other sources. Unlike the fat-soluble vitamins, water-soluble vitamins cannot be stored by the body. Therefore, it is important to eat foods that supply them every day. Figure 8 outlines the food sources and functions of the water-soluble vitamins.

Water-Soluble Vitamins

Vitamin	Good Sources	Main Functions
B1 (Thiamin)	Pork products; liver; whole-grain foods; legumes	Aids in carbohydrate use and nervous system function
B2 (Riboflavin)	Milk; eggs; meat; whole grains; dark green vegetables	Aids in metabolism of carbohydrates, proteins, and fats
B3 (Niacin)	Poultry; meat; fish; whole grains; nuts	Aids in metabolism
B6 (Pyridoxine)	Meat; poultry; fish; whole-grain foods; green vegetables	Aids in metabolism of carbohydrates, proteins, and fats
B12 (Cobalamin)	Meat; fish; poultry; eggs; milk; cheese	Maintains healthy nervous system and red blood cells
Pantothenic acid	Organ meats; poultry; fish; eggs; grains	Aids in metabolism
Folate (Folic acid)	Green, leafy vegetables; legumes	Aids in formation of red blood cells and protein
Biotin	Organ meats; poultry; fish; eggs; peas; bananas; melons	Aids in metabolism
C (Ascorbic acid)	Citrus fruits; green vegetables; melons; potatoes; tomatoes	Aids in bone, teeth, and skin formation; resistance to infection; iron uptake

FIGURE 8 Water-soluble vitamins are found in many food sources. **Reading Tables** Which vitamins aid in metabolism?

TEENS Are Asking . . .

Q: How do I know if I need to take a vitamin or mineral supplement?

A: Talk to your doctor honestly about your diet. In general, if you are eating a well-balanced diet with adequate fruits and vegetables, it is likely that you are receiving the recommended amounts of vitamins and minerals through your diet. You would not need a supplement. However, if your diet is made up mostly of fast food or if you do not eat many fresh fruits and vegetables, you may not be getting enough vitamins and minerals. In such cases, your doctor may recommend that you make changes in your diet or that you take a supplement.

Antioxidants Vitamins called **antioxidants** help protect healthy cells from the damage caused by the normal aging process as well as from certain types of cancer. Vitamins C and E are two of the most powerful antioxidants. Sources of vitamin C include citrus fruits, strawberries, broccoli, tomatoes, and potatoes. Sources of vitamin E include vegetable oils, whole grains, seeds, nuts, and peanut butter.

Minerals

Your body requires only small amounts of **minerals,** which are nutrients that occur naturally in rocks and soil. Plants absorb minerals from rocks and soil through their roots. Animals obtain these nutrients by either eating the plants or eating animals that have eaten the plants.

Twenty-four different minerals have been shown to be essential for good health. **You need seven minerals—calcium, sodium, potassium, magnesium, phosphorus, chlorine, and sulfur—in significant amounts.** You need only trace amounts of others, such as iron, fluorine, iodine, copper, and zinc. Minerals perform a wide variety of functions in the body.

Calcium Some minerals are of special nutritional concern. For example, many people's diets do not include enough calcium. Calcium is important in blood clotting and the functioning of your nervous system. It is an essential ingredient in the formation and maintenance of bones and teeth. Milk and other dairy products are good sources of calcium, but many people cannot digest dairy products. Beet greens, collard greens, broccoli, and tofu are also good sources of calcium.

A lack of calcium can sometimes lead to osteoporosis, a condition in which the bones gradually weaken. Osteoporosis is usually a disease of older people, but your calcium intake during adolescence can help you build stronger bones now to avoid osteoporosis later in life. Osteoporosis will be discussed in Chapter 11.

Connect to Your Life What are you doing now to prevent osteoporosis in the future?

85% of teenage girls do not get enough calcium in their diets.

FIGURE 9 Calcium is essential for building the strong bones you need to play sports now and to maintain bone strength as you age.

Food and Nutrition **205**

Minerals

L2 Class Discussion

Discuss with students what minerals are. *(nutrients that occur naturally in rocks and soil)* Point out that plants can absorb minerals from the soil. Animals can get minerals only by eating plants or by eating animals that have eaten plants. Ask: **How can you get minerals into your diet?** *(by eating plants or animals)* **Which minerals are needed by the body in significant amounts?** *(calcium, sodium, potassium, magnesium, phosphorus, chlorine, and sulfur)* List these minerals on the board. While teaching about minerals, list each mineral's sources and functions.

L3 Building Health Skills

Advocacy Ask: **Why is it important for teens to get enough calcium?** *(Building strong bones by getting enough calcium will help prevent osteoporosis later in life.)* Have students write an e-mail to a fictional friend in which they encourage her to add calcium to her diet. Students should give facts about the body's calcium requirements, sources of calcium, and how to prevent osteoporosis later in life. **WRITING**

L3 Cultural Connection

Explain to students that although dairy products are sources of calcium for many people, some people cannot easily digest these foods. About 90 percent of Asian Americans are lactose intolerant. Up to 75 percent of African Americans, Hispanic Americans, and Native Americans are lactose intolerant. Many older adults of all ethnic origins become lactose intolerant naturally over time. Challenge students to find alternative sources of calcium that people with lactose-intolerance can digest. *(Food sources include dark, green leafy vegetables such as spinach, collard greens, broccoli; legumes; juices fortified with calcium; aged cheeses like cheddar; tofu or soy milk. Another option is to take a lactase enzyme supplement before eating dairy products.)*

Connect to Your Life *Sample answer:* I am drinking milk and eating foods that are good sources of calcium.

Differentiated Instruction

L2 Less Proficient Readers

Before students read about minerals, ask them what they already know about minerals. List their responses on the board. Then ask students to think about what they would like to know about minerals. Encourage students to pose their thoughts as specific questions. List these questions on the board. After students have read about minerals, use their questions on the board to guide a discussion on what they learned.

L2 Cooperative Learning

Assign student groups a specific mineral, and have them create a descriptive poster about it. Consider assigning additional minerals that are not specifically described in this section. On their posters students should describe the roles of the mineral in the body, food sources of the mineral, and symptoms of being deficient in the mineral or of taking in too much of the mineral. Have groups present their posters to the class.

EL Building Vocabulary

Explain that the word *anemia* comes from the Greek word *anaimia,* in which the prefix *an-* means "without" and *haimia* means "blood." Tell students that anemia can be caused by a loss of blood, the inability to make new blood cells, or the destruction of blood cells. Explain that an iron deficiency can prevent new blood cells from being made, as well as deficiencies in vitamin B12 and folic acid.

L3 Building Health Skills

Analyzing Influences Ask students: **Why is it easier to consume far more sodium than one needs, but difficult to consume enough potassium?** *(Sample answer: People eat more processed snack foods that are high in sodium than fresh foods that are high in potassium.)* Give students several minutes to list two or three reasons why they think teens choose to eat foods that are high in sodium. Then have students share their ideas with the class. Ask: **What are the underlying influences that cause teens to choose foods high in sodium?** *(Sample answer: advertising, convenience, flavor)* Point out that what a person likes to eat is often based on what the person is in the habit of eating. Challenge students to replace the habit of eating salty foods with eating foods high in potassium.

Sample answer: The crackers that I ate contained 135 milligrams (mg) of sodium.

Potassium Potassium and sodium work together to maintain water balance in the body. In addition, people who consume enough potassium each day generally have lower blood pressure than people who do not. The problem is that most Americans do not consume enough potassium. Foods that are rich in potassium include baked potatoes, spinach, bananas, dried fruits, oranges, soybeans, and tomato products.

Iron Iron is necessary for healthy red blood cells. These cells have an iron-containing substance called hemoglobin, which carries oxygen from your lungs to all parts of your body. Adolescent girls and adult women need extra iron, because they lose iron during menstruation. Both adolescent girls and boys also need iron to build muscle mass.

There are many good sources of iron. During one day, for example, you might fulfill your iron requirements by eating an iron-fortified breakfast cereal, a salad containing garbanzo beans, a serving of cooked spinach, several dried apricots, and a serving of lean beef. If a person's diet does not include enough iron, he or she may develop **anemia** (uh NEE me uh), a condition in which the red blood cells do not contain enough hemoglobin. People suffering from anemia are often weak and tired, and they may become sick easily.

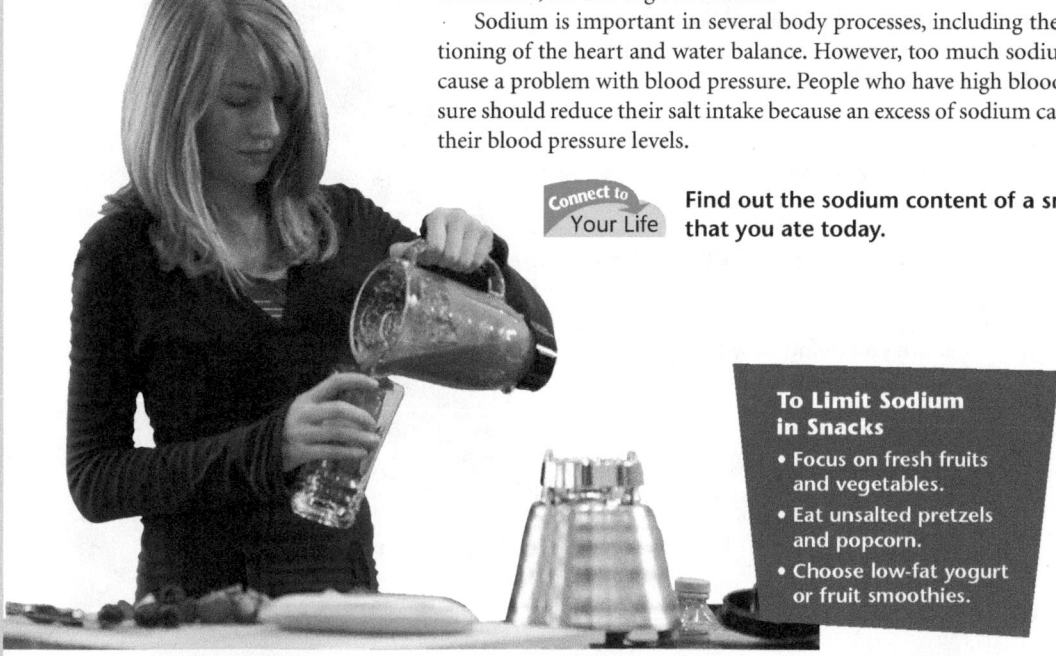
FIGURE 10 You can limit sodium by making your own snacks instead of eating processed foods or fast foods.

Sodium In contrast to calcium, most people consume far more sodium than they need. Table salt, or sodium chloride, is a major source of this mineral. So are some processed, or manufactured, foods, such as canned soups and frozen pizza. Salty snack foods, including chips and salted nuts, are also high in sodium.

Sodium is important in several body processes, including the functioning of the heart and water balance. However, too much sodium can cause a problem with blood pressure. People who have high blood pressure should reduce their salt intake because an excess of sodium can raise their blood pressure levels.

Connect to Your Life Find out the sodium content of a snack that you ate today.

To Limit Sodium in Snacks
- Focus on fresh fruits and vegetables.
- Eat unsalted pretzels and popcorn.
- Choose low-fat yogurt or fruit smoothies.

MATH and Health

L2 Graphing

Give students the following statistics, and tell them to graph the data. According to the *Dietary Guidelines for Americans,* the amount of sodium in an American's diet comes from four different sources: 12 percent occurs naturally in food, 5 percent is added during cooking, 6 percent is added at the table, and 77 percent is added during processing by food manufacturers. *(Students should make a circle graph to illustrate these data.)*

FIGURE 11 Minerals are found in a variety of foods and perform many essential functions in the body. **Reading Tables** Which minerals aid in the function of the nervous system?

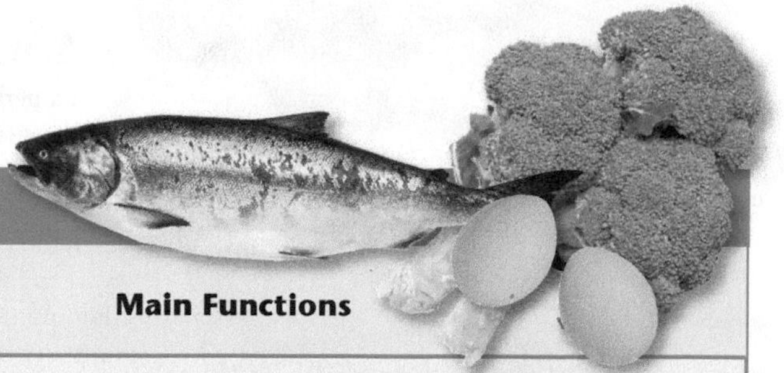

Minerals

Mineral	Good Sources	Main Functions
Calcium	Milk and milk products; dark green, leafy vegetables; tofu; legumes	Helps build and maintain bones and teeth; nerve and muscle function; blood clotting
Phosphorus	Meat; eggs; poultry; fish; legumes; milk and milk products	Helps build and maintain bones and teeth; energy metabolism
Magnesium	Leafy green vegetables; legumes; nuts; whole-grain food	Helps build bones and protein; energy metabolism; muscle contraction
Sodium	Table salt; processed food; soy sauce	Helps maintain water balance; nerve function
Chlorine	Table salt; soy sauce; processed foods	Helps maintain water balance; digestion
Potassium	Vegetables, fruits, meat, poultry, fish	Helps maintain water balance and make protein; functioning of heart and nervous system
Sulfur	Milk and milk products; meat; poultry; fish; legumes; nuts	Forms part of some amino acids and B vitamins
Iodine	Seafood; iodized salt	Helps in metabolism as part of thyroid hormone
Selenium	Seafoods; meats; organ meat	Helps break down harmful substances
Iron	Red meats; seafood; legumes; green, leafy vegetables; fortified cereals; dried fruits	Part of red blood cells; helps in energy metabolism
Zinc	Meats; poultry; seafood; milk; whole-grain foods	Part of many substances that help carry out body processes
Fluorine	Fish; fluoridated water	Helps form strong teeth and bones

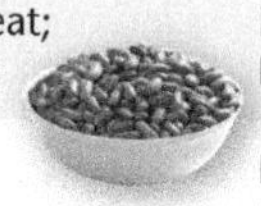

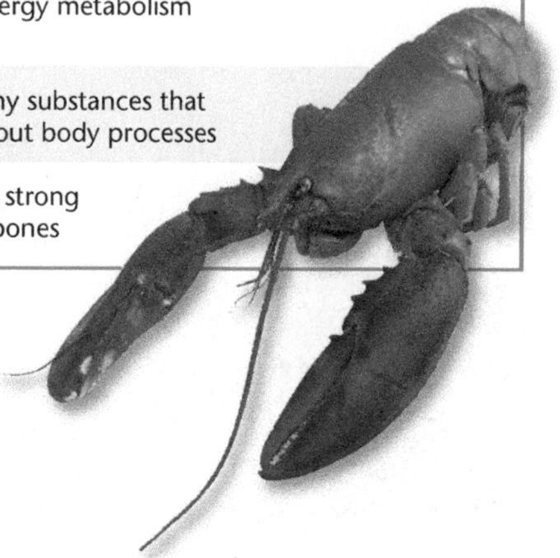

L3 Visual Learning: Figure 11

Refer students to the chart of minerals in Figure 11. Ask questions such as: **What are good sources of magnesium?** *(leafy, green vegetables; legumes; nuts; whole-grain foods)* **What is the role of iron in the body?** *(makes up part of red blood cells, helps in energy metabolism)* **What minerals help build and maintain bones and teeth?** *(calcium, phosphorus, magnesium, fluorine)* Point out that many different minerals are often required for a single body function. Ask: **What is the best source of minerals for the body?** *(food)*
Caption Answer calcium, sodium, potassium

L2 Active Learning

Have students prepare index cards with a mineral written on one side and the foods that are good sources of the mineral on the other side. Have students exchange cards with a partner. Partners can take turns reading the name of a mineral and identifying good sources of it. Students can check their answers by turning over the cards.

L4 Cooperative Learning

Divide the class into small groups. Challenge each group to write a short poem or song about each of the different minerals. The poems and songs can be humorous or serious, but should include important information about the mineral. Choose the best ones, and have students create a class poetry book or song book about minerals.

Differentiated Instruction

L1 Special Needs

Have students collect food labels from an assortment of food products, including processed foods, snack foods, canned fruits and vegetables, and frozen fruits and vegetables. Have students use the nutrition information on the labels to identify the amount of sodium in a serving of each food. Instruct students to put the foods in order from the one with the lowest amount of sodium to the highest.

Food and Nutrition **207**

Vitamin and Mineral Supplements

L3 Building Media Literacy

Have students find an advertisement for a vitamin or mineral supplement. Ask them to write a paragraph analyzing what the ad is selling, who the ad is targeted at, and what claims the ad makes. In a second paragraph, have students explain how a balanced diet can provide this nutrient without the added expense or danger of overdosing on vitamins or minerals. **WRITING**

Water

L3 Building Vocabulary

Write the word *electrolyte* on the board. Explain that the prefix *electro-* means electric or electricity. The suffix *-lyte* refers to a substance that can be dissolved. Explain that electrolytes are substances that, when dissolved in water, break into separate positive and negative charged particles. It is these positive or negative particles of important minerals, such as sodium, potassium, and magnesium, that are required for many of the chemical reactions that occur in the body.

L2 Teacher Demo

Demonstrate how much water is contained in a variety of foods, such as slices of apple, potato, carrot, and bread. Borrow a scale from the science department and weigh the foods when they are fresh. Then, leave the foods out to dry on paper plates for a few days. Weigh the foods again, and compare the fresh and dry weights. Discuss which foods contained the most water and how such foods contribute to people's daily water intake.

FIGURE 12 Salad bars loaded with fresh vegetables are a great way to get all the vitamins and minerals you need without taking supplements.

Vitamin and Mineral Supplements

If a person does not get enough of a specific nutrient, a nutrient deficiency can occur. People who eat a wide variety of healthy foods, however, seldom suffer from nutrient deficiencies. Vitamin and mineral supplements, therefore, are not usually necessary if your diet is nutritious and well-balanced. In fact, an excess, or overdose, of vitamins or minerals may damage your health. Some common symptoms of overdose include nausea, vomiting, diarrhea, and rash.

If you want to boost your intake of a particular vitamin or mineral, first consider how to meet your needs by making small adjustments to your daily diet. For example, if you need to increase your calcium intake, consider eating yogurt as a snack, or drinking milk with dinner instead of a soft drink.

If you do take a vitamin or mineral supplement, take one that meets, but does not exceed, your needs. A health care provider can advise you about how much is the right amount. Beware of megadosing, or taking in larger amounts of a nutrient than your body needs. For fat-soluble vitamins, the excess amounts would be stored in body fat and can cause vitamin poisoning. Symptoms of vitamin poisoning include nausea, vomiting, joint pain, severe headaches, and hair loss. For water-soluble vitamins, on the other hand, the excess amount would be excreted by your body. Therefore, taking megadoses of these vitamins may not be a wise investment.

Water

About 65 percent of your body weight is water. You do not get energy from this nutrient directly. Nevertheless, water is essential for all life processes, including the production of energy. **Nearly all of the body's chemical reactions, including those that produce energy and build new tissues, take place in a water solution.** Water is the primary component of blood and tissue. It carries dissolved waste products out of the body and helps digest food.

Water and Homeostasis Homeostasis (ho mee oh STAY sis) is the process of maintaining a steady state inside your body. What roles does water play in homeostasis?

▶ When you become overheated, your body excretes perspiration, which cools your body. Thus, water regulates body temperature.

▶ Water contains dissolved substances called **electrolytes** that regulate many processes in your cells. For example, your nervous and muscular systems depend on electrolytes, such as sodium and potassium.

TEENS *Are Asking . . .*

Q: I have heard that you can die from drinking too much water. Is this really true?

A: Yes, but it is a very rare occurrence. Drinking too much water can cause a condition called hyponatremia, or water intoxication. This condition is usually associated with marathon runners or long-distance bikers who sweat heavily and lose both water and electrolytes from their bodies. If these athletes drink large amounts of water to prevent dehydration, but do not replace the lost electrolytes, water intoxication can result. In this condition, the body cells swell up with water. The swelling puts pressure on the brain and the nerves, causing seizures, coma, and death. This condition has also occurred on college campuses during pledging rituals in which a pledge is forced to "chug" pitchers of water.

Water intoxication is almost unheard of in the average person, or even in average athletes. Just remember to drink the recommended amount of water and eat a well-balanced diet to supply your body with the right balance of electrolytes.

Preventing Dehydration   Very heavy perspiring or severe diarrhea can result in **dehydration** (dee hy DRAY shun), a serious reduction in the body's water content. When the body becomes dehydrated, it loses important electrolytes along with the water. Symptoms of dehydration can include weakness, rapid breathing, and a weak heartbeat. Whenever your body loses a lot of water, you need to be careful to increase your intake of water and electrolytes to prevent dehydration.

How Much Water?   Every day, you need at least ten 8-ounce cups of water if you are a female 14 to 18 years old. Males in the same age group need 14 cups of water per day. This water can be in the form of foods that contain a lot of water, such as fruits and vegetables, or juices. Drinks that contain caffeine—coffee, tea, and some sodas—may not be good sources of water for your body. This is because caffeine increases the amount of water your body excretes. It is probably better to obtain water from foods that do not contain caffeine.

Water Versus Sports Drinks   Experts in the field of sports medicine recommend that you drink about 2 cups of fluid 2 hours before exercise. During exercise, take a drink about every 15 minutes. Are sports drinks a better choice than water? A sports drink is not necessary if you exercise for 60 minutes or less. If you exercise longer, a sports drink that contains carbohydrates may be beneficial. However, sports drinks with electrolytes are not necessary unless you exercise for 5 hours or more.

You can lose 4 cups of water during every hour of heavy exercise.

FIGURE 13   It is important to drink plenty of water every day.

Section 2   Review

Key Ideas and Vocabulary

1. What are **vitamins?** How do they differ from **minerals?**

2. What are the two classes of vitamins? Which vitamins fall into each class?

3. Which seven minerals are needed by the body in significant amounts?

4. What roles does water play in the body?

5. Define **homeostasis.**

Critical Thinking

6. Classifying   What vitamins are supplied by green, leafy vegetables? By citrus fruits?

🔊 GO ONLINE PearsonSuccessNet.com   Audio Summary Section 8.2

Health and Community

Fluoride and the Water Supply   Find out whether your community adds fluoride to its water supply. If possible, talk to a town official, dentist, or other knowledgeable adult in your community. Write a paragraph summarizing your findings.   **WRITING**

7. Applying Concepts   What are some ways that people with high blood pressure can reduce their sodium intake?

8. Relating Cause and Effect   Explain how feelings of thirst can help a person maintain homeostasis on a hot day.

Food and Nutrition   **209**

ⓛ₃ Building Health Skills

Setting Goals Have students measure the amount of water or other water-based foods or beverages they consume in one day. Students should compare their water intake with the recommended daily amount. Then have them write a sentence in their private journals stating how they will adjust their daily water intake to meet their nutritional requirements.

3. Assess

Evaluate

These assignments can help you assess students' mastery of the section content.

Section 2 Review

Answers appear below.

Teaching Resources
• Practice 8-2
• Section 8-2 Quiz

ⓛ₂ Reteach

Have students write five questions about vitamins, minerals, and water that relate to the section objectives. Then ask students to exchange questions with a partner and answer them.

ⓛ₄ Enrich

Teaching Resources
• Enrich 8-2

Health and Community

Fluoride and the Water Supply Students will find that most municipal water supplies are fluorinated to help reduce dental cavities. Students who have private wells do not have fluorinated water, but the groundwater may contain enough fluoride naturally to meet nutritional requirements. These students should have their water tested to determine its fluoride content.

Section 2 Review

1. Vitamins are nutrients made by living things, are required in small amounts, and assist in chemical reactions. Minerals occur naturally in rocks and soil.

2. fat-soluble: A, D, E, K; water-soluble: all the B vitamins and vitamin C

3. calcium, sodium, potassium, magnesium, phosphorus, chlorine, sulfur

4. Nearly all the body's chemical reactions take place in water; water is the primary component of tissues; water removes wastes from the body and aids digestion.

5. Homeostasis is the process of maintaining a steady state in the body.

6. green, leafy vegetables: A, E, K, B2, B6, folate, C; citrus fruits: C

7. *Sample answer:* Don't add salt to foods at the table, and eat less processed food.

8. When you're thirsty, you tend to want to drink something, which restores water balance in the body.

Objectives
Before class begins, write the objectives on the board. Have students copy the objectives into their notebooks at the start of class.

1. Focus

Warm-Up Advice Line

After students complete the writing assignment, invite volunteers to share their responses. Discuss how their suggestions could help the family obtain all of the nutrients they need. *(Advice could include choosing low-fat foods for take-out and adding whole-grain breads and fresh fruits and vegetables to prepackaged meals.)*

Presentation 8-3

Sensitive Issues

This section discusses guidelines for making healthy food choices and balancing physical activity with food intake to maintain a healthy weight.

• Some students may be sensitive to these issues because they are overweight or think they are, or feel that they are not active enough. Allow students to keep food and exercise diaries private. Do not ask students to share their eating or exercise habits with other students.

• Be careful not to label foods as either "bad" or "good." Some students associate the foods they eat with who they are, thinking: "If I eat bad food, then I must be a bad person."

Section 3 | Guidelines for Healthful Eating

Objectives
▶ **Explain** how the *Dietary Guidelines for Americans* can help you plan a healthful diet.

▶ **Summarize** the recommendations in the MyPlate plan.

Vocabulary
• *Dietary Guidelines for Americans*
• nutrient-dense food
• MyPlate plan

Warm-Up

Dear Advice Line,

My family is really busy, and we don't have a lot of time to cook. It seems like we eat an awful lot of take-out, packaged meals, and frozen dinners. I wonder if we are getting too much sodium, sugar, and fat. I also don't think we get enough fresh vegetables and whole grains. What can we do?

WRITING Write a response to this teen to help solve the problem.

The Dietary Guidelines

How can you make sure you get enough nutrients while consuming the number of calories that is right for you? The United States Department of Agriculture (USDA) and the U.S. Department of Health and Human services have published the *Dietary Guidelines for Americans* to help you figure out the answer to this question. The **Dietary Guidelines for Americans** is a document developed by nutrition experts to promote health and help people reduce their risk for heart disease, cancer, and diabetes through diet and physical activity. **The *Dietary Guidelines* provide information on how to make smart food choices, balance food intake with physical activity, get the most nutrition out of the calories you consume, and handle food safely.**

Make Smart Food Choices To obtain all the nutrients you need, choose a wide variety of foods. Include plenty of whole-grain foods, vegetables, and fruits. These foods are rich in complex carbohydrates and fiber. Milk and milk products are an important part of a healthful diet, especially for adolescents who are still growing. Milk products provide the calcium needed to prevent bone loss. Choose low-fat or nonfat milk and milk products to keep cholesterol down and thus reduce your risk of heart disease.

WRITING and Health

L3 Public Service Announcement
Have students write a script for a radio public service announcement (PSA) that teaches the public about one of the four recommendations contained in the *Dietary Guidelines for Americans.* First have students identify the type of radio station that will play their PSA. Their PSA should be written for the type of audience that listens to the radio station. For example, a PSA written for a pop music radio station should use different language and examples than one written for a classical music station.

Hungry for a snack? Try these nutrient-dense foods:

* Fresh fruit
* Low-fat yogurt
* Nuts and raisins
* Raw veggies

Balance Food and Physical Activity Regular physical activity is important for your overall health and fitness. Maintaining a healthy weight is a matter of balancing the calories you take in with how active you are. Health problems can develop if you are overweight or underweight. The *Dietary Guidelines* recommend that teenagers be active for 60 minutes most days.

Get the Most Nutrition Out of Your Calories Choose foods that are nutrient-dense. **Nutrient-dense foods** contain lots of vitamins and minerals relative to the number of calories. At the same time, nutrient-dense foods are low in saturated fat, trans fat, added sugar, and salt. Lean meats, fish, poultry, and legumes are nutrient-dense foods. If you are hungry for a snack, some good nutrient-dense choices are shown in Figure 14. Limit your intake of sweet snacks and soft drinks. These foods contain lots of sugar but few other useful nutrients.

Most people consume too much sodium but not enough potassium. Eating more fruits and vegetables can boost your potassium intake. To reduce your sodium intake, limit salty snacks, pickled foods, luncheon meats, and canned soups.

Handle Food Safely Part of good nutrition is using safe procedures to prepare, handle, and store the food you eat. Food borne illnesses can be prevented if you follow a few simple steps.

▶ Keep your hands and surfaces that come into contact with food clean.

▶ Separate raw and cooked foods while preparing or storing them.

▶ Cook meat, poultry, and fish to safe internal temperatures.

▶ If food is perishable, chill it right away.

▶ Thaw foods in the refrigerator, not on the counter.

 **What kinds of things could you do to be more active each day?**

FIGURE 14 If you're hungry for a snack, it is still possible to make healthy food choices.

Food and Nutrition **211**

2. Teach

L3 **EL** Reading/Note Taking 8-3

L2 Adapted Reading/Note Taking 8-3

The Dietary Guidelines

L3 Cooperative Learning

Have small groups of students create a brochure that describes the four recommendations given in the *Dietary Guidelines*. In the brochure, students should explain how each recommendation promotes health and give practical tips about how to incorporate the recommendations into a teen's lifestyle. Consider placing copies of the brochures in the school lunchroom or library. **WRITING**

L2 Building Health Skills

Advocacy Have student pairs work together to write a script for a role-play in which one person tries to convince a friend to substitute a nutrient-dense snack for a salty snack. Invite students to perform their role-plays for the class.

L1 Teacher Demo

Put on an apron and pretend to be a television chef. As you pretend to prepare food, commit as many food handling violations as you can. Encourage students to interrupt you at any time to identify the mistakes you have made. Students should then describe the safer way of handling the food.

 Sample answer: Walk to school, play basketball with friends, vacuum my room

Differentiated Instruction

L2 Less Proficient Readers

Hand out supermarket advertisements and have students cut out pictures of different foods. Students should include the price of the food with its picture. Help students sort the foods into those that are nutrient-dense and those that are high in sugar, fat, or sodium. Have students compare the prices of nutrient-dense foods with the prices of foods high in sugar, fat, and sodium to see if there are any differences.

The "MyPlate Plan"

L3 Visual Learning: Figure 15

Image Bank Figure 8-15

Preview with students the MyPlate diagram shown in Figure 15. Point out how each group corresponds to the five food groups. Ask: **What are the five food groups?** (grains, fruits, dairy, vegetables, and protein) **What does the size of each part of the plate refer to?** (the proportion of your diet that should come from that food group) **Which food group should you consume more of—vegetables or protein?** (vegetables) **Caption Answer** grains and vegetables

L2 Active Learning

Give students pictures of various foods or a copy of the lunch menu. Ask students to classify each food into one of the five food groups. For food items that contain more than one food group, have students place the food into each group. Then, have students organize the foods in each group from those that contain the least fat and sugar to the most. Tell students to place foods low in fat and sugar at the bottom of a column with foods higher in fat and sugar at the top.

EL Cooperative Learning

List the six classes of nutrients that students learned about in Sections 1 and 2 on the board. Pair students up to review these terms and to list foods that contain each nutrient. Then challenge student pairs to identify which classes of nutrients are supplied by each of the food groups in Figure 15. (Grains: carbohydrates; Vegetables: carbohydrates, vitamins, minerals; Fruits: carbohydrates, vitamins, minerals, water; Dairy: fat, carbohydrates, minerals; Protein: protein, fat)

FIGURE 15 The MyPlate plan emphasizes a balance between the various groups of foods that you eat.
Interpreting Diagrams Which two groups should you consume in the largest amounts?

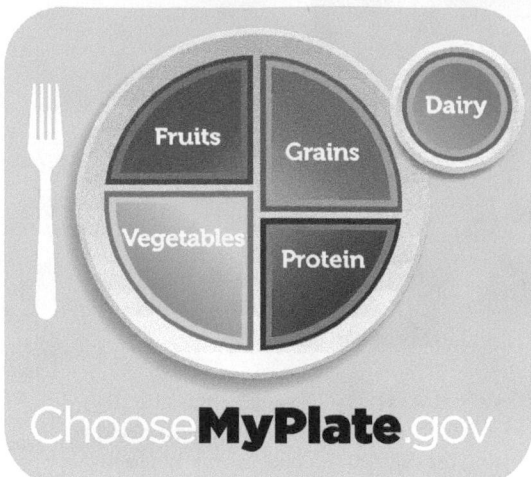

MyPlate

ChooseMyPlate.gov

Grains

Make half the grains you eat whole grains. Look for the word *whole* before the name of the grain. Good choices are
- breads: whole-wheat or rye, pita, rolls, tortillas
- pasta: macaroni, spaghetti, rice noodles
- other grains: rice, crackers, couscous, bulgur, breakfast cereals

Vegetables

Vary your vegetables. Include in your diet
- dark green vegetables: spinach, kale, mustard or collard greens
- orange vegetables: carrots, squash, sweet potatoes
- dry beans and peas
- starchy vegetables: potatoes, corn, lima beans

Fruits

- Eat a variety of fruits, such as apples, bananas, mangoes, oranges, papayas, grapes, and pineapples.
- Limit your fruit juices.

Dairy

- Get plenty of calcium-rich foods.
- Choose low-fat or fat-free when you consume milk, yogurt, or cheese.

Protein

Choose low-fat or lean meats and poultry. Vary your protein by choosing
- fish, nuts, seeds
- beans or peas, such as kidney, garbanzo, fava, navy, lentils

For Your INFORMATION!

The MyPlate Plan

In 2010, the USDA replaced MyPyramid with MyPlate. MyPlate is intended to be a simpler companion to the 2010 Dietary Guidelines for Americans. The USDA chose a plate for the diagram because it is a familiar mealtime visual. The size of each group corresponds with how much of each food group should be in a person's diet. Grains and vegetables should make up the largest proportion of a meal, followed by fruits, protein, and dairy. What was formerly listed as Meat and Beans has been condensed into Protein, and the Oils group has been eliminated from the diagram. The USDA has more information about a healthy diet on its website, including which foods to increase, which foods to reduce, and how to switch to low-fat and low-sodium foods.

MyPlate

You now know that you need to eat a variety of foods. To help you remember this advice, the USDA has designed a visual based on a familiar mealtime object—a plate. The **MyPlate** diagram illustrates the five food groups that you need to eat regularly, and provides a visual indication of how much of each group you need. Figure 15 shows the basic parts of the MyPlate diagram.

Balancing Calories The MyPlate diagram reminds you to balance your calories. You can enjoy your food, but often you should eat less of some food groups and more of others. It is always a good idea to avoid oversized portions.

Foods to Increase and Foods to Reduce The MyPlate diagram suggests that half of your plate at each meal needs to be made up of fruits and vegetables. The USDA also suggests that at least half of your grains should be whole grains, and that you switch to fat-free or low-fat (1%) milk. Other foods that you should reduce include those that are high in sodium (salt). You should also drink water instead of sugary drinks to reduce the sugar in your diet.

Creating Your Own MyPlate Plan You can create your own personalized MyPlate plan by visiting the USDA's Web site. It contains details about the foods in each group, suggestions for planning menus, and calorie counts.

 **Connect to Your Life** How could you include more whole grains in your diet?

 **GO ONLINE**
PearsonSuccessNet.com
For: More on MyPlate

Recommended Servings Per Day for 16-Year-Olds

Activity Level	Grains	Vegetables	Fruits	Dairy	Protein
Sedentary					
Male	8 ounces	3 cups	2 cups	3 cups	$6\frac{1}{2}$ ounces
Female	6 ounces	$2\frac{1}{2}$ cups	$1\frac{1}{2}$ cups	3 cups	5 ounces
Moderate					
Male	10 ounces	$3\frac{1}{2}$ cups	$2\frac{1}{2}$ cups	3 cups	7 ounces
Female	6 ounces	$2\frac{1}{2}$ cups	2 cups	3 cups	$5\frac{1}{2}$ ounces
Active					
Male	10 ounces	4 cups	$2\frac{1}{2}$ cups	3 cups	7 ounces
Female	8 ounces	3 cups	2 cups	3 cups	$6\frac{1}{2}$ ounces

L3 Online Activity  **GO ONLINE**
Visit Pearson SuccessNet to access an online activity about MyPlate. Have students complete the Web activity.

L3 Class Discussion
Begin a class discussion by asking: **Why does it make sense to have different nutrition plans based on a person's age, sex, and activity level?** (*Different groups of people have different energy requirements and therefore different food needs.*) Refer students to the table of recommended servings per day. Have students compare the recommended serving sizes. Ask: **Who should eat larger servings of food—sedentary teens or active teens?** (*active teens*) **Males or females?** (*males*)

L2 Addressing Misconceptions
Recommended Servings Students might get the impression from the chart of the daily recommended servings that they must eat those specific amounts of food from each food group each day. Explain that it is okay to eat more or less of each food on any given day. Point out that it is important, however, to try to achieve a balance of foods over time, such as over a week, to make sure the body gets all the nutrients it needs. Remind students that they also need to maintain an activity level that corresponds to the amount of food they consume.

L3 Building Health Skills
Accessing Information Suggest that students visit the USDA's Web site and create their own MyPlate plan. Challenge students to explore the Web site to find additional information about serving sizes in each food group, examples of good food choices, and sample menus. Suggest that students print a food calorie tracking sheet to track their daily calorie intake.

Connect to Your Life *Sample answer:* by eating whole-grain breads and breakfast cereals

Using the Food Guidelines

L2 Building Health Skills

Advocacy Have groups of students make posters offering practical tips for following the *Dietary Guidelines* and the MyPlate plan. Students should illustrate each tip to make the posters visually interesting. Display the posters in the school lunchroom.

3. Assess

Evaluate

These assignments can help you assess students' mastery of the section content.

Section 3 Review

Answers appear below.

Teaching Resources
- Practice 8-3
- Section 8-3 Quiz

L2 Reteach

Give students a copy of the MyPlate plan. Have them label each colored section with the food group it represents and explain the meaning of the different colors.

L4 Enrich

Teaching Resources
- Enrich 8-3

Health at Home

Improving Your Diet Allow students to keep their food journals and paragraphs private. Discuss with the class the difficulties of sticking with a healthful eating plan and ways to overcome these difficulties.

FIGURE 16 Eating a healthy breakfast will help you to resist unhealthy foods later in the day.

Using the Food Guidelines

Planning a nutritious diet does not mean you must forego all the foods you love. You can still have a dab of margarine on your toast and your favorite chocolate bar as a rare treat. Here are some tips for following the *Dietary Guidelines* and the MyPlate plan.

Meals You don't need to consume every food group at every meal. But you should try to vary your diet at each meal.

- ▶ **Breakfast** Don't skip breakfast. Choose whole-grain cereals, low-fat milk or yogurt, and fruit. Limit pastries, eggs, and bacon.
- ▶ **Lunch** Focus on whole grains, fruits, and vegetables. Use mustard or ketchup instead of mayonnaise. Try low-fat cheese on pizza.
- ▶ **Dinner** Trim excess fat from meats. Instead of fried meats or fish, try them grilled. Choose low-fat dressings, and limit butter.

Snacks When snacking, choose foods with high nutrient density.

- ▶ Try satisfying your sweet tooth with fruit instead of cookies.
- ▶ Make a whole-wheat bagel, not a donut, your after-school treat.
- ▶ When you go to the movies, choose unbuttered popcorn.

Eating Out When you eat at fast-food restaurants, follow these tips.

- ▶ Substitute low-fat milk, water, or fruit juice for shakes and soft drinks.
- ▶ Select the salad bar in place of fries or onion rings. But go easy on dressings, cheese, bacon bits, and croutons.
- ▶ Choose a grilled chicken sandwich instead of a burger.

Section 3 Review

Key Ideas and Vocabulary

1. What are the four main recommendations contained in the *Dietary Guidelines for Americans?*
2. What does it mean to say that food is **nutrient-dense?** Give an example of a nutrient-dense food.
3. What is indicated by the different colors in the MyPlate plan?

Critical Thinking

4. **Evaluating** Choose the row in the chart on page 213 that best applies to you. Evaluate whether your diet is in line with the recommended number of servings from each food group.

Health at Home

Improving Your Diet Keep track of how many fats and sweets you eat over the next three days. Then, come up with a plan to substitute nutrient-dense foods for the fats and sweets you eat. Monitor your diet for a week and evaluate how well you stuck to your plan. **WRITING**

5. **Classifying** You eat a meal that contains beans and peas. Using the MyPlate diagram, how would you classify this meal?

GO ONLINE PearsonSuccessNet.com   Audio Summary Section 8.3

Section 3 Review

1. make smart food choices, balance food and physical activity, get the most nutrition out of your calories, and handle food safely
2. Nutrient-dense foods contain lots of vitamins and minerals relative to the number of calories and are low in saturated fat, trans fat, added sugar, and salt. Examples: lean meat, fish, poultry, legumes
3. The colors represent the five food groups. The size of each section indicates the proportion of your diet that should come from that group.
4. Allow students to keep their dietary requirements private. Students' diets may or may not be in line with the recommendations.
5. Butter contains a large amount of saturated fat.

Chapter 8
At a Glance

VIDEO **TEENS** Talk ◉

Food for Thought List three ways the video helped you become a smarter consumer.

Section 1   Carbohydrates, Fats, and Proteins

Key Ideas

▶ Carbohydrates, fats, and proteins can all be used by the body as sources of energy.

▶ When your body uses the nutrients in foods, a series of chemical reactions occurs inside your cells. As a result, energy is released.

▶ Carbohydrates supply energy for your body's functions.

▶ Fats supply your body with energy, form your cells, maintain body temperature, and protect your nerves.

▶ The most important function of proteins is their role in the growth and repair of your body's tissues.

Vocabulary
- nutrient (192)
- metabolism (193)
- calorie (193)
- carbohydrate (194)
- fiber (195)
- fat (196)
- unsaturated fat (196)
- saturated fat (196)
- cholesterol (197)
- trans fat (197)
- protein (198)
- amino acid (198)

Section 2   Vitamins, Minerals, and Water

Key Ideas

▶ There are two classes of vitamins: fat-soluble vitamins, which dissolve in fatty materials, and water-soluble vitamins, which dissolve in water.

▶ You need seven minerals—calcium, sodium, potassium, magnesium, phosphorus, chlorine, and sulfur—in significant amounts.

▶ Nearly all of the body's chemical reactions, including those that produce energy and build new tissues, take place in a water solution.

Vocabulary
- vitamin (203)
- antioxidant (205)
- mineral (205)
- anemia (206)
- homeostasis (208)
- electrolyte (208)
- dehydration (209)

Section 3   Guidelines for Healthful Eating

Key Ideas

▶ The *Dietary Guidelines* provide information on how to make smart food choices, balance food intake with physical activity, get the most nutrition out of the calories you consume, and handle food safely.

▶ The MyPlate plan illustrates the five food groups that you need to eat regularly, and provides a visual indication of how much of each group you need.

Vocabulary
- *Dietary Guidelines for Americans* (210)
- nutrient-dense food (211)
- MyPlate plan (213)

Food and Nutrition **215**

Key Ideas Review

L3 Have each student write a quiz-show question about one of the Key Ideas in the chapter. Students should also supply the answer to the question. Collect the questions and answers, and use them for a class quiz game.

L2 Have students write true or false questions based on the Key Ideas from the chapter. Students can exchange questions with a partner and answer them. For each statement that is false, students should rewrite it to make it true.

Vocabulary Review

EL Have students use as many of the vocabulary terms as they can to make a concept map. Students should use the term *nutrients* to begin the map.

L3 Divide the class into groups of four, and have students write each vocabulary term on a separate index card to make a deck of terms. Then have students in each group sit in a circle. One student starts by holding the entire deck of terms and saying phrases that are related to the term on the top card. As soon as the term is identified, the student removes the card and passes the deck to the next student. Play continues until all the cards have been used. The group that finishes first is the winner.

Chapter 8 Review

 GO ONLINE

PearsonSuccessNet.com

Students can go online for a review activity on Chapter 8.

Reviewing Key Ideas

Section 1

1. d
2. d
3. Glucose provides energy to cells.
4. Fiber helps prevent constipation and may reduce the risk of colon cancer.
5. by substituting low-fat foods for meat and dairy products
6. Amino acids are substances that are linked together to make proteins. The body cannot make essential amino acids; they must be part of the diet.
7. By combining plant protein sources, such as legumes and grains, people obtain all the essential amino acids.

Section 2

8. a
9. b
10. Antioxidants help protect cells from damage caused by aging and certain types of cancer. Sources include citrus, strawberries, broccoli, tomatoes, potatoes, vegetable oils, whole grains, seeds, and nuts.
11. *Any one:* calcium—dark green, leafy vegetables; tofu; legumes; fluorine—fish, fluoridated water; phosphorus—meat, poultry, fish, legumes
12. *Any three:* Nearly all chemical reactions in the body take place in water. Water maintains homeostasis by regulating body temperature and electrolyte balance; is a primary component of tissue; carries wastes out of the body; helps digest food.
13. If a diet does not have enough iron, the body does not have enough hemoglobin to carry oxygen to tissues.
14. Diets high in fat and low in fiber can lead to heart disease and certain cancers in adulthood. Diets low in calcium can lead to osteoporosis.

Section 3

15. c
16. Making smart food choices means choosing a wide variety of foods to obtain all the necessary nutrients.

Chapter 8 Review

Reviewing Key Ideas

 GO ONLINE

PearsonSuccessNet.com

For: Chapter 8 review activity

Section 1

1. Complex carbohydrates are
   a. composed of sugars linked together.
   b. found in grain products.
   c. good sources of energy.
   d. all of the above.

2. Which of the following foods is high in protein?
   a. an apple   b. lettuce
   c. candy   d. chicken

3. What is the role of glucose in the body?

4. Why is fiber necessary for the proper functioning of the digestive system?

5. How can you limit your intake of fats and cholesterol?

6. What are amino acids? Why are some of them called "essential"?

7. **Critical Thinking** In many cultures, people get very little protein from animal sources. How might these people obtain the protein they need?

Section 2

8. Which of these nutrients is sometimes associated with high blood pressure?
   a. sodium   b. calcium
   c. iron   d. carbohydrate

9. Loss of water through heavy perspiring can result in
   a. homeostasis.   b. dehydration.
   c. anemia.   d. metabolism.

10. Explain how antioxidants are important to your health. Which foods are good sources of antioxidants?

11. Which mineral can help build strong bones and teeth? Name one nondairy source of this mineral.

12. Give three reasons why water is such an important nutrient.

13. **Critical Thinking** If a person's diet does not contain enough iron, his or her tissues may not get all the oxygen they need. Explain why this is so.

14. **Critical Thinking** How can your diet today affect your future health? Explain.

Section 3

15. Which of the following is *not* used to determine the amounts you should consume from each food group in the MyPlate plan?
   a. age   b. sex
   c. weight   d. activity level

16. The *Dietary Guidelines* recommend that you make smart food choices. Explain what this recommendation means.

17. Which two groups in the MyPlate diagram are the largest? Explain what this means.

18. **Critical Thinking** Several friends are planning a week-long backpacking trip in the mountains. They must carry all of their food in backpacks, so amounts must be limited. What kind of foods could they take to meet their nutritional needs?

 ## Building Health Skills

19. **Analyzing Influences** Many American teenagers have diets high in fats. Write a letter to the editor of your local newspaper explaining why. Suggest steps that can be taken to improve teen diets. **WRITING**

20. **Accessing Information** Laurie dislikes dairy products. Research and plan three meals that include calcium-rich foods.

21. **Setting Goals** Write down everything you eat for a week. Classify the foods into the groups in the MyPlate plan. Then, come up with a plan to align your diet with the amounts recommended for your age, sex, and activity level. See how you do for the next week.

Health and Community

Food Pantry Visit Volunteer at a local food pantry or soup kitchen for a day. You may be involved in preparing food, chatting with patrons, or cleaning up afterward. What did you find out that you didn't know before? Write an editorial describing your experience. **WRITING**

---

17. The vegetable and grain groups are the largest. These two food groups should make up the most of one's diet.

18. Foods suggested should be low in weight, but high in energy and nutrient density and cover all the food groups. Examples include whole-grain crackers, dried vegetables and fruits, powdered milk, nuts, legumes.

Building Health Skills

19. Letters should explain that teens tend to eat a lot of fast foods, chips, and processed foods because they like the taste and convenience. Suggestions might include making more low-fat choices available at fast-food restaurants and in the school cafeteria; providing fresh fruit, nuts, and other healthy snacks in vending machines; and more nutrition education.

Standardized Test Prep

Math Practice

The graphic below compares the typical American diet to the diet recommended by nutritionists. Use the graphic to answer Questions 22–24.

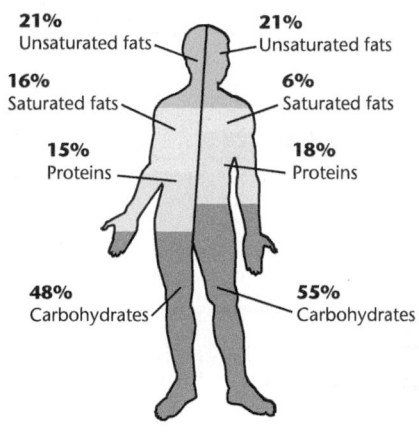

Typical Diet

21% Unsaturated fats
16% Saturated fats
15% Proteins
48% Carbohydrates

Recommended Diet

21% Unsaturated fats
6% Saturated fats
18% Proteins
55% Carbohydrates

22. Which nutrient do Americans typically eat more than double the recommended amount?
    A unsaturated fats
    B proteins
    C carbohydrates
    D saturated fats

23. In the typical diet, if a person consumed a total of 2,000 calories in a day, how many of those calories would be from fats?
    F 420 calories
    G 620 calories
    H 740 calories
    J 940 calories

24. To bring the typical diet more in line with the recommended diet, people should
    A cut their intake of unsaturated fats by one half.
    B cut their intake of saturated fats by two thirds.
    C cut their protein intake in half.
    D double their carbohydrate intake.

Reading and Writing Practice

Read the passage. Then answer Questions 25–28.

Trans fats are produced in a laboratory by heating vegetable oil and bubbling hydrogen through it. How then do animal products, such as beef or milk, contain small amounts of trans fats? In cows, the digestive process produces hydrogen. The hydrogen then mixes with unsaturated fats from the cow's diet to produce a small amount of trans fats. However, foods such as donuts, cookies, and other baked goods contain trans fats in much greater amounts. Thus, avoiding these processed foods is the most effective way to limit trans fats in your diet.

25. In a cow, trans fats are produced when hydrogen
    A mixes with saturated fats from the cow's diet.
    B mixes with vegetable oil.
    C is given off during respiration.
    D mixes with unsaturated fats during digestion.

26. Trans fats can best be limited in the diet by
    F eating chicken instead of beef.
    G limiting baked goods.
    H drinking low-fat milk.
    J eliminating milk.

27. Which of the following does *not* contain trans fats?
    A donuts
    B a cow's diet
    C milk
    D low-fat yogurt

Constructed Response
28. In a paragraph, compare how trans fats are formed in the lab versus in an animal.

> **Test-Taking Tip**
>
> Be sure to eat a good breakfast the morning of your test. The brain works better when it has fuel.

Standardized Test Prep

Math Practice
22. D
23. H
24. B

Reading and Writing Practice
25. D
26. G
27. B
28. Paragraphs will vary but should explain that in the lab, trans fats are produced by bubbling hydrogen through vegetable oil that has first been heated. In an animal, such as a cow, hydrogen mixes with unsaturated fats in the animal's diet.

---

20. Meals will vary but should include nondairy sources of calcium, such as dark green, leafy vegetables; tofu; and legumes.

21. Plans will vary but should focus on ways to eat a more balanced diet and better align the amount of food eaten with the recommended servings.

Health and Community

Food Pantry Visit Editorials should include information about the nutritional quality of the meals and the impact those meals have on the diets of the people served. Students might also describe how it felt to help people who are experiencing a difficult time in their lives.

Section Objectives	Standards Correlation	Instructional Resources L3	SE eTEXT	TE eTEXT	PRINT
1 Choosing Food Wisely ⏲ 1 period; 1/2 block **9.1.1 Summarize** three main reasons why you eat. **9.1.2 Analyze** the information contained on food labels.	NHES: 2.12.2, 2.12.3, 2.12.5, 2.12.10, 3.12.1	**SE** Warm-Up, p. 220	•	•	•
		RN Note Taking Guide 9-1	•	•	•
		IB Image Bank 9-1		•	
		TR Practice 9-1		•	
		TR Section 9-1 Quiz		•	
Reading a Food Label (BUILDING HEALTH SKILLS) ⏲ 1 period; 1/2 block **BHS.9 Evaluate** the information contained on a food label.	NHES: 2.12.10, 3.12.1, 3.12.2, 7.12.2	**SE** Practice the Skill, p. 225	•	•	•
		RN Building Health Skills 9	•	•	•
		IB Image Bank Page 224		•	
2 Safely Managing Your Weight ⏲ 2 periods; 1 block **9.2.1 Examine** how heredity, activity level, and body composition influence a person's weight. **9.2.2 Calculate** your body mass index. **9.2.3 Identify** health problems associated with being overweight and underweight. **9.2.4 Summarize** strategies for losing or gaining weight.	NHES: 1.12.4, 1.12.8, 2.12.5, 2.12.7	**SE** Warm-Up, p. 226	•	•	•
		SE Media Wise Evaluating Diet Plans, p. 230	•	•	•
		RN Note Taking Guide 9-2	•	•	•
		IB Image Bank 9-4		•	
		TR Practice 9-2		•	
		TR Section 9-2 Quiz		•	
3 Nutrition for Individual Needs ⏲ 2 periods; 1 block **9.3.1 Examine** how diabetics, vegetarians, people with food sensitivities, and athletes can meet their nutritional needs.	NHES: 1.12.1, 1.12.5, 8.12.2	**SE** Warm-Up, p. 233	•	•	•
		RN Note Taking Guide 9-3	•	•	•
		TR Practice 9-3		•	
		TR Section 9-3 Quiz		•	

Chapter Review and Assessment

SE Chapter 9 Review, p. 238 L3
CTB Chapter 9 Test L2 L3 L4
SE Standardized Test Prep, p. 239 L3

PROGRAM COMPONENTS

SE Student Edition	**CTB** Computer Test Bank
TE Teacher Edition	**AUD** Audio Section Summaries
TR Teaching Resources	
RN Reading and Note Taking Guide	**DVD** Teens Talk Video Series
	VVG Video Viewing Guide
ARN Adapted Reading and Note Taking Guide	**PPT** Presentation
IB Image Bank	

Differentiated Instruction

(L1) (L2) (L4) (EL)

		SE eTEXT	TE eTEXT	PRINT
ARN	Note Taking Guide 9-1 (L2)	•	•	
RN	Note Taking Guide 9-1 (EL)	•	•	•
AUD	Audio Summary 9-1 (L1) (L2) (EL)	•	•	
TE	Reteach Strategy, p. 223 (L2)		•	•
TR	Enrich 9-1 (L4)		•	
ARN	Building Health Skills 9 (L2)	•	•	
RN	Building Health Skills 9 (EL)	•	•	•
ARN	Note Taking Guide 9-2 (L2)	•	•	
RN	Note Taking Guide 9-2 (EL)	•	•	•
AUD	Audio Summary 9-2 (L1) (L2) (EL)	•	•	
TE	Reteach Strategy, p. 232 (L2)		•	•
TR	Enrich 9-2 (L4)		•	
ARN	Note Taking Guide 9-3 (L2)	•	•	
RN	Note Taking Guide 9-3 (EL)	•	•	•
AUD	Audio Summary 9-3 (L1) (L2) (EL)	•	•	
TE	Reteach Strategy, p. 236 (L2)		•	•
TR	Enrich 9-3 (L4)		•	

ABILITY LEVELS

(L1) **For students with special needs**

(L2) **For less proficient readers**

(L3) **For all students**

(L4) **For gifted and talented students**

(EL) **For English language learners**

Chapter 9 Digital/Video Pathway

This alternative pathway allows you to teach this chapter's content using only the video and online materials.

Preview

DVD **Video #9 Preview**

SE Video #9 Preview Activity

VVG Video #9 Worksheet

Goals for Healthy Eating

1

PPT 9-1 Presentation

RN/ARN 9-1 Note Taking

PPT 9-1 Section Quiz

2

DVD **Video #9 Explore/Wrap-Up**

VVG Video #9 Worksheet

PPT 9-2 Presentation

RN/ARN 9-2 Note Taking

PPT 9-2 Section Quiz

Goals for Healthy Eating

3

PPT 9-3 Presentation

RN/ARN 9-3 Note Taking

PPT 9-3 Section Quiz

Chapter Preview

Section 1 Choosing Food Wisely
People eat to meet their nutritional needs, satisfy their hunger, and supply their body with energy. Factors such as basal metabolic rate and activity level influence how much a person needs to eat. To make wise food choices, it is important to evaluate the information on food labels.

 Accessing Information
Reading a Food Label
Students practice reading the parts of a food label, including the ingredients list, calories per serving, percent Daily Values and any health or nutrient claims.

Section 2 Safely Managing Your Weight
Several factors determine what weight is healthy for an individual, including heredity, activity level, and body composition. Being overweight or underweight carries certain health risks. Reaching and maintaining a healthy weight can be achieved by recognizing eating patterns, choosing healthy weight management strategies, and exercising.

Section 3 Nutrition for Individual Needs
Diabetics, vegetarians, athletes, and people with food sensitivities must follow diets tailored to their health needs and lifestyles.

Making Healthy Food Choices

1 Choosing Food Wisely

◀ Building Health Skills
   • **Accessing Information** Reading a Food Label

2 Safely Managing Your Weight
   • **MediaWise** Evaluating Diet Plans

3 Nutrition for Individual Needs

> GO ONLINE PearsonSuccessNet.com

VIDEO 9

TEENS Talk

Goals for Healthy Eating

Preview **Activity**

Why Are Goals Hard to Reach?

Complete this activity before you watch the video.

1. Read the quote below.
   A goal without a plan is just a wish.
   Antoine de Saint-Exupéry

2. In a paragraph, discuss whether or not you agree with this quote. Cite specific examples from your life to support your view. **WRITING**

218

 GO ONLINE

PearsonSuccessNet.com

For resources and activities for this chapter.

Sensitive Issues

• Many students will be uncomfortable discussing issues related to body weight and body image. When you discuss topics such as body composition, heredity, body mass index, and gaining or losing weight, make sure to respect students' privacy. Also, remind students to treat each other with respect.

• Individual dietary habits may vary because of ethnic, religious, or socioeconomic differences. Take care not to embarrass students who eat differently because of home influences.

• Some students may suffer from medical problems that limit their food choices and make them unable to follow general instructions regarding diet.

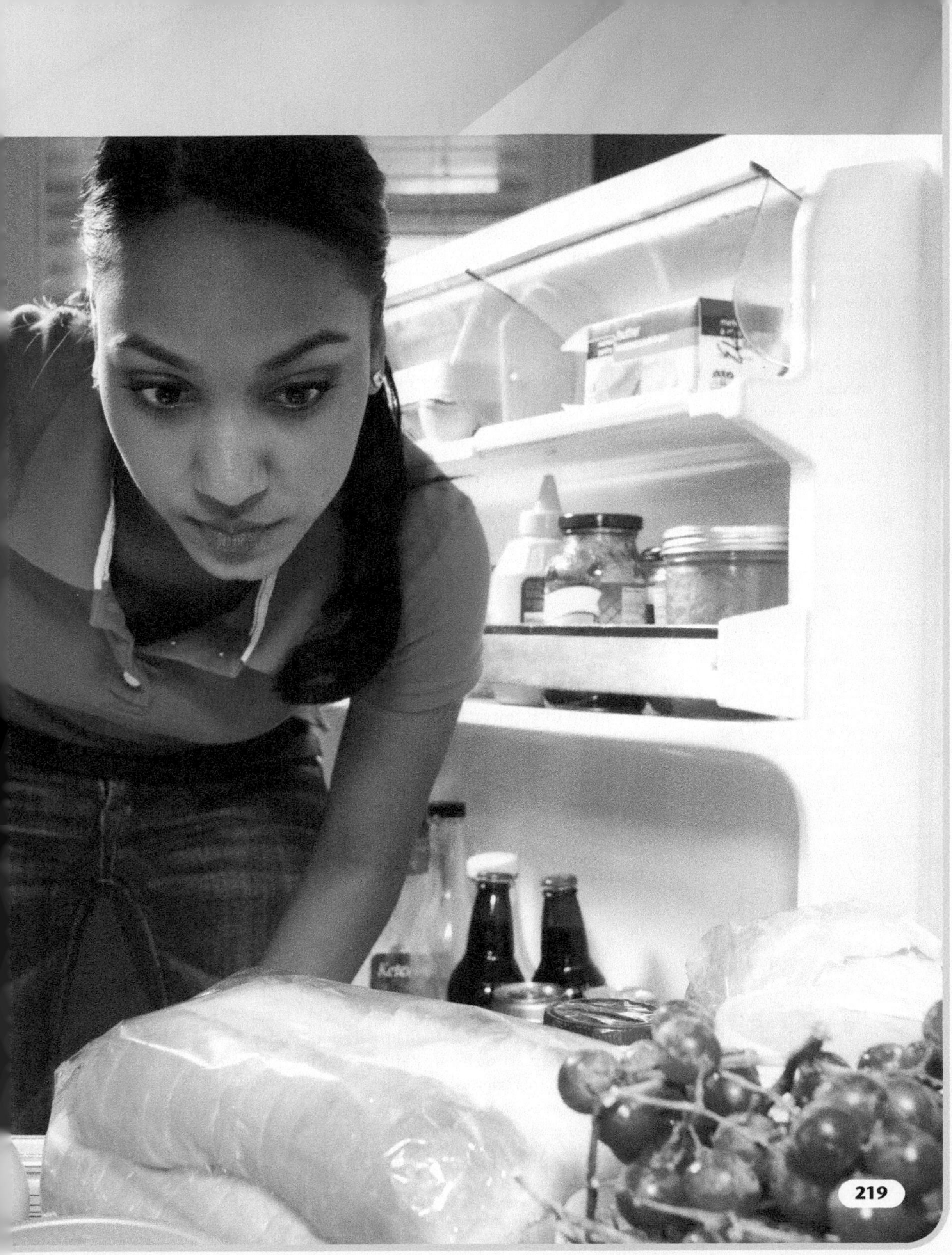

219

VIDEO 9 TEENS Talk

Goals for Healthy Eating

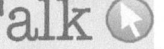

Video Objectives

Use this video to help students

Examine why people often fail to achieve goals that they set.

Identify the steps involved in successful goal-setting.

Improve their ability to set clear, concrete, achievable goals in their personal lives.

Preview **Activity**

Why Are Goals Hard to Reach?

Assign the Preview Activity for homework the night before you show the video. Ask volunteers to read their paragraphs to the class if they feel comfortable sharing their personal experiences. Discuss examples of both successful and failed goal-setting experiences. Use the discussion to start a class list of Goal-Setting "Do's" and "Don'ts."

From the Authors

Have you ever noticed how most grocery stores are arranged? You walk in the front door, and you see the fresh fruits and vegetables arranged along one of the store's wall. The canned fruits and vegetables are somewhere in the center of the store. You move to a different wall where you might find the fresh bread. Packaged bread products could be on the opposite side of the store. Fresh meats can be found along another wall, while canned or frozen meats might be located in the center of the store. Finally, you move to the last wall where you find the dairy products.

What is the pattern? Foods that involve little or no processing are located against the walls, while foods that have been processed are located toward the center of the store. Here's a pearl of wisdom for your students: "Shop the walls for the healthiest foods."

1. Focus

Warm-Up Quick Quiz

Use the Warm-Up Presentation slide to survey student responses.

Allow students to answer the questions privately. Then discuss why students think that certain moods and situations are common eating triggers. Ask students to suggest alternatives to eating when a person experiences an eating trigger *(for example, doing a puzzle or other activity while watching television).*

Presentation 9-1

2. Teach

L3 **EL** **Reading/Note Taking 9-1**

L2 **Adapted Reading/Note Taking 9-1**

Why You Eat

L2 **Building Vocabulary**

Make sure students understand the relationship between metabolism and basal metabolic rate. Call on a student to recall the definition of metabolism from Chapter 8. *(the chemical processes by which the body breaks down food to produce energy and then uses the energy to perform body functions)* Explain that basal metabolic rate is the speed at which metabolism occurs when the body is at rest. Then ask: **Is your body ever completely at rest?** *(No; processes such as breathing, heartbeat, and digestion are ongoing.)* **Do these processes require energy?** *(Yes.)*

Section 1
Choosing Food Wisely

Objectives
▶ **Summarize** three main reasons why you eat.
▶ **Analyze** the information contained on food labels.

Vocabulary
- hunger
- appetite
- basal metabolic rate (BMR)
- Daily Values

Warm-Up

Quick Quiz How many of these statements are true for you?

1. I eat when I am bored.
2. I eat when I feel stressed.
3. I eat when I am out with friends.
4. I eat when I am watching television, listening to music, or just sitting around.
5. I eat when I feel sad or depressed.

WRITING Look over your responses. What did you learn about your eating patterns?

Why You Eat

If asked why you eat, you might say, "Because I get hungry." But, is this always true? **You eat for several reasons: to meet your nutritional needs, to satisfy your appetite, and to supply your body with energy.**

Hunger is a feeling of physical discomfort that is caused by your body's need for nutrients. By contrast, **appetite** is a desire for food that is based on emotions and other factors rather than nutritional need. Unlike hunger, which is an inborn response, appetite is learned. For example, your appetite may make you want to eat popcorn because you have learned to associate its aroma with a delicious taste. Your appetite can make you eat even when you are not hungry.

Basal Metabolic Rate One factor that affects your calorie needs is your basal metabolic rate. Your **basal metabolic rate (BMR)** is the rate at which you use energy when your body is at rest. The higher your BMR, the more calories you burn. Various factors affect BMR. Younger people tend to have a higher BMR than older ones. People who have more muscle mass tend to have a higher BMR than those with less muscle mass because muscle burns calories.

Your level of activity also affects your calorie needs. The more active you are, the more calories you need. Figure 1 compares the number of calories burned per hour for various activities.

For Your INFORMATION!

Basal Metabolic Rate (BMR)

Most of the calories that the body burns in a given day go to support basal metabolism: breathing, heartbeat, maintaining body temperature, and other processes that are ongoing even when a person is at rest. BMR is controlled by the hormone thyroxine, which is secreted by the thyroid gland. The more thyroxine, the higher the BMR.

Other factors that affect BMR include
- Age: BMR decreases with age.
- Body Composition: Tall, thin people and lean, muscular people have higher BMRs.
- Stress: Stress hormones can raise BMR.
- Activity: Physical activity can raise BMR for up to 48 hours after the activity.
- Dieting: Extreme dieting, fasting, and malnutrition can lower BMR.

The Foods You Choose Do you eat breakfast? What's your favorite snack? Your answers to questions like these depend on many factors.

▶ **Personal Preferences** Of course, you choose many of the foods you eat simply because they taste good. You might love the taste of peanut butter, for example, while your sister might not. You might dislike fish, or choose not to eat red meat. Whatever your personal preferences are, they have a huge impact on your food choices every day.

▶ **Cultural Background** Your cultural background, or heritage, may also influence your eating habits. For example, one family might eat a traditional Korean breakfast of soybean soup and rice. Another family might eat a typical Mexican meal of tortillas with beans and rice.

▶ **Time and Convenience** Do you sometimes eat on the run? A busy schedule might lead you to choose foods that can be prepared quickly or that can be easily carried in your backpack. Alternatively, you might choose to eat at a fast-food restaurant rather than prepare a meal at home.

▶ **Friends** When you eat a meal with friends, you may choose different foods than when you are by yourself or with your family. Friends might influence you to try new foods or to change your eating habits.

▶ **The Media** Every day, you are bombarded with information about food—in advertisements, news articles, diet books, and more. All of these messages can influence your decisions about what foods to eat or to avoid.

Connect to Your Life Think about a food choice you made today. What factors influenced that choice?

GO ONLINE
PearsonSuccessNet.com
For: More on appetite and eating

FIGURE 1 The number of calories you burn depends on how active you are. More intense exercise burns more calories than less intense exercise or sitting. **Calculating** In terms of calories burned, about how many hours of talking on the phone would it take to equal one hour of karate? **MATH**

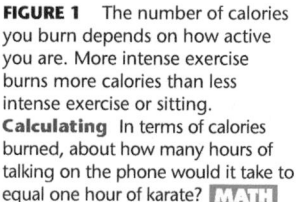

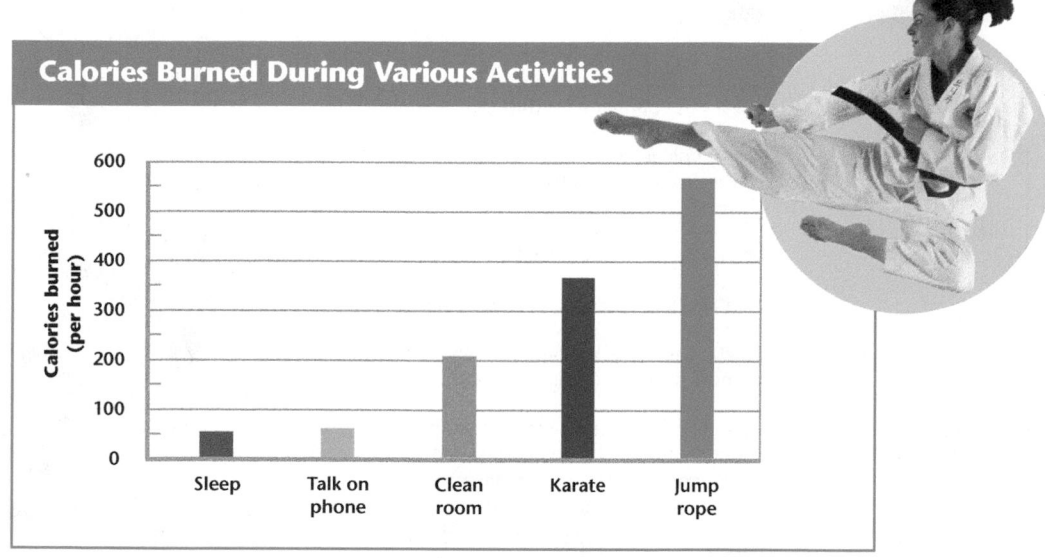
Calories Burned During Various Activities

Calories burned (per hour) — Sleep, Talk on phone, Clean room, Karate, Jump rope

Making Healthy Food Choices **221**

Differentiated Instruction

EL English Language Learners

Contrast the definitions of *hunger* and *appetite*. Point out that the definitions of the two words are similar but not identical because their causes are different. Help students understand the difference by asking: **Does hunger or appetite make you want dessert after a big meal?** *(appetite)* **If you've been sick and haven't eaten in a while, which causes you to eat even if no foods appeal to you?** *(hunger)*

L3 Building Health Skills

Analyzing Influences Have students write down each of the factors listed under the heading "The Foods You Choose." For each factor, students should note two or three ways in which that factor influences their food choices. For example, for "Time and Convenience," students might say that they grab a banana or a donut for breakfast as they rush to school. Ask for volunteers to share their responses with the class.

L1 Cultural Connection

Help students develop an appreciation for cultural diversity in food choices by suggesting that students of different cultures bring in foods to share with the class. Encourage them to talk about the cultural significance of the food. Refrain from making judgments about the nutritional value of the foods.

L2 Visual Learning: Figure 1

Image Bank Figure 9-1

Tell students that the data in the graph is for a person who weighs 125 pounds. The number of calories burned will be lower for a lighter person and higher for a heavier person. Have students use the number of calories burned during sleep to estimate the basal metabolic rate of a 125-pound person. (50 calories x 24 hours = 1,200 calories per day.) Point out that additional activity would increase the number of calories burned above the 1,200 basal level.
Caption Answer about 7 hours

Connect to Your Life *Sample answer:* I ate a hamburger with friends at a fast-food restaurant. Influencing factors: personal preferences, time and convenience, friends

Evaluating Food Choices

ⓛ Active Learning

Have students bring in clean, empty packages from a variety of foods. Ask them to identify the nutrition facts, any nutrient or health claims, Daily Values, and freshness dates. Ask if any students have used food labels to help them make food choices. If so, what information on the labels did they use? How did it help them make their choices?

ⓛ Visual Learning: Figure 2

Have students study the categories in the table. Ask them how the explanations differ from what they might have thought previously. For example, *Fat Free* and *Sugar Free* do not necessarily mean that foods contains no fat or sugar; they mean that the foods do not contain an appreciable amount of these nutrients in a serving.

Caption Answer Consuming foods that bear the claim "light" can help you manage your fat and calorie intake.

ⓛ Addressing Misconceptions

Nutrient and Health Claims Students may think all foods that carry nutrient or health claims are healthy choices. To dispel this misconception, ask: **Do you think the Caramel Popcorn shown in Figure 2 would be a healthy snack?** *(Not necessarily because it might be high in calories and sugar.)* Make sure students understand that nutrient and health claims do not provide a complete picture of the nutritional value of a food.

Evaluating Food Choices

Planning a sensible diet involves choosing nutritionally balanced meals and snacks. Your food choices may seem overwhelming, but tools are available to help you make good decisions. **When choosing foods, it is important to read and evaluate the information on the food label. The information includes nutrition facts, nutrient and health claims, Daily Values, and freshness dates.**

Food Labels The United States Food and Drug Administration (FDA) requires manufacturers to include food labels on most prepared foods, such as canned and frozen foods, breads, cereals, and drinks. Food labels must list specific nutrition facts about the food, including calorie and nutrient content, and the ingredients. The label is usually printed on the back or side of the package. You can practice reading food labels as you study the Building Health Skills on pages 224–225.

Nutrient and Health Claims Have you ever seen a label on a food that said "fat free"? Did you wonder what that claim meant? The FDA also sets standards regarding the nutrient claims that can be printed on a food label.

In addition, the FDA has approved the use of some health claims on food labels. Health claims are statements that link use of the food to certain health risks or benefits. Figure 2 explains some common nutrient and health claims you might see on food labels.

FIGURE 2 Claims about a food's nutrient or health benefits must follow standards set by the FDA. **Evaluating** How can foods that bear the claim "light" help you have a healthier diet?

Nutrient and Health Claims

What It Says	What It Means
…Free	*Fat Free:* Contains less than 0.5 g fat *Sugar Free:* Contains less than 0.5 g sugars
Low in…	*Low in Calories:* Contains less than 40 calories *Low in Sodium:* Contains less than 140 mg sodium
High in…	*High in Vitamin C:* One serving provides 20% or more of the Daily Value for vitamin C.
Light	Contains 50% less fat or at least $\frac{1}{3}$ fewer calories
Excellent source of…	*Excellent source of calcium:* One serving provides 20% or more of the Daily Value for calcium.
May reduce your risk of heart disease	Can appear on fiber-containing grain products, fruits, and vegetables that are also low in saturated fat and cholesterol.

WRITING and Health

ⓛ Advertisement

Provide students with two food labels from the same kind of food, for example two breakfast cereals. Ask them to compare the information on the food labels, including the percent Daily Values for the nutrients listed. Have them draw a conclusion about which food is the healthier choice. Then have students create an advertisement for that food, stressing why it is a healthy choice.

Daily Values How much protein do you eat each day? Do you eat too much saturated fat? To help you answer these questions, nutritionists have developed a tool called Daily Values. **Daily Values** are recommendations that specify the amounts of certain nutrients that the average person should obtain each day. Daily Values are only a general guide because they are calculated for the average person who consumes a total of 2,000 calories a day. Rapidly growing adolescents, for example, may need more nutrients than the Daily Values indicate. Other factors that affect nutrient needs include age, sex, heredity, and activity level.

When you buy a food, the food label lists the percent Daily Value for each nutrient in that food. For example, the food label on a package of crackers might indicate a percent Daily Value for iron of 12 percent. This means that one serving of the crackers provides 12 percent of the iron that the average person needs each day.

Open Dates The labels on prepared foods also include open dates. These dates give you an idea of how long the food will be fresh and safe to eat.

▶ The "sell-by" date tells you the last date the product can be sold. You can still use a product after the sell-by date.

▶ The "best-if-used-by" date tells you how long the product will be at peak quality.

▶ The "do-not-use-after" date is the expiration date. This is the last date you should consume the product.

FIGURE 3 This container of milk lists both a sell-by and a use-by date.

Section 1 Review

Key Ideas and Vocabulary

1. List three main reasons why people eat.

2. What is **hunger?** Distinguish hunger from **appetite.**

3. What is **basal metabolic rate?** How does your basal metabolic rate affect your calorie needs?

4. List three types of information included on a food label to help you evaluate the food.

5. What is meant by percent **Daily Value?** How are Daily Values useful as a guide to eating?

Critical Thinking

6. Evaluating How do time and convenience affect the food choices you make? Give two examples.

> ## Health and Community
>
> **Natural and Organic Foods** Some food manufacturers use the terms "natural foods" and "organically grown" to describe food products. Find out what these claims mean. In a paragraph, offer your opinion about whether these products are healthier than similar products that do not make those claims. **WRITING**

7. Predicting How do you think Daily Values for children would differ from Daily Values for the average person? How do you think Daily Values for professional athletes would differ from Daily Values for the average person? Explain.

Reading a Food Label

Objective

Evaluate the information contained on a food label.

Teaching Strategies

Image Bank Page 224

- As students look at the food label, point out the general structure—ingredients list, serving size information, calorie content, Daily Values, and any claims that might be listed.

- Go through the Nutrition Facts on this label line by line, noting both the absolute amounts of nutrients (in g or mg) and the percent Daily Values. Explain the distinction between the two measures.

- Discuss the ingredients list. Make certain that students understand the use of parentheses in the ingredients list—for example, wheat flour, niacin, iron, vitamins B1 and B2, and folic acid are the ingredients of which the enriched macaroni is composed. Also explain any unfamiliar terms on the list.

- Bring a variety of food labels to class so that students can compare them. Students will discover that, while the types of information are basically the same for all food products, the ingredients and nutritional value of individual foods can differ widely. This difference is especially noticeable for foods in the same general category, such as salad dressings or frozen dinners.

Reading a Food Label

Before you even enter a supermarket, advertisements in magazines, newspapers, and television try to convince you to buy certain foods.

To judge the nutritional value of a food, do not rely on advertisements or nice-looking packages. Instead, read the food label carefully. The FDA requires packaged foods to be labeled with nutrition information. For foods with more than one ingredient, the FDA also requires that ingredients be listed.

224

For Your INFORMATION!

Enriched Foods and Fortified Foods

The practices of enriching and of fortifying foods share a common goal—to improve the nutritional value of foods. However, the two practices differ in the reasons behind them. Foods are enriched to restore nutrients lost during food processing; thus, nutrients are added in amounts approximately equal to the amount naturally found in the food.

Foods are fortified to prevent specific nutrient deficiencies in a population. The nutrient added may not be present naturally in the food or may be present in a much smaller amount. Some commonly fortified foods include orange juice (fortified with calcium to prevent osteoporosis), salt (fortified with iodine to prevent goiter), and milk (fortified with vitamins A and D to prevent vitamin deficiencies).

❶ Read the ingredients list.

► Notice that ingredients are listed in order by weight, from most to least.

► Become familiar with terms for different kinds of ingredients. For example, words ending in *–ose* are often names of sugars.

► Check for food additives, such as artificial sweeteners (aspartame, sucralose) and preservatives (BHA, BHT, sulfites). Also check for other additives, such as food dyes.

► Note if the food is enriched (lost nutrients have been restored) or fortified (nutrients have been added).

► If you have dietary restrictions or allergies, look for those foods on the ingredients list.

❷ Note the number of servings per container.

Serving sizes are standardized for more than 100 different food categories. This allows you to compare similar food products by the number of servings they provide.

❸ Note the number of calories in one serving.

Keep in mind that daily calorie intake depends on a person's age, sex, weight, basal metabolic rate, and activity level.

❹ Look at the percentages of the Daily Values.

► Note the percentage Daily Values for nutrients that you should limit, such as saturated fat, cholesterol, and sodium. If a food is high in those nutrients, you may want to avoid it.

► Check the percentage Daily Values for fiber and valuable vitamins and minerals, such as iron and calcium.

Excellent source of calcium

❺ Look for any health or nutrient claims.

Because these claims are regulated by the FDA, they reveal useful information about the product.

Practice the Skill

1. Use the information on the macaroni and cheese label to answer these questions.
   a. What ingredients are contained in the cheese sauce part of the mix? Which of those ingredients is present in the largest amount?
   b. What percentage of the Daily Values for saturated fat does one serving contain? If you wanted to eat this macaroni and cheese as part of a balanced meal, should the other foods be high in fat? Explain.
   c. Do you think that this food would be a good choice for someone on a low-sodium diet? Why or why not?
   d. Is this food a good source of vitamin C?

2. Compare the food labels for several different breakfast cereals.
   a. How many different sugars are found in each cereal?
   b. Which cereal is highest in iron? What percentage of the Daily Value for iron does that cereal provide?
   c. Which cereal is the most nutritious overall? Explain your choice.

Making Healthy Food Choices **225**

Practice the Skill

1. a. whey, milk fat, milk protein concentrate, salt, calcium carbonate, sodium tripolyphosphate, citric acid, sodium phosphate, lactic acid, milk, yellow 5, yellow 6, enzymes, cheese culture; whey.
   b. 8% in the box and 20% prepared. The other foods should be low in saturated fat because a prepared serving already contains a lot of saturated fat.
   c. This would not be a good choice for someone on a low-sodium diet because one prepared serving contains nearly one third of the DV for sodium.
   d. No, this food has no vitamin C.

2. a. Sugars may include sucrose (listed as sugar), glucose (listed as honey), and high fructose corn syrup.
   b. Iron content varies, the average being from about 10 to about 25 percent of the DV in one serving.
   c. A nutritious cereal would be lower in fat, sodium, and sugars and higher in fiber, vitamins, and minerals.

Health at Home

 Food Label Survey

Have students survey food labels on products they have at home. Suggest that they pay particular attention to ingredients and percent Daily Values. Students can compare several labels of a particular food type, for example, soups. Or, they can select representative examples from various foods, such as soups, cereals, and frozen dinners. Encourage students to create charts to organize their findings.

Section 2

Safely Managing Your Weight

Objectives
Before class begins, write the objectives on the board. Have students copy the objectives into their notebooks at the start of class.

1. Focus

Warm-Up Health Stats

After students finish writing, call on a few volunteers to share their ideas about changes that could reverse the trend. Students might mention ideas such as increasing physical education requirements or tightening government regulations of advertisements and fast food offerings. Students' opinions will probably differ as to how successful such changes would be.

Presentation 9-2

 **Connect to Your Life** Many students probably have observed families in which family members tend to have similar body types and weights.

Sensitive Issues

• Many students will be sensitive about their body weight and body image. When discussing overweight and underweight, do not call on students with obvious weight issues or those who show signs of discomfort.

• Avoid implying that weight problems are more characteristic of one sex or group than another.

Section 2

Safely Managing Your Weight

Objectives

▶ **Examine** how heredity, activity level, and body composition influence a person's weight.

▶ **Calculate** your body mass index.

▶ **Identify** health problems associated with being overweight and underweight.

▶ **Summarize** strategies for losing or gaining weight.

Vocabulary

• body composition
• body mass index (BMI)
• overweight
• obesity
• underweight
• fad diet

Warm-Up

Health Stats What health trend do these statistics reveal?

> In 1965, 4.6 % of teens were overweight.

> 1980, 5.0 % of teens were overweight.

> Today, 18.4 % of teens are overweight.

WRITING What changes might help reverse this trend? How successful do you think the changes would be?

What Weight Is Right for You?

Cassie and her best friend, Ramona, are the same height. Although Cassie weighs 20 pounds more than Ramona, both girls have a weight that is appropriate for them. Ramona is small-boned, while Cassie has a larger bone structure. In addition, Cassie is more athletic than Ramona.

A person's weight is determined by various factors, including heredity, level of activity, and body composition. The weight that is right for you is the weight that does not present any health risks. A doctor or nutritionist can help you determine what weight is right for you.

Heredity You may have heard the expression, "it runs in the family." This expression means that certain traits are inherited and, therefore, appear regularly among family members. In the case of body weight, there is a link between body weight and heredity. This does not mean that you are "stuck with" a certain weight just because of your family history. It just means that you may have a natural tendency toward a certain weight.

Connect to Your Life What kinds of weight trends have you noticed in families you know?

TEENS *Are Asking . . .*

Q: My weight is normal for my height, but I don't like the way my body looks. Is there anything I can do to change the size of my body frame? I'd like to look more like the TV stars and models.

A: First, don't be misled by the images you see in magazines, TV, and movies—the images have been manipulated and touched up to make the stars look "perfect."

Also, understand that you can't change the overall size of your frame—your general body shape is inherited. But here are some tips for the things you *can* control.

• Exercise and eat right to maintain your weight.

• Engage in a variety of activities to give all areas of your body a workout.

• Appreciate your unique qualities.

Activity Level More important than family history in determining your weight is your activity level. The more active you are, the more calories you burn. If you are less active, you need fewer calories. Maintaining a healthy weight requires an energy balance. The number of calories consumed must equal the number of calories burned.

Tipping the energy balance can result in weight gain or weight loss. One pound of body weight is equivalent to 3,500 calories. If you take in 3,500 calories more than you burn, you gain a pound. You can gain a pound in two weeks by consuming only 250 extra calories a day. That's the number of calories in a small order of fast-food French fries.

Body Composition Another factor that affects weight is body composition. **Body composition** is a measure of how much body fat you have, as compared to muscle and bone. Remember Cassie and Ramona? Their body compositions were different—Cassie had more muscle mass than Ramona. One reason Cassie weighed more is that a given amount of muscle weighs more than an equal amount of fat. Strengthening exercises, such as lifting weights, can actually increase your weight as you build muscle.

Body composition is also affected by sex and age. Women tend to have more body fat and lower muscle mass than men. Body fat increases with age, while muscle mass decreases.

Body Mass Index

One simple way to assess whether your weight falls within a healthy range is to calculate your body mass index. **Body mass index (BMI)** is a ratio of your weight to your height. The following equation expresses this ratio.

$$BMI = \left(\frac{\text{Weight (in pounds)}}{[\text{Height (in inches)}]^2} \right) \times 703$$

Follow these steps to calculate your BMI.

1. Multiply your height (in inches) by your height (in inches).

2. Divide your weight (in pounds) by the number from Step 1.

3. Multiply the number from Step 2 by 703.

Although your BMI may be very different from your friend's, both of you may fall within a healthy range. You can use Figure 4 to assess your BMI. Notice that the BMI charts for teens take into account both age and sex. This is because teens are still growing. Also, males and females grow at different rates.

FIGURE 4 Your BMI is one way to assess whether your weight falls within a healthy range. **Calculating** Calculate your BMI, and compare it to the chart for your sex and age. `MATH`

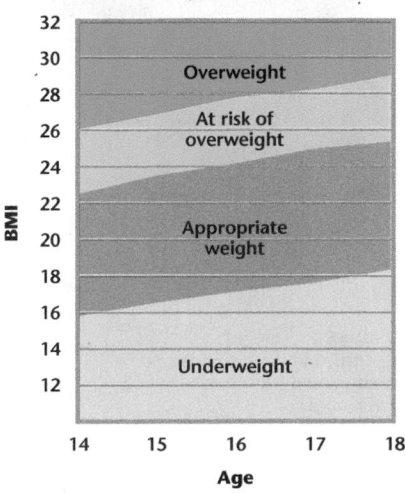

BMI Chart for Males

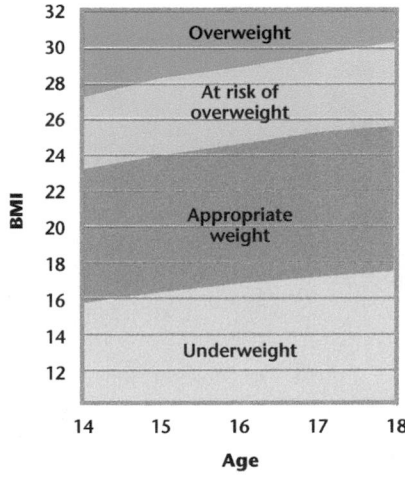

BMI Chart for Females

Making Healthy Food Choices **227**

2. Teach

L3 **EL** Reading/Note Taking 9-2

L2 Adapted Reading/Note Taking 9-2

What Weight Is Right for You?

L3 **Building Media Literacy**

Write this question on the board: **Are you satisfied with your weight?** Each student should write *yes* or *no* anonymously on a piece of paper. Collect the answers, tally them, and write the tally on the board. Discuss how media images, rather than true health concerns, may play the biggest role in teens' responses to this question. How much do ads, TV, and the movies shape their concept of the ideal body size?

L3 **Class Discussion**

Ask: **Of the three factors that influence weight, which do you think is most significant?** *(Students may think that heredity is the most important and simply can't be overcome.)* Point out that while heredity is important, eating a healthy diet and getting regular exercise can keep weight at a healthy level.

Body Mass Index

L2 **Visual Learning: Figure 4**

Image Bank Figure 9-4

Show students how to use the graphs for a hypothetical student, Joe, who is 15 and has a BMI of 24. Using the top graph, tell students to trace an imaginary line from 15 on the *x*-axis and from 24 on the *y*-axis. Ask: **Where do the two lines intersect?** *(in the green region marked "At risk for overweight")* `MATH`

Caption Answer Allow students to answer this question in their private journals.

`MATH` and Health

L2 **Calculating BMI**

Give students practice using the mathematical equation to calculate BMI with these questions. **Ramona is 16, weighs 100 pounds, and is 5 feet, 2 inches tall. What is her BMI?** *(100/3844 x 703 = 18.3)* **Cassie is 16, weighs 120 pounds, and is 5 feet, 2 inches tall. What is her BMI?** *(120/3844 x 703 = 21.9)* Then have students use the appropriate graph in Figure 4 to determine which range each girl falls in. *(Both girls fall in the "Appropriate weight" range.)*

Overweight and Obesity

L2 Addressing Misconceptions

Overweight Versus Obesity Make sure students understand the distinction between *overweight* and *obesity*. *Obesity* is not used to describe weight problems in children and teens, primarily because they are still growing. Instead, the categories "at risk of overweight" and "overweight" are used. However, the health problems associated with being at risk of overweight or overweight as a teen are just as significant as they are for an adult who is obese.

L3 Cultural Connection

Tell students that there is little obesity in China. One reason is that the Chinese consume about half as much fat as Americans do. Have students research other ways in which Chinese meals are different from traditional American meals.

L3 Cooperative Learning

In small groups, have students select one of the reasons why more calories are being consumed today—more prepared food choices, eating out, or portion size—and evaluate that influence. For example, students could visit a grocery store and collect calorie data on prepared foods for a particular category, such as chicken dinners. Students could research how often and where people eat out by conducting interviews. Or, students could visit restaurants and observe portion sizes for selected menu items. Students can then use guides to estimate the number of calories in the meals. Groups should prepare oral presentations to share their findings with the class.

EL Building Vocabulary

Offer everyday examples to help non-native speakers understand the meaning of colloquial phrases used in this section. For "prepared foods," give examples such as "takeout" or frozen dinners; for "leisure activities," mention "hanging out" with friends, listening to music, or playing video games.

A value meal is not a bargain if you cannot afford the extra calories.

FIGURE 5 One reason for the increase in calorie consumption is that portion sizes have increased dramatically.

Overweight and Obesity

Look back at Figure 4, and notice the label "overweight." **The number of people in the United States who are overweight is increasing. Being overweight can lead to serious health problems, including heart disease and diabetes.**

A Growing Problem From the 1960s until today, the percentage of overweight teens has quadrupled. **Overweight** is a term used to describe a person who is heavier than the standard for the person's height. You may have heard the term *obesity* used interchangeably with *overweight*. This is not accurate. **Obesity** (oh BEE sih tee) refers specifically to adults who have a BMI of 30 or higher.

More people are overweight today because calorie consumption has increased at the same time that calorie use has decreased. More calories are being consumed by people today because

▶ grocery stores offer more food choices, including many prepared foods

▶ more meals are eaten outside the home

▶ portion sizes have increased

Recall that calorie use is related to activity level. People today burn fewer calories because they

▶ are less active at school, work, and in their leisure activities

▶ rely more on technological devices, such as cars and computers

Health Risks Overweight people tend to develop several conditions that can lead to health problems. Two conditions are high blood pressure and excess cholesterol in the blood. A third condition, excess glucose in the blood, is associated with type 2 diabetes. Type 2 diabetes is a disease in which the body does not properly use insulin, a substance that controls blood glucose levels. Other health problems associated with being overweight include heart disease, stroke, and certain cancers.

228 *Chapter 9*

For Your INFORMATION!

Metabolic Syndrome

Being overweight or obese puts people at risk for a condition known as metabolic syndrome. One indicator of metabolic syndrome is abdominal obesity (excessive fat tissue around the abdomen). Others include high blood pressure, low HDL levels, high triglyceride levels, and high levels of glucose in the blood.

People with metabolic syndrome are at increased risk for heart disease and type 2 diabetes. It's estimated that more than 50 million Americans have this syndrome, and it is becoming increasingly common in children and teens. About 12 percent of children in the United States are estimated to exhibit metabolic syndrome.

What You Can Do Prevention is the key to avoiding the health problems associated with being overweight. It is easier to prevent weight gain than it is to take off excess pounds. Healthy eating and regular exercise can help you avoid becoming overweight in the first place.

If you are overweight, don't be discouraged. You are still growing, and your BMI may decrease as your height increases. Remember also that changing your habits can be easier when you are in your teens than when you are older. Setting goals to improve your diet, reducing portion sizes, and increasing your activity level can help you lose weight.

Underweight

The BMI charts in Figure 4 also identify people who are "underweight." **Underweight** is a term used to describe a person who is lighter than the standard for the person's height. Remember that some people are naturally thinner than others. In addition, some teens are very thin as they are growing. Eventually, as their growth rate slows, they start to put on weight.

Health Risks Thinness in itself is not a health problem unless it is excessive. However, underweight people should be checked by a doctor. **Being underweight can be linked to health problems, such as anemia, heart irregularities, and trouble regulating body temperature.**

What You Can Do First of all, be patient. As you mature, there probably will come a time when your weight will start to increase. Remember, too, that healthy eating and exercise are as important for putting on weight as they are for taking off weight.

Connect to Your Life List five things you did this week to help manage your weight.

GO ONLINE
PearsonSuccessNet.com
For: More on food and diet

FIGURE 6 No matter if you are underweight, overweight, or at an appropriate weight, exercise is important for staying fit and healthy.

229

L3 Content Update  **GO ONLINE**

Visit Pearson SuccessNet to access more information about food and diet. Have students complete the Web activity.

L3 Building Health Skills

Setting Goals Borrow a class set of pedometers from the physical education department. Students should wear the pedometer on a normal weekday (from morning until night) to determine how active they are on a typical day. Then, have students come up with a plan to increase their activity level over the next week. For example, students can plan to walk to school instead of ride. Have students use the pedometer to track their progress over the week.

Underweight

L2 Class Disscussion

Remind students that different factors influence a person's weight. Ask: **What factors can cause a person to be underweight?** (*Factors include heredity, activity level versus calorie intake, and body composition.*) Point out that being underweight is also influenced by other emotional and behavioral factors—for example, the behaviors associated with an eating disorder such as anorexia. Eating disorders are discussed in Chapter 4.

L4 Cultural Connection

Point out that people's concept of ideal weight and body shape differ from society to society, and even change in the same society as time passes. For example, advertisements from the Victorian period pictured women who were heavier than today's female models. Interested students can do research to identify factors that contribute to a society's definition of beauty. Cultures in which food is scarce, for example, tend to idealize plumpness rather than slenderness.

Connect to Your Life Allow students to answer this question in their private journals.

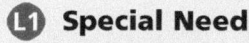
Differentiated Instruction

L1 Special Needs

Help students understand the significance of portion size. Bring in two French fry wrappers or two soft drink cups from a fast-food restaurant. Show students each container, and ask them to guess the number of calories contained in each food item.

Students might be surprised to learn that an extra-large serving of fries may contain two or three times the number of calories in a small or regular serving or that a large soft drink contains more than twice the calories of a small one.

Healthy Weight Management

Media Wise

Evaluating Diet Plans

Many diet plans promise fast weight loss with little or no effort. Ask students whether they think this expectation is reasonable and why. Make sure students understand that few diets live up to their claims.

Activity Make a class list of diet plans that are currently popular. Then assign the plans to different students to investigate. In addition to the questions in the checklist, ask students to consider the following about the diet: Is there any research to support the claims made about the diet? Can people eat ordinary food on the diet, or must they buy special foods? Are there any statistics on long-term effects?

L2 Active Learning

Collect a variety of diet ads from magazines with specific target audiences—teens, athletes, women, etc. Give each student one ad to analyze. Students should answer these questions.

- Is the ad for a fad diet, a diet aid, or another type of weight-loss plan?
- What claims does the ad make?
- What concerns do you have about the diet?
- Does it sound too good to be true?
- Would you recommend it to a loved one? Why or why not?

Media Wise

Evaluating Diet Plans

New diets seem to be everywhere—in magazines, on the Internet, in TV infomercials, and in best-selling books. Do these diets live up to their claims? Are they good for your health? Use this checklist to evaluate a diet.

Does the diet provide fewer than 1,200 calories a day?	Yes	No
Does the diet cut out fats, carbohydrates, or proteins?	Yes	No
Does the diet promise rapid weight loss in a short amount of time (more than 1 or 2 pounds per week)?	Yes	No
Does the diet ignore the need for long-term changes in eating habits?	Yes	No
Does the diet ignore the need for regular exercise?	Yes	No

"Yes" answers to one or more questions may indicate a diet that is unlikely to work. What's worse, the diet could harm your health in the long term.

Activity Choose a diet plan that you have seen advertised or have read about. Use the checklist to evaluate the diet. Then write a paragraph evaluating the diet plan. **WRITING**

Healthy Weight Management

There is no magic method for keeping your weight within a healthy range. Whatever your weight is, weight management should be part of your daily habits. **Sensible weight management involves avoiding dangerous diet plans, choosing nutritionally balanced meals and snacks, and getting regular exercise.**

Dangerous Diet Plans Most people who want to lose or gain weight want to do so very quickly. They may rely on strategies that promise quick results in a short period of time. Many of these approaches are unrealistic and can be unsafe.

▶ **Fad Diets** A **fad diet** is a popular diet that may help a person lose or gain weight but without proper regard for nutrition and other health issues. One example of a fad diet is a "high-protein, low-carbohydrate diet." Another example is a diet that includes a specific product that is supposed to burn fat.

Because fad diets often exclude important nutrients, they can put a dieter's health at risk. In addition, the weight loss achieved with a fad diet is usually temporary. Because fad diets often severely restrict food choices, people become bored with the diet's limitations. As a result, they stop dieting and return to their original eating habits.

Focus on ISSUES

L3 Debate: Is Obesity a Problem for Individuals or for Society?

Divide the class into two groups. One group should include students who feel that obesity is a personal issue that is best left to individuals to either confront or ignore. The other group should include students who think the government must take the lead in trying to control obesity in this country. Each group should prepare a position paper to support its viewpoint. The groups should select two representatives to debate the issue in front of the class. **WRITING**

▶ **Diet Aids** Diet aids include pills and candies that are supposed to suppress appetite. These diet aids are usually not effective, especially for long-term weight control. Also, diet aids can be habit-forming and cause unwanted side effects. For example, the main ingredient in many diet pills is caffeine, which may cause nervousness, sleeplessness, and high blood pressure.

▶ **Fasting** Some people fast, or refrain from eating, as a way to lose weight. Fasting for more than a brief period can lead to health problems. The body begins to break down muscle tissue to obtain the nutrients it needs. Long-term fasting may stunt your growth, put a strain on your kidneys, and cause hair loss. Fasting has also been linked with irregular menstrual periods in girls and women.

Sensible Weight Loss Losing weight sensibly and safely requires thought, planning, and patience.

▶ **Recognize Eating Patterns** Before you start a weight-loss program, keep a diary of your current eating habits. Record the foods that you eat and when you eat them. Also record any thoughts or feelings you have just before eating. As you review your diary, you may discover eating patterns you were not aware of. You may even identify triggers for overeating, such as boredom or stress.

▶ **Plan Helpful Strategies** Do not try to lose weight too fast. Remember that it took awhile to put on the weight. Change your eating habits gradually—your weight-loss program will be more successful in the long run. Figure 7 suggests some strategies to help you eat sensibly while losing weight.

▶ **Exercise** Your weight-loss program will be far more effective if you exercise. If you decrease your calorie intake but do not exercise, your basal metabolic rate goes down. As a result, your body will not burn calories as efficiently as it did before. Weight loss may slow down or stop even though you are still consuming fewer calories.

What emotions and behaviors trigger your desire to eat?

> **Weight-Loss Strategies**
> • Eat smaller portions.
> • Eat your food slowly to enjoy its taste.
> • Try not to eat while watching TV or reading.
> • Take a walk instead of eating when you are bored.
> • If you overeat occasionally, do not become upset. Just return to your sensible eating habits.

FIGURE 7 A successful weight-loss program combines sensible eating with regular exercise. Exercise helps your body burn calories more efficiently.

Making Healthy Food Choices **231**

L2 Addressing Misconceptions

Healthy Weight Loss Make sure students understand that there are no shortcuts to permanent weight loss. The only sure way for a person to lose weight is to eat nutritionally balanced, low-calorie meals and snacks and thereby consume fewer calories than the body uses. To maintain weight loss, healthy eating and exercise must become lifelong habits.

L3 Journal Writing

Ask students to keep a diet journal for one week. They should write down everything they eat, when they eat, whom they eat with, and how they feel when they eat. After the week, ask students to look over their journal entries to find out whether they sometimes eat for reasons other than being hungry. Were there times of day or night during which they were particularly prone to unnecessary eating? What other patterns can they uncover? **WRITING**

L1 Active Learning

Have students choose a physical activity they enjoy and create a poster to promote it. The poster should highlight both why the activity is enjoyable as well as why it is good for one's health. Display the posters around the classroom.

Connect to Your Life Allow students to answer this question in their private journals.

Differentiated Instruction

EL English Language Learners

The term *fad* may be unfamiliar to some students. Tell students that the word can apply to many categories other than diets. Offer examples of fashions or other fads from the recent past that are no longer popular with your students today. Then ask: **What are some other examples of fads?** *(Students might mention specific hairstyles, music, dances, or activities.)* Through the examples, make sure students understand the fleeting, or short-lived, nature of fads.

Visual Learning: Figure 8

Caption Answer Some other nutrient-dense snacks are peanut butter on celery or bean dip with tortillas.

3. Assess

Evaluate

These assignments can help you assess students' mastery of the section content.

Section 2 Review

Answers appear below.

Teaching Resources
- Practice 9-2
- Section 9-2 Quiz

 Reteach

Have students write e-mails to two hypothetical friends—one to an overweight friend offering advice on how to lose weight sensibly, and the other to an underweight friend on how to gain weight. **WRITING**

 Enrich

Teaching Resources
- Enrich 9-2

Health at Home

Lunch-Time Options Suggestions can include fruit with cottage cheese, bulgur wheat salad, bean taco, hot and sour soup, and cucumbers and mint mixed with yogurt. Students can cut out photos from cooking magazines or print photos from cooking sites on the Internet.

Frozen yogurt

Cheddar cheese on crackers

Trail mix

FIGURE 8 If you are trying to gain weight, snack on nutrient-dense foods such as the ones shown here. **Applying Concepts** List some other healthy nutrient-dense snacks.

Sensible Weight Gain A sensible plan for gaining weight is not unlike that for losing weight. The difference is that you need to *increase* your calorie intake while making sure to eat a balanced diet and to exercise. Here are some tips for changing habits that may be preventing you from gaining weight.

▶ Avoid snacks right before mealtimes because they could spoil your appetite.

▶ When you do snack, choose nutrient-dense foods that are high in calories. Figure 8 shows some good snack choices.

▶ Don't increase your fat intake over what is recommended in the MyPlate plan. Doing so can lead to other health problems.

▶ Try not to skip meals.

▶ At mealtimes, take bigger helpings of food than usual.

▶ While you are increasing your caloric intake, do not neglect exercise. Exercising will help you maintain fitness and gain healthy muscle mass.

Section 2 Review

Key Ideas and Vocabulary

1. Briefly describe how heredity, activity level, and body composition can affect a person's weight.

2. What is the formula for calculating body mass index? What does it mean for someone to have a healthy body mass index?

3. What are two diseases associated with being overweight? What health risks are associated with being underweight?

4. What is a **fad diet**? Describe two problems associated with fad diets.

5. Why is exercise an important part of a weight-loss program? Why is exercise also important for gaining weight?

Health at Home

Lunch-Time Options List some healthy lunch-time foods and snacks that students who are trying to lose weight can bring to school from home. Be creative—include some nontraditional foods on your list. Then design a poster that illustrates your suggestions.

Critical Thinking

6. **Applying Concepts** Many people have an unrealistic expectation of what their appropriate weight should be. What factors might contribute to their misconception?

7. **Evaluating** Being overweight is more common in the United States than in many other countries. Why do you think this is the case?

GO ONLINE PearsonSuccessNet.com   Audio Summary Section 9.2

Section 2 Review

1. You may inherit a tendency toward a certain weight. Activity level affects the number of calories you burn. Changing fat to muscle can increase your weight.

2. BMI = Weight/Height² × 703. It means that your weight is appropriate for your height.

3. overweight: type 2 diabetes, heart disease, stroke, certain cancers; underweight: anemia, heart irregularities, trouble regulating body temperature

4. Fad diets may help a person lose or gain weight but without regard for health and nutrition; excludes nutrients, weight loss is temporary, boredom with food choices

5. For weight loss: exercise burns calories; for weight gain: exercise builds muscles.

6. peer pressure, advertising, comparing yourself to movie stars or other popular role models

7. Americans have more unhealthy food choices, eat larger portions, and tend to be less active than people in other countries.

Nutrition for Individual Needs

Warm-Up

Dear Advice Line,

I've recently become a vegetarian, and it has my parents worried. They think I'm not getting enough nutrients, and they keep telling me that I have to eat meat to be healthy. How can I explain to them that a vegetarian diet can be healthy?

WRITING Write a response to this teen to help solve the problem.

Diets for Diabetics

People's circumstances may call for special diets. **Diabetes is a disease with dietary requirements that can help people manage their condition.**

Recall that one of the risks of being overweight is type 2 diabetes, a condition in which the blood contains high levels of glucose. Type 2 diabetes was once thought of as an adult disease. However, it is becoming more common in adolescents because of poor nutritional habits, such as eating too much sugar and fat.

Diabetes can be a life-threatening condition, so it is important for people to keep their diabetes under control. In addition to other treatments, diabetics can help control their disease by making changes in their diets. Here are some eating tips for diabetics.

▶ Eat balanced meals and snacks on a regular schedule.

▶ Keep track of your carbohydrate intake. You can replace some carbohydrates with foods that are high in unsaturated fats, such as peanut butter and almonds. If you have a sugary treat, avoid other carbohydrates that day.

▶ Control your weight. In addition to dietary changes, be sure to get regular exercise.

Connect to Your Life — How could you help a diabetic friend make the necessary changes in his or her diet?

Nutrition for Individual Needs

Objectives

▶ **Examine** how diabetics, vegetarians, people with food sensitivities, and athletes can meet their nutritional needs.

Vocabulary

- vegetarian
- vegan
- food allergy
- food intolerance
- carbohydrate loading

Objectives

Before class begins, write the objectives on the board. Have students copy the objectives into their notebooks at the start of class.

1. Focus

Warm-Up Advice Line

After students finish writing, call on a few volunteers to share their responses with the class. Students can check the accuracy of their advice against the information on page 234.

Presentation 9-3

2. Teach

L3 EL **Reading/Note Taking** 9-3

L2 **Adapted Reading/Note Taking** 9-3

Diets for Diabetics

L3 **Class Discussion**

Refer students to the graph on page 615 so they understand that diabetes, especially type 2, is a growing problem in this country. Review the relationship between being overweight and diabetes.

Connect to Your Life — *Sample answer:* I could help my friend research healthy foods for diabetics and I could exercise with my friend.

Differentiated Instruction

L4 Gifted and Talented

Many long-term diabetics develop vision problems. Have students research these visions problems and why they develop in diabetics. Encourage them to investigate current treatments. Ask students to share their findings with the class.

L2 Less Proficient Readers

Have students make a concept map for type 2 diabetes. They should include a definition of the condition, symptoms, and dietary requirements.

Sensitive Issues

Diabetic students may be uncomfortable discussing their condition. Do not request that they discuss their diet or any other aspects of their disease.

Vegetarian Diets

L3 Online Activity GO ONLINE

Visit Pearson SuccessNet to access an online activity about meals for individual needs. Have students complete the Web activity.

L3 Cooperative Learning

Have groups of students develop a menu of vegetarian meals and snacks for one day. The meal plan should provide complete protein combinations, adequate vitamins and minerals, and a good balance of protein, fats and carbohydrates. Encourage students to look in vegetarian cookbooks for ideas. Advise them that many vegetarian recipes include a significant amount of cheese and other dairy products that are high in fat, and that they should take this into consideration when planning their meals.

L2 Cultural Connection

Bring in a variety of restaurant menus or cookbooks from other cultures, including Indian, Mexican, Middle Eastern, Japanese, and Greek. Have students look through the menus or cookbooks to identify vegetarian meals that are complete protein combinations. Interested students can add the foods to the ones listed in Figure 9.

L1 Active Learning

Show students the weekly lunch menu from the school cafeteria. Ask students to select a healthy vegetarian lunch for each day of the week.

GO ONLINE

PearsonSuccessNet.com

For: More on meals for individual needs

Vegetarian Diets

A person who does not eat meat is called a **vegetarian.** Some vegetarians, called **vegans,** eat no food from any animal source. Other vegetarians, however, include eggs and dairy products in their diets. **Because vegetarians exclude certain foods from their diets, they need to plan their food choices carefully to avoid potential health risks.**

Benefits of a Vegetarian Diet   More people are turning to vegetarian diets because of the health benefits. Vegetarians tend to have a lower BMI than other people. In addition, vegetarians may have a lower risk of heart disease, which can result from eating too much animal fat. Vegetarians also tend to have lower blood pressure and a lower risk of type 2 diabetes.

Risks of a Vegetarian Diet   As you learned in Chapter 8, animal products such as milk, eggs, and meat are complete proteins because they contain all the essential amino acids. Plant products, however, are incomplete proteins. Vegetarians who eat no food from animal sources must make sure that their diets contain all the essential amino acids. Vegetarians must also make sure to obtain adequate supplies of vitamins and minerals.

There are some risks associated with a vegetarian diet.

▶ A vegetarian diet may not have sufficient vitamin B12, which is found primarily in animal products. Lack of vitamin B12 can result in nerve damage.

▶ Vegetarians may not consume adequate calcium, which can lead to bone loss.

▶ Vegetarians may experience a protein deficiency, which can result in hair and muscle loss.

Vegetarians can reduce their risk of health problems by eating a varied diet. Foods should be rich in vitamins and minerals or have those nutrients added. When eaten daily, foods such as brown rice, beans, corn, nuts, seeds, and whole grains help ensure that a vegetarian gets all the essential amino acids. Tofu and dark, green leafy vegetables are good sources of calcium for vegetarians.

FIGURE 9   Protein combinations such as tofu with pasta or rice are good choices for vegetarian meals. Vegetarians who eat foods from animal sources can also get protein from milk products and eggs.

Some Complete Protein Combinations
• Peanut butter on a whole-wheat bagel
• Refried beans on a corn tortilla
• Split pea soup with rice cakes

TEENS *Are Asking . . .*

Q: I want to become a vegetarian, but where do I start?

A: You will want to maintain a healthy diet, so here are some tips.

• First, talk to a doctor or nutritionist. Ask for help planning meals to make sure you will get the nutrients you need.

• Soy is a good substitute for meat. It has a lot of protein. Read food labels to determine if an item has soy in it. Tofu, which is made from soy, can be used in lots of recipes.

• Make sure you get enough vitamins and minerals, especially vitamin B12, calcium, and iron. Find out if your doctor recommends a vitamin or mineral supplement.

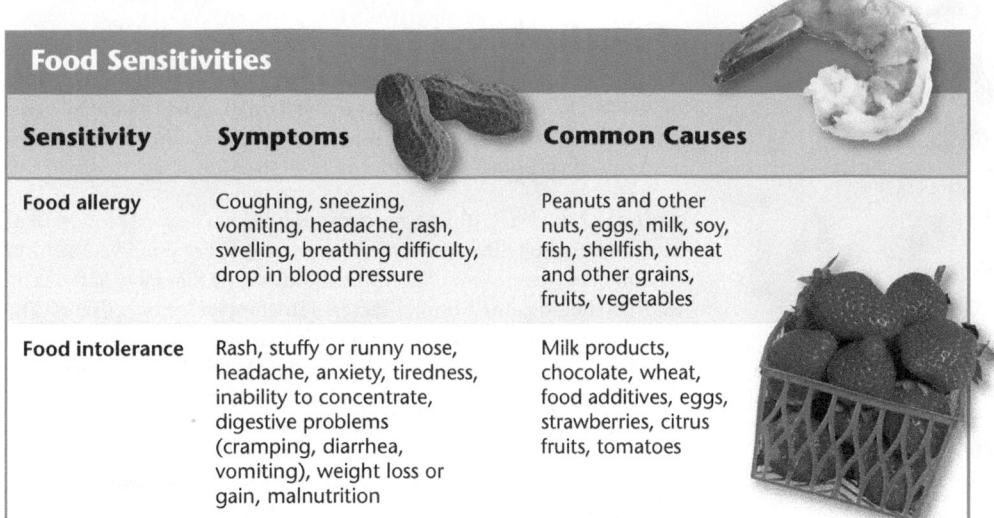

Food Sensitivities

Sensitivity	Symptoms	Common Causes
Food allergy	Coughing, sneezing, vomiting, headache, rash, swelling, breathing difficulty, drop in blood pressure	Peanuts and other nuts, eggs, milk, soy, fish, shellfish, wheat and other grains, fruits, vegetables
Food intolerance	Rash, stuffy or runny nose, headache, anxiety, tiredness, inability to concentrate, digestive problems (cramping, diarrhea, vomiting), weight loss or gain, malnutrition	Milk products, chocolate, wheat, food additives, eggs, strawberries, citrus fruits, tomatoes

Food Sensitivities

Do you know people who itch after eating strawberries or get a stomach ache from ice cream? Reactions like these may be due to food sensitivities. **People with food sensitivities, which include food allergies and food intolerances, may require special diets.**

Food Allergies A **food allergy** is a response by your immune system to the proteins in certain foods. Some common foods associated with food allergies are listed in Figure 10. An allergic reaction is usually fast and intense. In severe cases, the tongue swells, breathing becomes difficult, and blood pressure drops. This type of reaction requires emergency treatment.

Food labels sometimes contain statements, such as "may contain traces of peanuts." If you are allergic to peanuts, be careful to avoid such foods. Fortunately, food allergies are rare. In children, the frequency ranges from 6 to 8 percent. In adults, it is about 4 percent.

Food Intolerances Food intolerances are more common than food allergies. A **food intolerance** is an inability to digest a particular food or food additive. Symptoms of food intolerance may be slower to appear and harder to recognize than those of a food allergy. Figure 10 lists symptoms and foods associated with food intolerance.

Figuring out which food is causing a food intolerance reaction can take months. The person must eliminate foods from the diet one at a time until symptoms disappear.

 **Connect to Your Life** What are some ways you could help a family member deal with a food intolerance?

FIGURE 10 Food allergies are quick responses by the immune system to certain foods. Allergic reactions may require medical treatment. Food intolerances may not be as serious, but can make a person ill.
Reading Tables Which foods can cause both food allergies and food intolerances?

Food Sensitivities

EL Visual Learning: Figure 10

Clarify the difference between the two types of food sensitivities. Explain that both food allergies and food intolerances may require medical intervention and treatment. However, allergic reactions to foods are especially dangerous because the body recognizes the food as a foreign protein, or allergen. This may cause a reaction known as anaphylactic shock, which can lead to breathing failure.
Caption Answer milk, eggs, wheat, certain fruits, vegetables (tomatoes)

L3 Addressing Misconceptions

Food Sensitivities The line between food allergies and food intolerances is not always clear. In addition, the symptoms of food sensitivities often mimic symptoms of other ailments. Migraines, digestive upsets, upper respiratory symptoms, and anxiety can also be symptoms of other, unrelated illnesses. If a food sensitivity is suspected, keeping a diet journal can help to isolate the cause of symptoms.

L2 Active Learning

Provide students with food labels. Have them use the list in Figure 10 to identify possible sources of food allergies or intolerances listed on the labels. Advise students that grains can include corn or anything made with corn (corn syrup) as well as wheat. Fructose, a monosaccharide contained in fruit, is also a common ingredient in processed foods that may not contain any fruit per se. Have students make lists of all the different sources of food sensitivities they find on the labels.

 Connect to Your Life *Sample answer:* Help them keep track of foods that appear to cause symptoms; discourage them from eating foods that are known to be a problem; don't tempt them with problem foods.

Differentiated Instruction

L4 Gifted and Talented

Have students interview the school dietitian or food service manager. They should find out if the school cafeteria offers meals geared toward people who must follow special diets. Suggest that students create a brochure listing all the items that are available for special diets. Have them present their findings to the class.

Healthy Diets for Athletes

L3 Building Media Literacy

Have students do Internet research on carbohydrate loading. They should look at several sites and determine if the sites are research-based, based on personal anecdotes, or selling a product. Which sites do students consider trustworthy?

3. Assess

Evaluate

These assignments can help you assess students' mastery of the section content.

Section 3 Review

Answers appear below.

Teaching Resources
- Practice 9-3
- Section 9-3 Quiz

L2 Reteach

Help students create a chart listing the special dietary requirements for each of the conditions or lifestyle choices discussed in this section.

L4 Enrich

Teaching Resources
- Enrich 9-3

Health at School

Vending Machine Snacks Nuts, dried fruit, plain popcorn, and pretzels are good choices. A diabetic must monitor carbohydrates, so nuts or fruits might be the best choice. A vegetarian could choose any item. An athlete might prefer nuts for their calories.

Section 3 Review

1. They should eat balanced meals and substitute other foods, such as peanut butter, for carbohydrates.
2. Vary your diet and combine foods to get complete proteins.
3. Your body's response to a particular food could be life-threatening.
4. Consume extra calories, take in plenty of fluids during competition, and eat a well-balanced diet.

Healthy Diets for Athletes

A lot of conflicting information has been written about the dietary needs of athletes. **However, nutritionists in the field of sports medicine agree on one thing: athletes need a well-balanced diet with the recommended amounts of carbohydrates, fats, and proteins.**

Calorie Intake Athletes need to consume extra calories to fuel their higher level of physical activity. Where these calories should come from is a subject of controversy. Many nutritionists state that most of the extra calories should come from an increase in complex carbohydrates. The extra calories should not come from high-fat foods, otherwise athletes risk developing the health problems associated with them. However, athletes should not restrict fat intake to less than that recommended in the MyPlate plan.

Fluid Intake During competition, athletes should drink plenty of fluids, preferably water, to replace the fluid lost in perspiration. Just how much water athletes need depends on the duration and intensity of the competition. It also depends on weather factors, such as how hot and humid it is. Excessive heat and humidity require higher fluid intake.

Carbohydrate Loading You may have heard about endurance athletes, such as runners, loading up on carbohydrates before a long race. **Carbohydrate loading** is the practice of greatly increasing carbohydrate intake and decreasing exercise on the days immediately before a competition. By doing this, athletes hope to make extra energy available to the muscles during the competition. For marathon runners or other endurance athletes, carbohydrate loading may help supply needed energy. For the average athlete, however, it probably is unnecessary.

FIGURE 11 Athletes need a balanced diet with larger portions of food for additional calories.

Section 3 Review

Key Ideas and Vocabulary

1. How can diabetics control the amount of carbohydrates in their diets?
2. What recommendation would you make to a vegetarian about his or her diet?
3. Why is it important to identify any food sensitivities that you may have?
4. List three diet-related recommendations that athletes should follow.
5. What is **carbohydrate loading?** What do athletes hope to gain from this practice?

Health at School

Vending Machine Snacks Suppose you were choosing snacks to be included in a vending machine at school. What would be some good choices for diabetics? Vegetarians? Student athletes? List your choices and note the reason for each choice. **WRITING**

Critical Thinking

6. **Comparing and Contrasting** How do food allergies differ from food intolerances? Why might it be difficult to distinguish the two?
7. **Evaluating** Suppose an athlete decides to limit his caloric intake to keep his weight down. How could you convince him of the dangers of his decision?

 GO ONLINE PearsonSuccessNet.com   Audio Summary Section 9.3

---

5. The practice of greatly increasing carbohydrate intake and decreasing exercise on the days before a competition; they hope to make extra energy available to fuel the muscles during the competition.
6. Food allergies are a response of the immune system. They are faster and more intense than food intolerances, which are the inability to digest a particular food. Symptoms and the foods that cause them are sometimes similar.
7. Without enough calories, the athlete would not have enough energy to perform well. Also, health problems could result from too much weight loss.

Chapter 9
At a Glance

 **TEENS** Talk
VIDEO
Goals for Healthy Eating List three things you learned about goal-setting from this video.

Chapter 9
At a Glance

VIDEO
Goals for Healthy Eating Ask for volunteers to share their answers. Use examples from the video to review how to set goals for healthy eating.

Section 1   Choosing Food Wisely

Key Ideas

▶ You eat for several reasons: to meet your nutritional needs, to satisfy your appetite, and to supply your body with energy.

▶ When choosing foods, it is important to read and evaluate the information on the food label. The information includes nutrition facts, nutrient and health claims, Daily Values, and freshness dates.

Vocabulary
- hunger (220)
- appetite (220)
- basal metabolic rate (220)
- Daily Values (223)

Section 2   Safely Managing Your Weight

Key Ideas

▶ A person's weight is determined by heredity, level of activity, and body composition.

▶ One simple way to assess whether your weight falls within a healthy range is to calculate your body mass index.

▶ Being overweight can lead to serious health problems, including heart disease and diabetes.

▶ Being underweight can been linked to anemia, heart irregularities, and trouble regulating body temperature.

▶ Sensible weight management involves avoiding dangerous diet plans, choosing nutritionally balanced meals and snacks, and getting regular exercise.

Vocabulary
- body composition (227)
- body mass index (227)
- overweight (228)
- obesity (228)
- underweight (229)
- fad diet (230)

Section 3   Nutrition for Individual Needs

Key Ideas

▶ Diabetes is a disease with dietary requirements that can help people manage their condition.

▶ Because vegetarians exclude certain foods from their diets, they need to plan their food choices carefully to avoid potential health risks.

▶ People with food sensitivities, which include food allergies and food intolerances, may require special diets.

▶ Athletes need a well-balanced diet with the recommended amounts of carbohydrates, fats, and proteins.

Vocabulary
- vegetarian (234)
- vegan (234)
- food allergy (235)
- food intolerance (235)
- carbohydrate loading (236)

Key Ideas Review

L2 Have students write five multiple choice questions and use them to quiz each other. Prompt students to review the content in the text for any question they cannot answer.

L3 Have students write each objective on one side of an index card. On the other side, have them list some facts from the chapter that address the important points of the objective.

Vocabulary Review

L1 Have students make flash cards with vocabulary terms on one side and definitions on the other. Have them use the cards to quiz each other.

L2 Have students write a fill-in-the-blank question for each vocabulary word. Have them switch papers with a partner and try to fill in the blanks.

EL Tell students to use each vocabulary word in a complete sentence.

Chapter 9 Review

Reviewing Key Ideas

Section 1

1. b   2. c

3. Muscle burns calories, so the more muscle, the higher the BMR.

4. BMR declines as a person ages.

5. You tend to eat what your family eats, which is influenced by your cultural background, or heritage.

6. A friend can influence your desire for food (your appetite) by serving foods you find particularly tempting and encouraging you to eat them.

7. Reading food labels allows you to compare ingredients, nutrients, Daily Values, and freshness so that you can choose the food that provides the better overall nutritional value.

Section 2

8. c   9. d

10. BMI is determined by dividing your weight by the squared value of your height, and then multiplying the result by 703. BMI is one way to assess whether your weight falls within a healthy range.

11. Fad diets restrict food choices so that people become bored with the diet's limitations, stop dieting, and return to their former eating habits.

12. A diet diary can help a person keep track of calories and reveal eating patterns or behaviors of which the person might be unaware.

13. Skipping meals increases hunger at the next meal, which could lead to overeating at that time.

Section 3

14. c

15. Eating too much sugar and fat can lead to type 2 diabetes. Diabetics must eat balanced meals on a regular schedule and monitor their intake of carbohydrates.

Chapter 9 Review

Reviewing Key Ideas

Section 1

1. Basal metabolic rate (BMR) can be affected by
   a. Daily Values.   b. age.
   c. hunger.   d. appetite.

2. A Daily Value of 10 percent means that
   a. a food consists of 10 percent of a particular nutrient.
   b. 10 percent of your calories should come from a particular nutrient.
   c. one serving provides 10 percent of the daily amount for a particular nutrient.
   d. a food package can bear the nutrient claim "light."

3. How might a person's muscle mass affect BMR?

4. How does BMR change as a person ages?

5. How can a person's cultural background influence his or her diet?

6. **Critical Thinking** How do you think friends can influence your appetite?

7. **Critical Thinking** How can reading food labels help you choose between two similar foods?

Section 2

8. Body mass index (BMI) is a ratio of a person's weight to his or her
   a. age.   b. activity level.
   c. height.   d. basal metabolic rate.

9. People who are considered overweight
   a. are generally healthier than people who are not overweight.
   b. are decreasing in number.
   c. have a BMI of more than 30.
   d. are heavier than the standard for their height.

10. Joel has a BMI of 30. Explain how this number was determined and what it means.

11. Why aren't fad diets effective for long-term weight loss?

12. Why should a person use a diet diary when attempting to gain or lose weight?

13. **Critical Thinking** Explain why skipping meals is not an effective way to manage your weight.

Section 3

14. A food intolerance is
   a. a response by the immune system to certain proteins in foods.
   b. present in one percent of the population.
   c. the inability to digest a particular food.
   d. a fast and intense reaction to food.

15. How is type 2 diabetes related to diet?

16. How can vegetarians make sure they get all the amino acids they need?

17. Why is it important for an athlete to increase calorie intake?

18. **Critical Thinking** How could diabetics benefit from reading food labels? What information should they look for?

 ## Building Health Skills

19. **Accessing Information** Make a chart in which you compare different types and brands of yogurt. How do they compare for total fat, saturated fat, cholesterol, vitamins, and minerals?

20. **Advocacy** Tim, who is thin, has started eating a lot of potato chips and other high-fat foods in an attempt to gain weight. What advice would you give him? **WRITING**

21. **Setting Goals** Calculate your BMI. Determine if you have an appropriate weight, are overweight, or underweight. Plan meals that will increase, decrease, or keep your BMI the same. Try the meals for several weeks, and see if there is any change in your BMI.

Health and Community

Fast-Food Pamphlet Use the Internet to collect the nutrition information supplied by many fast-food restaurants. Use this data to analyze the fat and calorie content of different food items. Then, create a pamphlet comparing two meals: one that is low in fat and calories, and one that is high in fat and calories. **WRITING**

---

16. Vegetarians can combine foods, such as beans and grains, to get complete proteins.

17. Athletes need extra calories to fuel their higher level of activity.

18. Reading labels could help diabetics monitor their carbohydrate intake. They should look for carbohydrates under nutrition facts and for any information pertaining to diabetics, such as carbohydrate exchanges.

 ## Building Health Skills

19. Whole-milk yogurt has the most fat and cholesterol. Yogurt is high in protein and calcium.

20. If no health problem exists, Tim should eat large amounts of nutrient-dense foods that are rich in complex carbohydrates. Too much dietary fat could lead to other problems.

Standardized Test Prep

Math Practice

The food label below is from a box of breakfast cereal. Use the label to answer Questions 22–24.

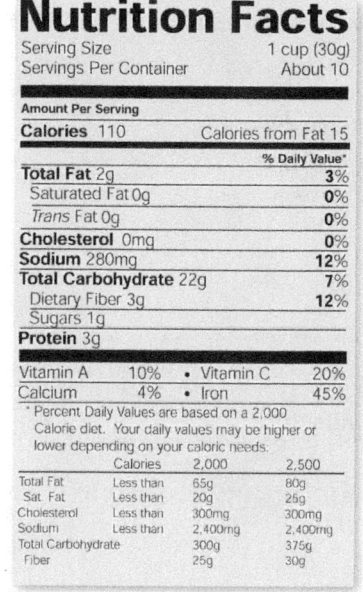

Nutrition Facts

Serving Size	1 cup (30g)
Servings Per Container	About 10

Amount Per Serving

Calories 110	Calories from Fat 15

	% Daily Value*
Total Fat 2g	3%
Saturated Fat 0g	0%
Trans Fat 0g	0%
Cholesterol 0mg	0%
Sodium 280mg	12%
Total Carbohydrate 22g	7%
Dietary Fiber 3g	12%
Sugars 1g	
Protein 3g	

Vitamin A	10%	•	Vitamin C	20%
Calcium	4%	•	Iron	45%

* Percent Daily Values are based on a 2,000 Calorie diet. Your daily values may be higher or lower depending on your caloric needs.

	Calories	2,000	2,500
Total Fat	Less than	65g	80g
Sat. Fat	Less than	20g	25g
Cholesterol	Less than	300mg	300mg
Sodium	Less than	2,400mg	2,400mg
Total Carbohydrate		300g	375g
Fiber		25g	30g

22. How many servings would an average person need to consume to get the total amount of vitamin C needed in a day?

A 2   B 5
C 10   D 25

23. What percentage of the calories in one serving comes from fat?

F about 3 percent
G about 6 percent
H about 14 percent
J about 20 percent

24. If you consume a diet of 2,500 calories per day, what percentage of your Daily Value for fiber would one serving provide?

A 8 percent
B 10 percent
C 12 percent
D 15 percent

Reading and Writing Practice

Read the passage. Then answer Questions 25–28.

Could a protein called leptin help explain why people gain or lose weight? Working with a genetically obese strain of mice, scientists found that these mice made very little leptin compared to normal mice. Perhaps leptin serves as a signal to the brain to suppress appetite, the scientists hypothesized. But, unlike the obese mice, overweight humans have plenty of leptin in their bodies. Nonetheless, the findings about leptin have opened the door for more research into weight control.

25. Leptin is a

A protein found only in mice.
B protein found only in humans.
C protein found in both mice and humans.
D medication that increases one's appetite.

26. In this passage, the word *suppress* means

F increase.
G reduce.
H stimulate.
J maintain.

27. According to the passage, which of these statements is true?

A Genetically obese mice produce high amounts of leptin.
B Normal mice produce very little leptin.
C Thin people produce very little leptin.
D Overweight people produce plenty of leptin.

Constructed Response

28. In a paragraph, explain the scientists' findings about leptin in mice and in humans.

Standardized Test Prep

Math Practice
22. B
23. H
24. B

Reading and Writing Practice
25. C
26. G
27. D
28. *Sample answer:* Genetically obese mice do not produce as much leptin as do normal mice. But overweight humans produce lots of leptin. These findings suggest that more research is needed about the role leptin plays in weight control.

21. Meals should include a balance of carbohydrates, proteins, and fats. Portion size and activity level can be adjusted to improve BMI.

Health and Community

Fast-Food Pamphlet If students don't have access to the Internet, they can gather data at fast-food restaurants or write to the company headquarters. Fried foods or items with dressings and sauces have more fat and calories than plain grilled items.

CHAPTER 10 Digestion and Excretion

Section Objectives	Standards Correlation	Instructional Resources L3			SE eTEXT	TE eTEXT	PRINT
1 Your Digestive System ⏱ 2 periods; 1 block	NHES: 2.12.6, 3.12.3	SE	Warm-Up, p. 242		•	•	•
10.1.1 Describe the three main functions of the digestive system.		SE	Hands-On Activity Enzymes in Action, p. 244		•	•	•
10.1.2 Identify the organs of the digestive system and their functions.		SE	Technology & Health Lights, Pill Camera, Action!, p. 247		•	•	•
		RN	Note Taking Guide 10-1		•	•	•
		IB	Image Bank 10-1, 10-2			•	
		TR	Practice 10-1			•	
		TR	Section 10-1 Quiz			•	
2 Keeping Your Digestive System Healthy ⏱ 1 period; 1/2 block	NHES: 1.12.1, 1.12.5, 7.12.2, 7.12.3	SE	Warm-Up, p. 248		•	•	•
10.2.1 Identify behaviors that keep your digestive system healthy.		RN	Note Taking Guide 10-2		•	•	•
		TR	Practice 10-2			•	
10.2.2 Evaluate whether you practice proper food safety methods.		TR	Section 10-2 Quiz			•	
Thinking Critically About Health News ⏱ 1 period; 1/2 block	NHES: 2.12.5, 3.12.1, 3.12.2, 5.12.1, 5.12.2	SE	Practice the Skill, p. 253		•	•	•
		RN	Building Health Skills 10		•	•	•
BHS.10 Evaluate current health information in newspapers and magazines.							
3 Your Excretory System ⏱ 1 period; 1/2 block	NHES: 1.12.1, 2.12.4	SE	Warm-Up, p. 254		•	•	•
10.3.1 Identify the organs of excretion in the body and their functions.		RN	Note Taking Guide 10-3		•	•	•
		IB	Image Bank 10-8			•	
10.3.2 Explain how the kidneys remove wastes from the blood and produce urine.		TR	Practice 10-3			•	
		TR	Section 10-3 Quiz			•	
10.3.3 Describe behaviors that can keep your excretory system healthy.							

Chapter Review and Assessment

SE Chapter 10 Review, p. 260 L3

CTB Chapter 10 Test L2 L3 L4

SE Standardized Test Prep, p. 261 L3

PROGRAM COMPONENTS

SE	Student Edition	**CTB**	Computer Test Bank
TE	Teacher Edition	**AUD**	Audio Section Summaries
TR	Teaching Resources		
RN	Reading and Note Taking Guide	**DVD**	Teens Talk Video Series
		VVG	Video Viewing Guide
ARN	Adapted Reading and Note Taking Guide	**PPT**	Presentation
IB	Image Bank		

Differentiated Instruction
L1 L2 L4 EL

		SE eTEXT	TE eTEXT	PRINT
ARN	Note Taking Guide 10-1 **L2**	•	•	
RN	Note Taking Guide 10-1 **EL**	•	•	•
AUD	Audio Summary 10-1 **L1 L2 EL**	•	•	
TE	Reteach Strategy, p. 246 **L2**		•	•
TR	Enrich 10-1 **L4**		•	
ARN	Note Taking Guide 10-2 **L2**	•	•	
RN	Note Taking Guide 10-2 **EL**	•	•	•
AUD	Audio Summary 10-2 **L1 L2 EL**	•	•	
TE	Reteach Strategy, p. 251 **L2**		•	•
TR	Enrich 10-2 **L4**		•	
ARN	Building Health Skills 10-3 **L2**	•	•	
RN	Building Health Skills 10-3 **EL**	•	•	•
ARN	Note Taking Guide 10-3 **L2**	•	•	
RN	Note Taking Guide 10-3 **EL**	•	•	•
AUD	Audio Summary 10-3 **L1 L2 EL**	•	•	
TE	Reteach Strategy, p. 258 **L2**		•	•
TR	Enrich 10-3 **L4**		•	

ABILITY LEVELS

L1 For students with special needs
L2 For less proficient readers
L3 For all students
L4 For gifted and talented students
EL For English language learners

Chapter 10 Digital/Video Pathway

This alternative pathway allows you to teach this chapter's content using only the video and online materials.

Preview

DVD Video #10 Preview
SE Video #10 Preview Activity
VVG Video #10 Worksheet

Feeding the Need

1
PPT 10-1 Presentation
RN/ARN 10-1 Note Taking
PPT 10-1 Section Quiz

2
DVD Video #10 Explore/Wrap-Up
VVG Video #10 Worksheet
PPT 10-2 Presentation
RN/ARN 10-2 Note Taking
PPT 10-2 Section Quiz

Feeding the Need

3
PPT 10-3 Presentation
RN/ARN 10-3 Note Taking
PPT 10-3 Section Quiz

Chapter Preview

Section 1 Your Digestive System
Digestion involves the mechanical and chemical breakdown of food into molecules that can be absorbed as it passes from the mouth to the stomach and through other organs of the digestive system. Most nutrients are absorbed in the small intestine. The large intestine then reabsorbs water and eliminates wastes.

Section 2 Keeping Your Digestive System Healthy
Many digestive system disorders can be controlled by changes in dietary habits and getting regular exercise. Practicing food safety includes cooking meats thoroughly, preventing cross-contamination between uncooked and cooked foods, quickly refrigerating leftovers, and washing hands thoroughly.

Analyzing Influences
Thinking Critically About Health News
Health information that is printed in newspapers and magazines needs to be evaluated critically.

Section 3 Your Excretory System
Waste products are filtered from the blood by the kidneys and then excreted from the body in urine. Besides the kidneys and urinary tract, the skin, lungs, and liver are also organs of excretion. Drinking plenty of water helps maintain optimal kidney function.

Digestion and Excretion

GO ONLINE PearsonSuccessNet.com

TEENS Talk

VIDEO 10

Feeding the Need

Preview **Activity**

Why Volunteer?

Complete this activity before you watch the video.

1. In a paragraph, discuss what "volunteering" means to you.
WRITING

2. Interview five teens to find out how they have volunteered their time in the community. Describe the types of volunteer activities they perform. What have they gained from their experiences?

240

GO ONLINE

PearsonSuccessNet.com

For resources and activities for this chapter.

Sensitive Issues

Some students may suffer from one of the disorders mentioned in the chapter, such as hemorrhoids or Crohn's disease. They may feel embarrassed by discussions that focus on these problems. Try to answer questions in a matter-of-fact way to make students feel more at ease with the subject matter.

Video Objectives

Use this video to help students

Identify ways that they can help people in need in their community.

Explore how both the volunteers and the people they help benefit from volunteer efforts.

Preview **Activity**

Why Volunteer?

A few days before watching the video, have students complete the Preview Activity. Ask students to share the most interesting volunteer experiences they learned about.

241

From the Authors

This chapter provides practical "take home" material on food safety (pages 250–251). Adults may be unaware of the concept of cross-contamination. They may not know that microorganisms can thrive in a kitchen sponge. Students have an opportunity to demonstrate that what they learn at school has practical applications. You have an opportunity to communicate with parents or guardians through their children. Opening a dialogue just might produce increased support for your efforts in other areas.

Objectives

Before class begins, write the objectives on the board. Have students copy the objectives into their notebooks at the start of class.

1. Focus

Warm-Up Myth/Fact

After students have finished writing, ask volunteers to read aloud a question that they could not answer. As an assignment, have students look for the answers to some of these questions.

Presentation 10-1

2. Teach

L3 **EL** **Reading/Note Taking 10-1**

L2 **Adapted Reading/Note Taking 10-1**

Functions of the Digestive System

L2 **Building Health Skills**

Analyzing Influences Most people sometimes eat when they are not hungry. Ask students to list external factors that influence their decision to have a snack even when they don't feel the signs of hunger. Likely answers include hanging out with friends, watching a game, or eating because someone else is eating. Use this opportunity to discuss how food provides people with more than nutrients and energy—it also has a strong role in social situations.

Connect to Your Life Answers will depend on what students had for their last meal or two.

Section 1

Your Digestive System

Objectives

▶ **Describe** the three main functions of the digestive system.

▶ **Identify** the organs of the digestive system and their functions.

Vocabulary

- digestion
- enzyme
- absorption
- pharynx
- epiglottis
- peristalsis
- chyme
- bile
- gallbladder
- villi

Warm-Up

Myth Food is digested in the stomach.

Fact Although protein digestion does begin in the stomach, most digestion occurs in the small intestine.

WRITING List three questions you have about how the digestive system functions. Look for the answers in the chapter.

Functions of the Digestive System

You've learned that your cells require nutrients for energy, growth, and repair. How do the nutrients from the apple you ate at lunch get to your cells? Before your body can use nutrients from your food, the food must be processed by your digestive system. **Your digestive system has three main functions—digestion, absorption, and elimination.**

Digestion   The process by which the digestive system breaks down food into molecules that the body can use is called **digestion.** There are two kinds of digestion.

▶ During mechanical digestion, foods are physically broken apart into smaller pieces.

▶ During chemical digestion, chemicals produced by your body break large molecules into smaller ones that your body can use.

Because mechanical digestion breaks food into small pieces, chemicals can digest the food faster. Most of the chemicals involved in digestion are **enzymes,** substances that speed up chemical reactions.

Absorption and Elimination   **Absorption** is the process by which nutrients pass through the lining of your digestive system into your blood. The blood then transports the nutrients throughout your body. Materials that are not absorbed are eliminated from the body as wastes.

 **Connect to Your Life**   What foods are being digested and absorbed by your body right now?

WRITING and Health

L3 **Descriptive Writing**

Before they read the section, have students compose a detailed essay describing how they think digestion and absorption of food occur. Ask them to trace the path of food from ingestion to elimination. After studying Section 1, have students revise their original essays. Then they should write a paragraph comparing what they wrote about the digestive process before studying the section to the knowledge they gained from reading the section.

Structures of the Digestive System

The organs of the digestive system include the mouth, pharynx, esophagus, stomach, small intestine, and large intestine. The liver, gallbladder, and pancreas also are involved in digestion. Figure 1 shows the organs of the digestive system.

GO ONLINE
PearsonSuccessNet.com
For: More on the digestive system

Mouth   Mechanical digestion occurs in your mouth as your teeth tear, crush, and grind your food and your tongue pushes the food around. Chemical digestion occurs as an enzyme in saliva begins to break down starches in your food. Saliva also moistens the bites of food into a slippery mass that can be easily swallowed.

Pharynx   The tongue pushes chewed food into the upper portion of the throat called the pharynx. The **pharynx** is the junction between the digestive tract and the respiratory system. As you swallow, a flap of tissue called the **epiglottis** seals off the trachea, or windpipe, preventing food and liquid from entering your lungs.

Esophagus   After passing through the pharynx, the food enters the esophagus, a muscular tube that connects the pharynx to the stomach. Muscle contractions push the food through the esophagus and toward the stomach. These waves of muscle contractions, called **peristalsis,** continue to push food through the rest of the digestive system.

The Digestive System

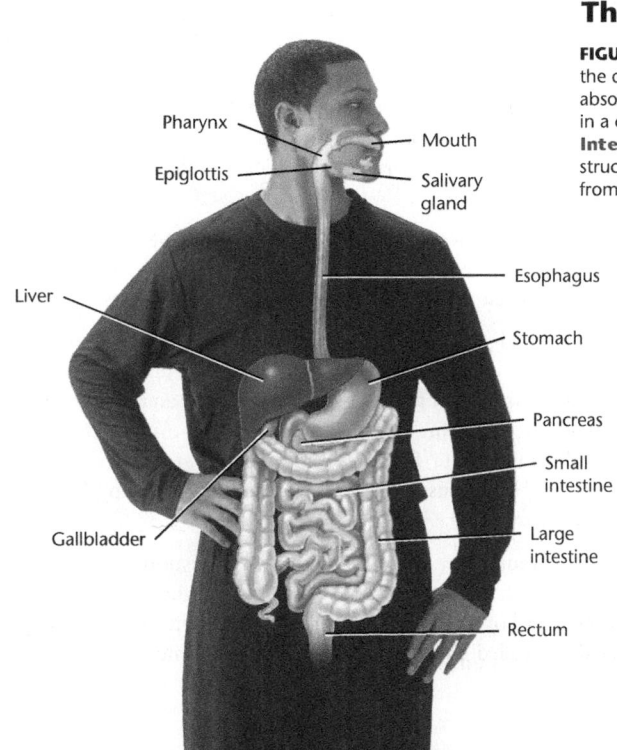

FIGURE 1   As food moves through the digestive system, digestion, absorption, and elimination occur in a continuous process.
Interpreting Diagrams Which structure prevents food and liquid from entering the trachea?

Labels on figure: Pharynx, Epiglottis, Liver, Gallbladder, Mouth, Salivary gland, Esophagus, Stomach, Pancreas, Small intestine, Large intestine, Rectum

Digestion and Excretion   **243**

L3 Class Discussion

Ask: **How can the body's cells use the food you ate for breakfast or lunch?** *(Food is broken down into nutrients, which are then absorbed and used for energy, growth, and repair.)* **What substances are involved in chemical digestion, and what is their function?** *(Enzymes; they help carry out chemical reactions.)*

Structures of the Digestive System

L3 Online Activity   **GO ONLINE**

Visit Pearson SuccessNet to access an online activity about the digestive system. Have students complete the Web activity.

L2 Visual Learning: Figure 1

Image Bank Figure 10-1
Have students examine the placement of the organs of the digestive system. Ask: **Where does food go after traveling through the esophagus?** *(the stomach)* **Do you think food enters the small intestine or the large intestine first?** *(small intestine)*
Caption Answer epiglottis

L3 Building Vocabulary

Explain that the prefix *peri-* is derived from the Greek word for "around." *Stalsis* is derived from the Greek word for "to draw in." Demonstrate peristalsis by holding a straw vertically and inserting a small bead into the straw (the bead should fit snugly). Pinch the straw above the bead so that it begins to move through the straw. Ask: **What do the straw and bead represent?** *(straw=the esophagus or intestines; bead=food or remnants of food)* **Why is *peristalsis* a fitting term for this process?** *(The muscles in the digestive tract surround food as they draw it through the body.)*

Differentiated Instruction

EL English Language Learners

Point to each part of the digestive system labeled in Figure 1. Pronounce the terms and have students repeat them. Then have students write the terms in English and in their native languages. As students read this section, have them write a sentence in their own words that describes the function of each labeled part. They can use their sentences to help them review for a test.

Hands-On *Activity*

Enzymes in Action

Give students oyster crackers or break apart soda crackers and tell them to take small bites. Remind students to keep the spoons and stirrers separate.

Think and Discuss Answers

1. Answers will vary, but most will observe that the taste became sweeter after a few minutes.

2. The enzymes in the mouth started to break down the starches in the cracker into sugars.

3. The milk solution thickened, but the orange juice solution did not change.

4. Papain acts on protein.

5. It breaks down the protein molecules in the meat.

Ⓛ **Active Learning**

To model the role of mechanical digestion, have half the class stand together in a cluster acting as a food mass. Then have the rest of the class approach the "food mass" acting as digestive chemicals. Ask: **Do the chemicals have easy access to all the areas of the "food mass"?** *(no)* Then tell the students in the "food mass" to act as though they are being thrown about by the churning motion of the stomach. Ask: **Now that the "food mass" is broken up, how will this affect chemical digestion?** *(Chemical digestion should happen faster.)*

Hands-On *Activity*

Enzymes in Action

In this activity, you will observe the effect of enzymes on foods.

Materials
crackers • meat tenderizer • milk
orange juice • 2 clear glasses • 2 stirrers

Try This

❶ Chew a cracker for 5 seconds. Do not swallow it. Note how the cracker tastes.

❷ Continue chewing the cracker for 5 minutes. Note how the taste of the cracker changes before swallowing it.

❸ Place 2 tablespoons of milk into one glass. Place 2 tablespoons of orange juice into another glass.

❹ Add 1 tablespoon of meat tenderizer to each glass. Stir well with separate stirrers.

❺ After 30 minutes, look closely at the contents of the two glasses. Record your observations.

Think and Discuss

❶ How did the taste of the cracker change during the five minutes it was in your mouth?

❷ Why do you think the taste of the cracker changed the longer it was in your mouth?

❸ After 30 minutes, how did the appearance of the milk solution compare to that of the orange juice solution?

❹ Meat tenderizer contains an enzyme called papain. Based on your observations, what nutrient does papain act on?

❺ Why do you think meat tenderizer makes cooked meat tender?

Stomach From the esophagus, food passes through a valve and into the stomach, a muscular pouch located in the abdomen. As you eat and drink, your stomach expands. The stomach can hold about one gallon of food and liquid. Most mechanical digestion and some chemical digestion occur in the stomach.

▶ Mechanical digestion occurs as three layers of muscle produce a churning motion. This action mixes the food with fluids in a similar manner as clothes and soapy water are mixed in a washing machine.

▶ Chemical digestion occurs as cells lining the stomach release gastric juice. Gastric juice contains pepsin, an enzyme that breaks down proteins. Hydrochloric acid in gastric juice creates an acidic environment in which pepsin works best. The acid also kills many bacteria that you swallow with your food. The lining of the stomach is coated with mucus. The mucus gives the stomach some protection from its own acidic gastric juice.

A few hours after you eat, mechanical digestion in the stomach is complete. By that time, most proteins have been chemically digested into shorter chains of amino acids. Peristalsis moves the food, which is now a thick liquid called **chyme** (kym), into the small intestine.

244 *Chapter 10*

Differentiated Instruction

Ⓛ **Less Proficient Readers**

Distribute sheets with the following heads printed on them: Mouth, Stomach, Small Intestine, and Large Intestine. Leave space for writing after each head. Work with students to help them write brief, simplified descriptions of the role of each of these organs in the digestive process.

Small Intestine The small intestine is where most chemical digestion and absorption of nutrients takes place. This 20-foot long tube gets its name from its small one-inch diameter. Three other organs play a role in the chemical digestion that takes place in the small intestine.

▶ **Liver** The liver plays a role in many body processes. The role of the liver in the digestive system is to produce bile. **Bile** is a substance that physically breaks up large fat droplets that clump together.

▶ **Gallbladder** Bile flows from the liver into the **gallbladder,** the organ that stores bile. As food leaves your stomach, the gallbladder releases bile through a tube into the small intestine.

▶ **Pancreas** The pancreas is a triangular organ that lies between the stomach and the first part of the small intestine. Like the liver, the pancreas plays a role in many body processes. In the digestive system, the pancreas secretes enzymes into the small intestine that complete the breakdown of carbohydrates, proteins, and fats.

Once pancreatic enzymes have broken down the food, the nutrients can be absorbed. The lining of the small intestine is covered with millions of tiny fingerlike projections called **villi** (singular, *villus*). The villi absorb nutrient molecules. As you can see in Figure 2, each villus contains tiny blood vessels. Most nutrients pass from cells on a villus into the blood vessels. Once in the blood, the nutrients are transported throughout the body.

 **Connect to Your Life** Choose one food that you ate today. Where did digestion and absorption occur?

Villus ▶

FIGURE 2 The lining of the small intestine is covered with tiny projections called villi. Nutrients pass through the thin surface of villi and into blood vessels for transport.

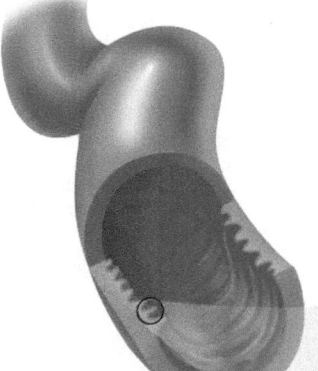
▲ **Small intestine**

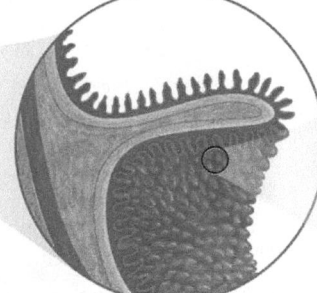
▲ **Fold covered with villi**

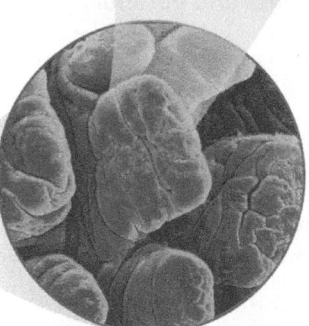
▲ **Close-up of villi**

Digestion and Excretion **245**

L3 Class Disscussion

Ask: **What are the digestive organs through which food does not pass as it travels through the digestive system?** *(liver, gallbladder, pancreas)* **What role does the liver play?** *(It produces bile, which helps with the break down of fats.)* **What type of problems would you expect to see in someone with a disorder of the pancreas?** *(problems with the digestion of carbohydrates, fats, and proteins; possible malnourishment as a result)*

L3 Active Learning

Provide pairs of students with 1 yard of string and a ruler. Tell students to place one hand palm-side down on a flat surface. While keeping their thumb and fingers tightly together, they should lay the string around the outline of their hand. They should measure the length of string that was needed to outline their hand. Next have students place their hand down with their thumb and fingers spread out. They should measure how much string is needed to outline their hand, thumb, and fingers. Have them compare the two measurements. Ask: **What does this reveal about the role of villi in absorption?** *(With villi, much more area is available for absorption.)*

L1 Visual Learning: Figure 2

Image Bank Figure 10-2
Make sure students understand that each diagram in the series is a closer view of the small intestine shown in the previous diagram. Ask: **What structures are inside the single villus in this diagram?** *(blood vessels)* **What happens to the nutrients after they enter the blood vessels?** *(They are transported throughout the body.)*

Connect to Your Life Mechanical digestion occurred in the mouth and stomach. Although chemical digestion of starch began in the mouth and protein digestion began in the stomach, most digestion occurred in the small intestine.

Differentiated Instruction

L1 Special Needs
Have two students hold out a rope that is 22-feet long. Have two other students hold out a thicker rope that is 5-feet long. Point out that these ropes illustrate the lengths of the small and large intestine, respectively. Next have the students coil the rope into tight bundles to demonstrate how the intestines fit inside a body.

3. Assess

Evaluate

These assignments can help you assess students' mastery of the section content.

Section 1 Review

Answers appear below.

Teaching Resources

- Practice 10-1
- Section 10-1 Quiz

 Reteach

Write the names of the major parts of the digestive tract at the top of large index cards. Mix up the cards, and have students arrange them in the sequence in which food passes through the organs. After students have organized the cards, they can write a brief description of the organ's function on each card.

L4 Enrich

Teaching Resources

- Enrich 10-1

Health and Community

First Aid for Choking Classes in first aid for choking are available from the American Red Cross, many fire departments, and other organizations. Arrange for students to display their posters in the cafeteria.

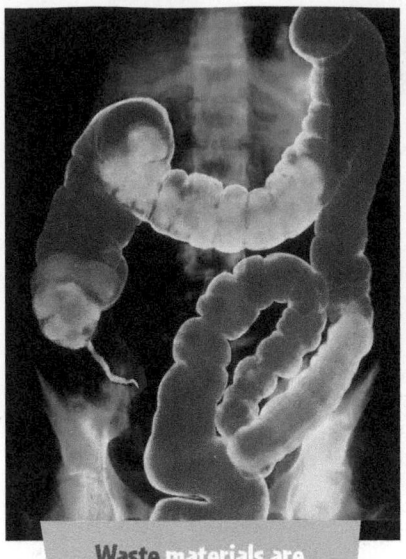

Waste materials are pushed slowly through the large intestine for about 12 to 24 hours.

The Large Intestine By the time material reaches the end of the small intestine, most nutrients have been absorbed. The remaining undigested material and unabsorbed water is pushed into the large intestine. The large intestine, also called the colon, is about 5 feet long and 3 inches wide. It runs up the right side of the abdomen, across the upper abdomen, and then down the left side. As the material moves through the large intestine, most of the remaining water is absorbed into the blood.

The large intestine ends in a short tube called the rectum. In the rectum, waste material is compressed into solid form. This waste material, called feces or stool, is eliminated from the body through the anus, a muscular opening at the end of the rectum.

Did you know that your large intestine is also a site of vitamin production? Billions of bacteria thrive in the warm and nutrient-rich environment of your large intestine. The bacteria produce several vitamins, including most of your daily requirement for vitamin K. The vitamin K is absorbed through the lining of your large intestine into your blood.

FIGURE 3 As waste materials pass through the large intestine, most of the remaining water is absorbed. The wastes are then eliminated from the body.

Section 1 Review

Key Ideas and Vocabulary

1. List the three main functions of the digestive system in the order that they occur.
2. What is **peristalsis**?
3. Trace the path of food through the digestive system. When does the food become chyme?
4. Describe the role of **bile**.

Critical Thinking

5. **Predicting** How would digestion be affected if the tube leading from the gallbladder to the small intestine became blocked?

Health and Community

First Aid for Choking Learning first aid for choking victims can help you save a friend, family member, or even a stranger. Find a program at your school or in your community that teaches first aid for choking. After taking the class, create a poster that summarizes what you learned. **WRITING**

6. **Applying Concepts** Why do you think that chewing your food well helps digestion?
7. **Classifying** Which three organs that participate in digestion are most likely known as accessory organs? Explain why.

 GO ONLINE PearsonSuccessNet.com Audio Summary Section 10.1

Section 1 Review

1. digestion, absorption, elimination
2. muscle contractions that push food through the digestive system
3. mouth, esophagus, stomach, small intestine, large intestine, rectum, anus; in the stomach after mechanical digestion and chemicals form a soupy mixture
4. Bile physically breaks up large fat droplets into smaller droplets.
5. It would be more difficult to digest fats because the gallbladder releases bile.
6. It increases the amount of surface area of food, thus aiding chemical digestion.
7. Liver, gallbladder, pancreas; food does not pass through these organs. However, they are important in digestion because they produce or release substances needed for digestion.

Technology & Health

Lights, Pill Camera, Action!

Disorders of the digestive system can be difficult to diagnose. The symptoms of many disorders are very similiar, and some parts of the digestive system are too deep within the body to examine. Today, however, a tiny new tool can provide doctors with clear color images of the small intestine. Patients simply swallow a pill-sized camera. During its journey, the camera transmits thousands of images to a recorder worn around the patient's waist.

WRITING The tiny parts of the pill camera are products of miniaturization. Think of another technology that has been changed by miniaturization. In a paragraph, describe how its small size impacted its use.

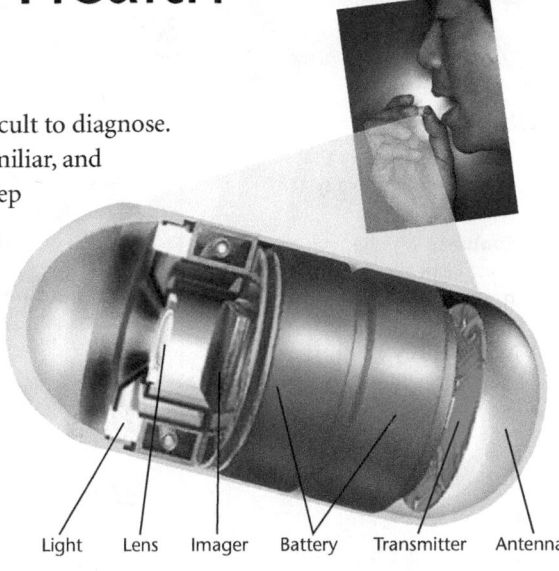

Light   Lens   Imager   Battery   Transmitter   Antenna

▲ The Pill Camera

After fasting overnight, the patient swallows the pill camera with water. As it tumbles through the small intestine, the camera captures about two images per second. About 24 hours later, the disposable pill camera is eliminated from the digestive tract.

▼ Reviewing the Images

A technician downloads the images from the recorder. A doctor examines the images for signs of bleeding, tumors, blockages, ulcers, or other disorders.

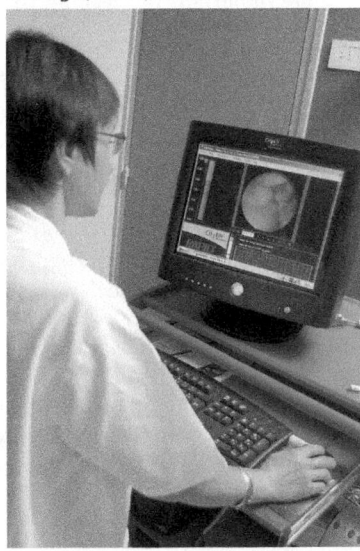

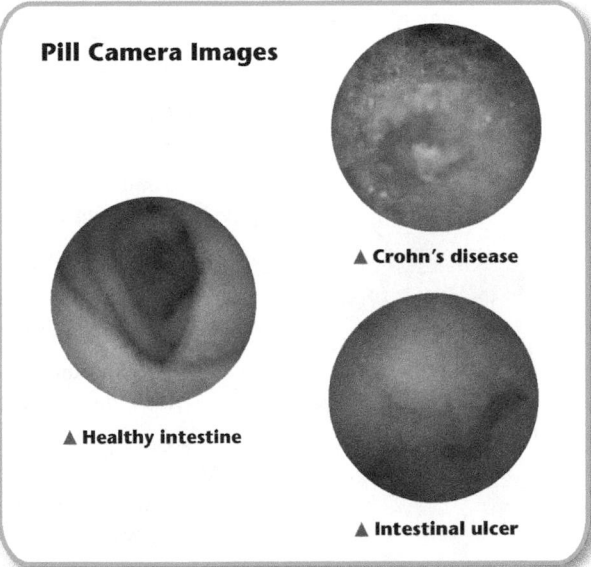

Pill Camera Images

▲ Crohn's disease

▲ Healthy intestine

▲ Intestinal ulcer

Digestion and Excretion **247**

For Your INFORMATION!

Lab-on-a-Chip

Another example of miniaturization is a type of device called lab-on-a-chip. "Lab-on-a-chip" is a generic term for small plastic devices containing tiny channels and pumps that can be used for a wide range of tests. Someday investigators may be able to use a credit-card sized "lab" to do DNA testing in the field without waiting weeks for crime-lab results. Healthcare workers in poor countries could use coin-sized devices that cost only cents to diagnose diseases. Also in development for NASA are labs-on-a-chip that will be used to search for chemical signs of life on other planets.

Technology & Health

Lights, Pill Camera, Action!

Teaching Strategies

• The pill camera requires no anesthesia, and the patient can resume normal activities immediately. Ask: **How is this beneficial to the patient?** *(It eliminates the risks involved with anesthesia and makes the patient less uncomfortable.)*

• Remind students that the pill camera images shown here represent only a few of the possibly thousands of images a pill camera takes on its way through the digestive system. The pill camera can take as many as five hours worth of images.

• A second type of pill camera is being used to diagnose diseases of the esophagus, such as reflux disease. Reflux affects about 45 percent of the U.S. population at least once per month. This pill camera is specially designed to take photos of the esophagus. Instead of wearing a recorder for many hours, the patient stays in the doctor's office for 20 minutes while the camera transmits several thousand images of the esophagus.

WRITING Answers will vary, but most students will probably think of the computer. While the first computers filled an entire room, they are small enough now to fit on a lap. Others may mention cell phones or digital music players.

Objectives

Before class begins, write the objectives on the board. Have students copy the objectives into their notebooks at the start of class.

1. Focus

Warm-Up Quick Quiz

Use the Warm-Up Presentation slide to survey student responses.

Use this Warm-Up activity to uncover misconceptions about food safety and digestive system health. Statement 4 is true; the other statements are false.

Presentation 10-2

Section 2

Objectives
▶ **Identify** behaviors that keep your digestive system healthy.
▶ **Evaluate** whether you practice proper food safety methods.

Vocabulary
• foodborne illness
• cross-contamination

Keeping Your Digestive System Healthy

Warm-Up

Quick Quiz Only one of the following statements is true. Which statement do you think it is?

1. Ulcers are caused by eating too much spicy food.

2. Hot foods should be cooled completely before putting them in the refrigerator.

3. There is nothing you can do to avoid food poisoning.

4. Harmful microorganisms can be found on fruits and vegetables.

5. Heartburn is a sign of heart disease.

WRITING Explain why you gave the answer that you did.

Avoiding Digestive Disorders

How can you help your digestive system function properly? **Healthy eating habits and regular exercise are important for keeping your digestive system healthy.**

▶ **Consume plenty of fiber.** High-fiber foods such as vegetables, fruits, and whole-grain products help food move through the intestines.

▶ **Limit fatty foods.** Fat is digested slowly. Eating a lot of fatty food in one sitting can lead to digestive problems such as heartburn.

▶ **Eat moderately.** Overeating can strain the digestive system.

▶ **Plan meals for a time when you can relax.** When you are relaxed, you are more likely to eat slowly and chew your food thoroughly.

▶ **Drink water.** Make sure to drink water during meals and at other times during the day.

▶ **Get regular exercise.** Regular exercise stimulates peristalsis, which can prevent constipation. If you exercise, you are also more likely to maintain a healthy weight. Excess weight is a risk factor for some digestive disorders.

248 *Chapter 10*

 Sensitive Issues

Some students may have chronic constipation, hemorrhoids, or other digestive disorders. Class discussion should not focus on individuals but should convey enough information to help those who might have problems. Point out that most people occasionally suffer from some of these disorders.

WRITING and Health

L4 Public Service Announcement

Have students write a public service announcement about the habits that can lead to a healthier digestive system. Tell them to write the PSA as though it will play on the radio during a show that is popular with older adults.

Disorders of the Digestive System

Condition	Cause	Symptoms	Treatments
Appendicitis	Microorganisms infect the appendix—a small pouch that projects from the colon.	Pain near the navel that spreads, nausea, diarrhea, and fever	Surgery to remove the appendix
Colon cancer	Uncontrolled cell division that leads to a cancerous tumor; risk factors include family history, high-fat diet, and lack of exercise.	Change in bowel habits, narrow stools, persistent gas or pain, unexplained weight loss	Surgery, radiation, and chemotherapy
Heartburn	Acid from the stomach irritates the esophagus; risk factors include obesity, asthma, pregnancy, ulcers, and overeating.	Burning sensation in chest, sour taste	Over-the-counter or prescription medications; rarely surgery
Hemorrhoids	Veins in the anus or rectum swell due to constipation, pregnancy and childbirth, sitting for long periods, or heavy lifting.	Bleeding, itching, pain	Over-the-counter treatments, warm baths, outpatient surgery
Inflammatory bowel disease (colitis and Crohn's disease)	Chronic inflammation of digestive tract; influenced by immune system, genetics, and environment.	Diarrhea, cramping, bleeding, loss of appetite, weight loss, fever; symptoms may come and go	Anti-inflammatory drugs, immune system suppressors, surgery to remove damaged sections of intestines
Irritable bowel syndrome	Abnormal peristalsis in the small intestine leads to bouts of diarrhea and constipation.	Diarrhea, constipation, gas, bloating; stress may worsen symptoms	Managing stress, diet changes, fiber supplements, drugs that affect nervous system activities
Lactose intolerance	Lack of the enzyme lactase in the small intestine leads to an inability to digest lactose, a sugar in milk.	Within 30 minutes to 2 hours after consuming milk products: nausea, cramps, gas, diarrhea	Drinking less milk, trying yogurt or hard cheeses, taking lactase drops or tablets, drinking lactose-free milk
Peptic ulcer (of esophagus, stomach, or small intestine)	Irritation caused by *H. pylori* infection leads to open sores.	Burning pain between the breastbone and the navel, especially at night or when the stomach is empty	Antibiotics, antacids, medications that protect the digestive tract lining

H. pylori ▶

Avoiding Digestive Disorders

L1 **Visual Learning: Figure 4**

Ask: **Which of these disorders can be cured only with surgery?** *(appendicitis)*
Ask: **Which of these disorders can be treated by removing one type of food from one's diet?** *(lactose intolerance)*
Caption Answer infection by the bacterium, *H. pylori*

L2 **Cooperative Learning**

Invite an internist to talk to the class about how medical knowledge regarding digestive system disorders has changed over the years. How has new knowledge changed the advice physicians give their patients? Before the class visit, have students break into small groups. Each group should brainstorm at least two or three questions about the digestive system to ask the speaker.

L3 **Cultural Connection**

Explain that lactose intolerance is a common occurrence in adults. As many as 90 percent of Asian Americans and 75 percent of African Americans, Native Americans, and Hispanic Americans are lactose intolerant. Adults who are lactose intolerant consume most of their calcium from sources other than dairy products. Ask students to bring in food labels from foods that they associate with their culture. As a class, examine which foods are good sources of calcium.

L3 **Building Media Literacy**

Ask students to analyze ads on television or in print for products that are said to relieve common digestive disorders, such as indigestion (heartburn). Do the ads make any suspicious claims about the products? How do the ads attempt to appeal to potential customers? Students can present their findings to the class.

Differentiated Instruction

L4 **Gifted and Talented**

Have small groups further research some of the disorders in the table, such as inflammatory bowel disease, irritable bowel syndrome, colon cancer, or ulcers. The groups should create presentations for the class explaining the available treatments and how the treatments help to cure the disorder or relieve symptoms.

Food Safety

L2 Cooperative Learning

Have small groups of students create a menu for a picnic and then exchange menus with another group. After reviewing their new menu, groups should develop a plan to prevent anyone at the picnic from contracting a foodborne illness. The plan should include information about how they will safely prepare the foods and what measures they will take to prevent contamination during the picnic.

L3 Active Learning

Coordinate with school food-service workers to organize a class tour of the cafeteria. During the tour, workers should discuss their daily tasks including menu planning and what they do to ensure the food is prepared and served safely. Encourage students to ask questions.

Connect to Your Life Answers will vary, but encourage students to adopt the practices outlined in the text.

L3 Content Update GO ONLINE

Visit Pearson SuccessNet to access more information about food safety. Have students complete the Web activity.

FIGURE 5 Protect yourself and your family from foodborne illnesses by cooking and storing foods properly.

Storing Food Safely
- Quickly refrigerate leftovers and cold food items.
- Keep your refrigerator set at a temperature of 40°F or below.
- Separate raw meat, poultry, and seafood from other foods in the refrigerator.

Grilling Foods Properly

Steak (medium)	160°F
Ground beef	160°F
Pork chops	160°F
Chicken breasts	170°F
Most fish	145°F

GO ONLINE
PearsonSuccessNet.com
For: More on food safety

Food Safety

Each year in the United States, about 76 million people become sick from contaminated food or beverages. **To avoid foodborne illnesses, it is very important to prepare and store food properly.**

Foodborne Illness **Foodborne illnesses** result from consuming a food or drink that contains either a poison or a disease-causing microorganism. Some mushrooms and fish, for example, contain poisons that can cause serious illness or even death.

Bacteria and viruses cause the most common foodborne illnesses. You may have heard about people becoming sick from consuming foods that were contaminated with the bacteria *E. coli* or *Salmonella*. Microorganisms are typically spread in one of three ways.

► When food is undercooked

► When raw food touches cooked food

► When people preparing food transfer the organisms onto their hands, countertops, or utensils

Typical symptoms of foodborne illnesses are diarrhea, vomiting, abdominal cramps, and fever. If you contract a foodborne illness, be sure to drink plenty of fluids to replace the fluids you lose. Seek medical care if symptoms include any of the following.

► Fever over 101.5°F

► Blood in stool or diarrhea for more than three days

► Prolonged vomiting or signs of dehydration, such as dry mouth and dizziness

Connect to Your Life What steps do you take at home to avoid foodborne illness?

For Your INFORMATION!

Irradiated Food

The process of irradiation can be used to kill microorganisms, parasitic worms, and other pests that cause foodborne illness or spoilage. Ionizing radiation destroys genetic material in these organisms, which prevents them from reproducing. Radiation does not result in radioactive food. The USDA has approved the use of irradiation for meat, poultry, fresh produce, spices, and wheat flours. Irradiated foods sold in the United States must be labeled with an international sign called a *radura*. The label should also say "treated with radiation" or "treated by irradiation."

Food Preparation and Storage How can you avoid becoming infected with microorganisms in foods? A few simple precautions can reduce your risk.

▶ **Cook** Cook meat, seafood, poultry, and eggs thoroughly. Eggs should be cooked until the whites and the yolks are firm. Fish should be cooked until it is opaque and flakes easily with a fork.

▶ **Separate** Keep uncooked food separated to prevent **cross-contamination,** the spread of microorganisms from one food to another food. For example, do not cut vegetables on the same cutting board you used to cut raw meat. Use plastic cutting boards for meat and poultry. Also, do not place cooked food on a platter that held uncooked food.

▶ **Chill** Quickly refrigerate leftovers, including cut-up fruits and vegetables, to slow the growth of bacteria. Do not defrost foods at room temperature.

▶ **Clean** Wash your hands with soap before preparing food and again after handling raw meat, poultry, or fish. Use paper towels, rather than sponges, to clean kitchen surfaces with a disinfectant cleaner. Rinse fruits and vegetables in running water.

FIGURE 6 Many microorganisms thrive in the moist environment of a kitchen sponge. The inset photo is a micrograph that shows bacteria (blue) and fungi (white) on the surface of a sponge.

Section 2 Review

Key Ideas and Vocabulary

1. List three eating habits that can help keep your digestive system healthy. Why is exercise important for digestive health?

2. What are two possible contaminants in food that can lead to **foodborne illness?**

3. List four tips for preparing and storing foods safely.

4. Explain how **cross-contamination** can lead to foodborne illnesses.

Critical Thinking

5. Evaluating List three changes you can make to your daily eating habits to keep your digestive system healthy.

Health at Home

Food Safety at Home For one week, evaluate the food safety methods practiced in your home. At the end of the week create a food-safety checklist for your family. The list could include items such as quickly putting milk back into the refrigerator and washing hands before preparing a snack.

6. Predicting A food worker wears plastic gloves while he works with raw chicken. Later, he chops vegetables for the salad bar while wearing the same gloves. What could be a consequence of his actions? Explain.

Thinking Critically About Health News

Objective

Evaluate current health information found in newspapers and magazines.

Teaching Strategies

- Advise students that medical and scientific journals can be difficult for the average reader. Tell them that reading an article's abstract is one way to glean information. Remind students that abstracts are useful if you want a summary of the article, but not if you want to evaluate research methods.

- Remind students that the nature of health research underscores the need for multiple studies and large studies. Multiple studies with similar results or a very large, ongoing study offer more compelling evidence than a study with a small sample size that has not been repeated.

- Students can organize the information they find in table format or by using a checklist. Organizing information in this way will make it easier to see at a glance how reliable the article is. Ask volunteers to present their findings to the class.

Analyzing Influences

Thinking Critically About Health News

Every day, newspapers and magazines report the latest scientific findings on health topics. Sometimes, it may seem that this information changes from day to day. For example, one day you might read that a certain food is good for you. The next day, you may read that the same food can lead to health problems.

How can you sort out all the information? When reviewing new health information, keep a critical, but open, mind. Use the following questions to evaluate health reports.

252

For Your INFORMATION!

Health Organizations

Organizations that provide information to the public include the Centers for Disease Control and Prevention, the National Institutes of Health, the American Cancer Society, the American Heart Association, the Food and Drug Administration, and many others. Tell students that these organizations provide reliable information that is understandable to the average reader.

① Who conducted the research?

Find out the credentials of the person or group who conducted the research. Usually, health professionals are the best-qualified researchers.

② Is the source trustworthy?

Always consider the type of source where the information appears.

▶ The most reliable sources are medical or scientific journals. These journals only accept articles that have been thoroughly reviewed by experts.

▶ Articles written by trained health or science writers also are generally reliable. These people have been trained in how to report scientific findings accurately.

▶ The least reliable sources are ads or publications funded by people with a financial interest in the information.

③ Is the evidence convincing?

Assess the quality of the evidence upon which the news is based. Look for signs of weak evidence.

▶ Vague statements that lack supporting information, such as "doctors recommend."

▶ Statements based on opinions rather than experimental results.

▶ Phrases such as "in animals," "of that age group," or "in laboratory tests," indicate that the findings may not be applicable to all groups.

④ Has the information been verified?

The best way to assess new health information is to compare findings in more than one reliable source. When a number of researchers report similar findings, the results are more likely to be accurate. However, this is not always easy. Experts often disagree about conclusions drawn from the same information. But becoming familiar with all the views on an issue can help you make decisions based on the best available information.

Practice the Skill

1. Find an article from a local newspaper or a popular magazine that discusses health information related to nutrition.

2. Evaluate the article by asking the following questions.
   ▶ Who conducted the research?
   ▶ Is the source of the information trustworthy? Explain.
   ▶ Is the evidence convincing? Why or why not?

3. Find out whether the information has been supported by other studies. Summarize your findings.

4. Based on your evaluation, do you think you can trust the information in the article? Explain your viewpoint. **WRITING**

253

Health at School

 Poster Presentation

Have students make a poster presenting how they evaluated the article. Encourage them to use pictures and data tables when available. Mount the posters in the classroom, or get permission to put them in a central location, such as the school cafeteria.

Section 3

Your Excretory System

Objectives

Before class begins, write the objectives on the board. Have students copy the objectives into their notebooks at the start of class.

1. Focus

Warm-Up Health Stats

After students finish writing, call on volunteers to share their responses. Make sure that students understand water loss methods change as the body regulates temperature.

Presentation 10-3

 **Connect to Your Life** You can see water; the lungs are at work.

Section 3

Your Excretory System

Objectives

▶ **Identify** the organs of excretion in the body and their functions.

▶ **Explain** how the kidneys remove wastes from the blood and produce urine.

▶ **Describe** behaviors that can keep your excretory system healthy.

Vocabulary

- excretion
- urea
- kidney
- urine
- nephron
- glomerulus
- dialysis

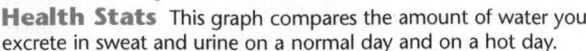 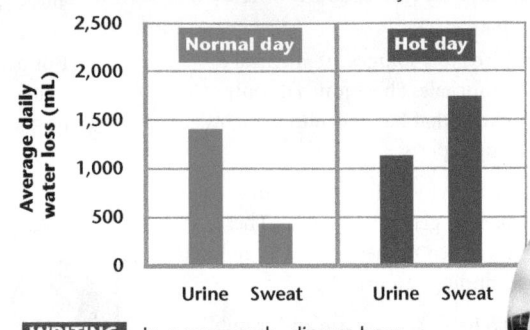

Warm-Up

Health Stats This graph compares the amount of water you excrete in sweat and urine on a normal day and on a hot day.

WRITING In a paragraph, discuss how weather affects water loss.

Organs of Excretion

Every cell in your body produces waste products that must be removed before they build up and make you sick. **Excretion** is the process by which the body collects and removes wastes. **Several organs in the body are involved in waste collection and removal, including the liver, lungs, and skin. The major organs of excretion, however, are the kidneys, which are part of the body's excretory system.**

Liver The liver converts impurities and poisons in the body to less harmful substances. For example, the liver forms **urea** from a harmful waste product of protein breakdown. Urea can be safely transported via blood to the kidneys. Some substances processed by the liver become a part of bile. After aiding fat digestion in the small intestine, bile is eliminated from the body in stool.

Lungs and Skin When you exhale, the lungs remove carbon dioxide and some water from the body. Sweat glands in the skin also serve an excretory function because water and urea are excreted in perspiration.

 **Connect to Your Life** When you exhale on a cold day, what waste product can you see? What excretory organ is at work?

TEENS *Are Asking . . .*

Q: I'm so embarrassed because I perspire more than anyone else I know. What causes this, and what can I do about it?

A: You may have hyperhidrosis, or excessive sweating. This is a medical condition that can involve the armpits, palms, feet, face, or torso. The most common treatment is a prescription antiperspirant containing aluminum hydrochloride. Other possible treatments include oral medication or electric therapy that turns off the sweat glands. Surgery to disable nerves also exists, but it is only performed in extreme cases.

Even if you feel that you don't want to seek treatment, you should still mention the problem to your doctor. Excessive sweating can be a sign of other conditions such as a thyroid problem or anxiety.

Kidneys You have two kidneys, each about the size of a fist. The **kidneys,** which are the major organs of the excretory system, filter urea and other wastes from the blood. Figure 7 shows where the kidneys and other organs of the excretory system are located.

The wastes are eliminated in **urine,** a watery fluid produced by the kidneys that contains urea and other wastes. Urine flows from the kidneys, through the other organs of the excretory system, and out of the body.

In addition to cleansing your body of wastes, the kidneys are also the main organs involved in water balance. Hormones sent from the brain signal the kidneys to release more or less water in urine depending on the amount of water in your body. For example, on a hot day you might sweat a lot but drink little water. If so, your kidneys will not release much water. On a cool day, you might not sweat much and drink plenty of water. If so, your kidneys will release more water.

The Excretory System

FIGURE 7 The main structures of the excretory system include the kidneys, ureters, bladder, and urethra. Together they remove wastes from your body.

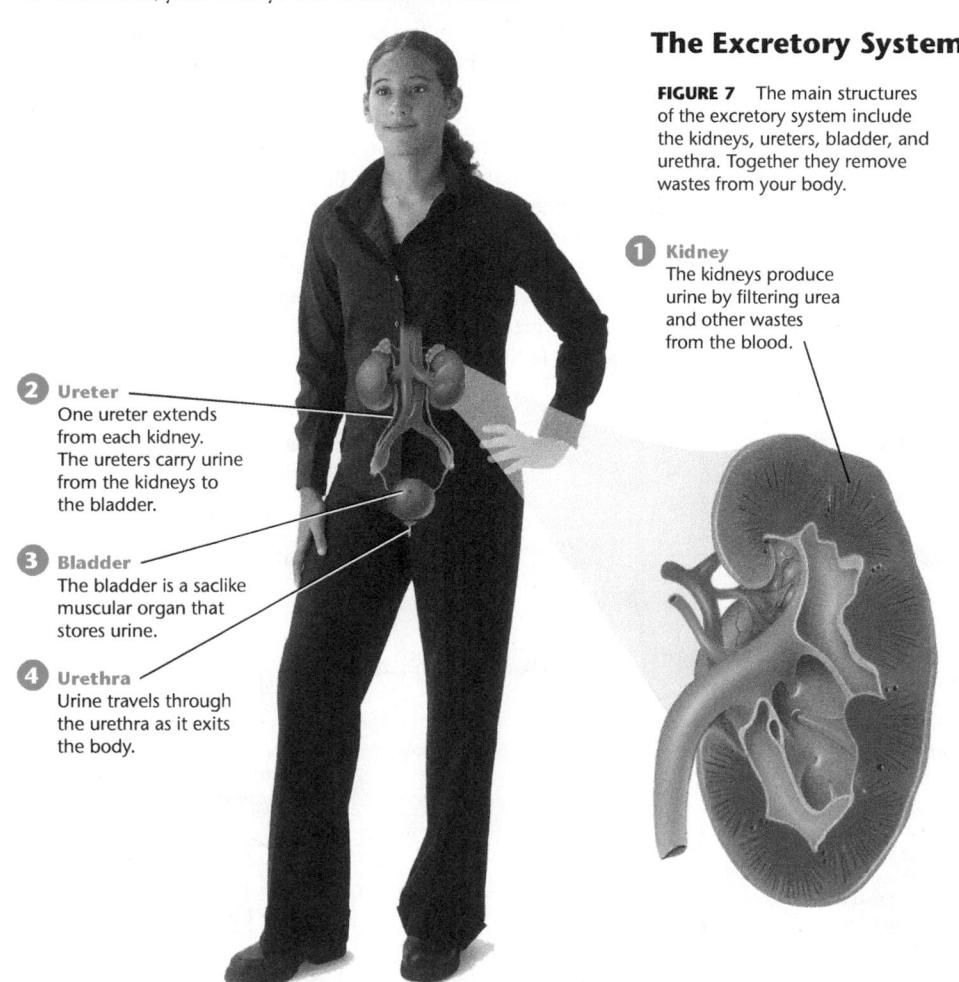

1 Kidney
The kidneys produce urine by filtering urea and other wastes from the blood.

2 Ureter
One ureter extends from each kidney. The ureters carry urine from the kidneys to the bladder.

3 Bladder
The bladder is a saclike muscular organ that stores urine.

4 Urethra
Urine travels through the urethra as it exits the body.

2. Teach

L3 EL Reading/Note Taking 10-3
L2 Adapted Reading/Note Taking 10-3

Organs of Excretion

L2 Class Discussion

Present the class with the following problem: You place two goldfish in a tank. You have an aerator to provide them with oxygen and plenty of food. Therefore, the fish have a home, oxygen, and food. What is missing? Why will the fish die in a short amount of time? *(There is no filter to remove the wastes produced by the fish.)* Help students relate this example to the importance of the excretory system.

L3 Teacher Demo

Breathe onto a mirror, and hold it up for students to see. Ask: **What is on the mirror?** *(water)* **Where did it come from?** *(lungs)* Tell students that the body gives off water as a waste product. Emphasize that the lungs play a part in both respiration and excretion.

L2 Visual Learning: Figure 7

Tell students that the numbered labels show the sequence in which wastes are removed by the excretory structures in the diagram. Ask: **Where is urine produced?** *(the kidneys)* **How does urine get from the kidneys to the bladder?** *(It travels through tubes called ureters.)*

EL Building Vocabulary

Ask students to find the ureters and urethra in Figure 7. Then have students brainstorm ways that they can recall the correct name for each structure.

Differentiated Instruction

L1 Special Needs

Have each student place a small plastic bag over one hand and then use masking tape to close the bag at the wrist. After a few minutes, students should observe condensation inside the bag. Ask: **Does the skin excrete wastes from the body all the time, or just when you are aware you are perspiring?** *(all the time)*

Filtration of Wastes

L2 Building Vocabulary

Tell students that the word *glomerulus* is from the Latin words for "ball" and "to carry." Ask: **How does this description fit the glomerulus?** *(It is shaped like a ball and carries materials filtered from the blood.)*

L3 Visual Learning: Figure 8

Image Bank Figure 10-8

Write the following on the chalkboard: Enters Tube, Stays in Blood, Returns to Blood, Exits Body. Ask students to tell you what substances belong with each heading. *(Enters Tube: urea, glucose, water. Stays in Blood: blood cells and protein. Returns to Blood: water, glucose. Exits Body: urea and other wastes.)*
Caption Answer water, glucose

Filtration of Wastes

How do your kidneys remove wastes from your body, but not substances that your body needs? To answer this question, you need to understand how the kidneys filter wastes. Each kidney contains about a million **nephrons,** tiny filtering units that remove wastes and produce urine.

The nephrons filter wastes in stages. **First, both needed materials and wastes are filtered from the blood. Then, most needed materials are returned to the blood, and the wastes are eliminated from the body.** Follow the process of waste filtration and urine formation in Figure 8.

Filtering Out Wastes   During the first stage of waste removal, blood enters the kidneys. Here, the blood flows through smaller and smaller blood vessels until it reaches a cluster of tiny blood vessels in a nephron called a **glomerulus** (gloh MUR yoo lus). Urea, salts, glucose, and some water are filtered from the glomerulus into a thin-walled capsule. Blood cells and most protein molecules usually remain in the blood because they are too large to pass through the walls of the glomerulus.

Formation of Urine   The capsule around the glomerulus is connected to a long, twisting tube. The tube is surrounded by tiny blood vessels. As the filtered material flows through the tube, the glucose, most of the water, and other needed materials pass from the tube back into the blood. Urea and other wastes, such as excess vitamins and harmful substances, stay in the tube. The fluid that remains in the tube is urine. Eventually, the urine drains into a larger tube called a ureter, which carries it from a kidney to the bladder.

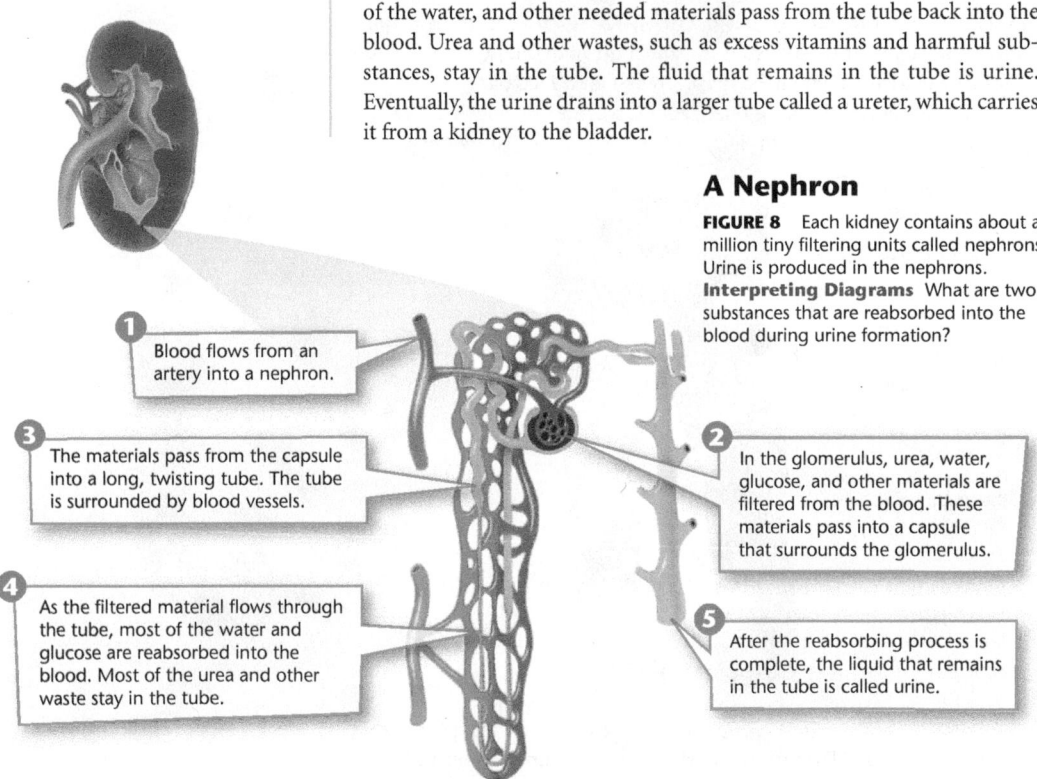

A Nephron

FIGURE 8   Each kidney contains about a million tiny filtering units called nephrons. Urine is produced in the nephrons.
Interpreting Diagrams What are two substances that are reabsorbed into the blood during urine formation?

1 Blood flows from an artery into a nephron.

3 The materials pass from the capsule into a long, twisting tube. The tube is surrounded by blood vessels.

4 As the filtered material flows through the tube, most of the water and glucose are reabsorbed into the blood. Most of the urea and other waste stay in the tube.

2 In the glomerulus, urea, water, glucose, and other materials are filtered from the blood. These materials pass into a capsule that surrounds the glomerulus.

5 After the reabsorbing process is complete, the liquid that remains in the tube is called urine.

256   *Chapter 10*

Differentiated Instruction

L2 Less Proficient Readers

Pass out several index cards to each student. Then have them write the answer to each of the following questions on a separate index card. **What is the purpose of the filtering stage that occurs in nephrons?** *(the removal of wastes from the blood)* **Why are some materials reabsorbed into the blood?** *(Some materials that end up in the tube, such as glucose, are needed by the body.)* **What does urine contain?** *(water, urea, excess vitamins, and other wastes)* Partners should review each other's answers. Ask pairs if they need help sorting out inconsistencies in their answers.

Tips for Increasing Fluid Intake
- Eat more fruit.
- Add a splash of fruit juice to water.
- Add lemon or lime to your water.

FIGURE 9 If you find drinking plain water boring, you can increase your fluid intake in other healthful ways.

Keeping Healthy

Because the kidneys remove harmful wastes from your body, proper functioning of your kidneys is essential for your overall health. **To help your kidneys function at their best, it is important to drink plenty of water and to see a doctor if you have symptoms of an infection.**

Routine medical checkups often include a urine test, which can reveal a lot about a person's health. For example, if glucose is present in the urine, it may be a sign that a person has diabetes. Protein in urine can be a sign of high blood pressure or of poorly functioning kidneys.

Drinking Water Because many of the waste products filtered by your kidneys are harmful, it is best if they are diluted as much as possible. Drinking plenty of water is the best way to dilute these substances. In Chapter 8, you learned about the importance of drinking water. How much you should drink depends on various factors such as your health status, activity level, and the weather. In general, if you are not thirsty and your urine is only slightly yellow, you are consuming enough fluid.

Treating Infections Urinary tract infections, which are bacterial infections of the urethra or bladder, are common disorders. Most cases occur when bacteria from the digestive system come in contact with the urethra. Symptoms of urinary tract infections include frequent, painful urination and blood in the urine. Prompt treatment with antibiotics is important to prevent the infection from spreading to the kidneys. Infections of the kidneys can lead to kidney damage.

Connect to Your Life How much water do you consume in a typical day? Do you think that you consume enough?

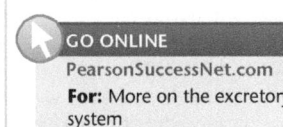
GO ONLINE
PearsonSuccessNet.com
For: More on the excretory system

Keeping Healthy

L3 Building Health Skills

Practicing Healthful Behaviors
Encourage students to keep track of how much water they drink each day in their journals. An easy way to keep track is by making a chart with days of the week across the top. Students enter a checkmark for each glass of water they drink. At the end of the week, they can find the average number of glasses per day.

L2 Cooperative Learning

Ask student pairs to brainstorm more tips for increasing fluid intake. For example, they could carry a bottle of water with them during the day.

Connect to Your Life Allow students to answer this question in their private journals.

L3 Content Update  GO ONLINE

Visit Pearson SuccessNet to access more information about the excretory system. Have students complete the Web activity.

For Your INFORMATION!

Diabetes and Kidney Disease

Diabetes is the leading cause of kidney failure in the United States. The high level of sugar in the blood of diabetics damages small blood vessels in nephrons. As damage accumulates, the kidneys cannot filter the blood adequately. Fluids and wastes start to build up in the blood leading to a rise in blood pressure. High blood pressure contributes to more damage to small blood vessels in the kidneys and accelerates kidney failure. Not all people with diabetes will develop kidney disease and kidney failure, but those who also have hypertension are at high risk.

3. Assess

Evaluate

These assignments can help you assess students' mastery of the section content.

Section 2 Review

Answers appear below.

Teaching Resources

- Practice 10-3
- Section 10-3 Quiz

L2 Reteach

Mix water, marbles, and a few drops of food coloring. Tell students that the marbles represent blood cells, the water represents the liquid part of blood, and the food coloring represents the wastes dissolved in blood. Pour the mixture into a colander, and let the students observe how the marbles stay behind while the colored water passes through. Reinforce that this is similar to the first step of the filtration process in a nephron.

L4 Enrich

Teaching Resources

- Enrich 10-3

Health at School

Water at School Remind students that they are creating an advertisement for water. Their ads should include information about its availability at school and health benefits.

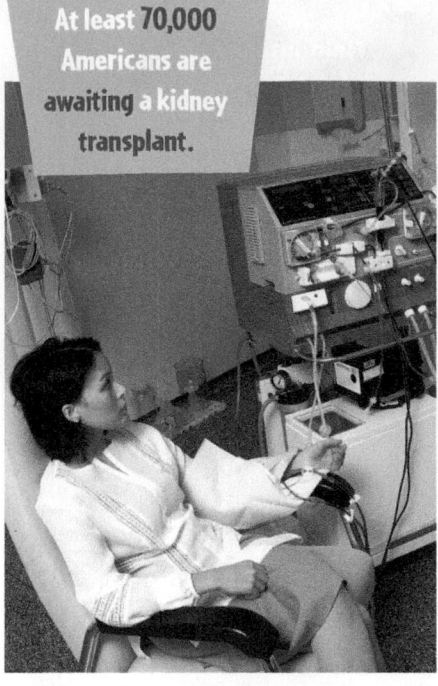

At least **70,000** Americans are awaiting a kidney transplant.

FIGURE 10 Dialysis is a treatment for kidney failure. During dialysis, a machine removes wastes from a patient's blood. Eventually, some of these patients will undergo a kidney transplant.

Preventing Kidney Stones Kidney stones are pebble-like masses that form in the kidneys. The most common stones contain calcium. When kidney stones become stuck, they are very painful. Many kidney stones eventually pass out of the excretory system in urine on their own. If a large stone blocks urine flow or damages the kidney, a procedure may be performed to shatter the stone. Drinking plenty of water and eating a low-sodium diet will reduce your risk of developing kidney stones.

Treating Kidney Failure Kidneys that are damaged from an injury, diabetes, uncontrolled high blood pressure, or other diseases may fail. When kidney failure occurs, the kidneys are unable to remove wastes and excess fluid. Kidney failure can be treated with dialysis or a kidney transplant.

▶ **Dialysis** During dialysis, a machine is used to filter wastes from the blood. Tubes carry blood from the body through the machine. The machine removes wastes and excess water. Then the blood is returned to the body. Dialysis must be performed three times a week for three to five hours. Many complications can arise from dialysis.

▶ **Kidney transplant** A transplant is a better option for some patients. During a kidney transplant, a patient's damaged kidney is replaced with a healthy kidney from another person. The kidneys often come from people who sign organ donation forms while they are alive.

Section 3 Review

Key Ideas and Vocabulary

1. What is the body's main organ of excretion? What are other organs in the excretory system?
2. Briefly describe the process of filtration and urine production that occurs in the nephrons.
3. What are two ways that you can help keep your excretory system healthy?
4. How is **dialysis** used to treat kidney failure?

Critical Thinking

5. **Predicting** Suppose you went for a long walk on a hot day and did not drink very much water. How might this affect urine formation?

Health at School

Water at School Does your school have working water fountains? Can you choose water with lunch? Do school vending machines sell water? Create a poster reminding students of the importance of drinking water.

6. **Relating Cause and Effect** Why is protein in the urine a sign that something could be wrong with the kidneys?
7. **Calculating** The kidneys filter about 50 gallons of fluid from the blood each day. Only 1 percent of this fluid is excreted from the body as urine. About how many gallons of urine do the kidneys produce in a day? **MATH**

 GO ONLINE PearsonSuccessNet.com | Audio Summary Section 10.3

Section 3 Review

1. kidney; liver, lungs, skin
2. Urea, glucose, water, and salts are filtered from the blood. Glucose and water re-enter the blood. Urea and other wastes stay in the tube that eventually reaches the ureter. These pass out of the body in urine.
3. drink water, see a doctor if you have symptoms of an infection
4. During dialysis, a machine performs the function of the kidneys by filtering wastes from the blood. The filtered blood is then returned to the body.
5. You would produce less urine than usual.
6. Protein should remain in the blood because protein molecules are too large to pass through the walls of the glomerulus.
7. 1% of 50 gallons = 0.5 gallon

Chapter 10
At a Glance

Feeding the Need What are three ways that you could volunteer to help people in your community?

Section 1   Your Digestive System

Key Ideas

▶ Your digestive system has three main functions—digestion, absorption, and elimination.

▶ The organs of the digestive system include the mouth, pharynx, esophagus, stomach, small intestine, and large intestine. The liver, gallbladder, and pancreas also are involved in digestion.

Vocabulary
- digestion (242)
- enzyme (242)
- absorption (242)
- pharynx (243)
- epiglottis (243)
- peristalsis (243)
- chyme (244)
- bile (245)
- gallbladder (245)
- villi (245)

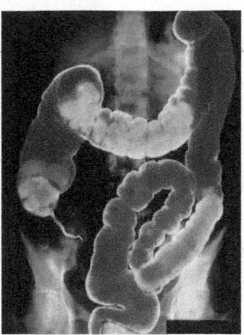

Section 2   Keeping Your Digestive System Healthy

Key Ideas

▶ Healthy eating habits and regular exercise are important for keeping your digestive system functioning properly.

▶ To avoid foodborne illnesses, it is very important to prepare and store food properly.

Vocabulary
- foodborne illness (250)
- cross-contamination (251)

Section 3   Your Excretory System

Key Ideas

▶ Several organs in the body are involved in waste collection and removal, including the liver, lungs, and skin. The major organs of excretion, however, are the kidneys, which are part of the body's excretory system.

▶ First, both needed materials and wastes are filtered from the blood. Then, most needed materials are returned to the blood, and the wastes are eliminated from the body.

▶ To help your kidneys function at their best, it is important to drink plenty of water and to see a doctor if you have symptoms of an infection.

Vocabulary
- excretion (254)
- urea (254)
- kidney (255)
- urine (255)
- nephron (256)
- glomerulus (256)
- dialysis (258)

Digestion and Excretion   **259**

Chapter 10
At a Glance

VIDEO **Feeding the Need** Ask for volunteers to share their answers. Use examples from the video to review ways to volunteer in the community.

Key Ideas Review

L2 Draw the outline for a flowchart that traces the pathway of food through the digestive system. Have students complete the flowchart by providing names for digestive organs and processes.

L3 Have students write the words *Problem* and *Solution* on a piece of paper. Have them list some digestive problems and their solutions. Remind students to include foodborne illnesses on their lists.

L2 Have students work in pairs. While one student writes a summary of how the kidney filters wastes, the other can summarize excretory disorders and how to keep the excretory system healthy. Students can then quiz each other.

Vocabulary Review

L2 Let students write matching questions using the vocabulary terms. Then, have students quiz each other.

L3 Have students write multiple choice questions on foodborne illnesses and cross-contamination. Use the questions for review.

EL Have pairs of students make flash cards with words on one side and definitions on the other side. Let students quiz each other.

Chapter 10 Review

Chapter 10 Review

GO ONLINE

PearsonSuccessNet.com

Students can go online for a review activity on Chapter 10.

Reviewing Key Ideas

Section 1

1. b

2. c

3. Enzymes speed up chemical reactions. They allow chemical digestion of starch, fat, and protein.

4. Nutrient molecules are absorbed in villi and then move into blood vessels.

5. The pancreas secretes enzymes into the small intestine for the breakdown of carbohydrates, proteins, and fats.

6. Mechanical digestion breaks food into smaller pieces so that chemicals have more access to the food and can digest it more efficiently.

7. Bacteria in the large intestine produce several vitamins, including vitamin K. Without these bacteria, vitamin levels in your body could decrease.

Section 2

8. a

9. b

10. It stimulates peristalsis, which can prevent constipation. It helps a person maintain a healthy weight.

11. undercooked food, raw food touching cooked food, contaminated hands

12. A person might lose weight due to lack of appetite. Or, maybe they eat enough calories, but the small intestine cannot absorb the nutrients.

Section 3

13. c

14. b

15. ureter, bladder, urethra

16. Drinking water is the best way to dilute waste products filtered by the kidneys.

17. It may block urine from reaching the ureter.

Reviewing Key Ideas

GO ONLINE

PearsonSuccessNet.com
For: Chapter 10 review activity

Section 1

1. The mixture of food and gastric juice that passes from your stomach to your small intestine is called
   a. peristalsis.
   b. chyme.
   c. bile.
   d. absorption.

2. Most mechanical digestion takes place in the
   a. epiglottis.
   b. gallbladder.
   c. stomach.
   d. large intestine.

3. What are enzymes? What is their role in digestion?

4. Describe how nutrients move from your digestive system into your blood.

5. How is the pancreas involved in digestion?

6. **Critical Thinking** Why is mechanical digestion important for chemical digestion?

7. **Critical Thinking** Some antibiotics used to fight disease also kill harmless bacteria in your body. How might this affect vitamin levels in your body?

Section 2

8. Exercise and consuming plenty of fiber may help you avoid
   a. constipation.
   b. foodborne illness.
   c. lactose intolerance.
   d. inflammatory bowel disease.

9. Cross-contamination is most likely to occur when foods are not properly
   a. cooked.
   b. separated.
   c. chilled.
   d. cleaned.

10. Describe two ways in which exercise benefits your digestive system.

11. List three ways that microorganisms that cause foodborne illnesses can be spread.

12. **Critical Thinking** Why do you think that weight loss is a symptom of several different digestive disorders?

Section 3

13. In which organ is urea produced?
    a. the kidney   b. the skin
    c. the liver   d. the bladder

14. The filtering unit of the kidney is the
    a. bladder.   b. nephron.
    c. ureter.   d. urethra.

15. List the organs in the order through which urine travels from the kidney out of the body.

16. Why is drinking plenty of water a benefit to your excretory system?

17. **Critical Thinking** How could a large kidney stone block urine flow?

Building Health Skills

18. **Making Decisions** A food worker at a take-out restaurant does several things that make you question the safety of the food you ordered. In a paragraph, describe how you would handle this situation. **WRITING**

19. **Communicating** For several weeks, a family member has had abdominal cramps and diarrhea. In an e-mail, explain to your family member why he or she should seek medical care. **WRITING**

20. **Setting Goals** Track the amount of water you consume each day over a three-day period. Also note when you drink water—with every meal or only when you are thirsty? Then develop and follow a plan to consume more water for one week. At the end of the week, evaluate how you did.

Health and Community

Organ Donors In many states, when people apply for a driver's license, they can sign a form indicating a desire to be an organ donor. Contact your state's department of motor vehicles to find out what a person needs to do to indicate a willingness to donate organs. Write a fact sheet summarizing what you learned. **WRITING**

Building Health Skills

18. Answers should demonstrate an assertive, but rational response. They could calmly explain the problem to the worker. Or, they could ask to speak with a manager.

19. Answer should include the dangers of prolonged diarrhea, particularly dehydration. Also, most digestive problems can be treated.

20. Students' plans will vary but could include some of the recommendations for water intake discussed in Chapter 8.

Standardized Test Prep

Math Practice

A scientist wanted to find out the amount of time needed for the stomach to digest protein. He placed pieces of hard-boiled egg white in a solution of hydrochloric acid, water, and pepsin. Use the graph of his data to answer Questions 21–23.

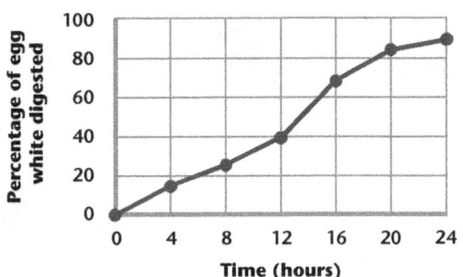

21. After how many hours would you estimate that half of the protein was digested?
- **A** 12
- **B** 14
- **C** 16
- **D** 20

22. During which four-hour period did the most digestion occur?
- **F** 0 to 4 hours
- **G** 8 to 12 hours
- **H** 12 to 16 hours
- **J** 20 to 24 hours

23. What was the average rate of egg-white digestion in this experiment?
- **A** 4% an hour
- **B** 40% a day
- **C** 50% an hour
- **D** 60% a day

Test-Taking Tip

Bring water with you the day of the test so that you will not be distracted by thirst.

Reading and Writing Practice

Read the passage. Then answer Questions 24–27.

Pasteurization is the partial sterilization of foods by heat treatment to destroy disease-causing and food-spoiling microorganisms. The process is named for the French scientist Louis Pasteur, who developed it in the 1860s. Before pasteurization, people boiled many foods. Unlike boiling, however, pasteurization doesn't significantly change a food's flavor. Pasteurization can be performed on liquids such as milk, juice, and cider, and on foods such as spices and cheese. The temperature and length of exposure vary based on the food being treated.

24. What did Louis Pasteur develop?
- **A** a pasteurization process that works only on milk
- **B** a way to kill all microorganisms
- **C** a way to change the flavor of foods
- **D** a method to prevent foodborne illness and slow food spoilage

25. Based on the information in this passage, which statement is most likely true?
- **F** Milk is boiled to preserve its flavor.
- **G** Pasteurization is only used on dairy products.
- **H** The pasteurization process is not the same for all foods.
- **J** Pasteurization can involve either heating or freezing.

26. Why do you think pasteurized milk still spoils eventually?
- **A** Pasteurization only partially sterilizes milk.
- **B** The milk was probably not treated at the right temperature.
- **C** Pasteurization doesn't kill any of the microorganisms that cause milk to spoil.
- **D** The heat used during pasteurization contributes to the spoiling of milk.

Constructed Response

27. In a paragraph, describe some of the benefits of pasteurization.

Standardized Test Prep

Math Practice
- **21.** B
- **22.** H
- **23.** A

Reading and Writing Practice
- **24.** D
- **25.** H
- **26.** A
- **27.** Pasteurization can destroy microorganisms that spoil food and cause diseases without changing the flavor of food. Pasteurization can be used on a wide variety of foods, including milk, juice, cider, spices, and cheese.

Health and Community

Organ Donors Possible answers include carrying a donor card, signing up with your state's donor registry, discussing your decision with your family.

Focus on ISSUES

Should Food Ads Be Allowed in Schools?

Teaching Strategies

- Ask students to describe any food or beverage ads or signs they have seen in their school, other schools, or school buses. Discuss the foods or beverages that are advertised. Are they part of a healthy diet? Why or why not?

- Have students read the cases for and against in-school food ads. Challenge students to think of other pros and cons of in-school food ads. (Some additional pros and cons are listed in the FYI: Advertising in Schools)

- After students complete the questions on page 263, ask a few volunteers to represent each side of the issue. Give students on each side a chance to meet and organize their ideas. Allow class time for the two sides to debate the issue. After the debate, ask the rest of the students if they feel their opinion was influenced by the debate.

Focus on ISSUES

Should Food Ads Be Allowed in Schools?

Teens spend 140 billion dollars each year on products ranging from food and beverages to clothing, electronics, and more. Because of their spending power, teens are the fastest growing market for advertising dollars today. Food marketers, especially those who sell soft drinks and snack foods, are especially interested in reaching teens.

Food marketers see schools as the ideal place to target teens with ads. In exchange for displaying the ads, schools may receive free equipment or money to fund needed programs. Are food ads on scoreboards, school buses, vending machines, and other places in schools a good idea?

262

For Your INFORMATION!

Advertising in Schools

The issue of food ads in schools is part of the larger and highly controversial issue of advertising in schools. Pro arguments for in-school advertising include:

- Schools need the increased revenues.

- Ads are everywhere else already.

- Educators will use good judgment in selecting the ads they allow in schools.

Con arguments include:

- Ads give non-educators influence over students.

- Ads give the impression that schools endorse the advertised products.

- Ads promote materialism in students.

The Case for In-School Food Ads

With schools facing budget cuts for athletics, arts, and other programs, advertising provides a needed source of money for schools. How can schools prepare students for the real world if they don't have money to buy computers and other equipment? As long as the ads are approved by the school administration, they seem like a reasonable trade-off. Teens live in such a media-rich world anyway. It's unlikely that in-school ads would have an additional effect on their purchasing behavior.

66 A few years ago, we could barely afford to have a football team or a marching band. Now we have new uniforms and a really cool scoreboard. Sure, we have a few vending machines and some posters around the school now. But I don't really pay attention to them anyway. My coaches, parents, and teachers have taught me about the importance of healthy eating. No logo on a scoreboard can convince me otherwise. 99

The Case Against In-School Food Ads

Schools have a responsibility to present factual information and to help students make wise decisions. If schools teach healthy eating habits, but allow the placement of ads for unhealthy foods, they are sending mixed messages to students. On what basis would someone decide which ads are acceptable and which are not? Schools should remain "ad-free zones"—places where students know they can trust the messages they see and hear.

66 I don't think that schools should look and feel like malls. Some of my friends think that the ads wouldn't affect them, but that's not true. If ads didn't work, companies wouldn't spend so much money on them. I'm sure the ads would influence students much more than what they learn in health class. Schools should be a place for learning. Teachers shouldn't have to compete with a bunch of slick ads for students' attention. 99

What do **YOU** think?

Use these steps to analyze and express your opinion about in-school food ads.

1. Analyze the Issue Carefully consider both sides of the argument. Make a table listing the pros and cons of in-school food ads.

2. Consider Your Values Would in-school ads be a reasonable way to save programs that would otherwise be lost due to budget cuts? Why or why not?

3. Take a Stand Write a paragraph expressing your opinion about in-school food ads. Provide several reasons to support your opinion. **WRITING**

263

What do **YOU** think?

1. Students' tables can include any reasonable pros and cons for in-school food ads. For example, a pro might be that food ads provide money for school sports programs. A con might be that food ads promote unhealthy food choices.
2. Students may take a stand on either side of the issue. Students who oppose in-school food ads might argue that the ads imply the products are endorsed by the school. Students who favor the ads might argue that a few ads at school are irrelevant because students are already exposed to so many ads.
3. Paragraphs will vary. Students may choose either side of the issue, provided they give several valid reasons in support of their opinion.

GO ONLINE

PearsonSuccessNet.com

Visit Pearson SuccessNet for more information on in-school food ads.

CHAPTER 11 Movement and Coordination

Section Objectives	Standards Correlation	Instructional Resources (L3)	SE eTEXT	TE eTEXT	PRINT
1 **Your Skeletal System** ⏱ 2 periods; 1 block **11.1.1** **Identify** the five main roles of the skeletal system. **11.1.2** **Describe** the functions of bones and joints. **11.1.2** **Explain** how you can keep your skeletal system healthy.	NHES: 1.12.1, 1.12.5, 2.12.6, 6.12.1, 7.12.2, 8.12.4	SE Warm-Up, p. 266	•	•	•
		RN Note Taking Guide 11-1	•	•	•
		IB Image Bank 11-1, 11-3		•	
		TR Practice 11-1		•	
		TR Section 11-1 Quiz		•	
2 **Your Muscular System** ⏱ 1 period; 1/2 block **11.2.1** **Describe** the functions of the three types of muscles. **11.2.2** **Explain** how you can keep your muscular system healthy.	NHES: 1.12.1, 1.12.5, 1.12.8, 7.12.3	SE Warm-Up, p. 272	•	•	•
		RN Note Taking Guide 11-2	•	•	•
		IB Image Bank 11-6		•	
		TR Practice 11-2		•	
		TR Section 11-2 Quiz		•	
🔺 **Warming Up, Stretching, and Cooling Down** ⏱ 1 period; 1/2 block **BHS.11** **Identify** warm-up, stretching, and cool-down exercises to prevent muscle injuries.	NHES: 1.12.5, 7.12.3	SE Practice the Skill, p. 276	•	•	•
		RN Building Health Skills 11	•	•	•
3 **Your Nervous System** ⏱ 3 periods; 1 1/2 blocks **11.3.1** **Explain** the functions of the nervous system and the role of neurons. **11.3.2** **Describe** the roles of the central nervous system and the peripheral nervous system. **11.3.3** **Identify** the most important thing you can do to keep your nervous system healthy.	NHES: 1.12.1, 1.12.5, 7.12.1, 7.12.3	SE Warm-Up, p. 278	•	•	•
		SE Hands-On Activity Mixed Messages, p. 281	•	•	•
		RN Note Taking Guide 11-3	•	•	•
		IB Image Bank 11-9, 11-10, 11-12		•	
		TR Practice 11-3		•	
		TR Section 11-3 Quiz		•	

Chapter Review and Assessment

- **SE** Chapter 11 Review, p. 288 L3
- **CTB** Chapter 11 Test L2 L3 L4
- **SE** Standardized Test Prep, p. 289 L3

PROGRAM COMPONENTS

SE Student Edition	**CTB** Computer Test Bank
TE Teacher Edition	**AUD** Audio Section Summaries
TR Teaching Resources	
RN Reading and Note Taking Guide	**DVD** Teens Talk Video Series
	VVG Video Viewing Guide
ARN Adapted Reading and Note Taking Guide	**PPT** Presentation
IB Image Bank	

Differentiated Instruction

L1 L2 L4 EL

		SE eTEXT	TE eTEXT	PRINT
ARN	Note Taking Guide 11-1 L2	•	•	
RN	Note Taking Guide 11-1 EL	•	•	•
AUD	Audio Summary 11-1 L1 L2 EL	•	•	
TE	Reteach Strategy, p. 271 L2		•	•
TR	Enrich 11-1 L4		•	
ARN	Note Taking Guide 11-2 L2	•	•	
RN	Note Taking Guide 11-2 EL	•	•	•
AUD	Audio Summary 11-2 L1 L2 EL	•	•	
TE	Reteach Strategy, p. 275 L2		•	•
TR	Enrich 11-2 L4		•	
ARN	Building Health Skills 11 L2	•	•	
RN	Building Health Skills 11 EL	•	•	•
ARN	Note Taking Guide 11-3 L2	•	•	
RN	Note Taking Guide 11-3 EL	•	•	•
AUD	Audio Summary 11-3 L1 L2 EL	•	•	
TE	Reteach Strategy, p. 286 L2		•	•
TR	Enrich 11-3 L4		•	

ABILITY LEVELS

L1 **For students with special needs**
L2 **For less proficient readers**
L3 **For all students**
L4 **For gifted and talented students**
EL **For English language learners**

Chapter 11 Digital/Video Pathway

This alternative pathway allows you to teach this chapter's content using only the video and online materials.

Preview

DVD	**Video #11 Preview**
SE	Video #11 Preview Activity
VVG	Video #11 Worksheet

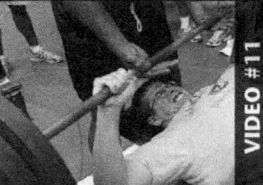

The Risks of Steroids

1

PPT	11-1 Presentation
RN/ARN	11-1 Note Taking
PPT	11-1 Section Quiz

2

DVD	**Video #11 Explore/Wrap-Up**
VVG	Video #11 Worksheet
PPT	11-2 Presentation
RN/ARN	11-2 Note Taking
PPT	11-2 Section Quiz

The Risks of Steroids

3

PPT	11-3 Presentation
RN/ARN	11-3 Note Taking
PPT	11-3 Section Quiz

Chapter Preview

Section 1 Your Skeletal System
The skeletal system supports the body, protects internal organs, allows the body to move, and stores and produces materials that the body needs. You can keep your skeletal system healthy by eating well, exercising, avoiding injuries, and getting regular medical checkups.

Section 2 Your Muscular System
Smooth muscle causes involuntary movements in the body. Cardiac muscle, found only in the heart, pumps blood through the body. Skeletal muscle causes body movements by moving bones. Muscles get stronger with regular exercise. Warming up and cooling down help prevent muscle injuries.

 Practicing Healthful Behaviors

Warming Up, Stretching, and Cooling Down
Warming up and stretching before exercise, and then cooling down afterward helps prevent muscle injuries.

Section 3 Your Nervous System
The nervous system senses information inside and outside the body, processes the information, and forms a response to it. The nervous system is divided into the central nervous system and the peripheral nervous system. The central nervous system consists of the brain and spinal cord. The peripheral nervous system is the network of nerves that links the body to the brain and spinal cord. Protecting the nervous system from injury is the most important way to maintain its health.

 GO ONLINE

PearsonSuccessNet.com
For resources and activities for this chapter.

Movement and Coordination

1 Your Skeletal System

2 Your Muscular System

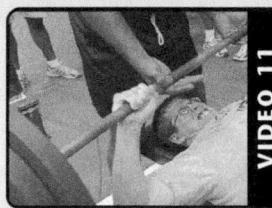 **Building Health Skills**
- **Practicing Healthful Behaviors** Warming Up, Stretching, and Cooling Down

3 Your Nervous System
- **Hands-On Activity** Mixed Messages

GO ONLINE PearsonSuccessNet.com

VIDEO 11

TEENS Talk
The Risks of Steroids

Preview **Activity**

What Do You Know About Steroids?

Complete this activity before you watch the video.

1. List three statements about steroids that you think are true.
2. Get together with a partner to discuss the statements you each wrote. Try to come to an agreement about whether each statement is true or false.
3. In a paragraph discuss what you learned from this activity. **WRITING**

264

Sensitive Issues

- Students with impaired mobility may feel uncomfortable studying this chapter. When you discuss movement, try to use examples that these students can perform. For example, if you have a paraplegic student, choose an action like dialing a phone or playing a musical instrument as an example of voluntary movement.

- Throughout this chapter, exercise is mentioned as a way to maintain the health of the skeletal, muscular, and nervous systems. Students who do not participate in exercise or sports may ignore the benefits of exercise, thinking the information does not apply to them. Stress the need to find suitable physical activities. Remind students that brisk walking is great exercise.

Video Objectives

Use this video to help students

Identify pressures that lead some teens to take steroids and supplements.

Describe the short- and long-term risks of steroid use.

Apply decision-making skills to situations that affect their health.

Preview **Activity**

What Do You Know About Steroids?

Just before watching the video, have students complete the Preview Activity. Ask volunteers to read the statements that both partners agreed were true. Choose statements that you know to be myths. Write those statements on the board so that students can see them while watching the video. Be sure to revisit these statements after showing the video to discuss why the statements are not true.

265

From the Authors

There are several ways you can make this chapter exciting for students. First, emphasize the interaction of all three systems with physical activity. Second, make sure students understand that strength training not only improves muscle strength and endurance and motor coordination, but can also increase bone mass. Third, remind students that attention to their skeletal and muscular systems can improve posture and overall physical appearance.

Activities such as the Quick Quiz on page 266 should help students realize that the choices they make are important for good physical and mental health.

Section 1

Your Skeletal System

Objectives

Before class begins, write the objectives on the board. Have students copy the objectives into their notebooks at the start of class.

1. Focus

Warm-Up Quick Quiz

Use the Warm-Up Presentations slide to survey student responses.

Have students answer the questions to the Quick Quiz on their own. When students have completed the quiz, invite them to infer how these healthy behaviors help protect the body from injury. Challenge students to choose one of the behaviors from the quiz that they sometimes or never do and incorporate it into their lifestyle.

Presentation 11-1

Objectives

▶ **Identify** the five main roles of the skeletal system.

▶ **Describe** the functions of bones and joints.

▶ **Explain** how you can keep your skeletal system healthy.

Vocabulary

- joint
- cartilage
- ossification
- marrow
- ligament
- osteoporosis
- fracture
- sprain
- dislocation
- scoliosis

Warm-Up

Quick Quiz Complete each of these statements with *always, sometimes,* or *never.*

1. I ___?___ warm up before exercising.

2. When I ride a bicycle or play contact sports, I ___?___ wear a helmet and other protective gear.

3. When I ride in a vehicle, I ___?___ fasten my seat belt.

4. My backpack for school is ___?___ less than 15% of my body weight.

5. I ___?___ make an effort to exercise on a regular basis.

WRITING Why do you think that teens might not always practice these healthful behaviors?

Functions of the Skeletal System

Have you ever seen a new building under construction? Before the roof or walls can take shape, the building's frame must be built. Like a building, your body needs a frame to give it shape and support. Your body's framework is your skeletal system. **Your skeletal system has five main roles. It provides support, protects internal organs, allows your body to move, and stores and produces materials that your body needs.**

Support and Protection As you can see in Figure 1, your skeleton is made up of all the bones in your body. Your skeleton gives your body its basic shape and provides the support that you need as you move through your day. The center of your skeleton is your backbone, or vertebral column. The backbone consists of 33 bones called vertebrae (VUR tuh bray). The vertebrae support your head and give flexibility to your neck and back.

Many bones of the skeletal system protect internal organs. Your ribs and breastbone, for example, form a protective cage around your heart and lungs. Your backbone protects the spinal cord, which runs through holes in the vertebrae. The hard, thick skull protects your brain.

WRITING and Health

 Web Site

Have student groups plan a Web page that describes the functions and structures of the skeletal system. They can describe their plan for the Web site by using posters as storyboards. Students should provide details about how users will navigate through the site.

Movement In coordination with your muscular and nervous systems, your skeletal system allows you to move. The range of movements can be as simple as striking a key on a keyboard, or as spectacular as pushing your body off the ground to spike a volleyball.

Storage and Production of Materials Your bones store essential substances, such as phosphorus and calcium, which are released when other parts of the body need them. Some bones, such as the breastbone and part of the thighbone, also produce blood cells.

 **Connect to Your Life** If you run your fingers down the center of your back, which bones can you feel?

The Skeletal System

FIGURE 1 Your skeleton provides a framework that supports and protects many other body parts.

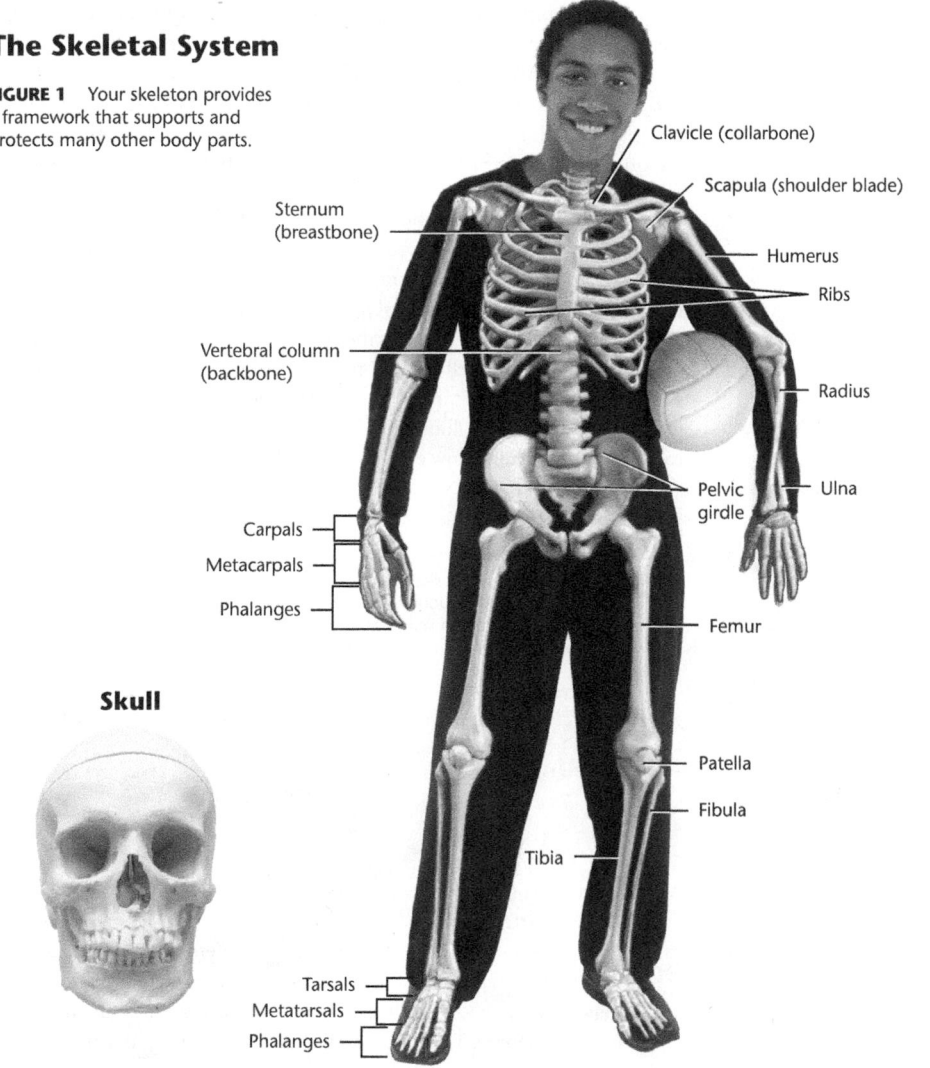

- Clavicle (collarbone)
- Scapula (shoulder blade)
- Sternum (breastbone)
- Humerus
- Ribs
- Vertebral column (backbone)
- Radius
- Pelvic girdle
- Ulna
- Carpals
- Metacarpals
- Phalanges
- Femur
- Skull
- Patella
- Fibula
- Tibia
- Tarsals
- Metatarsals
- Phalanges

Movement and Coordination **267**

2. Teach

L3 **EL** Reading/Note Taking 11-1
L2 Adapted Reading/Note Taking 11-1

Functions of the Skeletal System

L2 Class Discussion

Invite volunteers to describe how a house is built. Guide them in their descriptions so that they focus on the frame, regardless of whether it is made of wood, steel, or brick. Then challenge the class to describe how the frame protects and supports the house. Relate how the frame of a house is similar to the skeletal system. Have students make comparisons between the five main roles of the skeletal system and the role of a house frame. Ask: **What does the skeletal system do that a house frame does not?** (*A house frame does not allow the house to move and it does not produce materials.*)

L3 Active Learning

Challenge student groups to use common classroom materials to demonstrate how specific parts of the skeletal system protect and support the body.

L3 Visual Learning: Figure 1

Image Bank Figure 11-1

Refer students to Figure 1 and ask: **How would you describe the structure of the ribs?** (*Students might describe the ribs as a cage.*) **Based on their structure, what function do you think ribs have?** (*Ribs protect the heart and lungs and support the body so those organs have space to work.*) **What other bones protect internal organs?** (*Sample answer: skull, backbone, breastbone, pelvic girdle*) Then have students compare the number of bones in a finger to the number of bones in an arm. Ask: **How might the number of bones in a structure affect movement?** (*Students might infer that more bones allow for finer movements.*)

 **Connect to Your Life** the vertebrae that make up the backbone

Bones and Joints

L3 Online Activity GO ONLINE

Visit Pearson SuccessNet to access an online activity about movable joints. Have students complete the Web activity.

L3 Teacher Demo

About a week before you discuss the skeletal system, obtain two similar bones from a cooked chicken or turkey. Clean the bones. Then boil them and allow them to dry. Place one bone in a jar with white vinegar. Cover the jar and leave it undisturbed. Demonstrate how the bones differ. *(The bone soaked in vinegar is rubbery.)* Explain that the acid in the vinegar dissolved the bone's calcium. Ask: **What can you infer about the function of calcium in bones?** *(It makes bones hard and rigid.)*

L2 Visual Learning: Figure 2

Tell students to read about the parts of a bone in Figure 2. Ask: **How does compact bone differ from spongy bone?** *(Compact bone is more solid and denser than spongy bone. Spongy bone has spaces created by flat, needlelike structures. Spongy bone may contain red bone marrow.)* Point out that only long bones have space in the central cavity to store fat. Then have students describe how bone structure contributes to the five functions of the skeletal system.
Caption Answer in the central cavity

L3 Building Vocabulary

Show students the derivation of the word *ossification* by writing the following on the board: The word *ossify* comes from the Latin word *os,* which means "bone" and the suffix *–fy,* meaning "to make" or "cause to become." Ask: **What does ossify mean?** *(to make into bone)* Then write that the suffix *–ation* means "an action or process." Ask: **What does ossification mean?** *(the process of becoming bone)*

GO ONLINE
PearsonSuccessNet.com
For: More on movable joints

Bones and Joints

Did you know that your skeletal system is made up of just over 200 bones? A place in your body where two or more of your bones come together is called a **joint.** Your bones and joints work together every time you move.

Development of Bones **Your bones are living structures that undergo change throughout your life.** A newborn's skeleton is made mostly of **cartilage,** a tough supportive tissue that is softer and more flexible than bone. By young adulthood, most of this cartilage is replaced by bone in a process called **ossification** (ahs uh fih KAY shun). During this process, minerals, such as calcium and phosphorus, are deposited within the developing bone, making it hard. By young adulthood, the only cartilage left in your body will be in the outer part of your ears and nose, covering the ends of some bones, and cushioning some joints.

After ossification is complete, cells in the bones continue to maintain and repair the tissue. If you were to break a bone, the cells would form new tissue to fill the gap between the broken ends. Eventually, the healed region containing new bone might be stronger than the original bone.

Structure of Bones Bones are remarkably strong, although they are light in weight. This is because bone consists of two different types of tissue—compact bone and spongy bone. Figure 2 shows the location of these tissues and other structures in the thighbone, or femur. Another type of tissue called **marrow** fills the spaces in bones. There are two types of marrow—red and yellow. Red marrow, found in the spaces of some spongy bone, produces many types of blood cells. On average, red marrow produces 100 billion blood cells every day. Yellow marrow, which can be found in the hollow centers of long bones, stores fat.

FIGURE 2 Bones are intricate living structures that contain several types of tissue.
Interpreting Diagrams In which part of a bone is fat stored?

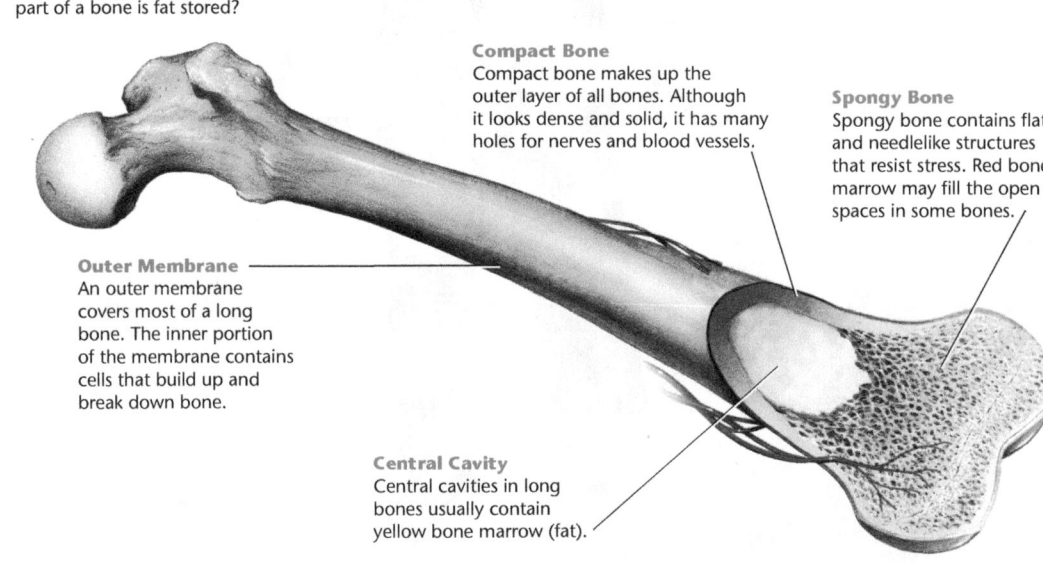

Compact Bone
Compact bone makes up the outer layer of all bones. Although it looks dense and solid, it has many holes for nerves and blood vessels.

Spongy Bone
Spongy bone contains flat and needlelike structures that resist stress. Red bone marrow may fill the open spaces in some bones.

Outer Membrane
An outer membrane covers most of a long bone. The inner portion of the membrane contains cells that build up and break down bone.

Central Cavity
Central cavities in long bones usually contain yellow bone marrow (fat).

268 *Chapter 11*

For Your INFORMATION!

Bone Cells

Bone tissue is made up of three kinds of cells: osteocytes, osteoblasts, and osteoclasts. Osteocytes are mature bone cells. Osteoblasts make new bone by producing collagen and filling it with mineral deposits (calcium, phosphorus, and sodium). Osteoblasts are active during growth, the repair of fractures, and bone remodeling that occurs with changes in exercise and nutrition. Osteoclasts break down old or damaged bone. Osteoclasts are active during fracture repair, remodeling, and when the body needs stored calcium. The osteoclasts produce an enzyme that removes calcium from the bone and releases it into the blood.

FIGURE 3 The different kinds of joints allow you to move and position your body in a variety of ways.

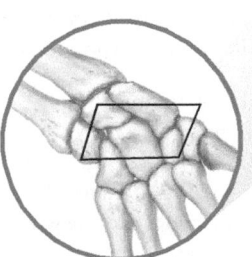

Pivot Joint
A pivot joint connects your head to the first vertebra in your backbone. It allows you to turn your head from side to side.

Ball-and-Socket Joint
A ball-and-socket joint allows movement in all directions. Your shoulders and hips are ball-and-socket joints.

Gliding Joint
Gliding joints allow movement in many directions as the bones slide along each other. Your wrists and ankles contain several gliding joints.

Hinge Joint
A hinge joint allows bending and straightening movements. Your knees and elbows are hinge joints.

Joints Without joints, your body would be like a chair with arms and legs that cannot move. **Joints allow for movement and protect bones from friction and force.** Some joints, such as those in your skull are immovable—they allow no motion. Other joints, such as those in your elbows, knees, and shoulders are movable. Four different types of movable joints are shown in Figure 3.

Bones are held together at joints by strong, fibrous bands called **ligaments.** A smooth layer of tough cartilage cushions and protects the ends of bones where they meet. Membranes around some joints secrete a fluid that lubricates the joint and reduces friction between the bones.

Connect to Your Life
What joint allows you to wave hello to a friend? What type of joint is it?

L3 Visual Learning: Figure 3
Image Bank Figure 11-3

Refer students to the different kinds of joints in Figure 3. Encourage students to move their own joints and visualize how the joint works by looking at the corresponding image in the figure. Then ask: **What would happen if the knee were a ball-and-socket joint?** *(The lower leg would be able to rotate like the upper arm.)* **How would the upper arm move if it were a hinge joint?** *(The arm would not be able to move in all directions.)*

L2 Class Discussion

Ask students to picture what their lives would be like if their fingers had no joints. Ask: **What types of activities would be impossible to perform?** *(typing, buttoning shirts, opening jars, putting on makeup)* **What is the difference between the joints in your fingers and the joints in your skull?** *(The joints in fingers are movable, but the joints in the skull are not.)* Point out that though the skull seems to be one piece, it is actually made of several bones fused together at immovable joints.

L3 Addressing Misconceptions

Double-Jointed Ask students to define "double-jointed" and explain how a double-jointed person can move. Then explain that people who are able to move fingers or limbs farther than average do not have an extra joint. Rather, they have greater muscle flexibility or looser ligaments that allow for a significant range of motion.

Connect to Your Life
Sample answer: the wrist; a gliding joint

Differentiated Instruction

L2 Less Proficient Readers
Have students carefully read about bone development and create a flowchart that describes the way in which bones change throughout life. Students should include details about each stage and definitions for *ossification* and *cartilage* in their own words. Encourage students to use their flowcharts to study for the chapter test.

Keeping Healthy

L3 **Cultural Connection**

Some people have a low calcium intake due to the foods they commonly eat. Have students list foods that are associated with specific cultures. Ask volunteers to find nutrition information for these foods. Are there certain cultures that may consume more calcium than others? Which of the foods are highest in calcium?

L1 **Building Health Skills**

Analyzing Influences On the board, write a list of sports and activities for which helmets are worn to prevent head injuries. *(football, baseball, hockey, biking, and horseback riding)* Invite students to add to the list. Then, ask students to make their own list of activities they participate in and indicate whether or not they wear a helmet. For each activity, have students write why they do or do not wear a helmet. For activities during which they do not wear helmets, have students consider what is influencing their behavior and what it would take to change their opinion about helmets.

L3 **Teacher Demo**

Put on a backpack and exaggerate how your body compensates to carry an overloaded pack. Explain how this poor posture strains the back, causing back and neck pain. Tell students that a backpack should weigh no more than 15 percent of their body weight. Then, demonstrate how to wear a backpack properly: each shoulder strap on one shoulder, straps tightened so the pack lies close to the back, waist straps buckled to pull in the bottom of the pack, which should be above the waist.

Connect to Your Life *Sample answers:* dancing, running, racquet sports, soccer, basketball, lacrosse

Healthy bone

Bone with osteoporosis

FIGURE 4 Weight-bearing activities, such as running, make your bones stronger by stimulating bone cells to make more bone. Building up bone mass in your teen years can decrease your chance of developing osteoporosis.

Keeping Healthy

Because your skeletal system performs so many functions, it is important to keep it healthy. **A combination of eating well, physical activity, and avoiding injuries contributes to lifelong bone and joint health. In addition, regular medical checkups can help detect skeletal system problems.**

Eating Well Adequate intake of calcium and phosphorus will help your bones grow to their maximum size and strength. Your body stores these minerals during childhood and adolescence. As you age, your bones will begin to lose some of these stored minerals. Significant mineral loss can lead to **osteoporosis,** a condition in which the bones become weak and break easily. If you enter your adult years with a good supply of stored minerals, you can decrease your risk for osteoporosis.

Other nutrients that are important for bone health include potassium, magnesium, and vitamins A, C, and D. See Chapter 8 for examples of foods that are rich in these nutrients.

Exercising Another way to build strong bones and prevent osteoporosis is to get plenty of weight-bearing physical activity. Activities in which the bones support the entire weight of your body help your bones grow strong and dense. Some examples of weight-bearing activities are dancing, running, racquet sports, soccer, basketball, and lacrosse.

Avoiding Bone Injuries One common injury of the skeletal system is a **fracture,** or a break in a bone. In a simple fracture, the bone may be cracked or completely broken in two or more pieces. In a compound fracture, the broken ends of the bone pierce the skin. Fractures are treated by putting the broken ends of the bone back together. Splints or casts are used to prevent movement of the bone until the bone tissue can repair itself. In some cases, surgery is required.

You can protect your bones from fractures. When participating in a physical activity, wear appropriate safety equipment, such as helmets and pads. Always wear a seat belt when traveling in a vehicle.

 **Connect to Your Life** **What are three weight-bearing activities that you enjoy?**

270 *Chapter 11*

TEENS *Are Asking . . .*

Q: Is it safe for teens to lift weights?

A: Yes, even though your bones and joints are still developing, it is safe to strength train as long as you do it properly. Strength training will improve your strength and endurance and will help reduce the risk of injuries to bones and joints. Strength training can also prevent or delay osteoporosis later in life because it makes bones denser. Before starting a strength-training program, work with a coach, athletic trainer, or physical education teacher to learn proper techniques. To prevent injury, start slowly, avoid heavy weights, use proper form, and gradually increase workouts.

Avoiding Joint Injuries   As you participate in physical activities, keep in mind that your bones and joints are still developing. Some injuries can lead to permanent damage. Proper warm-up and stretching exercises are important to help prevent joint injuries.

▶ **Sprains** Most likely you or someone you know has experienced a **sprain,** an overstretched or torn ligament. Treatment for mild sprains can include ice to reduce swelling and pain relievers. Severe sprains may require a brace or surgery.

▶ **Dislocations** In a **dislocation,** the ends of the bones in a joint are forced out of their normal positions. To treat a dislocation, the bones are typically put back into their proper positions and held in place by a cast or bandage until the joint heals.

▶ **Torn Cartilage** Serious damage to the cartilage between the bones in a joint is known as torn cartilage. The knees are particularly susceptible to this injury. Surgery, such as arthroscopic surgery, is often necessary to repair or remove torn cartilage.

▶ **Overuse Injuries** When an activity is performed too often or too strenuously, joints may become irritated and inflamed. In teens, overuse injuries most commonly occur to the shoulders or knees. Teens who play the same sport year-round are susceptible to overuse injuries. Also, carrying a heavy backpack improperly may cause overuse injuries to the back and shoulders.

Medical Checkups   If you experience bone or joint pain it is a good idea to see a doctor. He or she can advise you on how to prevent serious injury or recommend other professionals who can help you.

During yearly physical examinations, a nurse or doctor may check your spine for **scoliosis** (skoh lee OH sis), an abnormal curvature of the spine. Scoliosis usually develops during childhood, but it may not be detected until the teen years. Your doctor will also monitor your height and weight to make sure you are growing properly.

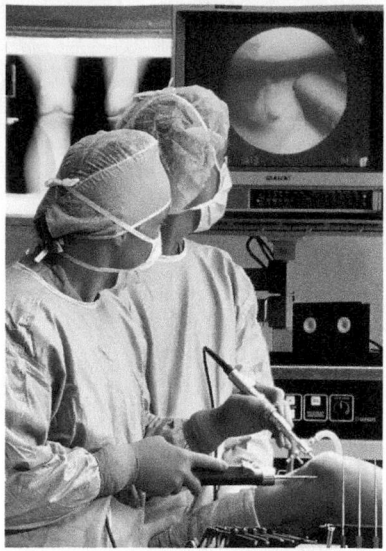

FIGURE 5   During arthroscopic surgery, doctors insert an instrument called an arthroscope into the joint. A camera attached to the arthroscope projects an image onto a monitor. Tiny instruments are then used to make repairs.

Section 1 Review

Key Ideas and Vocabulary

1. List the five main roles of the skeletal system.
2. Explain the function of bones.
3. Describe the two types of bone **marrow.**
4. What is a **joint?** Describe the function of movable joints in the body.
5. Identify four ways you can help your skeletal system stay healthy.

Health and Community

Safety Poster Create a poster aimed at young children that explains how to prevent bone, joint, and muscle injuries. With permission, display the poster in an elementary school, library, or other public place.

Critical Thinking

6. **Comparing and Contrasting** How is a newborn's skeleton different from your own?
7. **Classifying** Which type of joint allows you to kneel down? To move your arm in a circle?

Evaluate
These assignments can help you assess students' mastery of the section content.

Section 1 Review
Answers appear below.

Teaching Resources
• Practice 11-1
• Section 11-1 Quiz

L2 Reteach
Work with students to create a concept map that shows the five main functions of the skeletal system. Students should copy the concept map into their notebooks. Ask students to describe the role of bones and joints and how these components enable the skeletal system to carry out its functions. Invite students to suggest ways to add this information to the concept map.

L4 Enrich
Teaching Resources
• Enrich 11-1

Health and Community
Safety Poster Divide the class into groups, and give each group poster paper and markers. Suggest that students choose one type of joint injury to prevent, such as a sprain, or one way of protecting against injury, such as wearing a helmet. Suggest that students draw illustrations, design graphics on the computer, cut pictures from magazines, or take digital pictures and print them on paper. Have groups present their posters to the class.

Section 1 Review

1. The skeleton provides support, protects organs, allows for movement, and stores and produces materials the body needs.
2. Bones store fat, calcium, and other minerals; produce blood cells; support the body; and protect organs.
3. Red marrow, found in the spaces of some spongy bone, produces many types of blood cells. Yellow marrow, found in the center of long bones, stores fat.
4. A joint is where two or more bones come together. Movable joints allow the body to move in various ways.
5. eat well, exercise, avoid injuries, and get regular medical checkups
6. A newborn's skeleton is made mostly of cartilage. At my age, most of the cartilage has been replaced by bone.
7. hinge; ball-and-socket

Objectives
Before class begins, write the objectives
on the board. Have students copy the
objectives into their notebooks at the
start of class.

1. Focus

Warm-Up Myth/Fact

After students complete the writing
assignment, invite volunteers to
share their responses. Then, challenge
students to identify the underlying
motivation for groups or individuals
who advocate the "no pain, no gain"
myth.

Presentation 11-2

Connect to Your Life   skeletal muscles

Section 2

Your Muscular System

Objectives
▶ **Describe** the functions of
the three types of muscles.
▶ **Explain** how you can
keep your muscular
system healthy.

Vocabulary
• smooth muscle
• cardiac muscle
• skeletal muscle
• tendon
• muscle tone
• atrophy
• anabolic steroid
• strain
• tendonitis

Warm-Up

Myth No pain, no gain.

Fact Pain is not a sign of a good workout. Rather, pain is
a signal from your body that you are working too hard or
you have an injury. Continuing to exercise through
the pain could lead to a more serious injury.

WRITING   Where do you think most teens get
their information about muscles? How factual do
you think their information is?

The Muscles in Your Body

To open this book and turn its pages, you use muscles in your arms and
hands. Muscles move your eyes as you read the printed words. Muscles in
your chest allow you to breathe, and muscles in your heart pump your
blood. Every time your body moves, muscles are at work.

Types of Muscle   Your body has three types of muscle tissue that
perform different functions—smooth muscle, cardiac muscle, and
skeletal muscle. Some of these muscle tissues are involuntary muscle,
which means they are not consciously controlled. Other muscles are voluntary muscle, which means they can be consciously controlled.

▶ **Smooth muscle** is involuntary muscle that causes movements within
your body. Smooth muscles in the walls of your esophagus and intestines push food through your digestive system. Other smooth muscles
in your blood vessels help circulate your blood.

▶ **Cardiac muscle** is involuntary muscle that is found only in the heart.
Throughout your life, cardiac muscle allows your heart to beat and
pump blood throughout your body.

▶ **Skeletal muscles** are the muscles that you control to do activities,
such as walk or play a musical instrument. As the name indicates,
skeletal muscles are attached to the bones of your skeleton. A thick
strand of tissue called a **tendon** attaches a muscle to a bone.

Connect to Your Life   Which type of muscle helps you move your jaw to
chew your food?

WRITING and Health

L3 News Report

Instruct students to write a news story in
which they report the functions of the
three types of muscles. Students can
choose to treat the story as breaking news
or a health update. In their stories, students should describe the three types of
muscle tissue, the functions of each muscle
tissue, and how muscles work.

How Muscles Work All muscles do work by contracting, or becoming shorter and thicker. Muscle cells, which are often called fibers, contract when they receive a nerve message to do so. As you can see in Figure 6, many skeletal muscles work in pairs. One muscle in the pair contracts to move the bone in one direction. Then, the other muscle in the pair contracts to move the bone back.

Muscle Tone Even when a skeletal muscle is not contracting to cause movement, a few of its individual muscle fibers are still contracting. These contractions are not strong enough to cause movement, but they do tense and firm the muscle. This slight tension is called **muscle tone**. For example, at any given moment the muscles in your neck contract just enough to keep your head upright, even when you are not moving your head. Muscle tone also keeps your muscles healthy and ready for action. Muscles that cannot contract due to injury, or are not used often, will weaken and shrink, a condition known as **atrophy**.

FIGURE 6 Skeletal muscles are attached to bones and participate in movement. Your biceps and triceps are an example of a muscle pair. When a biceps contracts and a triceps relaxes, your arm bends. Your arm straightens when a biceps relaxes and a triceps contracts.
Relating Cause and Effect Which muscle contracts when you wrinkle your forehead?

The Muscular System

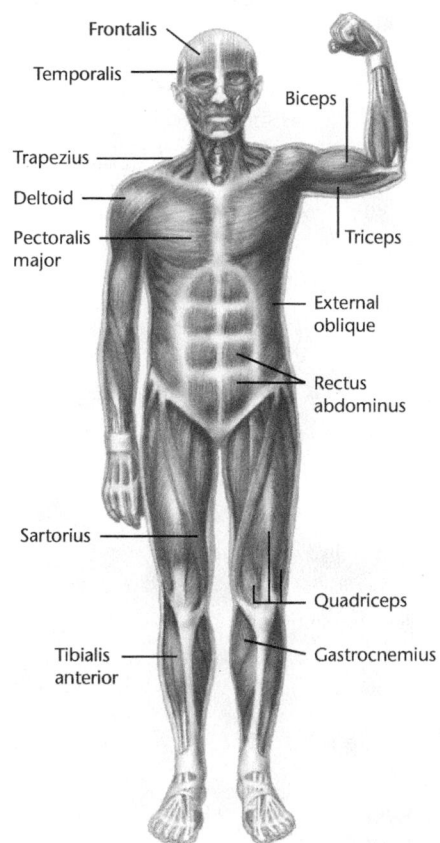

Frontalis
Temporalis
Trapezius
Deltoid
Pectoralis major
Biceps
Triceps
External oblique
Rectus abdominus
Sartorius
Quadriceps
Tibialis anterior
Gastrocnemius

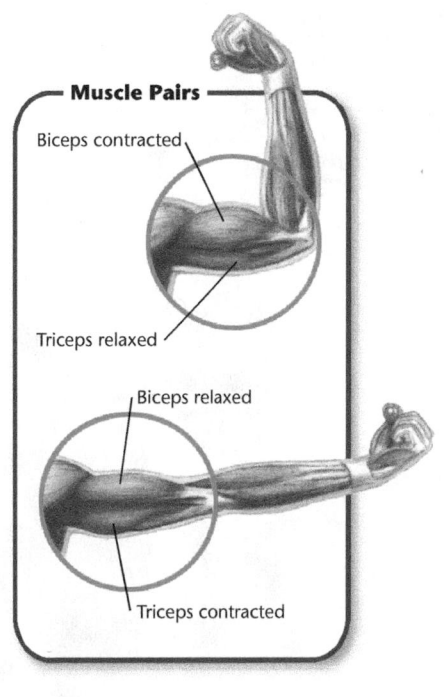

Muscle Pairs

Biceps contracted
Triceps relaxed

Biceps relaxed
Triceps contracted

Movement and Coordination **273**

2. Teach

L3 EL Reading/Note Taking 11-2
L2 Adapted Reading/Note Taking 11-2

The Muscles in Your Body

L3 Cooperative Learning

Give student pairs two strips of stiff paper or poster board, two lengths of string, paper fasteners, and a hole punch. Challenge students to use the materials to make a model of how skeletal muscles contract to move bones. Suggest they use the diagram of muscle pairs in Figure 6 as a guide. Then have students write a short description of how the model shows how skeletal muscles work.

L2 Visual Learning: Figure 6

Image Bank Figure 11-6

Refer students to the muscle pair shown in Figure 6. Encourage students to bend and straighten their arm at the elbow, feeling for the biceps and triceps contracting and relaxing. Ask: **Why are the biceps and triceps called a muscle pair?** *(They are both needed to bend and straighten the arm at the elbow. As one contracts, the other relaxes.)* Challenge students to identify what body part moves when the quadriceps contract. *(The lower leg bends at the knee.)* **Caption Answer** the frontalis

L4 Building Media Literacy

Challenge students to analyze a television commercial that advertises fitness equipment. Students should describe what the television commercial is advertising and how the product is supposed to improve muscle tone or strength. Then using reliable sources, students should evaluate the claims made by the television commercial. Have students give reasons for or against purchasing the fitness equipment.

Differentiated Instruction

L1 Special Needs

Smooth muscle movements are the most difficult for students to understand because they usually cannot feel these muscles move. Give students a cracker to eat. After they swallow the cracker, ask them to describe how it gets from their mouth to their stomach. Identify the location of the stomach if necessary. Explain that the throat and esophagus have muscles all around them that squeeze the food down and into the stomach. Students can squeeze a tube of toothpaste to model this movement.

Keeping Healthy

L3 Content Update GO ONLINE

Visit Pearson SuccessNet for more information about keeping muscles healthy. Have students complete the Web activity.

L3 Building Health Skills

Setting Goals Have students assess their own exercise routine. They should list the activities they participate in and indicate whether these activities increase muscle strength or endurance. Also have students assess the amount of time they spend warming up and cooling down for these activities. Have students list in their journal the weaknesses in their exercise program. Then ask students to create an exercise plan that addresses these weaknesses and try it for two weeks. After two weeks, students should evaluate how well they implemented their plan and how their fitness improved.

L3 Cultural Connection

Discuss the perception of girls and exercise that may differ from culture to culture. Are girls expected to work out as hard as boys? Are they encouraged to strengthen their muscles in the same way as boys? Have students interview their parents and grandparents about how this trend has changed since they were your age.

Connect to Your Life Allow students to answer this question in their private journals.

GO ONLINE

PearsonSuccessNet.com

For: More on keeping muscles healthy

Keeping Healthy

Like your bones, your muscles get stronger when you use them often. But you must take care to avoid overuse and injury. **You can maintain a healthy muscular system by regularly participating in different types of exercise. To help prevent injuries, exercise sessions should include a warm-up and cool-down period.**

Working Your Muscles Some types of exercise, such as running, increase a muscle's endurance—how long it can contract without tiring. Other exercises, such as lifting weights, make individual fibers grow, which causes the muscles to thicken and increase in strength.

To increase muscle size and strength, some athletes are tempted to use **anabolic steroids,** artificial forms of the male hormone testosterone. Doctors prescribe these drugs to treat people with certain muscle disorders. When used illegally, anabolic steroids are dangerous and can cause serious damage to many body systems. You will read more about the dangers of steroid use in Chapter 13.

FIGURE 7 Muscular strength and endurance are important in sports and in everyday activities.

Connect to Your Life How many different types of exercise do you participate in?

Building muscle strength

Building muscle endurance

274

Differentiated Instruction

L4 Gifted and Talented

Have students compare different local fitness centers, including some less-expensive ones such as Boys and Girls Clubs. Students should find out if the focus of each center is on muscle strength training or cardiovascular fitness; whether instructors have training in physical education or physical therapy; and whether programs can be individually tailored to meet a person's needs and limitations. Students can make a chart to summarize their findings and present those findings to the class.

Avoiding Muscle Injuries You likely have felt muscle soreness immediately after exercise or in the days that followed. Some muscle soreness is normal, but pain can be a sign of a more serious injury.

▶ **Strains** A muscle **strain,** or a pulled muscle, is a painful injury that may happen when muscles are overworked or stretched too much or too quickly. Sometimes muscle fibers rip, resulting in a torn muscle.

▶ **Tendonitis** Overuse of tendons may lead to painful swelling and irritation called **tendonitis** (ten duh NY tis). Tennis elbow, which consists of pain in the forearm, is one example of tendonitis. Excessive use of a hand-held control while playing video games can also lead to tendonitis. You should not play video games for more than one hour without taking a break.

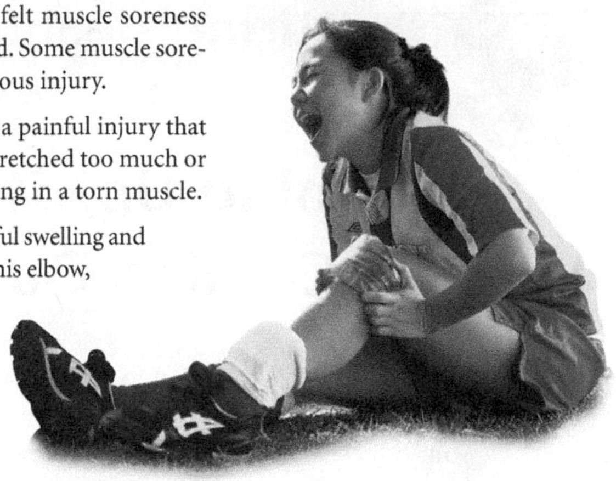

FIGURE 8 To help prevent muscle and tendon injuries, you should warm up properly and rest from exercise if you feel pain.

Treatment for muscle injuries usually includes rest, over-the-counter pain medication, and ice packs. If the injury is severe, surgery may be required.

Regular strengthening and stretching exercises can help you prevent injuries. Vary your exercise routine so that you are not always using the same muscles. Warm up before vigorous exercise, and include a cool-down period of mild exercise. Also, stop exercising if you feel sharp or sudden pain.

Preventing Muscle Cramps Have you ever felt a sudden, sharp pain in your leg or arm? If so, you may have experienced a muscle cramp, which is a strong, uncontrolled muscle contraction. To relieve a cramp, try massaging the affected area and exercising the limb gently. Stretching and drinking plenty of water before and during exercise can help you avoid muscle cramps.

Section 2 Review

Key Ideas and Vocabulary

1. Identify the three types of muscles and describe the location and function of each.
2. What is a **tendon**?
3. Explain what causes **muscle tone**. What causes the condition known as **atrophy**?
4. What can you do to prevent muscle injuries?
5. What is the cause of a muscle **strain**?

Critical Thinking

6. Evaluating Why is it an advantage that you do not have control over all of your muscles?

Health at School

Martial Arts Class Find out whether classes in martial arts such as judo, kendo, or tae kwon do are offered in your community. If so, observe a class. Then in a paragraph, describe to your classmates how the activity can help build muscular strength and endurance. **WRITING**

7. Applying Concepts Describe how a muscle pair in your thigh would work to bend and straighten your knee.

3. Assess

Evaluate

These assignments can help you assess students' mastery of the section content.

Section 3 Review

Answers appear below.

Teaching Resources
• Practice 11-2
• Section 11-2 Quiz

L2 Reteach

Have students make a table that lists the three types of muscle tissue in the muscular system, the functions of each muscle tissue, and where the muscle tissue is found in the body.

L4 Enrich

Teaching Resources
• Enrich 11-2

Health at School

Martial Arts Class Advise students that they should speak with an instructor first to get permission for observing a class. Suggest that students tell the instructor they wish to observe how martial arts helps build muscular strength and endurance.

5. muscles are overworked or stretched too quickly

6. Muscles that cause important body functions, such as digestion or circulation, continue to act without your control.

7. When the quadriceps at the top of the thigh contract and the muscles at the back of the thigh relax, the knee straightens. When the muscles at the back of the thigh contract and the quadriceps muscles relax, the knee bends.

Section 2 Review

1. Smooth muscle is found in many organs. It causes involuntary movements, such as pushing food through the digestive system. Cardiac muscle is found only in the heart and pumps blood through the body. Skeletal muscle is attached to bones and causes all skeletal movements.

2. A tendon attaches muscle to bone.

3. Muscle tone is caused by the slight tension of individual muscle fibers. Atrophy is caused when muscles weaken and shrink due to injury or disuse.

4. regular strengthening and stretching exercises, warming up and cooling down, and stopping exercise when feeling a sharp or sudden pain

Warming Up, Stretching, and Cooling Down

Objective

Identify warm-up, stretching, and cool-down exercises to prevent muscle injuries.

Teaching Strategies

- If you plan to do this activity as a class, remind students to wear appropriate clothing the day of the activity.

- Emphasize the dangers of bouncing during stretching exercises. Teach students not to force any stretch, but to allow the body to deepen the stretch with each repeat.

- Encourage students to keep a fitness diary in conjunction with Step 2 in Practice the Skill. They should record which stretching exercises they perform, and the length of time spent warming up and cooling down. They should also record how they felt before and after stretching, including any soreness or stiffness. At the end of the week, have students reread their diary entries from the beginning of the week to assess their progress.

Practicing Healthful Behaviors

Warming Up, Stretching, and Cooling Down

Suppose that you are about to go on a ten-mile bicycle ride or play your favorite sport. These are strenuous activities that put stress on your bones, muscles, and tendons. How should you prepare your body for these activities? And after the activity, what should you do to minimize the effects of the stress your body has just experienced?

1 Warming up

Before a workout, use slow movements to warm up the muscles that you will use. You should walk, jog slowly, or do the activity that you are about to participate in at a reduced pace. This warms up your muscles, preparing them for the more intense activity of the workout itself.

2 Stretching

▶ Once your muscles are warmed up, stretch them. Stretching "cold" muscles is not effective and can cause injury.

▶ Although no single stretching routine is appropriate for every activity, the stretching exercises shown here provide a base for you to build on. It is important not to rush when you perform these movements. A pulled muscle can hold you up much longer than the few minutes of warming up/stretching and cooling down/stretching needed with each workout.

▶ When you perform stretching exercises, do not bounce. Bouncing can tear muscle fibers. Scar tissue can form as a result limiting how much the muscle can stretch in the future.

3 Cooling down

After your workout, cool down by slowly moving the muscles you used at a reduced pace, much as you did to warm up. Do this for about five to ten minutes. Then stretch your muscles as you did before the workout. This cool-down period helps ease your body back to normal levels of muscular activity.

Practice the Skill

1. After warming up, take five to ten minutes to practice these stretching exercises.

2. Each day for a week, do the stretching routine and record how you felt before and after the routine, including any soreness or stiffness. At the end of the week, evaluate the stretching routine and your reactions to it. What are its benefits?

3. Select a favorite sport or other physical activity. Ask your physical education teacher or coach to suggest an appropriate warm-up, stretching, and cool-down routine for that activity. Then perform the activity along with the routine. Record how your muscles feel before, during, and after the activity.

276 *Chapter 11*

Sensitive Issues

Students who are physically inactive, overweight, or physically disabled may not be comfortable participating in these stretching exercises. Allow them to observe if they feel self-conscious. Emphasize that every person has different flexibility abilities.

Lower Back Curl

Lie on your back with legs extended. Draw your knees toward your chest. Grasp your legs just below your knees and gently pull your legs into your chest. Hold for 15 seconds.

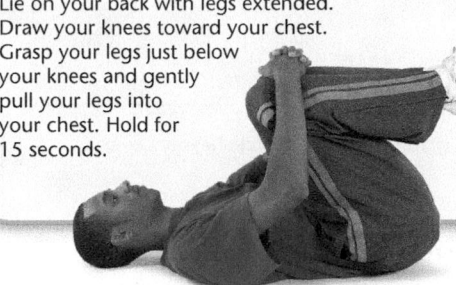

Side Stretch

Stand with feet apart, knees slightly bent, and one hand on your hip. Extend the opposite arm overhead and stretch to the side. Hold for 15 seconds. Repeat in the other direction. Do five times in each direction.

Hamstring Stretch

Sit on the floor and extend one leg, toes facing up. Tuck your other foot against your extended thigh. Reach forward over your extended leg and slide your hands down your leg until you feel a stretch. Bend from your waist, not from your neck and shoulders. Hold for 15 seconds. Switch to the other leg. Repeat with each leg twice.

Calf Stretch

Stand in a stride position with your left leg forward and hands on your hips. Lean your upper body forward. At the same time, bend your left leg and extend your right leg back in a continuous line with your upper body. Push your right heel to the ground. Hold for 15 seconds. Switch legs and repeat. Do this five times on each side.

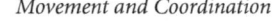

Triceps Stretch

Raise your right arm over your head. Bend at the elbow and place the hand at the center of your back. Place your left hand on your right elbow and pull gently. Hold for 15 seconds. Repeat with other arm.

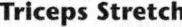

Movement and Coordination **277**

Practice the Skill

1. Assess student technique to be sure they are performing the stretch correctly without bouncing or straining.
2. By the end of the week, most students will feel more limber and energetic.
3. Students should feel that their muscles become stronger and more limber, causing them to feel more comfortable before, during, and after the activity. Students might also experience less muscle cramping.

Health at School

L2 Preparing for Other Activities

Encourage students to apply their knowledge of warming up to other activities. Explain that many different activities involve preparation, such as playing a musical instrument or getting into character for a play. Challenge students to think of other examples of how they prepare their body or mind for school activities. Then have them write a paragraph about their warm-up routine. **WRITING**

Section 3
Your Nervous System

Objectives
Before class begins, write the objectives on the board. Have students copy the objectives into their notebooks at the start of class.

1. Focus

Warm-Up **Health Stats**

After students finish completing the writing assignment, ask volunteers to share their responses. Ask the class if they have ever known anyone who suffered a head injury because they were not wearing a helmet. Did this experience affect their attitudes about helmets?

Presentation 11-3

Section 3 — Your Nervous System

Objectives
▶ **Explain** the functions of the nervous system and the role of neurons.
▶ **Describe** the roles of the central nervous system and the peripheral nervous system.
▶ **Identify** the most important thing you can do to keep your nervous system healthy.

Vocabulary
- neuron
- cerebrum
- cerebellum
- brain stem
- spinal cord
- reflex
- concussion
- coma
- paralysis
- meningitis
- seizure
- epilepsy

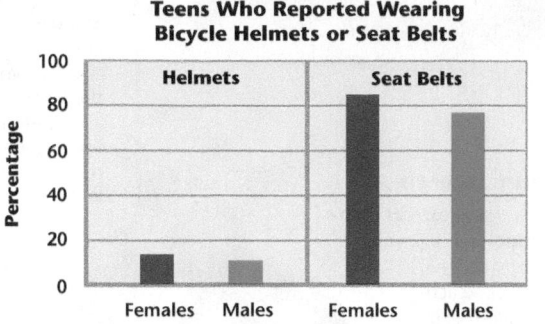

Warm-Up

Health Stats This graph compares bicycle-helmet use and seat-belt use among teens.

Teens Who Reported Wearing Bicycle Helmets or Seat Belts

WRITING Why do you think many more teens wear seat belts than bicycle helmets?

What Is the Nervous System?

Many of the actions you perform each day seem simple, but in reality, they are quite complex. For example, as you walk to class, the movement of your legs must be coordinated and your balance maintained. Also, your speed must be continually adjusted. Amazingly, your nervous system allows you to perform all of these actions while you think about your upcoming math test. **Your nervous system receives information about what is going on inside and outside of your body. Then it processes the information and forms a response to it.** These functions are accomplished with the help of the basic unit of the nervous system—a type of cell called a **neuron** (NOOR ahn).

Neuron Structure You can examine the structure of a neuron in Figure 9. **Neurons carry messages, or impulses, from one part of your body to another.** Notice that a neuron has three basic parts: dendrites, a cell body, and an axon. The junction where one neuron sends impulses to another neuron or another type of cell is called a synapse.

MATH and Health

 Ratios

The axon of a motor neuron that carries impulses to a foot is about 1 meter (1,000 mm) long. The diameter of its cell body is about 100 μm (0.1 mm). If students were to create a model of a nerve using a ping-pong ball as the cell body, how long would its axon be? They should assume the diameter of a ping-pong ball is 3.8 cm. *(The length of the model's axon can be calculated using the ratio: 0.1 mm/1,000 mm = 38 mm/x. When solving for x, x = (38 × 1,000) ÷ 0.1 = 380,000 mm. The axon would be 380 m long.)*

Types of Neurons Three types of neurons are found in your nervous system. Each type of neuron has a specific role.

▶ **Sensory Neurons** Information about your external and internal environment is gathered by sensory neurons through your sense organs or other parts of your body. For example, when your phone rings, sensory neurons carry information about the noise from your ears to your brain.

▶ **Interneurons** Located only in the brain and spinal cord, interneurons pass impulses from one neuron to another. When your phone rings, interneurons receive the messages from your sensory neurons about the ringing noise. Your brain determines that the noise is coming from your phone and you make the decision to answer it.

▶ **Motor Neurons** By command of other neurons, motor neurons send nerve impulses to muscles and glands. In the example of your ringing phone, interneurons signaled thousands of motor neurons. The motor neurons then signaled your muscles to pick up the phone.

 **Connect to Your Life** Which type of neuron signals your eyes to move across this page?

Neuron Structure

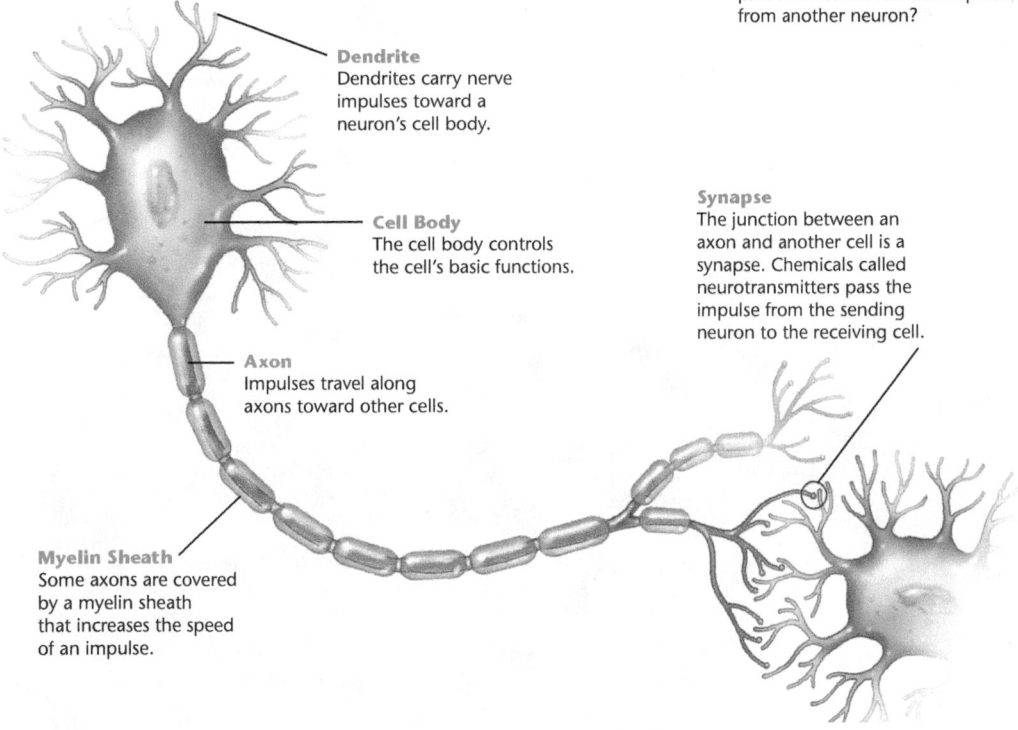

Dendrite
Dendrites carry nerve impulses toward a neuron's cell body.

Cell Body
The cell body controls the cell's basic functions.

Axon
Impulses travel along axons toward other cells.

Myelin Sheath
Some axons are covered by a myelin sheath that increases the speed of an impulse.

Synapse
The junction between an axon and another cell is a synapse. Chemicals called neurotransmitters pass the impulse from the sending neuron to the receiving cell.

FIGURE 9 Neurons relay impulses to other neurons, or they may send commands, in the form of chemical signals, to muscles or glands. **Interpreting Diagrams** Which part of a neuron receives impulses from another neuron?

Movement and Coordination **279**

Central Nervous System

⑬ Addressing Misconceptions

Static Brain Students may think that their brains are already fully developed. Explain that the brain continues to develop into a person's twenties. During the teen years, further connections are made between neurons that affect emotions and between those that affect physical and mental skills. This allows for more efficient thinking as an adult. It also means that neuron connections that are not used during the teen years will be pruned away. Invite students to list in their journals the activities they are often engaged in, such as music, art, academics, sports, video games, television. Challenge students to assess whether they are training their brains to be the kind of adult they wish to be.

⑫ Visual Learning: Figure 10

Image Bank Figure 11-10

Use Figure 10 to discuss the parts of the brain and their functions. Have students locate the three major parts of the brain in the figure. Ask such questions as: **What does the cerebrum control?** *(movement, memory, communication, and reasoning, and receives information from the senses)* **How do the left and right hemispheres of the cerebrum differ?** *(The right hemisphere generally controls muscles on the left side of the body and is associated with creativity and artistic ability. The left hemisphere generally controls muscles on the right side of the body and is associated with mathematical and logical thinking.)*
Caption Answer the brain stem

Central Nervous System

The nervous system consists of two major divisions—the central nervous system and the peripheral nervous system. **The central nervous system is the control center of the body. It includes the brain and spinal cord.** The peripheral nervous system (puh RIF ur ul) includes all the other parts of the nervous system, except for the brain and spinal cord.

The Brain The brain is a moist, spongy organ that weighs about 3 pounds. It is made up of about 100 billion neurons that control almost everything you do, feel, and remember. Within the skull, your brain is protected and cushioned by layers of membranes and fluid. The three major regions of the brain—the cerebrum, the cerebellum, and the brain stem—are shown in Figure 10.

FIGURE 10 Each of the three main regions of the brain—the cerebrum, the cerebellum, and the brain stem—carries out specific functions. **Predicting** Which region of the brain most likely controls blinking?

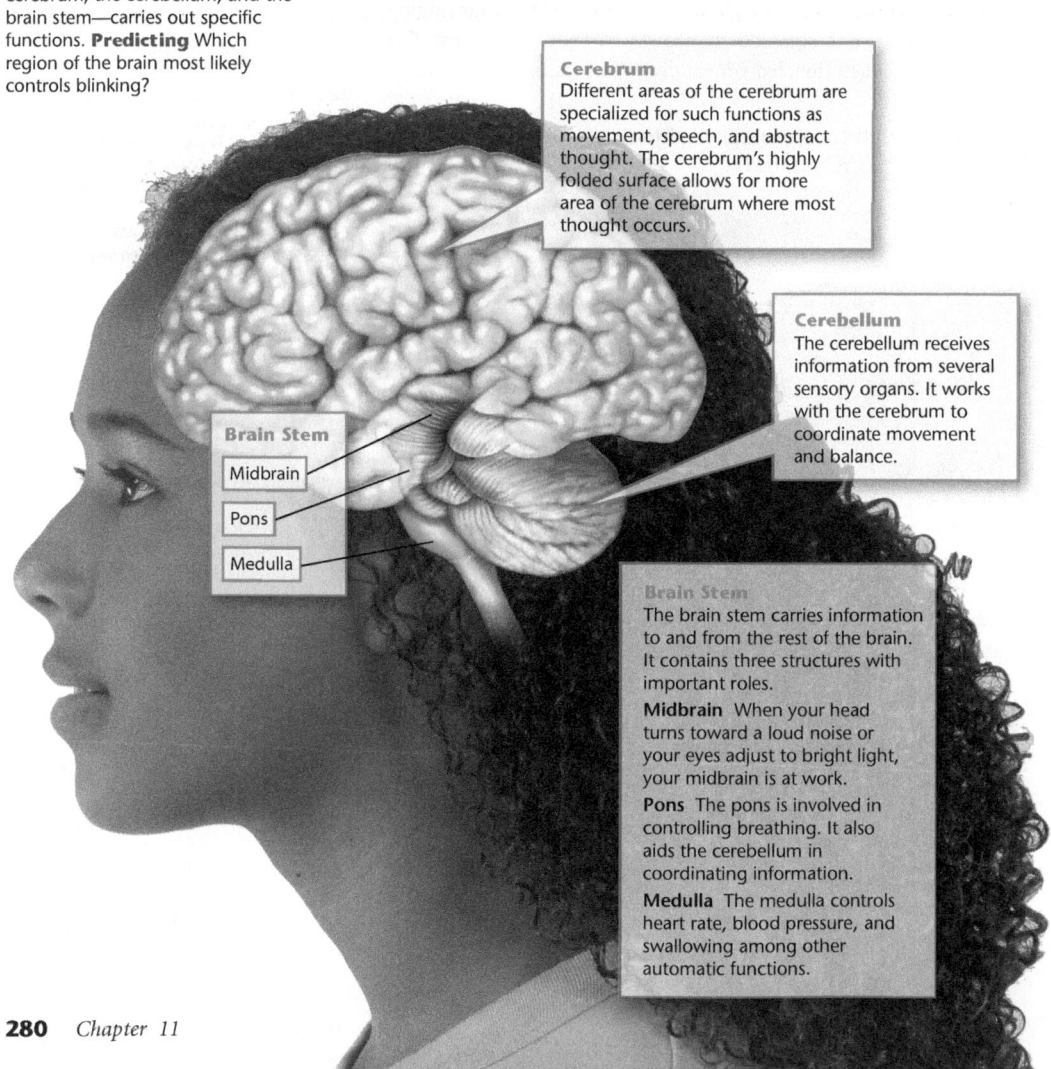

Cerebrum
Different areas of the cerebrum are specialized for such functions as movement, speech, and abstract thought. The cerebrum's highly folded surface allows for more area of the cerebrum where most thought occurs.

Cerebellum
The cerebellum receives information from several sensory organs. It works with the cerebrum to coordinate movement and balance.

Brain Stem
Midbrain
Pons
Medulla

Brain Stem
The brain stem carries information to and from the rest of the brain. It contains three structures with important roles.
Midbrain When your head turns toward a loud noise or your eyes adjust to bright light, your midbrain is at work.
Pons The pons is involved in controlling breathing. It also aids the cerebellum in coordinating information.
Medulla The medulla controls heart rate, blood pressure, and swallowing among other automatic functions.

280 *Chapter 11*

For Your INFORMATION!

Nerves vs. Neurons

A nerve is a bundle of thousands of fibers, or axons, from different neurons. Nerves are part of the peripheral nervous system. Not all neurons form nerves; the brain contains billions of neurons, but no nerves. When a neuron is stimulated, it responds by initiating and conducting an impulse along the length of the cell. The nerves that conduct impulses to the central nervous system are called afferent, or sensory, nerves. Nerves that conduct impulses away from the central nervous system are called efferent, or motor, nerves. Efferent nerves stimulate muscles and glands.

Hands-On *Activity*

Mixed Messages

Test how well your brain can handle conflicting messages.

green	blue	yellow
red	green	blue
blue	yellow	green
yellow	red	red
red	green	blue

Material
watch or clock with second hand

Try This

❶ Read the list of words while your partner times how long it takes you.

❷ Notice that the words in the list are written in different colors. This time you should say the color of each word as your partner times you. Do not read the words, rather, identify their colors.

Think and Discuss

❶ Did it take you more time to read the words or say the colors? Describe the experience of saying the colors.

❷ Which part of your brain most likely works hardest during this activity? Which task is your brain better at—reading the words or identifying their colors?

❸ Once people master basic skills such as tying shoes or reading, they perform them with little thought. How do you think this fact affected your results in this activity?

❹ What do you think would happen if you asked a young child who has just learned to read to do this activity? Explain.

▶ The **cerebrum** makes up about 85 percent of the brain's weight. It consists of several specialized regions that receive messages from sense organs, and control movement, memory, communication, and reasoning. A deep groove divides the cerebrum into left and right hemispheres. The right hemisphere generally controls the muscles on the left side of your body and the left hemisphere generally controls the muscles on the right side of your body. The right hemisphere is associated with creativity and artistic ability. The left hemisphere is associated with mathematical and logical thinking.

▶ The **cerebellum** (sehr uh BEL um) coordinates your body's movements and helps you keep your balance. Without the cerebellum, simple movements, such as picking up a glass of water without spilling it, would be impossible.

▶ The **brain stem** lies between the cerebrum and the spinal cord. The brain stem consists of three structures—the midbrain, pons, and medulla. These structures control many of your body's involuntary actions, such as breathing, sneezing, and your eyes' reaction to light.

Which of the three main parts of your brain is most likely involved in yawning?

Hands-On *Activity*

Mixed Messages

Invite student pairs to work on the activity together. Students can use the classroom clock or share watches to time each other. Encourage students to test family members at home.

Think and Discuss Answers

1. It usually takes longer to say the colors. Students might describe how they had to concentrate on thinking what the color was and ignoring that the letters spelled a word.

2. *Sample answer:* My cerebrum was most likely working hardest during the activity. My brain was better at reading the words.

3. *Sample answer:* Reading has become an activity that can be performed with little thought. My brain's first response was to read the word.

4. *Sample answer:* The child may have more difficulty reading the correct words, but say the correct colors easily. The words have less meaning to a child learning to read, especially because their reading requires a lot of thought. Naming colors is more automatic for young children than reading.

L2 Building Vocabulary

Guide students in creating a concept map for the nervous system. Students should show the parts of the central nervous system and their functions. Direct students to show the role of the peripheral nervous system and how it is related to the central nervous system. Suggest they also include neurons and their role in the nervous system.

the brain stem

Differentiated Instruction

EL English Language Learners

When introducing the three major parts of the brain, use a symbol that alludes to each part's function. For example, when you talk about the cerebrum, write *cerebrum* on the board and draw a light bulb to represent ideas. Briefly mime a "light bulb" moment to make sure students understand the meaning of the symbol. (For the cerebellum, draw a dancer standing on one leg to represent balance. For the brain stem, draw a heart to represent involuntary activities.) Give students phonetic spellings of the words accompanied with their symbols and a copy of Figure 10 to write notes on.

L3 Class Discussion

Emphasize that the spinal cord, while part of the central nervous system, links the brain to much of the peripheral nervous system. Briefly explain that the peripheral nervous system includes all the nervous tissue in the body except the brain and spinal cord. Ask: **How do most nerve impulses get to the brain?** *(by traveling through the spinal cord)* **When does the body react to the environment without nerve impulses reaching the brain?** *(during a reflex action)*

L3 Teacher Demo

While students are distracted, drop a large book so that it slams loudly onto your desk. Invite students to describe their response or the response they observed in others. Guide students in realizing that they reacted to the sudden noise before they recognized what had really happened. Explain that the startle response is a reflex action, which is an automatic response to the environment. Ask: **How could your response to the sudden noise help protect you?** *(prepares the body to avoid danger)*

L1 Visual Learning: Figure 12

Image Bank Figure 11-12

Have student pairs get together. On separate pieces of paper, one student should write down the four steps of a reflex action in his or her own words. The steps should not be numbered. Then the second student should place the separate pieces of paper in the proper order.

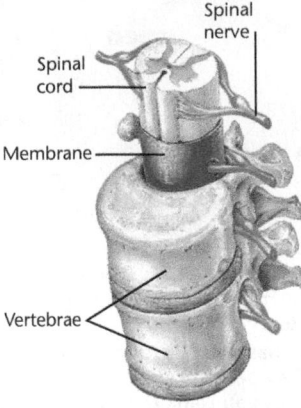

FIGURE 11 The spinal cord links the brain to the peripheral nervous system. Information and commands travel to and from the central nervous system via spinal nerves.

Spinal nerve

Spinal cord

Membrane

Vertebrae

The Spinal Cord The **spinal cord** is a thick column of nerve tissue that links the brain to most of the nerves in the peripheral nervous system. The spinal cord extends from the brain down the back. As you can see in Figure 11, the vertebrae of the backbone surround and protect the spinal cord. In addition, like the brain, the spinal cord is covered with protective membranes and bathed in fluid.

Nerve impulses travel from the brain, through the spinal cord, and then out to the rest of the body via spinal nerves. In the opposite direction, impulses travel from parts of your body via spinal nerves to the spinal cord, and then to the brain. Spinal nerves are part of the peripheral nervous system.

Reflexes What happens when you accidentally touch something hot, such as a flame? Most likely you have noticed that your hand automatically jerks away. This type of automatic response to your environment is called a **reflex.** A reflex action is shown in Figure 12.

In some reflex actions, the actions of the skeletal muscles are controlled by the spinal cord only—not the brain. These reflexes help protect your body from harm because they enable you to react very quickly. The brain receives separate signals but they take longer to arrive there. By the time the brain interprets the signals and you feel pain, the reflex action has already occurred.

A Reflex Action

FIGURE 12 Reflex actions allow you to react quickly in potentially harmful situations.

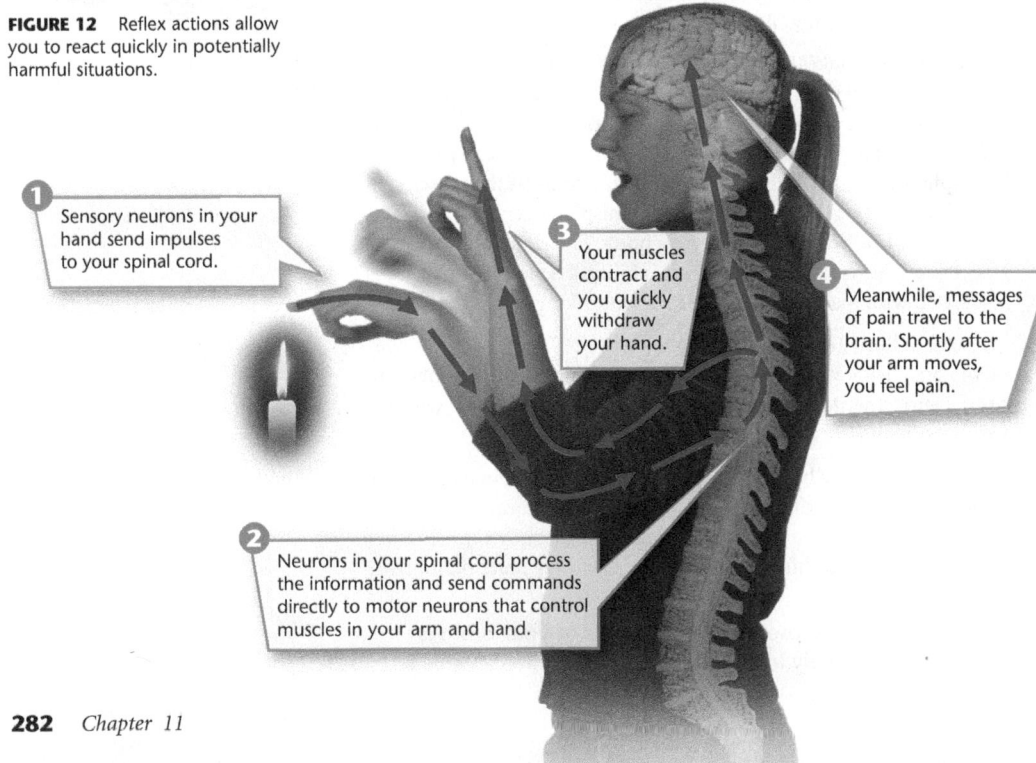

1. Sensory neurons in your hand send impulses to your spinal cord.

2. Neurons in your spinal cord process the information and send commands directly to motor neurons that control muscles in your arm and hand.

3. Your muscles contract and you quickly withdraw your hand.

4. Meanwhile, messages of pain travel to the brain. Shortly after your arm moves, you feel pain.

282 *Chapter 11*

WRITING and Health

L3 Firsthand Account

Invite students to write a detailed description of a reflex response they have experienced. In their firsthand account, they should describe what the reflex response was and what caused it to occur. They should also describe any feelings they might have had immediately after the response. Common reflex actions include the startle response, goose bumps, shivering, blinking or ducking, coughing, and sneezing.

Peripheral Nervous System

The peripheral nervous system includes the network of nerves that links the rest of your body to your brain and spinal cord. A nerve is a bundle or bundles of axons packaged with connective tissue. Notice in Figure 13 that the nerves of the peripheral nervous system branch from the central nervous system. The peripheral nervous system carries information to the central nervous system, and then carries responses from the central nervous system to the rest of the body. Based on these two functions, the peripheral nervous system is divided into a sensory division and a motor division.

Sensory Division Some nerves in the sensory division carry information about your outside environment from your ears, eyes, and other sense organs. Other sensory nerves carry information about internal body conditions such as blood pressure and heart rate. Both sets of sensory nerves deliver this information to the central nervous system.

Motor Division Once the central nervous system has processed the information from the sensory nerves, the motor division carries the responses back to your muscles and glands. The nerves of the motor division are divided into two groups based on the functions they control.

▶ **Somatic Nervous System** Motor nerves in the somatic nervous system carry signals that control voluntary actions such as chewing food or putting on a sock. For example, these motor neurons might signal skeletal muscles in your arm to raise your hand in class.

▶ **Autonomic Nervous System** Motor nerves in the autonomic nervous system regulate actions that happen automatically. These actions include such things as your breathing rate and digestion. For example, these motor neurons might carry signals to your heart to speed it up or glands in your eyes to release tears.

 **Connect to Your Life** How does your brain receive information about the smell of cookies baking?

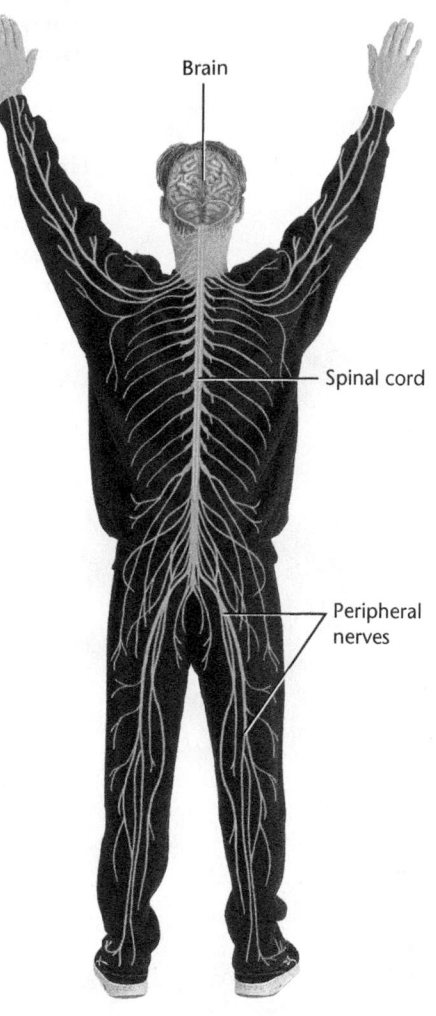

FIGURE 13 The peripheral nervous system includes all the nerves that branch out from the brain and spinal cord.

Brain

Spinal cord

Peripheral nerves

Movement and Coordination **283**

Peripheral Nervous System

Ⓛ2 Building Vocabulary

Help students develop ways to remember the names of the different divisions of the peripheral nervous system. For example, linking the words *autonomic* and *automatic* will help them remember that the autonomic nervous system controls actions that happen without conscious thought.

Ⓛ2 Cooperative Learning

Give student pairs a list of actions and have them identify whether sensory nerves or motor nerves are involved. If motor nerves are involved, students should identify whether the somatic or autonomic nervous system is involved. (Some examples of actions are scratching your arm, sneezing, watching television, walking, tasting a lemon, digesting food.) Then challenge students to name at least one example that involves each type of nerve.

Ⓛ3 Building Health Skills

Communicating While communicating with another person, sensory neurons supply the brain with information about the other person's nonverbal communication. A large majority of the communication between people is nonverbal communication, or body language. Ask students to provide examples of body language. *(facial expressions, hand or body movements, eye movements, touching)* Although body language is an integral part of communication, most of the time people are not aware of its significance. When these nonverbal cues are missing, misunderstandings are more likely to happen. As an example, ask students to share a time when they misunderstood the meaning of an e-mail or text message. Then discuss how body language may have prevented this misunderstanding.

Connect to Your Life Sensory nerves deliver the information about the smell to the brain.

Movement and Coordination **283**

Keeping Healthy

L2 Class Discussion

Discuss the differences between a concussion and a coma. *(A coma is a period of deep unconsciousness caused by disease, injury, or drugs. A concussion is a bruiselike injury to the brain.)* Ask students to describe the symptoms of a concussion. *(vomiting, drowsiness, loss of consciousness, confusion, or nose bleeds)* Ask: **Why should you stop what you are doing when you get a concussion?** *(You could risk further injury to the brain.)* **Why should head injuries be avoided?** *(Head injuries can impact all aspects of your health because the brain interacts with all body systems.)*

L3 Building Health Skills

Making Decisions Have students decide whether or not they should wear a helmet while biking. Instruct students to write the problem and list the possible alternatives. Then have them list the consequences of each alternative, both positive and negative. Finally, have students consider their values and make a decision. Students should write a paragraph that identifies the decision they made and explains why they made it.

L3 Cooperative Learning

Invite an athletic trainer, physical education teacher, or coach to class to talk about injuries they commonly see and how these injuries can be prevented. Before the class visit, have students break into small groups. Each group should brainstorm at least two or three questions to ask the speaker.

Connect to Your Life Allow students to answer this question in their private journals.

Keeping Healthy

Rest, good nutrition, and daily exercise can help keep your nervous system functioning properly. **The most important step you can take to care for your nervous system is to protect it from injury.** Because your nervous system interacts with all your body systems, damage due to trauma, disease, or drugs can have a significant impact on your health.

Avoiding Head Injuries A severe bump to the head could cause brain tissue to hit the skull. This bruiselike injury to the brain is known as a **concussion.** Seek medical attention if, following a blow to the head, you lose consciousness, vomit, feel drowsy or confused, or your nose bleeds. These symptoms can indicate a concussion or an even more serious head injury, such as a cracked skull or bleeding within the brain.

Certain diseases or drugs that damage or kill nerve cells can also lead to impaired brain function. A severe brain injury from trauma, disease, or drugs could possibly result in a **coma,** which is a prolonged period of deep unconsciousness.

Helmets greatly lower the risk of head injuries. Wear a helmet when you play contact sports, ski or snowboard, or ride a bicycle or skateboard. Always fasten your seat belt when traveling in a vehicle. Before diving, be sure the water is deep enough and that there are no underwater hazards. Avoid drugs and alcohol. Many head injuries occur when people are under the influence of drugs and alcohol.

Avoiding Spinal Cord Injuries Spinal cord injuries can result in **paralysis,** or the loss of the ability to move and feel some part of the body. Paralysis to the legs or to the arms and legs occurs when some nerves are so damaged that they can no longer signal the muscles they control. The extent of the paralysis is often related to the location of the spinal cord injury. Spinal cord injuries can be avoided in much the same way as head injuries—fasten your seat belt in a moving vehicle, take care when diving, and avoid drugs and alcohol.

 **Connect to Your Life** What activities do you participate in that carry a risk of head or spinal cord injury?

FIGURE 14 In a sport such as soccer the risk of concussions is high. Teens who have had several concussions may have impaired memory and learning abilities. A doctor should decide when it is safe for a person who has had a concussion to play again.

TEENS *Are Asking . . .*

Q: I recently got a concussion. My doctor said I shouldn't participate in sports for several weeks. If I feel fine, why do I have to wait so long?

A: A concussion is a brain injury. Although you may not have symptoms, brain injuries need time to heal properly. The amount of time you need to rest depends on the severity of the concussion and if you have had other head injuries recently. Someone with a head injury is more susceptible to repeated injury. Therefore, it is important that you follow your doctor's instructions.

Avoiding Nerve Injuries

Individual peripheral nerves also can be injured. For example, people with jobs that include hours of cash register or keyboard use, or who play some musical instruments are prone to a nerve injury called carpal tunnel syndrome. The "carpal tunnel" is a passageway through which a nerve and many tendons travel from the forearm to the hand. Repeated movements of the wrist and fingers can cause the tendons to swell and squeeze the nerve. Other risk factors for this injury include obesity and diabetes.

Symptoms include weakness and numbness in the fingers and pain that travels from the wrist to the upper arm. Treatments include wrist splints, medications to control the swelling, or surgery. To help prevent carpal tunnel syndrome and similar nerve injuries, it is important to take breaks from repetitive motions and to maintain good posture.

Preventing Infections

Nervous system infections are rare because its tissues are well protected. When infections do occur, however, they are often serious. For example, **meningitis** (men in JY tis) causes inflammation of the membranes surrounding the brain and spinal cord.

Meningitis symptoms are very similar to flu symptoms, but also include a stiff neck and severe headache. If you have not been vaccinated and have been exposed to a person with meningitis, talk to your doctor about preventive treatments. The most serious form of meningitis can be prevented with a vaccine. The vaccine is recommended for high school students and for college students living in dormitories.

A bite from an infected animal can transmit rabies, an infection of the central nervous system. Rabies is almost always fatal if not treated. Avoid contact with animals that act sick or behave strangely. If an animal bites you, seek medical attention.

FIGURE 15 Repetitive movements of the fingers and wrists can lead to a painful condition called carpal tunnel syndrome.

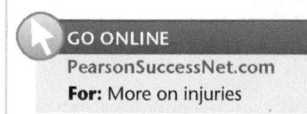

GO ONLINE
PearsonSuccessNet.com
For: More on injuries

Movement and Coordination **285**

3. Assess

Evaluate

These assignments can help you assess students' mastery of the section content.

Section 3 Review

Answers appear below.

Teaching Resources

- Practice 11-3
- Section 11-3 Quiz

L2 Reteach

Have student pairs use the figures in the lesson to describe the roles of neurons, the central nervous system, and the peripheral nervous system. Pairs should write at least one sentence for each. Then invite pairs to share their sentences with the class.

L4 Enrich

Teaching Resources

- Enrich 11-3

Health at Home

Memories Introduce the activity by explaining that memories are stored in the cerebrum. What is remembered and what is not may depend on how frequently the memory is accessed. Also, the feelings associated with a memory may influence how it is stored. After students have written their paragraph, invite them to make inferences about why the memories of the same event are different.

Living With Epilepsy Under certain conditions, a person's brain may experience sudden, uncontrolled nerve impulses. This flood of brain activity can lead to a **seizure.** Anyone can experience a seizure due to an injury or a bad reaction to a medication. However, people with a disorder called **epilepsy** are prone to seizures. Epileptic seizures vary widely in type and intensity, but include facial twitching, loss of awareness, and muscle spasms. Epilepsy has many causes including genetics, problems during prenatal development, diseases, and head injuries. Medication can reduce seizures in most people with epilepsy.

Preventing Headaches The most common problem of the nervous system that people experience are headaches. Tension headaches may be brought on by physical or emotional stress. Migraine (MY grayn) headaches are especially severe, long-lasting headaches. A person with a migraine is usually sensitive to light and noise and may experience nausea and blurred vision. The cause of migraines is not clear. Some scientists think that the brains of migraine sufferers may overreact to environmental signals.

In general, proper diet, exercise, and sleep can help prevent headaches. If you can identify certain foods or odors that trigger headaches, you may be able to avoid those triggers.

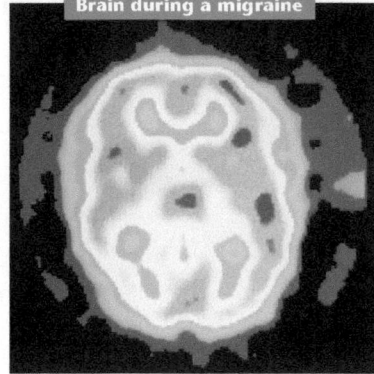
Brain during a migraine

FIGURE 16 One feature of a migraine is a change in blood flow in the brain. Researchers use imaging technology to learn more about brain activity during a migraine.

Section 3 Review

Key Ideas and Vocabulary

1. What functions does the nervous system perform?
2. What is a **neuron**? Name the three types of neurons and describe the function of each.
3. What is the role of the central nervous system? List the three main areas of the brain.
4. What is a **reflex**? How do reflexes protect the body?
5. How does the peripheral nervous system connect the central nervous system to the rest of the body?
6. Why is it so important to protect your nervous system from injury?

Health at Home

Memories Consider some of your early memories such as learning to ride a bike or a particular family vacation. Ask family members to describe their memories of the same event. In a paragraph, discuss how the memories of the same event differ from person to person. **WRITING**

Critical Thinking

7. **Evaluating** Suppose that after an accident, a person cannot feel or move his or her legs. What type of injury would you suspect? Explain.
8. **Classifying** After falling and hitting the back of her head, Lynn notices that she is having trouble catching her breath. Which part of her brain may have suffered damage in the fall?

---

286 *Chapter 11*

GO ONLINE PearsonSuccessNet.com   Audio Summary Section 11.3

Section 3 Review

1. receives information, processes information, and forms a response
2. A neuron is a type of cell that carries messages. Sensory neurons gather information from inside and outside the body. Interneurons pass impulses from one neuron to another. Motor neurons signal muscles and glands.
3. The central nervous system is the control center of the body. The cerebrum, cerebellum, and brain stem
4. A reflex is an automatic response to the environment. It protects the body by allowing it to react very quickly.
5. A network of nerves throughout the body links the body to the spinal cord and brain.
6. Because the nervous system interacts with all body systems, damage to it can significantly impact health.
7. Paralysis, or the loss of the ability to feel and move some part of the body, is often caused by injuries to the spinal cord.
8. the brain stem

Chapter 11
At a Glance

Section 1   Your Skeletal System

Key Ideas

▶ Your skeletal system provides support, protects organs, allows your body to move, and stores and produces materials that your body needs.

▶ Bones are living structures that undergo change throughout your life.

▶ Joints allow for movement and protect bones from friction and force.

▶ A combination of eating well, exercising, and avoiding injuries contributes to lifelong bone and joint health. Regular medical checkups can help detect skeletal system problems.

Vocabulary
- joint (268) • cartilage (268)
- ossification (268) • marrow (268)
- ligament (269) • osteoporosis (270) • fracture (270)
- sprain (271) • dislocation (271) • scoliosis (271)

Section 2   Your Muscular System

Key Ideas

▶ The three types of muscle tissue are smooth muscle, cardiac muscle, and skeletal muscle.

▶ You can maintain a healthy muscular system by regularly participating in different types of exercise. To help prevent injuries, exercise sessions should include a warm-up and cool-down period.

Vocabulary
- smooth muscle (272)
- cardiac muscle (272)
- skeletal muscle (272)
- tendon (272)
- muscle tone (273)
- atrophy (273)
- anabolic steroid (274)
- strain (275)
- tendonitis (275)

Section 3   Your Nervous System

Key Ideas

▶ Your nervous system receives information about what is going on inside and outside of your body. Then it processes the information and forms a response to it.

▶ Neurons carry messages, or impulses, from one part of your body to another.

▶ The central nervous system, which is made up of the brain and spinal cord, is the control center of the body.

▶ The peripheral nervous system includes the network of nerves that links the rest of your body to your brain and spinal cord.

▶ The most important step you can take to care for your nervous system is to protect it from injury.

Vocabulary
- neuron (278) • cerebrum (281)
- cerebellum (281) • brain stem (281)
- spinal cord (282) • reflex (282)
- concussion (284) • coma (284) • paralysis (284)
- meningitis (285) • seizure (286) • epilepsy (286)

Movement and Coordination **287**

Chapter 11
At a Glance

The Risks of Steroids Ask volunteers to share their answers. Use examples from the video to review the risks of steroids.

Key Ideas Review

L3 Have students create a table for each lesson in which they describe the function of the body system, structures of the body system, and ways to keep the system healthy.

L3 Invite students to create a multiple-choice quiz with ten questions that address the Key Ideas from this chapter. Students can exchange quizzes and answer the questions.

Vocabulary Review

L2 Have students group the vocabulary terms into different categories of their choosing. Suggest students exchange categories, and regroup the words based on the new categories.

EL Instruct students to create a fill-in-the-blank paragraph using as many vocabulary terms as possible. Students can exchange paragraphs and write in the missing terms.

Chapter 11 Review

Reviewing Key Ideas

Section 1

1. b   **2.** c

3. Ossification is the process in which cartilage is replaced by bone. It occurs throughout childhood.

4. Bones consist of two types of tissue—compact bone, which makes up the outer layer, and spongy bone, which is located under compact bone. Spongy bone may contain spaces filled with red bone marrow. Some bones have a central cavity that is filled with yellow marrow.

5. Simple fracture: bone is either cracked or broken in two or more pieces; compound fracture: broken ends of bone pierce the skin

6. eating adequate amounts of calcium and phosphorus and getting plenty of weight-bearing exercise

7. In a fracture, a bone breaks. In a dislocation, the ends of the bones in a joint are forced out of position.

Section 2

8. c   **9.** d

10. A tendon attaches a muscle to a bone. A ligament holds bones together.

11. Muscle tone helps hold up the body and keeps the muscles healthy and ready for action.

12. Muscular strength relates to how many and how large the muscle fibers are. Muscular endurance refers to how long a muscle can contract without tiring.

13. Muscle tone is the slight tension in muscle fibers that makes a muscle firm. Atrophy occurs when muscles weaken and shrink from injury or lack of use.

14. The muscles could be strained or the muscle fibers torn.

Chapter 11 Review

Reviewing Key Ideas

Section 1

1. Where is red bone marrow found?
 a. compact bone
 b. spongy bone
 c. hollow center of bones
 d. the ends of bones

2. What type of joint allows you to turn your head?
 a. ball-and-socket   **b.** hinge
 c. pivot   **d.** gliding

3. What is ossification and when during a person's life does it occur?

4. Describe the structure of a typical bone.

5. What is the difference between a simple and a compound fracture?

6. Describe two things you can do now to help avoid osteoporosis later in life.

7. Critical Thinking Compare and contrast fractures and dislocations.

Section 2

8. Where is cardiac muscle found?
 a. digestive system   **b.** arms and legs
 c. heart   **d.** blood vessels

9. Which type of muscle works by shortening and thickening?
 a. smooth muscle
 b. cardiac muscle
 c. skeletal muscles
 d. all of the above

10. Explain the difference between a tendon and a ligament.

11. Why is good muscle tone important?

12. Explain the difference between muscular strength and muscular endurance.

13. Critical Thinking What is the difference between muscle tone and atrophy?

14. Critical Thinking Why could it be harmful to your muscles to suddenly start exercising intensely and for long periods of time?

Section 3

15. The part of the central nervous system that controls memory and reasoning is the
 a. cerebrum.   **b.** cerebellum.
 c. brain stem.   **d.** spinal cord.

16. What is the function of sensory neurons?

17. Describe the relationship between the central and the peripheral nervous systems.

18. Critical Thinking Blinking your eye whenever something touches your eyelashes is a reflex action. Explain the protective funtion of this reflex.

 ## Building Health Skills

19. Making Decisions At swim practice, you hit your head while attempting a flip turn. Later that day, you feel nauseated and a little confused. If you go to a doctor, you will miss an important swim meet. In a paragraph, describe how you will make your decision. **WRITING**

20. Communicating Your friend is supposed to wear a brace to help correct her scoliosis. She wears it at home, but takes it off at school because she is embarrassed. Write an email to convince her she should wear her brace. **WRITING**

21. Setting Goals Track the amount of calcium you consume each day over a three-day period. List each food item you eat and use food labels to identify the amount of calcium in each food. Then develop and follow a plan to consume 1,300 mg of calcium a day for one week. At the end of the week evaluate how you did. **WRITING**

Health and Community

Rehabilitation Center Visit Volunteer at a local rehabilitation center for people with skeletal or nervous system injuries. Duties could include helping at mealtime, greeting patients and visitors, and assisting at special events. Write an editorial describing your experience. **WRITING**

Section 3

15. a

16. to gather information about the internal and external environment

17. The peripheral nervous system links the body to the brain and spinal cord, which make up the central nervous system.

18. Blinking keeps objects out of the eye and protects it from injury.

Building Health Skills

19. Students should describe the steps in the decision-making process they would use to make the decision.

20. Students might advise wearing the brace because true friends will not tease her. Without the brace the curvature will not straighten as quickly or could even get worse.

Standardized Test Prep

Math Practice

The graph shows the average amount of bone mass in men and women through most of the life span. Use the graph to answer Questions 22–24.

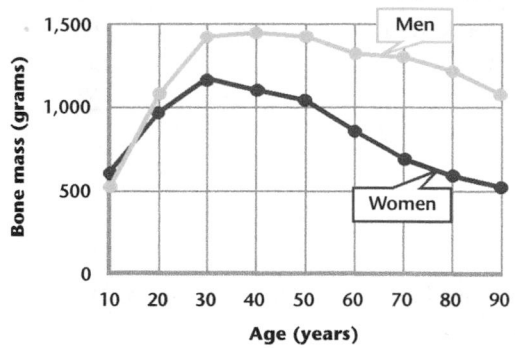

22. Between which ages do both men and women gain bone mass at the highest rate?
   A 10–20 years
   B 20–30 years
   C 30–40 years
   D 50–60 years

23. At what age does bone mass reach its peak in women?
   F age 20
   G age 30
   H age 40
   J age 50

24. Which conclusion *cannot* be drawn from this graph?
   A As men age, they lose less bone mass than women do.
   B During adolescence and early adulthood, women accumulate less bone mass than men do.
   C Men accumulate more bone mass because they consume more calcium.
   D Bone mass does not change much in men from 30 to 40 years of age.

Reading and Writing Practice

Read the passage. Then answer Questions 25–28.

Why are people apt to recall false memories? In a study, subjects were read lists of related words such as candy, cake, sugar, and taste. Later, they were shown written lists that contained these words and other similar words, such as sweet and sticky. Often, the subjects claimed that the similar words had been read aloud to them. Tests of their brain activity during the study revealed that the brain's memory center may prompt people to find memories that aren't really there, but are similar to ones that are.

25. In this study, what were the scientists studying?
   A where people store memories
   B how long certain memories can be stored
   C factors that affect memory loss
   D how the brain recalls memories

26. Which of the following words would the subjects most likely have falsely recalled?
   F sour   **G** fork
   H frosting   **J** table

27. According to the passage, which of these statements is true?
   A Human memory is flawless.
   B People are apt to remember what they see more than what they hear.
   C When processing information, the brain searches for similar experiences.
   D The brain cannot categorize information.

Constructed Response

28. In a paragraph, summarize what scientists learned about memory from this study.

> ### Test-Taking Tip
>
> **When you take a test, remember to change your body position now and then. Otherwise, neck or back cramps might distract you from the test.**

Standardized Test Prep

Math Practice
22. A
23. G
24. C

Reading and Writing Practice
25. D
26. H
27. C
28. Paragraphs will vary, but should explain that scientists learned that the brain may make up memories that are not really there, but are similar to real memories.

---

21. Students should list foods they will consume to help them reach their calcium goal. They should also evaluate their success at meeting their goal.

Health and Community

Rehabilitation Center Visit Editorials will vary, but should include a description of how the experience impacted their attitude about people with disabilities and helping others.

Section Objectives	Standards Correlation	Instructional Resources L3	SE eTEXT	TE eTEXT	PRINT
1 **Your Cardiovascular System** ⏱ 2 periods; 1 block	NHES: 1.12.1	SE Warm-Up, p. 292	•	•	•
		RN Note Taking Guide 12-1	•	•	•
12.1.1 **Describe** the main functions of the cardiovascular system.		IB Image Bank 12-1		•	
12.1.2 **Trace** the pathway of blood through the heart.		TR Practice 12-1		•	
12.1.3 **Identify** three types of blood vessels and the four components of blood.		TR Section 12-1 Quiz		•	
2 **Cardiovascular Health** ⏱ 2 periods; 1 block	NHES: 1.12.1, 1.12.4, 1.12.5, 6.12.1, 7.12.2	SE Warm-Up, p. 299	•	•	•
		SE Media Wise Fast Foods and In-Store Ads, p. 301	•	•	•
12.2.1 **Identify** two factors that contribute to cardiovascular disease.		RN Note Taking Guide 12-2	•	•	•
12.2.2 **Describe** behaviors that can reduce your risk of cardiovascular disease.		TR Practice 12-2		•	
		TR Section 12-2 Quiz		•	
Improving Your Cardiorespiratory Fitness ⏱ 1 period; 1/2 block	NHES: 6.12.1, 6.12.3	SE Practice the Skill, p. 305	•	•	•
		RN Building Health Skills 12	•	•	•
BHS.12 **Implement** a plan to improve your cardiorespiratory fitness.					
3 **Respiratory Health** ⏱ 1 period; 1/2 block	NHES: 1.12.1, 1.12.3, 7.12.2	SE Warm-Up, p. 306	•	•	•
		RN Note Taking Guide 12-3	•	•	•
12.3.1 **List** the functions of the respiratory system.		IB Image Bank 12-9, 12-10		•	
12.3.2 **Describe** how air travels through your respiratory system, and how you breathe.		TR Practice 12-3		•	
12.3.3 **Identify** ways to keep the respiratory system healthy.		TR Section 12-3 Quiz		•	

Chapter Review and Assessment

SE Chapter 12 Review, p. 312 L3
CTB Chapter 12 Test L2 L3 L4
SE Standardized Test Prep, p. 313 L3

PROGRAM COMPONENTS

SE Student Edition	**CTB** Computer Test Bank
TE Teacher Edition	**AUD** Audio Section Summaries
TR Teaching Resources	
RN Reading and Note Taking Guide	**DVD** Teens Talk Video Series
ARN Adapted Reading and Note Taking Guide	**VVG** Video Viewing Guide
IB Image Bank	**PPT** Presentation

Differentiated Instruction

L1 L2 L4 EL

		SE eTEXT	TE eTEXT	PRINT
ARN	Note Taking Guide 12-1 **L2**	•	•	
RN	Note Taking Guide 12-1 **EL**	•	•	•
AUD	Audio Summary 12-1 **L1 L2 EL**	•	•	
TE	Reteach Strategy, p. 298 **L2**		•	•
TR	Enrich 12-1 **L4**		•	
ARN	Note Taking Guide 12-2 **L2**	•	•	
RN	Note Taking Guide 12-2 **EL**	•	•	•
AUD	Audio Summary 12-2 **L1 L2 EL**	•	•	
TE	Reteach Strategy, p. 303 **L2**		•	•
TR	Enrich 12-2 **L4**		•	
ARN	Building Health Skills 12 **L2**	•	•	
RN	Building Health Skills 12 **EL**	•	•	•
ARN	Note Taking Guide 12-3 **L2**	•	•	
RN	Note Taking Guide 12-3 **EL**	•	•	•
AUD	Audio Summary 12-3 **L1 L2 EL**	•	•	
TE	Reteach Strategy, p. 310 **L2**		•	•
TR	Enrich 12-3 **L4**		•	

ABILITY LEVELS

L1 For students with special needs
L2 For less proficient readers
L3 For all students
L4 For gifted and talented students
EL For English language learners

Chapter 12 Digital/Video Pathway

This alternative pathway allows you to teach this chapter's content using only the video and online materials.

Preview

DVD	Video #12 Preview
SE	Video #12 Preview Activity
VVG	Video #12 Worksheet

Living With Asthma

1

PPT	12-1 Presentation
RN/ARN	12-1 Note Taking
PPT	12-1 Section Quiz

2

PPT	12-2 Presentation
RN/ARN	12-2 Note Taking
PPT	12-2 Section Quiz

3

DVD	Video #12 Explore/Wrap-Up
VVG	Video #12 Worksheet
PPT	12-3 Presentation
RN/ARN	12-3 Note Taking
PPT	12-3 Section Quiz

Living With Asthma

Chapter Preview

Section 1 Your Cardiovascular System
The cardiovascular system consists of the heart, blood vessels, and blood. The functions of the system include delivering materials, removing wastes, and fighting disease.

Section 2 Cardiovascular Health
Hypertension and high blood cholesterol are two factors that increase the risk of heart attack and stroke. Exercising regularly, eating a nutrient-rich diet, and avoiding smoking will help maintain cardiovascular health.

 Practicing Healthful Behaviors

Improving Your Cardiorespiratory Fitness
Implementing a plan to exercise regularly is a way to improve cardiorespiratory fitness.

Section 3 Respiratory Health
The respiratory system brings oxygen into the body and removes carbon dioxide from the body. Keeping the respiratory system healthy includes avoiding smoking and air pollution as well as treating asthma if you have it.

Cardiovascular and Respiratory Health

1 Your Cardiovascular System

2 Cardiovascular Health
- **MediaWise** Fast Foods and In-Store Ads

 Building Health Skills
- **Practicing Healthful Behaviors** Improving Your Cardiorespiratory Fitness

3 Respiratory Health

GO ONLINE PearsonSuccessNet.com

VIDEO 12

TEENS Talk

Living With Asthma

Preview **Activity**

What Is It Like To Live With Asthma?

Complete this activity before you watch the video.

1. Complete the following sentences.
   a. Having asthma means ___?___ .
   b. People have asthma attacks when ___?___ .
   c. I think an asthma attack feels like ___?___ .
2. Get together with a partner to compare how you completed each of the sentences.
3. In a paragraph, discuss what you learned from this activity.
   WRITING

290

 GO ONLINE

PearsonSuccessNet.com
For resources and activities for this chapter.

Sensitive Issues

- The topics in this chapter may bring back painful memories for students whose families have been affected by cardiovascular and respiratory diseases.
- Students with a family history of cardiovascular disease may become fearful of their future. Reassure students that they might reduce their risk by practicing the healthy habits discussed in Section 2.
- You should also be aware when introducing respiratory health that asthma may be a sensitive issue among some of your students.

VIDEO 12

TEENS Talk ⊙

Living With Asthma

Video Objectives

Use this video to help students

Identify what asthma is, how it is triggered, and how it is treated.

Learn how teens with asthma can successfully manage their disease.

Preview **Activity**

What Is It Like to Live With Asthma?

Just before watching the video, have students complete the Preview Activity. Discuss what students learned from the activity.

From the Authors

Cardiovascular disease is the leading cause of death in the United States. Yet, teaching about the importance of cardiovascular health to young people is challenging, because most adolescents are not concerned with how their current behaviors can affect what may happen in 30 or more years.

In addition, the dramatic increase in the prevalence and impact of asthma—especially among urban minority populations—is of great concern. Asthma attacks often lead to costly visits to the emergency room and keep young people out of school. Because of such interference with academic achievement, teaching youths to self-manage asthma is an important goal of health education.

The activities and questions in this chapter are designed to inform young people about what they can do to reduce risk factors for cardiovascular and respiratory diseases. See, for example, the Teens Talk video "Living With Asthma," the Building Health Skills activity "Improving Your Cardiorespiratory Fitness" on page 304, and the Health at School activity on page 310.

Cardiovascular and Respiratory Health **291**

Objectives

Before class begins, write the objectives on the board. Have students copy the objectives into their notebooks at the start of class.

1. Focus

Warm-Up **Myth/Fact**

After students complete the writing assignment, call on a few volunteers to read their ideas to the class. Typical responses might include hoping to understand how a heart beats, what the difference is between veins and arteries, or what blood consists of. After students have studied the cardiovascular system, ask them whether they learned what they had hoped to learn. If there are topics that have not been addressed, discuss where students could find the information.

Presentation 12-1

Connect to Your Life *Sample answer:* When you exercise, your cells need more oxygen to function. The cells also release more carbon dioxide as a waste product. You breathe harder to take in more oxygen and to release more carbon dioxide.

Section 1

Your Cardiovascular System

Objectives

▶ **Describe** the main functions of the cardiovascular system.

▶ **Trace** the pathway of blood through the heart.

▶ **Identify** three types of blood vessels and the four components of blood.

Vocabulary

- atrium
- ventricle
- pacemaker
- artery
- capillary
- vein
- blood pressure
- hypertension
- plasma
- red blood cell
- white blood cell
- platelet

Warm-Up

Myth Blood is blue in color when it is not carrying oxygen.

Fact Blood is bright red when it is carrying oxygen and dark red when it is not. Veins appear blue in some people because of the way light reflects from their skin.

WRITING What other knowledge about the cardiovascular system do you hope to gain from this chapter?

Functions of the Cardiovascular System

Whenever you feel the thumping of your heart or the steady pulse in your wrist, you are experiencing your cardiovascular system in action. Your cardiovascular system, or the circulatory system, consists of your heart, blood vessels, and blood. **The main functions of the cardiovascular system include delivering materials to cells and carrying wastes away. In addition, blood contains cells that fight disease.**

Delivering Materials Your heart continually pumps the blood in your blood vessels throughout your body. Many substances that your body needs dissolve in the blood. For example, blood picks up glucose from your digestive system and brings it to cells where it is used for energy.

Removing Wastes Your cardiovascular system also transports wastes from your cells. For example, when your cells break down glucose for energy, carbon dioxide is released as a waste product. Your blood picks up carbon dioxide and transports it to the lungs, where it is exhaled.

Fighting Disease Your blood contains cells that attack microorganisms that cause disease. It also contains substances that seal cuts, preventing blood loss and the entry of microorganisms.

 **Connect to Your Life** Why do you think you breathe harder when you exercise?

MATH **and Health**

L1 **Averages**

Maria checked her pulse three times in one day. Her first pulse rate was 75 bpm (beats per minute). The second rate was 68 bpm. The third rate was 80 bpm. What is Maria's average heart rate? *(72 + 68 + 79 = 219;* *219 ÷ 3 = 73. Her average heart rate is 73 bpm.)* Have students estimate how many times Maria's heart beats in one hour. *(73 bpm X 60 min/hr = 4,380 beats per hour.)*

The Heart

Your cardiovascular system contains a network of blood vessels with two major loops. The first loop leads from your heart to your lungs, where the blood releases carbon dioxide, picks up oxygen, and then returns to your heart. The second loop circles through to the rest of your body, where the blood delivers oxygen and nutrients and picks up wastes. The two loops cross paths at your heart. Each time the heart beats, strong cardiac muscles push blood through the blood vessels.

Structure of the Heart Figure 1 shows the structure of the heart. Notice that the heart has a right side and a left side, separated by a thick wall. Each side has two chambers: an upper chamber called an **atrium** (plural, *atria*) and a lower chamber, or **ventricle**. **The atria receive blood entering the heart. Blood flows from the atria to the ventricles, which pump blood out of the heart.** Between each atrium and ventricle, and between each ventricle and large blood vessel, is a flap of tissue called a valve. The valves allow blood to flow in only one direction.

FIGURE 1 Your heart is about the size of your fist. Blood travels from the right side of your heart to your lungs. The blood then returns to your heart's left side and is pumped throughout the body.
Interpreting Diagrams Which heart chamber receives blood from the lungs?

The Heart

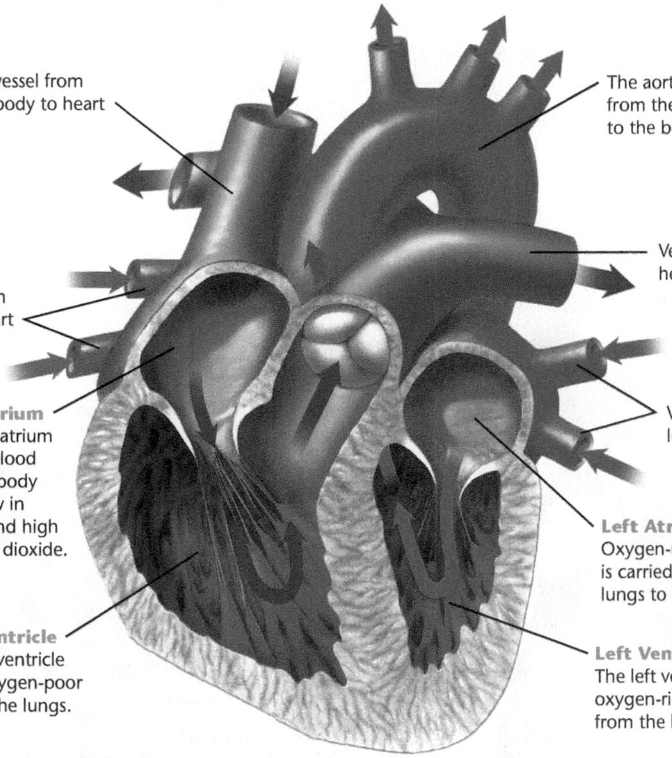

Major vessel from upper body to heart

The aorta carries blood from the left ventricle to the body.

Vessel from heart to lungs

Vessels from lung to heart

Vessels from lung to heart

Right Atrium
The right atrium receives blood from the body that is low in oxygen and high in carbon dioxide.

Left Atrium
Oxygen-rich blood is carried from the lungs to the left atrium.

Right Ventricle
The right ventricle pumps oxygen-poor blood to the lungs.

Left Ventricle
The left ventricle pumps oxygen-rich blood from the heart.

Cardiovascular and Respiratory Health **293**

2. Teach

L3 EL Reading/Note Taking 12-1

L2 Adapted Reading/Note Taking 12-1

Functions of the Cardiovascular System

L2 Building Vocabulary

Reinforce students' understanding of the cardiovascular system by examining the derivation of *cardiovascular*. Explain that *cardio-* comes from a Greek word for "heart," and *–vascular* comes from a Latin word for "vessel." Ask: **What does the cardiovascular system consist of?** *(heart, blood vessels, and blood)* Point out that although the system is often called the circulatory system, the term *cardiovascular system*—or "heart-vessel system"—is more descriptive of the system's structure.

The Heart

L3 Visual Learning: Figure 1

Image Bank Figure 12-1

Have students examine the diagram of the heart. Point out that the arrows in the diagram indicate the direction that blood flows. Ask: **What chamber of the heart pumps blood to the lungs?** *(the right ventricle)* **What happens to the blood that circulates through the lungs?** *(The blood releases carbon dioxide and picks up oxygen.)* **What chamber completes the first major loop of the cardiovascular system?** *(the left atrium)* **What two chambers are involved in the second major loop of the cardiovascular system?** *(The left ventricle pumps blood to the body, and the blood from the body returns to the right atrium.)*

Caption Answer the left atrium

Differentiated Instruction

L1 Special Needs

Pass out an unlabeled diagram of the heart that shows the four chambers and the valves between. Help students label each of the chambers. Then have students draw one box labeled "lungs" and a second box labeled "body" next to the heart. Have each student use a red crayon and a blue crayon to draw the pathway of blood through the cardiovascular system. A red line should be drawn from the box labeled "lungs" to the left atrium, to the left ventricle, and through the valve to the aorta to the box labeled "body." A blue line should be drawn from the box labeled "body" to the right atrium, to the right ventricle, and through the valve to the vessels to the box labeled "lungs."

L3 Online Activity GO ONLINE

Visit Pearson SuccessNet to access an online activity about the heart. Have students complete the Web activity.

L3 Cooperative Learning

Help students locate the pulse near the wrist of the left hand. Direct them to the photo on page 305. Explain that the pulse they feel is the artery expanding and contracting as the heart pumps blood through the body. After all students have found their pulse, have students work in pairs to answer the Connect to Your Life question on page 295. Make sure all students have a watch or are in sight of a clock with a second hand. One partner can watch the clock while the other partner counts his or her pulse beats.

Blood Vessels

L2 Active Learning

Use this activity to help students understand gas exchange between cells and capillaries. Pass out blue and red markers. Half the class should draw a large red dot on a piece of paper to represent oxygen. The rest of the class should draw a large blue dot to represent carbon dioxide. Have the "blue dots" stand clustered together as though they are in a cell. Have the "red dots" walk single file toward the "blue dots." Remind students that during diffusion, substances move from an area of higher concentration to an area of lower concentration. Ask: **What will happen when the oxygen in the capillary meets the carbon dioxide in the cell?** (The red dots will diffuse into the cell and the blue dots will diffuse into the capillary.)

GO ONLINE
PearsonSuccessNet.com
For: More on the heart

Your Heartbeat The action of the heart has two main phases. In the first phase, the heart relaxes and the atria fill with blood. In the second phase, the heart contracts and pumps blood. First the atria contract, pumping blood into the ventricles. Then the ventricles contract, pumping blood into the large blood vessels going toward the lungs or toward the rest of the body. The familiar *lub-dub* sound of a heartbeat occurs during the pumping phase. As the valves between the atria and ventricles close, the *lub* sound is made. The *dub* sound is heard when the valves between the ventricles and large blood vessels close.

The rate at which your heart muscles contract is regulated by the **pacemaker,** a small group of cells in the wall of the right atrium. The pacemaker receives messages from your brain to increase or decrease your heart rate.

Average heart rate varies from one person to the next and from one situation to the next. Your heart most likely beats about 70 to 80 times per minute when you are inactive. When you exercise, your heart speeds up in response to the body's need for more oxygen and nutrients and to remove excess carbon dioxide.

Blood Vessels

Your heart pumps blood through an extensive network of blood vessels. If all the blood vessels in your body were placed end to end, they could wrap around Earth more than two times. **The three main types of blood vessels in your body are arteries, capillaries, and veins.**

FIGURE 2 Blood flows from the heart through arteries, capillaries, and then veins.

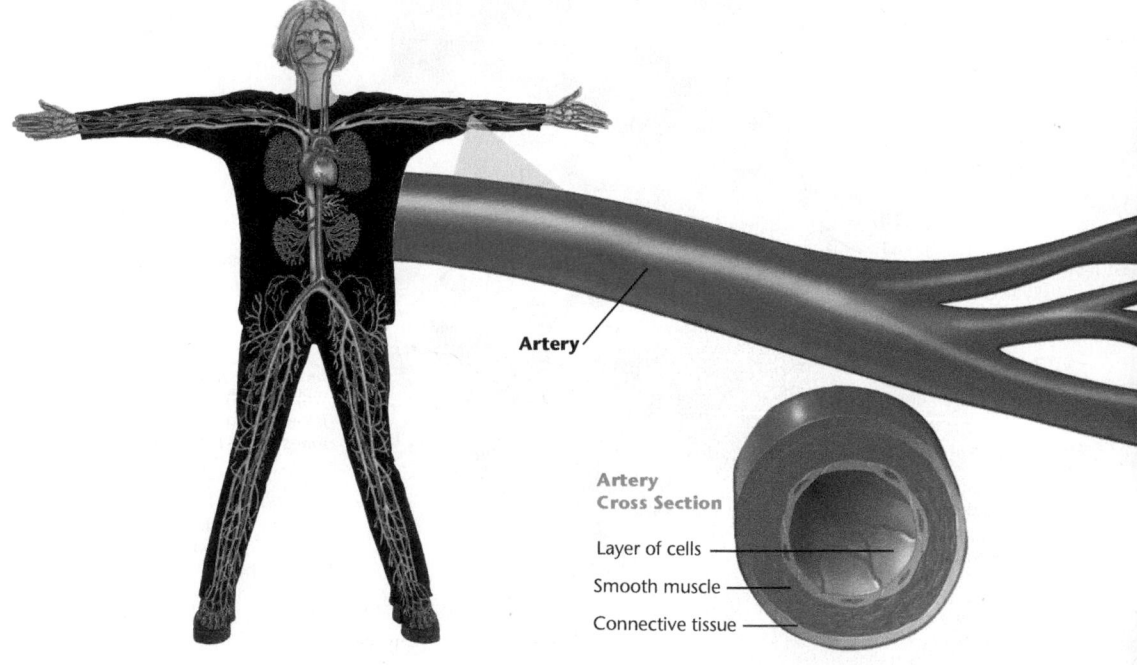

Artery

Artery
Cross Section

Layer of cells

Smooth muscle

Connective tissue

294 *Chapter 12*

WRITING and Health

L3 Descriptive Writing

Have students describe the beating of the heart and what happens inside the heart as if they were writing to inform a middle school student—that is, someone who has little detailed knowledge about the heart. Ask students to use terms from the chapter. Their descriptions should be clear and detailed. This activity requires students to describe the heart so thoroughly that any gaps or misconceptions in their knowledge will be revealed to them as they write. Let students use their textbooks as needed to fill any gaps and correct any errors.

Arteries Blood vessels that carry blood away from the heart are called **arteries.** Most arteries carry oxygen-rich blood. The exceptions are the arteries that carry oxygen-poor blood from the heart to the lungs.

The largest artery in the body is the aorta (ay AWR tuh). Blood leaves the left ventricle through the aorta, which branches into many smaller arteries that carry blood to your organs, muscles, and bones.

As you can see in Figure 2, arteries have thick walls that are both strong and flexible. When your ventricles contract, blood surges through your arteries, causing their elastic walls to expand and then relax. The pulse you feel in your wrist occurs when an artery expands.

Capillaries Branching from the smallest arteries are **capillaries,** the smallest blood vessels in your body. As blood flows through the capillaries, oxygen and dissolved nutrients diffuse through the capillary walls and into your body's cells. At the same time, wastes from body cells, such as carbon dioxide, diffuse into the blood. Capillaries also are involved in temperature regulation. When you are cold, the capillaries near the surface of your skin narrow and keep heat in your body. When you are warm, they expand and allow excess heat to escape your body.

Veins From the capillaries, blood flows into small blood vessels that join together to form veins. **Veins** are large, thin-walled blood vessels that carry blood to the heart. By the time blood reaches veins, the pumping force of the heart has little effect. Skeletal muscle contractions help to squeeze blood back toward the heart. Valves inside the veins prevent blood from flowing backward.

 **Connect to Your Life** Locate the pulse in your wrist. How many times does your pulse beat in one minute?

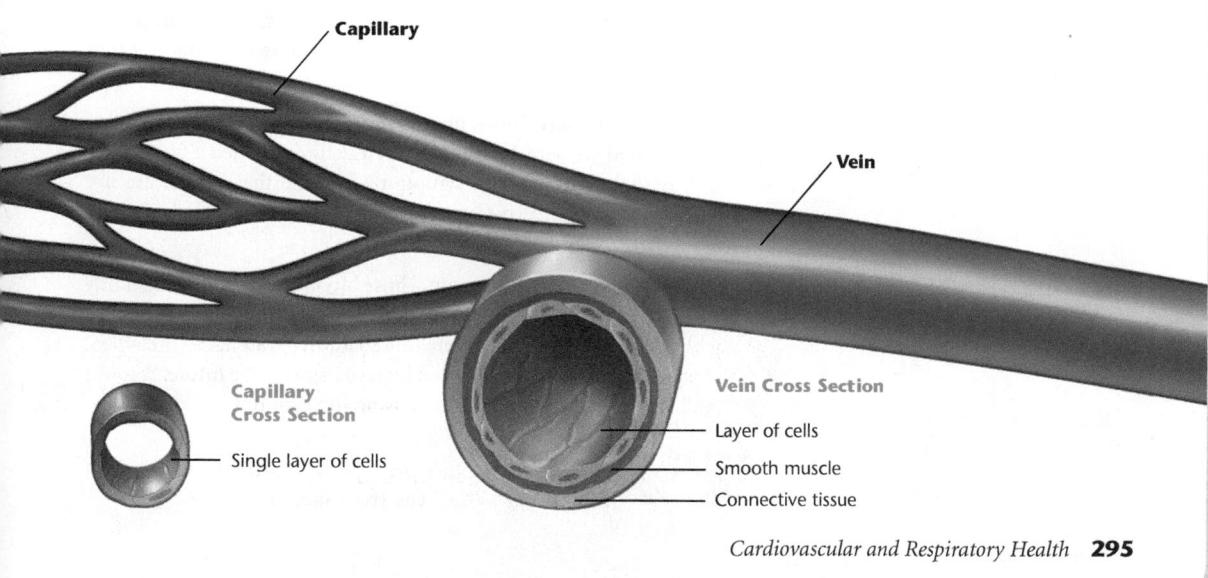

Capillary

Vein

Capillary Cross Section

Single layer of cells

Vein Cross Section

Layer of cells

Smooth muscle

Connective tissue

Cardiovascular and Respiratory Health **295**

L2 **Cooperative Learning**

Ask a school nurse to demonstrate to the class how a blood pressure reading is taken. The nurse's presentation should include an explanation of how a sphygmomanometer works and an explanation of systolic and diastolic readings. Before the class visit, have students break into small groups. Each group should brainstorm at least two questions about blood pressure to ask the nurse.

L3 **Building Health Skills**

Advocacy Have groups make posters to inform the public about what blood pressure is, what blood pressure readings mean, what different ranges of blood pressures indicate, and why people should have their blood pressure checked. The poster may include drawings, cartoons, or other images that would catch a person's eye. Encourage students to find places in the community to display their posters with permission.

L3 **Addressing Misconceptions**

Age and Blood Pressure Many people think of high blood pressure as a normal part of the aging process. Explain that blood pressure does not naturally rise as one gets older. Factors that contribute to high blood pressure include a poor diet, lack of exercise, and an increase in body weight. Explain that there appears to be a connection between hypertension and age because years of poor health habits tend to catch up on people as they age.

Connect to Your Life Allow students to answer this question in their private journals.

Blood Pressure Readings

Reading (in millimeters of mercury)	Condition
Less than 90/60	Low blood pressure
90/60 to 119/79	Normal
120/80 to 139/89	Prehypertension
140/90 or greater	Hypertension

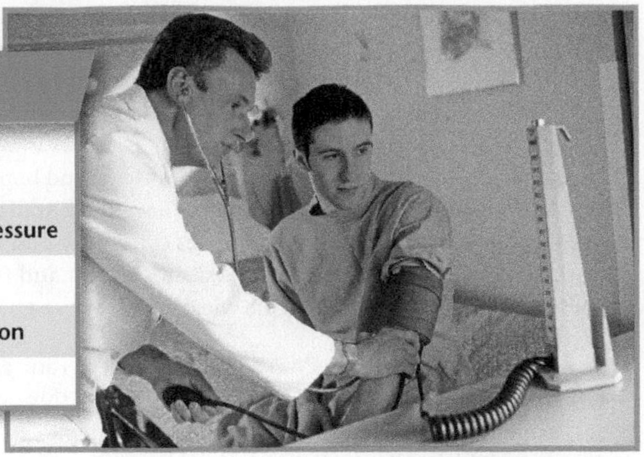

FIGURE 3 Blood pressure varies from person to person. Factors such as age, weight, fitness, and mood affect blood pressure.

Measuring Blood Pressure Visits to a doctor usually include having your blood pressure measured. **Blood pressure** is the force with which blood pushes against the walls of your blood vessels.

Figure 3 shows a sphygmomanometer (sfig moh muh NAHM uh tur), an instrument used to measure blood pressure. The healthcare provider pumps air into the cuff around the patient's upper arm until a large artery presses closed. As air is released from the cuff, the provider listens for the sound of flowing blood and records the reading from the sphygmomanometer. This first reading represents the *systolic pressure*—the pressure caused when the heart's ventricles contract. When the sound stops, the provider records the second reading. This second reading is the *diastolic pressure*—the pressure when the ventricles are relaxed.

Blood pressure readings are recorded as the systolic pressure over the diastolic pressure. For example, a person with a reading of 120/80 has a systolic pressure of 120 and a diastolic pressure of 80.

▶ **Normal Blood Pressure** Blood pressure readings vary from person to person. A blood pressure reading is considered normal if it falls within the range of 90/60 to 119/79.

▶ **Low Blood Pressure** Blood pressure lower than 90/60 is considered to be low blood pressure. Doctors are not usually concerned if blood pressure is slightly low, unless symptoms indicate that organs are not receiving enough oxygen. Causes of low blood pressure include medications, dehydration, and allergic reactions.

▶ **High Blood Pressure** A person whose blood pressure is consistently 140/90 or greater has high blood pressure, or **hypertension.** People with a blood pressure between 120/80 and 139/89 have "prehypertension," and are likely to develop hypertension in the future. You will read about the dangers of hypertension in Section 2.

Connect to Your Life When was the last time your blood pressure was measured? What was the measurement?

For Your INFORMATION!

Blood Pressure Near the Heart

For many years doctors have relied on blood pressure readings from the upper arm to track the effect of blood-pressure medicines. A recent study, however, revealed that some blood pressure medicines affect the pressure in the arm and the aorta differently. With some medicines although pressure in the arm lowered, pressure in the aorta did not. With other medicines pressure in the aorta lowered, although pressure in the arm did not. Patients in the study who took medicine that lowered blood pressure in the aorta, but not necessarily the arm, experienced fewer heart attacks.

Blood

The average adult has about 4 to 6 quarts of blood circulating through his or her blood vessels. Blood is a complex tissue that consists of cells and cell pieces in a watery solution. **The four components of blood are plasma, red blood cells, white blood cells, and platelets.**

Plasma The liquid component of the blood is called **plasma.** This straw-colored liquid makes up about 55 percent of the blood. Plasma is mostly water, with substances such as nutrients, hormones, and salts dissolved in it. These substances are necessary for many processes that occur in cells. Plasma also carries waste products such as urea to the kidneys for removal from the body.

Red Blood Cells The cells that carry oxygen from the lungs to all the parts of your body are **red blood cells.** Red blood cells contain hemoglobin, which is an iron-containing substance to which oxygen binds. The reaction between oxygen and the iron in hemoglobin gives blood its bright red color. Once oxygen has diffused to tissues, blood becomes a dull red.

White Blood Cells Your body's **white blood cells** help protect you against diseases and foreign substances. They are larger than red blood cells, but far less numerous. There are several kinds of white blood cells. Some white blood cells make chemicals that help your body resist diseases such as cancer. Others destroy invading microorganisms by surrounding and consuming them.

Platelets Platelets (PLAYT lits) are cell fragments that play an important role in the blood clotting process. When you get a cut, platelets stick to the edges of the cut and release proteins called clotting factors. Clotting factors and other plasma proteins form a net of fibers across the cut. The fibers trap more platelets and blood cells until a plug forms to seal the cut. When the plug dries, it forms a scab.

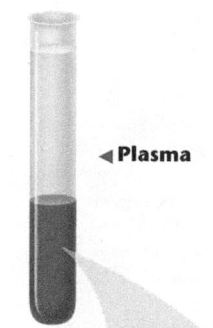

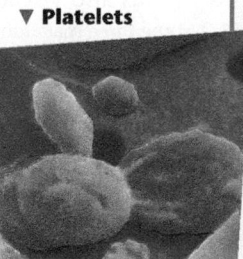

FIGURE 4 Blood consists of liquid plasma, red blood cells, white blood cells, and platelets.

◄ Plasma

▼ Red blood cell

◄ White blood cell

▼ Platelets

297

L2 Visual Learning: Figure 5

Have students examine the table about safe blood transfusions. Ask: **If a patient has blood type B, what blood types can that patient safely be given in a transfusion?** *(type B or type O)* **What would happen if that patient were given blood type A?** *(The blood would clump together in the patient's blood vessels.)*
Caption Answer blood types A and O

3. Assess

Evaluate

These assignments can help you assess students' mastery of the section content.

Section 1 Review

Answers appear below.

Teaching Resources
- Practice 12-1
- Section 12-1 Quiz

L2 Reteach

List the section's vocabulary terms on the board. Point to each word and have students brainstorm facts about that term. Record the key facts. For terms that students know little about, have them reread relevant passages. Suggest that students record the facts for each term in their notebooks.

L4 Enrich

Teaching Resources
- Enrich 12-1

Health and Community

Blood Drive You may want to divide the class into small groups for this activity and have each group produce its own fact sheet and list of local blood drives.

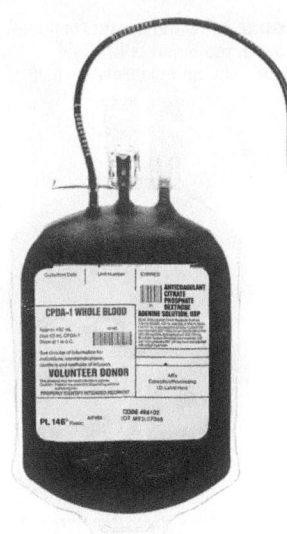

FIGURE 5 If you ever need a transfusion, your blood type will be checked to make sure you receive the correct blood.
Reading Tables If you have blood type A, what blood type(s) could you safely receive?

Safe Blood Transfusions				
If You Have Blood Type	A	B	AB	O
You Can Receive Blood Type(s)	A and O	B and O	A, B, AB, and O	O

Blood Types A person's blood type is determined by the proteins present on the surface of the red blood cells. Depending on which proteins are present, a person's blood type can be type A, B, AB, or O.

A second blood type is determined by the presence or absence of the Rh factor protein. If your red blood cells have the Rh factor, your blood is said to be Rh positive. If your red blood cells lack the Rh factor, your blood is Rh negative. About 85 percent of people are Rh positive.

Transfusions After an injury, surgery, or some illnesses, a person may require a blood transfusion. During a transfusion, blood from a donor is transferred to the patient's bloodstream. Donated blood is tested to identify the blood type. It is also screened for the presence of some microorganisms such as those that cause hepatitis or AIDS.

Why is blood type important? If a patient is given the wrong blood type during a transfusion, the blood will clump together in the patient's blood vessels. This is a life-threatening reaction. Figure 5 shows which blood types can be given safely during a transfusion.

Section 1 Review

Key Ideas and Vocabulary

1. List the three main functions of the cardiovascular system.
2. Describe the pathway of blood through your heart starting at the right **atrium**.
3. List the three types of blood vessels in the order in which they receive blood from the heart.
4. Name the four components of blood and their role in the body.

Critical Thinking

5. **Applying Concepts** What is the function of a closed heart valve?

Health and Community

Blood Drive Contact your local chapter of the American Red Cross to find out about upcoming blood drives in your community. With their guidance, prepare a fact sheet describing the requirements for and the importance of donating blood. Get permission to display the fact sheet and a list of local blood drives in a community building or your school.

6. **Predicting** How might low levels of iron affect the blood's ability to transport oxygen?
7. **Evaluating** Why are people with blood type O called "universal donors"? Why are people with blood type AB called "universal recipients"?

GO ONLINE PearsonSuccessNet.com   Audio Summary Section 12.1

Section 1 Review

1. delivering materials, removing wastes, and fighting disease
2. Blood flows from the right atrium into the right ventricle, through the lungs, into the left atrium, and into the left ventricle.
3. arteries, capillaries, veins
4. Plasma: transports many necessary substances and wastes. Red blood cells: carry oxygen. White blood cells: protect the body from disease and foreign substances. Platelets: help in the clotting process.
5. A closed heart valve prevents blood from flowing in the wrong direction.
6. Iron is needed to make hemoglobin—the substance that transports oxygen.
7. Anyone can receive blood type O. People with blood type AB can receive all types.

Cardiovascular Health

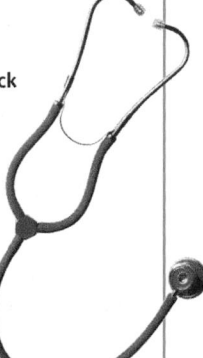

Warm-Up

Quick Quiz Only one of the following statements is true. Which statement do you think it is?

1. Heart attacks and strokes can't be prevented.

2. Teens do not need to be concerned about cardiovascular disease.

3. Smokers are more likely to have a heart attack than are nonsmokers.

4. To be healthy, you need to exercise intensely every day.

5. You do not need to be concerned about what you eat if you exercise regularly.

WRITING Explain why you gave the answer that you did.

Cardiovascular Diseases

Cardiovascular diseases are the leading causes of death in the United States. These diseases develop over many decades, often without symptoms. **Hypertension and high blood cholesterol are two factors that increase your risk of heart attack and stroke. Both factors may begin in your teens.**

Hypertension   As you read in Section 1, a person whose blood pressure is consistently 140/90 or greater has hypertension. Hypertension damages blood vessel walls due to the increased force of the blood. Also, the heart must work extra hard to pump blood through the body. The heart muscle may weaken and eventually fail to pump blood adequately.

Hypertension is known as the "silent killer" because most people have no symptoms. The only way to know if your blood pressure is high is to have it measured. Hypertension can sometimes be controlled with weight loss, exercise, and a low-sodium diet. In many cases, medication is necessary.

 **Do any members of your family have high blood pressure? How do they control it?**

Cardiovascular and Respiratory Health **299**

Objectives

▶ **Identify** two factors that contribute to cardiovascular disease.

▶ **Describe** behaviors that can reduce your risk of cardiovascular disease.

Vocabulary

- low-density lipoprotein
- plaque
- atherosclerosis
- high-density lipoprotein
- arrhythmia

Objectives

Before class begins, write the objectives on the board. Have students copy the objectives into their notebooks at the start of class.

1. Focus

Warm-Up Quick Quiz

Use the Warm-Up Presentation slide to survey student responses.

Call on volunteers to explain which statement they think is true. Hold off telling students which statement is true (Statement 3). Rather, have students retake the quiz after reading about cardiovascular health. Then ask students to explain why the other four statements are false.

Presentation 12-2

2. Teach

L3 **EL** Reading/Note Taking 12-2

L2 Adapted Reading/Note Taking 12-2

Cardiovascular Diseases

L3 **Class Discussion**

State that in 2009, hypertension was listed as the primary cause of death for over 60,000 Americans. Ask: **What is one reason that so many people die from hypertension?** *(Sample answer: Most people have no symptoms.)* **What is one way that you can help prevent damage to your heart and blood vessels from hypertension?** *(Sample answer: Have my blood pressure checked regularly.)*

Connect to Your Life Allow students to answer this question in their private journals.

Differentiated Instruction

EL English Language Learners

Help students with both the pronunciation and meaning of *atherosclerosis*. Pronounce the word clearly, and have students repeat it back to you. Explain that the word part *athero-* comes from a Greek word meaning a pasty food like cooked oatmeal. The word part *–sclerosis* means "hardening." The term *atherosclerosis*, then, means the hardening of arteries due to the buildup of a pasty substance.

L2 Teacher Demo

Use a bicycle pump and rubber tubing to demonstrate atherosclerosis. At a hardware store, find tubing that fits snugly over the air nozzle of a bicycle pump. In class, fit the tubing over the air nozzle. Tell students that the pump represents the heart and the tubing represents an artery. Invite volunteers to pump air through the tubing. Then, ask a student to pinch the tubing almost closed. Have the same students pump air through the tubing again. Ask them to describe the difference to the class. *(They must work harder to pump air through the pinched tubing than through the open tubing.)* Ask: **In this demonstration, we narrowed the tubing by pinching it. What can narrow the inside of an artery?** *(the buildup of plaque)* **When the tubing is narrowed, airflow is constricted. What is constricted when an artery narrows?** *(blood flow)*

L3 Building Health Skills

Practicing Healthful Behaviors Use Figure 6 to help students think about a diet that may prevent the development of atherosclerosis. Point out that habits of the childhood and teenage years contribute to the development of the condition later in life. Ask students to plan two meals, one that would contribute to the development of atherosclerosis and another that might help prevent that condition. Ask volunteers to share menus with the class.

FIGURE 6 Your diet affects your blood cholesterol levels. Foods that are rich in fiber, certain vitamins, and monounsaturated fats may help prevent atherosclerosis.

Blood Cholesterol Your body produces cholesterol to be used as a component of cells, hormones, and nerve tissue. You take in additional cholesterol when you eat animal products. Cholesterol is transported in your blood by carriers known as lipoproteins.

▶ **Low-density lipoproteins** (LDL) carry cholesterol to body tissues for use or storage. LDL is called "bad cholesterol" because it may become a component of **plaque,** a substance that builds up in artery walls. If the level of LDL cholesterol in your blood is continually high, you could develop atherosclerosis (ath uh roh skluh ROH sis). **Atherosclerosis** is a condition in which an artery wall hardens and thickens due to plaque buildup. Figure 6 gives you tips on how you can reduce your risk of atherosclerosis.

▶ **High-density lipoproteins** (HDL) pick up excess cholesterol from body tissues and artery walls and carry it to the liver. HDL is called "good cholesterol" because it cleans your arteries of excess cholesterol. The liver excretes the excess cholesterol in bile, which is eventually eliminated from the body. If your HDL levels are low, you could be at increased risk for atherosclerosis.

Your LDL level should be lower than 129 mg/dL (milligrams per deciliter of blood). Your HDL cholesterol level should be 40 mg/dL or higher.

Heart Attack and Stroke Why is it so important to reduce your risk of atherosclerosis? As artery walls thicken, blood flow is constricted. Eventually, some cells may not receive adequate oxygen or a blood clot could block the narrowed artery. If the artery carries blood to your heart muscles, a heart attack may result. If the artery carries blood to your brain, a stroke may result. In Chapter 23 you will learn more about heart attacks and strokes.

To Prevent Atherosclerosis

• **Choose** fruits, vegetables, nuts, fish, and grains.

• **Limit** red meats, fried foods, and whole milk products.

300 *Chapter 12*

TEENS *Are Asking . . .*

Q: Why should I worry about cardiovascular disease now?

A: Teens should worry. According to the American Heart Association, about 1 million American teens are at high risk for developing heart disease because of high blood pressure, high blood-sugar levels, or other conditions. Studies show that atherosclerosis can begin in a person's late teens without symptoms showing. Teens with diabetes are especially at risk for the development of cardiovascular disease. Research shows that teens with type 1 diabetes—especially boys—tend to have a buildup of cholesterol in their arteries. In addition, type 2 diabetes is becoming increasingly common among American teens, and this disease can lead to heart disease and stroke.

Media Wise

Fast Foods and In-Store Ads

Have you ever entered a fast food restaurant intending to order something healthy or to eat light? Once inside, though, did you change your mind? These questions can help you understand how restaurants influence your food choices.

Do photos of tempting foods entice you to order them?	Yes No
Is it difficult to find nutrition information about the foods?	Yes No
Does the restaurant offer large servings at "bargain" prices?	Yes No
Are there more high-fat foods and high-sugar options than healthy foods?	Yes No
Does the person taking your order suggest additional foods for you to try?	Yes No

"Yes" answers reveal some of the techniques restaurants use to get you to order different foods or more food than you originally planned.

Activity On the Internet, look for nutrition information for the fast food restaurants you visit. Record the information about foods you commonly order. Keep the information in your backpack or another place where you can easily access it.

Other Cardiovascular Disorders Structural problems in the heart may also prevent it from functioning properly. Some of these problems are present at birth, whereas others develop over time.

▶ **Heart Murmur** Almost half of all children are diagnosed with a heart murmur. The "murmur" is an extra sound, in addition to the lub-dub, a doctor hears when listening to a heartbeat. Often murmurs disappear over time without treatment. Occasionally, a murmur is a sign of a problem in the heart, such as a valve not closing properly.

▶ **Opening in Heart Wall** Before birth, all babies have a hole in the wall separating the two atria. If the hole does not seal after birth, oxygen-rich and oxygen-poor blood will mix in the heart, reducing its efficiency. Some people may live their entire lives with such a hole and never know it. Others may have complications and require surgery to close it.

▶ **Arrhythmia** Have you ever felt a strange fluttering in your chest? If so, you may have experienced an **arrhythmia,** or irregular heartbeat. It is normal to experience this from time to time. However, some arrhythmias are signs of serious heart conditions, such as the inability of the pacemaker to regulate the heartbeat.

Media Wise

Fast Foods and In-Store Ads

Call on volunteers to share their answers. Try to get responses about several different restaurants in your area. Discuss why "Yes" answers to the questions may indicate that a restaurant has influenced food choices.

Activity After discussion, have students carry out the Internet assignment. After students have looked for nutrition information on fast food restaurants, ask volunteers to share their findings.

L3 Cultural Connection

About 72,000 people in the United States have a blood disorder called sickle cell disease. The red blood cells of people with the disease are rigid, sticky, and sickle-shaped. The misshapen cells cannot transport as much oxygen as healthy cells and tend to clog small blood vessels, which leads to many health problems. Sickle cell disease most often affects people of African heritage. About 1 out of 600 African Americans has the disease.

Differentiated Instruction

L1 Special Needs

For students having difficulty grasping the difference in function between low-density lipoprotein and high-density lipoprotein, try this analogy. You can compare these cholesterol carriers to two kinds of trucks. LDL is like a freight truck that carries cholesterol to storage facilities. HDL is like a garbage truck that transports cholesterol to a place where it can be disposed. A high level of LDL leads to cholesterol being stored as part of plaque within the artery walls. Meanwhile, a high level of HDL leads to more "garbage" cholesterol being collected and removed from the body.

Keeping Healthy

L3 Content Update  GO ONLINE

Visit Pearson SuccessNet to access more information on preventing heart disease. Have students complete the Web activity.

L2 Visual Learning: Figure 7

Have students examine the photo and answer the caption question. Ask: **How does exercise help you improve cardiovascular health?** (*Exercise can strengthen heart muscles, decrease blood pressure, increase HDL levels, and lower stress levels.*) Call on volunteers to suggest a way to be active, and write their suggestions on the board. Have students copy the list into their journals. **Caption Answer** *Sample answer:* play soccer after school, participate in a dance program, swim laps at the pool

L3 Building Health Skills

Communicating Ask groups to each create a pamphlet that explains habits that would help teenagers maintain cardiovascular health. Explain that the pamphlet should include basic information about the cardiovascular system and how to reduce the risk of cardiovascular disease. **WRITING**

 **Connect to Your Life** Allow students to answer this question in their private journals.

 GO ONLINE
PearsonSuccessNet.com
For: More on preventing heart disease

FIGURE 7 With a little planning, you can achieve 60 minutes of physical activity a day. **Evaluating** What three activities would you add to this list?

Ways to Be Active

► Walk the dog.
► Ride your bike to school.
► Rake the lawn.
► Sweep the sidewalk.
► Jump rope during TV commercials.
► Walk briskly around the mall.

Keeping Healthy

Although few young people have heart attacks or strokes, signs of atherosclerosis can be seen in people in their late teens. And cases of teens with hypertension and high cholesterol are on the rise.

What is your risk for cardiovascular disease? One risk factor that you cannot control is heredity. Heredity plays a significant factor in the amount of LDL and HDL cholesterol your body produces. Having a family history of heart disease also puts you at higher risk for cardiovascular disease. But, many risk factors are within your control. Establishing healthy habits now will decrease your risk of serious health problems in the future. **To help maintain cardiovascular health, you should exercise regularly; eat a nutrient-rich, balanced diet; and avoid smoking.**

Exercise Teens should spend 60 minutes performing physical activity every day, or at least most days. Regular exercise has many benefits for your cardiovascular system.

► Heart muscles strengthen, allowing more blood to be pumped with each beat.

► Blood pressure may decrease.

► HDL levels may increase.

► Stress levels may lower.

Everyday activities can also help keep your cardiovascular system healthy. Anytime you walk to a friend's house instead of getting a ride, take the stairs instead of the escalator, or turn off a video game and take out the trash, you are contributing to your 60 minutes of physical activity.

 **Connect to Your Life** How many minutes of physical activity have you performed today?

WRITING and Health

L3 Advertisement

Ask students to create a magazine advertisement that illustrates the heart benefits of exercising regularly, eating a healthy diet, and avoiding smoking. Point out that the text under the heading Keeping Healthy provides information students can use in their ads. In creating this ad, students should choose information that they think would be most persuasive to a reader. Explain that a good advertisement should be designed so it catches a reader's attention with a bold title, a catchy phrase, or attractive illustrations.

Healthy Food Swaps

Instead of...	Try...
Mayonnaise	Mustard or low-fat mayonnaise
Whole milk	Low-fat or skim milk
Ice cream	Frozen yogurt
Cookies	Fruit
Hamburgers	Turkey burgers

FIGURE 8 Cardiovascular disease can start to develop during your teen years. Now is the time to begin heart-healthy eating habits.

Diet No matter how much you exercise, you still need to pay attention to what and how much you eat. To reduce your risk of cardiovascular disease, limit your intake of fried or processed foods and of foods made from animal products. The cholesterol, saturated fat, and trans fat in these foods increase the levels of LDL in your blood. Eating high-fiber foods such as oatmeal, beans, fresh fruits, and fresh vegetables may help keep your blood cholesterol levels low. Also, limiting your salt intake may help to keep your blood pressure in a normal range.

Avoid Smoking Tobacco products damage blood vessels and contribute to the development of atherosclerosis and hypertension. Some of the cardiovascular damage heals in the years after a smoker quits. However, your chances of living a long and healthy life are better if you never start smoking. In fact, smokers are two to three times more likely to have a heart attack than nonsmokers.

Section 2 Review

Key Ideas and Vocabulary

1. What are two factors that contribute to cardio-vascular disease that may begin in your teens?
2. What is **low-density lipoprotein**? What is **high-density lipoprotein**?
3. What is one symptom of an **arrhythmia**?
4. Describe three ways you can help keep your cardiovascular system healthy.

Critical Thinking

5. **Relating Cause and Effect** How can atherosclerosis and hypertension affect the heart and brain?

Health at Home

Monitoring Saturated Fat Intake For one week, read food labels to track how much saturated fat you consume each day. Remember to keep track of snacks as well as meals. Less than 10 percent of your total calories should come from saturated fats. In a paragraph, discuss ways you can reduce your saturated fat intake. **WRITING**

6. **Predicting** Why do you think cardiovascular diseases are more common in the United States than in some other countries?

3. Assess

Evaluate
These assignments can help you assess students' mastery of the section content.

Section 2 Review
Answers appear below.

Teaching Resources
• Practice 12-2
• Section 12-2 Quiz

L2 Reteach
Have students work in pairs, with one student naming a cardiovascular disorder described in the lesson and the other student stating two facts about that disorder. Pairs should alternate roles and continue the process until each disorder discussed in the section has been reviewed. If a partner disagrees about a fact, the pair should work together to find the sentence in the text that addresses that fact.

L4 Enrich
Teaching Resources
• Enrich 12-2

Health at Home

Monitoring Saturated Fat Intake
Remind students that saturated fats are found most commonly in animal products. Some of these products may be used in preparing other foods. Show students a Nutrition Facts label on a box of crackers, and point out where they can find the amount of saturated fat in a serving of the crackers. Assure students that they can keep the information about their saturated fat intake private. Ask volunteers to share ideas about how to reduce saturated fat intake.

Section 2 Review

1. hypertension and high blood cholesterol
2. Low-density lipoprotein transports cholesterol to body tissues for use or storage. High-density lipoprotein picks up excess cholesterol from body tissues and artery walls and transports it to the liver.
3. fluttering in the chest
4. You can exercise regularly; eat a nutrient-rich, balanced diet; and avoid smoking.
5. Both atherosclerosis and hypertension damage blood vessels which can lead to a heart attack or stroke.
6. *Sample answer:* Many Americans eat poorly and do not get enough exercise.

Improving Your Cardiorespiratory Fitness

Objective

Implement a plan to improve your cardiorespiratory fitness.

Teaching Strategies

- Explain to students that the resting heart rates of teenagers and adults vary according to their levels of cardiovascular fitness. Some very fit athletes have a resting heart rate as low as 30 to 40 beats per minute. Most people have a resting heart rate of 60 to 80 beats per minute.

- To build cardiovascular fitness, a person's target heart rate must be maintained for at least 15 to 20 minutes.

- Invite a fitness instructor, an exercise physiologist, or a physical education teacher to talk about the importance of intensity, duration, and frequency of exercise in any fitness program.

- As students design their fitness programs, remind them to set reasonable goals. Once a goal is reached, students should exercise at the same level of intensity about three times a week to maintain the level of fitness.

- You might suggest to students who have access to a pedometer to use the pedometer to monitor the number of steps they take during exercise. Students can also keep a log for a week to record how many steps they take each day. Tell students that their goal should be 10,000 steps a day.

Improving Your Cardiorespiratory Fitness

How can you improve your cardiorespiratory fitness—the ability of your heart, blood vessels, and lungs to deliver nutrients and oxygen to your muscles? When you are active, your heart and lungs must be able to supply your body with the oxygen it needs. In fact, when you exercise, your heart needs to pump up to five times more blood each minute than when you are resting. Here is a simple test for assessing your cardiorespiratory fitness and guidelines for improving it. *CAUTION: Before you do this test or start an exercise program, have a physical exam to make sure you are healthy enough for vigorous exercise. Do not attempt this test if you are ill or if you have a history of health problems.*

① Test your cardiorespiratory fitness.

▶ To prepare for the test, do the warm-up and stretching exercises described on pages 276–277.

▶ Run or walk for one mile as fast as you can. You can alternate running with walking. A partner should time how long it takes you.

▶ Compare your time to the times listed in the table. For an average fitness level, your time should be less than those listed in the table.

Mile Walk/Run Times (min)

Age	Females	Males
14	10:30	7:45
15–18	10:30	7:30

304 *Chapter 12*

⚑ Sensitive Issues

Students who are overweight or in poor physical condition may be uncomfortable participating in the walk/run activity at school with classmates. Some students may also have a medical condition that precludes vigorous exercise. Make alternative arrangements for such students.

② Calculate your target heart rate.

How will you know if you are exercising hard enough to improve your cardiorespiratory health, but not too hard? Your target heart rate is the heart rate you should maintain during exercise to improve your fitness. Follow these steps to calculate your target heart rate.

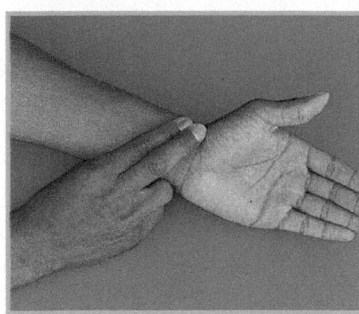

Step 1: Subtract your age from 220 if you are male; from 226 if you are female. This is an estimate of your maximum heart rate.

Step 2: Determine your resting heart rate. Use your index and middle finger to find your pulse in your wrist. Count the number of pulse beats in one minute.

Step 3: Subtract your resting heart rate from your maximum heart rate.

Step 4: Multiply the number from Step 3 by 0.6. Round to the nearest whole number. Then multiply the number from Step 3 by 0.8 and round to the nearest whole number.

Step 5: Add your resting heart rate to each of the two numbers from Step 4. The two sums give you the range in which your heart rate should be during exercise, or your target heart rate.

③ Choose an exercise program.

► Ask your physical education teacher to help you select appropriate activities for building cardiorespiratory fitness. Select moderate intensity activities at first, such as walking, tennis, and volleyball. Then, as your fitness improves, include activities of higher intensity such as basketball, jogging, or jumping rope. Try to do these activities for 60 minutes a day at least 5 days a week.

► To check that you are exercising in your target heart rate range, take your pulse immediately after you stop exercising. Count the beats for 10 seconds. Multiply by 6 for the number of beats in one minute.

► After you've been exercising regularly for several weeks, repeat the walk/run fitness test to check your progress.

🔺 Practice the Skill

1. After a physical exam by a healthcare professional, complete the one-mile walk/run test to determine your cardiorespiratory fitness level. Be sure to do warm-up and stretching exercises before you begin the test. Record your results.

2. Calculate your target heart rate range. Remember to check your heart rate while you exercise.

3. Work with your physical education teacher or another trained professional to design a cardiorespiratory fitness program that will improve your fitness level.

4. Perform the one-mile walk/run every few weeks. Keep a log of your progress.

🔺 Practice the Skill

1. Students should review the warm-up and stretching exercises in the Building Health Skills on pages 276–277. Times to complete the one-mile walk/run will vary. Many students will take longer to complete one mile than the averages listed in the table.

2. Students should use the procedure described in part 2 to determine their target heart rate range. Target heart rate ranges will generally be from a low of about 140 to a high of about 180.

3. The program that a student designs should consider his or her current fitness level as well as his or her interests. A typical program might include walking or running, playing soccer, or swimming.

4. Periodically encourage students to continue their cardiorespiratory fitness programs. Help students set up a log in their journals.

Health and Community

⒀ Teen Fitness

Explain that many places in the community focus on helping teens and adults achieve and maintain fitness. Ask a few volunteers to find out what fitness programs for teens are available at a community center, the YMCA or YWCA, or at a neighborhood health club. Ask students to report back to class both about what programs are offered and how much they cost.

Objectives
Before class begins, write the objectives on the board. Have students copy the objectives into their notebooks at the start of class.

1. Focus

Warm-Up Health Stats

After students have completed the writing assignment, have volunteers share their ideas with the class. Students should point out that the trend of the graph line shows a rise in ER visits for asthma from 2001 until 2002, after which there is a fall. Students might suggest that air pollution contributed to rising asthma rates. Perhaps emergency room visits dropped because at-home treatments became more effective.

Presentation 12-3

Objectives
▶ **List** the functions of the respiratory system.
▶ **Describe** how air travels through your respiratory system, and how you breathe.
▶ **Identify** ways to keep the respiratory system healthy.

Vocabulary
- alveoli
- diaphragm
- asthma
- bronchitis

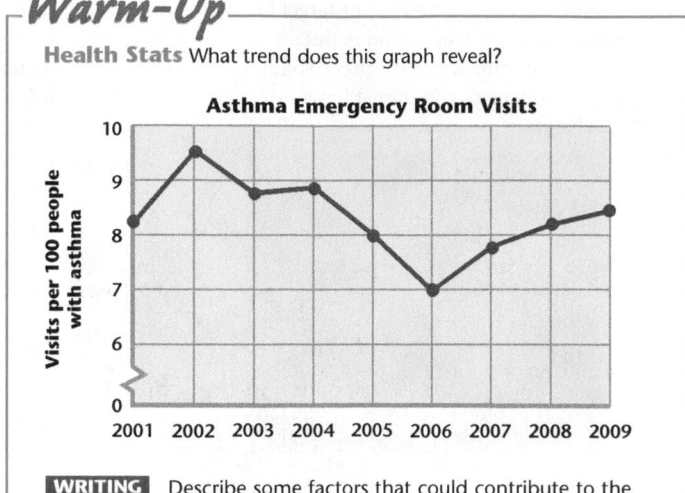

Warm-Up
Health Stats What trend does this graph reveal?

Asthma Emergency Room Visits

Visits per 100 people with asthma

2001 2002 2003 2004 2005 2006 2007 2008 2009

WRITING Describe some factors that could contribute to the rise and fall of asthma emergencies.

The Respiratory System

A person can survive weeks without food and days without water, but only minutes without oxygen. Your respiratory system brings a continuous supply of oxygen from the air into your body. As you have read, your cardiovascular system transports this oxygen to all of your body cells. After the cells use the oxygen to break down glucose for energy, they are left with carbon dioxide that must be expelled from the body. **The respiratory system is responsible for bringing oxygen from the outside environment into the body. It also removes carbon dioxide from the body.**

The Pathway of Air   When you breathe in, or inhale, much more than just air enters your body. With every breath, you also take in such things as dust, pollen, and microorganisms that can cause disease. Most of these substances never reach your lungs. Cells lining your nasal cavities release mucus, which traps particles. Mucus also warms and moistens the air as it passes through your nasal cavities. **On its way to the lungs, air passes through the nose, pharynx, larynx, trachea, and bronchi.** Follow the pathway of air from the environment to your lungs in Figure 9.

Sensitive Issues
Be aware that some students with asthma may be sensitive about sharing their experiences with the class. If you know students with asthma in your class, ask them ahead of time if they mind talking about their experiences.

For Your INFORMATION!

Asthma and Physical Activity
Physical activity is important for the health of the body and the mind. There are ways to help teens with asthma stay active and reap the benefits of physical activity. *Asthma and Physical Activity in the School,* available through the National Heart, Lung, and Blood Institute, offers advice to teachers and coaches who want to help students with asthma participate in physical activities.

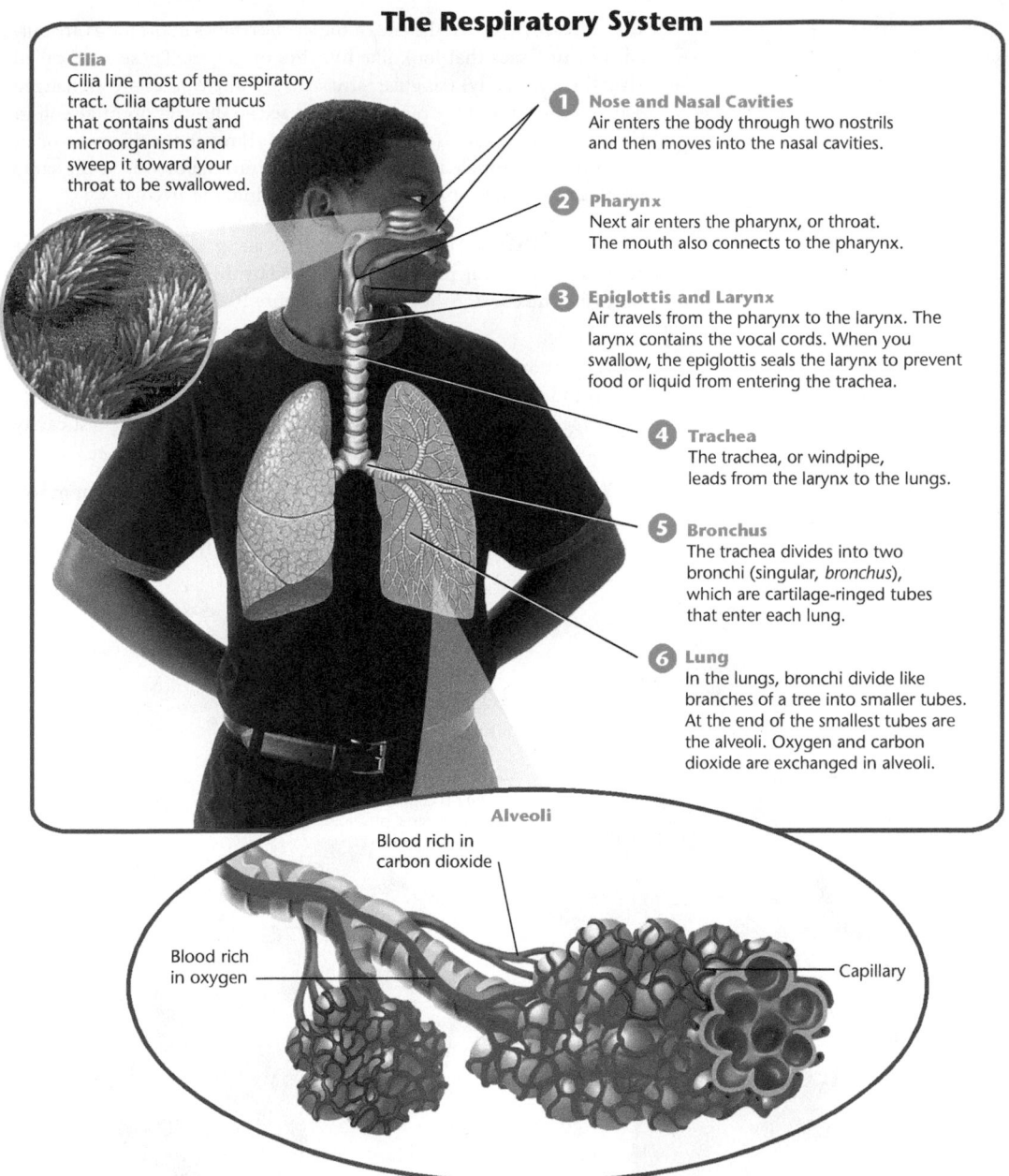

The Respiratory System

Cilia
Cilia line most of the respiratory tract. Cilia capture mucus that contains dust and microorganisms and sweep it toward your throat to be swallowed.

1 **Nose and Nasal Cavities**
Air enters the body through two nostrils and then moves into the nasal cavities.

2 **Pharynx**
Next air enters the pharynx, or throat. The mouth also connects to the pharynx.

3 **Epiglottis and Larynx**
Air travels from the pharynx to the larynx. The larynx contains the vocal cords. When you swallow, the epiglottis seals the larynx to prevent food or liquid from entering the trachea.

4 **Trachea**
The trachea, or windpipe, leads from the larynx to the lungs.

5 **Bronchus**
The trachea divides into two bronchi (singular, *bronchus*), which are cartilage-ringed tubes that enter each lung.

6 **Lung**
In the lungs, bronchi divide like branches of a tree into smaller tubes. At the end of the smallest tubes are the alveoli. Oxygen and carbon dioxide are exchanged in alveoli.

Alveoli
Blood rich in carbon dioxide
Blood rich in oxygen
Capillary

FIGURE 9 On its path to the lungs, air passes through several structures where it is filtered, warmed, and moistened. **Predicting** What path does carbon dioxide take on its way out of the body?

2. Teach

L3 **EL** Reading/Note Taking 3-1
L2 Adapted Reading/Note Taking 3-1

The Respiratory System

EL **Visual Learning: Figure 9**

Image Bank Figure 12-9

Have students write the name of each label in Figure 9 on an index card. Have them organize the labels by the order in which air passes through the respiratory system. Suggest they write a question they have about each structure on the card. Have them fill in the answers as they read the section.

Caption Answer Carbon dioxide moves from the lungs through the bronchi, through the trachea, through the larynx, through the pharynx, and out through the nose or mouth.

L2 **Active Learning**

Ask students to tilt their heads backward and place the fingers of one hand on the front of the neck. Then ask students to move the fingers up and down the neck. Ask: **What are the ridges you feel up and down your neck?** *(the rings of the trachea)* Ask students to keep their fingers in place as they swallow. Explain that the movement they feel is the epiglottis sealing the larynx. Ask: **What does the sealing of the larynx by the epiglottis prevent?** *(It prevents food or liquid from entering the trachea.)*

Differentiated Instruction

L1 **Special Needs**

Students who need extra help, as well as visual and tactile learners, may learn more about the respiratory system by drawing it. Give each student a sheet of tracing paper or thin unlined paper. Ask students to trace the outline of the person in Figure 9. Then students should draw the structures, label them, and describe them in their own words. Check students' completed drawings for errors and omissions.

L3 Class Discussion

After students have read about gas exchange, reinforce the connection between the cardiovascular system and the respiratory system. Ask: **Where does the carbon dioxide come from that passes from blood into the alveoli?** *(It is a waste product that passes from body cells into the blood.)* **When the oxygen in the alveoli passes into the blood, to what chamber of the heart does that blood first go?** *(to the left atrium)* **Why is the oxygen that is part of the exchange in the alveoli needed by the body?** *(Body cells use oxygen in the process that extracts energy from nutrients.)*

L2 Teacher Demo

To demonstrate how the diaphragm works, borrow a model of the lungs and diaphragm from a biology teacher. A common apparatus consists of one or two small balloons to represent the lungs. These balloons are attached to a tube within a glass bell jar. The bottom of the jar is sealed with latex, which represents the diaphragm. When you pull down on the "diaphragm," the "lungs" inside the bell jar inflate. Ask: **What will happen to the "lungs" when the "diaphragm" moves upward?** *(The "lungs" will deflate as air moves out of them.)* Tell students that this model illustrates how changes in air pressure cause the lungs to expand and contract.

L3 Visual Learning: Figure 10

Image Bank Figure 12-10

Have students examine the process of inhalation and exhalation shown in the figure. Then ask them to place one hand on their abdomen as they breathe normally. Ask: **Why does your abdomen move in and out as you breathe?** *(When the diaphragm contracts and flattens, it pushes the abdomen out. The reverse occurs when the diaphragm relaxes and moves upward.)*

Gas Exchange   At the end of the smallest tubes in the lungs are millions of tiny sacs that look like bunches of grapes. These sacs, called **alveoli** (al VEE uh ly) (singular, *alveolus*), are where gases are exchanged between the air and the blood. You can see an illustration of alveoli in Figure 9 on the previous page. Oxygen passes through the thin walls of an alveolus and through a thin capillary wall into the blood. At the same time, carbon dioxide passes from the blood into the alveoli.

The Breathing Process   How does air get into and out of your body? **The breathing process is controlled by the actions of muscles in your ribs and chest.** As you can see in Figure 10, breathing takes place in two stages.

▶ **Inhalation** When you inhale, or breathe in, rib muscles pull the ribs up and out. At the same time the **diaphragm** (DY uh fram), a dome-shaped muscle that lies below the lungs, flattens. The chest cavity enlarges, the volume of the lungs increases, and air flows in.

▶ **Exhalation** When you exhale, or breathe out, the diaphragm moves upward. The rib muscles relax and the ribs drop. These movements make the chest cavity smaller and squeeze air from the lungs.

FIGURE 10   When you inhale, the diaphragm flattens. Pressure in the expanded lungs decreases, causing air to flow in. When you exhale, the diaphragm curves upward. Pressure in the lungs increases, pushing air out of your lungs.

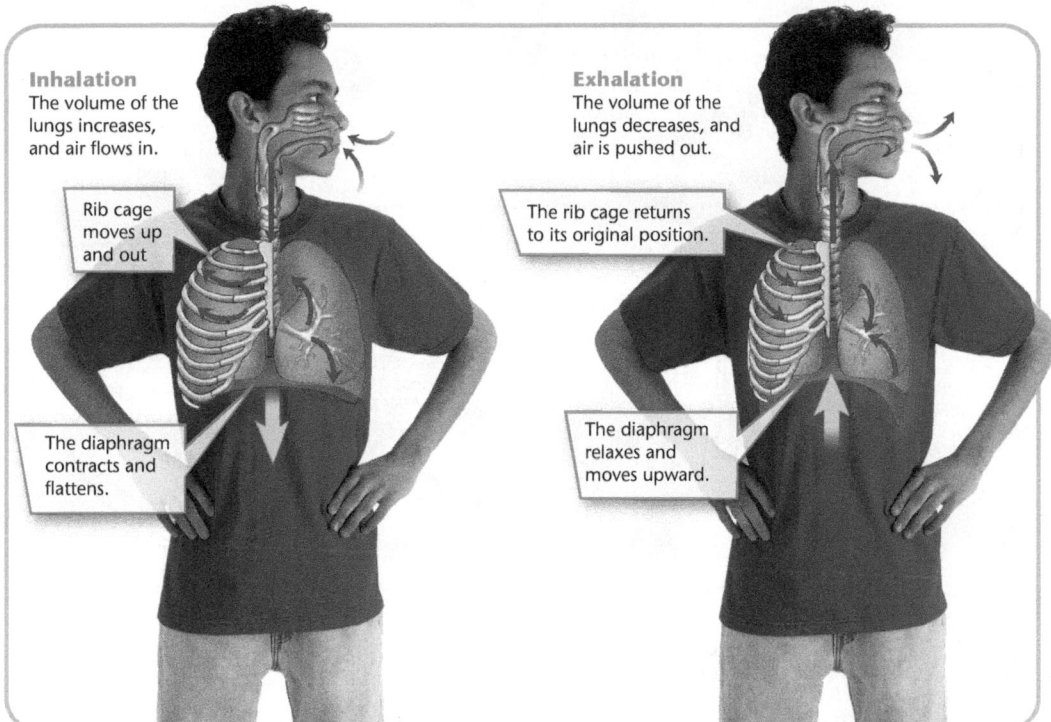

Inhalation
The volume of the lungs increases, and air flows in.

Rib cage moves up and out

The diaphragm contracts and flattens.

Exhalation
The volume of the lungs decreases, and air is pushed out.

The rib cage returns to its original position.

The diaphragm relaxes and moves upward.

308   *Chapter 12*

MATH and Health

L3 Percentages

On page 309, students will learn that approximately 26 million people in the United States have asthma. Based on this data, have students estimate the percentage of people in the United States with asthma. For this exercise, assume that the United States population is 300 million. *(26 ÷ 300 = 0.086; 0.086 × 100 = 8.6 percent)*

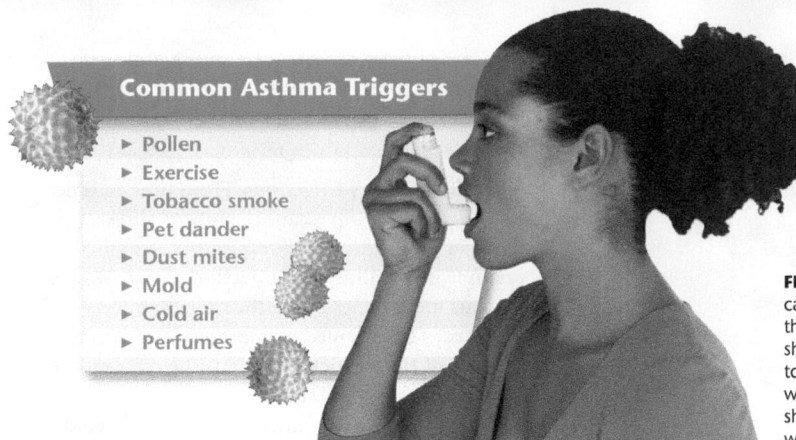

Common Asthma Triggers

► Pollen
► Exercise
► Tobacco smoke
► Pet dander
► Dust mites
► Mold
► Cold air
► Perfumes

FIGURE 11 People with asthma can lead active lives if they follow their treatment program. They should also avoid or limit exposure to their particular triggers. People with exercise-induced asthma should work with a doctor to find ways to exercise safely.

Keeping Healthy

What can you do to keep your respiratory system healthy? **You can keep your respiratory system healthy by avoiding tobacco smoke and air pollution and treating asthma if you have it. In addition, avoid respiratory infections, get regular exercise, and maintain a healthy weight.**

Avoiding Smoking and Air Pollution The most important thing you can do to protect your respiratory system is not to smoke. Over time, exposure to tobacco smoke and other air pollutants can seriously harm your respiratory health. In Chapter 16 you will learn how smoking can lead to serious respiratory system disorders such as chronic bronchitis and emphysema.

It is also important to avoid exposure to air pollutants whenever possible. If you do work that generates fumes or dust, such as sweeping a garage, wear a mask. Work in a well-ventilated area when you paint or use other chemicals that produce fumes. Before exercising outdoors on a hot, sunny day, check local news reports for warnings about air quality.

Living With Asthma About 19 million adults and 7 million children in the United States have asthma. **Asthma** (AZ muh) is a disorder in which respiratory passageways become inflamed. During an asthma attack, the passageways narrow until air can barely pass through. As a result, the person wheezes, coughs, and has difficulty breathing. Attacks can range from irritating to life threatening. Substances or behaviors that cause asthma attacks are called triggers. Common asthma triggers are exercise, allergic reactions, and stress.

Asthma is usually first diagnosed in childhood. Sometimes children outgrow the condition. Many people with asthma take medications daily to control their symptoms and avoid attacks. If an attack does occur, other medications are taken for immediate relief.

 **Connect to Your Life** What things do you do to keep your respiratory system healthy?

GO ONLINE
PearsonSuccessNet.com
For: More on respiratory health

Keeping Healthy

L2 Class Discussion

Write the following question on the chalkboard: How often are you exposed to automobile exhaust, smoke, or dust each day? Where do these exposures occur? Have students call out responses and make a running list on the board. Students will likely be surprised at the long list of respiratory system irritants they are exposed to every day.

L3 Cooperative Learning

Have small groups work together to make a list of "Do's" and "Don'ts" regarding respiratory health. *(For example, students might list: "Do get regular exercise" and "Don't exercise outdoors on days when the air is very polluted.")* Give groups a chance to share their lists. Call on students to explain how following these "Do's" and "Don'ts" contributes to a healthy respiratory system.

L3 Journal Writing

Ask students to write a journal entry in which they explain why it is important for a person to keep his or her respiratory system healthy. Ask students to think of times when they've been tempted to smoke tobacco and describe why refusing tobacco is important to maintain good respiratory health. **WRITING**

Connect to Your Life Allow students to answer this question in their private journals.

L3 Content Update **GO ONLINE**

Visit Pearson SuccessNet to access more information about asthma. Have students complete the Web activity.

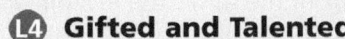 **Instruction**

L4 Gifted and Talented

Have interested students further investigate asthma. Ask them to find out about the causes of asthma, the triggers that produce an asthma attack, the symptoms of the disorder, and the treatment of asthma. Point out to students that asthma is a growing problem in the United States and other industrialized countries. Ask students to try to find explanations for the increase of asthma. Have them focus some of their attention on how air pollution affects a person with asthma. Ask students to share what they learn with the class.

3. Assess

Evaluate
These assignments can help you assess students' mastery of the section content.

Section 3 Review
Answers appear below.

Teaching Resources
- Practice 12-3
- Section 12-3 Quiz

 Reteach

Play a quiz game in which you describe the function of a part of the respiratory system and students try to name that part. Go around the room, calling on one student after another, until most students show mastery of the information.

 Enrich

Teaching Resources
- Enrich 12-3

Health at School

Asthma Attacks Encourage students to ask what the procedures are when a student experiences an asthma attack. To manage this activity, you might assign pairs of students or small groups to interview the nurse or a specific physical education teacher. Each student can then write a paragraph summarizing the findings.

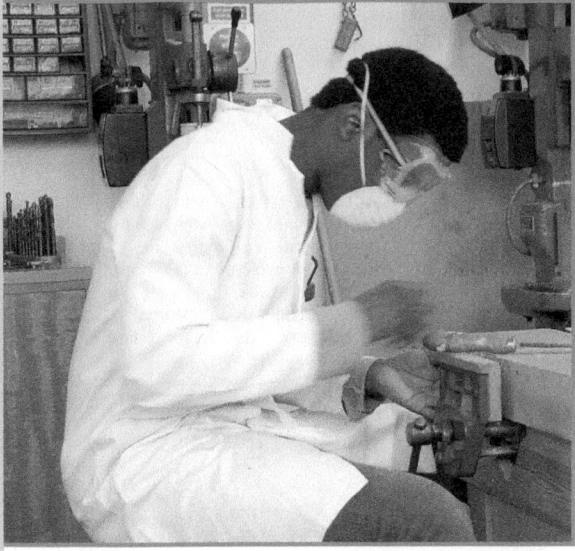

FIGURE 12 Protect your respiratory system by wearing a mask when you do work that generates dust or fumes.

Other Healthful Behaviors You can practice other important behaviors to protect the health of your respiratory system.

▶ **Avoid Respiratory Infections** From time to time, microorganisms will escape the mucus and sweeping cilia and infect your respiratory system. For example, **bronchitis** is an infection that causes the mucous membranes lining the bronchi to become inflamed. The inflamed membranes secrete a large amount of thick mucus that must be removed by coughing. In Chapter 21 you will learn about other common respiratory infections such as colds, influenza, and pneumonia. You will also learn ways to prevent and treat these infections.

▶ **Get Regular Exercise** A regular exercise program that involves several minutes of repetitive, non-stop physical activity is extremely important for maintaining respiratory health. Exercise helps your lungs become more efficient at taking in oxygen and eliminating carbon dioxide.

▶ **Maintain a Healthy Weight** Regular exercise will also help you maintain an ideal weight. The respiratory system of an overweight person must work harder to deliver adequate oxygen than the system of a normal weight person. Maintaining a reasonable weight will help you avoid straining your respiratory system.

Section 3 Review

Key Ideas and Vocabulary
1. What two functions does your respiratory system perform?
2. List the structures that air flows through on its way to the lungs.
3. Explain the action of the **diaphragm** when you inhale and exhale.
4. Identify five ways you can help your respiratory system stay healthy.

Critical Thinking
5. **Relating Cause and Effect** In a healthy person, how might coughing and sneezing protect the respiratory system?

Health at School

Asthma Attacks Talk to your school nurse, physical education teacher, or other students about asthma. What are the most common triggers for asthma attacks at school? Are attacks more common at certain times of day or times of year? How are asthma attacks treated? Summarize your findings in a paragraph. **WRITING**

6. **Comparing and Contrasting** Explain the difference between the movement of oxygen and carbon dioxide in the alveoli.
7. **Evaluating** Why is it important for someone with exercise-induced asthma to find ways to participate in physical activity?

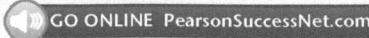 GO ONLINE PearsonSuccessNet.com | Audio Summary Section 12.3

Section 3 Review

1. It brings oxygen into the body and removes carbon dioxide from the body.
2. nose, pharynx, larynx, trachea, and bronchi
3. When the diaphragm flattens, you inhale. When the diaphragm moves upward, you exhale.

4. avoid smoking and air pollution, treat asthma if you have it, avoid respiratory infections, get regular exercise, and maintain a healthy weight
5. *Sample answer:* Coughing and sneezing can remove microorganisms and foreign particles from the respiratory tract.

6. Oxygen moves from the air in the alveoli into the blood in the capillaries. Carbon dioxide moves from the blood in the capillaries into the air in the alveoli.
7. *Sample answer:* Exercise helps your lungs become more efficient at taking in oxygen and eliminating carbon dioxide. Exercise also benefits the cardiovascular system and other systems of the body.

Chapter 12
At a Glance

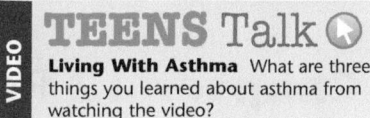

Section 1   Your Cardiovascular System

Key Ideas

▶ The main functions of the cardiovascular system include delivering materials to cells and carrying wastes away. In addition, blood contains cells that fight disease.

▶ The atria receive blood entering the heart. Blood flows from the atria to the ventricles, which pump the blood out of the heart.

▶ The three main types of blood vessels in your body are arteries, capillaries, and veins.

▶ The four components of blood are plasma, red blood cells, white blood cells, and platelets.

Vocabulary
- atrium (293)
- ventricle (293)
- pacemaker (294)
- artery (295)
- capillary (295)
- vein (295)
- blood pressure (296)
- hypertension (296)
- plasma (297)
- red blood cell (297)
- white blood cell (297)
- platelet (297)

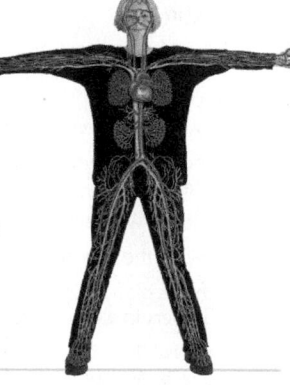

Section 2   Cardiovascular Health

Key Ideas

▶ Hypertension and high blood cholesterol are two factors that increase your risk of heart attack and stroke. Both factors may begin in your teens.

▶ To help maintain cardiovascular health, you should exercise regularly; eat a nutrient-rich, balanced diet; and avoid smoking.

Vocabulary
- low-density lipoprotein (300)
- plaque (300)
- atherosclerosis (300)
- high-density lipoprotein (300)
- arrhythmia (301)

Section 3   Respiratory Health

Key Ideas

▶ The respiratory system is responsible for bringing oxygen from the outside environment into the body. The respiratory system also removes carbon dioxide from the body.

▶ On its way to the lungs, air passes through the nose, pharynx, larynx, trachea, and bronchi.

▶ The breathing process is controlled by the actions of muscles in your ribs and chest.

▶ You can keep your respiratory system healthy by avoiding tobacco smoke and air pollution and treating asthma if you have it. In addition, avoid respiratory infections, get regular exercise, and maintain a healthy weight.

Vocabulary
- alveoli (308)
- diaphragm (308)
- asthma (309)
- bronchitis (310)

Chapter 12
At a Glance

VIDEO   **Living With Asthma** Ask for volunteers to share their answers. Use examples from the video to review strategies for living with asthma.

Key Ideas Review

L2 Restate the boldfaced sentences as questions and have teams take turns answering them. If one team cannot answer a question, give other teams a chance. Award points for correct answers.

L3 Invite students to create a multiple-choice quiz with ten questions that address the Key Ideas from this chapter. Students can exchange quizzes and answer the questions.

Vocabulary Review

L2 Ask each student to write a paragraph that uses ten vocabulary terms from the chapter but using a blank instead of the word each time a term is required. Then have students exchange and try to fill in the blanks of each other's paragraphs.

EL Ask students to make flashcards to review the chapter's vocabulary. Students should write a term on one side of an index card and the definition and an example of the term. Ask students to choose partners and quiz each other using the flashcards.

Chapter 12 Review

GO ONLINE

PearsonSuccessNet.com

Students can go online for a review activity on Chapter 12.

Reviewing Key Ideas

Section 1

1. b   **2.** b

3. One loop leads from the heart to the lungs, where the blood releases carbon dioxide, picks up oxygen, and then returns to the heart. A second loop circles through the rest of the body, where the blood delivers oxygen and nutrients and picks up wastes.

4. In the first phase, the heart relaxes and the atria fill with blood. In the second phase, the ventricles contract and pump blood out of the heart.

5. Platelets play an important role in the blood clotting process.

6. Blood pressure is the force with which blood pushes against blood vessel walls. Systolic pressure is the pressure when the ventricles contract. Diastolic pressure is the pressure when the ventricles relax.

7. The patient with blood type B can receive only blood type O. The patient with blood type AB can receive either blood type A or blood type O. The patient with blood type O can receive only blood type O.

Section 2

8. b   **9.** d

10. Atherosclerosis is a condition in which an artery wall hardens and thickens due to plaque buildup. LDL may become a component of plaque, and as a result can contribute to atherosclerosis. HDL removes excess cholesterol from arteries, and as a result can prevent atherosclerosis.

11. because most people have no symptoms of hypertension

12. It can strengthen heart muscles, decrease blood pressure, increase HDL levels, and lower stress levels.

13. Having a family history of cardiovascular disease puts a person at higher risk for cardiovascular disease.

Chapter 12 Review

Reviewing Key Ideas

GO ONLINE

PearsonSuccessNet.com

For: Chapter 12 review activity

Section 1

1. In which kind of blood vessel are materials exchanged between the blood and body cells?
- **a.** aorta
- **b.** capillary
- **c.** vein
- **d.** artery

2. Which component of blood is responsible for the transport of oxygen?
- **a.** plasma
- **b.** red blood cells
- **c.** white blood cells
- **d.** platelets

3. Describe the two loops of the cardiovascular system.

4. Describe what happens during a heartbeat.

5. What is the role of platelets?

6. What is blood pressure? What do the two numbers in a blood pressure reading indicate?

7. **Critical Thinking** Three patients with blood types B, AB, and O are waiting for blood transfusions. The hospital's blood bank only contains blood types A and O. Which patient should receive which type of blood? Explain.

Section 2

8. Cholesterol is a fatty substance most closely associated with
- **a.** white blood cells.
- **b.** atherosclerosis.
- **c.** hemoglobin.
- **d.** blood pressure.

9. Which of the following foods are healthy for your cardiovascular system?
- **a.** butter and cheese
- **b.** beef and whole milk
- **c.** ice cream and potato chips
- **d.** fruits and fish

10. What is atherosclerosis and how is it related to LDL and HDL?

11. Why is hypertension called the "silent killer"?

12. Explain how exercise is beneficial to your cardiovascular health.

13. **Critical Thinking** Why is it important to know your family's history of cardiovascular disease?

Section 3

14. In which structure does gas exchange take place?
- **a.** alveolus
- **b.** bronchus
- **c.** trachea
- **d.** pharynx

15. Which of the following is *not* a respiratory infection?
- **a.** bronchitis
- **b.** influenza
- **c.** asthma
- **d.** pneumonia

16. Describe the path oxygen takes as it moves from the air outside your body into your blood.

17. How does the movement of the diaphragm affect the size of the chest cavity?

18. **Critical Thinking** Some respiratory diseases reduce the ability of the lungs to take in oxygen. How could this lead to damage of the cardiovascular system as well?

Building Health Skills

19. **Communicating** Develop an analogy to explain hypertension to a younger sibling.

20. **Analyzing Influences** Each day you make decisions about which foods you eat. Most likely there are many factors that influence your choices. Choose three of these influences and describe their effects on your decisions. **WRITING**

21. **Setting Goals** Between school, homework, and an after-school job, you have no time for school sports or other exercise. But, you want to stay fit. In a paragraph, describe how you can incorporate exercise into your busy schedule. **WRITING**

Health and Community

Blood Pressure Screenings Contact local medical centers, doctors' offices, and pharmacies to find out where people can have their blood pressure checked. Ask about free or low-cost blood-pressure screening programs. Write a letter to your local newspaper providing information about these screening programs. **WRITING**

Section 3

14. a   **15.** c

16. Oxygen travels through the nose, pharynx, larynx, trachea, bronchi, and alveoli.

17. When the diaphragm flattens, the chest cavity enlarges. When the diaphragm moves upward, the chest cavity becomes smaller.

18. *Sample answer:* Heart cells depend on oxygen from the lungs. Lack of oxygen can lead to heart muscle damage.

Building Health Skills

19. *Sample answer:* Hypertension is like having too much water in a hose. If the water pressure becomes too high, the hose may split.

20. A typical answer might mention what a parent prepares for lunch or dinner, what friends are eating, and what food is most convenient.

Standardized Test Prep

Math Practice

The graph below compares lung function in smokers and in people who have never smoked. Use the graph to answer Questions 22–24.

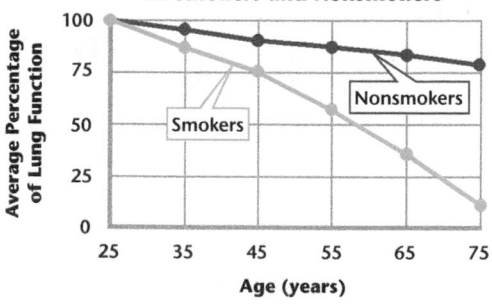

Comparing Lung Function in Smokers and Nonsmokers

22. At about what age are a smoker's lungs functioning at only 50% of their capacity?
    A 40
    B 50
    C 60
    D 70

23. At approximately what age do a smoker's lungs have the same capacity as the lungs of a 75-year-old nonsmoker?
    F 25
    G 45
    H 65
    J 75

24. What general conclusion about lung function and smoking can you draw from this graph?
    A Smoking does not affect lung function.
    B Smokers have greater lung function than people who do not smoke.
    C By the age of 50, a smoker will likely have 50 percent lung function.
    D Smoking significantly reduces a person's lung function.

Test-Taking Tip

When you take a test, try to stay relaxed. If you start to feel nervous, sit back and take a few deep breaths to calm yourself down.

Reading and Writing Practice

Read the passage. Then answer Questions 25–28.

The larynx contains two elastic folds of tissue called the vocal cords. As muscles pull on the vocal cords, air moves between them, causing them to vibrate. The vibrations produce the sounds you make when you speak, shout, or sing.

High-pitched sounds are produced when muscles shorten the vocal cords. Low-pitched sounds are produced when the muscles lengthen the vocal cords. Controlled pitch, a requirement for quality singing, can be improved by exercising the vocal cord muscles.

25. In this passage, the term *pitch* is most closely related to
    A high or low sounds.
    B the quality of one's voice.
    C the shortening of the vocal cords.
    D the lengthening of the vocal cords.

26. Children's voices are usually higher-pitched than adult's voices. This is most likely because
    F their vocal cord muscles are weak.
    G they cannot control the movement of their vocal cords.
    H they cannot control the volume of their voices.
    J their vocal cords are shorter than the vocal cords of adults.

27. The ability to control pitch while singing depends on
    A the singer's age.
    B the strength of the vocal cord muscles.
    C the arrangement of the vocal cords.
    D the amount of air passing through the vocal cords.

Constructed Response

28. In a paragraph, summarize how the vocal cord muscles control the pitch of your voice.

Standardized Test Prep

Math Practice
22. C
23. G
24. D

Reading and Writing Practice
25. A
26. J
27. B
28. Vocal cord muscles control the pitch of a voice by shortening and lengthening the vocal cords.

21. Answers will vary. A typical answer might suggest doing exercises before going to school in the morning or walking instead of riding to the after-school job.

Health and Community

Blood Pressure Screenings Lead a class discussion about which local medical centers or pharmacies might be good places for students to find out where people can get their blood pressure checked. After the information has been gathered, display letters to the editor from a local newspaper so that students can get a sense of how to form their letters.

CHAPTER 13 Exercise and Lifelong Fitness

Section Objectives	Standards Correlation	Instructional Resources ⓛ₃	SE eTEXT	TE eTEXT	PRINT
1 The Importance of Physical Activity ⏱ 2 periods; 1 block	NHES: 1.12.1, 1.12.2, 3.12.3	**SE** Warm-Up, p. 316	•	•	•
13.1.1 Explain some of the physical, psychological, and social benefits of physical activity.		**RN** Note Taking Guide 13-1	•	•	•
		IB Image Bank 13-3			•
13.1.2 Define the five components of fitness.		**TR** Practice 13-1			•
13.1.3 Describe five types of physical activity.		**TR** Section 13-1 Quiz			•
Assessing Flexibility, Muscular Strength, and Endurance ⏱ 1 period; 1/2 block	NHES: 6.12.1, 6.12.2	**SE** Practice the Skill, p. 323	•	•	•
		RN Building Health Skills 13	•	•	•
BHS.13 Demonstrate healthful behaviors by assessing levels of flexibility, muscular strength, and muscular endurance.					
2 Setting Goals for Lifelong Fitness ⏱ 2 periods; 1 block	NHES: 1.12.7, 2.12.6, 6.12.1, 6.12.2, 6.12.3, 6.12.4	**SE** Warm-Up, p. 324	•	•	•
		SE Technology & Health Out on a Limb, p. 330	•	•	•
13.2.1 Develop a plan for achieving lifelong fitness.		**RN** Note Taking Guide 13-2	•	•	•
		IB Image Bank 13-8			•
13.2.1 Describe the three phases of exercise.		**TR** Practice 13-2			•
		TR Section 13-2 Quiz			•
3 Physical Activity and Safety ⏱ 2 periods; 1 block	NHES: 1.12.5, 1.12.8, 2.12.4, 2.12.5, 3.12.1, 3.12.4, 5.12.5, 7.12.1, 7.12.2	**SE** Warm-Up, p. 331	•	•	•
		SE Media Wise Evaluating Exercise Devices, p. 335	•	•	•
13.3.1 List five safety considerations related to physical activity.		**RN** Note Taking Guide 13-3	•	•	•
13.3.2 Evaluate the risks of using substances to enhance performance.		**TR** Practice 13-3			•
13.3.3 Identify ways to avoid overtraining and prevent sports-related injuries.		**TR** Section 13-3 Quiz			•

Chapter Review and Assessment

SE Chapter 13 Review, p. 338 ⓛ₃
CTB Chapter 13 Test ⓛ₂ ⓛ₃ ⓛ₄
SE Standardized Test Prep, p. 339 ⓛ₃

PROGRAM COMPONENTS

SE	Student Edition	**CTB**	Computer Test Bank
TE	Teacher Edition	**AUD**	Audio Section Summaries
TR	Teaching Resources		
RN	Reading and Note Taking Guide	**DVD**	Teens Talk Video Series
		VVG	Video Viewing Guide
ARN	Adapted Reading and Note Taking Guide	**PPT**	Presentation
IB	Image Bank		

Differentiated Instruction
(L1) (L2) (L4) (EL)

		SE eTEXT	TE eTEXT	PRINT
ARN	Note Taking Guide 13-1 (L2)	•	•	
RN	Note Taking Guide 13-1 (EL)	•	•	•
AUD	Audio Summary 13-1 (L1) (L2) (EL)	•	•	
TE	Reteach Strategy, p. 321 (L2)		•	•
TR	Enrich 13-1 (L4)		•	
ARN	Building Health Skills 13 (L2)	•	•	
RN	Building Health Skills 13 (EL)	•	•	•
ARN	Note Taking Guide 13-2 (L2)	•	•	
RN	Note Taking Guide 13-2 (EL)	•	•	•
AUD	Audio Summary 13-2 (L1) (L2) (EL)	•	•	
TE	Reteach Strategy, p. 329 (L2)		•	•
TR	Enrich 13-2 (L4)		•	
ARN	Note Taking Guide 13-3 (L2)	•	•	
RN	Note Taking Guide 13-3 (EL)	•	•	•
AUD	Audio Summary 13-3 (L1) (L2) (EL)	•	•	
TE	Reteach Strategy, p. 336 (L2)		•	•
TR	Enrich 13-3 (L4)		•	

ABILITY LEVELS

(L1) **For students with special needs**
(L2) **For less proficient readers**
(L3) **For all students**
(L4) **For gifted and talented students**
(EL) **For English language learners**

Chapter 13 Digital/Video Pathway

This alternative pathway allows you to teach this chapter's content using only the video and online materials.

Preview

DVD Video #13 Preview
SE Video #13 Preview Activity
VVG Video #13 Worksheet

Fit for Life

1
PPT 13-1 Presentation
RN/ARN 13-1 Note Taking
PPT 13-1 Section Quiz

2
DVD Video #13 Explore/Wrap-Up
VVG Video #13 Worksheet
PPT 13-2 Presentation
RN/ARN 13-2 Note Taking
PPT 13-2 Section Quiz

Fit for Life

3
PPT 13-3 Presentation
RN/ARN 13-3 Note Taking
PPT 13-3 Section Quiz

Chapter Preview

Section 1 The Importance of Physical Activity

Physical activity has physical, psychological, and social benefits. Physical activity improves five components of physical fitness: cardiorespiratory endurance, muscular strength, muscular endurance, flexibility, and body composition. Physical activities can be classified as aerobic or anaerobic. Muscle training activities are further classified as isometric, isotonic, or isokinetic.

 Practicing Healthful Behaviors

Assessing Flexibility, Muscular Strength, and Endurance

Assessing levels of flexibility, muscular strength, and muscular endurance will help students identify improvement goals for their fitness programs.

Section 2 Setting Goals for Lifelong Fitness

A plan for achieving lifelong fitness requires defining goals, developing a program, and monitoring progress. Three phases of exercise are the warm-up, workout, and cool-down. Stretching exercises should be part of both warm-up and cool-down periods.

Section 3 Physical Activity and Safety

Most injuries can be avoided if one gets proper medical care, wears safety equipment, and pays attention to surroundings and the weather. Proper water and food intake is also important. To achieve and maintain lifelong fitness, a person should avoid harmful substances, overtraining, and sports-related injuries.

Exercise and Lifelong Fitness

GO ONLINE PearsonSuccessNet.com

TEENS Talk

Fit for Life

VIDEO 13

Preview **Activity**

How Has Physical Activity Changed?

Complete this activity before you watch the video.

1. Make a list of the sports or recreational activities you do with friends.
2. Interview one or two adults and ask them to describe the types of sports or recreational activities they did with friends when they were your age.
3. Write a paragraph comparing the activities you listed with the activities that the adults listed. Based on this comparison, would you say that activity levels have increased, decreased, or stayed the same? **WRITING**

314

 GO ONLINE

PearsonSuccessNet.com

For resources and activities for this chapter.

 Sensitive Issues

* Students who are not athletic or who are overweight may find discussions of physical fitness or body composition uncomfortable. Be attuned to their comfort levels when you discuss these issues in class.

* When you teach this chapter, avoid calling attention to individual students. For example, do not discuss or post students' fitness scores, goals, or plans.

Video Objectives

Use the video to help students

Understand the importance of making physical activity a lifelong habit.

Identify the benefits of an active lifestyle.

Evaluate their current level of physical activity and plan ways to incorporate more physical activity into their daily lives.

Preview **Activity**

How Has Physical Activity Changed?

A day or two before watching the video, have students complete the Preview Activity. Discuss what students learned from the survey. How have the types of physical activities and amount of time devoted to physical activity changed since their parents were young?

315

From the Authors

A combination of a sedentary lifestyle and poor diet is the second leading contributor to preventable deaths in the United States. Many experts predict that the combination will soon overtake smoking as the leading contributor to preventable deaths. Helping students become physically active for a lifetime is one of the most important challenges health teachers face. This chapter makes the case for physical activity by describing the physical, psychological, and social benefits of an active lifestyle.

The chapter also helps students incorporate physical activity into their lives. It describes the components of physical fitness, types of activities that build the components, and how to plan and monitor a personal fitness program. Use the Building Health Skills Activity on page 322 to help students assess their fitness levels before they plan their fitness programs.

Section 1

The Importance of Physical Activity

Objectives

Before class begins, write the objectives on the board. Have students copy the objectives into their notebooks at the start of class.

1. Focus

Warm-Up Myth/Fact

Ask several students to share the fitness myths they wrote about. (Possible myths might include that all athletes are fit or that protein supplements build muscle.) Challenge students to explain why the myths are false.

Presentation 13-1

Section 1

The Importance of Physical Activity

Objectives

▶ **Explain** some of the physical, psychological, and social benefits of physical activity.

▶ **Define** the five components of fitness.

▶ **Describe** five types of physical activity.

Vocabulary

- physical activity
- endorphins
- physical fitness
- body composition
- aerobic exercise
- anaerobic exercise
- isometric exercise
- isotonic exercise
- isokinetic exercise

Warm-Up

Myth Being thin is a sign of fitness.

Fact Appearance is not a good indicator of overall fitness. Thin people who do not exercise are likely to have poor heart, lung, and muscular fitness.

WRITING Identify another fitness misconception that teens may hold. Why do you think they have that misconception?

The Benefits of Physical Activity

How physically active are you? To answer this question, you first need to know that physical activity includes more than just sports. Any movement that requires your large muscle groups to work is considered **physical activity.** Thus, physical activity includes actions such as walking briskly around the mall or doing household chores. Teens should spend 60 minutes or more each day performing some form of physical activity.

What happens inside your body when you rake leaves, swim, or dance? The most obvious changes affect your heart, lungs, and muscles. But did you also know that chemical changes occur in your brain that influence your mood? **The changes that occur due to physical activity are beneficial to your body, your mind, and your social interactions.**

Physical Benefits The physical benefits of exercise extend to many of the systems in your body.

▶ **Cardiovascular System** Your heart and blood vessels receive the most benefits from regular physical activity. As your heart becomes stronger, it can pump more blood with less effort. The number of capillaries in your muscles increases, which may reduce blood pressure. Exercise also lowers blood cholesterol levels.

▶ **Weight Maintenance** Regular physical activity increases your basal metabolic rate—the amount of energy your body uses when you are at rest. An active metabolism makes it easier to remain at a healthy weight. Staying at a healthy weight can reduce your risk for developing diseases such as diabetes, heart disease, and certain cancers.

WRITING and Health

L3 Persuasive E-mail

After students read about the benefits of physical activity, ask them to write an e-mail to an inactive friend. In the e-mail, they should try to persuade the friend to get more exercise by describing the benefits of physical activity. Ask a few students to read their e-mails to the class.

► **Bone Strength** Your physical activities should include some weight-bearing exercises such as jumping rope or walking. These activities make your bones stronger and denser. Having strong, dense bones may reduce your chances of developing osteoporosis later in life.

► **Balance and Coordination** Physical activity improves your balance and coordination, which may, in turn, improve your athletic ability. In addition, good balance and coordination can also reduce your risk of injury while performing chores such as climbing ladders or carrying packages down stairs.

Psychological Benefits During continuous exercise, your brain releases **endorphins,** chemicals that block pain messages from reaching your brain cells. Endorphins are also responsible for the feelings of satisfaction and pleasure you feel after a good workout.

People who exercise regularly are likely to be more self-confident and focused, and have reduced stress levels. Simple stretching exercises, for example, can relax tense muscles and help you sleep better. If you are upset or depressed, physical activity can help improve your mood. In fact, many health professionals consider physical activity an important part of treatment for depression.

Social Benefits Exercise is also an opportunity to have fun. Whether you play on a sports team or join an aerobics class, physical activity can be a way to bond with family and friends or build new relationships.

 **Connect to Your Life** What benefits do you think you gain from regular physical activity?

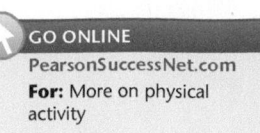
GO ONLINE
PearsonSuccessNet.com
For: More on physical activity

FIGURE 1 Physical activity can be an opportunity to bond with friends or meet new people.

Studies show that regular physical activity also improves academic achievement.

---

2. Teach

L3 EL **Reading/Note Taking** 13-1

L2 **Adapted Reading/Note Taking** 13-1

The Benefits of Physical Activity

L3 **Content Update**  GO ONLINE

Visit Pearson SuccessNet to access more information about physical activity. Have students complete the Web activity.

L2 **Active Learning**

On the board, start a concept map with the concept "Benefits of Physical Activity." Below that, draw three boxes for the types of benefits (physical, psychological, and social). Call on students to go to the board and fill in the boxes. Ask other students to give examples of specific benefits of each type.

L3 **Building Health Skills**

Communicating Have students make an illustrated poster to persuade other teens to get 60 minutes of physical activity every day. Posters should show several benefits of exercise that are especially important to teens, such as improved appearance and athletic ability. Arrange for students to display their posters throughout the school.

Connect to Your Life *Sample answer:* greater endurance, weight control, and fun with friends

---

Differentiated Instruction

EL **English Language Learners**
Sum up the benefits of exercise in three simple sentences: "Exercise keeps you healthy. Exercise makes you happier. Exercise lets you have fun with others."

Then ask students to find pictures in magazines that show these benefits. Have them share their pictures and explain which sentence(s) each picture represents.

The Components of Fitness

L3 Cooperative Learning

Explain that many different activities—not just sports or organized activities such as dance classes—can contribute to fitness. Have groups of students brainstorm a wide variety of activities to build each component of fitness. (e.g., *inline skating to build cardiorespiratory endurance; rock-wall climbing to build muscular strength*) Ask groups to share their ideas.

L2 Active Learning

Create a bulletin board entitled, "Building Components of Physical Fitness." Divide the bulletin board into five columns, and head each column with one of the five components of fitness. Ask students to find photos or draw pictures of activities that build each component and post the pictures in the correct columns.

L1 Class Discussion

Help students distinguish between the concepts of *muscular strength* and *muscular endurance*. Explain that picking up one heavy rock requires muscular strength. Picking up hundreds of light rocks requires muscular endurance. Then ask students to complete these sentences. **You need muscular _____ to push a car 2 feet.** (*strength*) **You need muscular _____ to push a bicycle for 2 miles.** (*endurance*)

L3 Addressing Misconceptions

Fitness Is for Athletes Some students might think that only athletes need to be physically fit. Help students appreciate the importance of fitness in everyday life. Ask them to name common daily activities (*e.g., running up stairs, doing active chores, playing sports*) and identify which components of fitness they involve. Discuss how difficult the activities would be without adequate levels of fitness in those components.

Your Life Allow students to answer this question in their private journals.

The Components of Fitness

Most people do not have the ability to become an Olympic swimmer or a professional football player. But, with dedication, just about everyone can be physically fit. **Physical fitness** means that you have the energy and strength to participate in a variety of activities. **There are five components of fitness: cardiorespiratory endurance, muscular strength, muscular endurance, flexibility, and body composition.**

Cardiorespiratory Endurance Cardiorespiratory endurance means that your heart, blood vessels, and lungs are able to distribute nutrients and oxygen and remove wastes efficiently during prolonged exercise. People with poor cardiorespiratory endurance become short of breath and have a very high heart rate after even light exercise. Regular exercise improves cardiorespiratory endurance.

▶ As the heart muscles become stronger, more blood is pumped with each beat.

▶ The lungs become more efficient at delivering oxygen to the blood and removing carbon dioxide.

Muscular Strength The ability of a muscle to produce force is called muscular strength. The amount of weight you can lift is one measure of your muscular strength. Developing muscular strength requires exerting your muscles for short periods of time, such as doing push-ups.

Muscular Endurance Muscular endurance is the ability of your muscles to work for an extended time. How long you can hold a barbell—or how many times you can lift it—is a measure of your muscular endurance. Developing muscular endurance requires repeated actions over an extended period of time, such as raking leaves, rowing, or walking.

Flexibility The ability to move a joint through its entire range of motion is called flexibility. This means that you can bend, stretch, and twist your body easily. Flexibility can vary in different joints. For example, some people can't lean over and touch their toes. But their shoulders are flexible enough to help them throw a javelin a great distance. Stretching exercises, if done correctly, can increase flexibility and may reduce the risk of injury during exercise.

Body Composition Your weight is not the best indicator of your fitness. In fact, when you begin an exercise program, you may gain some weight as you gain muscle. A better fitness indicator is your body composition. **Body composition** is the amount of fat tissue in your body compared to the amount of lean tissue, such as muscles and bones. Having too much, or too little, body fat can lead to health problems.

FIGURE 2 A skinfold test is one way to estimate body composition. A caliper is used to measure the top layer of skin and underlying layer of fat in different areas of the body. Then the measurements are used to estimate body fat percentage.

Connect to Your Life In which components of fitness are you the strongest? In which do you need to improve?

MATH and Health

L3 Converting Units

Tell the class that Ashley wants to get four hours of cardiorespiratory exercise each week. She plans to swim for 30 minutes, three times a week, and walk briskly for 60 minutes, twice a week. Ask: **How many hours per week of cardiorespiratory exercise will her plan give her?**

(30 min × 3 = 90 min of swimming; 60 min × 2 = 120 min of brisk walking; 90 min + 120 min = 210 min; 210 min ÷ 60 min/hr = 3.5 hr of cardiorespiratory exercise each week) **How could she modify her plan to get enough exercise?** *(Sample answer: She could swim four times a week instead of three.)*

A Physical Activity Pyramid

Sedentary Activities
• gaming
• watching TV
• "IM-ing"

FIGURE 3 This pyramid can guide you as you divide your time among activities to improve your fitness. **Applying Concepts** List three activities that you would add to the everyday activities list.

Occasionally

Flexibility
• stretching exercises
• ballet
• martial arts

Muscular Training
• weightlifting
• sit-ups
• push-ups

2 to 5 times a week

Cardiorespiratory
• swimming
• jogging
• dancing
• brisk walking
• rowing

3 to 5 times a week

Everyday Activities
• washing the car
• walking the dog
• cleaning your room
• sweeping the garage
• biking to school

Every day

Exercise and Lifelong Fitness **319**

Ask students to give examples of other activities in each category of the pyramid. *(e.g., "shooting hoops" for everyday activity, biking for cardiorespiratory activity)* Ask students to point out which everyday activities are also cardiorespiratory, flexibility, or muscular training activities.
Caption Answer *Sample answer:* delivering newspapers, using stairs instead of elevators, vacuuming

L3 **Building Health Skills**

Practicing Healthful Behaviors
Challenge students to create a schedule for a week's worth of activities based on the physical activity pyramid. Urge students to follow their schedules for the week and keep a diary of their activities. At the end of the week, ask students to evaluate their schedules. How could they improve upon their schedules? How could they change them to better fit their lifestyles? Encourage students to create and follow weekly activity schedules throughout the school year. **WRITING**

EL **Cooperative Learning**

Some students may not be familiar with the American names for the many different activities you will talk about in class. Have student pairs make flashcards with about ten index cards. On one side of the card they should write the name of the activity. On the other side they should draw a person participating in the activity or equipment required for the activity. Have pairs swap cards with other pairs. Then students in each pair can test each other. The students being tested should be able to name the activity by looking at the drawing.

Differentiated Instruction

L2 **Less Proficient Readers**
Guide students in relating the information on physical activities in Figure 3 to the information on fitness components on page 318. Explain how the types of physical activities shown in the figure improve particular components of fitness described in the text. For example, point out that muscular training activities (in the figure) improve both muscular strength and muscular endurance (in the text). Follow this example for the other activities and fitness components.

Types of Physical Activity

L2 Building Vocabulary

Define *an-* (not) and *aerobic* (using oxygen). Then, ask: **Based on these definitions, what does anaerobic mean?** (*not using oxygen*) Have students read the definitions of *aerobic* and *anaerobic exercise* on this page. Relate the two definitions by explaining that anaerobic exercise is work produced by muscle cells without using oxygen for energy.

L3 Visual Learning: Figure 4

Have students examine the photos and answer the caption question. Call on a student to read his or her answer. Discuss the fact that many activities improve more than one component of fitness. For example, swimming improves muscular strength and endurance as well as cardiorespiratory endurance. Ask students to identify other examples.

Caption Answer aerobic exercise—cardiorespiratory endurance, muscular endurance; anaerobic exercise—muscular strength and endurance, flexibility; isometric exercise—muscular strength; isotonic exercise—muscular strength and endurance; isokinetic exercise—muscular strength

L3 Cultural Connection

Help your class expand their knowledge of different types of physical activities. Invite students to discuss active pastimes, such as a dance or a game, that are unique to their cultures. Also ask other teachers if they would share examples of active pastimes from their cultures. Invite the students and teachers to demonstrate or explain the activity to the class. Ask students to comment on the activity in their private journals. Is this activity something they could integrate into their personal fitness program?

Aerobic Exercise

Anaerobic Exercise

FIGURE 4 To be truly physically fit, you should participate in a variety of activities so that your muscles are worked in different ways. **Classifying** Which components of fitness do each of these activities improve?

Types of Physical Activity

No single activity can improve or maintain all five components of fitness. Instead, it is important to participate in a variety of physical activities. **Physical activities can be classified as aerobic exercise or anaerobic exercise. Strengthening and endurance activities can be further classified as isometric exercise, isotonic exercise, or isokinetic exercise.**

Aerobic Exercise Ongoing physical activity that raises your breathing rate and heart rate is called **aerobic exercise** (ehr OH bik). Aerobic exercises increase the amount of oxygen that your body takes in and uses. Swimming, running, brisk walking, and cross-country skiing are all forms of aerobic exercise.

By performing aerobic exercise for at least 20 minutes at a time on a regular basis, you can improve your cardiorespiratory endurance. Many aerobic activities also improve muscular endurance.

Anaerobic Exercise Intense physical activity that lasts for a few seconds to a few minutes is called **anaerobic exercise** (an uh ROH bik). Because anaerobic exercise is so intense and quick, your cardiovascular system cannot supply muscles with enough oxygen to produce energy. Unlike your other body cells, muscle cells do not need oxygen to meet this rapid demand for energy.

Lifting weights, doing push-ups, and sprinting are examples of anaerobic activities. Most anaerobic exercises develop muscular strength, muscular endurance, or flexibility.

Isometric Exercise Place your palms together and push them against each other. This is an **isometric exercise** (eye suh MET rik), an exercise in which muscles contract but very little body movement takes place. If you do isometric exercises on a regular basis, the muscles you use will become stronger.

320 *Chapter 13*

TEENS *Are Asking . . .*

Q: **I have been doing sit-ups for months, but my stomach does not look trimmer. What am I doing wrong?**

A: Although sit-ups and other abdominal exercises will increase the strength and endurance of your abdominal muscles, these exercises will not necessarily make you trimmer. You cannot get rid of fat tissue in a specific area of your body by "spot training" muscles. The only way to get rid of fat tissue is through exercise and eating a healthy, balanced diet. However, it is important to remember that strong abdominal muscles have many benefits— they help you maintain good posture and reduce strain on your lower back during everyday activities.

Isometric Exercise

Isotonic Exercise

Isokinetic Exercise

Isotonic Exercise Isotonic exercise (eye suh TAHN ik) involves contracting and relaxing your muscles through the full range of a joint's motion. Pull-ups are an example of isotonic exercise. Exercises with free weights, such as barbells, are also isotonic. Through repetition of isotonic exercises, you can develop muscular strength and endurance.

Isokinetic Exercise In isokinetic exercise (eye soh ki NET ik) muscles contract at a constant rate. Isokinetic exercises require fitness machines that provide resistance to muscle movement. These exercises are often used as therapy to rebuild muscle strength after an injury.

3. Assess

Evaluate

These assignments can help you assess students' mastery of the section content.

Section 1 Review
Answers appear below.

Teaching Resources
• Practice 13-1
• Section 13-1 Quiz

L2 Reteach

Side by side on the board, write the headings *Components of Fitness* and *Types of Physical Activity*. Call on one student after another to list an item under the appropriate heading until both lists are complete. Call on other students to draw arrows matching each component of fitness with a type of activity that helps build it.

L4 Enrich

Teaching Resources
• Enrich 13-1

Section 1 Review

Key Ideas and Vocabulary

1. Define the term **physical activity.** List three physical activities that are not sports.

2. List four physical benefits of regular physical activity. Then list three psychological benefits and two social benefits.

3. Briefly explain the five components of fitness.

4. List the five types of physical activity and give an example of each.

5. Explain why muscles do not use oxygen to produce energy during **anaerobic exercise.**

Critical Thinking

6. **Comparing and Contrasting** Explain how aerobic exercise differs from anaerobic exercise.

Health and Community

Exercise Classes Contact local community groups, fitness centers, or universities to find free or low-cost exercise classes that are open to the public. Summarize the information in a chart or poster to display at your school. **WRITING**

---

7. **Sequencing** Put the following activities in order from the one that would contribute the most to cardiorespiratory endurance to the one that would contribute the least: golf, basketball, tennis, volleyball. Explain your order.

8. **Applying Concepts** How would you convince a friend to start an exercise program?

🔊 GO ONLINE PearsonSuccessNet.com   Audio Summary Section 13.1

Exercise and Lifelong Fitness   **321**

Health and Community

Exercise Classes If there is a local community center, it may have low-cost classes. Charts and posters should include information on locations, phone numbers, and times of classes. Arrange for students to display their work at school.

4. aerobic (running), anaerobic (push-ups), isometric (push palms together), isotonic (pull-ups), isokinetic (therapy machines)

5. Anaerobic exercise is so intense that the cardiovascular system cannot supply muscles with enough oxygen.

6. Aerobic exercise: Increased breathing and heart rates supply cells with more oxygen. Anaerobic exercise: Muscle cells produce bursts of energy without oxygen.

7. Golf should be listed last, but the other sports may be listed in any order that can be justified.

8. by explaining the benefits of exercise

Section 1 Review

1. movement that works large muscle groups; *sample answer:* walking the dog, ballet, sit-ups

2. physical: cardiovascular health, weight maintenance, bone strength, balance and coordination; psychological: self-confidence, less stress, better mood; social: bonding with family, making new friends

3. cardiorespiratory endurance: ability of cardiorespiratory system to deliver enough oxygen; muscular strength: ability to produce force; muscular endurance: how long muscles can work; flexibility: how well joints move through their range of motion; body composition: amount of fat tissue compared to lean tissue

Assessing Flexibility, Muscular Strength, and Endurance

Objective

Demonstrate healthful behaviors by assessing levels of flexibility, muscular strength, and muscular endurance.

Teaching Strategies

- Before students assess their fitness, have them obtain written permission to participate from a parent or guardian.

- Any students who do not feel well on the day of the tests should be excused temporarily from testing. You can schedule a make-up day or have students assess their fitness at home with a family member.

- Help students with physical disabilities find alternative ways to assess their fitness levels. There are many adapted physical education Web sites with relevant information.

- Have students do the activities in the gymnasium or a wide corridor. Or, push desks and chairs to one side of the classroom to provide students with a large, open floor space. Each pair of students will need a yardstick, masking tape, and a watch with a second hand.

- Make sure students do light stretching exercises for at least five minutes before doing the flexibility test.

- As pairs of students do the activities, go from pair to pair, monitoring that they are doing the activities correctly.

Practicing Healthful Behaviors

Assessing Flexibility, Muscular Strength, and Endurance

Do you know how you rate in the areas of flexibility, muscular strength, and muscular endurance? It is important to know your current level of fitness before planning a fitness program. Although the tests described here do not evaluate all your muscles, they are good indicators of your fitness. Before you perform any of these tests, get a medical checkup by a doctor or other healthcare professional.

1 Assess your flexibility.

- Tape a yardstick to the floor. Place the tape across the 18-inch mark.

- Sit on the floor so that the 18-inch mark of the yardstick lines up with the bottom of your feet. Your legs should be straight in front of you. Your feet should be about 8 to 12 inches apart.

- Clasp your thumbs. With your palms down and your knees straight, slowly stretch forward and rest your fingertips on the yardstick.

- Repeat four times. On the fourth try, hold the stretch while your partner counts the inches above or below the 18-inch mark. For example, if you reach the 21-inch mark, your score is +3. If you reach the 15-inch mark, your score is -3.

Flexibility: Average Fitness Level

Age	Males	Females
13	+0.5 in.	+3.5 in.
14	+1.0 in.	+4.5 in.
15	+2.0 in.	+5.0 in.
16–17	+3.0 in.	+5.5 in.

🚩 **Sensitive Issues**

- Students who have low levels of flexibility, strength, or endurance may be uncomfortable assessing their fitness with classmates. Give students the option of doing the assessments at home with the help of a family member.

- For students who do the assessments in class, urge them to keep their scores confidential. Point out that virtually everyone can improve at least one or two components of fitness and that the scores are only a starting point for improving fitness levels.

Curl-ups: Average Fitness Level

Age	Males	Females
13–17	45/min	37/min

❷ Assess your abdominal muscular strength and endurance.

▶ Lie on your back with your knees flexed and feet about 12 inches from your bottom. Cross your arms. Your hands should be on your shoulders and your elbows against your chest. Your partner should hold your feet.

▶ Curl up until your elbows touch your thighs. Then lower down until your shoulder blades touch the floor.

▶ Your partner should count how many curl-ups you complete in one minute.

Push-ups: Average Fitness Level

Age	Males	Females
13–14	24	11
15–16	30	15
17	37	16

❸ Assess your upper body muscular strength and endurance.

▶ Lie face down. Your hands should be flat on the ground under your shoulders. Your legs should be straight back and slightly apart, with toes tucked.

▶ Push up with your hands until your arms are straight. Keep your legs and back straight.

▶ Lower your body until your elbows are at a 90-degree angle and your upper arms are parallel to the floor. An entire push-up should take 3 seconds.

▶ Repeat until you cannot do a push-up every 3 seconds.

1. Students' flexibility scores are the difference (negative or positive) between 18 inches and the distance they could reach. Students should compare their score with the average fitness level in the chart for their age and gender.

2. Students should compare the numbers of curl-ups and push-ups they could do with the numbers in the charts for their age and gender.

3. Most students should aim to meet or exceed the average fitness levels in the charts and try to improve in areas in which they are below average. Encourage students to work with a physical education teacher to plan a fitness program based on the results of their fitness tests.

 **Practice the Skill**

1. Pair off with a partner and perform the flexibility test. Warm up before performing this test. Compare your results with the average fitness levels noted in the chart.

2. With your partner, perform the curl-ups and push-ups tests. Compare your results with the average fitness levels in the charts.

3. Evaluate your results for the three tests. Do you feel that you need to improve in one or more of these areas? If so, work with your physical education teacher to plan an appropriate fitness program.

Exercise and Lifelong Fitness **323**

Health at Home

Family Fitness

Have students demonstrate to family members the fitness tests for flexibility, muscular strength, and muscular endurance that they learned in the activity. Students can encourage family members to do the tests to assess their levels of fitness. Suggest that students ask family members to be their workout partners. They can help motivate each other to adopt and stick with an exercise program.

Objectives

Before class begins, write the objectives on the board. Have students copy the objectives into their notebooks at the start of class.

1. Focus

Warm-Up **Health Stats**

Call on a few students to share their responses to the writing activity. *(Sample answer: Fewer teens are physically active as they get older because they have less time for exercise.)* Ask: **If the graph continued into adulthood, how do you think it would look?** *(Students may predict correctly that the line would continue to decline.)* Tell students they will learn in this section how to set fitness goals that will help motivate them to stay active for life.

Presentation 13-2

 **Connect to Your Life** *Sample answers:* canoeing, bowling, gardening

Sensitive Issues

• Overweight and unfit students may not feel comfortable sharing their fitness goals and plans. Allow students to work with a parent or guardian.

• It is especially important for overweight and unfit students to get medical clearance before starting an exercise program. However, do not single out these students. Encourage all students to check with a doctor before undertaking any significant change in their level of physical activity.

 **Section 2**

Setting Goals for Lifelong Fitness

Objectives

► **Develop** a plan for achieving lifelong fitness.

► **Describe** the three phases of exercise.

Vocabulary

• lifelong fitness
• FITT formula
• target heart rate
• cross-training

Warm-Up

Health Stats This graph shows the percentage of teens who participate in vigorous physical activity on a regular basis.

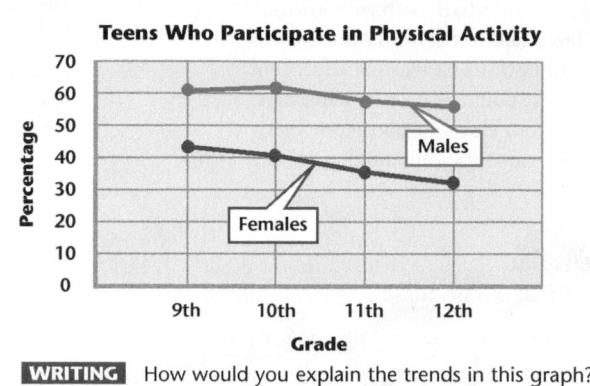

Teens Who Participate in Physical Activity

Males

Females

WRITING How would you explain the trends in this graph?

Planning a Fitness Program

One of the most important things you can do for your health is to start exercising now. If you get into the habit of exercising, it will help you maintain **lifelong fitness**—the ability to stay healthy and fit as you age. **To plan a successful fitness program you should define your goals, develop your program, and monitor your progress.**

Define Long-Term Goals An important long-term goal of any fitness program should be lifelong fitness.

► Choose activities that you enjoy and can continue as you age.

► Vary your activities from day to day. This can lower your risk of injury, allow you to meet your schedule needs, and reduce boredom.

► Combine exercise with social activities whenever possible. For example, go for a hike with friends or rake leaves with your family.

 **Connect to Your Life** What activities do you enjoy now that could become lifelong activities?

324 *Chapter 13*

For Your INFORMATION!

Inactivity and Weight Gain in Teen Girls

In addition to the statistics in the Warm-Up activity, data from several recent studies show that the majority of females experience a steep drop in activity levels during their teens. Declines in activity levels are accompanied by increases in weight and body fat, even without significant increases in calorie intake. During adolescence, inactive females gain 50 percent more weight than active females, and the difference in body mass index between active and inactive females triples. Emphasize the link between inactivity and weight gain in females. It may help motivate female students to become more active.

Define Short-Term Goals In planning a fitness program, you also need to know your more immediate, or short-term goals. For example, do you want to increase your cardiorespiratory endurance? If so, your exercise program could include basketball, brisk walking, or other aerobic activities. If you want to gain more muscle mass, your program should include anaerobic exercises such as lifting weights. Or, you may have a combination of goals in mind.

Your goals should be specific to help you measure your progress. For example, "I want to be able to run an eight-minute mile" is more specific than "I want to run faster." Your time frame for reaching your goals also needs to be realistic. Otherwise, you may become discouraged and give up.

Develop Your Fitness Plan Once you have decided on your goals, think about your current schedule and fitness level. Then develop a fitness plan by marking a calendar with your typical weekly schedule. Decide what days and times are best for you to exercise. Each week, plan what activities you will do and when you will do them. Figure 5 shows an example of a weekly exercise plan.

Besides your interests and goals, there are several other things to consider when forming your plan.

▶ **Your Health** If you have health concerns, such as diabetes or asthma, work with your doctor to devise an appropriate fitness plan.

▶ **Your Budget** Do the activities require special equipment or fees?

▶ **Where You Live** What activities are appropriate for the area where you live? Will you have to alter your plans when the seasons change?

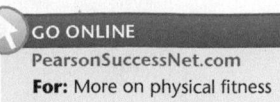

GO ONLINE

PearsonSuccessNet.com

For: More on physical fitness

FIGURE 5 Here is an example of a weekly exercise plan to improve cardiorespiratory endurance. For help in developing an exercise plan, talk to your physical education teacher or a fitness coach.

A Weekly Exercise Plan

Sunday	Wednesday
• Rake leaves for 40 minutes	• Alternate 90 seconds of jogging and
• Play basketball with neighbors	2 minutes walking for a total of 20 minutes
Monday	**Thursday**
• Alternate 90 seconds of jogging and	• Bike to school
2 minutes walking for a total of 20 minutes	• Gym class
	• Bike home
Tuesday	**Friday**
• Walk to school	• Walk to school
• Gym class	• 30-minute swim after school
• Walk home	• Walk home
	Saturday
	• Alternate 90 seconds of jogging and 2 minutes walking for a total of 20 minutes

Exercise and Lifelong Fitness **325**

---

2. Teach

L3 EL Reading/Note Taking 3-2

L2 Adapted Reading/Note Taking 3-2

Planning a Fitness Program

L3 Content Update

Visit Pearson SuccessNet to access more information about physical fitness. Have students complete the Web activity.

L2 Cooperative Learning

Ask students to bring in pictures from old newspapers or magazines that show older adults engaged in activities, such as swimming, golfing, and bicycling. Display the pictures in the classroom, and give students a chance to look at them. Encourage students to find activities they can start now and continue to enjoy lifelong.

L3 Building Health Skills

Accessing Information With the class make a list of physical activities on the board. Have students brainstorm as many activities as possible. Then assign small groups three or four activities. Have the groups research whether the activities are available in your area, how much each activity costs, and what equipment is needed. Have groups present their findings to the class.

L2 Active Learning

Walking may be the best method for some teens to increase their physical activity because it requires no money and little planning. However, to improve fitness, students need to assess their current activity level. Borrow a set of pedometers from the physical education department. Have students keep track of how many steps they take each day for three days. Work with students to help them plan ways of increasing their steps each day. Remind students that they must walk briskly to improve cardiorespiratory endurance.

Differentiated Instruction

L1 Special Needs

Help students with physical disabilities find exercises that are suitable for them. They could look on the Internet or talk to a physical education teacher who is knowledgeable about adapted physical education. Guide students in incorporating the exercises in their fitness plans.

L4 Gifted and Talented

Ask students to write a weekly exercise plan for improving muscular strength and endurance. They can use Figure 5 as a model for their own plan. Display students' plans in the classroom anonymously. **WRITING**

L3 Visual Learning: Figure 6

Have students read how the FITT formula was applied in the figure. Ask: **Which factor of the FITT formula should you choose first?** *(type)* Have students choose a type of exercise that would help them reach one of their own fitness goals. Then have them use that exercise to answer the caption question.

Caption Answer *Sample answer:* goal—improve cardiorespiratory endurance; frequency—5 days a week; intensity—4 mi/hr; time—1/2 hr; type—walking

L2 Building Health Skills

Practicing Healthful Behaviors Show students who need review how to take their pulse and estimate their heart rate. Then, call on a volunteer to go to the board and review how to calculate target heart rate range. Remind students that their cardiorespiratory endurance improves only as a result of exercising in their target heart rate zone. Urge students who want to improve cardiorespiratory endurance to monitor their heart rate whenever they exercise.

The FITT Formula and Muscular Strengthening

▶ **Frequency**	3 days a week (nonconsecutive days)	
▶ **Intensity**	Do as many pull-ups as possible without resting.	
▶ **Time**	Include pull-ups as part of a 15-minute strengthening session.	
▶ **Type**	Isotonic exercise that strengthens the biceps.	

FIGURE 6 You can use the FITT formula to improve any of the components of fitness.
Applying Concepts How would you apply the FITT formula to your own fitness goals?

The FITT Formula The success of your fitness plan depends on four factors: how often you exercise, how hard you exercise, how long you exercise, and the types of exercise you choose. These factors make up the **FITT formula,** which stands for frequency, intensity, time, and type. Figure 6 includes an example of applying the FITT formula.

▶ **Frequency** To become or stay physically fit, you should exercise at least 3 to 5 times a week. Spread out your exercise over the week. Being inactive during the week does not prepare your body for an intense weekend workout and can lead to injury.

▶ **Intensity** The only way to improve your physical fitness is to make your body do more than it normally does. To increase cardiorespiratory endurance, for example, you must exercise within your target heart rate range. Your **target heart rate** is the rate at which your cardiovascular system receives the most benefits from exercise without working too hard. See page 305 to calculate your target heart rate range.

The "talk test" is an easy way to check your exercise intensity. If you are so out of breath that you cannot talk while exercising, your exercise level is too intense. If you can sing, however, you are probably not working hard enough.

▶ **Time** The amount of time you spend exercising affects your level of fitness. If you are just starting an exercise program, limit your time to only about 10 or 15 minutes a day. Then increase your exercise time gradually. Once your workout program is established, you should exercise for at least 20 to 30 minutes, 3 to 5 times a week.

▶ **Type** The types of activities you choose are also important for your success. Make sure that your exercise choices correspond to your goals and interests. To prevent boredom and overuse injuries, you should practice **cross-training** by participating in a wide variety of activities. Cross-training also ensures that more areas of your body become fit. For example, people who primarily walk for exercise could benefit from biking, which works different muscle groups in the legs.

326 *Chapter 13*

Focus on **ISSUES**

L3 Female Athlete Triad

Explain that female athlete triad may develop when a female athlete exercises intensely and severely restricts food intake to keep her weight low. Girls with the disorder might exhibit one or all three aspects of the triad including disordered eating, amenorrhea, and osteoporosis.

Ask students to list the activities in which they think girls feel pressure to be thin. They should understand that girls who participate in all sorts of activities are susceptible to the triad. Some activities such as martial arts classify athletes by weight. Other activities such as ballet and figure skating place an emphasis on having a lean, thin body. Some

girls may feel that losing a few pounds will give them an extra edge in soccer or lacrosse.

Advise students to tell a trusted adult if they suspect someone they know has female athlete triad. The condition can lead to lifelong health problems or even death.

FIGURE 7 It is important to monitor your progress. Create a chart, such as this one, that reflects your goals.

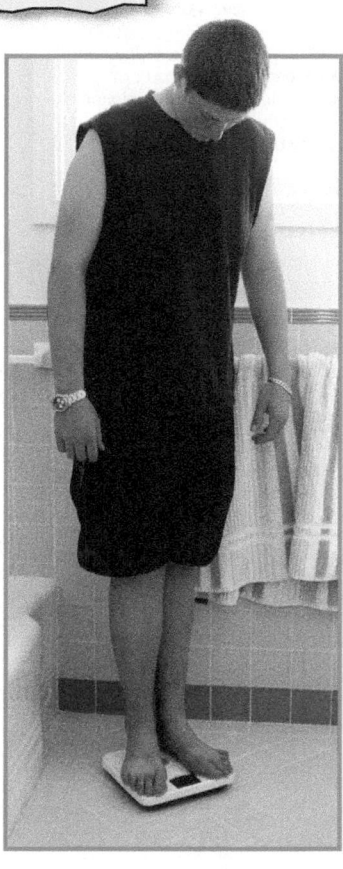

Week	Weight	Resting Heart Rate	Appetite	Sleep Pattern
0				
3				
6				
9				
12				
15				
18				

Monitor Your Progress One of the most gratifying aspects of sticking with a fitness program is noticing progress. It is a good idea to track your overall progress using a chart like the one in Figure 7.

With most exercise programs, you will begin to notice significant changes within 12 weeks. You may find that you look better, sleep better, and feel more alert. You might also notice that you have gained muscle strength or lost weight. As you track your progress, keep in mind that monitoring your weight alone is not a good idea. Because muscle tissue is heavier than fat tissue, you may actually gain some weight as you become more fit.

One good indicator of improved fitness is a drop in your resting heart rate. Your resting heart rate is the number of times your heart beats each minute when you are at rest. A resting heart rate that is below 72 beats per minute usually indicates a good level of fitness. To find your resting heart rate, take your pulse for one minute when you first wake up in the morning.

Alter Your Fitness Plan As your fitness improves, your workouts may become too easy. You may become frustrated because you do not notice any further progress. This may be a sign that your body has adjusted to your fitness routine. By slightly increasing the intensity or time of your workout, you should continue to see positive results.

Remember that, no matter what your fitness goals are, you need to combine your exercise program with healthy eating habits. Chapter 9 includes suggestions for what to eat and how much to eat when you are physically active.

 **How would your chart differ from the sample in Figure 7?**

Phases of Exercise

L3 **Visual Learning: Figure 8**

Image Bank Figure 13-8

Have students review the phases of the exercise session shown in the figure. Ask students to discuss their experiences with exercise sessions. Has anyone noticed a difference in their experience when they didn't warm up or cool down? Has anyone had an injury that may have been prevented by stretching?

L2 **Active Learning**

Ask a few volunteers to review the warming-up, stretching, and cooling-down activities on pages 276–277 and demonstrate them to the class. Ask the class to identify which of the stretches might be best for different types of workouts. *(Students should identify stretches that use the same muscles that are used in the workout, such as muscles of the lower body for running.)*

 *Sample answer:* walking and stretching

Warm-up

Slowly move muscles to be used in workout.

5–10 minutes

Stretch

Stretch muscles to be used in workout.

5–10 minutes

Cardiorespiratory workout

Exercise in target heart rate range.

20–30 minutes

FIGURE 8 This is just a suggestion for an exercise session. You can choose to do both cardiorespiratory and strengthening workouts on the same day or on different days.

Phases of Exercise

The safest workouts begin with a warm-up period and end with a cool-down period. Stretching exercises should be part of both the warm-up and cool-down periods. You can find suggestions for warming up, stretching, and cooling down on pages 276–277.

Warming Up and Stretching A warm-up is a five- to ten-minute period of mild exercise that prepares your body for a vigorous workout. During the warm-up, your body temperature rises, your heart rate speeds up, and your muscles become more flexible. A warm-up should include some of the same motions as your planned activity, but at a slower pace. If you are planning to run, for example, start out by walking. Then gradually increase your speed until you reach your running pace.

Your warm-up should also include five to ten minutes of stretching. It is very important to pay attention to your body's limits when stretching. Do not bounce when you stretch, because bouncing can tear muscle fibers. You should feel tension while you stretch, but not pain. Hold stretches for 15 seconds.

The Workout The workout is when you perform an activity at its peak level. To be effective, your workout should follow the FITT formula you just read about.

Some people choose to do cardiorespiratory and muscular training during the same workout session. Others do cardiorespiratory training one day and muscular training another day. It is important that you do not do muscular training exercises with the same muscle groups two days in a row. Your muscles need an entire day of rest between strengthening workouts to repair and rebuild.

 What activities do you perform to warm up before exercise?

328 *Chapter 13*

TEENS *Are Asking . . .*

Q: I have noticed that many people stretch before they warm up, but my physical education teacher told us we should warm up before we stretch. Which way is right?

A: Your physical education teacher's advice is right. In the past, experts recommended stretching before warming up in order to "limber up" muscles. Current recommendations are that you should do at least five minutes of light activity, such as walking or jogging, to warm up muscles before stretching. Cold muscles are more prone to injury.

Strength/Endurance workout

Do strength-endurance exercises, such as weightlifting; take short breaks frequently.

30–45 minutes

Cool-down

Move muscles used in workout at a reduced pace.

5–10 minutes

Stretch

Stretch muscles used in workout.

5–10 minutes

Cooling Down and Stretching The cool-down is a period of mild exercise, such as walking, performed after a workout. Your cool-down should be at least as long as your warm-up. During the cool-down period, your body and your heart rate return slowly to their resting states. If you were to stop exercising abruptly, blood could collect in your muscles and not return quickly enough to your heart and brain. As a result, you could become dizzy and faint.

Stretching after your cool-down loosens muscles that may have tightened during exercise. Stretching can prevent muscle and joint soreness. Spend at least five minutes repeating the stretches you did during your warm-up period.

Section 2 Review

Key Ideas and Vocabulary

1. List the steps involved in developing a successful fitness program.
2. Name the four factors of an exercise program that are included in the **FITT formula.**
3. Describe the benefits of **cross-training.**
4. List the phases of an exercise session.

Critical Thinking

5. **Evaluating** Maria considers herself to be physically fit because she runs and swims almost every day in the summer. In the winter, however, she exercises very little. Do you agree or disagree with Maria's self-assessment? Explain.

Health at Home

Family Activity Day Plan a day of physical activity with your family. Some possibilities include a hike, a bicycle trip, or a softball game with other neighborhood families. At the end of the day, write a paragraph describing what you did and how you felt. **WRITING**

6. **Relating Cause and Effect** Why do you think that people's resting heart rates decrease as they become more fit?
7. **Comparing and Contrasting** How might a fitness program to improve muscular strength differ from one to improve flexibility?

GO ONLINE PearsonSuccessNet.com   Audio Summary Section 13.2

Exercise and Lifelong Fitness **329**

---

3. Assess

Evaluate

These assignments can help you assess students' mastery of the section content.

Section 2 Review

Answers appear below.

Teaching Resources
• Practice 13-2
• Section 13-2 Quiz

L2 Reteach

Using a projector, display the headings and subheadings to create an outline of the section, leaving spaces for additional information. Have students copy the outline and complete it by adding definitions, important details, and examples.

L4 Enrich

Teaching Resources
• Enrich 13-2

Health at Home

Family Activity Day Suggest to students that they first check with their parents before planning the details of their family activity day. Allow students to keep their writing confidential.

Section 2 Review

1. define goals, develop the program, monitor progress
2. frequency, intensity, time, type
3. It helps prevent boredom and overuse injuries.
4. warm-up and stretching, workout, cool-down and stretching

5. Students should disagree, because a person needs to exercise year-round to be physically fit.
6. *Sample answer:* The heart of someone who is fit pumps more blood with every beat. Therefore, it does not need to beat as often.

7. The fitness program might differ in the types of exercises or other activities it includes. For example, to improve muscular strength, you might lift weights. To improve flexibility, you might do ballet.

Exercise and Lifelong Fitness **329**

Technology & Health

Out on a Limb

Teaching Strategies

- Introduce the feature by telling students that over a million people in the United States have had part of or an entire lower limb amputated. Health limitations or financial restraints limit some people from receiving artificial limbs.

- Before computerized prostheses were developed, prosthetic legs were relatively crude. The knees locked into place to provide stability and support, and this made it very difficult to walk, except on smooth, flat surfaces. Going downstairs was slow and awkward. In contrast, a prosthesis with a microprocessor automatically maneuvers the knee, so wearers can walk naturally over all kinds of surfaces and even run downstairs.

- This prosthesis, like other prosthetic limbs, is removable. The user straps it onto the amputated limb. Friction between the end of the limb and the artificial limb is a universal problem. It causes irritation and restricts how long people can comfortably wear prosthetic limbs. Under development are artificial limbs that can be permanently attached to the body, using a technology similar to dental implants. This will eliminate the friction problem and give wearers more freedom.

WRITING Ads should highlight the benefits of using a computer chip to control movements of the knee, which allows the wearer to walk smoothly over uneven terrain or down steps.

Technology & Health

Out on a Limb

Staying active is often a struggle for people who have lost a limb. Many types of artificial legs are heavy and awkward. Recently, however, the same computer technology used to improve aircraft stability is also being used in artificial limbs. Tiny sensors in the artificial limb monitor movement at least 50 times per second. The data is sent to a computer chip, which controls the hydraulics that move the knee. With split-second timing, the limb adjusts to changes in terrain, and movement is smooth and stable.

WRITING Create an ad for this new artificial limb that highlights its benefits.

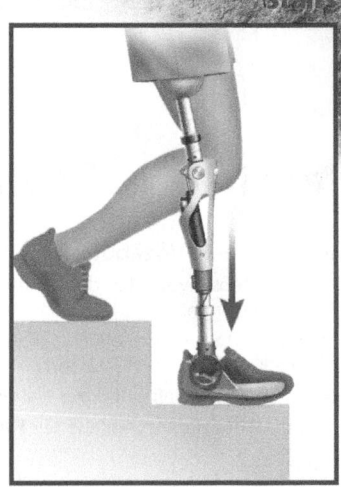

Walking

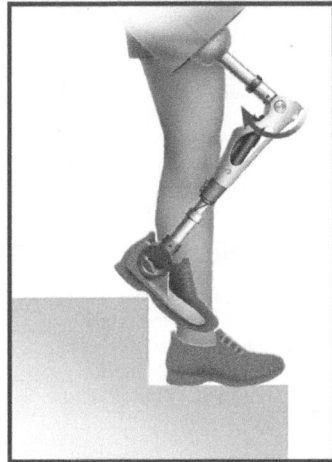

▲ **Knee Bends**

Sensors in the artificial leg detect when weight is being placed on the natural leg. The computer chip reduces the pressure on the artificial knee, and the knee bends.

Down

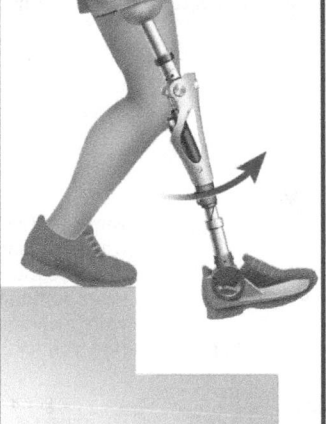

▲ **Leg Swings**

Sensors in the knee detect both the decrease in pressure and the knee movement. The computer chip reduces the pressure even more, allowing the leg to swing forward.

▲ **Knee Straightens**

As the person puts weight on the artificial leg, sensors detect the extra weight. The computer chip increases the pressure to support the person's weight.

For Your **INFORMATION!**

Neural Prosthetics

A goal of scientists who are working on artificial limbs is to develop neural prostheses, which would be prostheses directly controlled by the user's brain. Researchers are investigating the feasibility of implanting computer chips in the brain that could send to and receive signals from prosthetic limbs. Wearers would be able to control the limbs much as real limbs are controlled. The technology could also be used to help people with spinal cord injuries and stroke victims who have lost the ability to control parts of their body.

Physical Activity and Safety

Warm-Up

Quick Quiz Complete each of these statements with *always*, *sometimes*, or *never*.

(1) I __?__ wear proper safety equipment when I am physically active.

(2) I __?__ follow the rules and regulations of the site where I participate in physical activity.

(3) I __?__ make sure I am properly hydrated during physical activity.

(4) I __?__ allow my body adequate time to recover from physical activity.

(5) I __?__ see a doctor if I experience an injury while exercising.

WRITING Why do you think that teens might not always practice these healthful behaviors?

Exercising Safely

Anyone who exercises faces the risk of injury. But there are many things you can do to stay healthy and safe while exercising. **Most injuries can be avoided if you get proper medical care, wear safety equipment, and pay attention to your surroundings and the weather. Proper water and food intake is also important.**

Medical Care A safe fitness plan starts with a visit to your doctor. Even if you think you are perfectly healthy, it makes good sense to get a checkup before beginning an exercise program. If you have any conditions that limit your activity level, your doctor can offer advice about your fitness plan. You should also see your doctor whenever you experience any injuries or pain that doesn't go away.

Safety Equipment You do not necessarily need expensive equipment to exercise safely. The key is to choose the right equipment for your particular activity.

Exercise and Lifelong Fitness **331**

Objectives

▶ **List** five safety considerations related to physical activity.

▶ **Evaluate** the risks of using substances to enhance performance.

▶ **Identify** ways to avoid overtraining and prevent sports-related injuries.

Vocabulary

- dehydration
- dietary supplement
- overtraining

Objectives

Before class begins, write the objectives on the board. Have students copy the objectives into their notebooks at the start of class.

1. Focus

Warm-Up Quick Quiz

Use the Warm-Up Presentation slide to survey student responses.

For any questions with many *sometimes* or *never* responses, ask students to describe what might happen to a teen who did not practice the behavior. Call on a few students to share their responses to the writing assignment. Stress that excuses for not practicing the behaviors are not as important as the reasons for practicing them, which are to prevent serious injury or death.

Presentation 13-3

2. Teach

L3 **EL** **Reading/Note Taking** 13-3

L2 **Adapted Reading/Note Taking** 13-3

Exercising Safely

L2 **Teacher Demo**

Demonstrate protective gear for a variety of sports. Ask a few students who participate in different sports to bring their protective gear to school and put it on correctly. Discuss the types of injuries that are common in each sport, and explain how the gear protects players from the injuries.

Differentiated Instruction

L1 **Special Needs**

Ask students to bring pictures to class that show people exercising or playing sports or active games. Have students point out people who are practicing safe behaviors and those practicing unsafe behaviors. *(They might point out someone bicycling with a helmet or someone not wearing* *kneepads while they inline skate.)* For each example, ask students to explain which guideline is being followed or broken. For pictures of people breaking the guidelines, ask students to explain what the person should be doing in order to exercise safely.

L1 Building Media Literacy

Ask students to bring in magazine ads for athletic shoes. Display the ads in the classroom, and give students a chance to study them. Then, ask students to identify the messages that the ads convey. If students have trouble identifying the messages, use one of the ads as an example and point out aspects of the ad that indicate the message. For example, an ad that shows a runner crossing a finish line ahead of other runners might convey the message that the shoes she is wearing help her run faster. Discuss how the messages in the ads might influence buying decisions.

L3 Journal Writing

Ask students to identify their three favorite sports or other physical activities. For each one, have them write two lists: a list of potential risks of participating in that sport or activity and a list of corresponding ways of minimizing or preventing the risks. **WRITING**

L3 Online Activity  GO ONLINE

Visit Pearson SuccessNet to access an online activity about exercise safety. Have students complete the Web activity.

Shopping for Athletic Shoes

► **Fit**	Shop late in the day when your feet are a bit swollen. Wear the same socks you wear for exercise.
► **Size**	Be sure your toes do not slide forward or feel pinched. Your heels should not rise as you walk.
► **Shoe Type**	Consider buying sport-specific shoes if you perform the same activity more than 3 times a week.
► **Price**	Unless you have a specific medical problem, moderately priced shoes will do the trick.
► **Style**	Just because your friends like a certain type of shoe doesn't mean it is the right one for you.

FIGURE 9 Choosing the right athletic shoes will not make you a state champion, but they can protect you from discomfort and injury.

GO ONLINE
PearsonSuccessNet.com
For: More on exercise safety

► **Clothing** Clothing should be comfortable and allow unrestricted movement. Avoid any clothing that could cause you to trip or get caught on equipment. For example, do not wear loose-fitting pants when bicycling. Wear light-colored, reflective clothing if you must exercise at night.

► **Footwear** To protect your feet from injury, footwear must fit properly, be in good condition, and provide support and protection. Be sure to buy footwear that fits your particular needs. For example, do not buy running shoes if your main activities are walking and bicycling. Figure 9 gives some tips for purchasing footwear.

► **Protective Gear** Shoulder pads, helmets, mouthguards, and other protective gear are designed to prevent injuries during contact sports. Hard-shell helmets worn by football, hockey, and baseball players protect the head from a direct blow. A helmet also should be worn any time you use wheeled sports equipment such as a bicycle, a skateboard, or inline skates. Kneepads, elbow pads, and wrist guards are also important to prevent injuries while skateboarding or skating.

Your Surroundings In planning your exercise program take into account where you live and where it is safe for you to exercise. For example, if walking to school would involve traveling along busy roads with no sidewalks, this is not a safe plan. Other safety issues to consider include whether an area is well-lit and whether there are other people around. If you listen to music while exercising, keep the earphone volumes low enough so that you can hear what is happening around you.

332 *Chapter 13*

For Your INFORMATION!

Hyponatremia

Marathon runners and other people who exercise for long periods are at risk of developing hyponatremia, a condition in which the blood contains too much water. In their efforts to avoid dehydration, they take in too much fluid, which causes the salt concentration in their blood to fall and their cells to swell with water. In the brain, the swelling cells push against the skull, which may lead to headache and confusion. Because these symptoms are similar to those of dehydration, athletes with hyponatremia may continue drinking, causing more damage. Hyponatremia can eventually lead to seizures, coma, and even death. Experts recommend that marathon runners and other endurance athletes drink a maximum of eight ounces of fluid every 20 minutes, regardless of whether they are drinking water or sports drinks.

Weather Considerations Make sure your clothing is appropriate for the weather. Regardless of the air temperature, you should feel slightly cool at the beginning of your workout. When you exercise outdoors on warm, sunny days, wear light-colored clothing to reflect the sun's rays, and dress lightly to prevent overheating. Always wear sunscreen to protect your skin.

In cold weather, wear gloves or mittens and a hat to prevent heat loss. If you wear layers of clothing, you can regulate your temperature by taking off layers as you warm up. See the First Aid Appendix, pages 730–731, for ways to recognize and treat emergencies caused by extreme weather conditions.

Proper Water and Food Intake Proper hydration, or fluid intake, is important while exercising. You should drink about 16 ounces of water one to two hours before you exercise. Replacing the water you lose in sweat will prevent **dehydration,** or excessive water loss. Dehydration can lead to a dangerous rise in body temperature, muscle cramps, and unnecessary strain on your heart.

You have probably seen many sports drinks and foods advertised for athletes. How do you know if these products are necessary? Sports drinks replace sodium and other important substances you lose in sweat. But they also contain calories and sugar, whereas water does not. Unless you exercise for more than an hour, you only need to drink water.

Products such as sports-nutrition bars and gels also may have the most benefits for athletes who exercise for long periods of time. Your body needs nutrients for energy, maintenance, and repair, but nutritionists agree that fruits, vegetables, and whole-grain products provide the best nutrients. Chapter 9 offers examples of good foods for physical activity.

 **Connect to Your Life** What steps do you take to ensure your safety during physical activity?

During exercise, drink water every 15 to 20 minutes.

FIGURE 10 Plan ahead to make sure you have enough water to drink while you exercise.

Exercise and Lifelong Fitness **333**

L3 Cooperative Learning
Recent studies have found that teens are less likely to exercise when they do not live near a park or similar outdoor space. Challenge groups of students to brainstorm ways teens could exercise at home and present their ideas to the class. *(Possible ideas might include running in place, using food cans as free weights, or working out with a library exercise video.)*

L2 Class Discussion
Make sure students understand the pros and cons of sport drinks so they can be better consumers. Ask: **What do sports drink advertisements imply about the products?** *(They will help you get in shape; they will make you a better athlete; you need to drink them whenever you exercise.).* **What have you learned in this chapter that will make you think about sports drinks differently?** *(You need to work at being in shape, a sports drink will not help you; they have calories and contain sugar.)* **When are sports drinks useful?** *(When you will be exercising for a long period of time.)*

Connect to Your Life *Sample answer:* I wear protective gear, avoid exercising alone after dark, and dress for the weather.

Differentiated Instruction

L2 Less Proficient Readers
Guide students in making a concept map of the information on exercising safely. This will help them remember that exercising safely includes guidelines in five different areas: getting proper medical care, wearing safety equipment, paying attention to surroundings, being prepared for the weather, and taking in the proper water and food. Under each of these five secondary concepts, students should list one or more specific details or examples. Suggest that they save their concept maps for section and chapter reviews.

Avoiding Harmful Substances

L3 Addressing Misconceptions

Protein Requirements Many athletes think that muscle building requires protein supplements. Show students that the extra protein needs of athletes can be met with food alone. Remind them that excess protein will not give them larger muscles; it will be stored as fat. State that athletes need a maximum of 1.8 grams of protein per kilogram of body weight. Ask: **How much protein does a 60-kilogram (132-pound) athlete need?** *(108 g)* Have students use nutrition charts on food labels to plan meals for a day that would provide this much protein.

L1 Building Media Literacy

Bring in examples of articles from the Internet or print media that discuss a supplement, such as creatine, or a hormone, such as HGH. Choose an article from a reliable source and one that is not reliable. Read and summarize the articles as a class. Then evaluate the articles based on the following questions. Where did the information appear? What is the source? Are there references? Is the information current? Does the article use persuasive language? In a paragraph, have students explain which article they think is trustworthy. Ask volunteers to read their paragraphs to the class. **WRITING**

Visual Learning: Figure 11

Caption Answer Steroids could cause mood swings and depression.

Avoiding Harmful Substances

When developing a fitness plan, it can be easy to get caught up in the here and now. Although your immediate goals are important, you also need to think about the future. **To achieve and maintain lifelong fitness, you need to avoid substances that can harm you.**

Dietary Supplements A **dietary supplement** is any product that contains one or more vitamins, minerals, herbs, or other dietary substances that may be lacking in the diet. Many supplement products promise shortcuts to greater fitness, such as increased muscle strength or extra energy. Keep in mind that supplements do not undergo the same strict testing as medications do. Therefore, some harmful side effects might not be discovered until after the supplement has been widely used. Also, there is no guarantee that the supplement will provide the benefits it claims.

In some situations, a doctor may recommend that you take a multivitamin or a similar supplement. But for most teens, a proper diet is the best way to provide your body with all the materials it needs to be healthy and physically active.

Anabolic Steroids Anabolic steroids are artificial forms of the hormone testosterone, a hormone that is involved in muscle development. Doctors may prescribe anabolic steroids for patients with muscular disorders. Some people take steroids without a prescription, which is illegal. They want to improve their athletic performance or change their appearance. This illegal use of steroids presents serious health risks. Steroids can damage organs, increase the risk of cancer, and cause depression. Some athletes inject artificial growth hormone (HGH) to increase muscle mass. But HGH also has health risks, such as organ damage.

When people illegally use steroids or HGH they risk more than their health. They risk being banned from sports and other punishments.

FIGURE 11 Anabolic steroids have serious effects on many body systems. Short-term goals are not worth the long-term risks. **Classifying** What effect could steroids have on mental health?

Effects of Steroids on the Body

In Males and Females
- Cardiovascular disease
- Liver and kidney cancer
- Stunted growth
- Mood swings
- Liver problems
- Hair loss
- Acne

In Males Only
- Enlarged breasts
- Infertility

In Females Only
- Facial hair growth
- Deepening of voice

334 *Chapter 13*

For Your INFORMATION!

Preventing Steroid Abuse

Studies show that simply teaching students about the dangers of anabolic steroid use is not very effective in preventing steroid use. A new anti-steroid program for high school athletes, called ATLAS, is proving to be much more effective. In the ATLAS program, coaches, special trainers, and student leaders work together to discourage steroid use in players. The program teaches students how steroids can negatively affect immediate sports performance. It also shows students how to refuse drugs and how to eat and weight train so they can build muscle without using drugs.

Media Wise

Evaluating Exercise Devices

The Internet, magazines, and TV infomercials are used to sell exercise devices to help reshape your body. The ads often show impressive before and after photographs. How can you know whether the products being sold are safe and effective? Use this checklist to evaluate the products.

Work out while you work!

Does the ad guarantee you will see major changes in a week or a month?  Yes No

Does the ad say that you can use the device to get fit in just a few minutes a day?  Yes No

Does the ad say that the device can "spot reduce" specific parts on the body?  Yes No

Does the ad promise a total body workout?  Yes No

"Yes" answers may reveal that you should think carefully about your purchase. Instead, choose exercises that require little or no equipment.

Activity Find an ad for an exercise device. Use the checklist to evaluate the product. Would you buy the product? Would you recommend it to a friend? Why or why not? **WRITING**

Preventing Sports-Related Injuries

Practice is important in order to improve at any sport or activity. However, sometimes teens feel pressure to be too competitive. Pushing your body too hard can lead to injury. **An important part of achieving lifelong fitness is avoiding overtraining and preventing injuries.**

Overtraining If you exercise too intensely or for too long without allowing enough time for rest, you may be **overtraining.** The first sign of overtraining is fatigue during exercise or a few hours after a workout. Fatigue is a signal that you are overworking your body. Other signs of overtraining include nausea or vomiting during or after a workout, loss of appetite, and irritability. If you experience any of these symptoms, reduce the intensity and length of your workout. If the symptoms do not subside, seek medical care.

You can avoid overtraining by sticking to a consistent exercise schedule that includes days of rest. In addition, always exercise within your comfort level. Pushing yourself to achieve fitness goals too quickly can lead to injuries.

 **Connect to Your Life** Have you ever experienced signs of overtraining? What were the signs?

Differentiated Instruction

L4 Gifted and Talented

Have a student or group of students choose a common sports injury to research in depth. Some examples of injuries that students may be familiar with are Achilles tendon injuries, torn knee ligaments, and hamstring injuries. Have students prepare a presentation for the class that includes a detailed description of the injury. The presentation should also answer these questions. Who is most susceptible to this type of injury? What are typical treatments for this injury? How can it be prevented?

Media Wise

Evaluating Exercise Devices

Help students find infomercials or other ads for products like the "Hawaiian" chair shown in the illustration. (The seat rotates "like a hula dancer.") Ask why infomercials are often used to sell exercise devices.

Activity Students should be wary of buying a product that receives two or more "Yes" responses to the questions on the checklist.

Preventing Sports-Related Injuries

L4 Building Media Literacy

Ask students to name criteria that would be suitable for judging the reliability of magazine articles on training. *(Sample answers: written by a sports physician, based on scientific research, recently published)* Have the class discuss the criteria and then vote on which criteria they think are most important. Ask a few volunteers to find and share articles that meet these criteria.

L3 Building Health Skills

Making Decisions Present the following scenario to your class: For many years, you have wanted to play varsity soccer. You finally made the team. However, you find that your coach pushes you so hard during practice that you are developing signs of overtraining. You have noticed similar signs in some of your teammates. After all of your hard work, you do not want to quit the team. Have students write a paragraph describing how they would handle this situation. **WRITING**

 Connect to Your Life *Sample answer:* I have experienced fatigue, nausea, and loss of appetite.

3. Assess

Evaluate

These assignments can help you assess students' mastery of the section content.

Section 3 Review

Answers appear below.

Teaching Resources

- Practice 13-3
- Section 13-3 Quiz

L2 Reteach

Have students make an illustrated "do" and "don't" poster that describes ways to stay safe while being physically active. Have students illustrate at least one point from each blue heading in Section 3.

L4 Enrich

Teaching Resources

- Enrich 13-3

Health at School

Improving School Fitness Help students choose practical ideas. In their papers, students might try to convince administrators of such potential benefits of exercise as improved school attendance and better grades. If possible, arrange to have students present their papers at a meeting of school administrators.

FIGURE 12 The small break in this leg bone is a stress fracture. Exercise places stress on bones. If the bones do not have time to heal before repeated, intense exercise, a stress fracture could develop.

Sports-Related Injuries Using the same joints repetitively during your workouts can lead to overuse injuries. Tendonitis, a painful swelling of a tendon, is an injury that can result from overuse. Overuse of a bone can lead to a stress fracture, like the one shown in Figure 12. Participating in a variety of activities and allowing your body to recover between workouts can help prevent overuse injuries.

In Chapter 11, you learned about two common sports-related injuries—sprains, the tearing of ligaments, and strains, the tearing of tendons. Treatment for sprains and strains usually involves controlling the swelling with rest, ice, compression, and elevation. These treatment steps are often referred to by the initials R.I.C.E. See the First Aid Appendix for more information on R.I.C.E.

Allowing injuries to heal properly is extremely important for lifelong fitness. Reinjuring bones, tendons, ligaments, or muscles before they heal can lead to ongoing problems and limit your ability to stay active. If you have an injury, work with a doctor to find ways to exercise while allowing the injured area to heal.

Section 3 Review

Key Ideas and Vocabulary

1. What are five safety considerations to keep in mind when planning a fitness program?
2. What is **dehydration**? What physical problems can dehydration cause?
3. Describe the health risks associated with dietary supplements and anabolic steroids.
4. Why is the prevention of injuries important to lifelong fitness?

Critical Thinking

5. **Comparing and Contrasting** How might the safety concerns of a physically active person living in a large city differ from those of a person living in a small town?

Health at School

Improving School Fitness With permission from school administrators, interview students to identify ways to encourage physical activity at school. For example, would more students exercise if the gym were open for a few hours after school? Choose one practical idea. In a paper, present your idea to school administrators. **WRITING**

6. **Making Judgments** Do you think that exercising with a partner would increase or decrease your risk of overtraining? Explain your reasoning.
7. **Evaluating** Felicia has never exercised regularly, but has decided to start a fitness program. She has committed to running for one hour every day regardless of the weather or the time of day. Critique her fitness plan from a safety perspective.

 GO ONLINE PearsonSuccessNet.com   Audio Summary Section 13.3

Section 3 Review

1. medical care, safety equipment, your surroundings, the weather, and proper water and food intake
2. Dehydration is excessive water loss. It can cause dangerously high body temperature, muscle cramps, and strain on the heart.
3. Dietary supplements may have unknown, harmful side effects.

Anabolic steroids can damage organs, increase the risk of cancer, and cause depression.
4. because ongoing injuries can limit the ability to stay active
5. *Sample answer:* City: crime, traffic, pollution. Town: few organized activities, poor street lighting

6. *Sample answer:* It would increase my risk by motivating me to exercise harder than I would if I exercised alone.
7. *Sample answer:* She is too ambitious. She might get hurt by overtraining or by exercising in bad weather or at night.

Chapter 13
At a Glance

Section 1   The Importance of Physical Activity

Key Ideas

▶ The changes that occur due to physical activity are beneficial to your body, your mind, and your social interactions.

▶ There are five components of fitness: cardio-respiratory endurance, muscular strength, muscular endurance, flexibility, and body composition.

▶ Physical activities can be classified as aerobic exercise or anaerobic exercise. Muscular strengthening and endurance activities can be further classified as isometric exercise, isotonic exercise, or isokinetic exercise.

Vocabulary
- physical activity (316)
- endorphins (317)
- physical fitness (318)
- body composition (318)
- aerobic exercise (320)
- anaerobic exercise (320)
- isometric exercise (320)
- isotonic exercise (321)
- isokinetic exercise (321)

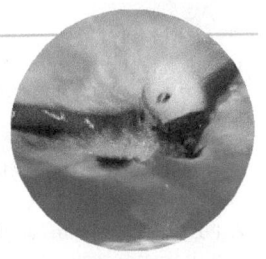

Section 2   Setting Goals for Lifelong Fitness

Key Ideas

▶ To plan a successful fitness program you should define your goals, develop your program, and monitor your progress.

▶ The safest workouts begin with a warm-up period and end with a cool-down period. Stretching exercises should be part of both the warm-up and cool-down periods.

Vocabulary
- lifelong fitness (324)
- FITT formula (326)
- target heart rate (326)
- cross-training (326)

Section 3   Physical Activity and Safety

Key Ideas

▶ Most injuries can be avoided if you get proper medical care, wear safety equipment, and pay attention to your surroundings and the weather. Proper water and food intake is also important.

▶ To achieve and maintain lifelong fitness, you need to avoid substances that can harm you.

▶ An important part of achieving lifelong fitness is avoiding overtraining and preventing injuries.

Vocabulary
- dehydration (333)
- dietary supplement (334)
- overtraining (335)

Exercise and Lifelong Fitness   **337**

Chapter 13
At a Glance

VIDEO **Fit for Life** Ask for volunteers to share their answers. Use examples from the video to review ways to stay physically active.

Key Ideas Review

L1 Ask students to copy the Key Ideas sentences in pencil on a sheet of paper. Then have them erase one important word in each sentence and exchange papers with a partner. Partners should try to fill in the blanks in the sentences.

L2 Tell students to write a concise paragraph about each Key Idea. They should use the Key Idea itself as the initial topic sentence(s) and follow it with supporting details.

Vocabulary Review

L1 Give examples or definitions of the vocabulary terms, and call on students at random to try to identify the terms. Retest students on any terms they cannot identify the first time around.

L2 Ask pairs of students to make flash cards of the vocabulary terms, with the terms on one side and the definitions on the other. Have partners take turns using the flash cards to quiz each other on the definitions.

Chapter 13 Review

GO ONLINE

PearsonSuccessNet.com

Students can go online for a review activity on Chapter 13.

Reviewing Key Ideas

Section 1

1. c   **2.** a

3. Cardiovascular system benefits include stronger heart, more capillaries, lower blood pressure, and lower cholesterol levels. Skeletal system benefits include stronger, denser bones. Muscular system benefits include bigger, stronger muscles.

4. chemicals that block pain messages from reaching brain cells; by promoting feelings of satisfaction and pleasure after a good workout

5. Muscular strength is the capacity of muscles to produce force. Muscular endurance is the ability of muscles to work for an extended time.

6. no, because they could have different proportions of fat and lean tissues

Section 2

7. b

8. by determining if your resting heart rate is getting lower

9. warm-up and stretching—prepare body for vigorous workout; workout—improve or maintain fitness; cooldown and stretching—slowly return body and heart rate to resting state and loosen muscles

10. *Sample answer:* Aerobic activities, stretching, and muscle strengthening exercises would be beneficial to both of us. I may benefit from anaerobic activities such as sprinting.

Section 3

11. b

12. *Sample answer:* Will there be physical contact with other players? Is there a risk for head injury? Are there equipment rules?

13. because supplements do not undergo the same strict testing

14. *Sample answer:* I would advise him to play less soccer because his fatigue suggests he may be overtraining.

Chapter 13 Review

Reviewing Key Ideas

Section 1

1. Which component of fitness receives the greatest benefit from jogging?
a. muscular strength
b. flexibility
c. cardiorespiratory endurance
d. body composition

2. Pushing your palms against a wall is an example of
a. isometric exercise.
b. isokinetic exercise.
c. isotonic exercise.
d. aerobic exercise.

3. Describe the benefits of physical activity for three different body systems.

4. What are endorphins? How do they contribute to the psychological benefits of physical activity?

5. Explain the difference between muscular strength and muscular endurance.

6. **Critical Thinking** Jane and Maria are the same height and the same weight. Does this mean that they have the same body composition? Why or why not?

Section 2

7. Which types of activities should you try to perform every day?
a. vigorous exercise such as soccer
b. recreational activities such as walking, throwing a frisbee, or riding a bike to school
c. watching television and playing video games
d. strengthening exercises such as lifting weights

8. How can you determine if your cardiovascular system is becoming more fit as a result of your fitness program?

9. List the three stages of a workout session. What is the goal of each stage?

10. **Critical Thinking** You are trying out for the basketball team in a few months. Your friend is trying out for the volleyball team. He asked you to train with him. What types of activities would be beneficial to both of you? What types of activities would be more beneficial to you?

Section 3

11. Which is the best way to avoid dehydration?
a. Avoid exercise when it is warm outside.
b. Drink as much water as you lose in sweat.
c. Do not wear a helmet so that heat can escape from your head.
d. Wear dark clothing so that sweat can evaporate.

12. What factors should you consider when choosing safety equipment for physical activity?

13. Why are the claims made by supplement manufacturers less trustworthy than the claims made by prescription drug manufacturers?

14. **Critical Thinking** Your friend plays soccer for several teams. He has practice or a game every day. Lately, he cannot finish his homework without falling asleep. What advice would you give him?

Building Health Skills

15. **Communicating** Your uncle has always said that he does not need to exercise because he eats well and is not overweight. In a letter, explain to your uncle why this is not true. **WRITING**

16. **Analyzing Influences** In a paragraph, describe how your family and friends have influenced your activity choices and level of activity. **WRITING**

17. **Setting Goals** Choose two or three fitness goals you want to achieve. Rank your goals by highest priority. Explain why you placed the goals in that order. Plan an exercise program that will help you achieve your first goal. **WRITING**

Health and Community

Endurance Event Find out about local charity events, such as walk-a-thons or bike-a-thons, that will require you to train. Develop a schedule to train for the event. Write a regular column for your school newspaper describing your experiences with training and fundraising. **WRITING**

Building Health Skills

15. Letters should describe benefits of exercise, such as improved cardiovascular health and reduced stress.

16. Students may say they play certain sports or stay active because family members or friends play the same sports or stay active.

17. Students might place the highest priority on losing weight, building muscle, or improving skills for various reasons. Exercise programs should be suited to students' goals. They should also be reasonable and safe.

Standardized Test Prep

Math Practice

The box below gives the formula for calculating a target heart rate range. Use the formula to answer Questions 18–20.

Calculating Target Heart Rate

1. 220 – person's age = maximum heart rate

2. Maximum heart rate – resting heart rate = __?__

3. Answer from Step 2 × 0.6 = __?__ (Round to the nearest whole number.)

4. Answer from Step 2 × 0.8 = __?__ (Round to the nearest whole number.)

5. Resting heart rate + answer from Step 3 = __?__
Resting heart rate + answer from Step 4 = __?__

The two sums from Step 5 are the target heart rate range.

18. Randy is 20 years old. He has a resting heart rate of 70 beats per minute (bpm). What is his target heart rate range?
A 148–174 bpm
B 78–104 bpm
C 90–120 bpm
D 168–198 bpm

19. After ten years, Randy's resting heart rate stays the same. What will happen to his target heart rate?
F It will stay the same.
G It will increase.
H It will decrease.
J It depends on his fitness level.

20. Ken's target heart rate range is 122–139 bpm. His resting heart rate is 73 bpm. What is his age?
A 82
B 73
C 65
D 59

Reading and Writing Practice

Read the passage. Then answer Questions 21–24.

In 1713, Italian physician Bernardino Ramazzini wrote about the association between inactivity and poor health. Ramazzini, who is considered the father of occupational medicine, noted that "those who sit at their work and are therefore called 'chairworkers,' suffer from their own particular diseases." He urged these workers to at least exercise on their days off to counteract the harm done by many days of sedentary life.

21. When Ramazzini refers to "chairworkers," he is most likely referring to people such as
A farmers and railroad workers.
B cobblers and tailors.
C miners and blacksmiths.
D furniture makers and carpenters.

22. What factor does Ramazzini blame for the poor health of "chairworkers"?
F their poor diet
G rare diseases
H being overworked
J lack of physical activity

23. Someone who practices occupational medicine is most likely concerned with
A diseases or hazards related to the workplace.
B helping those with sedentary lifestyles become more active.
C treating diseases related to sedentary lifestyles.
D diagnosing and treating rare diseases.

Constructed Response

24. In a paragraph, summarize Ramazzini's observations of inactive workers in the 18th century.

> ### Test-Taking Tip
>
> On the days before a test, keep to a regular physical activity routine. Because physical activity improves your mood and your focus, it may help your performance on the test.

Standardized Test Prep

Math Practice
18. A
19. H
20. C

Reading and Writing Practice
21. B
22. J
23. A
24. *Sample answer:* Ramazzini observed that inactive workers suffered from their own particular diseases. He blamed this on the harm done by their sedentary life.

Health and Community

Endurance Event Make sure students choose events that will allow them ample time to train. Check that their training schedules and fundraising ideas are appropriate and realistic. Arrange with the editor of the school newspaper for students to publish their columns.

Section Objectives	Standards Correlation	Instructional Resources L3	SE eTEXT	TE eTEXT	PRINT
1 Your Teeth and Gums ⏱ 1 period; 1/2 block 14.1.1 **List** the functions of teeth and gums. 14.1.2 **Identify** two structural problems of the teeth and mouth. 14.1.2 **Describe** ways to prevent teeth and gum problems.	NHES: 1.12.1, 1.12.5, 6.12.1	SE Warm-Up, p. 342	•	•	•
		SE Hands-On Activity Sports Drinks, Soft Drinks, and Your Teeth, p. 345	•	•	•
		RN Note Taking Guide 14-1	•	•	•
		IB Image Bank 14-1, 14-3		•	
		TR Practice 14-1		•	
		TR Section 14-1 Quiz		•	
2 Your Skin, Hair, and Nails ⏱ 2 periods; 1 block 14.2.1 **Identify** the functions of the skin. 14.2.1 **Describe** behaviors that can keep your skin healthy. 14.2.1 **Explain** the functions of your hair and nails and how to care for them.	NHES: 1.12.1, 1.12.5, 1.12.8, 8.12.1	SE Warm-Up, p. 347	•	•	•
		RN Note Taking Guide 14-2	•	•	•
		IB Image Bank 14-4		•	
		TR Practice 14-2		•	
		TR Section 14-2 Quiz		•	
Recognizing Misleading Claims ⏱ 1 period; 1/2 block BHS.14 **Apply** strategies for recognizing misleading claims.	NHES: 2.12.5, 3.12.1, 3.12.5	SE Practice the Skill, p. 355	•	•	•
		RN Building Health Skills 14	•	•	•
3 Your Eyes and Ears ⏱ 2 periods; 1 block 14.3.1 **Explain** how your eyes allow you to see. 14.3.2 **Identify** two ways to keep your eyes healthy. 14.3.3 **Explain** how your ears allow you to hear and maintain your balance. 14.3.4 **Identify** ways to keep your ears healthy.	NHES: 1.12.1, 2.12.6, 3.12.4	SE Warm-Up, p. 356	•	•	•
		RN Note Taking Guide 14-3	•	•	•
		IB Image Bank 14-11, 14-14		•	
		TR Practice 14-3		•	
		TR Section 14-3 Quiz		•	
4 Sleep and Feeling Fit ⏱ 1 period; 1/2 block 14.4.1 **Describe** why sleep is important for health. 14.4.2 **Explain** how circadian rhythms influence the sleep patterns of teens.	NHES: 1.12.1, 1.12.7, 6.12.1	SE Warm-Up, p. 364	•	•	•
		RN Note Taking Guide 14-4	•	•	•
		IB Image Bank 14-18		•	
		TR Practice 14-4		•	
		TR Section 14-4 Quiz		•	

Chapter Review and Assessment

SE Chapter 14 Review, p. 368 L3
CTB Chapter 14 Test L2 L3 L4
SE Standardized Test Prep, p. 369 L3

PROGRAM COMPONENTS

SE Student Edition
TE Teacher Edition
TR Teaching Resources
RN Reading and Note Taking Guide
ARN Adapted Reading and Note Taking Guide
IB Image Bank

CTB Computer Test Bank
AUD Audio Section Summaries
DVD Teens Talk Video Series
VVG Video Viewing Guide
PPT Presentation

Differentiated Instruction
L1 L2 L4 EL

		SE eTEXT	TE eTEXT	PRINT
ARN	Note Taking Guide 14-1 L2	•	•	
RN	Note Taking Guide 14-1 EL	•	•	•
AUD	Audio Summary 14-1 L1 L2 EL	•	•	
TE	Reteach Strategy, p. 346 L2		•	•
TR	Enrich 14-1 L4		•	
ARN	Note Taking Guide 14-2 L2	•	•	
RN	Note Taking Guide 14-2 EL	•	•	•
AUD	Audio Summary 14-2 L1 L2 EL	•	•	
TE	Reteach Strategy, p. 353 L2		•	•
TR	Enrich 14-2 L4		•	
ARN	Building Health Skills 14 L2	•	•	
RN	Building Health Skills 14 EL	•	•	•
ARN	Note Taking Guide 14-3 L2	•	•	
RN	Note Taking Guide 14-3 EL	•	•	•
AUD	Audio Summary 14-3 L1 L2 EL	•	•	
TE	Reteach Strategy, p. 363 L2		•	•
TR	Enrich 14-3 L4		•	
ARN	Note Taking Guide 14-4 L2	•	•	
RN	Note Taking Guide 14-4 EL	•	•	•
AUD	Audio Summary 14-4 L1 L2 EL	•	•	
TE	Reteach Strategy, p. 366 L2		•	•
TR	Enrich 14-4 L4		•	

ABILITY LEVELS
- L1 **For students with special needs**
- L2 **For less proficient readers**
- L3 **For all students**
- L4 **For gifted and talented students**
- EL **For English language learners**

Chapter 14 Digital/Video Pathway

This alternative pathway allows you to teach this chapter's content using only the video and online materials.

Preview
- **DVD** Video #14 Preview
- **SE** Video #14 Preview Activity
- **VVG** Video #14 Worksheet

Taking Care of You

1
- **DVD** Video #14 Explore/Wrap-Up
- **VVG** Video #14 Worksheet
- **PPT** 14-1 Presentation
- **RN/ARN** 14-1 Note Taking
- **PPT** 14-1 Section Quiz

Taking Care of You

2
- **PPT** 14-2 Presentation
- **RN/ARN** 14-2 Note Taking
- **PPT** 14-2 Section Quiz

3
- **PPT** 14-3 Presentation
- **RN/ARN** 14-3 Note Taking
- **PPT** 14-3 Section Quiz

4
- **PPT** 14-4 Presentation
- **RN/ARN** 14-4 Note Taking
- **PPT** 14-4 Section Quiz

Chapter Preview

Section 1 Your Teeth and Gums
Healthy teeth are essential for speaking clearly and chewing food. The gums hold the teeth firmly in place. Structural problems of the teeth and mouth can cause problems if they are not treated. Healthy teeth and gums can be maintained by eating a healthy diet, taking proper care of the teeth, and getting regular dental checkups.

Section 2 Your Skin, Hair, and Nails
The skin's functions include protection, temperature regulation, and information gathering. Steps for caring for the skin include avoiding damage from ultraviolet radiation and monitoring moles for signs of cancer. Hair protects the scalp and helps to insulate the body. Nails cover and protect the tips of the fingers and toes.

 Analyzing Influences

Recognizing Misleading Claims
Advertisements for health care products can be analyzed for signs of misleading claims.

Section 3 Your Eyes and Ears
The eyes and ears send impulses to the brain, which interprets the impulses as images and sounds. Having regular eye exams and wearing eye protection are two steps in caring for the eyes. Minimizing exposure to loud sounds can help prevent damage to the ears.

Section 4 Sleep and Feeling Fit
Sleep is just as important to the body as air, water, and food. Teens often have trouble getting enough sleep because puberty affects the body's circadian rhythms.

 GO ONLINE

PearsonSuccessNet.com
For resources and activities for this chapter.

Personal Care

GO ONLINE PearsonSuccessNet.com

TEENS Talk

VIDEO 14

Taking Care of You

Preview **Activity**

When Do You Follow Instructions?

1. Instructions with your new suede jacket tell you to treat it with a water-repellent spray, and to avoid wearing it in bad weather.
   a. Will you follow these instructions? Explain.
   b. What could happen if you don't follow the instructions? How would you feel?
2. Throughout your life, you have been told to wear sunscreen and to avoid the sun during the hottest time of the day.
   a. Do you follow these instructions? Explain.
   b. What could happen if you don't follow these instructions? How would you feel?
3. What did you learn about yourself from your answers to these questions? **WRITING**

340

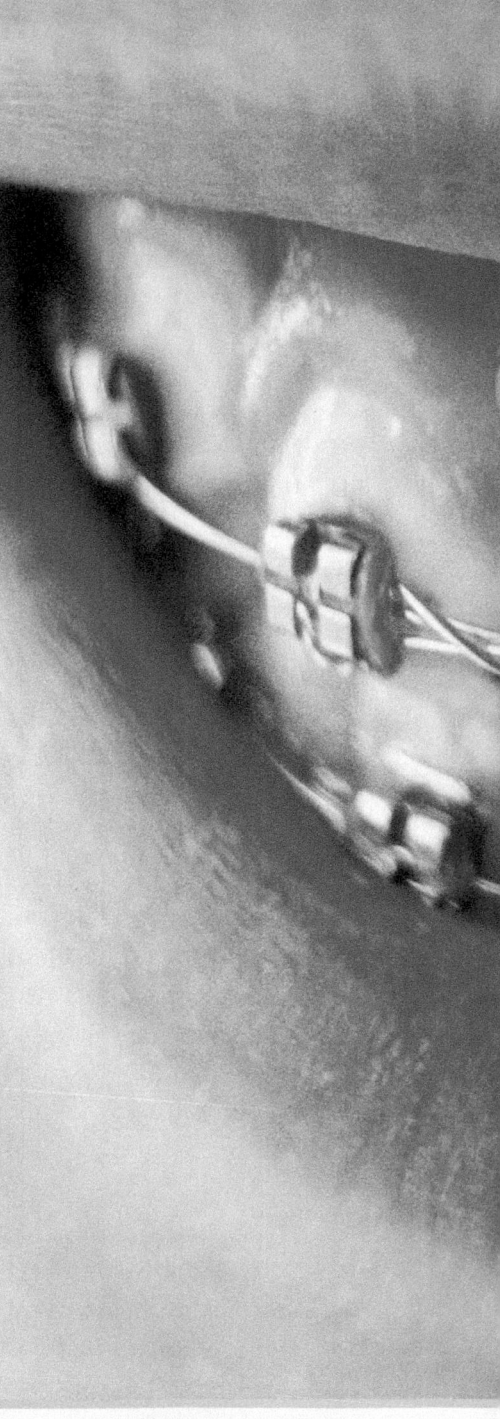

 **Sensitive Issues**

- Discussions of acne may cause discomfort to teens who are experiencing skin problems. Call on only those students who volunteer during class discussions of acne and other skin problems.

- Do not single out visually-impaired or hearing-impaired students during discussions of the functions of the eyes and ears. Provide a supportive atmosphere for students who volunteer to discuss the cause of their hearing or vision impairments.

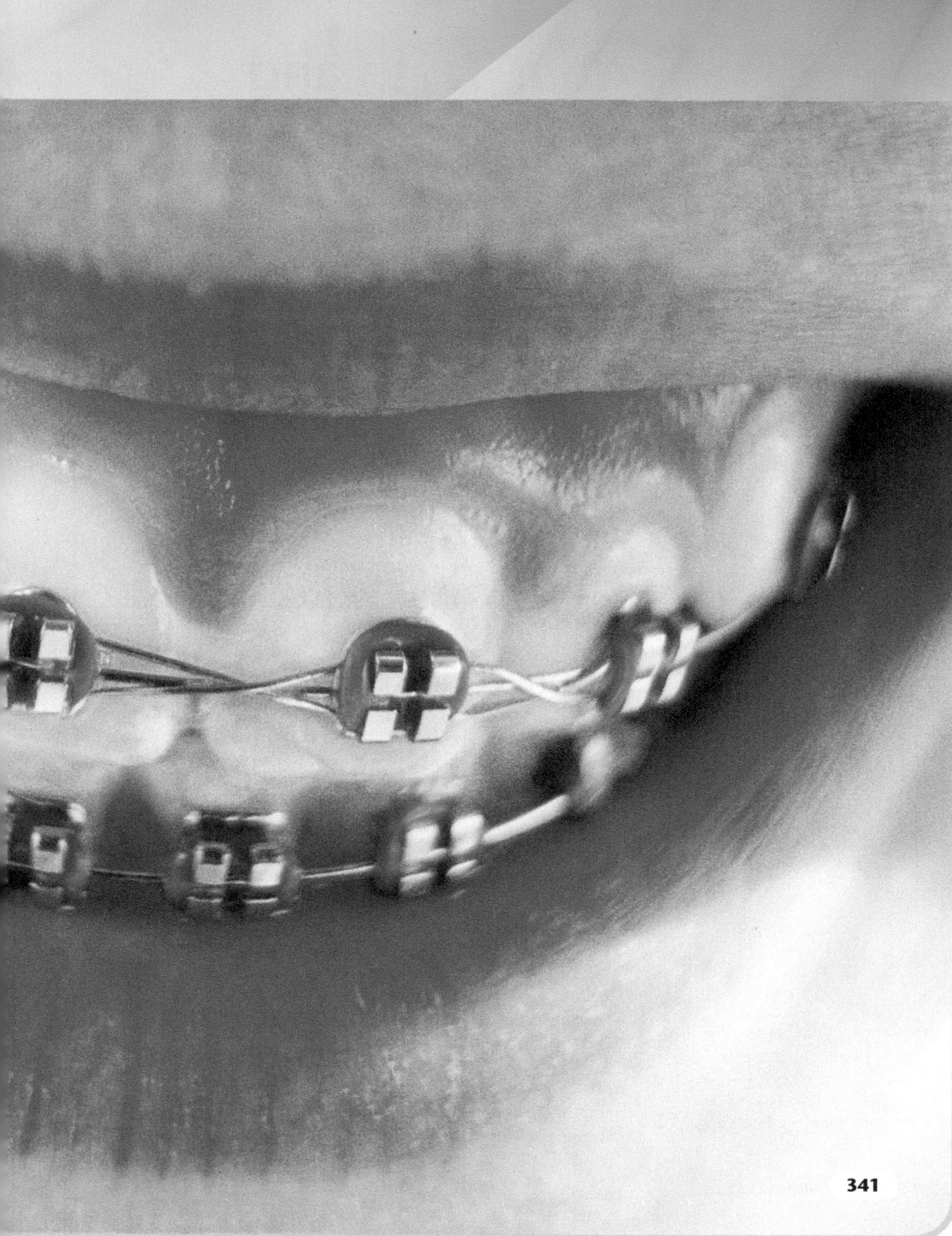

Video Objectives

Use this video to help students
Identify personal care concerns they may encounter during adolescence.
Evaluate their personal health behaviors.

Preview **Activity**

When Do You Follow Instructions?

Just before watching the video, have students complete the Preview Activity. Ask some students to share their responses to Steps 1 and 2. Discuss why some people are more apt to follow instructions for caring for their belongings than instructions for caring for themselves.

341

From the Authors

Good grooming...now that's an old-fashioned idea. Or is it? Good grooming is an indication of good health habits. Poor grooming is an indication of poor health habits and can lead to health problems. Be certain that students do not confuse hair or clothing styles with grooming. For example, baggy trousers or an all-black wardrobe are not indications of poor grooming. At the same time, a stylish wardrobe does not necessarily indicate good grooming. The activities and questions in the chapter are designed to help students develop good health and hygiene habits. See the Quick Quiz on page 342, the Hands-On Activity on page 345, and the Connect to Your Life questions throughout the chapter.

Section 1

Your Teeth and Gums

Objectives

Before class begins, write the objectives on the board. Have students copy the objectives into their notebooks at the start of class.

1. Focus

Warm-Up **Quick Quiz**

Use the Warm-Up Presentation slide to survey student responses.

Give students several minutes to read the choices and select their responses. Remind students that their responses will remain confidential. Then ask students to complete the writing assignment. Point out that this section describes ways to care for the teeth and gums. Give students the opportunity to review and revise their writing assignment after they finish reading the section.

Presentation 14-1

Section 1

Your Teeth and Gums

Objectives

▶ **List** the functions of teeth and gums.

▶ **Identify** two structural problems of the teeth and mouth.

▶ **Describe** ways to prevent teeth and gum problems.

Vocabulary

- enamel
- cementum
- dentin
- pulp
- malocclusion
- orthodontist
- halitosis
- plaque
- tartar
- periodontal disease

Warm-Up

Quick Quiz How many of these questions can you answer *yes* to?

① I brush my teeth at least twice a day.

② I floss my teeth every day.

③ I go to the dentist at least once a year.

④ I limit my intake of sugary foods.

⑤ When I play a contact sport, I always wear a mouthguard.

WRITING What changes can you make to take better care of your teeth?

The Teeth and Gums

Do you remember when you lost your baby teeth? Normal activities such as biting into an apple or making an *s* sound became difficult. You learned that your teeth are important for many reasons. **Healthy teeth allow you to chew your food properly and speak clearly.**

Structure of Teeth You have four types of teeth. Figure 1 shows where they are located and describes their functions. It also shows the three basic parts of a tooth—the crown, the neck, and the root.

Each tooth is made of three types of bonelike material. **Enamel,** the hardest material in your body, covers a tooth's crown. **Cementum** covers a tooth's root and helps to anchor the tooth to the jawbone. Under the enamel and cementum is **dentin,** a living material that makes up the majority of a tooth. A soft tissue called **pulp** fills the center of each tooth. The pulp contains nerves and blood vessels, which pass through a channel called the root canal.

The Gums The gum is the pink tissue that surrounds the base of your teeth and covers the bone around the teeth. **Healthy gums fit tightly around the neck of each tooth like a collar, holding it firmly in place.**

TEENS *Are Asking . . .*

Q: **When I sleep over at friends' houses they complain that I make a grinding noise in my sleep. What's going on?**

A: You may be experiencing bruxism, or teeth grinding. Dentists are not entirely sure why some people grind or clench their teeth while sleeping. Some may do so because they have a malocclusion. Stress also seems to be a factor. Bruxism can cause jaw damage and eventually wear down the enamel on your teeth. If you suspect you grind your teeth at night, you should talk to your dentist. Your dentist may suggest that you wear a nightguard to prevent you from grinding. Nightguards are similar to the mouth guards worn by football players. Learning to manage your stress may also help you stop grinding.

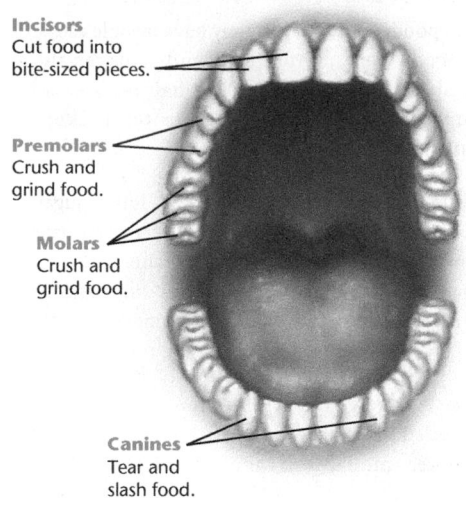

Incisors
Cut food into bite-sized pieces.

Premolars
Crush and grind food.

Molars
Crush and grind food.

Canines
Tear and slash food.

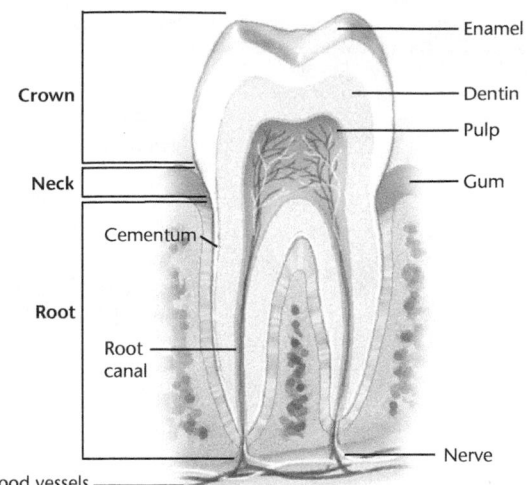

Enamel
Crown
Dentin
Pulp
Neck
Gum
Cementum
Root
Root canal
Nerve
Blood vessels

FIGURE 1 All of your teeth are made up of three parts—the crown, the neck, and at least one root.
Interpreting Diagrams What material covers a tooth's crown?

Structural Problems

By the age of 3, most children have all of their first teeth, or primary teeth. Around the age of 5 or 6, the primary teeth begin to fall out. Over the next few years, the primary teeth are replaced by 28 permanent teeth. An additional four teeth, called wisdom teeth, usually grow in between the ages of 17 and 21. **The changes that occur in the jaws throughout the growing years can lead to structural problems.**

Malocclusion When the upper and lower teeth do not meet properly, the condition is known as a **malocclusion** (mal uh KLOO zhun), or improper bite. When the upper teeth stick out too far, the condition is called an overbite. When the lower teeth stick out beyond the upper teeth, the condition is called an underbite. A severe malocclusion can make chewing difficult or cause the teeth to wear down unevenly.

People with malocclusions, or people with crooked teeth, may seek the help of an **orthodontist** (awr thuh DAHN tist). Orthodontists are specialists who correct the position of jaws and teeth. They use braces and other devices to move teeth into their proper positions.

Impacted Wisdom Teeth Some teens have their wisdom teeth surgically removed before they grow in because the teeth are impacted. Impacted wisdom teeth either do not have the space to emerge through the gum line or are positioned at an awkward angle. If impacted wisdom teeth are not removed, they may crowd the other teeth and cause serious gum infections.

Connect to Your Life

Have you worn braces? If so, how did they change your appearance?

2. Teach

L3 EL Reading/Note Taking 14-1

L2 Adapted Reading/Note Taking 14-1

The Teeth and Gums

L2 Visual Learning: Figure 1

Image Bank Figure 14-1

Have students examine the shape and structure of the various kinds of teeth. Ask: **How is the structure of each type of tooth related to its function?** *(Sample answer: Incisors are wedge shaped, for cutting food into bite-sized pieces. Premolars and molars have a flat surface, for crushing and grinding food. Canines are sharp and pointed, for tearing food.)*
Caption Answer enamel

Structural Problems

L1 Teacher Demo

Provide a model to help students understand structural problems of the jaws and teeth. Show students a three-ring binder. Ask: **What happens when the rings do not line up properly?** *(Sample answer: The binder does not open and close easily, and it does not hold paper well.)* Relate this to malocclusion. Then have students visualize a bookshelf that is full of books. Ask: **What would happen if I tried to push this three-ring binder onto the bookshelf?** *(Sample answer: Books would be damaged or pushed out of place.)* Explain that the eruption of an impacted wisdom tooth is similar to a book being pushed into an already-full bookshelf.

L4 Active Learning

Explain that orthodontics is one example of the many careers available in the field of dental care. Ask students to research a variety of careers related to dentistry. Have students share their findings with the class.

Connect to Your Life Allow students to answer this question in their private journals.

Caring for Your Teeth and Gums

L3 Content Update GO ONLINE

Visit Pearson SuccessNet to access more information about caring for your teeth. Have students complete the Web activity.

L3 Building Health Skills

Accessing Information A well-balanced diet that is low in sugar can contribute to good oral health. Ask students to use Nutrition Facts labels to find the sugar content of some of their favorite foods, including snack foods and foods they consider to be healthy. Have students work as a class to create a bulletin board display showing what they learned about the sugar content of various foods.

L2 Cooperative Learning

Have students read the tips for proper brushing and flossing. Then challenge students to incorporate one or more of these tips into a poster that could be used to teach younger students about proper oral care. Ask students to present their posters to the class. Arrange for students to share their posters with younger students.

Connect to Your Life Allow students to answer this question in their private journals.

GO ONLINE

PearsonSuccessNet.com

For: More on caring for your teeth

FIGURE 2 You should spend about two minutes brushing your teeth, twice a day. You should also floss every day to remove plaque from areas where a toothbrush does not reach.

Brushing
- Use a toothbrush with soft bristles.
- Brush all surfaces of your teeth—outer, inner, and top.
- Hold the toothbrush at a 45-degree angle.
- Brush away from your gums.
- Brush your tongue.

344

Flossing
- Use 18 inches of dental floss—waxed or unwaxed.
- Gently move the floss up and down between your teeth.
- At the gum line, curve the floss around each tooth and glide it up and down.
- Unwind, and use a clean section of floss for each tooth.

Caring for Your Teeth and Gums

If your teeth and gums are in poor condition, you may have trouble eating and speaking. Failing to properly maintain your teeth and gums can also cause mouth pain and an embarrassing condition called **halitosis,** or bad breath. **A healthy diet, proper tooth care, and regular dental checkups can prevent tooth decay and gum disease.**

Healthy Diet You should eat a well-balanced diet that is low in sugar. Bacteria in your mouth feed on sugar and produce acids that can damage your teeth. Limit your intake of sports drinks, which contain acids that can destroy your teeth's enamel. Your diet should include foods that contain calcium and phosphorus—two minerals that help strengthen teeth.

Brushing Your mouth is full of bacteria that adhere to your teeth in a sticky film called **plaque.** Brushing your teeth removes plaque. You should also brush your tongue to remove food particles. Brush at least twice a day, preferably after every meal. If you cannot brush after eating, rinse your mouth with water.

Flossing Dental floss removes food and plaque from areas that a toothbrush cannot reach, such as between your teeth. You should floss your teeth once a day, preferably before bedtime. Instructions for proper brushing and flossing are given in Figure 2.

Wearing a Mouthguard Although teeth are made of strong material, collisions can lead to broken or cracked teeth. To prevent damage to your teeth during contact sports, such as basketball or lacrosse, wear a mouthguard.

Connect to Your Life  How many times a day do you brush your teeth? How often do you floss?

For Your INFORMATION!

Fluoride

Fluoride describes a group of compounds found in soil, air, and water. In mouths, fluoride becomes a part of plaque and inhibits the removal of enamel from teeth. It also may prevent bacteria from producing acids. The amount of fluoride found naturally in water is not enough to combat tooth decay. Therefore, in the 1940s programs were initiated to add fluoride to community water supplies. Now, approximately 60 percent of the United States population has access to fluoridated water. It is recommended that those who exclusively drink well water, bottled water, or live in a region without fluoridated water use fluoride-containing products such as toothpaste or mouthwash.

Hands-On *Activity*

Sports Drinks, Soft Drinks, and Your Teeth

In this activity, you will observe how various drinks affect eggshells, which are composed of some of the same materials as your teeth.

Materials
three plastic cups
tape for labeling
three large pieces
of eggshell
sports drink
soft drink
water

Try This
1. Label the first cup "sports drink," the second cup "soft drink," and the third cup "water." Place a piece of eggshell in each cup.
2. Pour some of the sports drink into the appropriate cup. Pour the same amount of soft drink into the second cup and water into the third.
3. After three days, discard the liquids and examine each eggshell.

Think and Discuss
1. Describe the appearance of each eggshell after three days.
2. Compare the effects of the sports drink and soft drink. Was there any difference?
3. What did you learn from this experiment about the effects of water, sports drinks, and soft drinks on teeth?

Dental Checkups   Having regular dental checkups, about twice a year, can identify problems before they become painful or hard to treat. Because of checkups and other preventive care, young people today generally have fewer cavities than their parents did at the same age. An example of preventive care is the addition of fluoride to toothpastes and drinking water. Fluoride binds with enamel, making it stronger and more resistant to decay.

Some people also visit their dentist to discuss teeth whitening. Some beverages, foods, and medicines can stain teeth. The stains sometimes can be removed at the dentist's office or with products that can be used at home. Talk to your dentist before buying any teeth-whitening products.

Treating Tooth Decay   When plaque is not removed often enough or well enough, the bacteria in your mouth grow and multiply. The acid that they produce eats away at enamel. When the enamel is broken down, a tiny hole, or cavity, forms.

To repair a cavity, a dentist uses a drill to remove the decay and bacteria and then fills the hole. The type of filling used depends on the area being filled. If not treated, the decay can spread through all the layers of the tooth and eventually into the root. If this happens, the dentist must either remove the tooth or perform root canal therapy. During root canal therapy, the dentist removes the infected pulp and replaces it with a rubber-like material.

Personal Care   **345**

Hands-On *Activity*

Sports Drinks, Soft Drinks, and Your Health

White eggshells will work best for this activity. Allow students with special needs to work with a group or partner to complete the activity.

Think and Discuss Answers
1. *Sample answer:* The eggshell in the soft drink became stained. The eggshell in the water did not change in appearance. The eggshell in the sports drink started to break apart.
2. Students may or may not be able to detect a difference in the eggshells. Some studies have shown that the acids in sports drinks are more harmful to teeth than those in soft drinks.
3. *Sample answer:* Of the three drinks tested, water would have the least effect on teeth.

L3 Addressing Misconceptions

Whitening Products Students may have the misconception that whitening products can replace regular dental hygiene. Explain that tooth whiteners cannot replace regular brushing and flossing and cannot correct tooth decay. Teens may have questions about the use or safety of products that whiten teeth. Explain that most dentists recommend waiting until all of the adult teeth are fully grown in before proceeding with whitening. Otherwise, teeth may be mismatched or unevenly bleached. Teeth may continue to move above the gum line well into the teen years.

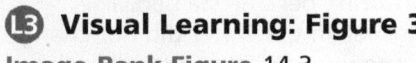

L3 Class Discussion

After students examine Figure 3 and read the text ask: **How does the body's reaction to tartar contribute to the development of gum disease?** *(When the gums swell and pull away from the teeth, pockets form. Food and plaque fill the pockets, further irritating the gums.)*

L3 Visual Learning: Figure 3

Image Bank Figure 14-3

3. Assess

Evaluate

These assignments can help you assess students' mastery of the section content.

Section 1 Review

Answers appear below.

Teaching Resources
• Practice 14-1
• Section 14-1 Quiz

L2 Reteach

Have students review each diagram and illustration in the section. For each diagram or illustration, ask a volunteer to give a verbal summary of the information presented.

L4 Enrich

Teaching Resources
• Enrich 14-1

Health at Home

Improving Dental Care Ask students to review the suggestions in the section for improving dental health. Allow students to keep their checklists confidential.

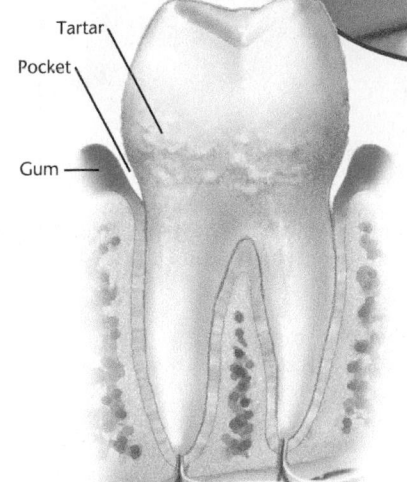

FIGURE 3 During cleanings, dental hygienists scrape away plaque and tartar buildup. If plaque and tartar are not removed, the gums may pull away from the teeth and form pockets.

Tartar

Pocket

Gum

Treating Gum Disease Plaque can also damage the gums. If plaque is not removed within 48 hours, it begins to harden into a material called **tartar,** which irritates the gums. The gum irritation caused by plaque and tartar eventually can lead to **periodontal disease,** or gum disease. During the first stage of periodontal disease, called gingivitis (jin juh VYT is), the gums become red and swollen and bleed easily.

In later stages of periodontal disease, the buildup of plaque and tartar causes the gums to pull away from the teeth and form pockets, as shown in Figure 3. Plaque, tartar, and food collect in the pockets, and the gums become inflamed and infected. Without treatment, the structures that hold teeth in place may be destroyed. The teeth may become loose and eventually fall out.

Periodontal disease can be treated surgically by dentists who specialize in gum disease. However, the need for these painful and expensive procedures can be prevented with good oral care including brushing, flossing, and regular visits to the dentist.

Section 1 Review

Key Ideas and Vocabulary

1. What are the functions of your teeth and gums?
2. What is **pulp**?
3. Describe two structural problems in the mouth and how they can be corrected.
4. What are three ways that you can prevent problems with your teeth and gums?

Critical Thinking

5. **Relating Cause and Effect** People with periodontal disease sometimes stop brushing their teeth because their gums hurt. What effect do you think this will have on their oral health? Explain.

Health at Home

Improving Dental Care Create a checklist of things you can do to improve your dental care. Your checklist can include brushing more often, flossing every day, and replacing your toothbrush every four months. Post your checklist on your bathroom mirror or somewhere else where you will see it.

6. **Predicting** Why do you think malocclusions are typically corrected during the teen years?
7. **Evaluating** Why do you think that some people ignore simple steps, such as brushing and flossing, that can help keep their teeth and gums healthy?

346 *Chapter 14*

🔊 **GO ONLINE** PearsonSuccessNet.com | Audio Summary Section 14.1

Section 1 Review

1. Teeth: chew food and speak clearly. Gums: hold the teeth in place.
2. soft tissue in teeth that contains nerves and blood vessels
3. Malocclusion is an improper bite; can be corrected with braces. Impacted wisdom teeth cannot grow properly; they must be removed.

4. *Sample answer:* eat a healthy diet, brush your teeth at least twice a day, floss once a day
5. *Sample answer:* Their oral health will become even worse as more plaque and tartar irritate the gums. Eventually, teeth may become loose and fall out.

6. *Sample answer:* because that is when all of the adult teeth are in place
7. *Sample answer:* Because the damage occurs over time, they may not realize how damaged their teeth and gums are becoming.

Your Skin, Hair, and Nails

Section 2
Your Skin, Hair, and Nails

Warm-Up

Myth Spending time in the sun can clear up acne.

Fact Tanned skin may temporarily camouflage the redness of acne, but it does not treat the condition. Also, many acne medications make skin more sensitive to the sun.

WRITING Identify another skin-care misconception that teens may hold. Why do you think they have that misconception?

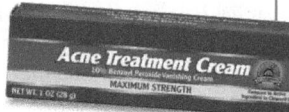

Objectives
▶ **Identify** the functions of the skin.
▶ **Describe** behaviors that can keep your skin healthy.
▶ **Explain** the functions of your hair and nails and how to care for them.

Vocabulary
- epidermis
- keratin
- melanin
- dermis
- pore
- follicle
- sebaceous gland
- melanoma
- acne
- dermatologist
- eczema

Your Skin

You may think that your skin is just a covering that separates the inside of your body from the outside environment. However, your skin is actually your body's largest organ and it plays several major roles in keeping you healthy. **The skin covers and protects the body from injury, infection, and water loss. The skin also helps to regulate body temperature and gathers information from the environment.**

▶ **Protection** The skin shields and protects the organs and tissues beneath it. The skin also keeps harmful substances and microorganisms out of the body. In addition, it keeps important fluids, such as water, in the body.

▶ **Temperature Regulation** When you are warm, sweat glands in the skin produce perspiration, which cools your body as it evaporates. In addition, blood vessels in your skin widen allowing more heat to be given off at the skin's surface. When you are cold, the blood vessels narrow, keeping more heat within your body.

▶ **Information Gathering** Nerves in the skin provide information to your central nervous system about outside factors such as pressure, pain, and temperature.

What information has your skin provided to your nervous system today?

Section 2
Your Skin, Hair, and Nails

Objectives
Before class begins, write the objectives on the board. Have students copy the objectives into their notebooks at the start of class.

1. Focus

Warm-Up Myth/Fact

After students have completed their writing, ask volunteers to share their responses with the class. Keep a list of common misconceptions on the board. Have students look for information about these misconceptions as they read the section.

Presentation 14-2

2. Teach

L3 **EL** **Reading/Note Taking** 14-2
L2 **Adapted Reading/Note Taking** 14-2

Your Skin

L2 **Cooperative Learning**

Ask students to work in small groups to create a rhyme, rap, or song that identifies and describes the three functions of skin. Have each group share its results with the class.

Connect to Your Life *Sample answer:* My skin informed my nervous system that my shower this morning was too hot.

L1 Special Needs

Some students may need to be coached on how personal care habits can affect the way others perceive them. Make sure students understand that in some situations they will be judged by the care they take of their skin, hair, and nails. Cleanliness and a neat appearance can be a major factor in how one is perceived during a job interview. These factors can also influence how someone is evaluated as an employee. After the lesson, ask students to create a simple checklist to summarize important hygiene and grooming skills.

L2 Visual Learning: Figure 4

Image Bank Figure 14-4

Have students use the figure to identify the components of each layer of skin. **Ask: In what layer of skin are blood vessels found?** *(dermis)* **Why do you think skin becomes flushed when people are warm?** *(More blood is at the surface of the skin.)*

Caption Answer The epidermis is thinner than the dermis.

EL Building Vocabulary

Have students copy these three words: *pore*, *pour*, and *poor*. Talk about how the words sound alike but have different spellings and different meanings. Have students look up the words in a dictionary, write the meaning of each, and then write sentences using the words in context. As an extension, ask students to find other homonyms, related to the vocabulary in this lesson, such as *cell* and *sell*, *hair* and *hare*, and *pain* and *pane*.

L2 Teacher Demo

Remind students that one function of skin is to keep water inside the body. To model this, dampen two identical sponges. Wrap one sponge tightly in plastic wrap. Place both sponges on a counter or desk. The next day, ask students to compare the amount of water in each sponge. Explain that the plastic wrap kept water in the sponge in the same way the skin keeps water in the body.

The Epidermis Your skin consists of two major layers. The outermost layer is the **epidermis** (ep uh DUR mis). The part of the epidermis that comes into contact with the environment is made up of dead cells. These dead cells contain a protein called **keratin** that makes the skin tough and waterproof. You shed dead cells when you brush against objects, bathe, or rub your skin.

Underneath the dead cells are living cells that continually produce new cells. The new cells push older cells toward the skin's surface. Eventually the older cells die and become part of the dead surface layer.

Cells deep in the epidermis produce the protein **melanin,** a dark pigment that gives skin some of its color. The more melanin produced by your skin, the darker it is. Sunlight can stimulate melanin production, which causes the skin to tan.

The Dermis The **dermis** (DUR mis) is the tough, elastic layer of skin that lies below the epidermis. In most areas of your body, the dermis is much thicker than the epidermis. Notice in Figure 4 that the dermis contains the nerves that send information to the central nervous system. The dermis also contains blood vessels that bring nutrients to the skin and carry wastes away.

Sweat glands in the dermis produce perspiration that helps keep your body cool. Sweat travels through a narrow channel, or duct, to the surface of the skin. There, it is excreted through a tiny opening called a **pore.** Strands of hair grow within the dermis in structures called **follicles.** Oil is secreted into follicles by **sebaceous glands.** The oil softens hair and skin and keeps both from becoming too dry and brittle.

FIGURE 4 The skin is made of two main layers. The top layer is called the epidermis. The bottom layer is called the dermis.
Interpreting Diagrams Which layer of skin is thinner?

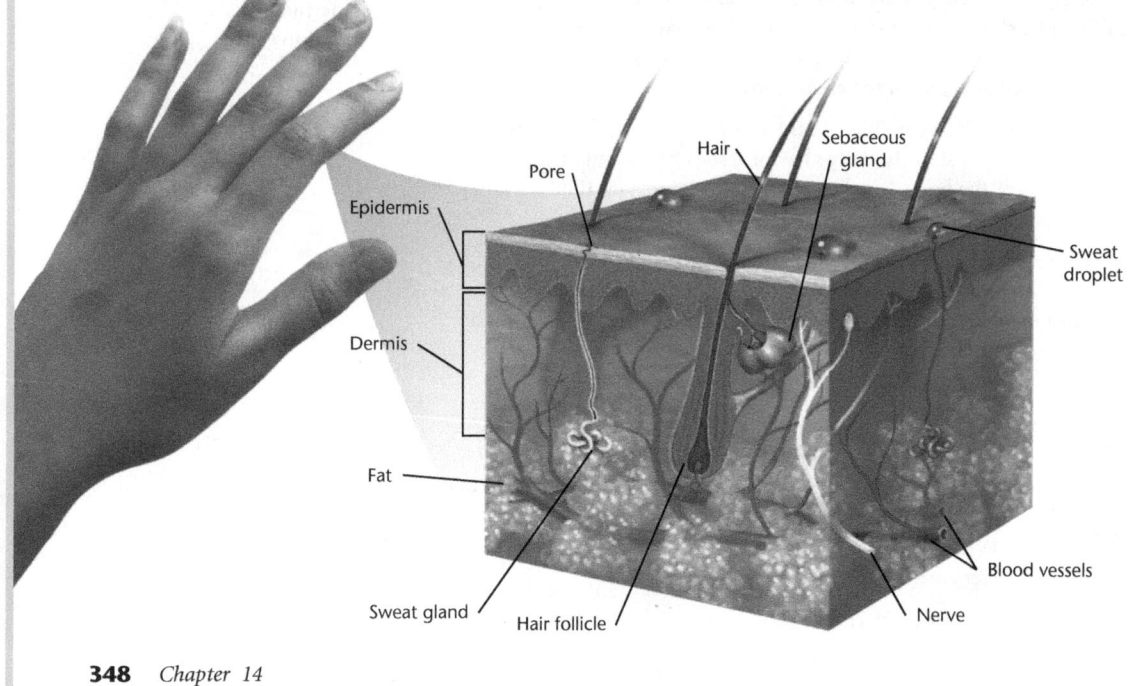

348 *Chapter 14*

MATH and Health

L3 Proportions

A sunscreen's SPF is the measurement of the amount of time the product protects against sunburn from UVB radiation. Broad-spectrum sunscreens offer some UVA protection, however SPF refers only to UVB protection. No sunscreen offers complete protection from UVB rays. When used correctly, SPF 15 blocks about 93 percent of the UVB rays and SPF 30 blocks about 97 percent. In general, a person wearing SPF 15 can be in the sun without burning 15 times longer than if he or she did not wear sunscreen. After sharing this information have students calculate this problem: If David does not wear sunscreen, he usually burns within 15 minutes. How long will a SPF 15 sunscreen protect his skin from sunburn? *(Answer = 3 hours, 45 minutes. However, remind students that this is just a guideline. Most experts recommend that sunscreen be reapplied no less than every two hours.)*

FIGURE 5 You can enjoy the outdoors and still protect your skin from the sun.

Caring for Your Skin

Most of the time, the skin requires only basic care such as regular washing with mild soap. Eating a balanced, healthy diet; drinking plenty of water; and sleeping enough will also keep your skin healthy. **The most important things you can do for your skin, however, are to avoid damage from the sun and tanning lamps and to monitor moles.** Treating acne and other skin problems can also help you feel and look your best.

Preventing Skin Damage Overexposure to ultraviolet (UV) radiation emitted from the sun and tanning lamps causes skin to become leathery, wrinkled, and discolored. It can also lead to skin cancer, including a sometimes deadly form called **melanoma.** Melanoma is the least common form of skin cancer. Yet it causes more deaths each year than other forms of skin cancer.

When you are outside, it is important to wear sunscreen that blocks UVA and UVB rays—two types of ultraviolet radiation that reach Earth. Sunscreens are numbered with a sun protection factor (SPF). The higher the SPF, the more protection a sunscreen provides. Sunscreen should be reapplied frequently, especially if you have been swimming or sweating. See Figure 5 for other ways to protect your skin from the sun.

Monitoring Moles The first sign of melanoma is usually an irregularly shaped mole, or brown spot, that increases in size. The mole may become blue-black or have blackish spots. Without early treatment, melanoma will spread to other organs. If you notice any change in a wart, birthmark, or mole—or any skin growth that appears abnormal—you should consult a doctor.

 **Connect to Your Life** How do you protect your skin from ultraviolet radiation damage?

FIGURE 6 The ABCD rule is a guide for detecting melanoma. Note the irregularities of the mole shown below.

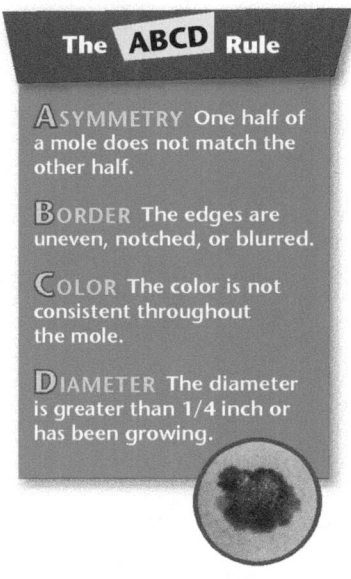

The ABCD Rule

ASYMMETRY One half of a mole does not match the other half.

BORDER The edges are uneven, notched, or blurred.

COLOR The color is not consistent throughout the mole.

DIAMETER The diameter is greater than 1/4 inch or has been growing.

L3 Addressing Misconceptions

Sun Damage to the Skin Students with dark skin may assume that they do not have to protect their skin from the sun. Make sure students understand that any tan is a sign of damage to the skin—even if the tan is not the result of sunburn. Also, although skin cancer may be more common in people with light skin, it can be more deadly in people with dark skin.

Caring for Your Skin

L3 Building Health Skills

Advocacy Have students read the tips for preventing damage to skin. Then have students work in small groups to make a pamphlet that can be used to share this information with other teens. Encourage students to restate the tips using their own words and to include pictures and graphics to make the pamphlet visually interesting to teens. **WRITING**

L3 Addressing Misconceptions

Value of Sunscreen Many people assume that they are protecting their skin from the harmful effects of the sun by wearing sunscreen. However, this is not completely true. Sunscreen does not usually block the full spectrum of UVA and UVB rays. Therefore, sunscreen alone may not prevent skin cancer and other problems caused by overexposure to UV rays. People should follow as many tips in Figure 5 as possible.

L2 Visual Learning: Figure 6

Ask students to read the description of the ABCD rules for monitoring moles. Then ask students to work with a partner to develop a slogan that can help others remember to use these guidelines. Have each pair share its slogan with the class.

Connect to Your Life *Sample answer:* I use sunscreen and wear a hat to protect my skin from the sun.

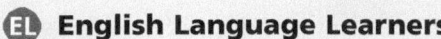

Differentiated Instruction

EL English Language Learners

Have students discuss the key words of the ABCD rule (asymmetry, border, color, and diameter) with a partner. Some or all of these terms may be unfamiliar to them. Have student pairs use a dictionary to find a definition for each term. Students should record a definition for each term in their own words. For some terms, students may want to include a drawing.

L4 **Active Learning**

Have students use library and Internet resources to learn more about treatments for acne. Students can research topical, over-the-counter treatments and prescription treatments. Students might also investigate laser treatments used to reduce acne. Have students combine their findings to create a bulletin board that gives information about various treatments for acne.

L3 **Cooperative Learning**

Invite a dermatologist to talk to the class about skin conditions they commonly see in teens and how they can be treated or prevented. Before the class visit, have students break into small groups. Each group should brainstorm at least two or three questions to ask the speaker. Encourage students to submit personal questions to you anonymously.

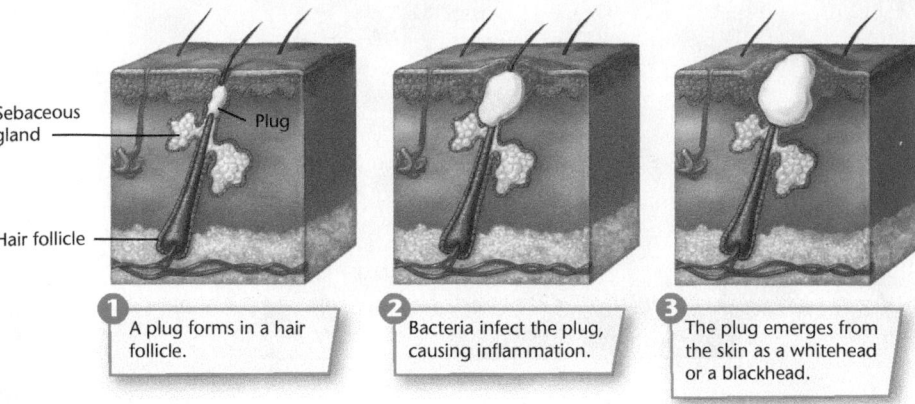

FIGURE 7 If a follicle becomes blocked, bacteria can infect it. Your body's reaction to the infection leads to a pimple. Keeping your face clean can help prevent pimples.

Sebaceous gland

Plug

Hair follicle

1 A plug forms in a hair follicle.

2 Bacteria infect the plug, causing inflammation.

3 The plug emerges from the skin as a whitehead or a blackhead.

Treating Acne   One common skin problem in teens is acne. **Acne** forms when excess oil and dead cells plug a hair follicle. Bacteria from the skin's surface multiply within the plug. The bacteria attract white blood cells, which cause the hair follicle to become inflamed and an acne lesion, or pimple, to form. Lesions that stay beneath the skin's surface are called whiteheads. Blackheads are lesions that open at the skin's surface.

Hormones, heredity, and stress are some factors that influence acne outbreaks. Greasy foods and chocolate do not cause acne. The best defense against acne is keeping your skin clean. If you have oily skin, wash with mild soap two or three times a day. More frequent washing may worsen acne because it will stimulate your oil glands to produce more oil.

Because your fingers and nails carry bacteria, do not scratch or squeeze acne. Products that contain benzoyl peroxide, a chemical that dries out pimples and kills bacteria, can help mild cases of acne. For a more severe case of acne, you should see a **dermatologist,** a doctor who specializes in treating skin problems.

Treating Eczema   Another skin disorder is **eczema** (EK suh muh), a condition in which an area of skin becomes red, swollen, hot, and itchy. Sometimes the skin blisters and oozes. Eczema is not contagious.

Substances that irritate the skin, including chemicals, soaps, or poison ivy, can cause eczema. Certain medicines and foods may also cause this skin irritation. Some people inherit a tendency to develop eczema. In most cases, eczema can be treated with a medication applied to the skin. To prevent eczema from recurring, a person should try to identify and avoid substances that irritate the skin.

350   *Chapter 14*

TEENS *Are Asking . . .*

Q: **Why does acne usually begin during the teen years?**

A: During puberty, the bodies of both girls and boys produce more androgens, a type of hormone. One effect of the hormones is the enlargement of sebaceous glands. The larger glands produce a greater amount of pore-clogging oil. These changes can lead to a mild or a severe case of acne. Heredity is not a factor in determining what type of acne you might have unless one of your parents had a very severe case of acne.

Treating Skin Infections Several types of microorganisms can infect the skin. Although the majority of these infections are not serious, they can be painful or embarrassing.

▶ **Boils** Boils are swollen, painful infections of hair follicles caused by bacteria. They start as red, tender lumps that fill with pus. Eventually they rupture and drain. Boils can occur anywhere on the body, but are most common on the face, neck, armpits, and thighs. If a boil does not heal after two weeks or is accompanied by a fever, you should see a doctor.

▶ **Cold Sores** Cold sores are clusters of watery blisters caused by a virus. These sores usually occur around the outside of the mouth and last about a week. To prevent the virus from spreading to other parts of the body, wash your hands after touching the affected area.

▶ **Warts** Warts are hardened growths on the skin that are also caused by a virus. Over-the-counter medication is available to treat warts. See a doctor if a wart persists or spreads after treatment.

▶ **Ringworm** Skin infections caused by fungi usually occur in warm, moist areas of the skin. The ringworm fungus, which is highly contagious, produces red, scaly, ring-shaped patches on the skin. Ringworm is treated with prescription medication.

▶ **Athlete's Foot** Another common fungal infection is athlete's foot. It causes burning, itching, cracking, and peeling of the skin on the feet and between the toes. Over-the-counter medication is available for athlete's foot. However, for a severe infection that does not respond to over-the-counter medication, you should see a doctor. Figure 8 lists some tips for preventing athlete's foot.

 **Connect to Your Life** Identify a problem that you have had with your skin. How did you care for it?

 **GO ONLINE**
PearsonSuccessNet.com
For: More on acne

Fungus that causes athlete's foot ▶

FIGURE 8 The fungus that causes athlete's foot thrives in the damp and warm environment of a shoe.

To Prevent Athlete's Foot
- Wear flip-flops or shower shoes in locker rooms and shared showers.
- Wash your feet more than once a day.
- Dry your feet thoroughly, especially between the toes.
- Powder your feet.
- If your feet perspire, change your socks during the day.

351

L3 **Online Activity**  **GO ONLINE**

Visit Pearson SuccessNet to access an online activity about acne. Have students complete the Web activity.

L2 **Active Learning**

Have students work in small groups to create a chart or other graphic organizer to record information about the skin infections described on the page. Ask students to fill in their chart or organizer with the name of each type of infection, symptoms, cause, and tips for prevention.

L2 **Class Discussion**

Have students read the tips for preventing athlete's foot. Ask: **Why is keeping your feet dry an important part of preventing athlete's foot?** *(The fungus that causes athlete's foot needs a moist environment to survive. By keeping the feet dry, you do not provide an environment in which the fungus can grow.)* **Is athlete's foot an accurate name for this infection? Why or why not?** *(Sample answer: No, this is not an accurate name; anyone can contract athlete's foot—it does not exclusively infect athletes.)*

 Connect to Your Life Allow students to answer this question in their private journals.

Differentiated Instruction

L1 **Special Needs**

Students should understand that problems with the skin should not be ignored. Remind them that infections that cause openings in the skin can make a person susceptible to worse infections. For each of the examples on this page, have students write or explain in their own words what they or a family member should do if they have the infection.

Your Hair

L2 **Visual Learning: Figure 9**

Ask your students if they can think of more hair-care tips to add to the list.

L3 **Building Media Literacy**

Entire aisles of stores are stocked with different types of shampoos, conditioners, and styling products. Help your students develop a survey to find out what influences the hair-care purchases of their friends. Some possible questions are "Do you choose your hair-care products?" "Do you have favorite products?" "What factors influence your purchases?" As part of the survey, have students show their friends hair-care product ads and record their reactions. Groups should present their findings to the class.

Connect to Your Life Allow students to answer this question in their private journals.

Your Nails

L1 **Class Discussion**

Call on students to read each tip for nail care in Figure 10. Then ask: **Why is it important to have healthy, strong nails?** *(Nails protect the tips of fingers and toes from damage.)* **Why is it important to have clean nails?** *(Microorganisms can live under nails and spread to other people or other areas of the body.)* **How could nail biting affect one's health?** *(Nail biting could lead to breaks in the skin surrounding nails. Also, nail biting could lead to the transfer of microorganisms from the nails to the mouth.)*

FIGURE 9 Healthy hair requires only basic care.

Hair Care Tips
- Wash your hair every two days.
- Have your hair trimmed regularly.
- When detangling your hair, start at the ends.
- Do not brush wet hair.
- Allow hair to air dry whenever possible.
- Avoid overuse of styling products.

Your Hair

Almost every exposed surface of the body is covered with hair, except the palms of the hands and soles of the feet. **Hair protects the scalp from sunlight and provides insulation from the cold. Hairs in the nostrils and ears and your eyelashes prevent debris from entering the body.**

Caring for Your Hair Keeping your hair clean and well-groomed enhances your appearance. Frequent brushing of your hair will remove excess dirt and make your hair shine. Shampooing removes dirt and oil buildup from sebaceous gland secretions. However, your hair may become dry and brittle if you wash it too frequently or use a shampoo made with harsh chemicals. In addition, dyeing or highlighting your hair may also cause dryness and brittleness.

Hair Problems Head lice are small insects that live on the scalp and lay their eggs on hair. Head-lice infection is not a sign of poor hygiene. Anyone who comes in contact with lice can be infected. The best way to prevent infections is to avoid sharing combs, brushes, or hats. Several shampoos are available to kill lice.

Another common hair problem is dandruff. Dandruff occurs when the epidermal cells of the scalp are shed at a faster than normal rate. Some factors that may contribute to dandruff are fungal infections, overactive oil glands, stress, and heredity. Regular hairwashing with dandruff shampoo should help control this problem.

 **Connect to Your Life** How does the appearance of your hair affect your mood? Why do you think this is so?

 **WRITING** **and Health**

L3 **Firsthand Account**

Ask students to write about a time when they had a negative experience with their hair. Examples could be a style that did not look good on them, a poor cut from a stylist, or an experiment with hair color that didn't work out as hoped. In their passages they should explain what the expected outcome of their experience was and why they were disappointed. How did they handle the disappointment? How did the experience influence how they will make future decisions about their hair?

Your Nails

Nails grow from an area of rapidly dividing cells near the tips of the fingers and toes. **The tough, platelike nails cover and protect the tips of your fingers and toes, which come in frequent contact with objects in your environment.** During cell division, the cells fill with keratin and become nails.

Caring for Your Nails   Keeping your nails clean will help prevent the spread of infectious microorganisms to other parts of your body and to other people. Clip and file your nails so that their edges are smooth. Jagged edges may dig into your skin and cause infections. Avoid biting your nails. Nail biting can lead to breaks in your skin that allow microorganisms to enter.

Nail Problems   An ingrown toenail results when the sides of a toenail grow into the skin. If not treated properly, ingrown nails can become infected. To prevent ingrown toenails, clip your toenails straight across.

Fungal infections of the nails are common in people who often have wet hands or feet. Infected nails appear thick and discolored with white markings. If you suspect that you have a fungal infection, see a doctor.

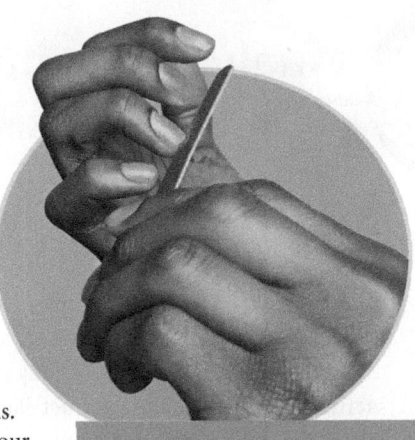

Nail Care Tips
- Keep your nails clean and dry.
- Do not rip hangnails, cut them with a nail clipper.
- Apply lotion daily to prevent nails from cracking.
- Seek treatment for infections.
- Use nail polish remover as infrequently as possible.
- If you go to a salon, ask how they prevent the spread of infections.

FIGURE 10   Proper nail care, which includes filing, clipping, and cleaning helps to prevent minor cuts and the spread of disease.

Section 2 Review

Key Ideas and Vocabulary

1. What are the three major functions of the skin?
2. What is a **sebaceous gland?** What is its function?
3. Besides basic care, identify four other ways to keep your skin healthy.
4. What is thought to be the cause of most cases of **melanoma?**
5. What are the functions of your hair and nails?

Critical Thinking

6. **Relating Cause and Effect** Victims of serious burns often suffer from infection and loss of body fluids. Explain why this happens.

Health at School

Sun Safety Poster Create a poster that alerts teens to the skin damage caused by ultraviolet radiation. Use a slogan and visuals to make your point in a compelling manner. With permission, hang the poster at school.

7. **Evaluating** Although most people know the dangers of tanning, some people still consider a tan to be a sign of good health. Why do you think this is the case?
8. **Making Judgments** You are hiring people as servers in a restaurant. A person that you interview has dirty nails. How might this fact affect your decision to hire the person?

 GO ONLINE PearsonSuccessNet.com   Audio Summary Section 14.2

Personal Care **353**

3. Assess

Evaluate

These assignments can help you assess students' mastery of the section content.

Section 2 Review

Answers appear below.

Teaching Resources
- Practice 14-2
- Section 14-2 Quiz

L2 **Reteach**

Make a three-column table on the board. Label the columns Skin Care, Hair Care, and Nail Care. Call on students to come forward and add a suggestion or tip to one of the columns.

L4 **Enrich**

Teaching Resources
- Enrich 14-2

Health at School

Sun Safety Poster Remind students that a slogan is a short, memorable summary of information. Have students share their completed posters with the class. Arrange for students to hang their completed posters in the hallways, cafeteria, or other high-traffic areas.

Section 2 Review

1. protection, temperature regulation, and information gathering
2. A sebaceous gland is a gland in the skin that secretes oil into follicles.
3. *Sample answer:* use sunscreen, monitor moles, treat acne, treat infections
4. overexposure to ultraviolet radiation
5. Hair protects the scalp, provides insulation from the cold, and prevents debris from entering the eyes, ears, and nose. The nails protect the tips of the fingers and toes.
6. *Sample answer:* Skin that is seriously damaged cannot protect the body from microorganisms or prevent fluid loss.
7. *Sample answer:* In magazines and on television, healthy people often are shown with tans, leading to the misconception that a tan is healthy.
8. *Sample answer:* I would not want to hire a person with dirty nails to work in a restaurant.

Personal Care **353**

Recognizing Misleading Claims

Objective

Apply strategies for recognizing misleading claims.

Teaching Strategies

- Ask students to examine the ad shown on this page. Have volunteers identify aspects of the ad that they find hard to believe. Challenge students to explain why teens are at particular risk of being misled by advertisements for health products. *(an overwhelming desire to solve problems such as acne, an emphasis on the importance of physical appearance, low self-esteem, poor body image, and inexperience purchasing items for themselves)*

- Show students an advertisement for a health product from a newspaper or magazine. Have students examine the ad. Analyze the ad with your students.

- Ask students to write an entry in their private journals that identifies the factors that influence which health products teens purchase. Challenge students to identify the influences that are most likely to lead to good purchasing decisions.

Analyzing Influences

Recognizing Misleading Claims

Each year millions of people spend billions of dollars on fraudulent health products, such as weight-loss aids, supplements, and "miracle" skin products. Many of these consumers fall victim to the persuasive product claims found in advertisements. In some situations, the loss is just monetary. But sometimes, people put their health at risk too. For example, people might not seek needed treatment from a healthcare professional if they think they have found their own "cure." These guidelines can help you avoid being a victim of misleading product claims.

Fight acne with Acne B-Gone

"If you use Acne B-Gone, you will have perfect, blemish-free skin!"

Have clear, glowing beautiful skin!

Guaranteed—or your money back!

Acne B-Gone has a special, secret ingredient that prevents pimples from forming. Scientists have proven that Acne B-Gone works better than any other product.

354 *Chapter 14*

🚩 **Sensitive Issues**

- Students with acne may be embarrassed by the discussion of acne products. During class discussions, remind students that acne is a normal part of adolescence.

- Some students may have purchased ineffective health products in the hopes of clearing up acne or improving appearance in another way. Do not give the impression that those who are misled by advertisements are uneducated or gullible. Instead, point out that most deceptive advertisements are cleverly worded.

① Examine the product's claims for misleading information.

Ask yourself these questions.

▶ **Do any of the claims contradict common knowledge?** For example, a diet supplement that promises weight loss without the need to change eating and exercise habits should not be taken seriously.

▶ **What wording is used in the claim?** Be wary of words and phrases such as miracle, secret ingredient, ancient remedy, or scientific breakthrough.

▶ **Is the claim based on a testimonial?** An endorsement from a famous person or a "happy customer" may convince people that a product works.

▶ **Can scientific studies be verified?** A claim may state that the product has proven effective in scientific studies. However, the claim will probably offer little information about the actual studies.

▶ **Does the ad use "hurry up" techniques?** Some ads may claim that there are only limited quantities available to push you into making a quick decision.

▶ **Does the ad promise you a money-back guarantee?** You should not count on these guarantees. It is not always easy or possible to get your money back.

② Try to check any claims made about the product.

▶ Before purchasing a product, read the packaging information, including the fine print. Does any of the information indicate the product is actually less effective or suitable than the claims imply?

▶ If you are unsure about the language used on the packaging, ask a healthcare professional for advice.

③ Request more information.

You can request more information from the product's manufacturer about any claims that seem suspicious. Or, you could visit the web site of the Federal Trade Commission to search for any customer complaints made about the particular manufacturer.

Practice the Skill

1. Analyze the ad for Acne-B-Gone.
   a. Describe the claims made by the ad.
   b. Do any of the claims make you suspicious? Why or why not?

2. Analyze three other magazine or television advertisements for personal-care products such as hairstyling products or deodorants.
   a. Evaluate whether the ads include misleading or suspicious claims.
   b. Look for one of the products in a local store. Does any of the packaging information indicate that the product is less effective than the ad implied?

3. Find an ad that makes claims about a scientific study that supports the effectiveness of the product.
   a. List some questions you would like to have answered about the study to believe its claims.
   b. How could you find this information?

Chapter 14 **355**

Practice the Skill

1. **a.** *Sample answer:* The ad for Acne-B-Gone claims that its use will result in blemish-free skin and that scientists have proven it works better than any other product.

   b. *Sample answer:* The claim that use of this product will result in perfect skin makes me suspicious, because this seems like an impossible promise to make.

2. **a.** Answers will vary, depending on the advertisements used for the activity. Check that students accurately identified misleading claims.

   b. Answers will vary. Students may note that the detailed information on the packaging indicates the product is less effective than implied in the advertisement.

3. **a.** *Sample answer:* I would like to know how many participants were included in the study. I would also like to know if the study included a control group.

   b. *Sample answer:* I could obtain this information by contacting the manufacturer.

Health at Home

Analyzing Advertisement Appeal

Have students discuss health-product advertisements with an adult family member. Have students ask the family member to identify the factors that influence his or her health-product purchases. Ask students to write a paragraph comparing the influences on adult's purchasing decisions to the influences on their own purchasing decisions. **WRITING**

Personal Care **355**

Objectives
Before class begins, write the objectives on the board. Have students copy the objectives into their notebooks at the start of class.

1. Focus

Warm-Up Advice Line

After students finish writing, have volunteers share their responses with the class. Use students' responses to spark a class discussion on the importance of advocating for your own health.

Presentation 14-3

Connect to Your Life *Sample answer:* My eyes are brown. The iris is the part of the eye that contains this color.

Section 3   Your Eyes and Ears

Objectives
▶ **Explain** how your eyes allow you to see.
▶ **Identify** two ways to keep your eyes healthy.
▶ **Explain** how your ears allow you to hear and maintain your balance.
▶ **Identify** ways to keep your ears healthy.

Vocabulary
• cornea
• pupil
• iris
• lens
• retina
• optometrist
• eardrum
• cochlea
• semicircular canals
• audiologist

Warm-Up

Dear Advice Line,

One of my friends likes to play loud music when I am at his house. Sometimes when I leave, my ears are ringing and I have trouble hearing for several hours. I've asked him to lower the music, but he just laughs at me. I don't want to stop hanging out with him. What should I do?

WRITING Write a response to this teen to help solve the problem.

Your Eyes

Much of the information you gather about your environment reaches your brain through your eyes. Because of your eyes, you can enjoy the beauty of colorful sunsets. Your eyes warn you when a car is approaching, and help you recognize the faces of friends. **The eyes are complex organs that respond to light by sending impulses. Your brain then interprets the impulses as images.**

How Light Enters Your Eye   When rays of light strike the eye, they pass through the structures shown in Figure 11. First the light strikes the **cornea** (KAWR nee uh), the clear tissue that covers the front of the eye. The light then passes through a chamber filled with a liquid that nourishes the eye. The light then reaches the **pupil,** the opening through which light enters the eye.

The size of the pupils adjusts based on the amount of light entering the eye. In bright light, the pupil becomes smaller. In dim light, the pupil becomes larger. The **iris** is a circular structure that surrounds the pupil and regulates its size. The iris also contains pigments that give your eyes their color.

 *Connect to Your Life* **What color are your eyes? What part of your eyes contain this color?**

For Your INFORMATION!

Teens and Eye Health

Many teens who wear glasses or contact lenses express an interest in laser eye surgery. There is no approved laser eye surgery for people under the age of 18. Some patients have to wait until they are 30 years old for their eyes to be ready for such surgery.

Some teens may like to experiment with decorative lenses. These lenses, which are designed to alter the appearance of the eye, are often distributed directly to consumers. The Food and Drug Administration has warned consumers about the dangers associated with contact lenses that are not fitted by an eye care professional. Use of decorative contact lenses without a prescription can lead to infection, scarring, and permanent vision impairment.

How Light Is Focused   Light that passes through the pupil strikes the lens. The **lens** is a flexible structure that focuses light. Muscles attached to the lens adjust its shape, producing an image that is in focus. The lens of your eye functions something like the lens of a camera, which focuses light on photographic film. Because of the way in which the lens of the eye bends the light rays, the image it produces is upside down and reversed.

How You See an Image   After passing through the lens, focused light rays pass through a clear, jellylike fluid. Then the light rays strike the **retina,** a layer of cells that lines the back of the eye.

The retina contains about 130 million cells called rods and cones that respond to light. Rods work best in dim light and allow you to see black, white, and shades of gray. Cones work best in bright light and allow you to see colors. One type of cone cell responds to red light, another to blue, and a third to green. This difference between rods and cones explains why you see colors best in bright light, but only gray images in dim light.

When light strikes the rods and cones, nerve impulses travel through the optic nerves to the brain. One optic nerve carries impulses from the left eye and the other from the right eye. In the cerebrum, the brain turns the flipped image right-side up. The brain also combines the information from each eye to produce a single image.

The Eye

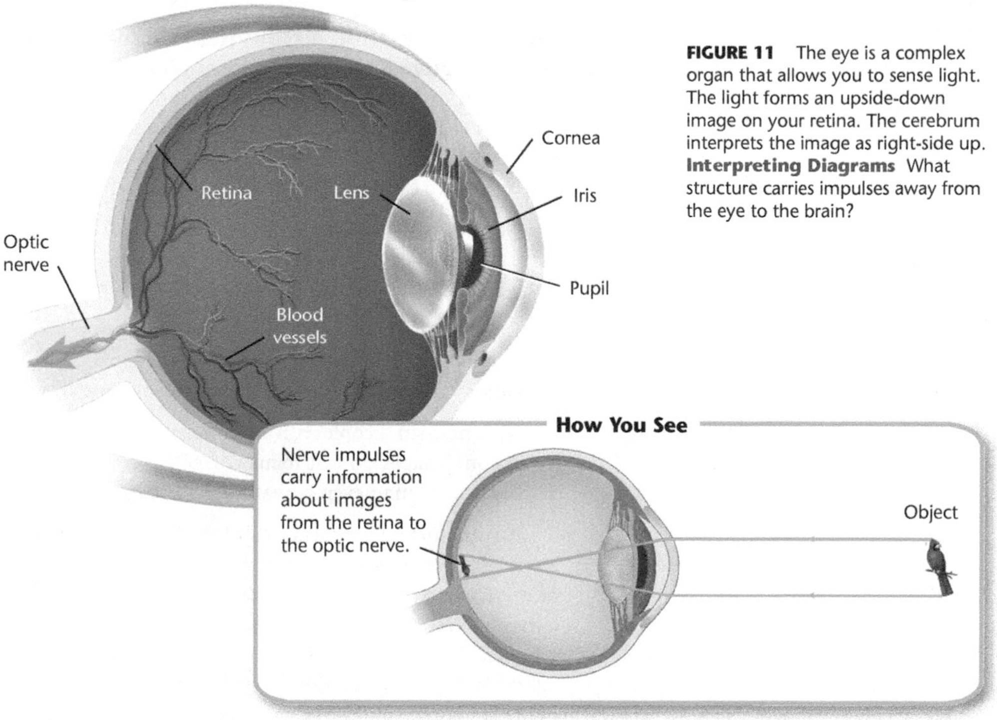

FIGURE 11   The eye is a complex organ that allows you to sense light. The light forms an upside-down image on your retina. The cerebrum interprets the image as right-side up. **Interpreting Diagrams** What structure carries impulses away from the eye to the brain?

Retina
Lens
Cornea
Iris
Optic nerve
Pupil
Blood vessels

How You See

Nerve impulses carry information about images from the retina to the optic nerve.

Object

357

2. Teach

(L3) (EL) Reading/Note Taking 14-3

(L2) Adapted Reading/Note Taking 14-3

Your Eyes

(L2) Active Learning

Turn off the lights. Ask students to compare their vision immediately after the lights are turned off to their vision after several seconds of darkness. Ask a volunteer to explain how his or her eyes "adjusted" to the darkness.

(L2) Visual Learning: Figure 11

Image Bank Figure 14-11

Have students examine the figure of the eye. Call on students to explain the function of each labeled structure. Ask: **Why do you think that rods and cones are not included in this diagram?** *(They are cells and cannot be seen in a diagram of this size.)*

Caption Answer The optic nerve carries impulses from the eye to the brain.

(L3) Teacher Demo

Explain to students that, just as they have a dominant hand, they also have a dominant eye. To demonstrate this, have each student hold a forefinger straight up at arm's length. Ask students to look at their forefinger with both eyes open and note the position of their forefinger relative to the position of a background object. Ask students to shut one eye at a time and note the position of their forefinger relative to the background in each case. The eye that produces an image most similar to the image produced by both eyes together is the dominant eye.

Differentiated Instruction

(EL) English Language Learners

Make a diagram of an eye on the board. Have students point out and label each part of the eye. Ask students to pronounce each term aloud as they label the structures of the eye. After students have labeled each structure, ask them to use a simple phrase to describe the function of each structure. Students can work with a partner to review this information as they prepare for the chapter review.

Caring for Your Eyes

L3 Building Health Skills

Accessing Information Have students use the Internet, a phone directory, or other resources to find information about free or low-cost vision screenings that are available in the school and community. The school nurse may be an excellent source of information for students. Also have students investigate services available through the local health department. Have students organize their information in the form of a list of resources and contact information.

L2 Visual Learning: Figure 12

Have students examine the figure that shows the causes of common vision problems. Ask: **What do these vision problems have in common?** (Sample answer: All cause a problem with the way the image forms on the retina. All can be corrected with glasses or contact lenses.) **If an individual needs glasses only for reading, what type of vision problem does he or she probably have?** (He or she is probably farsighted.)

L3 Class Discussion

Ask students to read the eye care tips in Figure 13. Ask: **What do the three foods listed in the fifth bullet point have in common?** (They are all a shade of red.) Explain to students that these foods are rich in carotenoids, pigments that your body can convert to vitamin A. Ask: **How does vitamin A help your vision?** (It helps rods to function properly.) Mention that dark green vegetables such as spinach and broccoli are also a good source of carotenoids.

FIGURE 12 Optometrists treat nearsightedness, farsightedness, and astigmatism with different types of lenses. The lenses make light focus on the ideal portion of the retina.

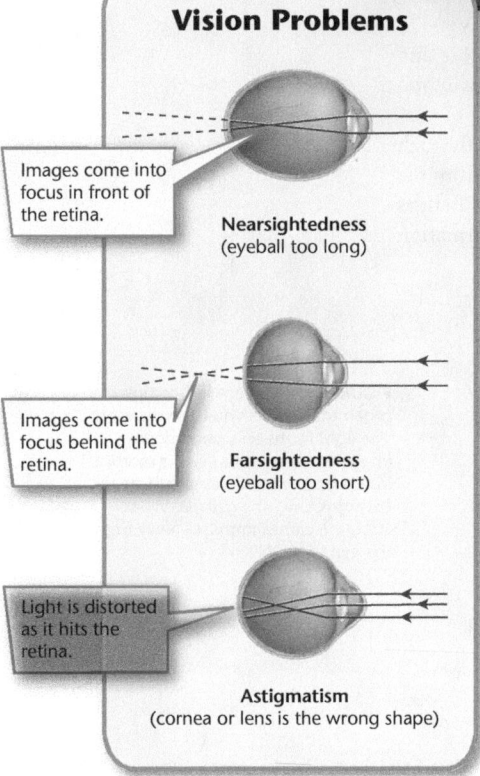

Vision Problems

Images come into focus in front of the retina.

Nearsightedness (eyeball too long)

Images come into focus behind the retina.

Farsightedness (eyeball too short)

Light is distorted as it hits the retina.

Astigmatism (cornea or lens is the wrong shape)

Caring for Your Eyes

There are some things you can do to help your eyes stay healthy throughout your lifetime. **It is important to protect your eyes from damage and to have regular eye exams.** To protect your eyes from damage wear protective goggles when you work with harmful substances or around machinery. Also, wear sunglasses that provide UV protection. Regular eye exams can help you prevent or identify vision problems, eye diseases, and eye infections.

Detecting Vision Problems During routine visits, an **optometrist,** a professional who provides eye and vision care, checks you for vision problems. Three common vision problems are nearsightedness, farsightedness, and astigmatism. All three problems usually can be corrected with eyeglasses or contact lenses.

▶ **Nearsightedness** People who are nearsighted can see nearby objects clearly, but not faraway objects. Nearsightedness is caused by an elongated eyeball.

▶ **Farsightedness** People who are farsighted can see faraway objects clearly, but nearby objects appear blurry. Farsightedness is caused by an eyeball that is too short.

▶ **Astigmatism** People with astigmatism have distorted vision. Images do not focus correctly on the retina because of an uneven curvature in the cornea or lens.

An optometrist may also check for colorblindness and night blindness. Colorblindness, the inability to detect one or more colors, occurs when a person is born with a deficiency in one or more sets of cones. This disorder is usually inherited. Night blindness is the inability to see well in dim light due to poorly functioning rods. This condition also can be inherited, or it can be caused by a lack of vitamin A.

358 *Chapter 14*

MATH and Health

L3 Converting Units

Ask students if they are familiar with the term *20/20 vision*. Explain that this is a way vision is assessed. A person with 20/50 vision, for example, can see at 20 feet what a person with normal eyesight can see at 50 feet. Have students use the following conversion factor to convert the distances 20 feet and 50 feet to meters.

1 foot = 0.3048 meters
(20 feet = 6.1 meters, 50 feet = 15.24 meters)
Explain that, in countries that use the metric system, the standard distance of 6 meters is used to measure vision. So, a person with perfect vision is said to have 6/6 vision. What would be the metric measurement for a person with 20/60 vision? *(6/18)*

Treating Eye Diseases   As a person ages, the eyes become susceptible to several diseases.

▶ **Glaucoma**   Age and certain diseases, such as diabetes and high blood pressure, may slow the drainage of liquid from the eye. The result is a buildup of pressure in the eye, a condition called glaucoma (glaw KOH muh). Glaucoma can damage the optic nerve and lead to sight problems. Glaucoma often develops so slowly that a person may have severe vision damage before it is detected. Regular eye exams can detect glaucoma before symptoms are noticed.

▶ **Cataracts**   The clouding of the eye's lens is known as a cataract. This condition is very common among older adults. Treatment involves surgical replacement of the clouded lens with an artificial lens. Wearing sunglasses with UV-ray protection and not smoking are two behaviors that may slow or prevent the development of cataracts.

▶ **Detached Retina**   Aging or an injury to the eye can cause the retina to separate from the lining of the eye. Surgery is the only effective treatment for a detached retina.

▶ **Macular Degeneration**   The leading cause of eyesight problems in older adults is macular degeneration. This condition occurs when cells in the center of the retina break down. Treatment for macular degeneration is limited and often depends on the extent of the damage.

Treating Eye Infections   Two common eye infections are sties and conjunctivitis. A sty is a painful swelling that occurs when an oil gland at the base of an eyelash becomes infected. Allergic reactions or infections related to colds can lead to conjunctivitis, an inflammation of the outside layer of the eye. The eye may ooze a yellowish fluid and become red and itchy. Sties and conjunctivitis can be treated with prescription medications.

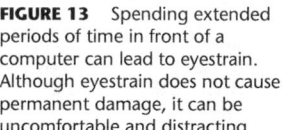
Connect to Your Life   Have you ever had an eye infection? How was it treated?

GO ONLINE
PearsonSuccessNet.com
For: More on eye diseases

FIGURE 13   Spending extended periods of time in front of a computer can lead to eyestrain. Although eyestrain does not cause permanent damage, it can be uncomfortable and distracting.

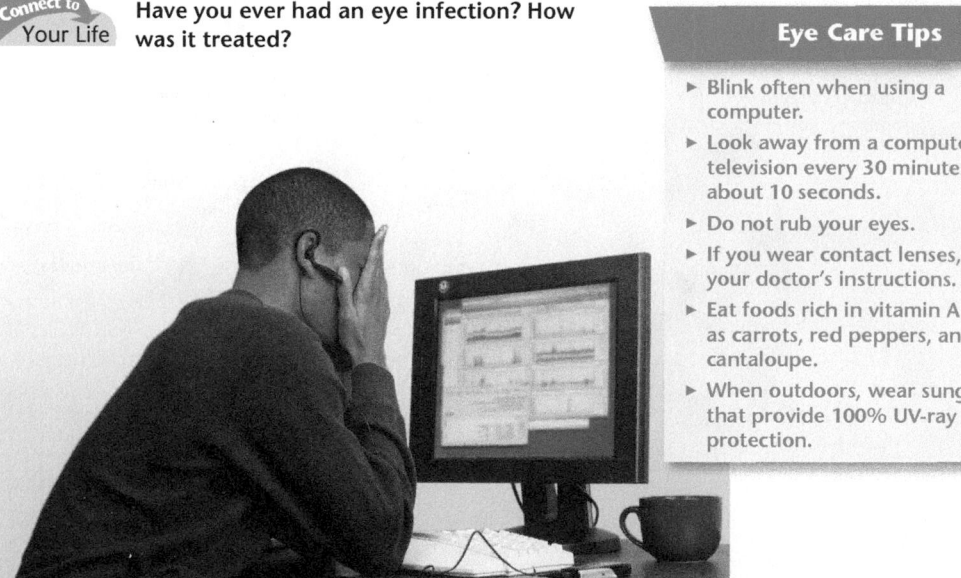

Eye Care Tips

▶ Blink often when using a computer.
▶ Look away from a computer or television every 30 minutes for about 10 seconds.
▶ Do not rub your eyes.
▶ If you wear contact lenses, follow your doctor's instructions.
▶ Eat foods rich in vitamin A such as carrots, red peppers, and cantaloupe.
▶ When outdoors, wear sunglasses that provide 100% UV-ray protection.

359

L3 Content Update   GO ONLINE

Visit Pearson SuccessNet to access more information about eye diseases. Have students complete the Web activity.

L2 Active Learning

Make a large table with four columns and four rows on a piece of poster board or newsprint. Label the columns Type of Disease, Description, Cause, and Treatment. Call on volunteers to fill in the information about eye diseases that are described in the text. After all the information has been recorded, cut the table so that each cell is separate. Ask students to reconstruct the table. Allow students to repeat this activity until they have mastered the information about various eye diseases.

L3 Class Discussion

Ask students to read the eye care tips listed in Figure 13. Ask: **One of the tips is "Do not rub your eyes." What are two reasons why rubbing your eyes can be harmful?** *(Sample answer: Rubbing your eyes with your hands can introduce dirt and germs into the eyes. Rubbing your eyes can cause dirt and dust in the eye to scratch the surface of the eye.)*

Connect to Your Life   Allow students to answer this question in their private journals.

Your Ears

L2 Active Learning

Tape three cardboard squares to the floor in a row, about two feet apart. Label the first square *outer ear,* the next square *middle ear,* and the last square *inner ear.* Have a student stand on the first square. Ask the student to describe what happens in the *outer ear* from the point-of-view of a sound. *(I enter the outer ear, and I travel to the eardrum.)* Then, have the student step to the square labeled *middle ear.* Again, have the student describe what happens in the *middle ear. (I cause the hammer to vibrate, which pushes against the anvil, which moves the stirrup.)* Finally, have the student step to the square labeled *inner ear* and describe what happens there. *(The vibrations pass through the oval window to the cochlea. When the fluid in the cochlea vibrates, impulses are generated in nerves. The nerve impulses travel to the brain, where they are interpreted as sounds.)*

L3 Visual Learning: Figure 14

Image Bank Figure 14-14

Ask a volunteer to read aloud the three numbered descriptions of how sound is converted to nerve impulses. Ask: **In what way is the ear similar to the eye?** *(Sample answer: It is a set of structures that converts information from the outside world to nerve impulses that can be interpreted by the brain.)*

Your Ears

You know that your ears allow you to hear, but do you know that they also help you keep your balance? **The ears convert sounds into nerve impulses that your brain interprets. In addition, structures in the ear detect the position and movement of your head.** By sensing movement and position, your ears help you to stand upright, walk smoothly, and adjust your body's position.

The Outer Ear Figure 14 shows the three regions of the ear—the outer ear, middle ear, and inner ear. When you look in a mirror, you can see part of the outer ear. This part, which is covered with a thin layer of skin, acts as a collecting funnel for sounds. Sounds travel to your ears as vibrations—movements in the air. In the outer ear, the vibrations are channeled into the ear canal, a narrow cavity that leads to the middle ear. At the end of the ear canal is a thin membrane called the **eardrum.** The eardrum vibrates when sound vibrations strike it.

The Middle Ear Vibrations from the eardrum pass to the middle ear, which contains three small bones—the hammer, the anvil, and the stirrup. The vibrating eardrum causes the hammer to vibrate, which pushes against the anvil, which then moves the stirrup.

Have you ever felt your ears pop in an elevator? This happens because the air pressure in the outer ear suddenly changes. Usually the pressure in the outer ear and the middle ear is the same. The auditory tube, which connects the middle ear with the back of the throat, keeps the pressure equal so that your eardrum vibrates correctly. Most of the time the auditory tube is closed. When you cough, swallow, or yawn, however, it opens. You hear a popping sound as the air pressure in the middle ear and outer ear equalize.

FIGURE 14 Sound vibrations enter the outer ear and cause structures in the middle ear to vibrate. When the vibrations reach the inner ear, nerve impulses travel to the brain via the auditory nerve.

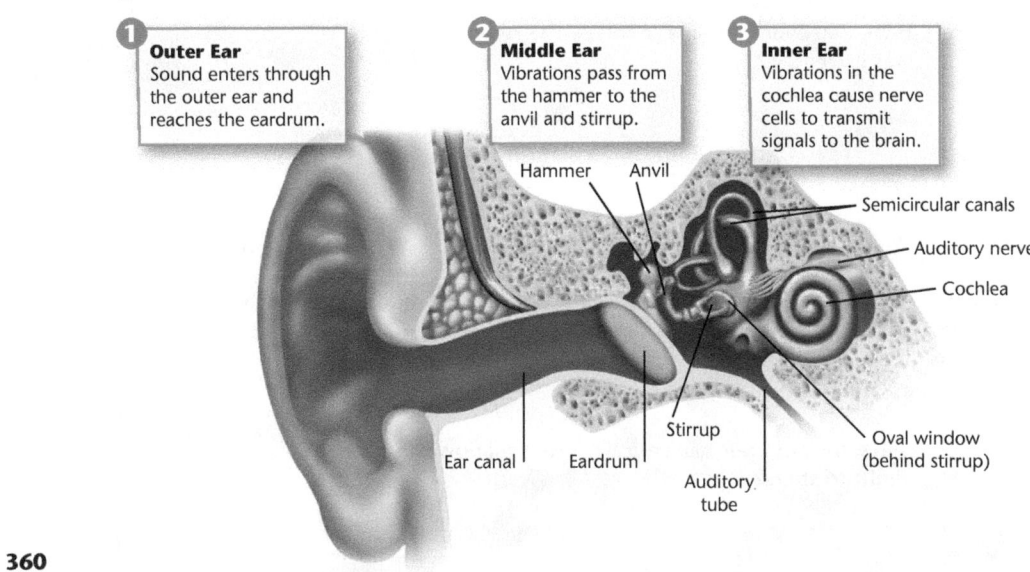

1 Outer Ear Sound enters through the outer ear and reaches the eardrum.

2 Middle Ear Vibrations pass from the hammer to the anvil and stirrup.

3 Inner Ear Vibrations in the cochlea cause nerve cells to transmit signals to the brain.

Hammer Anvil

Semicircular canals

Auditory nerve

Cochlea

Ear canal Eardrum Stirrup Oval window (behind stirrup)

Auditory tube

360

WRITING and Health

L3 Detailed Observation

Have students sit with their eyes closed for five minutes in the classroom, at home, or outdoors. During that time, ask students to listen closely to any sounds they hear. Then, ask students to write a detailed observation of the sounds they noticed during their five minutes of listening. Encourage students to use descriptive language in their writing. Model the use of descriptive language by providing students with several examples of descriptive phrases (the shuffle of footsteps, the crack of a bat, the whistling wind). Ask volunteers to share their writing with the class.

FIGURE 15 Structures in the surfer's inner ear, together with his eyes, muscles, and brain, help him keep his balance as he rides the waves.

Waves, car trips, and rides give some people motion sickness. They feel ill when their brains receive conflicting information from their ears and eyes.

The Inner Ear   After the anvil passes vibrations to the stirrup, the stirrup pushes on the oval window. The oval window is a membrane-covered opening that separates the middle ear from the inner ear. Vibrations are passed through the oval window to a hollow, coiled tube filled with fluid called the **cochlea** (KAWK lee uh).

The cochlea is lined with cells with hairlike extensions that sense vibrations. When the cochlear fluid moves, the cells stimulate impulses in nerves. The impulses travel through the auditory nerve to the brain, where they are interpreted as sound.

The Inner Ear and Balance   Above the cochlea in your inner ear are the **semicircular canals,** structures that send information to your brain about the movements of your head. Two sacs located behind the canals capture information about your head's position. The canals and sacs are also lined with tiny cells that have hairlike extensions.

When your head moves, the fluid inside the semicircular canals and sacs causes the "hairs" to move. The movement stimulates nerve cells, which send impulses to your brain. Your brain interprets these impulses to determine the position of your body. In response, the brain sends signals to your muscles to help you keep your balance.

 What part of your ear helps you to walk down a flight of stairs?

EL Building Vocabulary

Write the term *semicircular canal* on the board. Explain that the word part *semi-* means "partially or half." Have students use this information to infer the meaning of the word *semicircular.* Have students check their answer by locating the semicircular canals in Figure 14.

L3 Class Discussion

Ask students if they have ever experienced a brief sensation of dizziness after quickly changing position (for example, quickly leaning over to pick up something). Explain that this sensation is called vertigo. Point out that there are disorders in which this sensation occurs frequently or constantly. Ask students to discuss ways this would affect their everyday life.

L4 Cooperative Learning

Ask students to work in small groups to prepare a multimedia presentation about the structures and functions of the ear. Encourage students to perform library or Internet research to find additional information to include in their presentations. Challenge students to use creativity when preparing their presentation. Have each group share its presentation with the class.

Connect to Your Life   The inner ear helps me to maintain balance as I walk down stairs.

Differentiated Instruction

 Special Needs

Students with visual or hearing impairments should not be singled out during discussions of the eye and ear. Use three-dimensional models to allow visually impaired students to learn about the structures of the eye and ear. Have students work in small groups or with a partner to complete the activities in this section.

Caring for Your Ears

 Building Health Skills

Practicing Healthful Behaviors Challenge students to lower the level of their headphones. If they lower the volume gradually over time, they may not notice the difference. Suggest that they lower the volume by about five percent a week until they reach the volume recommended by health professionals (see Student Edition).

Visual Learning: Figure 16

After students examine the figure, challenge them to create a list of other sounds they are exposed to in their everyday lives, for example, a school basketball game, a car horn, a passing ambulance. Have students estimate where these everyday sounds would rank on the decibel scale. Ask students to work as a class to identify at least three sounds from their list that might damage hearing.

Connect to Your Life *Sample answer:* I avoid listening to loud music.

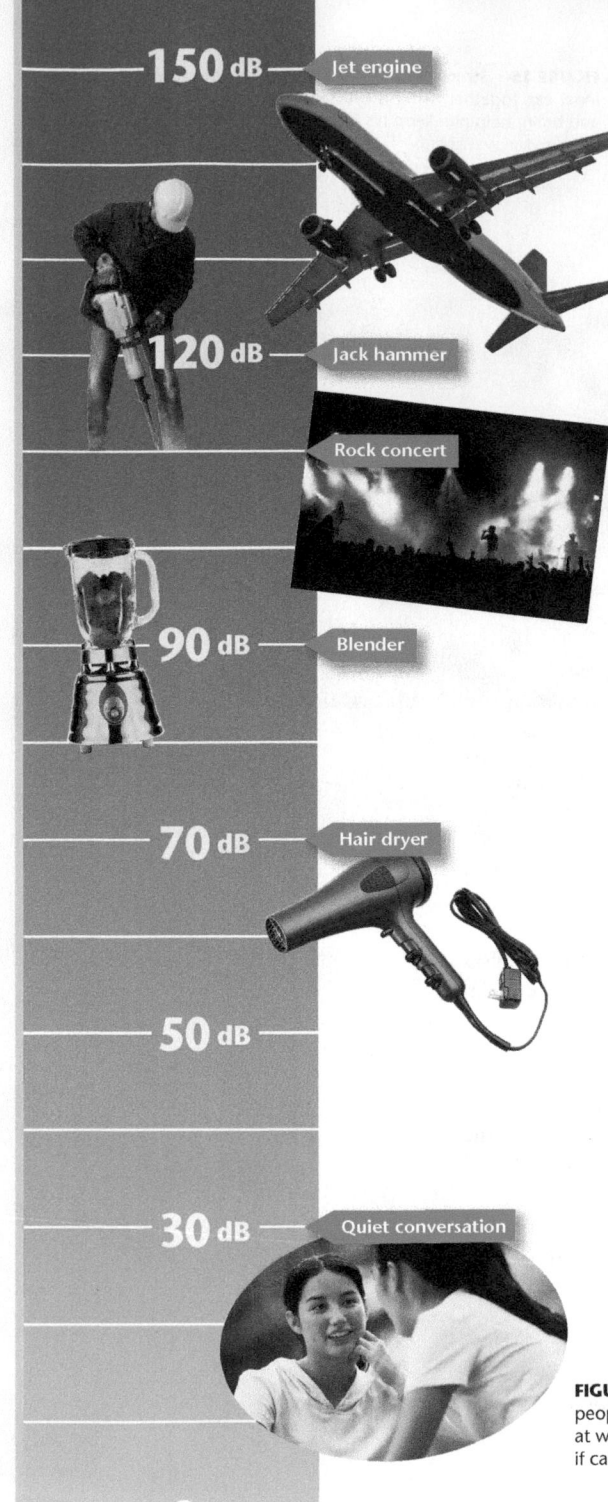

FIGURE 16 Many sounds that people are exposed to at home and at work can lead to hearing damage if care is not taken.

Caring for Your Ears

Proper ear care is fairly simple. **Besides keeping your ears clean, you also need to monitor noise levels. In addition, you should see a doctor if you experience ear pain or hearing difficulties.**

Ear Care Use a wet washcloth to clean your outer ear and the front part of your ear canal. Dry your ears thoroughly after you wash them.

Never insert a cotton-tipped swab or any other object into your ear canal. The swab can damage your eardrum. Swabs may also compress the earwax. Earwax, which is secreted by glands lining your ear canal, traps dust and microorganisms. If the earwax is compressed, it will not drain normally.

Monitoring Noise Levels Partial hearing loss or deafness can result from damage to nerves or to the vibration-sensing cells in the cochlea. This type of hearing damage is generally permanent. The longer and more often a person is exposed to loud noise, the more likely it is that noticeable hearing damage will occur.

The intensity, or loudness, of sound is measured in units called decibels (DES uh bulz). Exposure to sounds above 80 decibels (dB) for several hours at a time can damage hearing. Exposure to sounds above 120 dB for even a few seconds can damage hearing. Ringing in your ears or difficulty hearing normal conversation are signs that you have exposed yourself to ear-damaging noise levels.

To avoid hearing damage, keep your television and stereo low enough that you can comfortably hear a person speaking at a normal level. When listening to music with headphones or ear buds, you should never turn the music player up to more than 60 percent of its potential volume.

Connect to Your Life  In what ways do you try to protect your hearing?

TEENS *Are Asking . . .*

Q: I attend only one or two concerts a year. Do I really need to worry about my hearing?

A: After attending a rock concert, many people complain of ringing in their ears and muffled hearing for several hours or even days. This experience, called a temporary threshold shift, is the result of damage to the cells lining the cochlea. It is possible to recover completely from a temporary threshold shift, however repeated exposures to loud noises will lead to progressive hearing loss. Hearing loss from recreational noise such as concerts and sporting events is one hundred percent preventable. If you wear earplugs, you will not have to be concerned about damaging your hearing.

Treating Ear Infections Bacterial infections of the middle ear can sometimes result in some hearing loss—especially if the infections occur frequently and are not treated. A middle-ear infection may cause the eardrum to break, or rupture. Although the eardrum will heal, scarring will result. Scar tissue makes the eardrum less flexible and less able to transmit sound.

Middle-ear infections are especially common in young children. An infected ear usually aches, feels warm, and may feel filled with fluid. If you have an earache, see a doctor. If you are prone to ear infections or have ever had a damaged eardrum, you should wear earplugs when swimming.

Treating Hearing Problems Hearing loss, whether temporary or permanent, can be caused by factors other than loud noise or infections. Some types of hearing loss can be inherited. Diseases, high fevers, and certain medications can also cause hearing loss. A buildup of wax in the ear can cause temporary hearing loss when the wax blocks the passage of sound vibrations. A doctor can remove the wax or prescribe treatments to soften the wax.

People with hearing problems see an audiologist (aw dee AHL uh jist). **Audiologists** are professionals who are trained to evaluate hearing and treat hearing loss. In some cases, people with hearing loss use hearing aids. Most hearing aids increase the volume of sounds and transmit the sounds into the ear canal. Another treatment, called a cochlear implant, does not increase the volume of sounds. Instead, it acts as a replacement cochlea by converting sound waves to impulses that can be sent to the brain.

FIGURE 17 Cochlear implants do not restore hearing, but they do help a deaf person understand speech and other sounds going on around them.

Section 3 Review

Key Ideas and Vocabulary

1. List the structures in the eye through which light passes to allow you to see an image.
2. List two ways you can keep your eyes healthy.
3. Trace the path of sound from your outer ear until it is perceived by your brain.
4. How do the **semicircular canals** help you keep your balance?
5. List three ways you can keep your ears healthy.

Critical Thinking

6. **Classifying** If nearby objects seem blurry, what type of vision problem might you have? What does this indicate about the shape of your eyes?

Health and Community

Music and Hearing Loss Going to a concert with friends can be a lot of fun, but it can also put the health of your ears at risk. Research some strategies that allow you to protect your ears from loud music and still enjoy a concert. Make a pamphlet that shares these strategies with your classmates. **WRITING**

7. **Predicting** If a person were born with only green and blue cone cells, which color would the person have trouble seeing? How might this condition affect the person?
8. **Relating Cause and Effect** Why may an infection of the inner ear cause you to lose your balance?

---

3. Assess

Evaluate

These assignments can help you assess students' mastery of the section content.

Section 3 Review
Answers appear below.

Teaching Resources
• Practice 14-3
• Section 14-3 Quiz

L2 Reteach

Have students work with a partner to review the diagrams of the structure of the eye and the ear. Ask students to work together to review the function of each labeled structure.

L4 Enrich

Teaching Resources
• Enrich 14-3

Health and Community

Noise Ordinances Provide students with several examples of informational pamphlets to use as models as they write. Encourage students to contact local concert venues for more information about ear protection.

Section 3 Review

1. cornea, pupil, lens

2. wear protective goggles and sunglasses; have regular eye exams

3. Sound enters the outer ear and causes vibrations in the middle ear. The vibrations pass through the oval window to the cochlea in the inner ear. Nerves send impulses to the brain.

4. Semicircular canals send information to the brain about movements of the head and the position of the body.

5. *Sample answer:* keep your ears clean, monitor noise levels, see a doctor for ear pain or hearing difficulties

6. farsightedness; A problem that is caused by an eyeball that is too short.

7. red; *Sample answer:* This person might have a hard time seeing traffic lights.

8. *Sample answer:* Ear infections can impair the function of the semicircular canals, which help you to keep your balance.

Objectives
Before class begins, write the objectives on the board. Have students copy the objectives into their notebooks at the start of class.

1. Focus

Warm-Up Health Stats

Encourage students to reflect on their own experiences and the experiences of friends as they complete the writing assignment. Ask volunteers to identify factors they feel contribute to the sleep habits of teens. Record their responses on the board. Challenge students to add to the list as they read the section.

Presentation 14-4

Sample answer: My body feels numb, and my mind functions slowly.

Section 4
Sleep and Feeling Fit

Objectives
▶ **Describe** why sleep is important for health.
▶ **Explain** how circadian rhythms influence the sleep patterns of teens.

Vocabulary
• insomnia
• sleep apnea
• narcolepsy
• circadian rhythm

Warm-Up

Health Stats What trend does this graph reveal about teens and sleep?

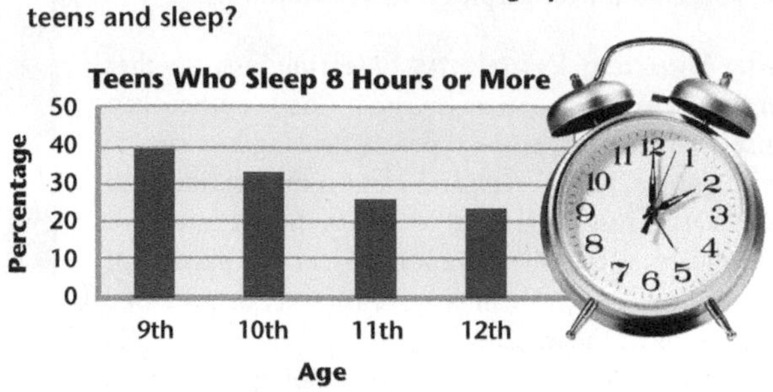

Teens Who Sleep 8 Hours or More

Bar graph: x-axis labeled "Age" with values 9th, 10th, 11th, 12th; y-axis labeled "Percentage" from 0 to 50. Bars decrease from about 40 (9th) to about 33 (10th) to about 26 (11th) to about 23 (12th).

WRITING What factors do you think contribute to the sleeping habits of teens?

What Is Sleep?

Sleep is the deep relaxation of the body and mind during which the eyes are usually closed and there is little conscious thought or movement. During sleep, your muscles relax, your breathing and heart rate decrease, and your body temperature drops slightly. **Although some people think of sleep as wasted time, it is actually just as important to the body as air, water, and food.**

Benefits of Sleep Scientists have yet to agree on the reason why people sleep. But their research has uncovered a number of possible benefits of sleep.

▶ During sleep, your brain sorts the day's information. Learning and the storage of memories may occur.

▶ The healing of body tissues occurs during sleep. For example, the damage done to muscle tissue after a workout heals while you sleep.

▶ Adequate sleep helps the immune system to function properly.

▶ Adequate sleep may help prevent some diseases, such as diabetes.

Connect to Your Life How does your body feel after a night of too little sleep? How does your mind function?

WRITING and Health

⑬ Public Service Announcement

Ask each student to develop a public service announcement (PSA) that mentions at least one benefit of sleep. Remind students that PSAs can be created for radio, television, or print media. Have students present their PSAs to the class. Evaluate the public service announcements based on accuracy and creativity.

The Sleep Cycle   As you sleep, your body and brain go through periods of light and heavy sleep. Figure 18 shows the typical sleep cycle. At first, you enter nonrapid eye movement sleep (NREM). As you pass through the four stages of NREM sleep, your body gradually reaches a state of deep relaxation.

After the stages of NREM sleep, you enter rapid eye movement sleep (REM). During REM sleep, your eyes flicker rapidly behind closed eyelids, and there is a high level of brain activity. This is also the stage of sleep in which you dream. Your muscles are paralyzed during REM sleep, which prevents you from acting out your dreams.

Notice in Figure 18 that you alternate between NREM and REM sleep during the night. About 25 percent of your sleeping time is REM sleep. This percentage decreases as you age. REM sleep may be when you form long-term memories and when your brain discards unneeded information.

Sleep Disorders   A number of sleep disorders can affect your health. Sleep disorders should not be ignored. If you experience symptoms of any of these disorders, you should see a doctor for treatment.

▶ **Insomnia** refers to difficulties falling asleep or staying asleep. Insomnia can be caused by stress or some physical problems.

▶ **Sleep apnea** (AP nee uh) is a disorder in which a person stops breathing for short periods during sleep and then suddenly resumes breathing. This may happen 20 to 30 times an hour without the person being aware of it. However, he or she may be extremely tired during the day.

▶ **Narcolepsy** is a disorder in which a person experiences severe sleepiness during the day, or falls asleep suddenly. The brain of someone with narcolepsy does not regulate the wake-sleep cycle normally.

GO ONLINE
PearsonSuccessNet.com
For: More on teens and sleep

FIGURE 18   During a typical eight-hour period, you cycle between NREM sleep and REM sleep several times. **Reading Graphs** How many times was this person in REM sleep? In stage 4 NREM sleep?

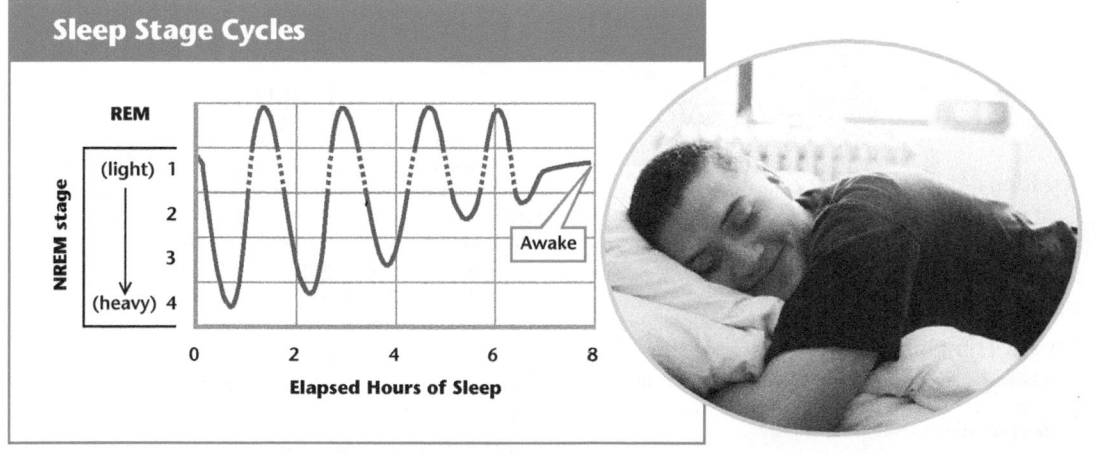
Sleep Stage Cycles

Personal Care **365**

Teens and Sleep

L2 Cooperative Learning

Assign small groups two or three of the tips for developing good sleep habits. Ask the groups to develop explanations as to why these tips may help someone sleep better. Have each group present their thoughts to the class.

3. Assess

Evaluate

These assignments can help you assess students' mastery of the section content.

Section 4 Review

Answers appear below.

Teaching Resources
• Practice 14-4
• Section 14-4 Quiz

L2 Reteach

Ask students to review with a partner the bulleted lists of information found on each page of this section.

L4 Enrich

Teaching Resources
• Enrich 14-4

Health at Home

Sleep Journal Throughout the two-week period, remind students to make entries in their sleep journals each day. Ask volunteers to describe any connections they noted between sleep and their mental, physical, or emotional health.

FIGURE 19 Sleeping less than you should leads to several negative consequences that will impact your daily life.

Some Effects of Sleep Loss
• Depression
• Problems with focusing and paying attention
• Difficulties learning
• Increased risk of illness
• Increased risk of motor vehicle crashes

Teens and Sleep

Do you have a hard time waking up for school, but do not feel tired at night? This is a common problem for teens. The sleep cycle is under the influence of the body's **circadian rhythm** (sur KAY dee un)—the body's internal system for regulating behavior patterns during a 24-hour cycle. **Puberty affects the body's circadian rhythm. One result is that teens want to sleep later into the day and stay awake later at night than adults.**

Most teens need about nine hours of sleep each night. However, teens sleep an average of seven hours. Some of the consequences of not getting enough sleep on a regular basis are listed in Figure 19. Here are some tips to help you develop good sleep habits.

▶ Go to bed and wake up at the same times each day, even on weekends.

▶ Avoid bright lights at night. After waking, expose yourself to bright light as soon as possible.

▶ Avoid caffeine and sugary foods after noon.

▶ Exercise regularly, but not right before bedtime.

▶ Don't fall asleep with the television on.

▶ Avoid all-nighters, which disrupt your sleep patterns.

▶ If you nap, do not let your naps interfere with your regular sleep patterns.

▶ If you can't fall asleep, get up and do something relaxing until you feel tired.

Section 4 Review

Key Ideas and Vocabulary

1. List three possible health benefits of sleep.
2. Explain the symptoms of **insomnia** and **narcolepsy**.
3. Describe how the typical circadian rhythm of teens affects their sleep patterns.

Critical Thinking

4. **Relating Cause and Effect** Why do people with sleep apnea feel tired even after sleeping for eight hours or more?

Health at Home

Sleep Journal For two weeks, keep track of what time you go to bed and wake up. Also note how you feel each day, both mentally and physically. At the end of the two weeks, review your journal. In a paragraph, describe any connections you notice between your sleep pattern and your health status. **WRITING**

5. **Evaluating** List four reasons why you think teens do not get enough sleep. What can be done to address these reasons?

🔊 GO ONLINE PearsonSuccessNet.com   Audio Summary Section 14.4

Section 4 Review

1. *Sample answer:* Tissues heal during sleep; sleep helps the immune system function properly; adequate sleep helps prevent some diseases.
2. insomnia: difficulty falling asleep or staying asleep; narcolepsy: sudden severe sleepiness during the day
3. Teens' circadian rhythms make them want to stay up late at night and sleep later in the day.
4. Although the person with sleep apnea does not realize it, his or her sleep may be disrupted many times during the night.
5. Answers will vary, but most students will probably mention overextending themselves in different activities or too much homework. Prioritizing activities may help solve the problem.

Chapter 14
At a Glance

VIDEO **TEENS Talk** ◉
Taking Care of You How has watching this video changed your attitudes about personal care?

Section 1   Your Teeth and Gums

Key Ideas

▶ Healthy teeth allow you to chew your food properly and speak clearly.

▶ Healthy gums fit tightly around the neck of each tooth like a collar, holding it firmly in place.

▶ The changes that occur in the jaws throughout the growing years can lead to structural problems.

▶ A healthy diet, proper tooth care, and regular dental checkups can prevent tooth decay and gum disease.

Vocabulary

- enamel (342) • cementum (342) • dentin (342)
- pulp (342) • malocclusion (343) • orthodontist (343)
- halitosis (344) • plaque (344) • tartar (346)
- periodontal disease (346)

Section 2   Your Skin, Hair, and Nails

Key Ideas

▶ The skin protects the body from injury, infection, and water loss. It also helps to regulate body temperature and gathers outside information.

▶ Care for your skin by avoiding damage from UV-rays. Also, you should monitor your moles carefully.

▶ Hair protects the scalp from sunlight and provides insulation from the cold. Hairs in the nostrils and ears and your eyelashes keep out debris.

▶ Tough, platelike nails cover and protect the tips of your fingers and toes.

Vocabulary

- epidermis (348) • keratin (348)
- melanin (348) • dermis (348)
- pore (348) • follicle (348)
- sebaceous gland (348) • melanoma (349)
- acne (350) • dermatologist (350) • eczema (350)

Section 3   Your Eyes and Ears

Key Ideas

▶ The eyes are complex organs that respond to light by sending impulses to your brain.

▶ It is important to protect your eyes from damage and to have regular eye exams.

▶ The ear converts sounds into impulses that your brain interprets. In addition, structures in the ear detect the position and movement of your head.

▶ Keep your ears clean. You should also monitor noise levels and see a doctor if you experience ear pain or hearing difficulties.

Vocabulary

- cornea (356) • pupil (356) • iris (356)
- lens (357) • retina (357) • optometrist (358)
- eardrum (360) • cochlea (361)
- semicircular canals (361) • audiologist (363)

Section 4   Sleep and Feeling Fit

Key Ideas

▶ Although some people think of sleep as wasted time, it is actually just as important to the body as air, water, and food.

▶ Puberty affects the body's circadian rhythm. One result is that teens want to sleep later into the day and stay awake later at night than adults.

Vocabulary

- insomnia (365) • sleep apnea (365)
- narcolepsy (365) • circadian rhythm (366)

VIDEO **Taking Care of You** Ask for volunteers to share their answers. Use examples from the video to assess changes in students' attitudes about personal care.

Key Ideas Review

L2 Divide the class into four groups. Assign each group one of the sections of the chapter. Within their groups, have students prepare lessons that convey the main points of the section. Have each group share its lesson with the class.

L1 Ask students to skim the chapter to locate each of the boldface key ideas in the text. Have students read each key idea aloud or listen as a partner reads the key idea to them.

Vocabulary Review

EL Have students make a flashcard for each chapter vocabulary term. Each flashcard should contain the term and a simple written definition or a drawing. Ask students to work in pairs while they use their flashcards to review the chapter vocabulary terms.

L2 Challenge students to develop a rap or rhyme that can be used to remember the definition of one chapter vocabulary term. Ask students to present their raps or rhymes to the class.

Chapter 14 Review

 GO ONLINE

PearsonSuccessNet.com

Students can go online for a review activity on Chapter 14.

Reviewing Key Ideas

Section 1

1. b   2. a

3. When plaque is not removed from teeth, bacteria multiply and produce acid. The acid breaks down tooth enamel, causing a cavity to form.

4. a tooth that does not have space to emerge or is positioned at an awkward angle

5. Regular visits to the dentist can identify problems before they become painful or hard to treat.

6. *Sample answer:* Molars crush and grind food. A person who has lost his or her molars might have a hard time eating foods that must be ground up before being swallowed.

Section 2

7. a

8. Sweat glands produce perspiration, which helps to cool the body. Blood vessels in the skin expand to allow heat to be given off or contract to keep heat within the body.

9. asymmetry, an uneven border, an inconsistent color, or a diameter larger than ¼ inch

10. *Sample answer:* Keeping nails smooth prevents nails from digging into the skin and causing infection. Keeping nails clean also helps prevent the spread of germs.

11. *Sample answer:* When skin is dry, the body may produce even more oil. This increase in oil production can lead to acne breakouts.

Section 3

12. d

13. The iris regulates the size of the pupil, the opening through which light enters the eye.

14. an uneven curve to the cornea or lens that causes distorted vision

---

Chapter 14 Review

Reviewing Key Ideas

 GO ONLINE

PearsonSuccessNet.com

For: Chapter 14 review activity

Section 1

1. What material covers the crown of a tooth?
   a. dentin   b. enamel
   c. pulp   d. gums

2. Which of the following is a condition in which the lower and upper teeth do not meet properly?
   a. malocclusion   b. gingivitis
   c. cementum   d. tooth decay

3. Explain the process by which tooth decay occurs.

4. What is an impacted wisdom tooth?

5. Why are regular visits to the dentist so important?

6. **Critical Thinking** Sometimes people lose their molars due to periodontal disease. How do you think this might affect their diet?

Section 2

7. Which of these structures are found in the dermis, but not the epidermis?
   a. blood vessels   b. pores
   c. living cells   d. hairs

8. How does your skin help to regulate your body temperature?

9. What characteristics of a new or changed mole might be signs of melanoma?

10. How can keeping your nails smooth and clean help you stay healthy?

11. **Critical Thinking** Soaps that dry out your skin can make acne breakouts worse. Why do you think this is true?

Section 3

12. The transparent structure that covers the front of the eye is the
    a. pupil.   b. lens.
    c. retina.   d. cornea.

13. How do the iris and the pupil work together to control the amount of light entering the eye?

14. What is astigmatism?

15. **Critical Thinking** What would happen if the bones of the middle ear were stuck together and could not move?

Section 4

16. Which sleep disorder involves the inability to fall asleep or stay asleep?
    a. insomnia   b. narcolepsy
    c. sleep apnea   d. circadian rhythm

17. What happens during NREM sleep? What happens during REM sleep?

18. What are some things you can do to help yourself get a good night's sleep?

19. **Critical Thinking** Studies have shown that night workers have a higher injury rate on the job than day workers. What do you think might account for the higher rate of injuries?

Building Health Skills

20. **Analyzing Influences** Watch an hour of children's television programs. Count the ads for sugary cereals and snacks. What techniques are used to capture the attention of children? How could these ads affect children's oral health?

21. **Communicating** Write a letter to your school newspaper offering reasons why school should start later in the day. **WRITING**

22. **Practicing Healthful Behaviors** Create a comic strip that uses humor to remind people about the importance of protecting the skin from the sun.

23. **Setting Goals** Come up with a plan for getting more sleep during the school week. Monitor your progress for one week, then make changes to your plan. Continue to monitor your sleep habits over the next few weeks.

Health and Community

Volunteering to Read Volunteer to read to people with impaired vision. You usually can find such programs at senior centers, nursing homes, or organizations for the blind. Once you have been reading for two weeks, write an editorial describing your experience. **WRITING**

---

15. No vibrations would reach the inner ear, and a person would be unable to hear.

Section 4

16. a

17. During NREM sleep, the body reaches a state of deep relaxation. During REM sleep, there is a high level of brain activity, dreams occur, and muscles are paralyzed.

18. *Sample answer:* avoid caffeine, exercise regularly, and keep the same sleep schedule every day

19. *Sample answer:* Due to circadian rhythms, people are naturally tired at night.

Standardized Test Prep

Math Practice

The graph compares the percentage of total sleep that is spent in REM sleep in different age groups. Use the graph to answer Questions 24–26.

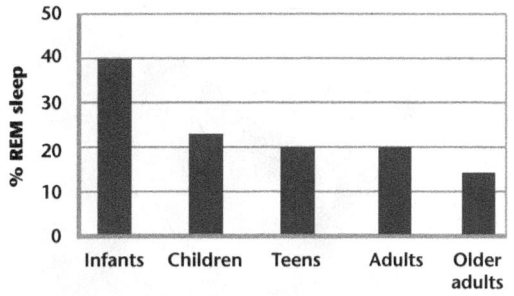

24. Which of the following statements is true according to the graph?
    - A Infants spend the most time sleeping.
    - B Children spend the same amount of time sleeping as adults.
    - C The oldest adults spend the lowest percentage of time in REM sleep.
    - D Not every age group spends time in REM sleep.

25. Which age group(s) spend 50% less time in REM sleep than infants?
    - F Children
    - G Children and teens
    - H Teens and adults
    - J Adults and older adults

26. Which title would be the best one for this graph?
    - A Total REM Sleep
    - B Total Percentage of Sleep
    - C Total Sleep and Age
    - D REM Sleep and Age

Test-Taking Tip

Get plenty of sleep the night before a test. You will be more alert and perform better if you are not tired.

Reading and Writing Practice

Read the passage. Then answer Questions 27–30.

UVA and UVB are two types of ultraviolet rays that reach Earth. Many people once thought that UVA rays caused tans, while UVB rays caused burns. Because tanning booths emit primarily UVA rays, people assumed that tanning booths were safer than sun exposure. However, recent research has shown this to be false. Although the two types of UV rays affect the skin in different ways, they both contribute to the development of skin cancer. Overexposure to either type of UV ray also damages proteins in skin, leading to signs of premature aging. In addition, the rays cause cataracts and suppress the immune system.

27. Which of the following statements is true according to this passage?
    - A UVB rays are emitted from tanning beds, but not from the sun.
    - B UVA rays are not dangerous to the skin, but UVB rays are.
    - C Overexposure to the sun may make people look older than they actually are.
    - D It is not yet known whether UVA rays contribute to the development of skin cancer.

28. In this passage, the word *premature* means
    - F early.
    - G abnormal.
    - H excessive.
    - J embarrassing.

29. What is the main idea of this passage?
    - A No amount of exposure to sunlight is safe.
    - B Both UVA and UVB rays have effects that are harmful to the body.
    - C Scientists continue to study the effects of UV rays on the skin.
    - D Overexposure to UV rays causes cataracts.

Constructed Response

30. In a paragraph, discuss the effects of UVA and UVB rays on the skin.

Standardized Test Prep

Math Practice
24. C
25. H
26. D

Reading and Writing Practice
27. C
28. F
29. B
30. Answers will vary, but should reflect the idea that both UVA and UVB rays are harmful to the skin.

 Building Health Skills

20. *Sample answer:* Ads directed at children use cartoon characters and bright, lively images and music. The sugary foods can lead to tooth decay and gum disease.

21. Arguments will vary, but might mention the circadian rhythms of adolescents.

22. Comic strips should include information about protecting the skin from UV rays.

23. Plans should include a realistic goal for getting more sleep using some of the tips from Section 4.

Health and Community

Volunteering to Read Provide students with several examples of editorials to use as models. Remind students that editorials usually express an opinion or encourage others to take a particular action. Ask students if they would encourage others to take part in a volunteer reading program.

CAREERS

Physical Fitness

Teaching Strategies

- At least two weeks before you discuss these careers in class, ask a few interested students to interview local professionals in the three careers discussed on page 370. Have students ask modified versions of the Career Focus questions and questions they develop on their own. As part of your class discussion, ask the students to share what they learned about the three careers.

- Call on a volunteer to explain how the fourth career—respiratory therapist—is related to physical fitness. *(Sample answer: Having a healthy respiratory system is a requirement of being physically fit.)* Then, have students read the Career Focus.

- Challenge students to think of other careers in physical fitness. *(Sample answers: aerobics instructor, athletic coach, physical education teacher, orthopedic surgeon, physical therapist)* **What do all of these careers have in common?** *(All involve helping people improve or maintain their physical fitness or deal with fitness-related problems, such as sports injuries or stress.)*

CAREERS

Physical Fitness

People in physical fitness careers help patients keep their bodies in top condition or rehabilitate from injuries.

Athletic Trainer

Athletic trainers work with athletes to help them prevent, treat, or recover from sports injuries. They may also provide first aid and non-emergency medical care at games and practices. Athletic trainers may work for college or professional sports teams, at sports medicine clinics, or in health clubs. For this career, you need a bachelor's degree in athletic training or a related field, and state certification. Some athletic trainers may also have a graduate degree.

Chiropractor

Chiropractors diagnose and treat problems of the skeletal, nervous, and muscular systems. For some conditions, chiropractors might use a treatment technique called spinal manipulation. They also might recommend exercise and rest rather than medications. This career requires two to four years of premedical undergraduate study, a four-year chiropractic degree, and state licensing.

Orthodontist

Orthodontists are dentists with specialized training in treating dental and facial irregularities. They use corrective appliances such as braces, retainers, and headgear to align teeth, jaws, and lips. To become an orthodontist, a person must obtain degrees from both a dental program and an orthodontic program after college. Licenses in dentistry and orthodontics are also required.

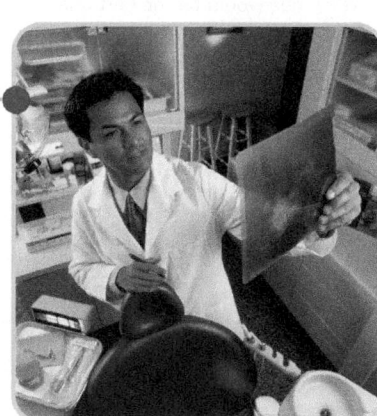

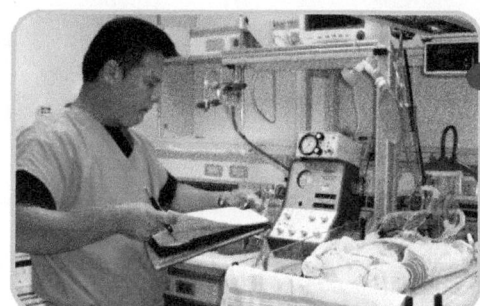

Respiratory Therapist

Respiratory therapists provide care for patients with chronic breathing problems such as asthma or emphysema. They may also treat premature infants whose lungs are not fully developed. This career requires a minimum of an associate's degree in respiratory therapy. Most states also require certification by the National Board for Respiratory Care and a state license.

Career Focus

Teodoro Tovar, Jr., Respiratory Therapist

How did you become interested in respiratory therapy?

"I became interested in respiratory therapy when my father was hospitalized after a near-fatal accident. While at his bedside, I witnessed the one-on-one care provided to him by the respiratory therapist. I was impressed by the therapist's knowledge and experience, and gained a lot of respect for the profession. After that experience I knew I wanted to become a respiratory therapist."

What does a respiratory therapist do?

"As a respiratory therapist, my job is to maintain an airway, assess oxygen needs, and give my patients ventilation assistance. I have worked with patients of all ages, but, for the past 15 years, I have specialized in neonates (premature babies)."

What challenges do the babies face?

"Because these babies have underdeveloped lungs, they can't get enough oxygen. I place them on special ventilators that breathe for them up to 400 times a minute."

What is the best part of your job?

"My favorite part is watching parents take their new baby home. The parents are so thankful, appreciative, and respectful of what respiratory therapists do. I become very close with the families. Sometimes the parents bring the baby back to the hospital just so I can see how well they are doing and how big and strong the baby has grown."

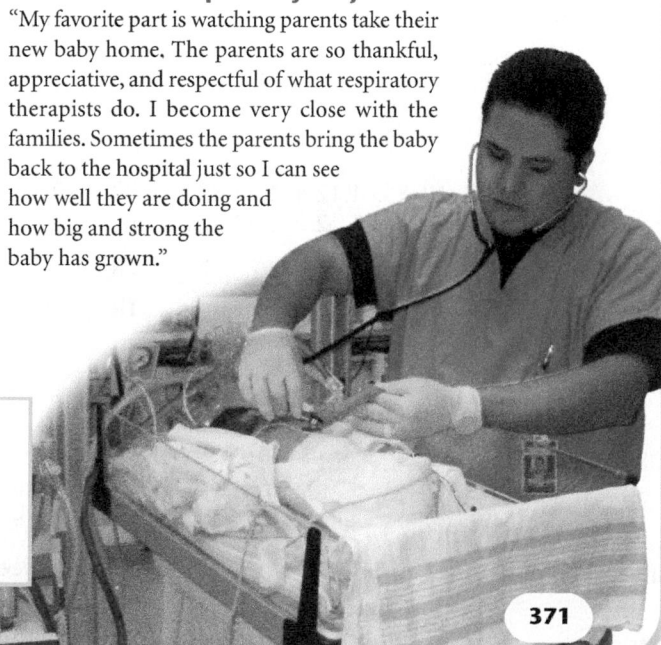

Health and Careers

Careers in Physical Fitness Research other physical fitness careers. Choose a career that interests you. Explain how keeping physically fit yourself would help you be successful at the career. **WRITING**

Health and Careers

Careers in Physical Fitness Check that students have used only up-to-date and reliable sources in their research. Suggest they use the Bureau of Labor Statistics' *Occupational Outlook Handbook* to find additional careers. Answers will vary, depending on the careers students chose to research. For example, a student who chose the career of physical therapy might say that keeping physically fit would set a good example for clients and give the therapist the strength and endurance needed to help clients through their therapy.

CHAPTER 15 Alcohol

Section Objectives	Standards Correlation	Instructional Resources L3	SE eTEXT	TE eTEXT	PRINT
1 Alcohol Is a Drug ⏱ 1 period; 1/2 block **15.1.1 Describe** how alcohol acts as a depressant in the body. **15.1.2 Identify** three major factors that influence underage drinking.	NHES: 2.12.1, 2.12.3, 2.12.4, 2.12.5, 2.12.7, 2.12.8, 2.12.9, 2.12.10, 6.12.1	SE Warm-Up, p. 374	•	•	•
		SE MediaWise Sports and Alcohol, p. 376	•	•	•
		RN Note Taking Guide 15-1	•	•	•
		TR Practice 15-1		•	
		TR Section 15-1 Quiz		•	
Developing Refusal Skills ⏱ 1 period; 1/2 block **BHS.15 Communicate** no in a way that tells others you mean it.	NHES: 2.12.3, 4.12.2	SE Practice the Skill, p. 379	•	•	•
		RN Building Health Skills 15	•	•	•
2 Alcohol's Effects on the Body ⏱ 2 periods; 1 block **15.2.1 Summarize** the effects of intoxication on the body systems. **15.2.2 List** four factors that affect blood alcohol concentration. **15.2.2 Identify** three ways that intoxication may lead to death.	NHES: 1.12.8, 1.12.9, 2.12.9, 2.12.10	SE Warm-Up, p. 380	•	•	•
		RN Note Taking Guide 15-2	•	•	•
		IB Image Bank 15-3, 15-5		•	
		TR Practice 15-2		•	
		TR Section 15-2 Quiz		•	
3 Long-Term Risks of Alcohol ⏱ 2 periods; 1 block **15.3.1 Identify** five serious physical effects of long-term alcohol abuse. **15.3.2 Describe** the three stages of alcoholism. **15.3.2 List** in order three steps taken during recovery from alcoholism.	NHES: 1.12.4, 1.12.8, 1.12.9, 3.12.3, 3.12.4	SE Warm-Up, p. 386	•	•	•
		RN Note Taking Guide 15-3	•	•	•
		TR Practice 15-3		•	
		TR Section 15-3 Quiz		•	
4 Choosing Not to Drink ⏱ 1 period; 1/2 block **15.4.1 Evaluate** how refusal skills help you stick to your decision not to drink. **15.4.2 Identify** two benefits of avoiding situations where alcohol is present.	NHES: 2.12.4, 4.12.2, 5.12.1, 5.12.2, 5.12.4, 5.12.6	SE Warm-Up, p. 392	•	•	•
		RN Note Taking Guide 15-4	•	•	•
		TR Practice 15-4		•	
		TR Section 15-4 Quiz		•	

Chapter Review and Assessment

SE Chapter 15 Review, p. 396 L3
CTB Chapter 15 Test L2 L3 L4
SE Standardized Test Prep, p. 397 L3

PROGRAM COMPONENTS

SE Student Edition
TE Teacher Edition
TR Teaching Resources
RN Reading and Note Taking Guide
ARN Adapted Reading and Note Taking Guide
IB Image Bank

CTB Computer Test Bank
AUD Audio Section Summaries
DVD Teens Talk Video Series
VVG Video Viewing Guide
PPT Presentation

Differentiated Instruction

L1 L2 L4 EL

		SE eTEXT	TE eTEXT	PRINT
ARN	Note Taking Guide 15-1 L2	•	•	
RN	Note Taking Guide 15-1 EL	•	•	•
AUD	Audio Summary 15-1 L1 L2 EL	•	•	
TE	Reteach Strategy, p. 377 L2		•	•
TR	Enrich 15-1 L4		•	
ARN	Building Health Skills 15 L2	•	•	
RN	Building Health Skills 15 EL	•	•	•
ARN	Note Taking Guide 15-2 L2	•	•	
RN	Note Taking Guide 15-2 EL	•	•	•
AUD	Audio Summary 15-2 L1 L2 EL	•	•	
TE	Reteach Strategy, p. 385 L2		•	•
TR	Enrich 15-2 L4		•	
ARN	Note Taking Guide 15-3 L2	•	•	
RN	Note Taking Guide 15-3 EL	•	•	•
AUD	Audio Summary 15-3 L1 L2 EL	•	•	
TE	Reteach Strategy, p. 391 L2		•	•
TR	Enrich 15-3 L4		•	
ARN	Note Taking Guide 15-4 L2	•	•	
RN	Note Taking Guide 15-4 EL	•	•	•
AUD	Audio Summary 15-4 L1 L2 EL	•	•	
TE	Reteach Strategy, p. 394 L2		•	•
TR	Enrich 15-4 L4		•	

ABILITY LEVELS

L1 For students with special needs
L2 For less proficient readers
L3 For all students
L4 For gifted and talented students
EL For English language learners

Chapter 15 Digital/Video Pathway

This alternative pathway allows you to teach this chapter's content using only the video and online materials.

Preview

DVD	Video #15 Preview
SE	Video #15 Preview Activity
VVG	Video #3 Worksheet

Drinking Dangers

1

PPT	15-1 Presentation
RN/ARN	15-1 Note Taking
PPT	15-1 Section Quiz

2

DVD	Video #15 Explore/Wrap-Up
VVG	Video #15 Worksheet
PPT	15-2 Presentation
RN/ARN	15-2 Note Taking
PPT	15-2 Section Quiz

Drinking Dangers

3

PPT	15-3 Presentation
RN/ARN	15-3 Note Taking
PPT	15-3 Section Quiz

4

PPT	15-4 Presentation
RN/ARN	15-4 Note Taking
PPT	15-4 Section Quiz

Chapter Preview

Section 1 Alcohol Is a Drug
Alcohol may cause confusion, decreased alertness, and other depressant effects. Using alcohol is illegal for anyone under age 21. The attitudes of peers, family, and the media strongly influence underage drinking.

Communicating
Developing Refusal Skills
Developing and practicing refusal skills will allow students to feel confident in their choice to say *no* to alcohol.

Section 2 Alcohol's Effects on the Body
Intoxication by alcohol causes many negative effects on a drinker's body and behavior, such as increased blood pressure and violence. Blood alcohol concentration (BAC) is affected by the rate of alcohol consumption, gender, body size, and amount of food in the stomach. Intoxication increases the risk of death from motor vehicle crashes, alcohol overdose, and interactions of alcohol with other drugs.

Section 3 Long-Term Risks of Alcohol
Long-term alcohol abuse may harm the brain, liver, heart, and digestive system. Drinking any amount during pregnancy may permanently harm the baby. Alcoholism progresses through three stages: problem drinking, absolute dependence, and late-stage alcoholism. Three steps in recovery from alcoholism are acknowledging the problem, detoxification, and rehabilitation.

Section 4 Choosing Not to Drink
Sticking to a decision not to drink means being able to say *no* with confidence in situations where other people are drinking. Avoiding situations in which alcohol is present can help one stay alcohol free and avoid related risks.

GO ONLINE

PearsonSuccessNet.com
For resources and activities for this chapter.

Alcohol

GO ONLINE PearsonSuccessNet.com

TEENS Talk
VIDEO 15
Drinking Dangers

Preview **Activity**

What's Your Take on Drinking?

Complete this activity before you watch the video.

1. Ask five students your age to complete each sentence with the first thought that comes into mind.
   a. Alcohol is __?__ .
   b. Teens who refuse alcohol are __?__ .
   c. Teens who get drunk are __?__ .
   d. Driving after drinking alcohol is __?__ .

2. In a paragraph, describe what your survey revealed about teens' attitudes towards alcohol. **WRITING**

Sensitive Issues

• Alcohol is likely to be a sensitive issue for students who have alcohol problems themselves or who have family members with alcohol problems. Such students may feel ashamed or be in denial about the problems. They may respond to direct questioning about alcohol by withdrawing or becoming angry.

• Never ask students to publicly identify problem drinking or alcoholism in themselves or others, especially their parents.

• Be sure to share with students how common alcohol problems are and to stress the dangers of alcohol.

SOMETIMES IT TAKES A FAMILY OF FOUR TO STOP A DRUNK DRIVER. **MADD**

373

VIDEO 15

TEENS Talk

Drinking Dangers

Video Objectives

Use this video to help students

Evaluate the risks of underage drinking.

Identify techniques that will help them refuse alcohol.

Apply their refusal skills in high-pressure situations.

Preview **Activity**

What's Your Take on Drinking?

Assign the Preview Activity for homework a few days before you plan to show the video. After students complete the activity, discuss the results of the students' surveys. Ask if students found the responses to the survey questions surprising or if they were as expected. Ask if they found teen attitudes toward drinking troubling. If so, how do students think these attitudes can be changed?

From the Authors

Many young adults, especially college students, practice binge drinking. Some of the college students we teach tell us that they started binge drinking in high school and did not know the dangers of binge drinking. Some of your students may already be practicing this risky behavior. Other students may feel peer pressure to binge drink.

Make sure students know what binge drinking is and why it is dangerous. Stress the risk of dying from binge drinking. Also stress the risky behaviors—such as driving under the influence—that often accompany binge drinking. Give students plenty of opportunities to develop the skills they need to avoid peer pressure to binge drink. For example, assign the Building Health Skills activity on pages 378–379 and the Connect to Your Life questions throughout the chapter.

Section **1**

Alcohol Is a Drug

Objectives

Before class begins, write the objectives on the board. Have students copy the objectives into their notebooks at the start of class.

1. Focus

Warm-Up Quick Quiz

Use the Warm-Up Presentation slide to survey student responses.

Make sure students are aware that answering *no* to the quiz questions can endanger not only their health but also their lives. Call on several students to share their responses to the writing activity. Try to get a diversity of ideas about ways to avoid drinking. Tell students they will learn in this section why it is so important to avoid alcohol.

Presentation 15-1

2. Teach

L3 **EL** **Reading/Note Taking** 15-1

L2 **Adapted Reading/Note Taking** 15-1

Facts About Alcohol

L2 **Class Discussion**

Ask: **Why is alcohol classified as a drug?** *(It is a chemical substance that changes behavior.)* **What type of effect does alcohol have on the body and brain?** *(a depressant effect)* Discuss the risks of alcohol's depressant effects, especially while driving. Make sure students realize that large amounts of alcohol can depress the body and brain so much that death results.

Objectives

▶ **Describe** how alcohol acts as a depressant in the body.

▶ **Identify** three major factors that influence underage drinking.

Vocabulary

- drug
- depressant
- fermentation
- zero-tolerance policy

Warm-Up

Quick Quiz See how many of these questions you can answer "yes" to.

① Do you observe the law that prohibits people under age 21 from purchasing or possessing alcohol?

② Do you avoid riding with drivers who have been drinking?

③ Do you say *no* to friends who pressure you to drink?

④ Do you know how to seek help for an alcohol problem?

WRITING What other things can you do to avoid the risks associated with drinking alcohol?

Facts About Alcohol

You may not think of alcohol as a drug, but it is. A **drug** is a chemical substance that is taken to cause changes in a person's body or behavior.

Alcohol Is a Depressant Alcohol acts as a powerful depressant. A **depressant** (dih PRES unt) is a drug that slows brain and body reactions. **In slowing the body's normal reactions, alcohol may cause confusion, decreased alertness, poor coordination, blurred vision, and drowsiness.**

The depressant effects of alcohol are very strong. If a person drinks large amounts of alcohol, vital functions such as heartbeat and breathing can be seriously affected. Death can result.

Alcohol Production The alcohol in beverages such as beer, wine, and liquor is produced by the process of fermentation. During **fermentation,** microorganisms called yeast feed on the sugars in foods such as malted grains, grapes, or berries. In the process, carbon dioxide and alcohol are produced.

MATH and Health

L3 **Calculating Proportions**

Have students calculate the proportion of alcohol per ounce of each kind of drink shown in Figure 1. (beer: 0.5 oz. ÷ 12 oz. = 0.04 oz. of alcohol per 1 oz.; wine: 0.5 oz. ÷ 5 oz. = 0.10 oz. of alcohol per 1 oz.; liquor: 0.5 oz. ÷ 1.25 oz. = 0.40 oz. of alcohol per 1 oz.) Have students compare the proportion of alcohol per ounce in liquor and beer. Then ask: **How much stronger is liquor than beer?** *(10 times stronger)* Remind students that some liquors are even stronger, depending on their proof.

How Much Alcohol Is in a Drink?

This 1.25-oz shot of liquor contains **40% alcohol, or 0.5 oz.**

This 12-oz beer contains **4% alcohol or 0.5 oz.**

This 5 oz-glass of wine contains **10% alcohol, or 0.5 oz.**

To Calculate Alcohol Content
Multiply drink volume by percent alcohol.
Example: 5 oz wine × 0.10 = 0.5 oz

FIGURE 1 All of these drinks contain the same amount of alcohol—0.5 oz.
Calculating How much alcohol is in an 18-oz beer? **MATH**

Alcohol Content Not all alcoholic beverages contain the same amount of alcohol. The alcohol content of alcoholic beverages typically ranges from 4 percent to 50 percent.

Beverages with a greater percentage of alcohol, such as whiskey, gin, and rum, list their proof on the label. To calculate alcohol content from proof, divide by two. Thus 100-proof vodka is 50 percent alcohol.

Teens and Alcohol

For teens and others under the age of 21, using alcohol is illegal. In addition, many schools have adopted a **zero-tolerance policy.** Under such a policy, students face stiff consequences—including suspension—starting with the first time they are caught with alcohol or other drugs. Even so, alcohol is the most widely abused drug among high school students.

What influences teens' decisions about drinking? **The attitudes of peers, family, and the media strongly influence underage drinking.** Teens who refuse alcohol avoid the serious health and legal risks of this dangerous drug.

Influence of Peers Some teens say they drink to fit in, or just to do what their classmates seem to be doing. Teens often mistakenly believe that everyone is drinking. In fact, millions of teens never use alcohol.

Teens who choose friends who avoid alcohol will have an easier time refusing it themselves. Some teens refuse because they have a friend with an alcohol problem and don't want to turn out that way. Some teens refuse because they know a friend or family member who was killed because of drinking.

 **How can you and your friends help each other avoid alcohol?**

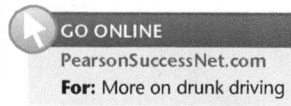

GO ONLINE
PearsonSuccessNet.com
For: More on drunk driving

Alcohol **375**

Alcohol **375**

Media Wise

Sports and Alcohol

Introduce the activity by asking: **What are ways that ads for alcohol try to connect sports and alcohol in people's minds.** *(Sample answer: They show fit, athletic-looking people in outdoor settings.)*

Activity Have students do the activity as a homework assignment. After students have completed the assignment, ask them to describe examples of ads that received *yes* answers. Discuss why *yes* answers indicate a link between alcohol and sports. Then ask how the attempt to connect alcohol to sports is misleading. *(Sample answer: Drinking alcohol doesn't improve a person's athletic performance.)*

L3 Journal Writing

Ask students to write a journal entry describing how a parent or other family member influences their decisions about alcohol. Reassure students that their writing will be kept private. In case this issue is too sensitive for some students, give the class a choice of writing assignments. Another option might be why drinking alcohol does not increase popularity. **WRITING**

L3 Cultural Connection

Discuss the role of alcohol in different religions. For example, Catholics and Jews use small amounts of alcohol in some of their religious rituals, whereas Muslims and Mormons have strict laws entirely prohibiting alcohol. Ask students to share other examples of religions that either use alcohol ritually or forbid its use. Point out that religions in which alcohol does play a role limit its use and discourage its abuse.

Media Wise

Sports and Alcohol

Think back to the last time you watched a sports event on TV. What kinds of products were advertised during the commercials? Chances are, some of the ads were for beer. Besides being aired during sports events, how do the ads try to connect sports and alcohol in people's minds?

Does the ad have a competitive or a sports-related theme?	Yes No
Does the beer have a "mascot," as many sports teams do?	Yes No
Is beer shown to improve athletic performance or increase enjoyment of sports?	Yes No
Does the ad make other connections to sports?	Yes No

A "Yes" answer to one or more questions indicates a link connecting an alcohol ad to sports.

Activity Watch two beer commercials that air during sporting events. Use the checklist above to evaluate whether the ads make a connection between sports and alcohol. Then explain how the connection to sports is misleading. **WRITING**

Influence of Family Teens report that parents and other family members are important influences on their decisions about alcohol. A majority of teens want their parents' guidance in making decisions about alcohol use. Although your parents may seem tough on you, their rules and advice can help you steer clear of alcohol and other drugs.

Influence of the Media Alcohol's wide availability makes it relatively easy to obtain. Alcohol use is also seen as generally acceptable in people who are over 21—even though it can be dangerous at any age.

Companies that sell alcohol bombard the public with advertisements for beer, wine, liquor, and other beverages. Television commercials and magazine ads often show drinkers in beautiful outdoor settings, at fun-filled parties, or enjoying sports. Although the ads never show underage drinking, the scenarios tend to appeal to teens as much as to adults.

Usually the message accompanying an alcohol ad says nothing about the product. Unlike ads for some drugs, alcohol ads are not required to list negative side effects. Instead, the ads promote a one-sided image of drinkers as athletic, healthy, and successful. The ads give the false impression that drinking will make you more popular and attractive.

376 *Chapter 15*

TEENS *Are Asking . . .*

Q: I see kids drinking in the parking lot during football games on Friday nights. They look like they know something that I don't know. Doesn't drinking sometimes make you look cool?

A: You might think these students look "cool" now, but think about how they would look if they were to drink and drive and end up in a car crash. Or how they might look the next morning when they are hung over and trying to recall what they said or did the night before. The next time you think kids look cool because they are drinking, think about those images as well.

Risks of Underage Drinking Teen alcohol use can have very serious consequences. In fact, alcohol is a huge factor in injury deaths, the leading cause of death among teens. Teens who use alcohol increase their risk of the following:

► Being injured or killed in a motor vehicle crash

► Committing or being the victim of sexual assault or other violence

► Long-term brain damage

► Problems with alcohol later in life

► Suspension from school, sports teams, or other school activities

Legal Risks Laws prohibiting minors—people under the age of 21—from buying or possessing alcohol are enforced with heavy fines and lawful seizure of property. For example, law-enforcement officers in some states can seize a car in which a minor is in possession of alcohol. Selling alcohol to someone under the age of 21 is a criminal offense for the seller. In many states, it is against the law to serve alcohol to people under the legal drinking age, even at a private party.

People found to be driving under the influence of alcohol may have their driver's licenses taken away or face other stiff penalties. In some states, those found guilty repeatedly can be sent to prison. You will learn more about driving laws in the next section.

FIGURE 2 Each year, crashes and other injuries related to underage drinking kill about 5,000 youth in the United States.

Section 1 Review

Key Ideas and Vocabulary

1. What is a **depressant**?
2. List at least three of the depressant effects alcohol may cause.
3. Describe how **fermentation** produces alcohol.
4. What are three major factors that influence underage drinking?

Critical Thinking

5. **Making Judgments** Some people argue that alcohol should not be considered a drug. After all, it is legal for adults to use alcohol. What do you think? **WRITING**

Health at School

School Policy on Alcohol Find out your school's policy on alcohol. Make a poster that informs your peers of the rules and the consequences. **WRITING**

---

6. **Predicting** What legal consequences could you face by possessing alcohol as a minor?
7. **Relating Cause and Effect** Students who use alcohol regularly are more likely than nondrinkers to get lower grades, drop out of school, and use other drugs. Offer some reasons why you think this is so. **WRITING**

🔊)) GO ONLINE PearsonSuccessNet.com Audio Summary Section 15.1

Alcohol **377**

Communicating

Developing Refusal Skills

Objective

Communicate *no* in a way that tells others you mean it.

Teaching Strategies

- Ask a volunteer to help you role-play a wishy-washy, half-hearted refusal to an offer of alcohol. Ask students to point out specific words, facial expressions, or body language that suggest you do not really mean *no*.

- Have students read through the guidelines for learning refusal skills. Point out that the second step is illustrated in the picture on page 378. Make sure students read the lists of Do's and Don'ts in the picture.

- Discuss why showing concern for others' drinking can help students refuse alcohol by reinforcing their own commitment not to drink. Ask students to think of other things they could say to friends who have decided to drink. *(Sample answer: If you drink, you might get kicked off the team.)*

- Challenge the class to brainstorm and list on the board other situations in which teens would want to say *no*. (Examples might include a boyfriend or girlfriend insisting on having sex, a friend asking you to lie for her, or a classmate pressuring you to smoke cigarettes.) For each situation, have students suggest two honest reasons for refusing.

Developing Refusal Skills

Erica's friends are pressuring her to drink alcohol with them. Though Erica does not use drugs of any kind, she worries about what her friends will think if she refuses. Perhaps you have felt this way about saying no to your friends. Maybe you worried that if you refused, your friends would be disappointed or not want to hang out with you. You might even have decided to go along with your friends just to avoid the discomfort of saying no.

Refusing your friends is never easy. Nevertheless, being true to yourself and honest with friends are two important values. To refuse an offer convincingly, you may need to do more than say *no*. These guidelines can help you learn to say *no* in a way that tells others you mean it.

When You Refuse...

Do
- Make eye contact.
- Stand up tall.
- Use a firm voice.

Don't
- Look at the ground or glance away.
- Show that you're nervous.
- Speak softly.

Sensitive Issues

- Students may not be comfortable writing about situations in which they said *no*. For example, they may have been at a party they were not supposed to attend when they said *no* to drugs. Give students the option of describing hypothetical situations.

- Tell students not to use the real names of other people that are involved in the situations they describe.

① Give a reason for your refusal.

When you say no, also state reasons for your refusal. Be honest—honest answers are more easily accepted by others. Some reasons might be:

"I want to keep a clear head."

"I could get suspended from the team."

"I'd rather have a soft drink."

② Use body language to reinforce what you say.

Your body language can either strengthen or weaken your message.

③ Show your concern for others.

Express your concern for those trying to persuade you. In the case of friends who have decided to drink, you might say things like:

"I'd be really sad if anything happened to you."

"Your parents would ground you for months if they ever found out."

④ Provide alternatives.

Try to persuade your friends to do something safer or more comfortable. Here are some suggestions:

"I'm bored. Let's hang out at the Teen Center."

"This isn't fun. Let's go to a movie."

⑤ Take a definite action.

If your friends still try to persuade you after you have made your feelings clear, it is best not to continue repeating the point. Instead, take a definite action that removes you from the situation. This will make it clear that you cannot be persuaded to change your mind.

If All Else Fails...

Get up and leave the party.

Call other friends and do something else.

Always call for help rather than ride with someone who has been drinking.

 Practice the Skill

1. Suppose that a friend asks you to sit close by during a test and share your answers.
   a. How would your friend's request make you feel? Why?
   b. If you were to refuse, what honest reason could you give? How would you express yourself?
   c. What are some possible consequences of saying no? What are some possible consequences of saying yes?

2. Think of two situations in which you said no to people who tried to convince you to do something you did not want to do.
   a. Describe each situation. List the things that allowed you to refuse in each case.
   b. In which situation was it more difficult to say no? Why?
   c. Did you use any of the steps presented in this skill when you refused? If so, describe the steps and how effective they were.

Alcohol **379**

---

1. a. Answers will vary. Students might say that the request would make them feel uncomfortable because it would involve doing something risky.

b. *Sample answer:* I could give the honest reason that I might get caught and accused of cheating. I would be reasonable and avoid sounding angry, but I would also be firm and look my friend straight in the eye.

c. Possible consequences of saying *no* might include the friend becoming angry, the friend studying harder, and neither student getting in trouble for cheating. Possible consequences of saying *yes* might include both students getting caught cheating, receiving failing grades in the course, and being grounded at home.

2. a. *Remind students not to use the real names of people involved in the situations they describe.* Answers will vary. Students might describe a situation in which a friend asked them to drink or use drugs. Things that allowed students to refuse might include thinking about their parents' reaction if they said *yes* and knowing that saying *no* was the only legal alternative.

b. Answers will vary depending on the situations students described in answer 2a. *Sample answer:* It was harder to say *no* to the offer of a beer than the offer of a ride home with a friend who had been drinking, because I knew that riding with a drunk driver could be deadly.

c. Answers will vary. *Sample answer:* I gave a reason for refusing to drink when I said I didn't want to get into trouble, and I provided an alternative to drinking when I said we should go to a movie instead. The steps were effective because my friends decided to leave the party and go to a movie with me.

Health at School

ⓛ⑶ Sharing Refusal Skills

After students complete the activity, ask some of them to share their knowledge of refusal skills with other students in their school. Have students write a public service announcement in which they use a brief dialogue to demonstrate the steps on this page. Arrange to have the students read their announcements over the school's public address system. **WRITING**

Objectives

Before class begins, write the objectives on the board. Have students copy the objectives into their notebooks at the start of class.

1. Focus

Warm-Up **Health Stats**

Ask a few volunteers to share their answers. Then ask other volunteers to describe a time when quick reactions helped them avoid a car crash or other accident. Discuss what might have happened if their reaction time had been slowed by alcohol. Tell students they will learn in this section why alcohol slows reaction time and causes other adverse effects.

Presentation 15-2

Connect to Your Life Students might describe such effects as slurring words, stumbling, falling down, acting aggressively, and passing out.

Section 2

Alcohol's Effects on the Body

Objectives

▶ **Summarize** the effects of intoxication on the body systems.

▶ **List** four factors that affect blood alcohol concentration.

▶ **Identify** three ways that intoxication may lead to death.

Vocabulary

• intoxication
• blackout
• blood alcohol concentration (BAC)
• hangover
• driving while intoxicated (DWI)
• overdose
• binge drinking

Warm-Up

Health Stats What trend does this graph reveal?

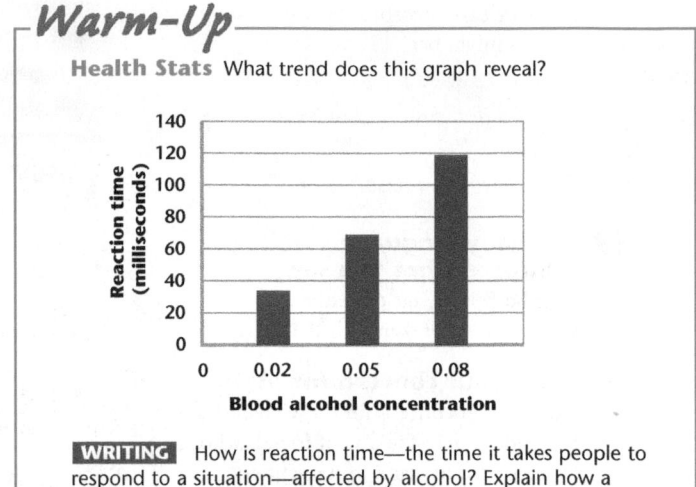

WRITING How is reaction time—the time it takes people to respond to a situation—affected by alcohol? Explain how a longer reaction time affects a person's safety on the road.

Physical and Behavioral Effects

When a person drinks alcohol, the alcohol follows the same pathway through the digestive system as food. But unlike food, alcohol does not have to be digested in the stomach before it is absorbed into the blood. Thus, alcohol gets into a person's bloodstream within minutes of being consumed. Once in the blood, alcohol circulates throughout the body, where it has widespread effects.

Effects on Body Systems When people drink alcohol faster than the body can break it down into harmless compounds they become intoxicated. **Intoxication** is the state in which a person's mental and physical abilities are impaired by alcohol or another substance. **Many negative effects on a drinker's body and behavior accompany intoxication by alcohol.** Some of these effects are shown in Figure 3.

Connect to Your Life Think of a movie or book in which a character became intoxicated. Describe the effects.

🚩 **Sensitive Issues**

Students who have experienced the loss of a classmate, friend, or family member due to drunk driving may be upset by the issue. Be attuned to their needs, and remind students of healthful ways to express grief, such as journal writing.

For Your **INFORMATION!**

Alcohol Use and Risky Behaviors

When teens use alcohol, they are also more likely to engage in other risky behaviors. Drinking alcohol increases the risk that a teen will also

• be in a physical fight or carry a weapon.
• commit a serious crime such as rape or be the victim of a serious crime.

• use illegal drugs such as marijuana or cocaine.
• die from a car crash or drowning.
• engage in sexual activity, especially unprotected sexual activity.
• attempt suicide.

Effects of Intoxication

FIGURE 3 Intoxication has many effects on a drinker's body and behavior. **Predicting** Which effects would reduce a person's ability to drive safely?

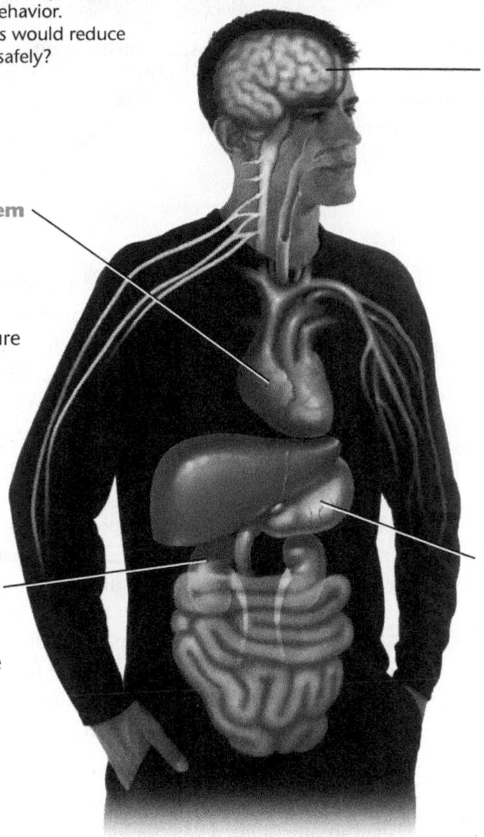

Nervous System
- Brain activity slows down.
- Coordination becomes impaired.
- Sensations and perception become less clear.
- Reflexes become sluggish.

Cardiovascular System
- Heart rate and blood pressure increase.
- More blood flows to the skin's surface.
- Core body temperature decreases.

Excretory System
- Kidneys increase urine production.
- Drinker loses more water from body than usual.

Digestive System
- Too much alcohol in the stomach may cause vomiting.

Effects on Behavior As intoxication takes effect, drinkers begin to lose judgment and self-control. At the same time, alcohol decreases drinkers' natural fears. When these two effects are combined, drinkers may behave in ways they normally would never consider. For example, a person under the influence of alcohol may express anger in violent or destructive ways. Shy people may behave in outgoing ways, and serious people may act foolishly.

A person who drinks a lot of alcohol may suffer a blackout. A **blackout** is a period of time that the drinker cannot recall. Other people may recall seeing the drinker talking, walking, and seemingly in control. The following day, however, the drinker may have no memory of some events from the day before. The drinker may harm others or be harmed during a blackout. Blackouts can happen to first-time drinkers as well as to experienced drinkers.

Alcohol **381**

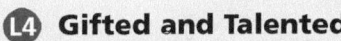
---

2. Teach

 **L3 EL** Reading/Note Taking 15-2

L2 Adapted Reading/Note Taking 15-2

Physical and Behavioral Effects

EL Building Vocabulary

Have students list on a sheet of notebook paper all the unfamiliar terms they encounter as they read this section. Then, ask students to write a definition for each term in English, using their own words. Suggest that they keep the list in their notebook and use it as a personal glossary for the section.

L2 Building Vocabulary

On the board, write the following word parts and their definitions: *in-* ("in"), *toxic-* ("poison"), and *-ation* ("process"). Ask students to put the word parts together to create a vocabulary term *(intoxication)* and then define the term *(e.g., in the process of being poisoned)*. Ask: **Based on this definition of intoxication, what is alcohol?** *(a poison)* Have students read the definition of intoxication on page 380 and the effects of intoxication in Figure 3.

L3 Visual Learning: Figure 3

Image Bank Figure 15-3

Challenge students to use information in the figure to explain two apparent contradictions about intoxication. Ask: **Why does intoxication cause dehydration even though drinkers consume a lot of liquid when they drink?** *(Intoxication causes the kidneys to produce more urine and the body to lose more water.)* **Why does intoxication make drinkers feel warmer in cold weather even though they are at increased risk of "freezing" to death?** *(Intoxication causes blood to flow to the skin's surface and core body temperature to decrease.)* Call on a student to answer the caption question.

Caption Answer nervous system effects, such as coordination becoming impaired and reflexes becoming sluggish

Alcohol **381**

Blood Alcohol Concentration

 **Visual Learning: Figure 4**

Remind students that the numbers for blood alcohol concentration (BAC) in the figure are percentages. For example, the blood alcohol concentration at which reflexes and alertness decline is 0.02 percent to 0.03 percent. Ask: **What percentage of alcohol in the blood may be life threatening?** *(0.40% or higher)* To put these numbers in terms that students might better understand, remind them that 0.40% means four-tenths of one percent and 0.02% means two-hundredths of one percent.

L3 Class Discussion

Discuss why BAC is a more reliable measure of intoxication than the number of drinks a person has consumed. Then describe various pairs of hypothetical individuals who vary in gender and body size. For each pair, challenge students to predict which individual they think would have the higher BAC if they drank the same amount of alcohol at the same rate on an empty stomach. Ask students to explain their predictions. **MATH**

L3 Online Activity **GO ONLINE**

Visit Pearson SuccessNet to access an online activity about blood alcohol concentration. Have students complete the Web activity.

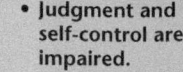

When Blood Alcohol Concentration Is . . .			
0.02–0.03	**0.04–0.06**	**0.07–0.09**	**0.12–0.15**
• Reflexes and alertness decline.	• Judgment and self-control are impaired. • Reaction time slows.	• Muscle coordination decreases.	• Vomiting usually occurs. • Emotions become exaggerated, unstable, or violent.

FIGURE 4 As blood alcohol concentration increases, physical and behavioral effects get more and more severe.

GO ONLINE
PearsonSuccessNet.com
For: More on blood alcohol concentration

Blood Alcohol Concentration

Two people who drink the same amount of alcohol may not be equally affected. Why? The effects of alcohol depend on how much is actually circulating in a person's bloodstream. This amount is termed the **blood alcohol concentration (BAC).** BAC is the amount of alcohol in a person's blood, expressed as a percentage. For example, a BAC of 0.1 percent means that one-tenth of 1 percent of the fluid in the blood is alcohol.

The higher a person's blood alcohol concentration, the more severe the physical and behavioral effects. Blood alcohol concentration is a more reliable measure of intoxication than the number of drinks consumed.

Factors Affecting BAC A variety of factors affect a drinker's BAC. You can see the effects of some of these factors in Figure 5. **The rate of alcohol consumption, the gender and size of the drinker, and how much food is in the stomach all affect BAC.**

▶ **Rate of Consumption** A person's liver chemically breaks down, or metabolizes, alcohol at a fairly constant rate. That rate is about one half to one ounce of alcohol per hour—the approximate amount of alcohol in one can of beer, one shot of liquor, or one glass of wine. Therefore, people who have a few drinks in one hour have a higher BAC than people who drink the same amount over several hours.

▶ **Gender** At the same rate and amount of alcohol consumption, males generally will have a lower BAC than females. This is because, for males, a larger portion of the alcohol gets metabolized in the stomach before it enters the bloodstream. In addition, the liver is more efficient at metabolizing alcohol in males.

▶ **Body Size** In general, smaller people—by weight and height—feel the effects of alcohol more than larger people. They will have a higher BAC after a similar number of drinks.

▶ **Amount of Food in the Stomach** Drinking on an empty stomach increases the rate of alcohol absorption into the bloodstream. A higher BAC will result.

WRITING and Health

 Firsthand Account

Based on the information in Figure 4, challenge students to write a first-hand account of how someone might behave if his or her blood alcohol concentration increased over a period of a few hours

from 0.00 to 0.20 percent. (Students should give an account of a person who shows increasing effects of intoxication, as listed in Figure 4. They should describe the person as though they were observing the person firsthand.)

0.20	0.30	0.40	0.50 and higher
• Confusion, dizziness, and disorientation occur. • Vision and speech are impaired. • Blackouts are typical.	• Ability to stand or walk is lost. • Loss of consciousness may occur.	• Loss of consciousness usually occurs. • Death may occur.	• Death usually occurs.

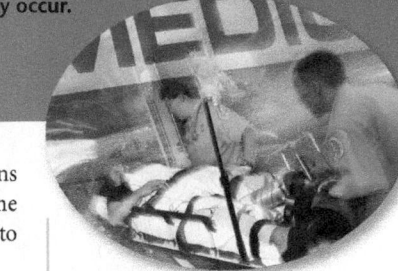

After Drinking Ends Once a person stops drinking, BAC begins to decrease. The intoxicating effects of alcohol slowly diminish, and the person's reflexes and coordination return to normal. Many people refer to this process as "becoming sober" or "sobering up."

You may have heard that cold showers, exercise, fresh air, or coffee will help a person sober up more quickly. But this is not true. Nothing can speed the liver's ability to break down alcohol. Fresh air may keep a person awake, but it does not eliminate the intoxicating effects of alcohol.

Hangovers Drinking heavily usually causes a person to wake up the next day with a hangover. **Hangover** is a term used to describe the after-effects of drinking too much alcohol. Symptoms of a hangover include nausea, upset stomach, headache, and a sensitivity to noise. It is not clear why some drinkers get a hangover and others do not. The only way a person can be sure to prevent one is to avoid alcohol altogether.

Your Life Your friend says he'll drive you home after he "sobers up" with a cup of coffee. What do you say?

FIGURE 5 Several factors besides number of drinks affect blood alcohol concentration. **Predicting** Predict the BAC of a 110-pound woman after she consumes three drinks in one hour.

Estimating Blood Alcohol Concentration

Number of Drinks* (per hour)	Males			Females		
	100–120 lb	120–140 lb	140–160 lb	100–120 lb	120–140 lb	140–160 lb
1	0.04	0.03	0.02	0.05	0.04	0.03
3	0.10	0.08	0.07	0.13	0.11	0.07
5	0.18	0.15	0.12	0.21	0.18	0.15
7	0.24	0.20	0.17	0.30	0.25	0.22

*One drink is 1.25 oz of 80-proof liquor, 5 oz of wine, or 12 oz of beer.

Alcohol **383**

L2 Teacher Demo

Show students how the rate of drinking affects BAC. Place a paper coffee filter in a funnel, and rest the funnel in a glass jar. Slowly pour water into the funnel through the filter. Tell students that the filter is like the liver and the water is like alcohol. Now pour the water faster, so it starts to overflow the filter. Tell students that this is like a person drinking too quickly for the liver to break down the alcohol. Ask: **What happens to the drinker when that occurs?** (The drinker becomes intoxicated.) **How can I stop the funnel from overflowing?** (Stop pouring water into it or pour more slowly.) **How can the drinker become less intoxicated?** (Stop drinking or drink over a longer period of time.)

L3 Visual Learning: Figure 5
Image Bank Figure 15-5

Ask: **Which three factors affecting BAC are represented in the table?** (rate of consumption, gender, and body size) **How do BAC estimates for females and males compare?** (For the same rate of consumption and body size, females have higher BAC estimates than males.) **What is the BAC estimate of a 150-pound man after he consumes five drinks in one hour?** (0.12). **Using the information in Figure 4, what are the likely effects on his body at this BAC?** (vomiting and exaggerated, unstable, or violent emotions) Call on a student to answer the caption question. Make sure students realize that the man has a lower BAC than the woman, even though he drank more than she did in the same amount of time.
Caption Answer 0.13

Your Life *Sample answer:* No, thanks. A cup of coffee will not help you sober up, so you will still be intoxicated and not fit to drive.

Differentiated Instruction

L1 Special Needs

Have students do a simple hands-on activity to help them understand the concept of blood alcohol concentration (BAC). Give each student two clear plastic cups half full of water, a small bottle of food coloring, a dropper, and a drinking straw. Tell students that the water represents blood and the food coloring represents alcohol. Have students add one drop of food coloring to one cup and thoroughly stir the water with the straw. Then have them add six drops of food coloring to the other cup and thoroughly stir the water. Explain that the water in the first cup is like the blood of a drinker with a low BAC and the water in the second cup is like the blood of a drinker with a high BAC.

Life-Threatening Effects

L4 Cooperative Learning

Have groups of students find rates of teen car crashes involving alcohol in different areas of their state. Have groups compare and discuss the rates. Ask: **Which areas have higher rates and why?** *(Sample answer: Rates might be higher in rural areas than in urban areas. Possible reasons might include higher speed limits, worse road conditions, and higher rates of teen drinking in rural areas.)* Urge students to investigate further and try to identify the most likely reasons for the different rates. Then have the class brainstorm ways to reduce rates of teen car crashes involving alcohol.

L3 Addressing Misconceptions

Alcohol and Safe Driving Point out that *legal* does not necessarily mean *safe* when it comes to alcohol and driving. For example, it is legal in some states for adults to drive with a BAC of 0.06 percent, but this level of alcohol doubles the risk of being involved in a car crash. Because alcohol affects different people differently, there is no truly "safe" level of alcohol.

L2 Building Health Skills

Practicing Healthful Behaviors Tell students to assume that some teens at a party are playing a "drinking game" and getting very drunk. Ask: **What would you do if you were at the party?** *(Sample answers: try to convince them to stop drinking, tell an adult, call 911)* Make sure students realize that someone who is very intoxicated is unlikely to listen to reason and may need emergency medical help. Take this opportunity to re-emphasize the seriousness of binge drinking due to the risk of overdose and death.

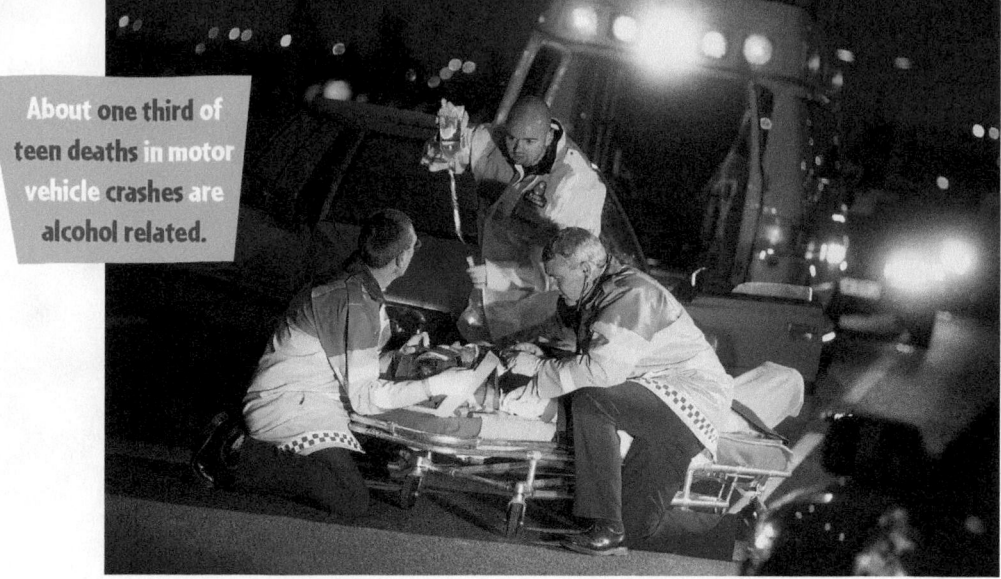

About one third of teen deaths in motor vehicle crashes are alcohol related.

FIGURE 6 Alcohol has a dramatic effect on fatality risk in motor vehicle crashes.

Life-Threatening Effects

The short-term effects of intoxication can put a drinker at serious risk. **Intoxication increases the risk of death from motor vehicle crashes, alcohol overdose, and interactions of alcohol with other drugs.**

Motor Vehicle Crashes Alcohol is involved in about 40 percent of fatal motor vehicle crashes. Driving can be impaired by any amount of drinking, even if it falls below legal limits.

Alcohol especially impairs the driving skills of underage drinkers. Because of their relative lack of driving experience, underage drivers are already more likely to crash, even without the influence of alcohol. The effects of alcohol and driving inexperience together are a particularly dangerous combination.

▶ **Driving Under the Influence** A driver over age 21 caught driving with a BAC that exceeds the legal limit of 0.08 is charged with **driving while intoxicated (DWI).** Law enforcement officers often measure BAC with a breath alcohol testing device. The device measures the alcohol level in the breath from the lungs, from which BAC is accurately estimated. Or a blood sample may be drawn and tested directly. People whose BAC is above the legal limit can have their driver's license taken away and can be prosecuted. They may have to pay stiff fines or serve jail time.

▶ **Zero Tolerance Laws** For drivers under the age 21, the law is different. The purchase and possession of alcohol by minors is already illegal. Therefore, there is no acceptable BAC for underage drivers. Laws vary a little from state to state, but in all cases, it is illegal for minors to drive after consuming any amount of alcohol. The penalties for underage drivers may be more strict than those for other drivers.

384 *Chapter 15*

Focus on **ISSUES**

L3 Debate: Drinking Age

Assign several students to represent each side of a debate about whether the minimum drinking age should be lowered to 18. Those arguing for a minimum drinking age of 18 might note that teens who are permitted to drive, join the military, and vote should also be allowed to make their own decisions about drinking. Those arguing against a lower drinking age might point out that there are already many drinking problems on college campuses, and that making drinking legal would only make problems worse. Give students a chance to present the debate in class. After the debate, ask other students to voice their opinions on the issue.

Overdose Taking an excessive amount of a drug that leads to coma or death is called an **overdose.** Alcohol overdose, also called alcohol poisoning, can cause the heart and breathing to stop. Many drinkers assume that they will pass out before drinking a fatal amount. This is not necessarily true. Alcohol continues to be absorbed into the blood for 30 to 90 minutes after a person's last drink. The drinker's BAC can increase even if the drinker becomes unconscious.

A person need not be a regular drinker or an alcoholic to die from an overdose. Even someone drinking for the first time can overdose and die from binge drinking. **Binge drinking** is the consumption of excessive amounts of alcohol at one sitting. Binge drinking is a particular problem among underage drinkers, who may consume many drinks on a bet or dare, or during a "drinking game." Binge drinking also affects teens more severely than older drinkers—teens enter comas at lower blood alcohol concentrations than adults.

Interactions With Other Drugs Sometimes, two drugs can interact to produce effects that are greater than either drug would produce by itself. Recall that alcohol is a depressant drug. When a person drinks alcohol and takes another depressant, such as sleeping pills, the combination can cause drastic changes in the body. Together, the two depressants' effects are more than doubled and can dangerously slow breathing and heart rates. In extreme cases, combining alcohol and other depressants leads to coma or death.

Warning Signs of Alcohol Poisoning
- Cold, clammy, pale, or bluish skin
- Slow or irregular respiration
- Vomiting while "sleeping"
- Cannot be wakened (unconscious)

FIGURE 7 If someone you know shows any of these warning signs, contact emergency medical services.

Section 2 Review

Key Ideas and Vocabulary
1. What is **intoxication?**
2. Describe the effects of intoxication on four body systems.
3. List four factors that affect blood alcohol concentration.
4. What are three ways that intoxication can lead to death?
5. For drivers over age 21, how is **driving while intoxicated (DWI)** defined?
6. What is an **overdose?** How could **binge drinking** cause an alcohol overdose?

Health and Community

BAC and Driving Laws Since state governments lowered the legal limit for adult drivers from a BAC of 0.10 to 0.08, thousands of lives have been saved. Is 0.08 low enough? Take a poll of teens and adults in your community. Summarize your findings in a letter to a local politician. **WRITING**

Critical Thinking
7. **Relating Cause and Effect** Teens who use alcohol are more likely to get into fights than those who don't. Relate this fact to the effects of intoxication on the nervous system. **WRITING**
8. **Comparing and Contrasting** How do drinking-and-driving laws differ for teens and adults?

Section 3
Long-Term Risks of Alcohol

Objectives
Before class begins, write the objectives on the board. Have students copy the objectives into their notebooks at the start of class.

1. Focus

Warm-Up Myth/Fact

Call on a few volunteers to share their answers. Restate correctly as fact any other common misconceptions of alcoholics that students reveal, such as "Alcoholics have a character flaw" (which might be restated as "Alcoholics have a disease"). Tell students they will learn more about alcoholics and alcoholism in this section.

Presentation 15-3

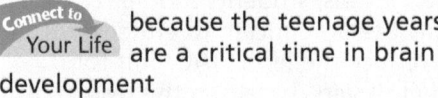 because the teenage years are a critical time in brain development

Sensitive Issues

• Some students might try to identify classmates or others with the various descriptions of problem drinkers. Make sure students do not publicly identify and embarrass any individual.

• Students who have alcoholic family members may feel uncomfortable during class discussions. Stress that all members of a family in which alcoholism occurs will not necessarily become alcoholics. Recognizing the problem and knowing the warning signs of problem drinking are helpful in avoiding the disease.

Section 3

Objectives
▶ **Identify** five serious physical effects of long-term alcohol abuse.
▶ **Describe** the three stages of alcoholism.
▶ **List** in order three steps taken during recovery from alcoholism.

Vocabulary
• fetal alcohol syndrome
• cirrhosis
• alcoholism
• tolerance
• dependence
• addiction
• reverse tolerance
• detoxification
• withdrawal
• rehabilitation

Long-Term Risks of Alcohol

Warm-Up

Myth Alcoholics sleep on park benches and wear shabby clothes.

Fact Alcoholics come from all cultures, backgrounds, and levels of education.

WRITING In what ways does the media contribute to this myth about alcoholics? How else does the media shape people's perception of alcoholics?

Damage to the Body

Adults over age 21 who use alcohol responsibly usually are not at risk of developing long-term health problems related to alcohol. But heavy drinking can cause serious damage to the body over time. **Long-term alcohol abuse may harm the brain, liver, heart, and digestive system. Furthermore, drinking any amount of alcohol during pregnancy may permanently harm the developing baby.**

Brain Damage Long-term alcohol abuse destroys nerve cells in the brain. Destroyed nerve cells usually cannot grow again. The loss of many nerve cells causes permanent changes that impair memory, the ability to concentrate, and the ability to make sound judgments. These losses interfere with normal everyday functions.

Effects on the brain can be especially damaging for underage drinkers. When teens drink, they expose the brain to alcohol during a critical time in its development. Teenage drinkers may suffer long-term learning and memory problems.

 **Why are teens especially vulnerable to brain damage caused by alcohol?**

TEENS *Are Asking . . .*

Q: I read that the effects of alcohol on the brain are cumulative. Does that mean drinking one drink a day for ten days is as harmful as drinking ten drinks in two hours?

A: The effects of alcohol are cumulative in that the brain damage done during a single bout of drinking adds to any prior damage. Drinking one drink vs. ten drinks at a time is a different matter. Drinking ten drinks in two hours is binge drinking. Research shows that binge drinking can permanently damage parts of the brain responsible for judgment, impulse control, and memory formation. The brains of teens are more susceptible to damage from binge drinking than the brains of adults. For a lightweight person, drinking ten drinks in an hour could result in coma or even death.

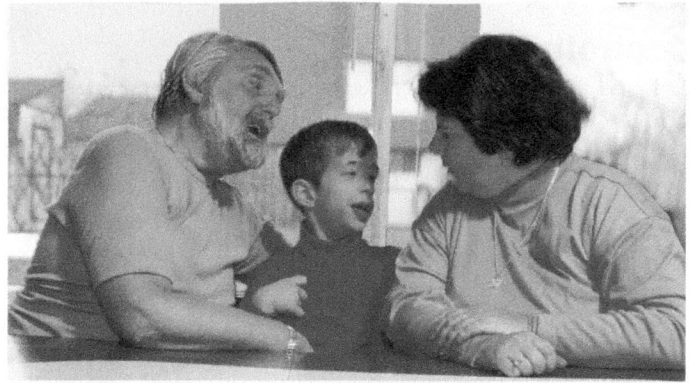

FIGURE 8 Drinking any amount of alcohol during pregnancy may cause fetal alcohol syndrome. This boy, shown with his adoptive parents, has severe symptoms.

Fetal Alcohol Syndrome Pregnant women who drink put the health of their future children at risk. **Fetal alcohol syndrome** is a group of birth defects caused by the effects of alcohol on an unborn child.

Babies born with this syndrome may suffer from heart defects, malformed faces, delayed growth, poor motor development, and mental retardation. Some show only brain and behavioral problems, without the other physical effects.

Tragically, drinking during pregnancy is the leading preventable cause of mental retardation in the United States. Even small amounts of alcohol consumed during pregnancy can cause brain damage. Any woman who is planning to become pregnant, or who is already pregnant or breast-feeding, should not drink any alcohol.

Liver Damage Alcohol interferes with the liver's ability to metabolize, or break down, fats. As a result of heavy drinking, the liver begins to fill with fat, which blocks the flow of blood in the liver. The fat-filled liver cells die, leaving behind useless scar tissue. This disease, called **cirrhosis** (sih ROH sis), may lead to liver failure and death.

Heavy drinkers also may suffer from alcoholic hepatitis, an inflammation of the liver caused by the toxic effects of alcohol. It too can cause the drinker to die.

Heart Disease Excessive drinking contributes to heart disease, the leading cause of death in the United States. Over time, alcohol causes increased blood pressure and heart rate, irregular heartbeat, and a buildup of fatty deposits in the heart muscle.

Digestive Problems Ongoing drinking also irritates the tissues that line the digestive system, causing inflammation. Repeated irritation increases the risk of

▸ cancers of the mouth, tongue, esophagus, and stomach.

▸ recurring diarrhea.

▸ chronic indigestion, heartburn, or ulcers.

▼ **Healthy liver**

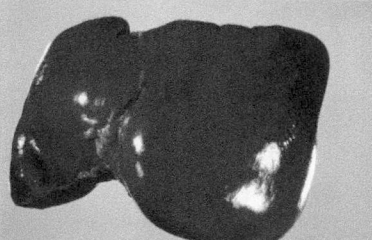

▼ **Liver damaged by cirrhosis**

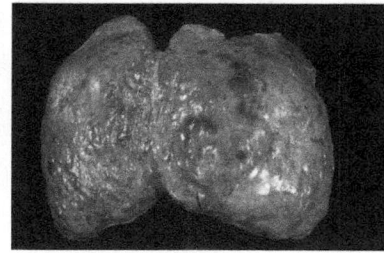

FIGURE 9 A healthy liver contains smooth tissue. The liver of a heavy drinker contains useless scar tissue.

Alcohol **387**

Alcoholism

EL Building Media Literacy

The terms *alcoholism, tolerance, dependence,* and *addiction* are easily confused. Write the terms on the board, and then ask: **What type of media could you search for more detailed definitions of these terms?** (*Sample answers: dictionaries, encyclopedias, medical reference books, nonfiction books about alcoholism, medical Web sites*) Ask students to search the different types of media for definitions of the terms and decide which type of media is most useful for this purpose.

L3 Addressing Misconceptions

The Nature of Alcoholism Many people think that alcoholics drink because they are irresponsible or morally weak. In fact, research shows that alcoholism is a complex disease involving serious social and psychological problems. It may also have a biochemical component that can be genetically transmitted. Help students understand that the progression of alcoholism can be stopped because it is a treatable disease.

L2 Visual Learning: Figure 10

Have students read the caption and examine the photos. Call on a volunteer to answer the caption question. Ask: **If the two teens whose brain scans are shown here were doing a math test, which teen do you think would get a lower score?** (*the heavy drinker*) **Caption Answer** the brain of the non-drinker

FIGURE 10 Teenage drinking affects the brain dramatically in the short term. Shown here (in red) is brain activity in two teens asked to perform the same task. **Interpreting Photos** Which brain has more activity?

Alcoholism

People who can no longer control their use of alcohol suffer from the disease known as **alcoholism.** Physically, an alcoholic's body requires alcohol to function. Psychologically, alcoholics consider drinking a regular, essential part of coping with daily life.

Changes to the Brain With repeated use of alcohol, its effects in the brain become reduced—the body has developed **tolerance** to alcohol. Tolerance causes a drinker's body to need increasingly larger amounts of alcohol to achieve the original effect.

With increasing tolerance, the body will eventually develop **dependence**—the brain develops a chemical need for alcohol and cannot function normally without it. Finally, **addiction** results—the drinker no longer has control over his or her drinking. Alcohol addiction is characterized by a craving, or strong emotional need, to use alcohol.

Because alcoholics can no longer control their alcohol use, they must receive help to recover from this disease. Scientists have found that during addiction, the structure and the chemistry of the brain changes—addiction is a disease of the brain.

Who Is at Risk? Anyone who drinks is at risk of becoming an alcoholic. However, some people seem to be at higher risk than others. For example, alcoholism is four to five times more common among the children of alcoholics than in the general population. The reason for this is likely a combination of the influence of genetics and the environment in which a person grows up.

Attitudes towards drinking and the availability of alcohol in the home play a strong role in determining whether or not a person will develop a drinking problem. Underage drinking also increases a person's risk of becoming an alcoholic.

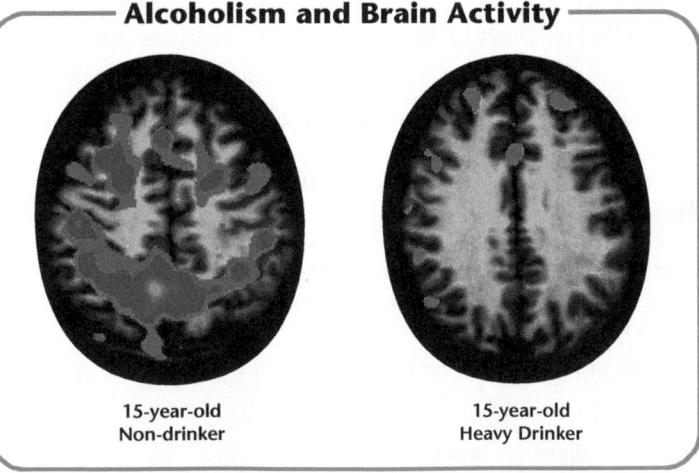

Alcoholism and Brain Activity

15-year-old
Non-drinker

15-year-old
Heavy Drinker

388 *Chapter 15*

Focus on ISSUES

L3 Early Drinking and Alcoholism

Tell students that the younger teens are when they start drinking, the more likely they are to become alcoholics. Ask: **Does this mean that early drinking causes alcoholism?** (*At least some students are likely to say "yes."*) Explain that the link between early drinking and alcoholism means only that the two are correlated, or tend to occur together. A teen who drinks may not end up an alcoholic, or may end up an alcoholic for reasons other than early drinking. Then tell students that both alcoholics and teens who start drinking early have higher-than-average rates of psychiatric problems. Ask: **Based on this fact, how do you think early drinking and alcoholism might be related?** (*Sample answer: Both might be caused by the same psychiatric problems.*)

The Stages of Alcoholism Alcoholics progress through several stages as their dependence strengthens. **What begins as problem drinking becomes absolute dependence, and finally, late-stage alcoholism.** Each stage may last weeks, months, or years. Teenage alcoholics tend to go through the stages faster than adult alcoholics.

Stage 1: Problem Drinking Even a "social drinker"—someone who occasionally drinks small amounts with meals, at parties, or on special occasions—can become an alcoholic. If social drinkers start to use alcohol to try to relieve stress or escape from problems at home, school, or work, their drinking habit may quickly become a problem. Some warning signs of problem drinking are listed in Figure 11.

Stage 2: Absolute Dependence At this stage, the drinker becomes totally dependent on the drug. Alcohol dominates the drinker's life. He or she usually cannot stop after one drink, and feels a constant need to drink.

Some alcoholics are able to hide their problem and appear to be fine. Others show signs of excessive alcohol consumption. Signs of alcoholism may include frequent absences from work or school and strained relationships.

Stage 3: Late Stage of Alcoholism During this stage, alcoholics rapidly lose their mental, emotional, and physical health. Because their entire lives revolve around drinking, they become isolated from society. Late-stage alcoholics also experience **reverse tolerance** for alcohol, a condition in which less and less alcohol causes intoxication.

Serious health problems, including malnutrition, liver and brain damage, cancer, lung disease, and heart disease, are common among alcoholics. Without medical and psychological help, an alcoholic may die.

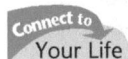

Connect to Your Life **How can you reduce your risk of alcoholism? Explain.**

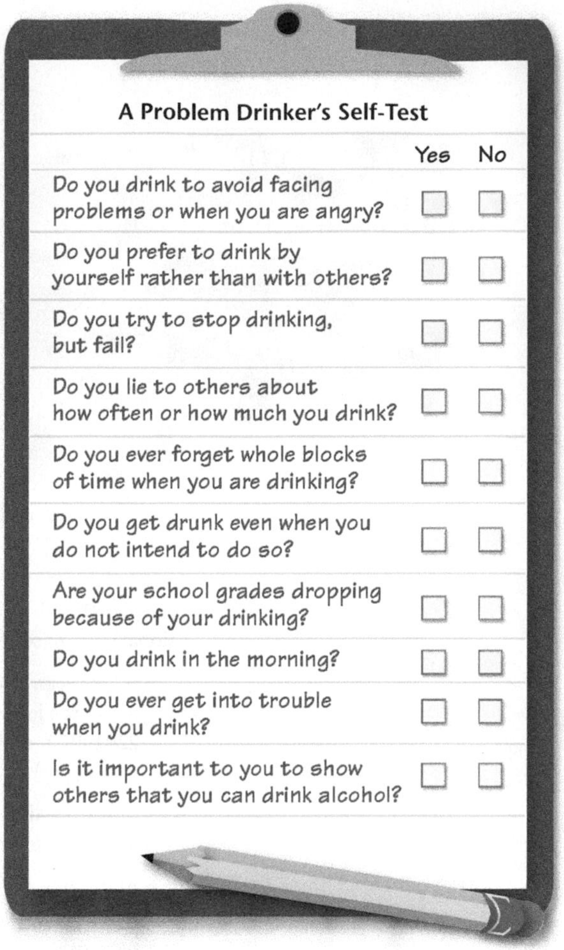

A Problem Drinker's Self-Test

	Yes	No
Do you drink to avoid facing problems or when you are angry?	☐	☐
Do you prefer to drink by yourself rather than with others?	☐	☐
Do you try to stop drinking, but fail?	☐	☐
Do you lie to others about how often or how much you drink?	☐	☐
Do you ever forget whole blocks of time when you are drinking?	☐	☐
Do you get drunk even when you do not intend to do so?	☐	☐
Are your school grades dropping because of your drinking?	☐	☐
Do you drink in the morning?	☐	☐
Do you ever get into trouble when you drink?	☐	☐
Is it important to you to show others that you can drink alcohol?	☐	☐

FIGURE 11 One or two "yes" answers to these questions may indicate a drinking problem.

L2 Visual Learning: Figure 11

Ask students to read the test questions in the figure. Discuss why *yes* answers indicate a drinking problem. For example, regarding the first question, explain that people who use alcohol to avoid problems or relieve stress tend to develop into problem drinkers. Encourage students to suggest positive solutions to these problem behaviors.

L1 Active Learning

Have students make a flowchart of the stages of alcoholism. Their flowcharts should sum up what occurs during the stages of problem drinking, absolute dependence, and late-stage alcoholism. Post students' flowcharts in the classroom.

L3 Journal Writing

After students read about the stages of alcoholism on this page, urge them to think about what their lives would be like if they became alcoholics. Ask them to write a journal entry explaining how alcoholism would interfere with the attainment of their goals and their potential to live a full and happy life. Tell students they may keep their journal entries confidential. **WRITING**

Connect to Your Life You can reduce your risk of alcoholism by not drinking. Anyone who drinks is at risk of becoming an alcoholic.

Differentiated Instruction

L1 Special Needs

Some students may be confused by the many terms relating to alcoholism, such as *tolerance, reverse tolerance, dependence,* and *absolute dependence.* To distill the information down into a single take-home message, have the students focus on the term *alcoholism.* Help students understand the concept of alcoholism by redefining it simply as "a disease in which people cannot stop drinking." Also, make sure students understand the dangers of alcoholism and what factors appear to raise the risk of developing alcoholism.

L2 Active Learning

L2 Active Learning

Ask each student to find a newspaper article that deals with emotional costs of alcoholism. For example, articles might describe alcohol-related vehicle crashes, homicides, or incidents of domestic abuse. Have students bring copies of the articles to class. Ask a few volunteers to organize the articles into categories (e.g., crimes, car crashes) and use them to make a bulletin board display.

Treating Alcoholism

EL Building Vocabulary

To help students understand the term *detoxification*, tell them that the prefix *de-* means "do the opposite of." Give students several examples of familiar words that begin with *de-*, such as *decaffeinated, decode, decompose, decongestant,* and *defrost.* For each word, ask students to explain how *de-* changes the meaning of the root word. Then challenge students to use this knowledge to define *detoxification* in their own words. *(doing the opposite of poisoning the body, or the process of getting rid of poison from the body)*

L3 Building Health Skills

Advocacy Ask students to make a brochure for other teens about Alateen. Brochures should encourage students who live with alcoholics to join Alateen. Brochures also should explain how Alateen can help them and how they can contact a local Alateen group. Arrange for students to place their brochures in community locations frequented by teens, such as shopping malls and concert venues. **WRITING**

L3 Content Update  **GO ONLINE**

Visit Pearson SuccessNet to access more information about alcoholism. Have students complete the Web activity.

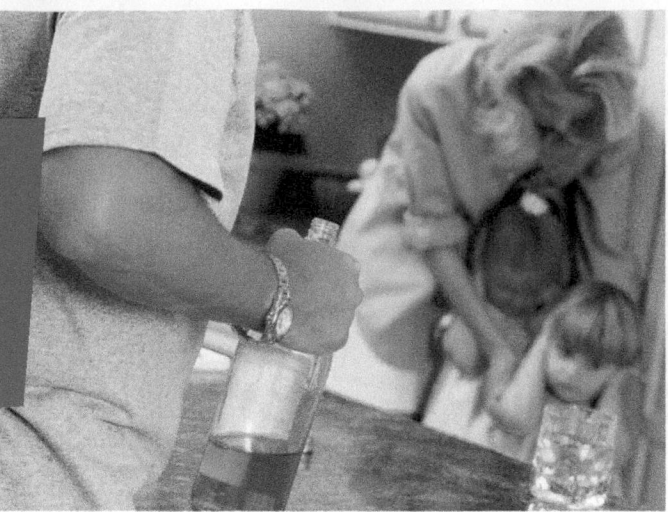

FIGURE 12 Alcoholism has many negative effects on families.

Effects of Alcoholism on the Family
- Unpredictable behavior
- Embarrassment
- Violence
- Neglect
- Money problems
- Legal problems
- Divorce

Effects on Others Alcohol abuse and alcoholism affect many people other than the drinker. Consider some of the financial and emotional costs to society and individual families.

▶ In one year, alcohol-related crimes, medical expenses, lost productivity on the job, and motor vehicle crashes cost the United States over 220 billion dollars.

▶ Alcohol is involved in over 80,000 deaths per year. Most of these deaths are due to violence committed under the influence of alcohol and to motor vehicle crashes involving drunk drivers.

▶ About one in every five Americans grows up in an alcoholic family. Spouses and children of alcoholics live in homes filled with stress arising from uncertainty and embarrassment.

▶ In some cases, alcoholics verbally or physically abuse family members. Family life centers around the drinking member as the needs of other family members are ignored.

Treating Alcoholism

With appropriate treatment, the progress of alcoholism can be stopped. Alcoholics can lead productive, happy lives if they stop drinking completely. **There are three stages in an alcoholic's recovery: acknowledging the problem, detoxification, and rehabilitation.**

Acknowledging the Problem In the first step of recovery, alcoholics must acknowledge their problem and ask for help. For some alcoholics, the shock of losing a job, being arrested, or being separated from their families motivates them to enter a treatment program.

GO ONLINE
PearsonSuccessNet.com
For: More on alcoholism

WRITING and Health

L3 Public Service Announcement

Ask pairs of students to write a public service announcement (PSA) to educate people about the costs of alcoholism to the family or society. Suggest that students focus on just one alcohol-related problem in their PSA. Give pairs a chance to present their PSAs to the rest of the class. **WRITING**

Detoxification The next step in recovery is **detoxification,** which involves removing all alcohol from a person's body. The alcoholic will suffer from **withdrawal,** a group of symptoms that occur when a dependent person stops taking a drug. Withdrawal symptoms last from three to seven days. They include shakiness, sleep problems, irritability, rapid heartbeat, and sweating. The drinker also may see, smell, or feel imaginary objects. Severe withdrawal symptoms can be extremely dangerous, requiring medical care or a hospital stay.

Rehabilitation After detoxification, the recovering alcoholic begins **rehabilitation**—the process of learning to cope with everyday living without alcohol. During rehabilitation, alcoholics receive counseling to help them understand their disease and behavior. In some cases, the recovering alcoholic takes medications that may help prevent a return to alcohol use.

Support Groups Community, religious, and health organizations often sponsor support groups for alcoholics. In one of the most successful groups, Alcoholics Anonymous (AA), recovering alcoholics offer encouragement and support to help other alcoholics stop drinking.

Two other groups, Al-Anon and Alateen, are designed to help friends and family members of alcoholics. Al-Anon helps adult friends and family members learn how they can help in the alcoholic's recovery process. Alateen provides help for teenagers living with alcoholics. You can find the phone numbers for local AA, Al-Anon, and Alateen groups on the Internet or in a telephone book.

FIGURE 13 Al-Anon members use understanding and education in their efforts to help alcoholics cope.

Section 3 Review

Key Ideas and Vocabulary

1. What are five long-term physical effects of alcohol abuse?

2. What is **cirrhosis?** Explain how the disease can be fatal.

3. What is **tolerance** to alcohol? How does it relate to **dependence?**

4. Describe each stage of alcoholism. What happens during absolute dependence?

5. List in order three steps alcoholics must take to recover from their alcohol dependence.

Health at School

Support for Teens What kinds of school programs do you think would help teenagers who have drinking problems? What elements would the program need to be effective? Prepare an oral report to present to school officials. **WRITING**

Critical Thinking

6. **Evaluating** "Alcoholism only affects the alcoholic." Do you agree or disagree with this statement? Explain your answer.

7. **Comparing and Contrasting** How are the goals of Alcoholics Anonymous, Al-Anon, and Alateen similar? How are they different?

Evaluate

These assignments can help you assess students' mastery of the section content.

Section 3 Review
Answers appear below.

Teaching Resources
• Practice 15-3
• Section 15-3 Quiz

L2 Reteach

Ask students to make an outline of the section, using the main headings as major topics and the subheadings as minor topics. Tell students to include the boldfaced sentences and the definitions of the vocabulary words in their outlines.

L4 Enrich

Teaching Resources
• Enrich 15-3

Health at School

Support for Teens Students may suggest different kinds of school programs, such as programs to educate teens about the dangers of drinking or programs to help teens learn refusal skills. To be effective, students might say a program needs the support of parents as well as teachers or that it must be relevant to today's teens. Ask permission for students to present their oral reports at a meeting of the school staff or school board.

5. acknowledging the problem, detoxification, and rehabilitation

6. Students should say they disagree with this statement. Alcoholism affects many people other than the drinker, including the drinker's family members.

7. All three groups aim to help people affected by alcoholism. Alcoholics Anonymous helps recovering alcoholics; Al-Anon helps adult friends and family members of alcoholics; Alateen helps teens who live with alcoholics.

Section 3 Review

1. harm to the brain, liver, heart, and digestive system and fetal alcohol syndrome

2. a disease of the liver in which cells die and leave behind useless scar tissue; by leading to liver failure

3. Tolerance to alcohol occurs when a drinker's body needs more and more alcohol to achieve the original effect. Increasing tolerance leads to dependence, in which the brain cannot function without alcohol.

4. In stage 1, a person drinks to avoid facing problems and may try to stop drinking but fail. In stage 2, the drinker becomes totally dependent on alcohol. In stage 3, the alcoholic rapidly loses mental, emotional, and physical health.

Section 4

Choosing Not to Drink

Objectives
Before class begins, write the objectives on the board. Have students copy the objectives into their notebooks at the start of class.

1. Focus

Warm-Up Advice Line

Ask several students to share what they wrote. Try to get at least one response that makes the point that it is better to give honest reasons for refusing to drink. Discuss why honest reasons make refusals more effective. (But remind students that any kind of refusal is better than drinking.) Tell students that they will learn in this section about other techniques for abstaining from alcohol.

Presentation 15-4

Objectives
▶ **Evaluate** how refusal skills help you stick to your decision not to drink.
▶ **Identify** two benefits of avoiding situations where alcohol is present.

Vocabulary
• refusal skills

Warm-Up

Dear Advice Line,

I was at a friend's house and we were bored. My friend got some liquor and offered me a drink. I said I couldn't because I had a game that night. The real reason is that I've decided not to drink at all. Was it wrong to give an excuse? What if she asks me again when I don't have a game?

WRITING Write a response to this teen. Offer advice on how to handle future situations.

Abstaining from Alcohol

You know that underage drinking is illegal and could risk your health and future plans. The best decision you can make is to abstain from alcohol, meaning not to drink at all. Once you turn 21, drinking will no longer be illegal, but the risks will remain. Many adults abstain from, or choose not to drink, alcohol.

At different times in your life—now or years from now—you will likely find yourself in situations where you are pressured to drink when you don't want to. How will you stick to your decision? **Sticking to your decision not to drink means being able to say no with confidence in situations where other people are drinking.**

The skills needed to say *no* are sometimes referred to as **refusal skills.** Refusal skills are especially important when others are pressuring you to do something against your will. You will feel better about yourself by sticking to your beliefs.

🚩 Sensitive Issues

Students who have struggled and failed to resist peer pressure to drink may find this to be a sensitive issue.

• Reassure students that peer pressure is hard for many people—even adults—to resist.
• Focus on the refusal skills students need to resist peer pressure in the future instead of dwelling on past failures to refuse.

TEENS *Are Asking . . .*

Q: **I don't want to drink, but all my friends drink and keep asking me to join them. How can I keep refusing when I'm under so much pressure from my friends?**

A: First of all, reconsider your choice of friends. Do you want to hang out with people who drink and pressure you to join them? No matter who your friends are, you are likely to face similar pressures throughout life. Use the "NICE" way to say *no*.

• **No!** Say it firmly, like you really mean it. Don't say "maybe" or "I guess not."
• **I** want to stay in control. I am not old enough to drink. Use these or other "I statements" to support your decision.
• **Change** the subject, change who you are talking to, or change rooms to avoid continued pressure to drink.
• **Exit** the situation if the other strategies do not help.

What to Say When Offered a Drink

"No thanks, I don't drink."

"I'm not old enough to drink."

"I want to stay in control."

FIGURE 14 There's more than one way to refuse a drink.

Prepare for Pressure To prepare yourself for the pressure you may face, ask yourself the following questions:

► What are my reasons for not drinking alcohol at this time in my life?

► How can I come across as confident in my decision?

► In what situations will I most likely encounter pressure to drink?

► Why are my friends pressuring me to drink?

► Are there other friends who can help me stick to my decision?

You may want to practice saying *no* in role-playing situations with friends or classmates. That way you can develop the refusal skills you will need in actual social situations.

Stick to Your Decision You may find that some people will not accept your decision not to drink. Many people who drink want to see others around them drink so that they can feel accepted.

Remember that you never need to apologize for not drinking. Most people will respect your decision, especially if you are clear in your response. Refer to the Building Health Skills on pages 378–379 for other tips for developing your refusal skills.

 **Connect to Your Life** How would you say no to alcohol if it were offered to you?

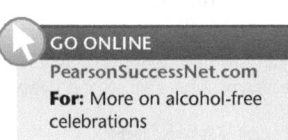

GO ONLINE

PearsonSuccessNet.com

For: More on alcohol-free celebrations

Alcohol **393**

---

2. Teach

L3 **EL** Reading/Note Taking 15-4

L2 Adapted Reading/Note Taking 15-4

Abstaining from Alcohol

EL Cooperative Learning

Pair English language learners with English-proficient students, and ask them to study the questions listed on this page under the heading, Prepare for Pressure. Ask the English-proficient students to help their partners understand the meaning of any difficult terms or idioms, such as *confident* and *sticking to a decision*. Then have the pairs formulate their responses. Give students the option of responding in their private journals to questions that are too personal for them to share with each other.

L3 Building Health Skills

Practicing Healthful Behaviors Have pairs of students write brief dialogues in which one teen uses refusal skills to resist pressure from another teen to drink. Ask several pairs to read their dialogues to the class. Urge other students to point out the most persuasive ways of refusing alcohol in the dialogues. **WRITING**

Connect to Your Life *Sample answer:* I would say *no* firmly, give my reasons, and leave if I were pressured to drink.

L3 Online Activity  **GO ONLINE**

Visit Pearson SuccessNet to access an online activity about alcohol-free celebrations. Have students complete the Web activity.

Differentiated Instruction

L2 Less Proficient Readers

As a homework assignment, ask less proficient readers to practice reading aloud the responses listed in Figure 14. Instruct them to read the sentences with feeling and to practice them in front of a mirror to make sure their facial expressions match their words. The next day, call on the students to read the sentences aloud in class. They should be able to read them easily and with expression and conviction. This activity will improve students' self-confidence in their reading skills as well as help them learn how to say *no* effectively.

Alcohol **393**

Avoiding High-Pressure Situations

L1 Building Health Skills

Advocacy Have students make posters showing other teens how to avoid high-pressure situations involving alcohol. Arrange for students to display their posters throughout the school.

3. Assess

Evaluate

These assignments can help you assess students' mastery of the section content.

Section 4 Review

Answers appear below.

Teaching Resources

• Practice 15-4
• Section 15-4 Quiz

L2 Reteach

Call on several students to demonstrate using refusal skills to turn down an offer of an alcoholic drink. Call on other students to point out specific ways—such as making eye contact and using a firm voice—that the students said *no* convincingly.

L4 Enrich

Teaching Resources

• Enrich 15-4

Health at Home

Reminder Card Suggest that students have their reminder cards laminated to protect them from wear and tear. If students do not carry a wallet, suggest that they keep their reminder card wherever they carry their ID card or driver's license.

A Safe Ride Home
• Find a sober driver.
• Call a parent or another adult.
• Take a taxi or bus.

FIGURE 15 Don't risk your life with a driver who has been drinking, even if they don't seem drunk.

Avoiding High-Pressure Situations

Besides using refusal skills, teens who choose not to drink also do something else that's smart: they stay away from situations where alcohol is present. **Avoiding situations in which alcohol is present will help you stay alcohol free. It will also help you avoid related risks, like being injured by someone who has been drinking.**

Alternatives to Parties Teenagers who abstain from alcohol are likely to participate in healthy activities. Think about the kinds of activities that interest you. You may be interested in sports, hobbies, playing an instrument, helping an organization raise money, or organizing a school activity. Try taking up a new activity or spending more time with a current activity as an alternative to parties.

Refusing Rides From Drinkers Even if you don't drink alcohol, you may have to deal with people who have had too much to drink. Remember that intoxicated people must not be allowed to drive. The driver may be a friend, a relative, or the parent of a child for whom you babysit. You should *never* get into a car with anyone who has been drinking. Don't worry about being rude—your life is more important than the driver's feelings. You should also do everything you can to prevent that person from driving.

If you find yourself dependent on a drinker for a ride home, ask someone for help. Some teens have an understanding with a parent or other adult that they can call for a ride home, no questions asked. Do not risk riding with an intoxicated driver.

Section 4 Review

Key Ideas and Vocabulary

1. What are **refusal skills**?
2. How can you stick to a decision not to drink?
3. What are two benefits of staying away from situations where alcohol is present?

Critical Thinking

4. **Applying Concepts** What reasons would you give for postponing drinking until you are of legal age?
5. **Evaluating** Make a list of pros and cons of going to a party where alcohol may be served. Then evaluate the list and decide what you would do.

Health at Home

Reminder Card Cut an index card to fit in your wallet. On it, list three ways that you would feel comfortable saying *no* if you were offered alcohol. Also list the names and phone numbers of three friends and family members you could contact if you needed a ride home. Carry the card with you so it's always handy.

6. **Making Judgments** The father of a child you've been baby-sitting is intoxicated when he returns. He offers you a ride back to your house. What would you do? **WRITING**

🔊 GO ONLINE PearsonSuccessNet.com   Audio Summary Section 15.4

Section 4 Review

1. the skills needed to say *no*
2. by learning how to say *no* with confidence in situations where other people are drinking
3. helps you stay alcohol free and helps you avoid related risks, such as being injured by someone who has been drinking

4. *Sample answer:* I don't want to do anything illegal. I don't want to get into trouble. I want to stay in control. I don't want to risk my future. I have more important things to do with my time.
5. Answers will vary. Pros might include spending time with friends and having fun. Cons might include being pressured

to drink and being around people who are drunk. Student decisions should be reasonable, given the pros and cons they listed.
6. *Sample answer:* I would refuse the ride home with the father and call my parents to get me.

Chapter 15
At a Glance

Section 1 Alcohol is a Drug

Key Ideas

▶ In slowing the body's normal reactions, alcohol may cause confusion, decreased alertness, poor coordination, blurred vision, and drowsiness.

▶ The attitudes of peers, family, and the media strongly influence underage drinking.

Vocabulary
- drug (374)
- depressant (374)
- fermentation (374)
- zero-tolerance policy (375)

Drinking Dangers Ask for volunteers to share their answers. Use examples from the video to review refusal skills.

Key Ideas Review

L1 Have students rewrite each of the key ideas in their own words. Make sure their rewritten ideas have the same meanings as the original key ideas. Have students work with partners to revise any ideas that do not have the same meanings.

Section 2 Alcohol's Effects on the Body

Key Ideas

▶ Many negative effects on a drinker's body and behavior accompany intoxication by alcohol.

▶ The rate of alcohol consumption, the gender and size of the drinker, and how much food is in the stomach all affect blood alcohol concentration.

▶ Intoxication increases the risk of death from motor vehicle crashes, alcohol overdose, and the interactions of alcohol with other drugs.

Vocabulary
- intoxication (380) • blackout (381)
- blood alcohol concentration (BAC) (382)
- hangover (383) • driving while intoxicated (DWI) (384)
- overdose (385) • binge drinking (385)

L2 Ask students to write responses to the section objectives throughout the chapter. They should look up the correct responses to any objectives they are unsure of.

Vocabulary Review

EL Have pairs of students make flashcards for each of the chapter vocabulary terms. Ask them to use the flashcards to quiz each other on the definitions.

Section 3 Long-Term Risks of Alcohol

Key Ideas

▶ Long-term alcohol abuse may harm the brain, liver, heart, and digestive system. Furthermore, drinking any amount of alcohol during pregnancy may permanently harm the developing baby.

▶ As alcoholism progresses, what begins as problem drinking becomes absolute dependence, and finally, late-stage alcoholism.

▶ There are three stages in an alcoholic's recovery: acknowledging the problem, detoxification, and rehabilitation.

Vocabulary
- fetal alcohol syndrome (387) • cirrhosis (387)
- alcoholism (388) • tolerance (388)
- dependence (388) • addiction (388)
- reverse tolerance (389) • detoxification (391)
- withdrawal (391) • rehabilitation (391)

L3 Tell students to write a meaningful paragraph using at least ten of the chapter vocabulary terms. Ask students to exchange paragraphs with a classmate and identify any terms they think have been used incorrectly. Help settle any cases in which partners disagree over the correct use of a term.

Section 4 Choosing Not to Drink

Key Ideas

▶ Sticking to your decision not to drink means being able to say no with confidence in situations where other people are drinking.

▶ Avoiding situations in which alcohol is present will help you stay alcohol free.

Vocabulary
- refusal skills (392)

Alcohol **395**

Chapter 15 Review

GO ONLINE

PearsonSuccessNet.com

Students can go online for a review activity on Chapter 15.

Reviewing Key Ideas

Section 1

1. a   2. c

3. being injured or killed in a motor vehicle crash, committing or being the victim of sexual assault or other violence, and long-term brain damage

4. *Sample answer:* Teens may decide to drink in order to fit in with their peers. They may decide not to drink because they have a friend with an alcohol problem and don't want to turn out that way.

Section 2

5. d

6. The liver breaks down alcohol.

7. When a person drinks alcohol and takes another depressant drug, the effects are more than doubled and can lead to death.

8. Intoxication depends on the amount of alcohol in a person's blood, which is measured by blood alcohol concentration. The amount of alcohol in the blood depends not only on the number of drinks consumed, but also on factors such as rate of consumption and gender.

Section 3

9. b

10. The drinker's body requires alcohol to function, and the drinker considers alcohol an essential part of coping with daily life.

11. *Sample answer:* Drinking to avoid facing problems, preferring to drink alone, trying but failing to stop drinking, or lying about drinking.

12. because he or she might suffer dangerous withdrawal symptoms

13. *Sample answer:* because they might not be able to stop drinking if they start again

Section 4

14. d

15. *Sample answer:* risk of becoming an alcoholic ("I don't want to ruin my future."); fear of doing something illegal ("I don't want to end up in jail."); danger of drinking and driving ("I don't want to crash my car and die.")

16. *Sample answer:* playing basketball, going to movies, shopping

Building Health Skills

17. *Sample answer:* I would tell my parents immediately.

18. All communities have laws prohibiting minors from purchasing alcohol. Students may or may not think that the laws are effective. They might say that more could be done to detect minors who use fake IDs or to curb alcohol advertising to teens.

Chapter 15 Review

Reviewing Key Ideas

Section 1

1. Alcohol is classified as a depressant drug because it
   a. slows brain and body reactions.
   b. reduces blood flow to skin.
   c. causes liver failure.
   d. increases heart rate.

2. The percentage of alcohol in 80-proof liquor is
   a. 4 percent.   b. 8 percent.
   c. 40 percent.   d. 80 percent.

3. Identify three ways that teens who drink put themselves at risks for physical harm.

4. **Critical Thinking** How do peers influence teens' decision whether to drink?

Section 2

5. Blood alcohol concentration measures
   a. the number of drinks consumed in one hour.
   b. the rate at which a person drinks alcohol.
   c. a person's risk of a car crash.
   d. the amount of alcohol in a person's blood.

6. Which organ breaks down alcohol?

7. How can alcohol's interaction with other drugs be fatal?

8. **Critical Thinking** Why is blood alcohol concentration a more reliable indicator of intoxication than number of drinks consumed?

Section 3

9. A condition in which less and less alcohol causes intoxication is called
   a. tolerance.   b. reverse tolerance.
   c. dependence.   d. problem drinking.

10. What are the physical and psychological signs of alcohol addiction?

11. What are some signs that a person may be a problem drinker?

12. During detoxification, why might an alcoholic need to be in a hospital?

13. **Critical Thinking** Doctors recommend that former alcoholics should avoid drinking even one drink. Why do you think so?

Section 4

14. The skills you need to say no to alcohol are called
    a. denial skills.   b. problem-solving skills.
    c. tolerance skills.   d. refusal skills.

15. List three reasons why teens should abstain from alcohol. Then, turn each reason into a way to say *no* to alcohol.

16. **Critical Thinking** What activities do you enjoy that take place in alcohol-free settings?

Building Health Skills

17. **Making Decisions** Your 18-year-old sister has a date with her boyfriend. He is driving. When he arrives you smell alcohol on his breath. What do you do?

18. **Accessing Information** What are the laws that regulate alcohol purchases in your community? Do you think they are effective at preventing underage drinking? What more could be done? Explain. **WRITING**

19. **Advocacy** What advice would you give someone who has an alcoholic parent? Be specific.

20. **Communicating** Three members of the football team were suspended from playing for the rest of the season because they were caught drinking at a private party. Write a letter to the editor of the school newspaper giving your opinion about the situation. **WRITING**

21. **Setting Goals** Develop a list of strategies you can use to refuse alcohol. Review your list over the course of the school year. Refine your strategies as necessary to make them more effective.

Health and Community

Public Service Announcement Work with a group of your classmates. Design a public service announcement (PSA) to educate the public about the dangers of binge drinking. **WRITING**

Standardized Test Prep

Math Practice

The graph shows the effect of a driver's blood alcohol concentration on motor vehicle crashes. Use the graph to answer Questions 22–24.

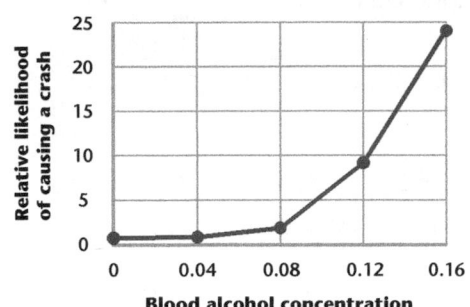

Blood alcohol concentration

22. About how much higher is crash likelihood at a BAC of 0.08 compared with a BAC of zero?
    - A About the same
    - B 2 times
    - C 5 times
    - D 10 times

23. By about what percentage does crash risk increase between a BAC of 0.08 and a BAC of 0.1?
    - F 25%
    - G 50%
    - H 100%
    - J 400%

24. What mathematical term best describes the relationship between BAC and crash risk?
    - A inverse correlation
    - B exponential
    - C linear
    - D constant

Test-Taking Tip

Read *all* of the answers to a question before you make your choice. An answer that seems correct at first might not be the best answer when you weigh it against all the other choices.

Reading and Writing Practice

Read the poem below. Then answer Questions 25–28.

My Papa's Waltz
by Theodore Roethke

The whiskey on your breath
Could make a small boy dizzy;
But I hung on like death:
Such waltzing was not easy.

We romped until the pans
Slid from the kitchen shelf;
My mother's countenance
Could not unfrown itself.

The hand that held my wrist
Was battered on one knuckle;
At every step you missed
My right ear scraped a buckle.

You beat time on my head
With a palm caked hard by dirt,
Then waltzed me off to bed
Still clinging to your shirt.

25. From the context of the poem, what's the best definition of *countenance?*
    - A a waltz step
    - B anger
    - C dizziness
    - D facial expression

26. Which two words make a soft, or inexact, rhyme?
    - F head, bed
    - G wrist, missed
    - H dizzy, easy
    - J dirt, shirt

27. Which of the following verbs contributes most to the poem's violent feeling?
    - A waltzed
    - B scraped
    - C romped
    - D battered

Constructed Response
28. What does the poem suggest are the boy's feelings about his father's alcoholism? Explain.

Alcohol **397**

Standardized Test Prep

Math Practice
22. B
23. H
24. B

Reading and Writing Practice
25. D
26. H
27. D
28. *Sample answer:* The poem suggests that the boy feels sad and afraid about his father's alcoholism. For example, the poem says that the boy hung onto his father "like death," while his father held the boy's wrist and beat time on his head.

19. *Sample answer:* I would encourage the person to join Alateen and to seek counseling.

20. In their letters, students should state whether they think the punishment is suitable and provide logical reasons for their opinion. For example, they might say that the punishment is suitable because drinking is illegal and students who break the law should not be allowed to play on school teams.

21. Strategies will vary but should include honest and effective reasons to refuse alcohol, such as "I'm not old enough to drink" or "I want to stay in control."

Health and Community

Public Service Announcement Have the teams consider which audience they are targeting—all segments of the public or a specific group. Will the PSA be heard on the radio as well as seen on television?

CHAPTER 16 Tobacco

Section Objectives	Standards Correlation	Instructional Resources (L3)		SE eTEXT	TE eTEXT	PRINT
1 Teens and Tobacco — 1 period; 1/2 block	NHES: 2.12.1, 2.12.3, 2.12.5, 2.12.7, 7.12.3	SE	Warm-Up, p. 400	•	•	•
16.1.1 Identify three factors that influence teens' decisions about tobacco use.		RN	Note Taking Guide 16-1	•	•	•
16.1.2 Describe the various forms of tobacco products.		TR	Practice 16-1		•	
		TR	Section 16-1 Quiz		•	
Examining Advertising Tactics — 1 period; 1/2 block	NHES: 2.12.5, 2.12.7	SE	Practice the Skill, p. 405	•	•	•
BHS.16 Develop skills to analyze advertisement messages.		RN	Building Health Skills 16	•	•	•
2 Chemicals in Tobacco Products — 1 period; 1/2 block	NHES: 1.12.9, 3.12.2	SE	Warm-Up, p. 406	•	•	•
16.2.1 Explain how nicotine affects the body.		RN	Note Taking Guide 16-2	•	•	•
16.2.2 Identify two other dangerous substances in tobacco smoke.		IB	Image Bank 16-4		•	
		TR	Practice 16-2		•	
16.2.2 Examine why using smokeless tobacco is not a safe alternative to smoking.		TR	Section 16-2 Quiz		•	
3 Risks of Tobacco Use — 2 periods; 1 block	NHES: 1.12.3, 1.12.8, 1.12.9, 2.12.10, 8.12.1	SE	Warm-Up, p. 410	•	•	•
		SE	Hands-On Activity Make a Model of a Smoker's Lungs, p. 412	•	•	•
16.3.1 Describe the long-term health risks of tobacco use.		RN	Note Taking Guide 16-3	•	•	•
16.3.2 Identify the long-term risks of exposure to secondhand smoke.		TR	Practice 16-3		•	
		TR	Section 16-3 Quiz		•	
16.3.2 Examine how smoking by a pregnant woman can affect her baby.						
4 Saying No to Tobacco — 1 period; 1/2 block	NHES: 1.12.7, 3.12.3, 3.12.4, 4.12.2, 4.12.4, 8.12.2	SE	Warm-Up, p. 417	•	•	•
		RN	Note Taking Guide 16-4	•	•	•
16.4.1 Examine how refusal skills will help you stick with your decision not to use tobacco.		IB	Image Bank 16-11		•	
		TR	Practice 16-4		•	
16.4.2 Describe the benefits of quitting tobacco use.		TR	Section 16-4 Quiz		•	
16.4.2 Identify the most important factor for successfully quitting tobacco.						

Chapter Review and Assessment

SE Chapter 16 Review, p. 422 **L3**

CTB Chapter 16 Test **L2 L3 L4**

SE Standardized Test Prep, p. 423 **L3**

PROGRAM COMPONENTS

SE	Student Edition	CTB	Computer Test Bank
TE	Teacher Edition	AUD	Audio Section Summaries
TR	Teaching Resources	DVD	Teens Talk Video Series
RN	Reading and Note Taking Guide	VVG	Video Viewing Guide
ARN	Adapted Reading and Note Taking Guide	PPT	Presentation
IB	Image Bank		

Differentiated Instruction

L1 L2 L4 EL

		SE eTEXT	TE eTEXT	PRINT
ARN	Note Taking Guide 16-1 L2	•	•	
RN	Note Taking Guide 16-1 EL	•	•	•
AUD	Audio Summary 16-1 L1 L2 EL	•	•	
TE	Reteach Strategy, p. 403 L2		•	•
TR	Enrich 16-1 L4		•	
ARN	Building Health Skills 16 L2	•	•	
RN	Building Health Skills 16 EL	•	•	•
ARN	Note Taking Guide 16-2 L2	•	•	
RN	Note Taking Guide 16-2 EL	•	•	•
AUD	Audio Summary 16-2 L1 L2 EL	•	•	
TE	Reteach Strategy, p. 409 L2		•	•
TR	Enrich 16-2 L4		•	
ARN	Note Taking Guide 16-3 L2	•	•	
RN	Note Taking Guide 16-3 EL	•	•	•
AUD	Audio Summary 16-3 L1 L2 EL	•	•	
TE	Reteach Strategy, p. 416 L2		•	•
TR	Enrich 16-3 L4		•	
ARN	Note Taking Guide 16-4 L2	•	•	
RN	Note Taking Guide 16-4 EL	•	•	•
AUD	Audio Summary 16-4 L1 L2 EL	•	•	
TE	Reteach Strategy, p. 420 L2		•	•
TR	Enrich 16-4 L4		•	

ABILITY LEVELS

L1 For students with special needs

L2 For less proficient readers

L3 For all students

L4 For gifted and talented students

EL For English language learners

Chapter 16 Digital/Video Pathway

This alternative pathway allows you to teach this chapter's content using only the video and online materials.

Preview

DVD	Video #16 Preview
SE	Video #16 Preview Activity
VVG	Video #16 Worksheet

Tackling Tobacco

1

DVD	Video #16 Explore/Wrap-Up
VVG	Video #16 Worksheet
PPT	16-1 Presentation
RN/ARN	16-1 Note Taking
PPT	16-1 Section Quiz

Tackling Tobacco

2

PPT	16-2 Presentation
RN/ARN	16-2 Note Taking
PPT	16-2 Section Quiz

3

PPT	16-3 Presentation
RN/ARN	16-3 Note Taking
PPT	16-3 Section Quiz

4

PPT	16-4 Presentation
RN/ARN	16-4 Note Taking
PPT	16-4 Section Quiz

Chapter Preview

Section 1 Teens and Tobacco
Friends, family, and the media have a great influence on teens' decisions about whether or not to use tobacco. Tobacco products include cigarettes, cigars, pipe tobacco, and smokeless tobacco.

Analyzing Influences

Examining Advertising Tactics
Analyzing how advertisements influence behavior can help students resist media messages about tobacco.

Section 2 Chemicals in
Tobacco Products
Nicotine causes increased heart rate and blood pressure and may lead to addiction. Tar and carbon monoxide are other dangerous substances in tobacco smoke. Smokeless tobacco contains many of the same dangerous chemicals.

Section 3 Risks of Tobacco Use
Long-term health risks of tobacco use include respiratory and cardiovascular diseases and cancers. Long-term exposure to secondhand smoke can cause many of the same problems. Pregnant women who smoke put their babies at risk for many health problems.

Section 4 Saying No to Tobacco
Being able to say *no* clearly and with confidence helps teens stick with their decision not to use tobacco. Health benefits of quitting tobacco use begin immediately and continue throughout life. The most important factor in successfully quitting tobacco is a strong personal commitment.

GO ONLINE

PearsonSuccessNet.com
For resources and activities for this chapter.

Tobacco

1 Teens and Tobacco

Building Health Skills
- **Analyzing Influences** Examining Advertising Tactics

2 Chemicals in Tobacco Products

3 Risks of Tobacco Use
- **Hands-On Activity** Make a Model of a Smoker's Lungs

4 Saying No to Tobacco

GO ONLINE PearsonSuccessNet.com

TEENS Talk

Tackling Tobacco

VIDEO 16

Preview **Activity**

Why Do Teens Start to Smoke?

Complete this activity before you watch the video.

1. List three reasons why you think that some teens start to smoke.

2. Get together with a partner to discuss the reasons you each wrote down. Between the two of you, how many different reasons did you come up with?

3. Design a T-shirt or bumper sticker with an anti-smoking message. The message should address at least one of the reasons why you and your partner think that some teens start to smoke.

 Sensitive Issues
Discussions about tobacco use may be a sensitive issue for some students. Be attuned to students' comfort levels. Avoid asking direct questions about personal tobacco use or tobacco use among family members. The health effects of smoking may be a tense topic in homes where a family member is reluctant to quit or has a smoking-related illness.

399

Video Objectives

Use this video to help students

Consider the factors that influence teens' decisions about tobacco.

Understand the long-term health consequences of smoking.

Identify ways to educate other teens about the dangers of smoking.

Preview **Activity**

Why Do Teens Start to Smoke?

A week or so before watching the video, have students complete the Preview Activity. Have students present their T-shirt or bumper sticker ideas to the class. Students should explain their ideas to the class. Students should explain the goal of their anti-smoking message and why they think their message would be effective.

From the Authors

When you encourage students to avoid or give up tobacco use, be aware that teens' priorities and concerns are typically different from those of adults. Concerns about appearance and hygiene may influence students more than the long-term health risks of tobacco use. For example, students are likely to be more worried about having bad breath or stained teeth in the present than they are about developing respiratory diseases or cancers in the future. Keep this in mind when you teach the chapter. Stress the health risks of tobacco use but also point out the consequences that are most bothersome to students.

Objectives

Before class begins, write the objectives on the board. Have students copy the objectives into their notebooks at the start of class.

1. Focus

Warm-Up **Health Stats**

After students complete the writing assignment, call on a volunteer to share his or her response. Ask: **Why do you think smoking is less popular with teens?** *(Sample answer: greater awareness of the health risks of smoking)* Ask students to discuss their reaction to the data in the graph.

Presentation 16-1

Section 1 Teens and Tobacco

Objectives

▶ **Identify** three factors that influence teens' decisions about tobacco use.

▶ **Describe** the various forms of tobacco products.

Vocabulary

• nicotine
• smokeless tobacco
• chewing tobacco
• snuff

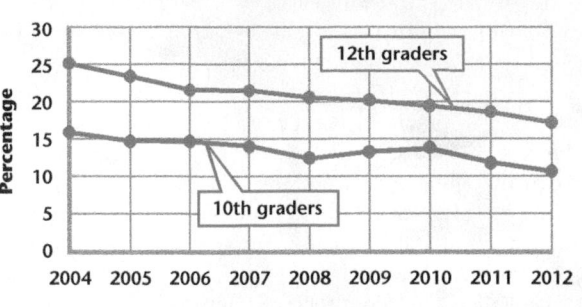

Warm-Up

Health Stats This graph shows how the percentage of 10th graders and 12th graders who smoke has changed.

WRITING What does this graph reveal about the popularity of smoking among high school students?

Why Teens Use Tobacco

When your parents were teens, they lived in a much smokier environment than you do today. Only a few decades ago, people smoked on airplanes, in movie theaters, in restaurants, and at work. Today, people know a lot more about the dangers of tobacco use. As a result, tobacco use has fallen sharply and it is not as socially acceptable as it once was.

Despite all of the health warnings, some people do start using tobacco. Few users can pinpoint the exact reason they started smoking or using smokeless tobacco. But, both users and nonusers refer to the same factors when discussing their decision. **Friends, family, and the media greatly influence whether someone starts to use tobacco.**

Influence of Friends Most people who become addicted to tobacco start using it during their teens. Friends are an important influence. Teens with friends who use tobacco are more likely to also use tobacco. They may feel pressure to be part of the group.

On the other hand, if a teen's friends do not use tobacco, it is less likely that he or she will make the decision to use it. Many teenagers credit their friends for helping them resist the temptation to use tobacco.

400 *Chapter 16*

 Sensitive Issues

Students who feel peer pressure to smoke may be uncomfortable during this discussion. Remind the class that the majority of teens do not smoke.

WRITING **and Health**

L3 Essay

Ask students to construct an essay that discusses their perceptions of smoking and popular culture. Encourage students to write about how the image of smoking has changed over the years. Inform students about laws that restrict the areas where smoking is permitted and lawsuits that have been brought against cigarette manufacturers.

Influence of Family Your parents may have first made you aware of tobacco's negative health effects. They also may have offered you advice on how to avoid tobacco use. Other family members, such as older sisters or brothers, may be positive role models for you.

Studies show that children of smokers are much more likely to smoke, even if their parents try to discourage them. Why are children of smokers more likely to smoke? These children may think of smoking as a behavior related to adulthood. They may simply assume that they will use tobacco just like their parents do.

Influence of Media Anti-tobacco advertising in magazines, television, and other media also may have influenced your decision not to smoke. You probably have read or heard much about the dangers of tobacco through the media. Many anti-tobacco ads are designed to get the attention of teens. Anti-tobacco programs were designed to compete with the appealing ads created by tobacco companies.

The advertising of tobacco products on radio and television has been banned for over 30 years. In the 1990s, further regulations were placed on tobacco advertising. Ads placed near schools were banned. Tobacco companies were told to discontinue cartoon-like ads that appeal to children and teens. In addition, tobacco companies were required to help pay for anti-smoking education.

Despite all these regulations, tobacco companies still find ways to promote their products. They advertise on Web sites and in places where cigarettes are sold. They use direct mail. The companies also sponsor events and offer discounts to keep prices low.

 **Connect to Your Life** What people or factors have influenced your decisions about tobacco use?

GO ONLINE
PearsonSuccessNet.com
For: More on teens and tobacco

Media

FIGURE 1 Friends and family can be positive influences that steer teens away from tobacco use. However, the media, especially the movies, have long been criticized for glamorizing tobacco use.

Friends

Family

Tobacco **401**

Why Teens Use Tobacco

L3 **Content Update** GO ONLINE

Visit Pearson SuccessNet to access more information on the anti-smoking campaign. Have students complete the Web activity.

L2 **Journal Writing**

Encourage students to examine their own views about tobacco use. Ask them to complete the following sentence and use it as a topic sentence for a paragraph about tobacco use: "I think that people who use tobacco are..." Have students write their paragraphs in their journals, and let them keep their journal entries confidential. **WRITING**

L3 **Cultural Connection**

Tell students that some tobacco products are marketed primarily to specific groups, such as Hispanics, African Americans, Native Americans, or women. Find (or ask students to find) examples of such ads, and pass them around the class. Discuss how the ads try to attract members of specific groups and why tobacco companies might want to target those groups in particular.

L3 **Building Health Skills**

Analyzing Influences Ask students what they think people mean when they say "Actions speak louder than words." Then discuss the challenge faced by adults who smoke when they talk about the risks of smoking with their children.

Connect to Your Life Allow students to answer this question in their private journals.

Differentiated Instruction

L1 **Special Needs**

Abstract concepts, such as "influence of media," may be difficult for some students to understand. Work with students to create a visual display showing each type of influence on teen tobacco use. Try to show both positive and negative influences. For example, a picture of a group of teens having fun without tobacco could represent the positive influence of friends. To show the influence of the media, you could use a public service announcement and a Web site with discount coupons for cigarettes.

Tobacco Products

L3 **Visual Learning: Figure 2**

Ask: **What does the graph show?** *(Cigarette use increased from 1900 to 1960 and then decreased.)* Point out that the graph represents cigarette consumption per capita, or per person. Ask: **Can you tell from the graph how the numbers of smokers changed over time?** *(no, only how the numbers of cigarettes used per person changed)* Call on a volunteer to answer the caption question.

Caption Answer It seems to have led to a decline in cigarette use. Cigarette use peaked around that time and then started to decrease.

L3 **Building Media Literacy**

Assign students to find a reliable health-related article about nicotine from different types of print or electronic media. Ask students to write a paragraph describing what they learned from their article and the difficulty level of the article. Have several students read their paragraphs aloud. Based on this example, discuss which types of media seem to be the most informative, reliable, and accessible to the general public. **WRITING**

L2 **Cooperative Learning**

Divide the class into groups of students with different ability levels. Ask groups to make charts comparing and contrasting smoked and smokeless tobacco products. Charts should include examples and dangers of each type of product. Make sure all members of each group play an active role in creating the chart.

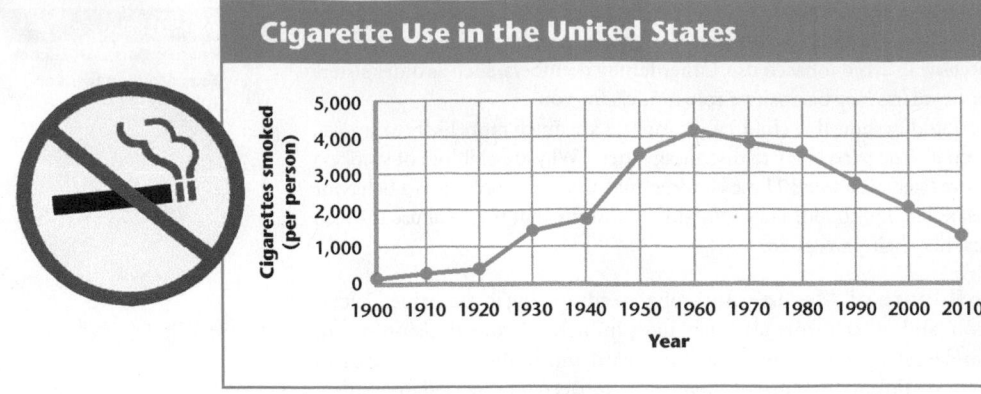

Cigarette Use in the United States

FIGURE 2 Cigarette use has fallen sharply since people have become more aware of its negative health effects. **Reading Graphs** In 1964, the Surgeon General issued the first report on the negative health effects of smoking. What effect did the report seem to have on cigarette use? Explain.

Tobacco Products

Tobacco products are made from the dried, processed leaves of tobacco plants. Tobacco plants naturally produce a chemical that acts as an insecticide to protect the plants' leaves from insects. This insecticide is **nicotine,** a very addictive chemical in tobacco products.

In its pure liquid form nicotine is extremely poisonous. In fact, each year thousands of young children are poisoned from eating cigarettes and cigars. Tobacco users are not immediately poisoned by nicotine because only a small amount enters the body at a time.

As you will learn in Sections 2 and 3, even small amounts of nicotine can have profound effects on several body systems. **Tobacco users take in nicotine whenever they use cigarettes, cigars, pipes, or smokeless tobacco products.**

Products That Are Smoked There is a wide variety of tobacco products that are smoked. When the tobacco is processed for these products, preservatives, flavorings, and other substances may be added. Some of these substances contribute to the harmful effects of smoking.

▶ Cigarettes are the most frequently used tobacco product. Cigarettes consist of cured and shredded tobacco leaves rolled in paper.

▶ *Bidis,* which are imported from India, are cigarette-like products that consist of tobacco wrapped in a leaf and tied with string.

▶ *Kreteks,* which are imported from Indonesia, contain ground clove. The clove alters the cigarette's flavor and numbs the lungs.

▶ Cigar and pipe tobacco is less processed than cigarette tobacco. It usually contains more nicotine than cigarette tobacco.

Many people think that products such as *bidis, kreteks,* cigars, pipes, and water pipes are safe alternatives to cigarettes. This is not true. No matter how tobacco is burned, cancer-causing chemicals and other harmful substances are produced.

402 *Chapter 16*

MATH **and Health**

L3 **Interpreting a Graph**

Have students look at the graph in Figure 2. Ask: **In which decade did the smoking rate increase the most?** *(the 1940s)* **By about how much did cigarette use increase in that decade?** *(from about 1,750 per person to about 3,500 per person, or by about 1,750 cigarettes per person)* **What percentage increase was that?** *(1,750 ÷ 1,750 = 1, or a 100 percent increase)* **Between 1960 and 2010, by what percentage did cigarette use decrease?** *(4000 − 1300 = 2700; 2700 ÷ 4000 = 0.675, or a 67.5 percent decrease)*

Smokeless Tobacco Tobacco that is chewed, placed between the lower lip and teeth, or sniffed through the nose is known as **smokeless tobacco.** As you will read in Sections 2 and 3, these products cause direct harm to the lining of the mouth, tongue, teeth, and gums. Smokeless tobacco also contains many of the same harmful chemicals found in tobacco smoke, including nicotine. In 1986, the Surgeon General concluded that smokeless tobacco is not a safe substitute for cigarettes.

▶ **Chewing tobacco,** also known as "dip" or "chew," consists of poor-quality, ground tobacco leaves mixed with flavorings, preservatives, and other chemicals. Wads of chewing tobacco are placed between the cheek and gum.

▶ **Snuff** is finely ground, powdered tobacco. It may be a dry powder, or oil may be added to make the snuff moist. Most snuff users place it in their mouths, between the lower lip and teeth. Some users sniff it through their nose.

When chewing tobacco and snuff are held in the mouth, the products cause increased saliva production. The user often spits out the excess saliva and tobacco juice. This is why smokeless tobacco is often called "spit" or "spitting tobacco."

FIGURE 3 Most smokeless tobacco products are held in the mouth. Although they do not harm the lungs like smoking does, these products pose other risks to a user's health.

Section 1 Review

Key Ideas and Vocabulary

1. Describe three factors that influence a person's decision about tobacco use.

2. What is **nicotine?**

3. List the types of tobacco products that are smoked and the smokeless tobacco products.

4. What part of the body is most affected by the use of smokeless tobacco?

Critical Thinking

5. Sequencing Consider the three factors that may influence a teen's decision about tobacco use—friends, family, and media. Which do you think has the greatest influence? Which has the least influence? Explain.

Health and Community

Smoking in Movies For many years, filmmakers have been accused of glamorizing smoking. Watch two movies in which one of the main characters smokes. In a report describe how smoking was treated in each film. Was smoking portrayed in an accurate way? Present your observations to your class. **WRITING**

6. Evaluating Which do you think have a greater influence on a teen's thoughts about smoking—tobacco ads or anti-tobacco ads?

7. Making Judgments At most schools, teens caught with alcohol face stronger punishments than teens caught with tobacco products. Do you think fewer teens would use tobacco if they faced stronger punishments?

GO ONLINE PearsonSuccessNet.com   Audio Summary Section 16.1

Tobacco **403**

Examining
Advertising Tactics

Objective

Develop skills to analyze advertisement messages.

Teaching Strategies

- Figure 12 on page 21 describes various advertising methods. You may want students to review this figure before they begin this activity.

- Explain that ads for tobacco products used to be common in all media. Tell students that the Hit Parade ad was produced in the 1950s. The woman shown in the ad, Dorothy Collins, was a star on the popular TV show for which the cigarettes were named. The use of a celebrity spokesperson is a variation on the testimonial tactic.

- Ask students to select an ad that contains claims about cigarettes that are not true. Have them suggest how to rewrite the ad to make it accurate.

- Ask students to read all the steps in analyzing an ad. Urge them to ask questions about any steps they are unsure of.

Analyzing Influences

Examining
Advertising Tactics

Tobacco companies used to spend billions of dollars a year to advertise their products. Their ads appeared on television, in magazines, in newspapers, and on billboards.

Why do companies spend so much money on advertising? The ultimate goal of advertising, of course, is to increase a company's profits. To do this, advertising is used to attract new users, increase customer use of a product, or to persuade people to switch brands. On a daily basis, you are bombarded with hundreds of advertisements. Use the following guidelines to help you identify and resist the techniques that advertisers use to influence you.

⚑ Sensitive Issues

Some cigarette ads may be provocative and suggestive. You may want to review the ads before students discuss them. Watch for ads that might elicit inappropriate conversations that could make some group members uncomfortable.

❶ Identify the tactics being used to sell the product.

These are some common advertising techniques.

▶ **Humor** Funny ads may cause you to associate a product with fun or feeling good.

▶ **Slogans and Jingles** Catchy phrases or tunes may help you remember the product.

▶ **Testimonials** "Satisfied customers" may convince you that the product works.

▶ **Attractive Models** The use of attractive models communicates the idea that attractive or successful people use the product.

▶ **Positive Images** The ad may imply that you need the product to be strong, independent, and successful.

▶ **Bandwagon Approach** The ad makes you think that everyone uses the product. You may want to "jump on the bandwagon" too.

▶ **Appeal to the Senses** The use of beautiful or exciting scenery, colors, or music appeals to the senses.

▶ **Price Appeal** The ad may imply the product is a better bargain than other products.

❷ Identify the ad's target audience.

These questions can help you determine whom an ad is trying to reach.

▶ In what setting does the ad take place? If it is a sporting event, for example, the ad is probably targeted at sports fans.

▶ What are the characters in the ad doing? If they are doing the latest fad, the ad may be targeted at teens or young adults.

▶ Where does the ad appear? Advertisers know which television shows and magazines attract the audience they want to reach.

❸ Identify the ad's message.

What exactly is the ad trying to convince you to believe?

▶ Write a one-sentence statement that describes what the ad wants you to believe about the product. Start your sentence as follows, "If I use this product, then . . ." For example, "If I use this product, then I will be happier and have more friends."

▶ Reread the statement you wrote. Do you think it could be true? Why or why not?

Practice the Skill

1. Examine the ad for a tobacco product on the previous page.
   a. Identify the tactics being used by the advertiser.
   b. Who do you think the ad is trying to reach? What is its message?

2. Search the Internet for vintage print ads for tobacco products. In this case, *vintage* means classic or old. Some Web sites have print ads grouped by decade.

3. Select and print three different cigarette ads. For each ad, describe the setting, characters, and behaviors. Decide which tactic is being used to sell the product. Then write a one-sentence statement that expresses the ad's message as you see it.

4. Work in a small group and compare ads. Identify the most common messages in cigarette ads. Are there different messages for different audiences? How have the messages changed over time?

5. Use one or more of the advertising tactics described to make an anti-tobacco poster.

Tobacco **405**

Practice the Skill

1. **a.** Tactics include slogans and attractive models.

   b. *Sample answer:* The ad is trying to reach young adults. Its message is "If I use this product, then I will have sophisticated friends."

2. Suggest that students choose ads that use a variety of advertising tactics.

3. Answers will vary depending on the ads students chose. Check that students have correctly described their ads. Statements about the ads' messages are subjective, so there are no right or wrong answers for this part of the question.

4. Groups are likely to find that the ads use different messages for different audiences. Many of the ads students find on the Internet will not be shown in their original context. So students will have to infer the intended audience from the characters and setting.

5. With their posters, students should try to convince others to avoid tobacco. They should use at least one of the advertising tactics described. Have students write a paragraph describing which tactics they used.

Health and Community

L3 Tobacco and the Internet

Although print cigarette ads are still permitted, tobacco companies may choose to spend their marketing dollars in other ways. One way companies attract and retain customers is to control the price of cigarettes. They offer rebates to retailers and coupons to consumers. These tactics help to offset increases in cigarette taxes.

People can register at Web sites to receive coupons and they can buy discounted cigarettes online. Ask students what advertising tactic is being used when manufacturers offer rebates and coupons. Also discuss how being able to purchase cigarettes online could affect a teen's interest in and access to cigarettes.

Section 2
Chemicals in Tobacco Products

Objectives

Before class begins, write the objectives on the board. Have students copy the objectives into their notebooks at the start of class.

1. Focus

Warm-Up Myth/Fact

After students complete the writing assignment, call on a few volunteers to describe their responses. Try to get a range of ideas for sources of information about tobacco products. Discuss whether the sources provide trustworthy information.

Presentation 16-2

Objectives

▶ **Explain** how nicotine affects the body.

▶ **Identify** two other dangerous substances in tobacco smoke.

▶ **Examine** why using smokeless tobacco is not a safe alternative to smoking.

Vocabulary

- stimulant
- tar
- carcinogen
- carbon monoxide

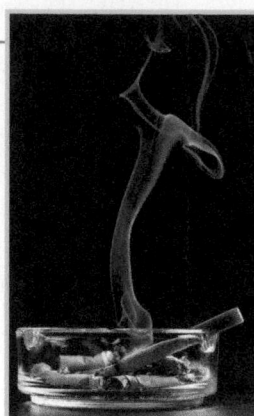

Warm-Up

Myth Low-tar and low-nicotine cigarettes are safer than regular cigarettes.

Fact Although the amount of tar and nicotine in these cigarettes may be reduced, carbon monoxide levels are not. Also, smokers tend to smoke more of these cigarettes and inhale more deeply in order to feel the same effects as they felt from regular cigarettes.

WRITING Where do you think that most teens get their information about tobacco products? How factual do you think this information is?

Nicotine and the Body

Nicotine is a type of drug called a stimulant. **Stimulants** are drugs that increase the activity of the nervous system. In smokers, nicotine enters the blood mainly through the lungs. In smokeless tobacco users, nicotine enters the blood through the lining of the mouth or nose.

Once in the blood, nicotine reaches the brain within seconds. There, it takes the place of certain neurotransmitters—chemicals that send signals between cells. By mimicking these neurotransmitters, nicotine affects breathing, movement, learning, memory, mood, and appetite.

Nicotine's Short-Term Effects The immediate effects of nicotine on the body depend largely on how much nicotine is used and on the user's history of tobacco use. **The major short-term effects of nicotine use are increased heart rate, increased blood pressure, and changes in the brain that may lead to addiction.** Figure 4 outlines nicotine's short-term effects on several body systems.

First-time tobacco users may experience mild signs of nicotine poisoning, which include rapid pulse, clammy skin, nausea, and dizziness. However, in frequent users, nicotine stimulates the area of the brain that produces feelings of reward and pleasure. These effects last for about 30 minutes. It is these feelings that make the continued use of tobacco seem appealing.

406 *Chapter 16*

For Your INFORMATION!

Nicotine

Nicotine is a substance in tobacco that causes addiction. In smokers, nicotine enters the lungs in tiny droplets of incompletely burned tobacco, or tar. From the lungs, it takes just seconds for nicotine to reach the brain.

Nicotine causes the adrenal glands to release the stress hormone epinephrine.

Many of the effects included in Figure 4 are the result of epinephrine. As a person uses more tobacco throughout the day, the level of nicotine in the blood rises. A tobacco user's blood still contains some nicotine even through the night. As a result, most tobacco users are constantly under the influence of nicotine.

Effects of Nicotine

FIGURE 4 Nicotine acts as a stimulant. It has many immediate effects on several body systems. **Interpreting Diagrams** How does nicotine affect the heart? How does it affect the brain?

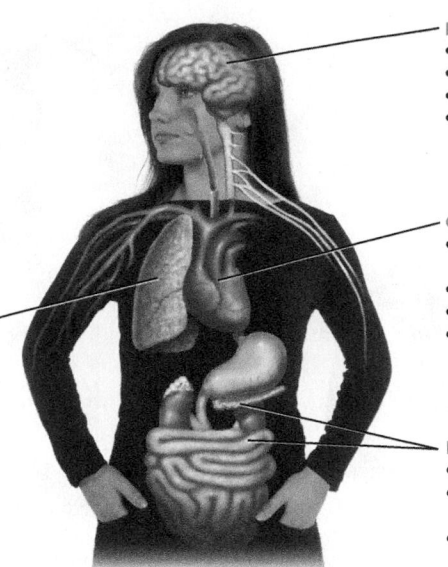

Nervous System
• Increases activity level
• Mimics neurotransmitters
• Decreases some reflex actions
• Activates the brain's "reward pathway"

Cardiovascular System
• Increases heart rate and the force of contractions
• Increases blood pressure
• Reduces blood flow to skin
• Increases risk of blood clotting

Respiratory System
• Increases mucus production
• Decreases muscle action in the lungs' airways
• Causes breathing to become more shallow

Digestive System
• Increases saliva production
• Decreases the amount of insulin released from the pancreas
• Increases bowel activity

Nicotine Addiction People who use tobacco frequently begin to rely on it for feelings of alertness and pleasure. Ongoing use of nicotine causes the body to develop a tolerance to nicotine. With tolerance, the user needs more and more nicotine to produce the same effects on the mind and body.

As tolerance increases, nicotine addiction develops. Once people are addicted, they experience strong cravings for nicotine. They might feel irritable or anxious in places or situations in which they cannot use tobacco.

The time it takes to become addicted depends on several factors including genetics, frequency of use, and age. Studies show that teens may become addicted faster and more intensely than adults. In fact, it may take only a few cigarettes for some teens to become addicted.

Psychological Dependence Tobacco users might also become dependent on nicotine for psychological reasons. Tobacco use may become a habit used to cope with stressful situations. Or, it may become associated with social situations, such as hanging out with friends. These psychological factors can make quitting difficult.

Nicotine Withdrawal If a nicotine addict goes without nicotine for even a short time, he or she may experience nicotine withdrawal. Symptoms of nicotine withdrawal include headaches, irritability, difficulty sleeping, inability to concentrate, and intense nicotine cravings. Withdrawal effects may begin as soon as 30 minutes after the last dose of nicotine.

 **Have you ever observed someone experiencing nicotine withdrawal? Describe his or her behavior.**

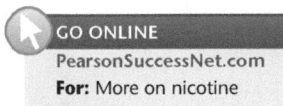
GO ONLINE
PearsonSuccessNet.com
For: More on nicotine

Tobacco **407**

---

2. Teach

L3 EL Reading/Note Taking 16-2
L2 Adapted Reading/Note Taking 16-2

Nicotine and the Body

L2 Visual Learning: Figure 4
Image Bank Figure 16-4

Challenge students to describe symptoms smokers might experience due to nicotine's effects on each system in the figure. *(e.g., Smokers might have breathing problems and chest congestion because of respiratory system effects.)*
Caption Answer Nicotine increases heart rate and the force of the heart's contractions. It activates the brain's "reward pathway."

L2 Addressing Misconceptions

Nicotine Addiction Most teens have likely observed that nicotine addiction does not lead to the same level of self-destructive or violent behavior as some illicit drugs such as heroin. As a result, they may underestimate the severity of nicotine addiction. Warn students that nicotine addiction is one of the toughest addictions to overcome. Nicotine is as addictive as the illicit drugs heroin and cocaine. As a result, it is far easier to never start smoking than to quit.

 *Sample answer:* Yes; the person acted nervous and irritable.

L3 Content Update  GO ONLINE

Visit Pearson SuccessNet to access more information about nicotine. Have students complete the Web activity.

Differentiated Instruction

L1 Special Needs

The detailed lists of nicotine's physical effects may be more information than some students need. To convince students to avoid using tobacco, make sure they have a clear understanding of nicotine and addiction. Write these three summary sentences on the board, and have students copy them into their notebooks.

• Nicotine is an addictive substance in tobacco.
• When people are addicted to nicotine, it is very hard for them to stop using tobacco.
• When addicted people first stop using tobacco, they feel sick and crave nicotine all the time.

Other Dangerous Chemicals

L2 Addressing Misconceptions

Tobacco Tar Explain to students that the tar in tobacco smoke is not the same substance that is used to pave roads. It consists of tiny droplets of burned tobacco resin. Ask: **Why do you think that tar is an appropriate name for burned tobacco resin?** *(It is dark and sticky like road tar.)*

EL Building Vocabulary

Give students definitions of the word parts *carcino-* ("cancer") and *-gen* ("producer"). Then ask students to define the term *carcinogen ("cancer producer").* Point out that there are many carcinogens, or cancer-causing agents, in tobacco smoke.

L3 Building Health Skills

Advocacy Have groups of students create posters advocating for avoiding tobacco because of its short-term dangers. Posters should show the dangers of both smoked and smokeless tobacco. Suggest that students illustrate their posters with pictures of some of the dangers (such as yellow teeth). Arrange for students to display their posters throughout the school.

FIGURE 5 Tobacco products contain many harmful chemicals. Some of these chemicals are a natural part of tobacco. Others are added when the tobacco is processed or form when tobacco is burned.

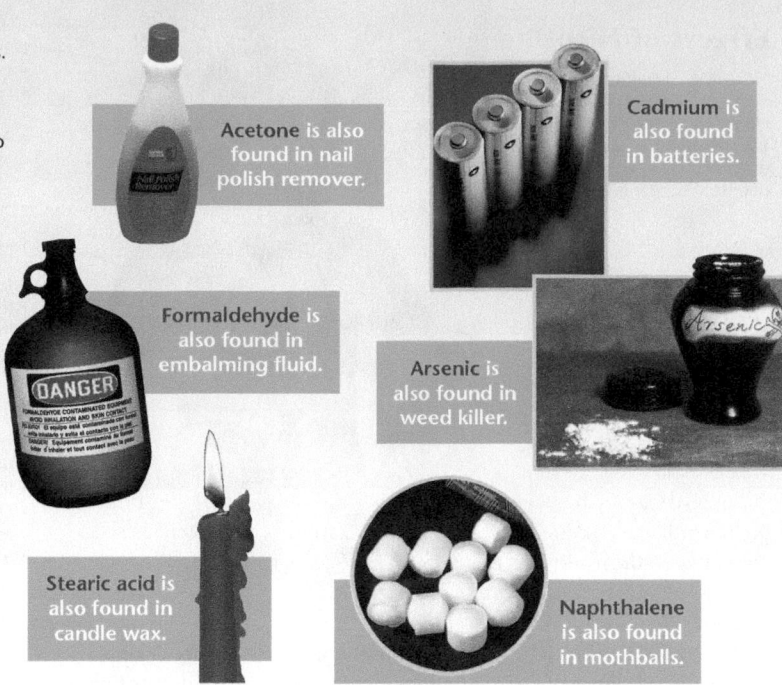

Some Chemicals in Tobacco Smoke
- Acetone
- Ammonia
- Arsenic
- Benzene
- Butane
- Cadmium
- Carbon monoxide
- Formaldehyde
- Hydrogen cyanide
- Methanol
- Naphthalene
- Nickel
- Propane
- Stearic acid
- Uranium
- Vinyl chloride

Acetone is also found in nail polish remover.

Cadmium is also found in batteries.

Formaldehyde is also found in embalming fluid.

Arsenic is also found in weed killer.

Stearic acid is also found in candle wax.

Naphthalene is also found in mothballs.

Other Dangerous Chemicals

As you can see in Figure 5, nicotine is only one of many chemicals in tobacco that can harm your body. In fact, tobacco smoke contains more than 4,000 chemicals. **In addition to nicotine, two of the most harmful substances in tobacco smoke are tar and carbon monoxide.**

Tar The dark, sticky substance that forms when tobacco burns is known as **tar.** Tar is a mixture of hundreds of chemicals. Smokers of any type of tobacco product—including cigarettes, herbal cigarettes, cigars, and pipes—expose their bodies to the short-term effects of tar.

▶ Brown stains on fingers and teeth

▶ Smelly hair and clothes

▶ Bad breath

▶ Paralysis of cilia lining the airways

▶ Increased number of respiratory infections, such as colds and the flu

▶ Impaired lung function, which leads to reduced athletic ability

In addition to these short-term effects, tar also causes long-term damage to the body. Tar contains many chemicals that are known **carcinogens** (kahr SIN uh junz), or cancer-causing agents. Tar can also damage the respiratory system to the point that it can no longer function. You will read more about the long-term effects of tar in Section 3.

TEENS *Are Asking . . .*

Q: I thought that cigarette filters protect the smoker from tar and other harmful chemicals?

A: Filters are designed to dilute smoke with air. In theory, this reduces the amount of nicotine, tar, and other substances inhaled by smokers. In laboratory studies performed with machines, the filters perform as designed. However, people do not smoke cigarettes like machines do. Smokers tend to inhale more deeply or smoke more frequently to reach the nicotine levels that satisfy their addiction. There is no convincing evidence that filters protect smokers from smoking-related diseases.

Carbon Monoxide When substances—including tobacco—are burned, an odorless, poisonous gas called **carbon monoxide** is produced. Once inhaled and absorbed into the blood, carbon monoxide binds to the hemoglobin molecules in red blood cells in place of oxygen. When this happens, red blood cells cannot transport as much oxygen as the body cells need.

To make up for the shortage of oxygen, a smoker's breathing and heart rates increase. Over time, this strain can damage the cardiovascular system and other organs.

Chemicals in Smokeless Tobacco Some people think that using smokeless tobacco products is safe because no smoke is produced or inhaled. **However, smokeless tobacco contains many of the same dangerous chemicals that are in tobacco smoke.** There are no safe tobacco products.

Smokeless tobacco is at least as addictive as cigarettes. In fact, with each dose of chewing tobacco, a user absorbs about two and a half times the nicotine as a person who smokes one cigarette. A snuff user absorbs about twice the nicotine as a person who smokes one cigarette.

The life-threatening effects of smokeless tobacco use, such as cancer, will be discussed in Section 3. Smokeless tobacco also has a number of other effects that are unpleasant or may lead to health problems.

▶ Stained teeth

▶ Bad breath and drooling

▶ Receding gums and tooth decay

To avoid these unpleasant side effects, many smokeless tobacco users eventually turn to smoking to satisfy their nicotine craving. Then they expose their bodies to the additional hazards of tar and carbon monoxide.

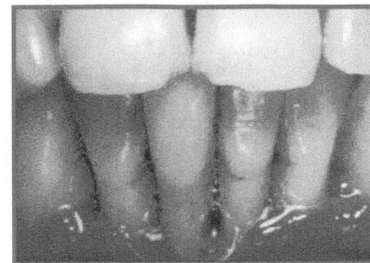

FIGURE 6 In addition to other harmful chemicals, many smokeless tobacco products contain sand and sugars. Both of these can damage the gums. Note how smokeless tobacco caused the gums to pull away from the teeth in this photo.

Section 2 Review

Key Ideas and Vocabulary

1. What type of drug is nicotine? How does nicotine affect the body?
2. What effects do tar and carbon monoxide have on the bodies of smokers?
3. What is a **carcinogen**?
4. Explain how smokeless tobacco products harm the body.

Critical Thinking

5. Applying Concepts What facts about tobacco would you use to convince a friend not to start using tobacco?

> **Health at Home**
>
> **Life After Quitting** Interview two family members, neighbors, or friends who have quit smoking. Ask them how they stopped smoking, how difficult it was, and how their lives have changed. In a paragraph, compare and contrast their experiences. **WRITING**

6. Making Judgments Do you think that drugstores, which sell medicines, should also sell tobacco products? Why or why not? **WRITING**

7. Evaluating Why do you think that tobacco users are willing to live with unpleasant side effects, such as stained teeth and bad breath?

3. Assess

Evaluate

These assignments can help you assess students' mastery of the section content.

Section 2 Review

Answers appear below.

Teaching Resources
• Practice 16-2
• Section 16-2 Quiz

L2 Reteach

Have pairs of students demonstrate their knowledge of the section's objectives to one another. For any objectives they are unsure of, students should reread the relevant passages in the section.

L4 Enrich

Teaching Resources
• Enrich 16-2

Health at Home

Life After Quitting Make sure students interview only trusted adults in safe settings. Advise students to ask both people the same questions so that they can directly compare both sets of responses.

Section 2 Review

1. stimulant; increased heart rate, increased blood pressure, and changes in the brain that may lead to addiction
2. Tar causes brown stains on fingers and teeth, smelly hair, bad breath, paralysis of cilia, more respiratory infections. Carbon monoxide reduces the amount of oxygen in blood and increases breathing and heart rates.

3. a cancer-causing agent
4. Smokeless tobacco products cause stained teeth, bad breath, drooling, receding gums, tooth decay, cancer, and addiction.
5. *Sample answer:* I would tell the friend how tobacco stains teeth, causes bad breath, and reduces athletic ability.

6. Some students might say that drugstores should not sell tobacco because it is harmful. Other students might say that drugstores should sell tobacco because it is legal for adults to buy and use.
7. *Sample answer:* because they are addicted to nicotine

Objectives

Before class begins, write the objectives on the board. Have students copy the objectives into their notebooks at the start of class.

1. Focus

Warm-Up **Quick Quiz**

Use the Warm-Up Presentation slide to survey student responses.

Statement three is the false statement. Explain that treatments exist for emphysema and chronic bronchitis, but no cures. Ask students if they were surprised that any of the other statements were actually true.

Presentation 16-3

Connect to Your Life *Sample answer:* I would use the label "Warning: Smoking these cigarettes can kill you!" I would use this label because tobacco use is the leading cause of preventable death in the United States.

⚑ Sensitive Issues

If students have family members with tobacco-related illnesses, the issue of long-term risks of tobacco use may be sensitive to them. Be careful not to imply that the sick individuals are responsible for their own illnesses because they chose to use tobacco. Point out that most older smokers were already addicted to tobacco when they learned of its health risks. Add that most tobacco users wish they had never started using tobacco because it is so hard to stop.

Section 3 Risks of Tobacco Use

Objectives

▶ **Describe** the long-term health risks of tobacco use.
▶ **Identify** the long-term risks of exposure to secondhand smoke.
▶ **Examine** how smoking by a pregnant woman can affect her baby.

Vocabulary

• chronic obstructive pulmonary disease (COPD)
• chronic bronchitis
• emphysema
• leukoplakia
• mainstream smoke
• sidestream smoke
• secondhand smoke

Warm-Up

Quick Quiz All of the following statements are true except for one. Which statement do you think is false?

① In the United States, over 400,000 people die from smoking each year.

② Children of people who smoke have a greater risk of developing asthma.

③ Scientists have developed cures for chronic bronchitis and emphysema.

④ Smokers die about 14 years earlier than nonsmokers.

⑤ Smokeless tobacco increases one's risk of cardiovascular disease.

 **WRITING** Explain why you gave the answer that you did.

Long-Term Risks

In Section 2, you read about the immediate effects that tobacco has on a person's health. You may have noticed some of these effects, such as stained teeth and bad breath, in tobacco users you know. What you cannot notice, however, is the development of much more serious problems. **With every dose of tobacco, users increase their risk of developing respiratory diseases, cardiovascular disease, and several different forms of cancer.**

Did you know that tobacco use is the leading cause of preventable death in the United States? Cigarette smoking alone is directly responsible for the deaths of over 400,000 Americans each year. Many more people die each year from cigar, pipe, and smokeless tobacco use. More than 6 million children living today may die early because of a decision they will make during their teen years—the decision to use tobacco.

Connect to Your Life What warning label would you put on cigarette packages? Why?

Focus on **ISSUES**

L3 Debate: Should Tobacco Be Illegal?

Point out that tobacco is the only legal product that can cause death and disability when used as intended. For this reason, many people think tobacco products should be illegal. Other people think tobacco products should remain legal. They argue that adults should have the right to do what they want as long as they do not harm others. Assign groups of students to debate this issue. Give groups a chance to present their debate to the rest of the class.

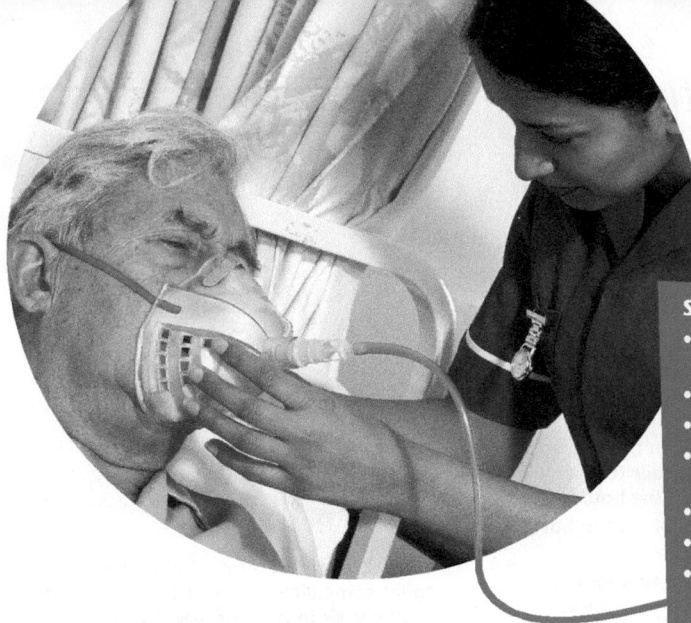

FIGURE 7 Over time, smoking can affect the function of many body systems and processes. Although some of these effects may be merely unpleasant, serious damage to the respiratory system can be life threatening.

Smoking also leads to . . .
- Increased risk of stomach ulcers
- Slower healing of injuries
- Increased colds and flus
- Increased allergies and asthma
- A constant runny nose
- Frequent headaches
- Dulled sense of taste and smell
- Premature wrinkling

Respiratory Diseases

You may know smokers who suffer from a hacking cough that does not go away. "Smoker's cough" is the result of damage caused by tar. Cells that line the respiratory tract have hairlike extensions called cilia. The cilia move in a sweeping motion and push mucus and particles away from the lungs and toward the throat to be swallowed.

Tar sticks to the cilia, prevents them from moving, and damages them over time. Dust, tobacco smoke toxins, and mucus then accumulate in the airways. Coughing is the body's attempt to clear the airways.

Tobacco smoke and other accumulating toxins also irritate the lining of the bronchi. Bronchi are the tubes that carry air between the trachea and the lungs. The bronchi become inflamed, which restricts the amount of air that can enter and leave the lungs.

Chronic Obstructive Pulmonary Disease If a person continues to smoke over a long period of time, the damage that occurs to the respiratory system becomes permanent. He or she may develop **chronic obstructive pulmonary disease (COPD),** a disease that results in a gradual loss of lung function.

COPD develops slowly, but its effects are severe. People with COPD find it difficult to fill their lungs with air. Simple activities, such as climbing stairs, may leave them gasping for breath. Chronic bronchitis and emphysema are two types of COPD. Many people with COPD have both chronic bronchitis and emphysema.

▶ **Chronic Bronchitis** In people with **chronic bronchitis,** the airways are constantly inflamed. Over time, mucus-producing cells increase in size and number, producing more and more mucus. The constricted airways and overproduction of mucus make breathing difficult.

Tobacco **411**

2. Teach

L3 **EL** Reading/Note Taking 16-3
L2 Adapted Reading/Note Taking 16-3

Long-Term Risks

L3 **Building Health Skills**

Accessing Information Challenge students to find several recent, reliable statistics about deaths related to tobacco use. (Examples might include: Tobacco kills half of the smokers who do not quit; and almost one in three cancer deaths is due to tobacco use.) Have students use the facts to create a brochure about the dangers of tobacco use. Display the brochures in the classroom. **WRITING**

Respiratory Diseases

L3 **Teacher Demo**

Obtain a three-dimensional model of the respiratory system from the science department or a physician's office, hospital, or anti-smoking clinic. Trace the path of smoke into the lungs and point out the respiratory structures that smoke affects. Call on students to describe how the structures are damaged by tobacco smoke.

L2 **Building Vocabulary**

Students who have had bronchitis may be confused by the use of the term in this context. Explain that it means "inflammation of the bronchi" and can be caused by infection or smoking. When bronchitis is caused by infection, it is called *acute bronchitis* and can be cured with antibiotics. When bronchitis is caused by smoking, it is called *chronic bronchitis* and cannot be cured.

Differentiated Instruction

EL **English Language Learners**

Some of the section vocabulary terms, including *emphysema* and *leukoplakia,* may be difficult for students to pronounce and learn. Read the vocabulary terms aloud, and ask students to repeat the terms after you. Students can also make vocabulary flashcards that include phonetic spellings of difficult terms. Pairs of students can practice pronouncing the terms and quiz each other on the definitions.

Hands-On *Activity*

Make a Model of a Smoker's Lungs

You may want to do this activity as a class demonstration. Use a 1-liter bottle. Rinse and dry both the bottle and cap. The tubing should be 5–10 cm long and about the same diameter as a cigarette. You can use a nail to make the holes in the cap and side of the bottle. Keep the room well ventilated to reduce students' exposure to sidestream smoke.

Make sure you get permission from school administrators before lighting a cigarette on school grounds.

Think and Discuss Answers

1. The cotton ball is brown because it is covered with sticky tar.

2. The inside of the bottle is coated with a brownish gray film of tar.

3. Smoking coats the teeth, throat, and lungs with tar, causing irritation and possibly cancer.

L4 Active Learning

Challenge students to create a model of lungs affected by emphysema. For example, students might use a new balloon to represent a healthy alveolus and a stretched out balloon to represent an alveolus that has lost its shape and elasticity. Torn balloons could represent alveoli that have started to break down. Set aside class time for students to demonstrate their models.

Hands-On *Activity*

Make a Model of a Smoker's Lungs

In this activity, you will construct a simple smoking machine to demonstrate how smoking affects the lungs.

Materials
- plastic bottle with cap • plastic tubing • clay
- cotton ball • twist tie • cigarette • safety matches

Try This

1. Your teacher will make a hole in the bottle cap about the size of the tubing. Your teacher will also poke a hole in the side of the bottle.
2. Thread the tubing into the hole in the bottle cap, and seal the edges with clay.
3. Place the cotton ball over the tubing on the underside of the cap. Use the twist tie to secure it.
4. Insert the cigarette into the other end of the tubing so that the side you light points up.
5. Screw the cap onto the bottle.
6. Squeeze the bottle to force some air out of it. Then cover the hole with your thumb.
7. Have your teacher light the cigarette. With your thumb over the hole, pump the bottle slowly and steadily. This will draw air in through the cigarette.
8. When the bottle is full of air, uncover the hole to let some air out. Cover the hole before drawing air in through the cigarette again.
9. Your teacher will extinguish the cigarette and dispose of it.

Think and Discuss

1. Describe the appearance of the cotton ball after the smoking test.
2. What does the inside of the bottle look like?
3. Use the model to describe what smoking does to a smoker's teeth, throat, and lungs.

Tubing and clay
Twist tie
Cotton ball
Puncture hole here

▶ **Emphysema** Recall that your lungs contain millions of tiny alveoli, or air sacs. Normally, the alveoli expand as you breathe in oxygen and contract as you breathe out carbon dioxide. Tobacco smoke damages alveoli tissue. The damage can lead to **emphysema,** a disorder in which alveoli in the lungs can no longer function properly.

With emphysema, the alveoli lose shape and elasticity. Less oxygen can get into the alveoli and less carbon dioxide can get out. Eventually, the alveoli walls start to break down, which reduces the area in which gas exchange can occur. As a result, people with emphysema are always short of breath.

COPD Treatments Cigarette smoking is responsible for about 90 percent of all COPD deaths. Although there is no cure for COPD, quitting smoking will prevent symptoms from getting worse. Treatments focus on relieving symptoms and slowing the progress of the disease. Possible treatments include medications that open airways, breathing exercises, oxygen treatments, and in severe cases, lung transplants.

412 *Chapter 16*

 and Health

L3 Public Service Announcement

Have groups of students write a public service announcement segment that warns about the long-term risks of smoking on the cardiovascular system. The PSA should mention increased risks of high blood pressure, high blood cholesterol, atherosclerosis, heart attack, and stroke. Arrange to have students present their PSAs at a meeting of the school board or parent-teacher organization.

Cardiovascular Disease

Cardiovascular disease—diseases of the heart and blood vessels—kill about 138,000 smokers in the United States every year.

▶ A smoker is two to three times more likely to have a heart attack than a nonsmoker.

▶ Cigarette smoking doubles a person's chances of suffering a stroke.

▶ Smokers are 10 times more likely to develop circulation problems in blood vessels that bring blood to the stomach, kidneys, legs, and feet.

These statistics are not surprising when you consider the damage that substances in tobacco products do to the heart and blood vessels. **The combined effects of nicotine, tar, and carbon monoxide force the cardiovascular system to work harder to deliver oxygen throughout the body.** Tobacco use also raises blood pressure, which, over time, weakens blood vessels and places strain on many organs.

Studies also show that the chemicals in tobacco smoke increase blood cholesterol levels and promote atherosclerosis—the thickening and hardening of artery walls. In addition, nicotine increases the blood's tendency to clot. Clots may block blood flow through narrowed arteries, leading to a heart attack or stroke.

 **Connect to Your Life** How do you think smoking would affect your ability to stay active as you age?

Cancer

Both tobacco smoke and smokeless tobacco contain many ingredients that are known carcinogens. **Tobacco use is a major factor in the development of lung cancer, oral cancers, and several other cancers.**

Many factors influence a tobacco user's risk of developing cancer. Some of these factors include when the person started using tobacco, how much tobacco the person has used, and how often the person is exposed to other people's smoke.

FIGURE 8 Most smokers are not fully aware of the damage occurring to their lungs until it is too late. **Comparing and Contrasting** Compare the lungs of a person with emphysema and a person with lung cancer to the healthy lung.

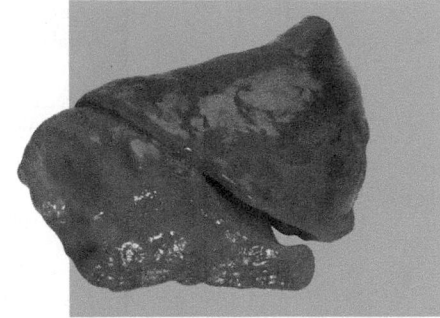

▲ **Healthy lung**

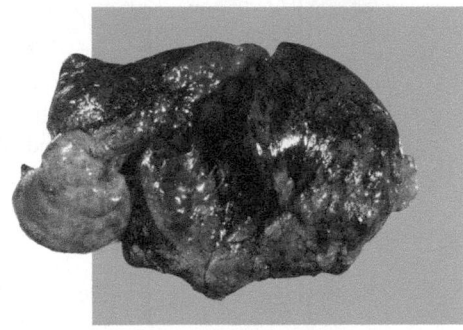

▲ **Lung with emphysema**

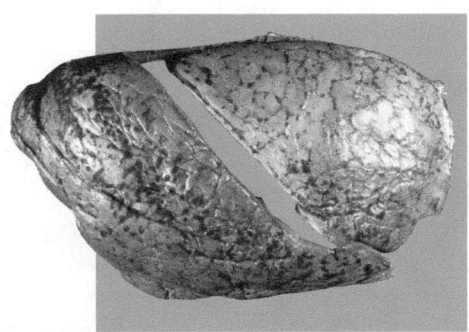

▲ **Lung with cancer**

Tobacco **413**

Cardiovascular Disease

L4 Building Health Skills

Communicating Have students make an intricate, illustrated concept map that demonstrates how the various risk factors for cardiovascular disease are related to or compounded by smoking. For example, three risk factors for cardiovascular disease are high blood pressure, high blood cholesterol levels, and physical inactivity. Concept maps should indicate smoking increases blood pressure and blood cholesterol. Smokers are also less able to be physically active.

L3 Cultural Connection

Some groups have high rates of certain conditions that can be worsened by smoking. For example, African Americans have high rates of high blood pressure compared to many other groups. Ask: **How might smoking affect someone with high blood pressure?** *(It might make the person's blood pressure higher and increase the risk of heart attack and stroke.)*

Connect to Your Life *Sample answer:* It would make it harder to stay active, because I would be out of breath and my heart would be unhealthy.

Cancer

L3 Class Discussion

Ask students to recall from Chapter 1 the kinds of factors that influence health. *(heredity, physical and social environments, culture, media, technology, healthcare, behavior)* Ask: **Which factors that influence a person's cancer risk are discussed on this page?** *(social and physical environments, behavior)* **What other factors might influence a tobacco user's risk of cancer?** *(heredity, other physical environment factors such as air pollution)*

L1 Visual Learning: Figure 8

Ask a student to answer the caption question. Ask other students to explain why the lungs of people with cancer or emphysema look so different from the healthy lung.

Caption Answer *Sample answer:* The lungs of people with emphysema or cancer look misshapen and discolored.

L2 **Teacher Demo**

Search for images of leukoplakia from the Internet and project them in your classroom. If you do not have an in-class projector, print the images and pass them around the class for students to examine. Whether or not students remember the term *leukoplakia,* they should remember what the condition looks like and that it may lead to cancer. Tobacco use leads to most cases of leukoplakia, but badly-fitted dentures and long-term alcohol use are other causes. People with an impaired immune system may have a similar condition called hairy leukoplakia. Point out that leukoplakia requires medical attention.

L2 **Class Discussion**

Discuss how smoking causes cancer in organs other than the lungs and mouth. Ask: **How can smoking cause cancer in organs that smoke does not contact, such as the pancreas and blood?** *(Carcinogens in smoke enter the blood through the lungs and travel through-out the body.)*

Secondhand Smoke

EL **Building Vocabulary**

Have students make a concept map showing their understanding of the terms *mainstream smoke, sidestream smoke,* and *secondhand smoke.* Concept maps should show that second-hand smoke consists of mainstream smoke and sidestream smoke. Concept maps should also show how mainstream and sidestream smoke differ. Suggest that students save their concept maps for section and chapter reviews.

Lung Cancer   Lung cancer is the leading cause of cancer death for both women and men. Scientists estimate that more than 85 percent of all deaths caused by lung cancer are related to smoking. Unfortunately, by the time most lung cancers are diagnosed successful treatment is unlikely. Only 15 percent of lung cancer patients survive for more than five years.

Oral Cancer   Smoking and smokeless tobacco are also associated with oral cancers—cancers of the mouth, tongue, and throat. About 90 percent of oral cancers occur in people who use or have used tobacco. The survival rate for oral cancer is higher than for lung cancer. However, surgery to remove the cancer may be disfiguring.

Tobacco users may develop white patches on their tongues or the lining of their mouths called **leukoplakia** (loo koh PLAY kee uh). Because the sores sometimes become cancerous, they should be monitored by a doctor.

Other Cancers   Tobacco carcinogens affect many organs in the body. As a result, tobacco users also have an increased risk of cancers of the esophagus, larynx, stomach, pancreas, kidney, bladder, and blood, among other sites.

Secondhand Smoke

When a person smokes, smoke enters the air from two sources. **Mainstream smoke** is exhaled from a smoker's lungs. Both the cigarette filter and the smoker's lungs trap a lot of substances before they can enter the air in mainstream smoke. The other source, **sidestream smoke,** is smoke that goes into the air directly from the cigarette. Sidestream smoke contains twice as much tar and nicotine as mainstream smoke.

The combination of mainstream and sidestream smoke is called **secondhand smoke,** or environmental tobacco smoke. Secondhand smoke is inhaled by everyone near the smoker.

414

TEENS *Are Asking . . .*

Q: **I live with a parent who smokes. How can I reduce my risk of health problems due to secondhand smoke?**

A: Start by trying to convince your parent to quit smoking. Encouragement generally works better than nagging. However, if that doesn't work, try to persuade your parent to stop smoking inside the house and car. It may help if you explain the health problems associated with secondhand smoke. If your parent continues to smoke inside, try to reduce your exposure to the smoke by going to your room, taking a walk outside, or opening a window when your parent lights up. Also, make sure you eat fruit. Studies suggest that the fiber in fruit might help protect lungs from damage due to childhood secondhand smoke exposure.

Dangers of Secondhand Smoke Long-term exposure to secondhand smoke can cause cardiovascular disease, many respiratory problems, and cancer. In fact, secondhand smoke exposure increases the risk of a sudden heart attack by about 30 percent. Each year, secondhand smoke causes about 50,000 deaths from heart attacks and lung cancer.

Children are especially vulnerable to secondhand smoke. Each year, secondhand smoke contributes to between 150,000 and 300,000 respiratory infections in children younger than 18 months. Children who are exposed to secondhand smoke are more likely to develop allergies and asthma. Their asthma symptoms are more likely to be worse than those of children who are not exposed. Inhaled secondhand smoke can cause recurring, long-lasting ear infections—a leading cause of hearing loss.

Avoiding Secondhand Smoke Although secondhand smoke is still a serious problem, great progress has been made to eliminate it. Federal, state, and local laws now prohibit or restrict smoking in many public places and workplaces. As smoking becomes less socially acceptable, smoking in public will become even less common.

Breathing clean air is a serious issue for everyone. The government and several health organizations have made great strides to protect you from secondhand smoke. But it is important that you also protect yourself.

▶ Ask smokers not to smoke around you.

▶ Be firm when telling guests that they can't smoke in your home or car.

▶ Pick restaurants that do not allow smoking or at least sit in no-smoking areas.

 **Connect to Your Life** Describe how you feel when you are exposed to secondhand smoke.

GO ONLINE **PLANETDIARY**
PearsonSuccessNet.com
For: More on secondhand smoke

FIGURE 9 About 22 percent of children in the United States are exposed to secondhand smoke at home on a regular basis.

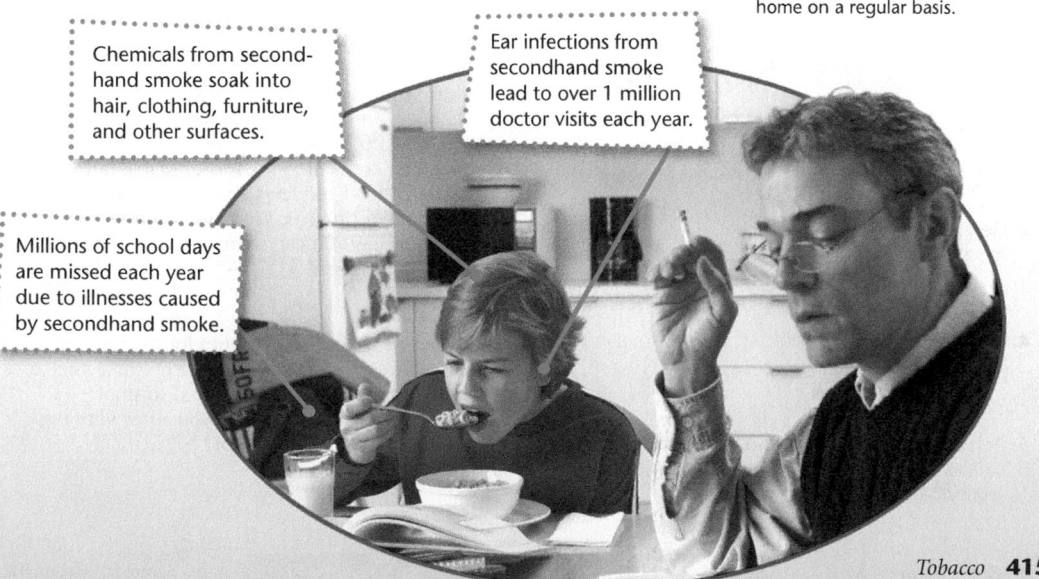

Chemicals from secondhand smoke soak into hair, clothing, furniture, and other surfaces.

Ear infections from secondhand smoke lead to over 1 million doctor visits each year.

Millions of school days are missed each year due to illnesses caused by secondhand smoke.

Tobacco **415**

L3 Online Activity **GO ONLINE**

Visit Pearson SuccessNet to access an online activity about secondhand smoke. Have students complete the Web activity.

L3 Building Health Skills

Advocacy Have students write a letter to the editor of a local newspaper encouraging smokers in their community to protect the people around them from secondhand smoke. Letters should identify the dangers of secondhand smoke, especially to infants and children. Ask pairs of students to exchange and critique each other's letters. Then, encourage students to send their letters to the editor. **WRITING**

L2 Journal Writing

Ask students to write a journal entry describing situations in which they are exposed to secondhand smoke. For each situation, have them describe a way they could reduce their exposure. (*e.g., If a friend or relative smokes, they could ask the person to smoke outside.*) **WRITING**

Connect to Your Life Students might say they feel irritated by the smoke and annoyed by the smokers.

Differentiated Instruction

L4 Gifted and Talented

Ask students who need an extra challenge to work together to create a Web site about secondhand smoke that uses a question-and-answer format. Suggest that they first learn more about the problem by visiting Web sites of the American Lung Association, Environmental Protection Agency, or similar organizations. Tell students that their Web sites should inform people of the dangers of secondhand smoke and suggest ways to reduce the dangers. Supervise their efforts to make sure the information they post is reliable and accurately represented. Encourage other class members to visit students' Web sites. **WRITING**

Tobacco Use and Pregnancy

L1 Visual Learning: Figure 10

Have students read the warning label for pregnant women. Then have them skim the text to find additional problems that may result when pregnant women smoke cigarettes. Ask students to rewrite the warning label so that it also includes these other problems. **WRITING**

3. Assess

Evaluate

These assignments can help you assess students' mastery of the section content.

Section 3 Review

Answers appear below.

Teaching Resources

• Practice 16-3
• Section 16-3 Quiz

L2 Reteach

Have students use the major headings in this section to make an outline they can use to study for a test. Their outlines should include all of the vocabulary terms.

L4 Enrich

Teaching Resources

• Enrich 16-3

Health at School

Anti-Smoking Quotes Suggest that students interview at least ten students. Remind students that the quotes should be suitable for younger children. Help students arrange to share their brochures with students in lower grades.

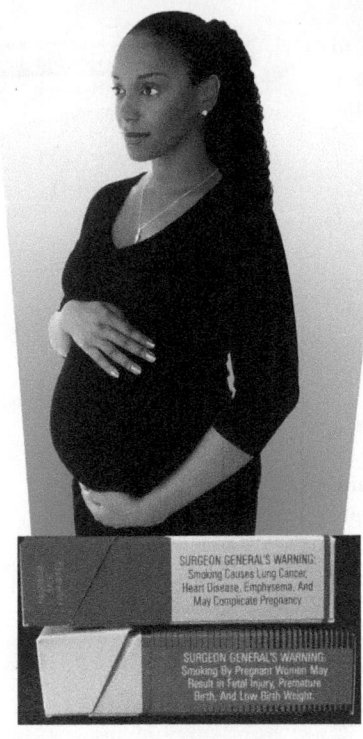

FIGURE 10 Despite warning labels, some pregnant women continue to smoke. However, the numbers are falling.

Tobacco Use and Pregnancy

Many of the harmful chemicals in tobacco smoke pass directly from a pregnant woman to her developing baby. **Pregnant women who smoke put their babies at risk for many health problems.** Tobacco smoke increases the baby's heart rate, reduces the baby's oxygen supply, and slows cell growth.

The babies born to mothers who smoke weigh, on average, six ounces less than the babies of nonsmokers. Low birthweight is a risk factor for many problems that could affect a baby throughout his or her entire life.

▶ Cerebral palsy

▶ Sight impairment

▶ Hearing problems

▶ Learning difficulties

Pregnant women who smoke also have higher rates of miscarriages, premature births, and stillbirths than women who do not smoke. Babies whose mothers smoked during pregnancy are also at much higher risk for sudden infant death syndrome (SIDS). SIDS is an unexplained disorder in which a seemingly healthy baby dies suddenly, usually while sleeping.

In addition, nursing mothers who smoke produce less milk than nonsmoking mothers. The nicotine in their milk can cause vomiting and diarrhea in nursing babies.

Section 3 Review

Key Ideas and Vocabulary

1. What are three long-term health risks associated with smoking?
2. Describe **leukoplakia.** Why should leukoplakia be monitored by a healthcare professional?
3. Identify three health risks associated with exposure to secondhand smoke.
4. List four problems for which babies of smoking mothers are at risk.

Critical Thinking

5. **Relating Cause and Effect** Do you think that smokers are also vulnerable to the dangers of secondhand smoke? Explain.

Health at School

Anti-Smoking Quotes Interview your peers who do not use tobacco. Ask them to describe how and why they made their decision. Create a brochure containing the most notable quotes along with related facts about tobacco. Do not use students' names. Work with your teacher to find out how you can share your brochure with younger students. **WRITING**

6. **Evaluating** People who fight for the rights of smokers claim that smoking is a personal choice and that they should be allowed to smoke anywhere they want to. Do you agree with this argument? Why or why not? **WRITING**

GO ONLINE PearsonSuccessNet.com   Audio Summary Section 16.3

Section 3 Review

1. respiratory diseases, cardiovascular disease, and several forms of cancer
2. white patches on the tongue or lining of the mouth; the patches can become cancerous
3. cardiovascular disease, respiratory problems, and cancer
4. *Any four:* low birthweight, cerebral palsy, sight impairment, hearing problems, learning difficulties, sudden infant death syndrome
5. *Sample answer:* yes, because they also breathe their own sidestream smoke
6. *Sample answer:* I think this argument is flawed, because it does not address the rights of nonsmokers, who deserve to be protected from secondhand smoke.

Saying No to Tobacco

Warm-Up

Dear Advice Line:

A bunch of my friends chew tobacco, especially when we get together to play sports. I know that it is not good for you, but I feel like a wimp when everyone else is chewing and I'm not. What if I just use chewing tobacco when we are playing?

WRITING Write a response to this teen to help with the decision he is facing.

Avoiding Tobacco Use

Your decision not to use tobacco will help you stay healthy now and reduce your risk of developing life-threatening diseases in the decades to come. As a nonuser, you are part of the growing majority of teens and adults who do not use tobacco. Your example may encourage others not to use tobacco.

At some point during your teen years, it is likely that someone will offer you a cigarette or another tobacco product. What will you do if this situation arises? **Sticking to your decision not to use tobacco involves being able to say no clearly and with confidence.**

It may be helpful to have a response prepared in advance so that you are not caught off guard. Simply stating, "I do not smoke," should be enough to end the conversation. Or, you could explain that you work hard to stay in shape and you do not want to spoil it. Fewer than one out of four teens smoke, which indicates that most teens do say no.

Do not assume that you can start using tobacco now and then quit. Studies show that people who start using tobacco in their teens have a more difficult time quitting than people who start using tobacco as adults. Refer to pages 378–379 for help in developing refusal skills.

 **How would you say no to a cigarette or other tobacco product offered to you?**

Objectives

▶ **Examine** how refusal skills will help you stick with your decision not to use tobacco.

▶ **Describe** the benefits of quitting tobacco use.

▶ **Identify** the most important factor for successfully quitting tobacco.

Vocabulary

• nicotine substitute

Tobacco **417**

Differentiated Instruction

 English Language Learners

Pair students who speak the same language, and ask them to practice using refusal skills for tobacco in their first language. After students feel confident saying *no* in their first language, ask them to practice using refusal skills for tobacco in English.

Section 4

Saying No to Tobacco

Objectives

Before class begins, write the objectives on the board. Have students copy the objectives into their notebooks at the start of class.

1. Focus

Warm-Up Advice Line

After students complete the writing assignment, call on a few volunteers to describe their responses. Try to get at least a few responses that advise the teen to avoid using tobacco because of the physical health risks and risk of addiction.

Presentation 16-4

2. Teach

L3 **EL** Reading/Note Taking 16-4

L2 Adapted Reading/Note Taking 16-4

Avoiding Tobacco Use

L3 **Cooperative Learning**

Have pairs of students write a brief dialogue in which one teen refuses an offer of a cigarette from another teen and provides convincing reasons for not smoking. Suggest that students first review refusal skills on pages 378–379. Give pairs a chance to present their dialogues to the class. Ask other students to decide which refusal statements were most effective and why. **WRITING**

Connect to Your Life *Sample answer:* I would say "No thanks, I don't want to harm my health."

Benefits of Quitting

L1 Visual Learning: Figure 11

Image Bank Figure 16-11

Ask students to read the lists of changes in the figure. Call on a volunteer to answer the caption question. Then, have students use the information in the figure to make a timeline of changes that occur after quitting. **Caption Answer** Lung function increases, coughing diminishes, respiratory infections become less frequent, and lung cancer death rate decreases.

L2 Addressing Misconceptions

Understanding Risk Some students may have difficulty understanding what the data in Figure 11 mean. For example, some students may think that after five years a person who quit smoking is no longer at risk for stroke. After quitting smoking for five years, a person's risk of stroke does drop to the same risk as someone of the same age who never smoked. But all people have some risk for stroke, and the risk increases with age. Ask students to read some of the other bullet points aloud and explain in their own words what they think the data mean.

Changes in a Smoker's Body After Quitting

First Days

After 20 minutes
- Blood pressure and heart rate return to normal
- Temperature of hands and feet increases to normal

After 8 hours
- Oxygen and carbon monoxide levels return to normal

After 24 hours
- Risk of sudden heart attack decreases

After 48 hours
- Senses of smell and taste start to improve

After 3 months
- Circulation improves; lung function improves

After 9 months
- Coughing and nasal congestion diminish
- Respiratory infections are less frequent
- Energy level increases

After 1 year
- Excess risk of heart disease is half that of a current smoker

FIGURE 11 Immediately after a person kicks the tobacco habit, the body begins to repair damage from the harmful substances to which it was exposed. Some of these repairs occur within days, while others may take decades. **Classifying** What benefits occur to the respiratory system after a smoker quits?

Benefits of Quitting

Surveys show that about nine out of ten smokers want to quit. Quitting tobacco use is not easy because it involves breaking an addiction. Nicotine may be just as addictive as some other drugs, such as cocaine and heroin. Quitting also involves breaking many habits associated with smoking. Taking time to consider the benefits of quitting, however, can make the difficult process seem even more worthwhile.

The tobacco user who quits can expect many immediate and long-term benefits. **The health benefits of quitting tobacco use begin immediately and continue throughout life. Society also benefits every time a tobacco user quits.** Figure 11 displays the changes that occur in a smoker's body after quitting.

Cardiovascular Benefits Immediately after quitting tobacco use, blood pressure lowers and heart rate returns to normal. As time passes, circulation improves and the risk of heart disease and stroke becomes similar to that of nonsmokers.

Respiratory Benefits Gradually, the cilia lining the air passages regain normal function. Breathing becomes easier as the lungs become free of tar, excess mucus, and other debris.

Psychological Benefits People who quit tobacco use usually feel increased confidence. They feel that they have regained control over their lives rather than allowing the tobacco to control them.

Benefits to Society Quitting tobacco also benefits society. Tobacco use costs society almost $200 billion per year. These expenses pay for healthcare for tobacco-related illnesses, damages and injuries from smoking-related fires, and loss of earnings from disease and early death.

Sensitive Issues

Students who have tried to stop using tobacco without success may be frustrated during this discussion. Point out that most people who quit do so only after trying multiple times. Make sure students know where to go for help to quit using tobacco.

TEENS *Are Asking . . .*

Q: My grandmother has been smoking for 40 years. She says it's too late to quit because the damage has already been done. Is she right?

A: No. Health improves when people quit smoking no matter how long they have smoked. In a study of smokers who quit at age 65, women gained about three years of life by quitting. Older smokers who quit experience the same health benefits as younger smokers. For example, within a year of quitting, their additional risk of heart disease is almost halved, and their risk of respiratory diseases and cancers declines. Improvements occur even in people who have already developed smoking-related illnesses.

After 5 years
- Stroke risk is the same as a nonsmoker
- Risk of mouth and throat cancer is half that of a current smoker

After 10 years
- Lung cancer death rate is about half the rate of a current smoker
- Life expectancy is comparable to a nonsmoker

Tips for Quitting

Breaking an addiction to tobacco is not easy, but millions of people have done it. **The most important factor in successfully quitting tobacco is a strong personal commitment.** Most people quit on their own. Others attend classes or seek other forms of professional help.

Some people who quit find that quitting abruptly, or going "cold turkey," works for them. Other people may quit by gradually reducing their use of tobacco over an extended period of time. No single method works best for everyone.

Quitting is most difficult within the first week or two after the last cigarette. By then, symptoms of nicotine withdrawal have usually subsided, but psychological symptoms may continue. There are many things you can do to help cope with withdrawal symptoms.

► Make a list of the reasons why you quit. Keep it handy.

► Throw away all tobacco products and anything that reminds you of tobacco use, such as ashtrays.

► Do little things to change your daily routine, such as sitting in a different seat at the kitchen table.

► Tell your family and friends that you have quit so that they can be there for support.

► Avoid being around people who use tobacco.

► Put aside the money you save. Reward yourself with a present.

► Exercise or call a friend to take your mind off smoking.

 **What would you do to support a friend or family member who is trying to quit tobacco use?**

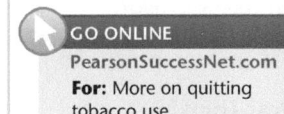

GO ONLINE
PearsonSuccessNet.com
For: More on quitting tobacco use

Tips for Quitting

L3 Building Health Skills

Setting Goals Ask students to develop an action plan for a person who has decided to quit smoking. Their action plan should have a time frame and incorporate the tips for quitting listed in the text. Suggest that students contact a group such as the American Lung Association or the American Cancer Society for additional tips for their action plan.

L2 Class Discussion

Ask: **What is the most important factor in successfully quitting tobacco?** *(a strong personal commitment)* **How can a smoker develop a strong personal commitment to quit?** *(Sample answers: consider the health risks of smoking; develop strategies to deal with cravings and setbacks)*

Connect to Your Life *Sample answer:* I would try to take the person's mind off smoking. I would also keep reminding the person of all the health benefits of quitting.

L3 Online Activity

Visit Pearson SuccessNet to access an online activity about quitting tobacco use. Have students complete the Web activity.

L2 Less Proficient Readers

Have students apply the tips for quitting tobacco listed on this page by writing a paragraph describing how a hypothetical person might quit smoking. The person they describe could quit abruptly or taper off slowly. Paragraphs should include at least some of the tips for quitting that are described in the text. For example, students might describe the person throwing out ashtrays or leaving a party where other people are smoking. Check that students' paragraphs show correct application of the tips. **WRITING**

3. Assess

Evaluate

These assignments can help you assess students' mastery of the section content.

Section 4 Review

Answers appear below.

Teaching Resources
• Practice 16-4
• Section 16-4 Quiz

L2 Reteach

On the board, write the headings Benefits of Quitting and Tips for Quitting. Call on students to go to the board and list items under the two headings until the lists include the most important information from these two passages in the text.

L4 Enrich

Teaching Resources
• Enrich 16-4

Health and Community

Resources for Quitting Students might learn about resources by looking in their telephone directory, contacting the American Cancer Society or American Lung Association, or calling area hospitals. Help students arrange to display their posters.

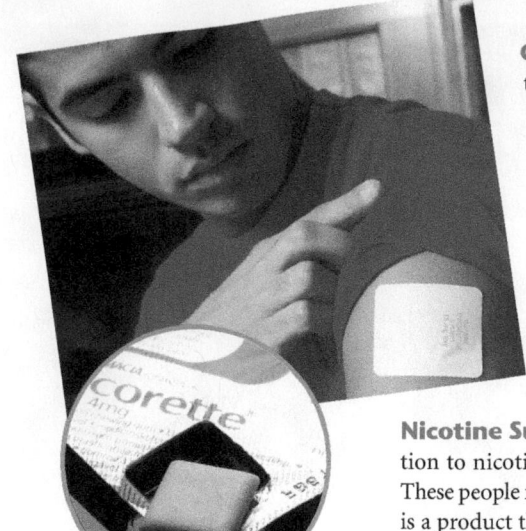

FIGURE 12 With the help of nicotine patches or gum, tobacco users can gradually overcome their nicotine addiction.

Getting Help Many resources are available to help tobacco users quit. For those who want to quit on their own, several health organizations offer booklets and pamphlets containing tips for quitting. Contact groups such as the American Lung Association or the American Cancer Society for more information and tips on quitting tobacco use.

Those who feel that they need professional help can attend local workshops or support groups. Some programs offer counseling on the phone or online. Local hospitals and other healthcare facilities frequently offer programs for helping tobacco users quit. A healthcare professional can advise you about where to get help.

Nicotine Substitutes Some tobacco users have such a strong addiction to nicotine that quitting can be very uncomfortable and difficult. These people may benefit from nicotine substitutes. A **nicotine substitute** is a product that contains nicotine, but not the other harmful chemicals found in tobacco. By slowly cutting back on the dose of a nicotine substitute, the user can reduce withdrawal symptoms.

The two most common types of substitutes are nicotine gum and nicotine patches. Inhalers and nasal sprays are also available. People younger than 18 need a prescription for any of these products.

Nicotine substitutes are only the first step in a program to break a nicotine addiction. People who use nicotine substitutes still expose their bodies to the negative effects of nicotine. Nicotine substitutes should never be used along with tobacco products.

Section 4 Review

Key Ideas and Vocabulary

1. Describe how refusal skills can help you say no to tobacco.
2. Identify four major benefits of quitting tobacco use.
3. What is the most important factor for successfully quitting tobacco? What are two ways that a person may choose to quit?
4. What is a **nicotine substitute**? Identify two types of nicotine substitutes.

Critical Thinking

5. **Evaluating** Do you think government money should be spent on programs to help people quit smoking? Why or why not? **WRITING**

Health and Community

Resources for Quitting What resources are available to help people in your community quit tobacco use? Create a poster that informs people of the services that are available, their costs, and other important details. With permission, hang the poster in the school library, nurse's office, or other visible location.

6. **Calculating** Brent used to spend $5 a day on cigarettes. Now that he has quit smoking, about how much extra money will he have each month? Each year? **MATH**

GO ONLINE PearsonSuccessNet.com | Audio Summary Section 16.4

Section 4 Review

1. When you use refusal skills, you say *no* clearly and with confidence. This shows other people that you mean what you say and strengthens your personal commitment to avoid tobacco use.

2. cardiovascular, respiratory, and psychological benefits; benefits to society

3. a strong personal commitment; abruptly or gradually

4. a product that contains nicotine, but not the other harmful chemicals in tobacco smoke; *any two:* gum, patches, inhalers, nasal sprays

5. *Sample answer:* Government money should be spent to help people quit smoking. Reducing healthcare costs and other costs associated with smoking will save money in the long run.

6. about $150 each month; about $1,800 each year

Chapter 16
At a Glance

VIDEO

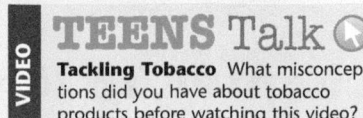

TEENS Talk

Tackling Tobacco What misconceptions did you have about tobacco products before watching this video?

Section 1   Teens and Tobacco

Key Ideas

> Friends, family, and the media greatly influence whether someone starts to use tobacco.

> Tobacco users take in nicotine whenever they use cigarettes, cigars, pipes, or smokeless tobacco products.

Vocabulary
- nicotine (402)
- smokeless tobacco (403)
- chewing tobacco (403)
- snuff (403)

Section 2   Chemicals in Tobacco Products

Key Ideas

> The major short-term effects of nicotine use are increased heart rate, increased blood pressure, and changes in the brain that may lead to addiction.

> In addition to nicotine, two of the most harmful substances in tobacco smoke are tar and carbon monoxide.

> Smokeless tobacco contains many of the same dangerous chemicals that are in tobacco smoke.

Vocabulary
- stimulant (406)
- tar (408)
- carcinogen (408)
- carbon monoxide (409)

Section 3   Risks of Tobacco Use

Key Ideas

> With every dose of tobacco, users increase their risk of developing respiratory diseases, cardiovascular disease, and several different forms of cancer.

> If a person continues to smoke over a long period of time, the damage that occurs to the respiratory system becomes permanent.

> The combined effects of nicotine, tar, and carbon monoxide force the cardiovascular system to work harder to deliver oxygen throughout the body.

> Tobacco use is a major factor in the development of lung cancer, oral cancers, and many other cancers.

> Long-term exposure to secondhand smoke can cause cardiovascular disease, many respiratory problems, and cancer.

> Pregnant women who smoke put their babies at risk for many health problems.

Vocabulary
- chronic obstructive pulmonary disease (COPD) (411)
- chronic bronchitis (411) • emphysema (412)
- leukoplakia (414) • mainstream smoke (414)
- sidestream smoke (414) • secondhand smoke (414)

Section 4   Saying No to Tobacco

Key Ideas

> Sticking to your decision not to use tobacco involves being able to say no clearly and with confidence.

> The health benefits of quitting tobacco use begin immediately and continue throughout life. Society also benefits every time a tobacco user quits.

> The most important factor in successfully quitting tobacco is a strong personal commitment.

Vocabulary
- nicotine substitute (420)

Tobacco **421**

Chapter 16
At a Glance

Tackling Tobacco Ask for volunteers to share their answers. Use examples from the video to review facts about the dangers of tobacco use.

Key Ideas Review

L2 Have students reword the section objectives as questions and then try to answer them. Students should find the answers in the text for any questions they cannot answer.

L2 Have pairs of students work together to rephrase in their own words the key ideas in each section.

Vocabulary Review

L1 Read definitions of the vocabulary terms and go around the class asking students to identify the terms. Have students look up and reread the definitions of any terms they miss.

L2 Have students use a pencil to write sentences using the vocabulary terms. Then have students erase the vocabulary term in each sentence, exchange sentences with a partner, and try to fill in the missing terms in the partner's sentences.

Chapter 16 Review

Reviewing Key Ideas

Section 1
1. b
2. because people are now more aware of the dangers of tobacco use
3. Having friends who use tobacco increases the risk of using tobacco. Having friends who do not use tobacco decreases the risk of using tobacco.
4. *Sample answer:* I think there should be more restrictions, because this might reduce the number of people who smoke.

Section 2
5. b
6. Nicotine mimics neurotransmitters and activates the brain's "reward pathway."
7. Teens may become addicted faster and more intensely than adults.
8. It decreases muscle action in air passages, increases mucus production, and paralyzes cilia lining air passages.
9. *Sample answers:* because they think bad things cannot happen to them; because they do not realize how addictive tobacco is

Section 3
10. b
11. *Any three:* cancer of the lung, mouth, esophagus, larynx, stomach, pancreas, kidney, bladder, and blood
12. *Any one:* cerebral palsy, sight impairment, hearing problems, learning difficulties, or sudden infant death syndrome
13. *Sample answer:* ban smoking in public places, because this is the only way to ensure that secondhand smoke does not affect other people

Section 4
14. a
15. Students can suggest any of the tips for quitting listed on page 419.

Chapter 16 Review

Reviewing Key Ideas

Section 1
1. In nature, nicotine acts as a(n)
   a. growth agent in plants.   b. insecticide.
   c. plant pigment.   d. nutrient.
2. Why is tobacco use less socially acceptable than it used to be?
3. How can friends be both positive and negative influences in regard to tobacco?
4. **Critical Thinking** Do you think there should be more or fewer restrictions on the advertising and sale of tobacco products? Explain.

Section 2
5. The odorless gas in tobacco smoke that binds to hemoglobin is
   a. carbon dioxide.   b. carbon monoxide.
   c. tar.   d. nicotine.
6. Describe how nicotine affects the brain.
7. How does the development of nicotine addiction differ in teens and adults?
8. How does tobacco smoke affect a smoker's air passages?
9. **Critical Thinking** Why do you think some people believe they can use tobacco without becoming addicted?

Section 3
10. The smoke that a smoker exhales into the air is called
    a. environmental tobacco smoke.
    b. mainstream smoke.
    c. sidestream smoke.
    d. secondhand smoke.
11. What are three types of cancer that have been linked to tobacco use?
12. Name one disorder that babies of mothers who smoked are at risk for.
13. **Critical Thinking** What do you think are the most effective ways to protect nonsmokers from the effects of secondhand smoke? Explain.

Section 4
14. Which benefit occurs first after someone quits smoking?
    a. Blood oxygen levels return to normal.
    b. Lung function improves.
    c. The risk of having a stroke returns to normal.
    d. Senses of taste and smell return to normal.
15. What would you suggest to an ex-smoker to help him or her not start smoking again?
16. Discuss the different methods a person could use to quit smoking.
17. **Critical Thinking** Some employers prefer not to hire smokers because their healthcare costs are higher. Do you think it is appropriate not to hire someone because he or she smokes? Why or why not? **WRITING**

Building Health Skills

18. **Making Decisions** Suppose that your favorite uncle has come to visit. He asks you for an ashtray. Smoking is not allowed in your home. How would you handle this situation tactfully?
19. **Advocacy** Suppose that you work for an advertising firm. The Surgeon General has hired your firm to work on a new anti-smoking campaign. Develop a 30-second public service commercial that will discourage young people from smoking. **WRITING**
20. **Setting Goals** Evaluate how smoking could affect your career goals.

Health and Community

Volunteering to End Smoking Contact a local chapter of the American Cancer Society, American Lung Association, or other similar agency. Find out about their efforts to reduce smoking in your community. Ask about volunteer opportunities for teens. Create a flyer describing the possible opportunities and share it with your health class. **WRITING**

---

16. A person could quit abruptly or gradually. The person could quit alone or with the help of classes or support groups. The person could use a nicotine substitute.
17. Students might think it is or is not appropriate. Evaluate the answer based on the quality of the argument.

Building Health Skills

18. *Sample answer:* I would explain my parents' rules and politely ask him to smoke outside.
19. Public service announcements should give convincing, teen-relevant reasons for not smoking.
20. *Sample answer:* Smoking might cause me to be unhealthy and unable to do my job.

Standardized Test Prep

Math Practice

The graph shows the number of cigarettes smoked per person from 1920 to 2000, and the number of lung cancer deaths from 1940 to 2000. Use the graph to answer Questions 21–23.

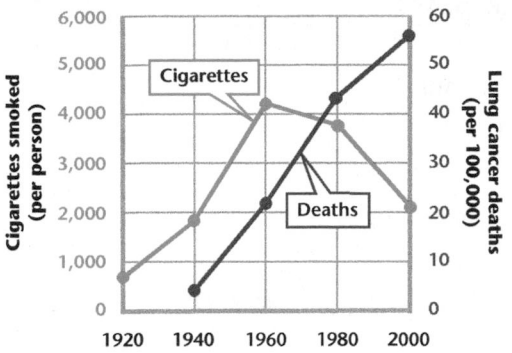

21. When did the number of cigarettes smoked per person reach its peak?
A 1940   B 1960
C 2000   D It has not reached its peak.

22. Why do you think that this graph does not show a significant decrease in lung cancer deaths?
F There is no relationship between cigarette smoking and lung cancer deaths.
G There has not been a significant decrease in cigarette smoking.
H Lung cancer takes years to develop.
J People survive longer with lung cancer now than in 1940.

23. What would be the best title for this graph?
A Lung Cancer Deaths From 1920–2000
B Causes of Lung Cancer
C Cigarettes Smoked vs. Lung Cancer Deaths
D The Rise and Fall of Cigarette Smoking

Test-Taking Tip

After you have completed the test, use any extra time to review your answers. Double check answers that you were unsure of.

Reading and Writing Practice

Read the passage. Then answer Questions 24–27.

In 1998, a settlement between the states and tobacco companies prohibited the companies from directly or indirectly targeting youth in their advertising or promotions. Some people argue that the order has been violated. For example, several companies introduced fruit or candy-flavored cigarettes. Anti-smoking activists complained that these flavors clearly appeal to young people who are not used to the taste of cigarettes. The flavored cigarettes are a way to attract young people to smoking. One tobacco company has agreed to stop selling fruit or candy-flavored cigarettes.

24. In this passage, the word *settlement* means a(n)
A establishment.
B colony.
C agreement.
D punishment.

25. Why are anti-smoking activists against the production of candy-flavored cigarettes?
F The tobacco companies did not have permission to produce candy-flavored cigarettes.
G The tobacco companies are violating the settlement by marketing a product to youth.
H The flavors hide the real taste of the cigarettes.
J The flavorings may be toxic.

26. From the context of this passage, you can conclude that
A the tobacco companies clearly violated the settlement.
B the settlement has a lot of room for interpretation.
C fewer young people have started smoking since the 1998 settlement.
D candy-flavored cigarettes are more harmful than regular cigarettes.

Constructed Response

27. In a paragraph, describe the anti-smoking activists' argument. Do you agree with this argument? Why or why not?

Standardized Test Prep

Math Practice
21. B
22. H
23. C

Reading and Writing Practice
24. C
25. G
26. B
27. *Sample answer:* Anti-smoking activists argued that tobacco companies were violating the 1998 settlement by producing cigarettes that specifically attract a younger group of people. I agree with this argument, because flavored cigarettes are less likely to appeal to adults.

Health and Community

Volunteering to End Smoking Make sure students describe volunteering opportunities that are safe for teens. For example, they should not include activities such as door-to-door canvassing.

CHAPTER 17 Preventing Drug Abuse

Section Objectives	Standards Correlation	Instructional Resources ⓛ₃	SE eTEXT	TE eTEXT	PRINT
1 Legal and Illegal Drugs ⏱ 3 periods; 1 1/2 blocks **17.1.1 Define** drug abuse and distinguish it from both appropriate use and misuse. **17.1.2 Describe** how psychoactive drugs affect the brain. **17.1.3 Summarize** the risks of drug abuse.	NHES: 1.12.8, 1.12.9, 2.12.6, 2.12.10, 3.12.1	SE Warm-Up, p. 426	•	•	•
		SE Technology & Health The Brain on Drugs, p. 433	•	•	•
		RN Note Taking Guide 17-1	•	•	•
		IB Image Bank 17-2		•	
		TR Practice 17-1		•	
		TR Section 17-1 Quiz		•	
2 Factors Affecting Drug Abuse ⏱ 1 period; 1/2 block **17.2.1 Evaluate** how family, friends, and personal factors can influence an individual's decisions about drugs.	NHES: 2.12.1, 2.12.3, 2.12.5, 2.12.7, 2.12.8, 2.12.9, 6.12.1, 7.12.1	SE Warm-Up, p. 434	•	•	•
		RN Note Taking Guide 17-2	•	•	•
		TR Practice 17-2		•	
		TR Section 17-2 Quiz		•	
BUILDING HEALTH SKILLS Intervening to Help a Friend ⏱ 1 period; 1/2 block **BHS.17 Demonstrate** advocacy by showing how to intervene to help a friend deal with drug abuse.	NHES: 3.12.4, 4.12.4, 8.12.2	SE Practice the Skill, p. 439	•	•	•
		RN Building Health Skills 17	•	•	•
3 Commonly Abused Drugs ⏱ 2 periods; 1 block **17.3.1 Compare** the effects of depressants, stimulants, and hallucinogens on the body. **17.3.2 Describe** the effects of marijuana. **17.3.2 Name** three classes of drugs of increasing concern in recent years.	NHES: 1.12.8, 1.12.9, 2.12.9	SE Warm-Up, p. 440	•	•	•
		RN Note Taking Guide 17-3	•	•	•
		IB Image Bank 17-10, 17-12, 17-15		•	
		TR Practice 17-3		•	
		TR Section 17-3 Quiz		•	
4 Choosing to Be Drug Free ⏱ 2 periods; 1 block **17.4.1 Identify** three treatment options for people who abuse drugs. **17.4.2 Name** three steps you can take to stay drug free.	NHES: 2.12.3, 3.12.3, 3.12.4, 4.12.2, 5.12.1, 5.12.2, 5.12.4, 5.12.6, 8.12.4	SE Warm-Up, p. 448	•	•	•
		SE Hands-On Activity Resisting Peer Pressure, p. 451	•	•	•
		RN Note Taking Guide 17-4	•	•	•
		TR Practice 17-4		•	
		TR Section 17-4 Quiz		•	

Chapter Review and Assessment

SE Chapter 17 Review, p. 454 ⓛ₃
CTB Chapter 17 Test ⓛ₂ ⓛ₃ ⓛ₄
SE Standardized Test Prep, p. 455 ⓛ₃

PROGRAM COMPONENTS

SE Student Edition	**CTB** Computer Test Bank
TE Teacher Edition	**AUD** Audio Section Summaries
TR Teaching Resources	
RN Reading and Note Taking Guide	**DVD** Teens Talk Video Series
	VVG Video Viewing Guide
ARN Adapted Reading and Note Taking Guide	**PPT** Presentation
IB Image Bank	

Differentiated Instruction
L1 L2 L4 EL

		SE eTEXT	TE eTEXT	PRINT
ARN	Note Taking Guide 17-1 L2	•	•	
RN	Note Taking Guide 17-1 EL	•	•	•
AUD	Audio Summary 17-1 L1 L2 EL	•	•	
TE	Reteach Strategy, p. 432 L2		•	•
TR	Enrich 17-1 L4		•	
ARN	Note Taking Guide 17-2 L2	•	•	
RN	Note Taking Guide 17-2 EL	•	•	•
AUD	Audio Summary 17-2 L1 L2 EL	•	•	
TE	Reteach Strategy, p. 437 L2		•	•
TR	Enrich 17-2 L4		•	
ARN	Building Health Skills 17 L2	•	•	
RN	Building Health Skills 17 EL	•	•	•
ARN	Note Taking Guide 17-3 L2	•	•	
RN	Note Taking Guide 17-3 EL	•	•	•
AUD	Audio Summary 17-3 L1 L2 EL	•	•	
TE	Reteach Strategy, p. 447 L2		•	•
TR	Enrich 17-3 L4		•	
ARN	Note Taking Guide 17-4 L2	•	•	
RN	Note Taking Guide 17-4 EL	•	•	•
AUD	Audio Summary 17-4 L1 L2 EL	•	•	
TE	Reteach Strategy, p. 452 L2		•	•
TR	Enrich 17-4 L4		•	

ABILITY LEVELS
- L1 For students with special needs
- L2 For less proficient readers
- L3 For all students
- L4 For gifted and talented students
- EL For English language learners

Chapter 17 Digital/Video Pathway

This alternative pathway allows you to teach this chapter's content using only the video and online materials.

Preview
DVD **Video #17 Preview**
SE Video #17 Preview Activity
VVG Video #17 Worksheet

The Risks of Drug Abuse

1
PPT 17-1 Presentation
RN/ARN 17-1 Note Taking
PPT 17-1 Section Quiz

2
PPT 17-2 Presentation
RN/ARN 17-2 Note Taking
PPT 17-2 Section Quiz

3
DVD **Video #17 Explore/Wrap-Up**
VVG Video #17 Worksheet
PPT 17-3 Presentation
RN/ARN 17-3 Note Taking
PPT 17-3 Section Quiz

The Risks of Drug Abuse

4
PPT 17-4 Presentation
RN/ARN 17-4 Note Taking
PPT 17-4 Section Quiz

Chapter Preview

Section 1 Legal and Illegal Drugs
Drug abuse occurs when people intentionally use any kind of drugs for nonmedical purposes. Drugs that are psychoactive cause temporary pleasurable feelings. When drugs are misused or abused, they can cause many serious health effects. Drug abusers may also face serious legal penalties, damage their relationships, and cause significant costs to society.

Section 2 Factors Affecting Drug Abuse
A variety of family, social, and personal factors influence whether a teen will abuse drugs. Having strong protective factors helps people stay drug free.

Advocacy
Intervening to Help a Friend

Practicing advocacy on behalf of a friend who abuses drugs can bolster one's own commitment to remain drug free.

Section 3 Commonly Abused Drugs
Depressants slow down body functions such as heart and breathing rates. Stimulants speed up body functions. Hallucinogens cause a distorted sense of reality. Marijuana changes the way information reaches and is acted upon by the brain. Club drugs, inhalants, and anabolic steroids are drugs of growing concern in recent years.

Section 4 Choosing to Be Drug Free
Treatment options for drug abusers include detoxification, therapeutic communities, and supervised medication. Teens can stay away from drugs by practicing refusal skills, seeking help when they need it, and getting involved in drug-free activities.

GO ONLINE

PearsonSuccessNet.com

For resources and activities for this chapter.

Preventing Drug Abuse

1 Legal and Illegal Drugs
- **Technology & Health** The Brain on Drugs

2 Factors Affecting Drug Abuse

Building Health Skills
- **Advocacy** Intervening to Help a Friend

3 Commonly Abused Drugs

4 Choosing to Be Drug Free
- **Hands-On Activity** Resisting Peer Pressure

GO ONLINE PearsonSuccessNet.com

TEENS Talk

VIDEO 17

The Risks of Drug Abuse

Preview **Activity**

What Do Different Generations Say?

Complete this activity before you watch the video.

1. Survey ten teens in your community, asking them which three drugs they think are abused by teens the most. Then ask what they think the greatest risk of teen drug abuse is.
2. Ask the same survey questions to ten adults in your community.
3. How were the perceptions of teens and adults alike? How were they different? Summarize the results of your survey. **WRITING**

424

Sensitive Issues

- Students may have a mixture of curiosity and anxiety about drugs and drug abuse. Keep this in mind when discussing chapter content. Watch for student reactions, and avoid discussing issues that appear to make students feel uncomfortable. However, do not shy away from stressing the dangers of drugs.

- Some students may worry that they will appear naive about drugs if they ask questions about them. As a result, they may pretend to understand issues even when they do not. Provide students with opportunities to ask questions anonymously.

Video Objectives

Use this video to help students

Identify some of the reasons why teens may abuse drugs.

Evaluate the risks that accompany drug abuse.

Analyze some myths about drug abuse, including the commonly held myths that over-the-counter substances and marijuana are not dangerous.

Preview **Activity**

What Do Different Generations Say?

Assign the Preview Activity for homework a few days before you plan to show the video. After students complete the assignment, compile the results of their two surveys. Discuss the similarities and differences between teen and adult perceptions of drug risks. Ask students what they think accounts for the differences.

From the Authors

The word *preventing* in the title of this chapter shows where emphasis should be placed when teaching about drug abuse. In the past, I spent too much time teaching about the drugs themselves—what they look like, how they are prepared—and not enough time teaching about how to avoid drugs. My students knew more about using drugs than staying away from them.

Students do not need to know how crack is smoked to avoid situations where it is used. They do not need to know the qualities of cannabis to refuse marijuana. Some information about drugs is useful, but knowing how to avoid drugs is far more important. Keep the focus on prevention and be sure to have your students answer the Connect to Your Life questions.

Section 1

Legal and Illegal Drugs

1. Focus

Warm-Up Myth/Fact

Call on students to identify other myths teens might believe about medicines or drugs. (e.g., You can use drugs for a long time before becoming addicted.) Tell students they will learn why the myths are not true when they read the facts about drug use in this section.

Presentation 17-1

 **Connect to Your Life** Allow students to answer this question in their private journals.

Sensitive Issues

Students with family members who abuse drugs might be upset by class discussions of this issue. Students who have had personal experiences with drug-related tragedies may be especially distressed by the issue of drug abuse.

- Be attuned to students' comfort levels when covering these topics.
- However, make sure you emphasize the seriousness of drug abuse.

Section 1

Legal and Illegal Drugs

Objectives

▶ **Define** drug abuse and distinguish it from both appropriate use and misuse.

▶ **Describe** how psychoactive drugs affect the brain.

▶ **Summarize** the risks of drug abuse.

Vocabulary

- medicine
- over-the-counter drug
- prescription drug
- illegal drug
- drug misuse
- drug abuse
- psychoactive drug
- side effect
- drug antagonism
- drug synergism

Warm-Up

Myth Medicines from a drugstore can't harm you.

Fact Medicines can be just as dangerous as "street drugs" if they are used inappropriately.

WRITING What other myths do teens believe about drugs? Write down some statements you have heard from your peers. Which ones do you think are true? Which are false?

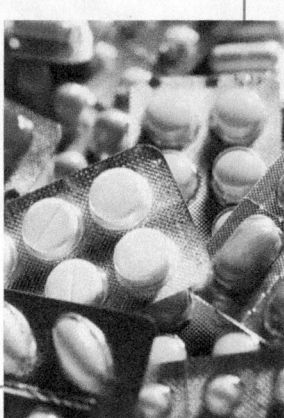

Facts About Drug Use

Drug use is part of life in the United States. Every year, doctors write countless prescriptions and consumers spend millions of dollars on nonprescription (over-the-counter) drugs. When taken as directed, prescription and nonprescription drugs treat many illnesses effectively. However, if drugs are not used as directed, serious health problems can result.

Recall from Chapter 15 that a drug is any chemical substance that is taken to cause changes in a person's body or behavior. **Medicines** are legal drugs that help the body fight injury, illness, or disease. Medicines can be classified into two groups: over-the-counter drugs and prescription drugs.

Over-the-Counter Drugs A medicine that is sold legally in pharmacies and other stores without a doctor's prescription is called an **over-the-counter drug.** Some examples are pain relievers such as aspirin, cold and cough remedies, and some sleep aids. Any over-the-counter drug can cause harm if the instructions on the label are not followed.

Connect to Your Life Which over-the-counter drugs have you used? Did you read the labels?

TEENS *Are Asking . . .*

Q: My sister has been taking cold medicine to help her fall asleep at night. I said it might be dangerous. She said it must be safe because she feels fine in the morning and, after all, you can buy it without a prescription. Who is right?

A: You are. Drugs are not necessarily safe just because you can buy them without a prescription. Furthermore, using a drug for a purpose other than what it is intended for is an example of drug misuse. Your sister may be putting herself at risk for problems such as addiction and drug interactions.

Q: What should I do?

A: Tell your sister about the dangers of misusing over-the-counter drugs. If that does not stop her, tell a parent or guardian about the situation.

Prescription Drugs A drug that can be obtained only with a written order from a doctor and can be purchased only at a pharmacy is known as a **prescription drug.** Prescription drugs require more government control than over-the-counter drugs because of their potential for harm. A doctor determines the correct amount of the medication that the individual patient needs at the time the prescription is written.

Illegal Drugs An **illegal drug** is a chemical substance that people of any age may not lawfully manufacture, possess, buy, or sell. Illegal drugs are also called street drugs.

Drug Misuse The improper use of medicines—either prescription or over-the-counter drugs—is called **drug misuse.** Examples of drug misuse include taking more than the prescribed amount of a drug, taking drugs with the wrong foods or at the wrong time of day, and not taking a drug for the correct period of time. Drug misuse is often by mistake or because of a patient's misunderstanding of a doctor's orders.

Drug Abuse When a drug is intentionally used improperly or unsafely, it is known as **drug abuse.** For example, a person is abusing prescription painkillers or over-the-counter cough medicines if he or she takes them to cause a "high," rather than to treat pain or a cough. And *any* use of illegal drugs is drug abuse. **Drug abuse occurs when people intentionally use any kind of drugs for nonmedical purposes.**

Proper Use
Using per label instructions to treat a cough

Misuse
Mistakenly taking more than is recommended to treat a cough

Abuse
Deliberately taking more than is recommended or taking for purposes other than treating a cough

FIGURE 1 Even legal drugs, such as cough syrup, can be misused or abused.

L3 **EL** Reading/Note Taking 17-1

L2 Adapted Reading/Note Taking 17-1

Facts About Drug Use

L2 Cooperative Learning

Pair students with differing ability levels, and have each pair make a concept map of the material under the heading Facts About Drug Use. Making a graphic organizer should help students distinguish between potentially confusing concepts such as drug misuse and abuse, which they need to know as a basis for the rest of the chapter.

L4 Active Learning

Explain that prescription pain relievers, such as Oxycontin, are often abused and may be sold as street drugs. Have students interview a pharmacist or pharmacy technician about how Oxycontin and other powerful prescription pain relievers are controlled. What extra measures are taken to ensure that they do not get into the wrong hands or that people who are prescribed the drugs do not abuse them? Ask students to share their findings with the class. Discuss why abuse of these drugs is especially risky.

Differentiated Instruction

L1 Special Needs

Make a display of several empty bottles and packages of over-the-counter and prescription medicines. Have students handle the items and discuss how they are similar and different. Use this hands-on experience to reinforce the major concepts on these pages. Ask: **How are the labels different?** *(Prescription labels carry the patient's name and the prescribing doctor's name.)* **How are they alike?** *(Both carry directions for proper use and warnings about potential negative effects.)* **Can either kind of medicine be misused or abused?** *(yes)* **Is using someone else's prescription medicine a form of drug abuse?** *(yes)*

Drug Abuse and the Brain

L2 Visual Learning: Figure 2

Image Bank Figure 17-2

After students examine the figure, ask: **What represents the pleasure signal in the diagrams?** *(the arrow)* **How does the arrow change in stages 1–3?** *(It gets bigger, then smaller.)* **How does the pleasure signal change?** *(It gets stronger than normal, then weaker than normal.)* Call on a volunteer to answer the caption question.

Caption Answer Brain cells lose receptors for dopamine, becoming less able to process the chemical. This causes the pleasure signal to weaken.

L2 Class Discussion

Stress that the "pleasurable feelings" associated with drug use are out-weighed by the risks of permanently dampening the pleasure signal. Call on volunteers to describe examples of normally pleasurable activities—such as hanging out with friends, playing sports, engaging in hobbies, or eating a favorite food—that might no longer be pleasurable to a long-term drug user.

L3 Building Health Skills

Communicating Discuss why it is important for children to learn about the risks of drug abuse. Then challenge small groups of students to write and illustrate a children's story that shows how drug abuse affects the brain. The story should explain what happens in Figure 2 in a creative way that is of interest to, and understandable by, fifth and sixth graders. Arrange to share the best stories with fifth and sixth grade classes in your school district. **WRITING**

How Drugs Affect the Brain

FIGURE 2 Drug users may eventually have trouble enjoying normal activities because they have harmed the brain's ability to feel pleasure.
Interpreting Diagrams How do brain cells change after repeated drug use?

Area of the brain's "reward pathway"

1 Under Normal Conditions
The chemical dopamine travels between brain cells, producing pleasurable sensations.

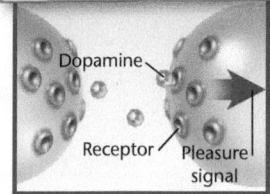

Dopamine

Receptor   Pleasure signal

2 On Drugs
Cells release extra dopamine, causing a stronger signal.

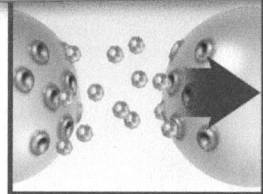

3 After Repeated Drug Use
Brain cells lose receptors for dopamine, becoming less able to process the chemical. The pleasure signal weakens.

Drug Abuse and the Brain

You have probably heard the phrase "mood-altering" used to refer to some drugs. A mood-altering drug, also called a **psychoactive drug** (sy koh AK tiv), is a chemical that affects brain activity. Most abused drugs are psycho-active. You will learn about commonly abused psychoactive drugs in Section 3.

The "Reward Pathway" Psychoactive drugs typically create a pleasurable feeling that the user wants to repeat. **Many psychoactive drugs trigger activity along a pathway of cells in the brain called the "reward pathway."**

As shown in Figure 2, brain cells along the activated reward pathway release a chemical called dopamine (DOH puh meen). Dopamine itself is not a dangerous chemical—your brain also releases it when you engage in healthy activities such as eating a delicious dessert or cuddling a puppy. In association with drug abuse, however, dopamine can have dangerous effects.

► The extra dopamine released during drug use can cause the user to ignore the harmful effects of the drug and want to continue using it.

► Flooding the reward pathway with dopamine may lead to intense cravings for the drug when it is not available.

► After a time, drug abuse can dull the brain's reactions to natural levels of dopamine. The user no longer feels pleasure from normal activities.

Addiction Abuse of psychoactive drugs may result in addiction. Recall from Chapter 15 that addiction is the compulsive use of a drug, despite any cost to health, family, or social standing. Addiction is a disease that changes the structure and chemistry of the brain.

For Your INFORMATION!

Psychoactive Drugs and the Teen Brain

Psychoactive drugs can turn off centers in the brain that control learning, vision, speech, and other abilities. When this happens to an adult brain, the brain can generally bounce back to normal or near-normal condition. When this happens to a teen brain, the brain can be damaged permanently. To develop normally, the brain must accomplish certain developmental tasks in a set sequence. If psychoactive drugs cause brain centers to shut down, some of the developmental tasks may never be accomplished. This can result in permanent deficits in mental and social abilities that may not be apparent until adulthood.

Dangers of Drug Misuse and Abuse

Drugs can produce powerful changes in the body. These changes are medically useful when a person uses a drug properly. **But when drugs are misused or abused, many serious health effects can result.**

Side Effects Whereas the immediate effect of a medicine may feel good, unpleasant side effects may follow. A **side effect** is an unwanted physical or mental effect caused by a drug. Side effects can include nausea, dizziness, and drowsiness. Because each person's body is unique, side effects of a particular drug vary from person to person. This is one reason why prescriptions should never be shared.

Medicines have been thoroughly tested to minimize side effects with appropriate use. On the other hand, drugs that are misused or abused often have side effects that can't be predicted and may be severe or even life threatening.

 **Connect to Your Life** What would you say to a friend who offers you her prescription medicine when you are sick? Why?

Tolerance and Dependence When a person uses a drug repeatedly, the body may develop tolerance to the drug. Recall from Chapter 15 that as tolerance grows, the user needs increasingly larger amounts of the drug to achieve the original effect. Tolerance may lead to drug dependence—the body develops a chemical need for the drug and can't function normally without it.

Withdrawal If a person who is dependent on a psychoactive drug stops taking the drug, that person will experience withdrawal symptoms. These symptoms are the body's reaction to not having the drug. Withdrawal symptoms range from mild to life threatening, depending on the drug that was used. Withdrawal symptoms include

▶ Nausea or vomiting

▶ Headaches or dizziness

▶ Fever

▶ Digestion problems

▶ Paranoia or panic

▶ Tremors, seizures, or death

FIGURE 3 Withdrawal symptoms range from mild to severe.

Dangers of Drug Misuse and Abuse

L1 Building Health Skills

Accessing Information Bring several package inserts to class from a variety of over-the-counter and prescription medicines. Pair special needs students with a partner and give each pair a package insert. Have the students find the side effects on their inserts and read aloud side effects that are common. Discuss with the class what to do when a medicine causes side effects.

 **Connect to Your Life** *Sample answer:* No, thanks; prescription medicines should never be shared.

L3 Journal Writing

Have students write a private journal entry describing what they think it would be like to be dependent on a drug. Write the following questions on the board for students to address in their journal entries: How would dependence on a drug affect your daily life? How would it affect your relationships with family and friends? Your ability to achieve your goals? Your chances of happiness? Remind students that what they write is confidential. **WRITING**

L3 Class Discussion

Discuss drug overdose as another important danger of tolerance. Help students recall from Chapter 15 that an overdose refers to taking so much of a drug that it leads to coma or death. Ask: **Why might developing tolerance for a drug lead to overdose?** (*As tolerance develops, the user needs more and more of the drug to achieve the original effect. The user might take so much of the drug that it causes coma or death.*)

Differentiated Instruction

L2 Less Proficient Readers

Some students may benefit from a review of the terms related to drug abuse that were covered in Chapter 15 on alcohol, including *addiction, tolerance, dependence,* and *withdrawal.* Suggest that students copy the definitions of these terms and keep them handy for easy reference while they read this chapter.

L4 Gifted and Talented

Challenge gifted and talented students to make three-dimensional models showing how drug abuse affects the brain, as described in Figure 2 on page 428. Give students an opportunity to explain their models to the class.

L1 Teacher Demo

Show students a few empty over-the-counter and prescription drug bottles that have drug interaction warnings on the labels. Point out where the warnings are located and read them aloud. Explain that medicines may also interact with vitamin supplements and foods. Urge students to always check the labels of medicines for information about drug interactions and other warnings.

L4 Cooperative Learning

The U.S. Controlled Substances Act of 1970 established a classification of drugs called the U.S. Drug Schedules. There are five schedules for drugs, based on the potential for their abuse. Have students work in small groups to research the U.S. Drug Schedules and create a poster that details their findings. The U.S. Drug Schedules are listed in many books about drugs, particularly those dealing with regulation and legalization issues. After groups have prepared their posters, have the class discuss whether the drugs in each schedule are prescription, over-the-counter, or illegal for use by the general public.

 *Sample answer:* You can ask a pharmacist or read drug container labels to see if there are any drug interactions.

L3 Content Update 🔵 GO ONLINE

Visit Pearson SuccessNet to access more information about drug misuse and abuse. Have students complete the Web activity.

WARNING:
Do not use if you are now taking blood pressure medication, or for two weeks after stopping that medication.

FIGURE 4 It is important to read prescription and over-the-counter drug labels to avoid dangerous drug interactions.

GO ONLINE
PearsonSuccessNet.com
For: More on drug misuse and abuse

Drug Interactions When a person takes more than one drug at a time, the drugs may interact. The result of this interaction is effects not seen when the drugs are taken alone.

▶ **Antagonism** A **drug antagonism** (an TAG uh niz um) occurs when each drug's effect is canceled out or reduced by the other. Neither drug has the predicted effect. For example, because nicotine causes blood pressure to rise, it can cancel out the beneficial effect of medications taken to lower high blood pressure.

▶ **Synergism** A **drug synergism** (SIN ur jiz um) occurs when drugs interact to produce effects greater than those that each drug would produce alone. For example, the combination of certain sleep medications with small amounts of alcohol may cause rapid loss of consciousness.

 When taking medicines, what precautions can you follow to prevent drug interactions?

Impurities The manufacture of illegal drugs is not regulated by law. Thus, there is no guarantee that they are pure. Many illegal drugs are contaminated with chemicals that may themselves be harmful or cause dangerous drug interactions. For example, a drug dealer may "cut," or dilute, heroin by adding cleansing powders or rat poison. Illegal drugs may also vary widely from batch to batch in the concentration of psychoactive chemicals they contain. Thus, the user can't easily predict what effect the drug will have each time.

430 *Chapter 17*

 **and Health**

L3 Proportions

Tell students that there were roughly 30 million juveniles (people aged 10–17 years old) in the United States during the 1990s. Have students estimate the total number of juveniles that were arrested for drug abuse violations in 1990, 1995, and 2000, based on the numbers of arrests per 100,000 juveniles in those three years, which are shown in Figure 5 on page 431. (1990: $30,000,000 \times 300/100,000 = 90,000$; 1995: $30,000,000 \times 640/100,000 = 192,000$ and 2000: $30,000,000 \times 600/100,000 = 180,000$)

Other Health Risks There are other serious health risks associated with drug abuse.

▶ **Hepatitis and HIV** If drug users share needles to inject drugs, contaminated blood left in the needle can carry disease-causing viruses from user to user. The viruses that cause hepatitis B and C can lead to serious, sometimes fatal, liver disease. The human immunodeficiency virus (HIV) causes AIDS, a disease that has no cure.

▶ **Risks to Fetus and Newborn** Drug abuse by a pregnant woman places her baby at risk for a broad range of developmental problems. This is because the drugs cross the placenta, the membrane separating the baby's blood from the mother's blood. The baby may even be born with a drug dependency. For example, "crack babies" are born dependent on the crack cocaine their mothers took during pregnancy. Drugs can also pass through a mother's breast milk to a nursing newborn and cause harm.

Legal Risks and Other Costs

In addition to health risks, people who abuse drugs face other risks. **Drug abusers risk facing serious legal penalties, damaging their relationships with family and friends, and causing significant costs to society.**

Legal Risks Penalties for individuals who produce, possess, transport, or sell illegal drugs include long prison terms and heavy fines. Sometimes the punishment for a drug-related crime is less severe. But the person will still have a criminal record. This record makes it difficult to get a job or to be admitted into schools and the military. In addition, many drug abusers commit other crimes, such as shoplifting and robbery, to support their drug addiction. The legal penalties for these drug-related crimes include fines and imprisonment.

FIGURE 5 Arrest rates for drug violations by juveniles age 10–17 were higher in 2000 than they were in 1990.
Interpreting Graphs Calculate the percentage change in juvenile drug violations between 1990 and 2000. **MATH**

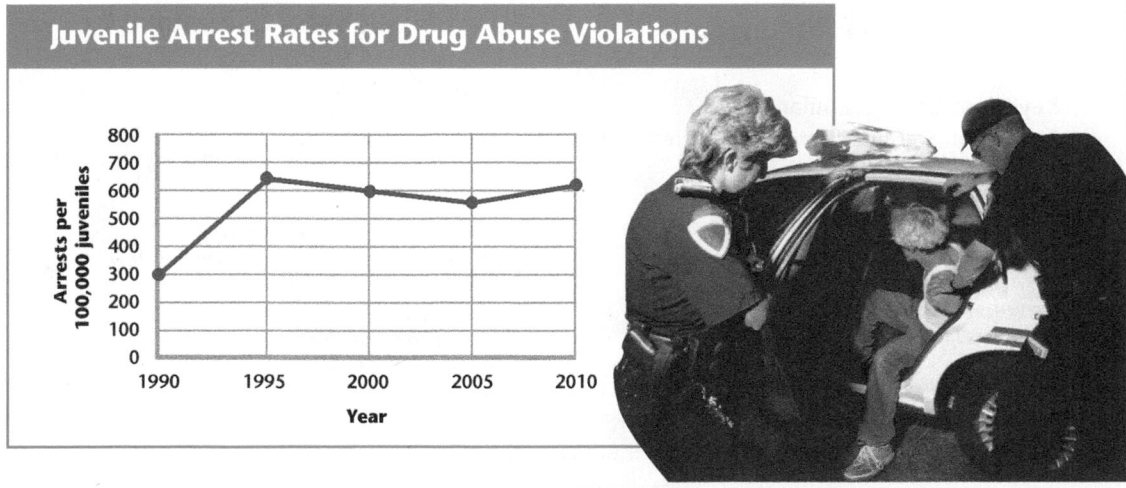

Juvenile Arrest Rates for Drug Abuse Violations

Preventing Drug Abuse **431**

3. Assess

Evaluate

These assignments can help you assess students' mastery of the section content.

Section 1 Review

Answers appear below.

Teaching Resources
• Practice 17-1
• Section 17-1 Quiz

L2 Reteach

Have students use the section vocabulary terms in sentences. For each term, call on a student to read his or her sentence. For terms used incorrectly, call on additional students to read their sentences.

L4 Enrich

Teaching Resources
• Enrich 17-1

Health and Community

Drug Penalties Penalties may depend on such factors as the amount and type of drug and whether it is a first offense. Charts should show how such factors affect the penalties. Post students' charts in the classroom.

FIGURE 6 Millions of tax dollars are spent each year in an effort to prevent illegal drugs from entering the United States.

Effects on Family and Friends Relationships with family and friends often become strained as the behavior and personality of a drug abuser change. A drug abuser may have unpredictable mood swings, become violent, or withdraw from relationships and responsibilities. The interests and activities that helped bind the person with family and friends may no longer exist. Drugs can cause friends to drift away and families to break up.

Costs to Society The United States government has spent billions of dollars in efforts to stop illegal drug manufacture and sales. Significant financial resources also go toward drug abuse prevention, education, treatment, and rehabilitation programs. These programs provide hope for many drug abusers. However, the demand for such programs often exceeds available funding.

Drug abuse affects many more people than just the abusers themselves. Consider a few of the other costs of drug abuse.

► The cost of imprisoning thousands of people for drug-related crimes

► Medical costs for drug-related illnesses and injuries, including many of the nation's cases of HIV/AIDS

► Premature deaths from drug-related homicides and motor vehicle crashes

► Lost work productivity because of drug dependency

Section 1 Review

Key Ideas and Vocabulary

1. How is an **over-the-counter drug** different from a **prescription drug**?
2. Define drug abuse. Give an example.
3. Briefly describe how psychoactive drugs affect the brain.
4. What is a **side effect**?
5. List three health risks and two other risks that drug abusers face.

Critical Thinking

6. **Comparing and Contrasting** How is drug abuse different from drug misuse?

Health and Community

Drug Penalties Find out what some of the penalties are for illegal drug possession in your state. Visit the Web sites of local law enforcement agencies for information. Prepare a chart that summarizes your findings. **WRITING**

7. **Relating Cause and Effect** How can drug dependence affect a person's family? How can it affect a person's community?
8. **Making Judgments** How do you think tax dollars could best be spent to prevent teen drug abuse? **WRITING**

 GO ONLINE PearsonSuccessNet.com | Audio Summary Section 17.1

Section 1 Review

1. An OTC drug can be sold legally without a doctor's prescription; a prescription drug cannot.

2. intentionally using a drug improperly or unsafely; for example, using pain relievers to get "high"

3. The drugs cause brain cells to release extra dopamine, which causes a stronger pleasure signal. After repeated drug use, brain cells lose receptors for dopamine, and the pleasure signal weakens.

4. an unwanted physical or mental effect caused by a drug

5. Health risks include (*any three*) side effects, dependence, drug interactions, hepatitis, HIV, and risks to fetuses and newborns. Other risks include legal risks and the risk of damaging relationships with friends and family.

6. Drug abuse is intentional, whereas drug misuse is accidental.

7. *Sample answer:* When people have a chemical need for drugs, they often lie to or steal from family members, friends, or neighbors to obtain money for drugs.

8. *Sample answer:* educating teens about the dangers of drug abuse

Technology & Health

The Brain on Drugs

Exactly how do different drugs affect the brain? A brain scanning technique called positron emission tomography (PET) can help scientists answer this question. PET scans measure the brain's ability to process brain chemicals, including dopamine and serotonin. These chemicals are critical to normal experiences of mood, emotion, and pain.

WRITING How might brain scans lead to new ways to treat drug addictions?

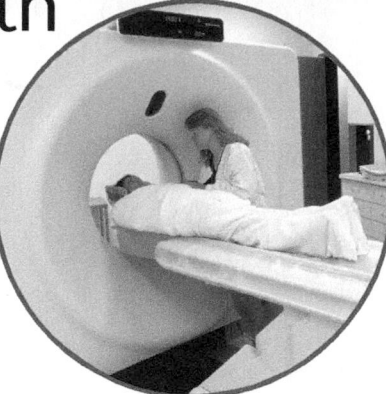

▲ A PET Scanner

The scanner produces images of the brain after specific chemicals in the brain are tagged with radioactive markers.

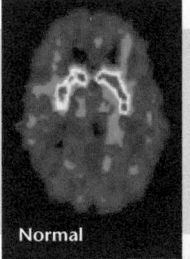 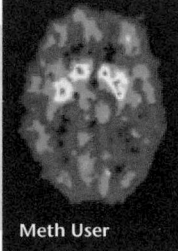

Normal | Meth User

◄ Effects of Meth

Notice the dramatic decrease in dopamine receptor activity (shown in red) compared with a normal brain. With fewer receptors to process dopamine, normal everyday feelings of pleasure are reduced.

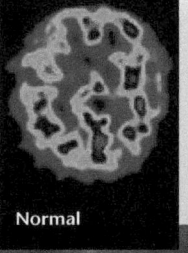 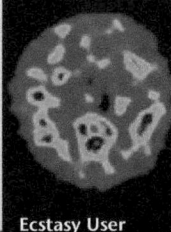

Normal | Ecstasy User

◄ Effects of Ecstasy

PET scans of an Ecstasy user show a significant decrease in the brain's ability to process serotonin. This effect makes it more difficult for the user to sleep, learn, and remember.

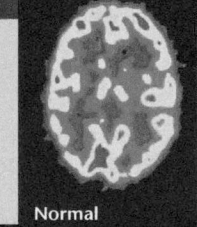 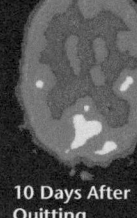 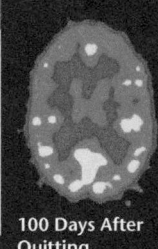

Normal | 10 Days After Quitting | 100 Days After Quitting

◄ Recovering from Cocaine Addiction

Even months after quitting cocaine, PET scans show that the brain's return to normal is very slow. Some addicts may never recover completely.

433

For Your INFORMATION!

Brain Scans at Brookhaven

In 1987, Brookhaven National Laboratory on Long Island, New York, became the first research laboratory to use PET scans to study the effects of drugs on the brain. Brookhaven is now world-renowned for its research on drug abuse using brain imaging. The laboratory has studied the effects on the brain of all commonly used legal and illegal drugs and has been designated a regional drug addiction study center by the National Institute on Drug Abuse. Advise any students who want to learn more about PET scans of brains on drugs to start their search with the Brookhaven National Laboratory Web site.

Technology & Health
The Brain on Drugs

Teaching Strategies

- Before students read the feature, have them re-examine Figure 2 on page 428. Tell students that addictive drugs deplete the brain's receptors for dopamine. Add that serotonin plays a role similar to dopamine and is similarly affected by addictive drugs.

- Explain how a PET scan is performed. A radioactive compound is injected into the blood, carried to the brain via the blood, and measured by the PET scanner. The injected compound becomes more concentrated in brain areas with higher activity (the type of activity depending on the compound injected). The PET image shows differences in concentration and, by inference, areas of higher and lower activity. As its name suggests, the PET scanner detects a type of subatomic particles called positrons.

- Tell students that PET scans of brains of people who use marijuana show abnormal blood flow, which may explain the drug's adverse effects on memory, learning, and problem solving.

WRITING *Sample answer:* Brain scans allow scientists to determine what happens in the brains of addicted people. This might suggest new ways to treat drug addictions.

1. Focus

Warm-Up Quick Quiz

Use the Warm-Up Presentation slide to survey student responses.

Discuss with students why *yes* answers to the questions can help protect them from drug abuse. Call on several volunteers to share other factors that help protect them from using drugs. *(Sample answer: friends who do not use drugs and parents who discourage drug use)* Tell students they will learn more in this section about factors that affect drug abuse.

Presentation 17-2

Section 2

Factors Affecting Drug Abuse

Objective
▶ **Evaluate** how family, friends, and personal factors can influence an individual's decisions about drugs.

Vocabulary
• protective factor

Warm-Up

Quick Quiz See how many of these questions you can answer "yes" to.

① Do you avoid situations where you think drugs might be used?

② Have you practiced refusing an offer of drugs?

③ Are there adults in your life whom you trust and with whom you can talk about your problems?

④ Do you manage stress in your life in healthy, constructive ways?

WRITING Each question you answer "yes" to is a way you protect yourself from drug abuse. What other factors in your life help protect you from using drugs? Explain.

Risk Factors

Why do some people abuse drugs? Some people turn to drugs as a way of coping with life's problems and stresses. Others use drugs because their friends do. Still others use drugs because they say they like the feeling of being "high." But, no matter the reason, the risks related to drug abuse are serious.

A number of factors make it either more or less likely that a teen will abuse drugs. They include family factors, social factors, and personal factors. Often, it is a combination of factors that influences drug use.

Family Factors Consider the following situation.

Since her mom died last year, Julie's dad has withdrawn into his own world. He rarely asks Julie or her brother about their weekend plans. One night, Julie was invited to a "rave" party where everyone seemed to be using drugs. Julie figured her dad would never find out, so she joined in.

For Your INFORMATION!

Risk Factors for Drug Abuse

The risk of drug abuse is greater if you

• inherit certain genes. Risk of drug abuse has a genetic component, which helps explain why having a family member who is a drug abuser increases the risk.

• have certain mental health disorders, especially undiagnosed disorders. For example, people with schizophrenia or

bipolar disorder may take drugs to alleviate symptoms, or self-medicate.

• are socially isolated. People who are socially isolated may be shy, have poor social skills, and feel as though they do not fit in. They may use drugs to try to feel better about themselves and overcome shyness.

FIGURE 7 Are your friends a good influence on you?

One risk factor for teen drug abuse is poor family relationships. When family relationships are not close and supportive, teenagers may not get needed guidance. The teen may feel alienated from the family. This alienation may make teens more vulnerable to the influence of peers who abuse drugs. In addition, if family members abuse drugs, a teen is at higher risk of using drugs, too.

Social Factors Do you know someone like Mike?

Mike has smoked marijuana almost every day for two years. Some of Mike's friends were using the drug and they offered it to him. Now, whenever Mike and his friends hang out, they smoke. Mike says that he can stop using marijuana at any time, although he has yet to try.

In addition to family factors, there are a number of social factors that influence teens to use drugs.

▶ **Peer Group** Many teens, like Mike, were first introduced to drugs by friends or by peers whose acceptance they wanted. They may have initially tried drugs because they were curious or felt pressured. Some continue to abuse drugs because they want to be "part of the crowd."

▶ **Role Models** Teens may see their role models—such as favorite actors—using drugs in movie roles or in real life, without seeing the negative effects. Such "glamorization" of drugs may influence their decision to try drugs.

▶ **Competitive Pressure** For some teens, a strong desire to excel at athletics may be a risk factor for drug use. For example, some teen athletes believe the myths that painkillers will allow them to play through an injury. Others mistakenly think that steroids will allow them to bulk up safely.

In fact, athletes who use painkillers during competition are more likely to sustain serious injuries that could end their athletic careers. Steroid abuse, especially in the teen years, can lead to lifelong or life-threatening disorders.

 **How would you react to news that your favorite professional athlete was abusing drugs?**

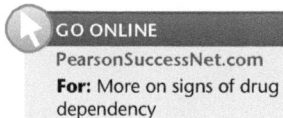

GO ONLINE
PearsonSuccessNet.com
For: More on signs of drug dependency

2. Teach

L3 EL **Reading/Note Taking** 17-2
L2 **Adapted Reading/Note Taking** 17-2

Risk Factors

L2 Active Learning

Have students create a chart with the following headings: Family Risk Factors, Social Risk Factors, Personal Risk Factors. Ask students to complete this chart by explaining how these risk factors can contribute to drug abuse among teenagers. Encourage students to use their own words and illustrations as they complete the chart.

L3 Cultural Connection

Have students research the International Olympic Committee's regulations prohibiting the use of certain drugs by Olympic athletes. What drugs are prohibited? Are athletes tested for drug use? Ask students to report their findings to the class.

Connect to Your Life *Sample answer:* I would be very disappointed and choose a new favorite athlete.

L3 Online Activity

Visit Pearson SuccessNet to access an online activity about signs of drug dependency. Have students complete the Web activity.

EL English Language Learners

Such terms as *alienation, vulnerable,* and *glamorization* may be unfamiliar to English language learners and other students. Have students make a list of these and any other unfamiliar terms on pages 434–435. Have students look up the terms in a dictionary. Then help students use the defini-

tions to rephrase the terms. They should use simpler words that fit the context. For example, *alienation* might be rephrased as "feeling excluded," *vulnerable* as "sensitive," and *glamorization* as "making attractive."

L2 Active Learning

Help students recall from Chapter 3 some healthy ways to reduce stress, such as physical activity and deep breathing. (You may wish to demonstrate some deep breathing techniques for the class to practice together or at home.) Then have students rewrite the paragraph about Keith so that he uses a healthy way to reduce stress instead of turning to drugs. Ask a few volunteers to share their paragraphs with the class. Discuss how Keith might feel if he reduced stress in healthful ways such as these, rather than by taking pills. **WRITING**

Protective Factors

L1 Building Health Skills

Practicing Healthful Behaviors Discuss how negative, drug-using role models may increase risk of drug use by teens. Then, have groups of students brainstorm examples of positive, drug-free role models. (Examples might include sports or movie stars, parents, coaches, or other drug-free adults whom students admire.) Ask groups to make collages of their examples. Display the collages in the classroom, and use them to start a discussion of how positive role models can help teens avoid drugs.

L3 Journal Writing

Have students read about protective factors for drug abuse and identify protective factors over which they have some control (for example, committing to success in academics and extracurricular activities). Ask students to write a private journal entry in which they list ways they could strengthen one or more of the protective factors they identified. **WRITING**

FIGURE 8 Drugs don't solve problems; they add problems.

"I can't concentrate in class anymore."

"What if my parents found out?"

"I need another hit!"

"What if I get suspended from the team?"

Personal Factors From time to time, all teens experience stress. But not all of them handle it like Keith.

Talia broke up with Keith after they had been going out for two years. Keith kept to himself and pretended the breakup did not bother him. Eventually, Keith began to feel depressed. He had heard that "uppers" improve mood. Soon, he was dependent on uppers and needed them just to get through the day.

There are many causes for stress in a teen's life—for example, a breakup like Keith's, an academic or social problem, or an illness or death in the family. Some teens might turn to drugs in an attempt to temporarily escape the negative feelings associated with stress. But, abusing drugs does nothing to address the underlying causes of stress. In fact, drug abuse ultimately makes life more stressful.

Another personal factor that may influence drug use is low self-esteem. When teens don't feel good about themselves, they are more likely to ignore the serious risks of drug abuse.

Protective Factors

Review the stories involving Julie, Mike, and Keith. Did their stories have to end in drug abuse? No. Even with the risk factors they faced—a distant parent, drug-abusing peers, and personal stress—their decision to use drugs was ultimately their own.

Just because risk factors exist in a teen's life does not mean the teen will abuse drugs. While most teens face at least some risk factors for drug abuse, protective factors can help them overcome those risks. A **protective factor** is a factor that reduces a person's potential for harmful behavior. **Having strong protective factors in your life will help you stay drug free.**

TEENS *Are Asking . . .*

Q: I've got many of the risk factors for drug abuse. Does that mean I'm doomed to becoming a drug abuser?

A: No, it does not. Risk factors are just that: factors that increase risk. Having risk factors—even having many risk factors—does not necessarily mean you will become a drug abuser. However, you should be aware that your chances of becoming a drug abuser are likely to be higher than they are for many other people. It is especially important for you to take positive steps to avoid drugs and the people who use them. You should also work hard to develop protective factors against drug abuse.

Family Factors Teenagers who have good relationships with their parents and other family members are better equipped to deal with life's problems and stresses. With close, supportive relationships, teens can seek guidance from parents or siblings and discuss the problems they face. Protective family factors include

▸ strong and positive family bonds

▸ parental awareness of a teen's social activities and peer group

▸ clear rules that are consistently enforced

FIGURE 9 Spending quality time with family members can help protect teens from drug abuse.

Social Factors Strong social bonds and supports can cushion the negative effects of stress in your life and act as powerful buffers against drug use. Protective social factors include

▸ having strong bonds to school and other community institutions

▸ associating with peers who are drug free

▸ having friends who are supportive and accepting

Personal Factors Stress and negative feelings are a part of life. With guidance from adult or peer role models, teens can learn healthy techniques for managing stress. Other protective personal factors include

▸ a commitment to success in academics and extracurricular activities

▸ a personal belief that drug abuse is unacceptable

Section 2 Review

Key Ideas and Vocabulary

1. What three general types of factors can either increase one's risk of drug abuse or protect against drug abuse?

2. What is a **protective factor**?

3. Why is it important to strengthen protective factors in your life?

Critical Thinking

4. Applying Concepts Explain how a teen's family life can either be a risk factor for drug abuse or a protective factor.

Health at Home

Anti-Drug Messages For one week, keep a record of all the information you receive from television, the Internet, and other media about drug use. What risk factors and protective factors do the media emphasize? Summarize your findings. **WRITING**

---

5. Communicating What advice would you give a friend who is abusing drugs to help him or her cope with negative feelings?

6. Evaluating Despite facing many risk factors, a person ultimately can still say "no" to drugs. Do you agree with this statement? Explain.

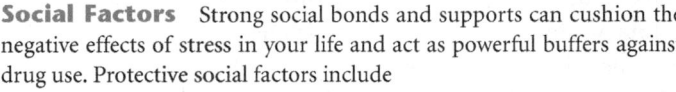
Evaluate

These assignments can help you assess students' mastery of the section content.

Section 2 Review

Answers appear below.

Teaching Resources

• Practice 17-2
• Section 17-2 Quiz

L2 Reteach

Ask students to use the headings and subheadings to make a concept map of section content. Then have students compare their concept maps with those of several classmates around them and correct any errors or omissions they notice in their own concept maps.

L4 Enrich

Teaching Resources

• Enrich 17-2

Health at Home

Anti-Drug Messages Suggest that students keep a notebook and pen handy when they watch television or use other media so they can record all the relevant information about drug use they receive. Students might note risk factors such as glamorization of drugs in movies. They might note protective factors such as strong family bonds in television programs.

Section 2 Review

1. family, social, and personal factors

2. a factor that reduces a person's potential for harmful behavior

3. Having strong protective factors in your life will help you stay drug free.

4. If a teen's family life is characterized by poor relationships and drug abuse by family members, it can be a risk factor for drug abuse. If a teen's family life is characterized by good relationships and clear, consistently-enforced rules, it can be a protective factor against drug abuse.

5. *Sample answer:* I would tell the friend that drug abuse will make the negative feelings worse. I would advise the friend to talk to a trusted adult or counselor to get help for dealing with the negative feelings and the drug abuse.

6. *Sample answer:* I agree with the statement, because people can choose not to use drugs no matter how many risk factors they have.

Intervening to Help a Friend

Objective

Demonstrate advocacy by showing how to intervene to help a friend deal with drug abuse.

Teaching Strategies

- You may want to have students read about marijuana and its dangers in Section 3 before they do the activity, but this is not necessary.

- Discuss how drug use may make users unable to think clearly and therefore unable to be persuaded by reasonable arguments or by facts about the risks. Ask: **When is a good time to talk to a friend about drug abuse?** *(when the friend is not under the influence of the drug)*

- Remind students that the best way to communicate feelings and concerns is by using "I statements" rather than "you statements." For example, they might say "I was worried when you showed up late," rather than "You always show up late;" or they might say "I felt hurt when you didn't listen to me," rather than "You never listen to me." Ask students to give additional examples.

- Guide the class in brainstorming local resources for people who abuse drugs. Give students suggestions if they need help thinking of resources. (See the answer to question 3 under Practice the Skill on page 439 for ideas, or look in a local telephone directory before class begins.)

 Advocacy

Intervening to Help a Friend

Jen had been concerned about her friend Christina's marijuana use for some time, but last night was the final straw. Jen and Christina were to meet at a friend's party, but Christina showed up two hours late and was "high." Christina was feeling drowsy and acting uncoordinated, so Jen drove her home. The next day, Christina told Jen that she was perfectly fine at the party and could have driven herself home. Christina also claimed that she could quit smoking marijuana at any time.

Jen wants to help Christina, but how can she when Christina is so out of touch with reality? Intervening to help a friend who abuses drugs is difficult. Here are some tips for helping a friend.

438

Sensitive Issues

- Marijuana use may be a sensitive issue for students who use marijuana. This might be a relatively large number of students. If the students in your classes are similar to students in recent national surveys, then at least one in five has used marijuana in the last twelve months.

- It is not necessary for students to discuss personal issues raised by this activity if it makes them feel uncomfortable. However, you should encourage students to do the activity, because it will reinforce reasons not to use drugs and identify sources of help to stop using drugs.

❶ Talk to your friend.

Talking to your friend about his or her behavior will not be easy, but it is worthwhile.

▶ **Express Your Concern** Tell your friend that you are intervening because you are worried about his or her well-being.

"I was worried something had happened to you when you showed up late."

▶ **Help Your Friend Face Facts** Share examples of your friend's destructive behavior as specific evidence of the problem. Describe behaviors accurately and simply, using dates and times when possible.

▶ **Describe Your Feelings** Tell how your friend's behavior affects you.

"When you showed up 'high,' it made me feel like you didn't care about my feelings."

▶ **Don't Criticize or Argue** Resist the temptation to be judgmental. You are objecting to the behavior, not the person. Do not get drawn into "No-I-didn't, Yes-you-did" arguments. Expect your friend to deny drug dependency or other destructive patterns of behavior. If your friend argues, say "I just want you to know how I feel," and then leave.

▶ **Offer Specific Help** Prepare a list of resources that your friend can go to for help. Include names, addresses, and phone numbers. Offer to go with your friend to the school counselor, a social service center, a member of the clergy, a health professional, or other local resource.

"Let's go talk to Mr. Ford together."

❷ Ask another friend to help.

The more people speaking the truth and offering support, the better. Be sure to discuss your concerns and guidelines for intervening with the second friend. Work together.

❸ Follow through.

Do what you said you would do to help your friend. Be sure your friend knows that your offers of support can be counted on.

❹ Seek adult or professional help.

If you think your friend is in a life-threatening or similarly serious situation, find a more experienced person to intervene directly.

❺ Recognize your limitations.

Remember, you can only be responsible for yourself. You cannot make another person get help or change behavior. If you have followed these guidelines, then you have done all you can, and you are a good friend.

Practice the Skill

1. Review Jen's situation. Write a dialogue between Jen and Christina following the guidelines presented in Step 1. **WRITING**

2. Under what circumstances do you think Jen should consider asking for adult or professional help for Christina? Explain.

3. Prepare a list of local resources for people facing drug dependency issues. Include addresses and phone numbers, as well as a brief description of the services.

Preventing Drug Abuse **439**

Health and Community

Objectives
Before class begins, write the objectives on the board. Have students copy the objectives into their notebooks at the start of class.

1. Focus

Warm-Up **Health Stats**

Call on several volunteers to share their answers with the class. Students might say, for example, that there are more prescription drugs available now than in the past or that there are more ads for prescription drugs than there used to be. Tell students they will learn more about the abuse of prescription drugs and other commonly abused drugs in this section.
Presentation 17-3

Section 3
Commonly Abused Drugs

Objectives
- ▶ **Compare** the effects of depressants, stimulants, and hallucinogens on the body.
- ▶ **Describe** the effects of marijuana.
- ▶ **Name** three classes of drugs of increasing concern in recent years.

Vocabulary
- depressant
- barbiturates
- opiate
- heroin
- stimulant
- amphetamines
- methamphetamine
- cocaine
- hallucinogen
- marijuana
- club drugs
- inhalant

Warm-Up

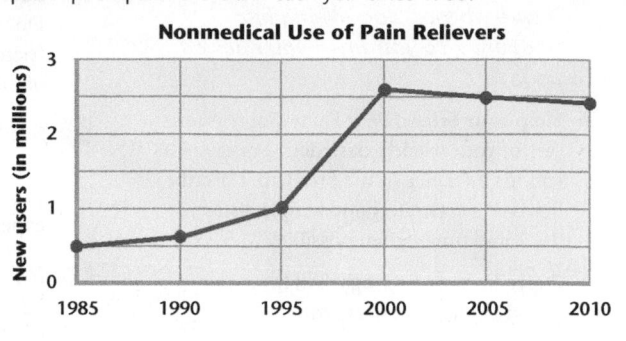

Health Stats The graph shows the number of new abusers of prescription pain relievers in each year since 1985.

WRITING What factors do you think are responsible for the increase in prescription drug abuse?

Depressants

Drugs are categorized according to their actions and effects on the body. A psychoactive drug that slows brain and body reactions is called a **depressant.** Figure 10 lists some commonly abused depressants and their effects. **Depressants slow body functions by decreasing heart and breathing rates and lowering blood pressure.**

Barbiturates One class of depressants is the **barbiturates** (bahr BICH ur its)—also called sedative-hypnotics. In small doses, barbiturates are sedatives—they relax a person. In high doses, barbiturates are hypnotics—they induce sleep. Today, physicians rarely prescribe barbiturates for sleep problems because barbiturates are dangerous and they have a high potential for abuse.

   A barbiturate abuser develops tolerance to the drug quickly. As tolerance increases, the abuser becomes dependent. Barbiturate abusers walk slowly, slur their speech, and react more slowly to their environment. Withdrawal from barbiturates can be fatal.

440 *Chapter 17*

WRITING and Health

L2 Summary

Ask students to write a paragraph summarizing the information in the passage headed Depressants. Have them start the paragraph with the definition of *depressant,* followed by the boldfaced key idea. Then suggest that they support the key idea by adding a sentence or two about each type of depressant described in the passage.

CNS Depressants A CNS depressant is a sedative that slows the activity of the central nervous system (CNS). This class of drugs used to be called tranquilizers. CNS depressants slow nerve activity, relax muscle tension, lower alertness, and cause drowsiness. CNS depressants have generally replaced barbiturates for medical uses. Doctors may prescribe CNS depressants to treat anxiety, sleep disorders, muscle spasms, and convulsions. However, as with barbiturates, abuse of CNS depressants can cause tolerance and dependence.

Opiates An **opiate** (OH pee it) is any drug made from psychoactive compounds contained in the seed pods of poppy plants. Some opiates can also be produced in a laboratory. In small doses, opiates act to dull the senses, relieve pain, and induce sleep. The opiates morphine and codeine, for example, are used in some prescription medications to reduce severe pain. Both morphine and codeine can produce tolerance and lead to dependence.

A growing area of concern is the use of opiate-containing painkillers or cough syrups for a "high." This kind of abuse usually involves taking a larger dose than is recommended for the intended medical purpose. Abusing opiates in this way can have dangerous or even life-threatening side effects.

Another frequently abused opiate in the United States is **heroin,** an illegal opiate made from morphine in a laboratory. Abusers of heroin appear dazed and disoriented. Heroin is also highly addictive.

 **Connect to Your Life** What news about painkiller abuse have you seen in the media?

▲ Poppy seed pod

FIGURE 10 Depressants have a number of dangerous side effects and long-term health effects when they are abused.

Depressants

Drug	Side Effects	Long-Term Effects
Barbiturates	Poor coordination, slurred speech, decreased alertness	Sleepiness, irritability, confusion
CNS Depressants	Blurred vision, dizziness, slurred speech, drowsiness, headache, skin rash	Blood and liver disease
Opiates	Nausea, vomiting, decreased alertness, drowsiness, depressed respiration	Constipation, infections associated with injecting
Alcohol	Impaired judgment, decreased alertness, lack of coordination, memory problems, vomiting	Liver damage, brain damage, anxiety and depression, malnutrition, memory loss

Preventing Drug Abuse **441**

2. Teach

L3 **EL** Reading/Note Taking 17-3

L2 Adapted Reading/Note Taking 17-3

Depressants

L2 **Visual Learning: Figure 10**

Image Bank Figure 17-10

Have students read the effects of depressant drugs that are listed in the figure. Ask: **How would the side effects influence a drug user's ability to pay attention in class?** (*Decreased alertness and drowsiness would make it hard to pay attention.*) **How would the side effects influence a drug user's ability to drive a motor vehicle?** (*Poor coordination, decreased alertness, blurred vision, and drowsiness would make a drug user unable to safely drive a motor vehicle.*) Remind students that when alcohol is consumed at the same time as other depressant drugs it produces drug synergism. The side effects are more than doubled and may be deadly.

L3 **Active Learning**

Have students design a detailed warning label for one of the depressant drug categories listed in Figure 10. Remind students to mention both the potential side effects (short-term effects) and long-term effects. **WRITING**

Connect to Your Life Answers will vary, depending on what news is in the media, but the news stories should relate to the abuse of legal pain relievers. An example might be a story about the arrest of an abuser for illegally obtaining prescription pain relievers.

Differentiated Instruction

L2 **Less Proficient Readers**

Pair less proficient with more proficient readers, and have pairs make a concept map about depressants. Organizing the material visually, without distracting details, will help students see how the drugs are categorized and related to one another. Urge students to make similar graphic organizers about the other categories of drugs in this section.

L4 **Gifted and Talented**

Ask the school librarian to direct students to works of fiction and nonfiction that give a cautionary account of drug abuse. Have students select and read one of the books and submit a book report. You may also want to ask the librarian if the students can help create a display of the books in the library or health classroom.

Stimulants

L2 Cooperative Learning

Divide the class into small groups. Ask each group to discuss: (1) differences between stimulant drugs and depressant drugs *(stimulants speed up the body, depressants slow down the body)*; and (2) similarities among different stimulant drugs *(e.g., all are addictive; all produce a "high" that is quickly followed by depression; all have dangerous side effects and long-term effects)*. Have groups write a few sentences summarizing the main points of their discussion. Give groups a chance to share their sentences. **WRITING**

L3 Class Discussion

Tell students that methamphetamine use has reached epidemic levels nationwide. Many law enforcement officers consider it the number one drug they battle today. Ask: **What might explain why methamphetamine is used so widely?** *(Sample answer: The drug is relatively inexpensive to make from over-the-counter ingredients, and strongly addictive.)*

L3 Visual Learning: Figure 11

Have students look at the graph and read the caption. Make sure they understand that the graph shows only the percent increase for crimes where meth was involved (e.g., there was not a 60 percent increase in *all* domestic violence crimes). Ask the class to brainstorm reasons why meth influences crime. *(Meth abusers may turn to crime to get money to buy the drug; meth makers may use crime to obtain supplies or money to make the drug; long-term meth abusers may become aggressive and engage in domestic violence.)* **Caption Answer 62 percent**

 *Sample answer:* Drug nicknames might make the drugs seem less dangerous and more attractive to teens.

Stimulants

A **stimulant** is a drug that speeds up activities of the central nervous system. **Stimulants increase heart rate, blood pressure, breathing rate, and alertness.** Physicians sometimes prescribe certain stimulants to treat sleep disorders and behavioral disorders such as attention-deficit hyperactivity disorder (ADHD). Abusers of stimulants may develop tolerance, some amount of dependence, and strong addiction. Figure 12 lists some commonly abused stimulants and their effects.

Amphetamines One group of powerful stimulants is the **amphetamines** (am FET uh meenz). Amphetamines are prescription drugs that are sometimes sold illegally as "speed" or "uppers." Amphetamine abuse produces feelings of well-being and high energy. However, the effects wear off quickly and the abuser is often left feeling depressed. The "down" often leads to taking another—and another—dose. The result may be drug dependence.

Methamphetamine A stimulant that is related to amphetamines, but is even more powerful, is **methamphetamine.** Abuse of this highly addictive drug, which is sometimes called "meth," "crank," "crystal," or "ice," is on the rise. The drug is made from relatively inexpensive over-the-counter ingredients in illegal laboratories called "meth labs."

Methamphetamine initially produces a rush, or "high." But, after the rush wears off, the user may become confused, shaky, anxious, irritable, or violent. Meth users ultimately become paranoid and psychotic due to brain damage. Meth use may also cause strokes and deadly convulsions.

▲ **Amphetamine powder**

FIGURE 11 In recent years, crimes linked to methamphetamine have soared. **Reading Graphs** By what percentage did domestic violence crimes linked to meth use increase?

Connect to Your Life How do you think drug nicknames affect the perceptions teens have of the drugs?

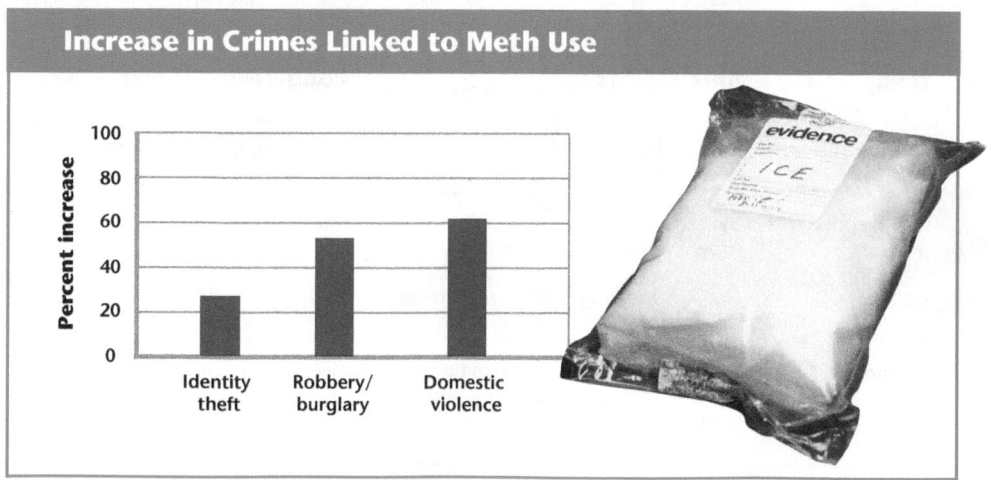

Increase in Crimes Linked to Meth Use

WRITING and Health

L3 Public Service Announcement

Have students write a public service announcement warning teens about the dangers of stimulant drugs. PSAs should include common names of several stimulant drugs (e.g., speed, meth, crack), as well as side effects and long-term effects of stimulant drugs. Suggest that students first prepare poster boards to help them identify important points to emphasize in their PSAs. If possible, arrange to have students present their announcements at a school assembly.

Stimulants

Drug	Side Effects	Long-Term Effects
Amphetamines	Restlessness, rapid speech, blurred vision, dizziness	Hyperactivity, irritability, irregular heart rate, liver damage, paranoia
Methamphetamine	Increased respiration, elevated body temperature, convulsions, stroke	Psychotic behavior, memory loss, aggression, brain damage, heart damage, severe tooth and gum disease, stroke
Cocaine	Sleep disorders, loss of appetite, increased blood pressure and heart rate	Depression, paranoia, irritability, weight loss, irregular heartbeat, seizures, respiratory failure, cardiovascular failure, liver damage
Nicotine/Tobacco Smoke	Nausea, loss of appetite, headache, increased blood pressure	Hacking cough, difficulty breathing, increased number of colds, heart and lung disease

Cocaine Cocaine is a powerful but short-acting stimulant. Cocaine abusers sniff the drug into the nose, smoke it, or inject it directly into their bloodstream.

Cocaine is highly addictive. Tolerance develops rapidly, causing abusers to need larger and larger amounts. When cocaine's effects wear off, abusers often experience depression, which can be severe. An overdose of cocaine, which can be caused by even a small amount, may result in seizures, heart failure, or respiratory failure. A cocaine overdose can be fatal.

A process called "free-basing" changes cocaine into a concentrated, smokable form known as *crack*. Crack is the strongest form of cocaine. The short but powerful effects produced by crack occur within eight seconds after it is smoked.

Hallucinogens

A **hallucinogen** (huh LOO sih nuh jun) is a drug that distorts perception, thought, and mood. **Hallucinogens overload the brain with sensory information, causing a distorted sense of reality.** Hallucinogens are illegal and have no medical use.

Hallucinogens can produce frightening and unpredictable mood swings. Sometimes abusers cannot tell what is real. They may also experience memory loss and personality changes, be unable to perform normal activities, or lose track of time and their surroundings. Tolerance to the mind-altering effects of hallucinogens develops quickly.

FIGURE 12 Stimulants have a number of dangerous side effects and long-term health effects.

▲ **Crack cocaine**

L2 Visual Learning: Figure 12

Image Bank Figure 17-12

Have students read the effects of stimulants that are listed in the figure. Call on volunteers to explain—or explain yourself, if necessary—the effects referred to as *paranoia* (thinking that everyone is "out to get you") and *psychotic behavior* (acting as though you are out of touch with reality). Have students look at the long-term effects of meth use. Tell them that meth abusers often lose their teeth, a condition that is commonly called "meth mouth."

Hallucinogens

L2 Building Vocabulary

On the board, write the following word parts and their meanings: *-ation* ("process") and *-gen* ("producer"). Ask: **If *hallucinate* means "to see or hear things that are not real," what does *hallucination* mean?** *(process of hallucinating, or seeing or hearing things that are not real)* **What does *hallucinogen* mean?** *(producer of hallucinations)* Conclude by saying that "producers of hallucinations" are drugs called *hallucinogens*.

EL Active Learning

The words for classes and kinds of drugs on these two pages and throughout the section are difficult to read and pronounce. Read the terms aloud while students read the phonetic respellings in the textbook. Ask students to repeat each term after you read it aloud.

Differentiated Instruction

L1 Special Needs

Help special needs students focus on the most important content. For example, it is more important for them to know that drugs such as meth and crack are very dangerous and should be avoided, rather than to know that drugs such as meth and crack are classified as stimulants and increase blood pressure.

L2 Cooperative Learning

Have pairs of students make flash cards on the material about hallucinogens. Ask partners to use the flash cards to help each other learn the information. Advise students to keep their flash cards and use them to review the material at the end of the section and again at the end of the chapter.

L3 Building Health Skills

Accessing Information Remind students that hallucinogens can cause permanent mental illnesses, such as schizophrenia. Have the class brainstorm where they could learn more about drug-related mental illness (e.g., dictionaries, encyclopedias, medical reference books, books about mental health or drugs, online encyclopedias, mental health or drug abuse Web sites). For each relevant source, assign one student to investigate it further. Ask students to report to the class on what they learn about hallucinogens and mental illness from their assigned source. Discuss which sources are most informative.

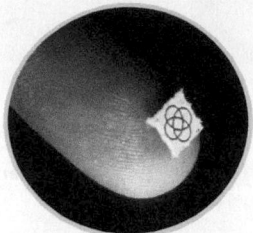

▲ LSD

▲ Psilocybin

LSD The strongest known hallucinogen is lysergic acid diethylamide, or LSD. LSD is also called "acid." LSD's effects are unpredictable—it can either stimulate or depress the central nervous system. Abusers experience hallucinations in which they may see colorful visions and mistakenly feel they have superhuman powers. The drug may also shorten a person's attention span, causing the mind to wander.

LSD use can lead to frightening episodes known as "bad trips." Another unpredictable effect of LSD is a "flashback." A flashback is an unexpected reoccurrence of a bad trip, sometimes years after LSD was taken. Flashbacks can happen at any time without warning.

Psilocybin Another hallucinogen is psilocybin (sil uh SY bin)—sometimes called "shrooms." Psilocybin is a chemical found in a certain type of mushroom. The mushrooms are eaten raw or mixed with food. The effects of psilocybin are much like those of LSD, but not as strong. Tolerance to psilocybin develops quickly. An added risk of this drug is that a similar-looking, but deadly, mushroom is sometimes mistaken for psilocybin.

PCP One of the most dangerous of all drugs is PCP, short for phencyclidine. PCP was once used as an anesthetic, or painkiller, for large animals. Today, PCP, or "angel dust," is only available illegally. Abusers may smoke the white powder with tobacco or marijuana, or inject, sniff, or eat it. Because the drug eliminates the sensation of pain, abusers may unintentionally injure or even kill themselves. Some PCP abusers develop signs of schizophrenia, a mental illness. PCP's effects remain long after drug use ends, and flashbacks may occur.

FIGURE 13 The hallucinogen PCP, a white powder, is sometimes added to marijuana joints.

Focus on ISSUES

L3 Situations Involving Marijuana

Divide the class into three groups. Assign each group to discuss a responsible solution to one of the following situations: (a) You're offered a ride home from a party by a friend who is smoking marijuana; (b) Your best friend went away for the summer and came home bragging about smoking marijuana every day—now he doesn't seem to care about anything that used to be important to him; (c) Your date says that you can't get hooked on marijuana like you can with cigarettes, then offers you a joint. After groups have discussed their scenario, have them write and act out a role-play that presents responsible ways to respond to the situation.

Marijuana

Marijuana (mar uh WAH nuh) is the leaves, stems, and flowering tops of the hemp plant *Cannabis sativa*. It is also called "pot," "dope," "weed," or "grass." Marijuana is smoked in a pipe or from a "joint" or "blunt," or mixed with food and eaten. The hemp plant is also the source of the illegal drug hashish (HASH eesh), or "hash."

Effects of Marijuana Marijuana is one of the most frequently abused psychoactive drugs. Its main ingredient changes the way information reaches and is acted upon by the brain. Side effects of marijuana use include

▶ distorted perceptions—sights, sounds, time, and touch

▶ difficulties with thinking and problem solving

▶ loss of motor coordination

▶ increased heart rate

▶ feelings of anxiety or paranoia

Frequent use of marijuana may permanently affect the brain. Users may damage their short-term memory and lose the motivation to perform at school or work. Smoking marijuana also increases the risk of certain cancers.

Marijuana and Driving Because marijuana can act as a depressant, users often feel sleepy or drowsy. Marijuana use can also make it difficult to judge distances and react quickly to signals and sounds on the road. Driving a car is extremely dangerous when under the influence of marijuana.

A Gateway to Other Drugs You may have heard the phrase "gateway drug" used to describe marijuana. This phrase reflects the fact that marijuana use is often a gateway to using other "harder" drugs, such as cocaine. As marijuana users build up tolerance, they may seek out other drugs to experience the "high" they first got from marijuana. In addition, a marijuana user is likely to be in contact with people who use and sell other illegal drugs. Studies show that almost all young people who use other illegal drugs first used marijuana.

 **How can refusing marijuana help you stay away from drugs in general?**

Facts About Marijuana
- May act as a depressant, stimulant, or hallucinogen
- Has lasting negative health effects
- May be deadly if combined with alcohol or another depressant

FIGURE 14 Contrary to what some people may think, marijuana is a dangerous drug.

 GO ONLINE
PearsonSuccessNet.com
For: More on commonly abused drugs

Marijuana

L3 Building Media Literacy

Ask students to find and print a reliable online source that deals with the physical health effects of smoking marijuana. Have small groups of students compare sources and select the source that is most reliable and relevant to the topic. Give groups a chance to share their choices and the reasons for them.

L2 Visual Learning: Figure 14

Have students read the facts about marijuana in the figure. Ask: **How is the user affected if marijuana acts as a depressant?** *(The user's body and brain slow down.)* **If marijuana acts as a stimulant?** *(The user's body and brain speed up.)* **If marijuana acts as a hallucinogen?** *(The user has hallucinations.)* **What are some lasting negative health effects of marijuana use?** *(damage to short-term memory, loss of motivation, increased risk of certain cancers)*

L1 Active Learning

Have students create a poster with illustrations that complete the following statement: "Marijuana is harmful because..." Display and discuss the ideas presented.

L3 Addressing Misconceptions

Marijuana Is Harmful Many people think that marijuana is not that harmful. Tell students that marijuana use by teens has been found to cause permanent changes in the brain and increased risks of depression, suicide, and schizophrenia later in life.

 Using marijuana may lead to use of other drugs, so refraining from marijuana can help you stay away from drugs in general.

L3 Online Activity

Visit Pearson SuccessNet to access an online activity about commonly abused drugs. Have students complete the Web activity.

Differentiated Instruction

L2 Less Proficient Readers

Because the term *marijuana* is used as a main heading, students might think it is another category of drug, like depressants, stimulants, and hallucinogens. Make sure students realize that marijuana is a single drug that can act as a depressant, stimulant, or hallucinogen, but it is not generally placed into any of these three categories of drugs.

L4 Gifted and Talented

Ask interested students to find statistics on marijuana as a "gateway drug." What percentage of marijuana users go on to use "harder" drugs? For which drugs is marijuana most often a gateway drug? Have students use tables or graphs to present their findings to the rest of the class.

Club Drugs, Inhalants, and Steroids

L3 Cooperative Learning

Divide the class into three groups, and assign each group to learn more about the dangers of club drugs, inhalants, or steroids. Ask groups to incorporate the information in a poster advocating avoidance of the drugs to other teens. Give groups a chance to share their posters, and then display the posters in the classroom.

L2 Visual Learning: Figure 15

Image Bank Figure 17-15

Have students read about club drugs in the figure. Stress that all the drugs can be fatal, even the first time they are used. Ask: **Which club drugs are hallucinogens?** *(ecstasy and ketamine)* Call on a student to answer the caption question. Then discuss the use of rohypnol and GHB in date rapes.
Caption Answer rohypnol and GHB

L3 Addressing Misconceptions

Dangers of Steroid Use Students may have the misconception that anabolic steroids are less dangerous than other drugs because they are not considered psychoactive and are used (sometimes with no apparent ill effect) by some famous athletes. Remind students of the dangers of steroid use especially to teens, from Chapter 13. Also, make sure students know that the psychological side effects of steroid use (extreme aggression and depression) can be as serious as the side effects of psychoactive drugs.

Club Drugs

Drug	Classification	Side Effects	Other Facts
Ecstasy (MDMA) *Also called XTC, X, Adam, clarity, love drug*	Combined stimulant and hallucinogen	Increased heart rate and blood pressure, blurred vision, muscle tension, severe sweating and chills, nausea, increased body temperature that can lead to organ failure	Drugs called "Ecstasy" often contain other substances besides MDMA that make them even more dangerous.
Rohypnol *Also called roofies, rophies, forget-me pill*	CNS depressant	Decreased blood pressure, drowsiness, dizziness, confusion, memory loss	Associated with "date rapes"; a small dose can impair a user for up to 12 hours.
GHB (Gamma-hydroxybutyrate) *Also called grievous bodily harm, G, liquid ecstasy*	CNS depressant; also has anabolic (body-building) effects	Drowsiness, nausea, headache, loss of reflexes	Associated with "date rapes"; high doses may result in sleep, coma, or death.
Ketamine *Also called K, Vitamin K, cat valium*	Hallucinogen	Hallucinations, increased heart rate and blood pressure, impaired motor function, memory loss, numbness, nausea	High doses may cause delirium and fatal respiratory problems.

FIGURE 15 Some of the known effects of club drugs are listed here. **Reading Tables** Which club drugs are CNS depressants?

▲ Ecstasy

Club Drugs, Inhalants, and Steroids

So far, you have learned about the traditional classes of drugs that are commonly abused. **Three classes of drugs that are of growing concern in recent years are club drugs, inhalants, and anabolic steroids.** The effects of club drugs and inhalants are extremely unpredictable and dangerous. The dangers of steroid abuse are less immediate. However, abuse of steroids causes lifelong damage to the body and brain.

Club Drugs **Club drugs** got their name from the fact that they first gained popularity at dance clubs and raves. They are now more widely available, but their use is still often associated with the club scene. The strength and quality of club drugs are highly unpredictable—their effects are different from person to person and very dangerous. Figure 15 summarizes the dangers of four of the more common club drugs. Other drugs associated with the club scene include methamphetamine and the hallucinogens LSD and PCP.

Some people are unknowing victims of club drugs. For example, rohypnol (roh HYP nawl) can be slipped into someone's drink without his or her knowledge. While under the effects of the drug, the person may be hurt or raped and not even be able to recall the event later on.

For Your INFORMATION!

Drug Use by Teens

Do you know which type of drug—ecstasy, inhalants, or anabolic steroids—is used by more teens? According to recent surveys, almost 10 percent of teens have used inhalants at least once, compared with about 5 percent of teens who have ever used ecstasy and 1.4 percent who have ever used anabolic steroids. While use of ecstasy has dropped dramatically from its peak use in 2001 and rates of steroid use are stable, rates of inhalant use have decreased from their peak use in 2000, though usage rates remain higher in young teens. In 2012, about 6 percent of eighth graders had used inhalants in the previous 12 months. In that same year, about 4 percent of tenth graders and 3 percent of twelfth graders had used inhalants in the previous 12 months.

The effects of rohypnol are most severe when it is taken with an alcoholic drink. This is because of the synergism of combining two depressant drugs. However, rohypnol can be dangerous in any drink. The best advice for avoiding club drugs is to stay away from places where these drugs are used.

Inhalants   A breathable chemical vapor that produces mind-altering effects is called an **inhalant** (in HAYL unt). Some inhalants have appropriate medical uses. For example, nitrous oxide is an anesthetic used by dentists and doctors during surgery. But most inhalants are not meant for human use.

Abusing inhalants—including glue and household cleaners—may produce brief feelings of excitement or giddiness, but the feelings are far from harmless. In fact, they are a sign that the oxygen in the inhaled breath has been replaced with a chemical that has either stimulated the heart or depressed brain function. Even a single session of inhalant abuse can cause death by cardiac arrest or suffocation.

Anabolic Steroids   Anabolic steroids are synthetic drugs that are similar to the hormone testosterone. Legal uses of this drug include treating growth disorders and certain types of anemia. But steroids are also abused, primarily by people who want bigger muscles.

You can review the many dangerous side effects of steroid abuse in Chapter 13. Steroid use is especially dangerous for teenagers, whose growing bodies can suffer permanent damage. Unlike other commonly abused drugs, steroids are not considered psychoactive. However, they can have serious long-term effects on a user's brain. Have you ever heard the phrase "roid rage"? Steroids can make a user's personality very aggressive. In addition, some steroid users become severely depressed.

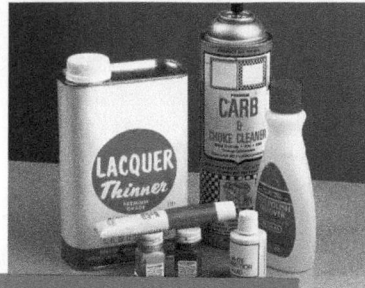

FIGURE 16   Inhalant abuse is extremely dangerous.

Some Dangers of Inhalant Abuse
• Liver and kidney damage
• Loss of bladder control
• Permanent hearing loss
• Brain cell death
• Loss of consciousness, coma, or death

Section 3 Review

Key Ideas and Vocabulary

1. Briefly describe the overall effects that depressants, stimulants, and hallucinogens have on the body.

2. What is an **opiate**? Give three examples.

3. What is **methamphetamine**? List three long-term effects of methamphetamine use.

4. How does marijuana affect the brain? List three side effects.

5. Name three classes of drugs of increasing concern today. In three sentences, summarize the dangers of each.

Health and Community

Steroid Abuse Rules   Choose three different sports where steroid abuse is a problem. Find out what rules and testing procedures are applied to professional athletes in these sports. Summarize your findings in a one-page report. **WRITING**

Critical Thinking

6. Relating Cause and Effect   Explain why prescription depressants or stimulants are dangerous when used for nonmedical purposes.

7. Comparing and Contrasting   How is methamphetamine different from other amphetamines?

GO ONLINE PearsonSuccessNet.com   Audio Summary Section 17.3   *Preventing Drug Abuse*   **447**

---

3. Assess

Evaluate
These assignments can help you assess students' mastery of the section content.

Section 3 Review
Answers appear below.

Teaching Resources
• Practice 17-3
• Section 17-3 Quiz

L2 **Reteach**

Have students use information in the section's figures to create a true-false quiz. Then have pairs of students exchange and try to solve each other's quiz. If partners disagree over the correct answers to any of the quiz questions, have them find the answers in the text.

L4 **Enrich**

Teaching Resources
• Enrich 17-3

Health and Community

Steroid Abuse Rules Students might choose baseball, football, or track, among many other sports. Rules and testing procedures are subject to frequent revision. Students are likely to find the most up-to-date rules and procedures online.

4. Marijuana changes the way information reaches and is acted upon by the brain. *Any three:* distorted perceptions, difficulties with thinking and problem solving, loss of motor coordination, increased heart rate, feelings of anxiety or paranoia

5. Three classes are club drugs, inhalants, and steroids. Club drugs change heart rate and blood pressure and can lead to death. Inhalants cause organ and brain cell damage and can be fatal. Steroids cause depression and aggression and can lead to permanent physical damage.

6. because they are usually used in higher doses, possibly in dangerous combinations with other drugs, and without medical supervision

7. It is more powerful.

Section 3 Review

1. Depressants slow body functions by decreasing heart and breathing rates and lowering blood pressure. Stimulants speed up the central nervous system and increase heart rate, blood pressure, breathing rate, and alertness. Hallucinogens overload the brain with sensory information, causing a distorted sense of reality.

2. any drug made from or simulating the psychoactive compounds in poppy seed pods; morphine, codeine, and heroin

3. a stimulant related to amphetamines; *any three:* psychotic behavior, memory loss, aggression, brain damage, heart damage, severe tooth and gum disease, stroke

Objectives
Before class begins, write the objectives on the board. Have students copy the objectives into their notebooks at the start of class.

1. Focus

Warm-Up **Advice Line**

If students need help thinking of ideas for the writing activity, have them review the steps in the Building Health Skills Feature on page 439. When students finish writing, call on several volunteers to share their answers. *(Students might say the friend could help Greg by informing a parent, guidance counselor, or other trusted adult about his drug use.)* Tell students they will learn in this section about other ways to help friends and themselves stay drug free.

Presentation 17-4

Connect to Your Life Allow students to answer this question in their private journals.

🚩 **Sensitive Issues**

Students who are involved in social circles with drug users may find it especially difficult to remain drug free because of fears about popularity and being accepted by their peer group. Emphasize that real friends care about one another, not about being "cool" at the expense of personal health and safety.

Section 4

Choosing to Be Drug Free

Objectives
▶ **Identify** three treatment options for people who abuse drugs.
▶ **Name** three steps you can take to stay drug free.

Vocabulary
• therapeutic community

Warm-Up

Dear Advice Line,

My friend Greg tried methamphetamine at a party a few months ago. Soon he started doing it regularly. He gets defensive and aggressive when I ask him if he needs help. I'm scared to talk to him anymore, but I want to help.

WRITING What advice would you give Greg's friend? How can she help Greg?

Treating Drug Abuse

What can you do to help someone who is abusing drugs? Before a person can be helped, the person needs to acknowledge that he or she has a drug problem. The next step would be for the person to explore possible treatment options.

Acknowledge the Problem Before drug abusers can be helped, they need to recognize their problem. Unfortunately, this may be difficult. Many abusers deny their behavior; others deny the underlying problems that led them to drug abuse.

Figure 17 lists some of the signs of drug abuse that you may recognize in yourself or in a friend or classmate. Review the Building Health Skills on pages 438–439 for tips on how to convince a friend that he or she has a drug problem.

 **Connect to Your Life** What trusted adult could you turn to for advice about a friend's drug problem?

TEENS *Are Asking . . .*

Q: **My boyfriend talked me into using cocaine several times, and now I think I'm hooked. My parents will die if I tell them! What should I do?**

A: First, tell your boyfriend to stop using cocaine and offering it to you, and drop him if he refuses. It will be much easier to avoid using cocaine if it is not around. Then, ask an adult you trust to help you tell your parents. Your parents may be very angry or upset when they find out. But, in time, they will probably be glad you confided in them. If they already suspected a problem, they will probably feel relieved to have it out in the open. You will probably feel relieved as well. You may also need drug couseling to help you overcome any cravings you may still have.

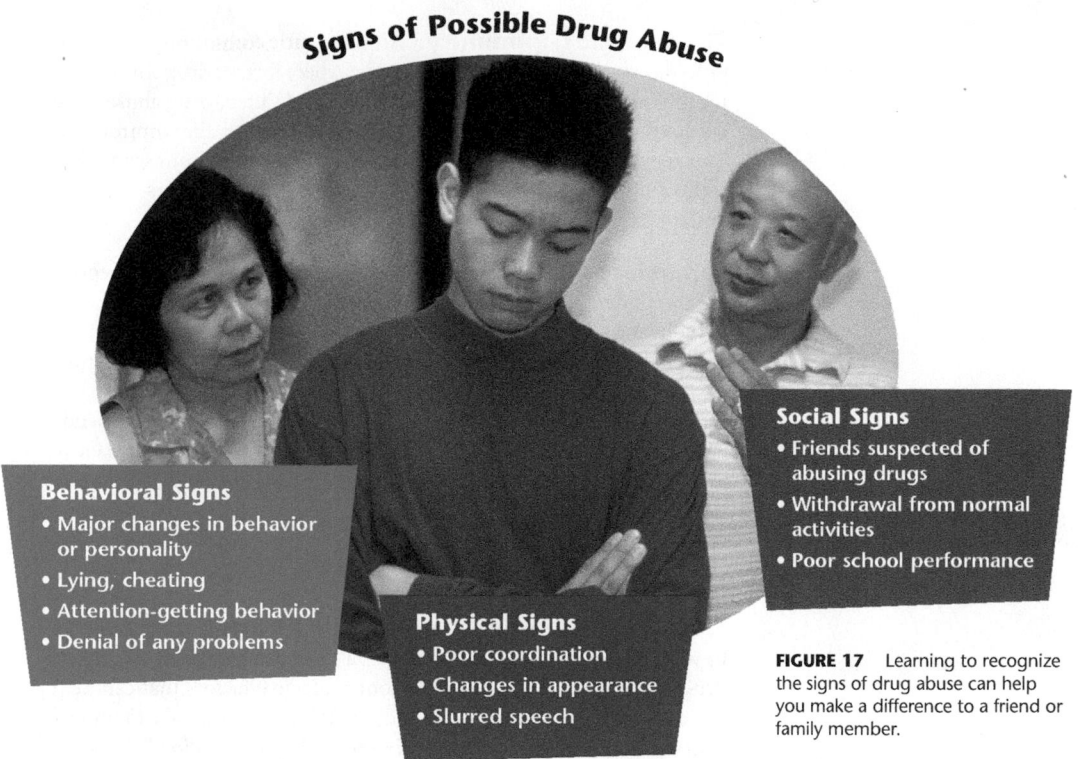

Signs of Possible Drug Abuse

Behavioral Signs
• Major changes in behavior or personality
• Lying, cheating
• Attention-getting behavior
• Denial of any problems

Physical Signs
• Poor coordination
• Changes in appearance
• Slurred speech

Social Signs
• Friends suspected of abusing drugs
• Withdrawal from normal activities
• Poor school performance

FIGURE 17 Learning to recognize the signs of drug abuse can help you make a difference to a friend or family member.

Explore Treatment Options Once drug abusers recognize their problem, several treatment options are available to them. **Treatment options for drug abusers include detoxification, therapeutic communities, and supervised medication.** Programs also exist for family members trying to understand their loved one's drug problem. Understanding the underlying cause for a loved one's drug abuse and getting involved in the person's treatment can help restore family stability.

Some drug treatment programs are available at little or no cost. Community hospitals, for example, may offer clinics or programs that provide low-cost or volunteer counseling for teenagers and adults. Local schools and governments also schedule parent meetings, peer group counseling, and drug-free programs.

Detoxification A person who enters a detoxification program undergoes gradual but complete withdrawal from the abused drug under medical supervision. Most detoxification programs are in hospitals. Doctors may reduce the drug dosage slowly to avoid painful withdrawal symptoms, or they may supervise the total withdrawal all at once. Detoxification programs include counseling to help people deal with their abuse and cope with the underlying problems.

GO ONLINE
PearsonSuccessNet.com
For: More on treating drug abuse

Preventing Drug Abuse **449**

2. Teach

L3 EL Reading/Note Taking 17-4
L2 Adapted Reading/Note Taking 17-4

Treating Drug Abuse

L2 Visual Learning: Figure 17

Ask students to read about the signs of possible drug abuse that are listed in the figure. For each category, describe a scenario in which a teen displays one of the signs. Then have students try to identify the signs. Discuss why people who abuse drugs might show the signs.

L3 Cooperative Learning

Ask pairs of students to write and act out role-plays in which a teen shows signs of drug abuse and a friend tries to convince the teen of the problem and suggests sources of help. Remind students to use strategies for intervening from the Building Health Skills feature on page 439. Give pairs a chance to present their role-plays to the class. Ask other students which strategies they think were most effective. **WRITING**

L3 Content Update GO ONLINE

Visit Pearson SuccessNet to access more information about treating drug abuse. Have students complete the Web activity.

Differentiated Instruction

L2 Less Proficient Readers

Guide students in reviewing what they learned about treating alcohol abuse in Chapter 15 to prepare them for reading about treating drug abuse in the present chapter. Have students reread the steps for treating alcohol abuse on pages 390–391. Ask: **Which steps in treating alcohol abuse are also steps in treating drug abuse?**

(acknowledge the problem and detoxification) Challenge students to predict the nature of these two steps in treating drug abuse, based on what they know about them in the context of treating alcohol abuse. They can check their predictions when they read the section.

L3 Active Learning

Ask interested students to look online or in a telephone directory for a therapeutic community for drug abuse in their area. Have students contact the community by phone, mail, or e-mail to learn about the kinds of therapy that are used to treat residents and what it is like to live in the community. Ask students to present what they learn to the class.

L4 Building Media Literacy

Find and copy articles from several different Web sites that list pros and cons of using drug replacements to treat drug abuse. Include articles from unbiased Web sites, as well as articles from Web sites of drug companies, treatment centers, or other organizations that might have a stake in one side or the other of the issue. Have students examine the articles and point out any clues they find that the articles might be biased. Discuss how biases might affect what information is presented and how the information is presented. Identify examples from the articles that demonstrate these points.

Staying Drug Free

L2 Teacher Demo

Before class, prepare a list of local options for helping teens stay drug free, such as school counselors, drug treatment programs, and support groups. In class, call on a volunteer to help you role-play a call to a drug-abuse hotline in which the caller (the student) describes a drug-related problem and asks for help and the hotline staffer (you) gives support and suggests options for help in the community.

L3 Building Health Skills

Advocacy Ask small groups of students to make posters demonstrating three ways to stay drug free: refusing drugs, seeking help, and alternatives to drugs. Have students illustrate their posters with pictures from magazines or the Internet. Urge students to make their posters informative yet direct and simple so the points can be grasped at a glance. Have groups ask local businesses to display their posters in their windows.

Therapeutic Community A **therapeutic community** (thehr uh PYOO tik) is a residential treatment center where former drug abusers live together and learn to adjust to drug-free lives. Often, drug abusers are required to undergo detoxification before joining the community. Therapeutic communities provide both medical care and counseling. The counseling may involve behavioral therapy to help drug abusers recognize and correct negative behaviors associated with their drug use.

Supervised Medication A third treatment option involves replacing the abused drug with a drug that produces some of the same effects, without the "high." For example, the drug methadone can help heroin abusers. Small, regular doses of methadone prevent withdrawal symptoms and craving for heroin.

Because methadone and other drug replacements can cause dependency, a trained professional must carefully monitor treatment and slowly lower the dosage. Long-term methadone use causes side effects such as liver damage.

Staying Drug Free

You face decisions every day. You need to decide what to eat, what clothes to wear, and how much to exercise. You may also face decisions about drugs. In Section 2, you learned about protective factors that can help you avoid drugs. There are some additional steps you can take to protect yourself from using drugs. **Practicing refusal skills, seeking help when you need it, and getting involved in drug-free activities can help you stay away from drugs.**

FIGURE 18 Teens in many communities are taking a stand against drugs. The teens at right are part of a program in Florida called "Drug Free Youth in Town."

Focus on **ISSUES**

L3 Debate: Methadone

Explain that the use of methadone to treat heroin addiction is a controversial issue. Assign a few interested students to learn more about the issue. After they do their research, ask them to choose sides and debate the issue in class. Ask other students which side of the issue they support. Point out that methadone treatment would be unnecessary if people stayed drug free in the first place. Briefly discuss refusing drugs as the best way to stay drug free.

Hands-On *Activity*

Resisting Peer Pressure

Materials
bag of jelly beans
set of five role-playing cards per group

Try This
1. Form a group with four other students.
2. Your teacher will distribute a different role-playing card to each group member.
3. Do not discuss your role with other group members.
4. Imagine that you are at a party with friends. Spend five minutes thinking about your assigned role and how you will act during the imagined party.
5. At your teacher's signal, begin acting out your role with the other members of your group.

Think and Discuss
1. Explain how you felt playing your role during the imagined party.
2. How do you think player 4 felt being pressured to eat the jelly beans?
3. How might player 3 have felt about eventually giving in?
4. How do you think player 1 felt about pressuring all the other players?
5. What refusal skills will you use to resist pressure from friends to use drugs?

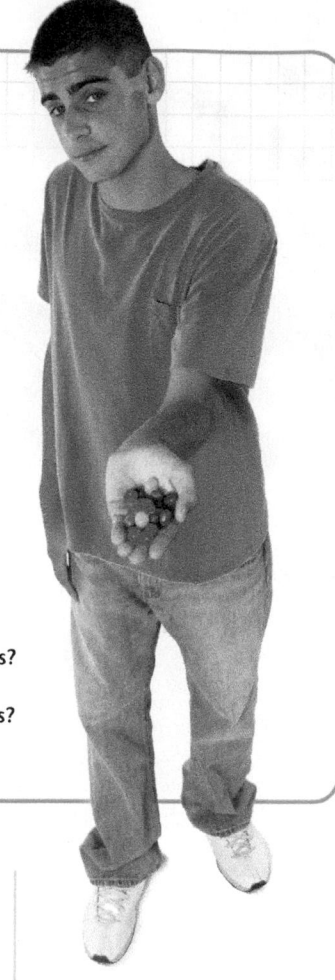

Refusing Drugs Refusing drugs can be difficult when you are faced with pressure to take them. You can sharpen your refusal skills by reviewing the Building Health Skills in Chapter 15 on pages 378–379. To be effective, be sure to clearly state your personal reasons for not wanting to take drugs. For example, you could say, "No thanks — I want to keep a clear head," or "I don't want to become addicted," or simply, "I don't do drugs."

If the person offering you drugs continues to pressure you, take a definite action and remove yourself from the situation. Your action will make it clear that you cannot be persuaded to change your mind.

Seeking Help If you decide that the stresses and problems in your life are too much to manage, find someone to talk to. Many people are willing to help, but you must first let them know that you need help. Parents, teachers, friends, siblings, school counselors, school nurses, and members of the clergy are usually available for guidance and support. A second option is to call a national drug-abuse hotline. Staffers can help you find support in your local community.

 **Connect to Your Life** What are your personal reasons for refusing drugs?

Hands-On *Activity*

Resisting Peer Pressure

Before the activity, prepare enough sets of the following role-playing cards for each group to have a set.

Player 1—Pressure all the other players to eat jellybeans; decide for yourself whether you will eat jellybeans.

Player 2—Pressure three other players to eat jellybeans; decide for yourself whether you will eat jellybeans.

Player 3—Do not pressure any other players to eat jelly beans; eventually give in when pressured to eat jellybeans.

Player 4—Do not pressure any other players to eat jellybeans; do not give in when pressured to eat jellybeans.

Player 5—Decide for yourself whether you will pressure any of the other players to eat jellybeans; decide for yourself whether or not you will eat jellybeans.

Think and Discuss Answers
1. Players who were allowed to decide for themselves how to act, as well as players who were told to act as they would have chosen, are likely to have felt better about playing their roles.
2. Player 4 might have found it hard to resist the pressure to eat jellybeans.
3. Player 3 might have felt guilty about eventually giving in to the pressure.
4. Player 1 might have felt pushy about pressuring all the other players.
5. *Sample answer:* say *no* with conviction and give honest reasons for refusing

Connect to Your Life Allow students to answer this question in their private journals.

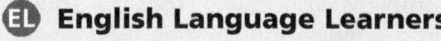

Differentiated Instruction

EL English Language Learners

A lack of English language mastery shouldn't stand in the way of a confident, assertive refusal. For this reason, explain to English language learners that a refusal does not have to be very long or detailed to work. In fact, the best refusals are usually short and to-the-point. Remind the students that body language is also key to an effective refusal. Good posture and eye contact will help them deliver their refusal with impact. Have English language learners practice speaking assertively the refusal statements that come most easily to them.

3. Assess

Evaluate
These assignments can help you assess students' mastery of the section content.

Section 4 Review
Answers appear below.

Teaching Resources
- Practice 17-4
- Section 17-4 Quiz

 **Reteach**

On the board, write the headings Ways to Treat Drug Abuse and Ways to Stay Drug Free. Go around the room, calling on one student after another to record a relevant item under one of the headings. Keep calling on students until they can no longer think of new ideas. Add any other important ideas students did not think of. Have students copy the lists in their notebooks.

 **Enrich**

Teaching Resources
- Enrich 17-4

Health at School

Drug Prevention Speech Tell students to try to begin their speeches with a "hook," or an opening that gets listeners' attention and interest. In their speeches, students might list such alternatives as playing sports, going to movies, or attending drug-free concerts or dances. If you arrange for students to present their speeches to younger students, make sure the style and content of the speeches are age appropriate.

FIGURE 19 Participating in a band helps these teens make friends, build self-confidence, and stay drug free.

Alternatives to Drugs Turning to drugs to try to feel good or to deal with problems is a risky choice. Imagine how you would feel if you had to tell lies, hide your physical condition, worry about police, and deal with the drug's side effects. People who become dependent on drugs spend almost all of their time either thinking about drugs, getting the money for drugs, or taking drugs. Drugs end up controlling their lives. By deciding not to use drugs, you can stay in control of your life.

There are many healthy and constructive activities that can lift your mood and help you handle the pressures in your life. In addition, you may make new friends who share your commitment to stay drug free.

▶ **Engage in physical activity.** Physical activity boosts your mood and relieves the negative effects of stress. Getting enough exercise and getting involved in sports can help you feel energetic, positive, and self-confident.

▶ **Volunteer.** Helping other people can give you a good feeling about yourself, too. Many social service agencies need volunteers. You can read to someone with a visual handicap, visit elderly people in a nursing facility, or teach a hobby or sport to young children.

▶ **Join a youth group.** Youth group leaders serve as role models and help you explore your values in a supportive environment. Youth groups often participate in community service projects. Participating in a youth group can give you a sense of belonging and a connection to others.

Section 4 Review

Key Ideas and Vocabulary
1. What are three options for drug abuse treatment?
2. Describe a **therapeutic community.** Identify two ways it helps drug abusers overcome their problems.
3. What are three steps you can take to stay away from drugs?

Critical Thinking
4. **Applying Concepts** What activities do you participate in that keep you away from drugs?

Health at School

Drug Prevention Speech Prepare a 5-minute speech for sixth graders about healthy alternatives to drug use. Use examples that will relate to this age group. Also pay attention to the style of speech that will most appeal to them. Practice your speech with friends and get suggestions for improvements. **WRITING**

5. **Comparing and Contrasting** How are detoxification and medication treatment programs similar? How are they different? **WRITING**

🔊 GO ONLINE PearsonSuccessNet.com   Audio Summary Section 17.4

Section 4 Review

1. detoxification, therapeutic communities, and supervised medication
2. It is a residential treatment center where former drug abusers live together without the drug. It helps drug abusers adjust to drug-free lives and recognize and correct negative behaviors associated with their drug use.
3. refuse drugs, seek help for stress and other problems, and practice healthy alternatives to drug abuse
4. *Sample answer:* playing sports, volunteering, participating in a youth group
5. Both help treat drug abuse under medical supervision. Detoxification involves complete withdrawal from the abused drug. Medication treatment involves replacing the abused drug with a drug that prevents withdrawal symptoms and craving.

Chapter 17
At a Glance

VIDEO **TEENS** Talk ⊙
The Risks of Drug Abuse What did you learn from the video about the risks of drug abuse?

Section 1   Legal and Illegal Drugs

Key Ideas

▶ Drug abuse occurs when people intentionally use any kind of drugs for nonmedical purposes.

▶ Many psychoactive drugs trigger activity along a pathway of neurons in the brain called the "reward pathway."

▶ When drugs are misused or abused, many serious health effects can result.

▶ Drug abusers risk facing serious legal penalties, damaging their relationships with family and friends, and causing significant costs to society.

Vocabulary
- medicine (426) • over-the-counter drug (426)
- prescription drug (427) • illegal drug (427)
- drug misuse (427) • drug abuse (427)
- psychoactive drug (428) • side effect (429)
- drug antagonism (430) • drug synergism (430)

Section 2   Factors Affecting Drug Abuse

Key Ideas

▶ A number of factors make it either more or less likely that a teen will abuse drugs. They include family factors, social factors, and personal factors.

▶ Having strong protective factors in your life will help you stay drug free.

Vocabulary
- protective factor (436)

Section 3   Commonly Abused Drugs

Key Ideas

▶ Depressants slow body functions by decreasing heart and breathing rates and lowering blood pressure.

▶ Stimulants increase heart rate, blood pressure, breathing rate, and alertness.

▶ Hallucinogens overload the brain with sensory information, causing a distorted sense of reality.

▶ Marijuana is one of the most frequently abused psychoactive drugs.

▶ Three classes of drugs that are of growing concern in recent years are club drugs, inhalants, and anabolic steroids.

Vocabulary
- depressant (440) • barbiturate (440) • opiate (441)
- heroin (441) • stimulant (442) • amphetamines (442)
- methamphetamine (442) • cocaine (443)
- hallucinogen (443) • marijuana (445)
- club drugs (446) • inhalant (447)

Section 4   Choosing to Be Drug Free

Key Ideas

▶ Treatment options for drug abusers include detoxification, therapeutic communities, and supervised medication.

▶ Practicing refusal skills, seeking help when you need it, and getting involved in drug-free activities can help you stay away from drugs.

Vocabulary
- therapeutic community (450)

Preventing Drug Abuse **453**

Chapter 17
At a Glance

VIDEO **The Risks of Drug Abuse** Ask for volunteers to share their answers. Use examples from the video to review risks of drug abuse.

Key Ideas Review

L2 Have students rewrite the bold-faced sentences in their own words on separate slips of paper. Ask them to shuffle and exchange their slips of paper with those of a partner. Students should try to match their partner's reworded sentences with the original sentences in the text. Partners can work together to revise any sentences that are incomplete or inaccurate.

L3 Turn each key idea on this page into a question, and call on students at random to answer the questions. Call on additional students as needed until each question has been answered correctly.

Vocabulary Review

L1 Ask students to find all the bold-faced terms in the chapter and copy each term on the front of an index card and its definition on the back. Have pairs of students use their cards to quiz each other on the terms.

L2 Have small groups of students play a quiz game in which one student acts as the moderator and reads definitions of chapter vocabulary terms and the other students try to identify the terms. Ask students to take turns being the moderator so all students in the group have a chance to identify terms.

Chapter 17 Review

 GO ONLINE

PearsonSuccessNet.com

Students can go online for a review activity on Chapter 17.

Reviewing Key Ideas

Section 1

1. c

2. Drug addiction changes the structure and chemistry of the brain.

3. Drug antagonism occurs when each drug's effect is canceled out or reduced by the other. Drug synergism occurs when drugs interact to produce effects greater than those that each drug would produce alone.

4. The drugs cross the placenta, the membrane separating the baby's blood from the mother's blood.

5. It is a crime to produce, possess, transport, or sell illegal drugs, such as methamphetamine or marijuana. In addition, many drug abusers commit other crimes, such as shoplifting and robbery, to support their drug habit.

Section 2

6. c

7. *Sample answer:* Examples of social risk factors are associating with peers who use drugs, having role models that use drugs, and feeling competitive pressure to use drugs. Examples of social protective factors are having strong bonds to school and other community institutions, associating with peers who are drug free, and having friends who are supportive and accepting.

8. They are healthy alternatives for dealing with stress, and stress is a risk factor for drug use.

Section 3

9. a

10. A flashback is an unexpected reoccurrence of a bad trip. It occurs with hallucinogenic drugs.

11. Immediate effects include distorted perceptions, difficulties with thinking and problem solving, loss of motor coordination, increased heart rate, feelings of anxiety or paranoia, and drowsiness. Long-term effects include

---

Chapter 17 Review

Reviewing Key Ideas

Section 1

1. Unwanted physical and mental effects caused by a drug are called
  a. psychoactive effects.
  b. withdrawal symptoms.
  c. side effects.
  d. tolerance.

2. How does drug addiction affect the brain?

3. Contrast two kinds of drug interactions.

4. How do drugs taken by a pregnant woman reach the fetus?

5. Critical Thinking In what ways are drug abuse and crime linked? Give at least three examples.

Section 2

6. Something that reduces a person's potential for harmful behavior is called a
  a. risk factor.
  b. social factor.
  c. protective factor.
  d. personal belief.

7. Give three examples of social risk factors and three examples of social protective factors for drug use.

8. Critical Thinking Explain why you think good stress management skills are a protective factor against drug use.

Section 3

9. Drugs that slow body functions are called
  a. depressants.
  b. stimulants.
  c. hallucinogens.
  d. club drugs.

10. What is a flashback and with which category of drugs does it occur?

11. What are the immediate and long-term effects of smoking marijuana?

12. Critical Thinking Is a drug dangerous only if it is addictive? Explain your position. **WRITING**

 GO ONLINE

PearsonSuccessNet.com
For: Chapter 17 review activity

Section 4

13. The objective of supervised medication in treating drug addicts is to
  a. provide a safe "high."
  b. prevent withdrawal symptoms and cravings.
  c. produce a controlled form of addiction.
  d. increase side effects.

14. Where can drug treatment programs be found for little or no cost?

15. Why does detoxification require close medical supervision?

16. List three alternative activities to doing drugs.

17. Critical Thinking Analyze the risks and benefits of a drug replacement such as methadone. When would the benefits outweigh the risks? **WRITING**

Building Health Skills

18. Analyzing Influences Studies show that students who regularly abuse drugs tend to get lower grades in school and are more likely to lie or steal. Why do you think this is true?

19. Making Decisions If you were an editor of a teen magazine, would you print a story about a movie star who overdoses on illegal drugs? Explain your answer. **WRITING**

20. Communicating How might you tell a friend that you suspect he or she is abusing drugs?

21. Setting Goals Pick an area of your life in which you feel you could add a protective factor for drug abuse. Write a goal to work on—for example, "Always let mom know where I'm going." Monitor your progress over the course of the school year.

Health and Community

Club Drugs Warning Write a public service announcement that warns people of the dangers of Ecstasy and other club drugs. Consider the audience you want to address. Choose words and images that best reach that audience. **WRITING**

---

permanent changes in the brain, damage to short-term memory, loss of motivation, and increased risk of certain cancers.

12. *Sample answer:* No; most drugs have the potential to cause dangerous side effects, drug interactions, or other risks if misused or abused.

Section 4

13. b

14. community hospitals, school and government programs

15. because withdrawal symptoms may be painful or dangerous

16. *Sample answer:* participating in a sport, becoming involved in a school club, or going to the movies

17. *Sample answer:* Risks: dependency and liver damage; Benefits: preventing withdrawal symptoms and craving for heroin. Benefits would outweigh the risks when fear of withdrawal symptoms prevents heroin addicts from giving up heroin.

Standardized Test Prep

Math Practice

The graphs below track changes in marijuana use and perceptions of marijuana risk among tenth and twelfth graders. Use the graphs to answer Questions 22–24.

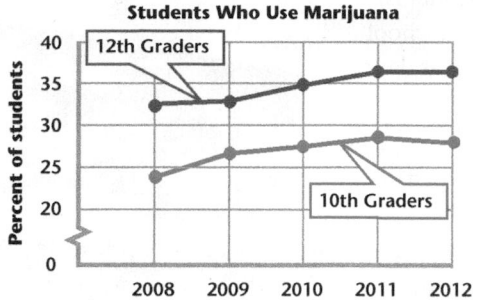

Students Who Use Marijuana

22. In what year was marijuana abuse by tenth and twelfth graders at its lowest level?
    A 2008   **B** 2009
    C 2010   **D** 2011

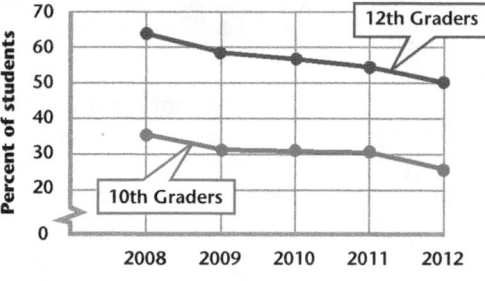

Students Who Agree Marijuana Use Is High Risk

23. In what year did most tenth and twelfth graders agree that marijuana use is high risk?
    F 2008   **G** 2009
    H 2010   **J** 2012

24. What phrase best summarizes the general trend shown by the graphs?
    A Marijuana abuse rises as perception of its risk falls.
    B More More tenth graders agree that marijuana use is high risk than do twelfth graders.
    C Marijuana use harmed more students in 2008 than in 2012.
    D Teaching youth the risks of marijuana use will make them want to try marijuana.

Reading and Writing Practice

Read the passage. Then answer Questions 25–27.

Many rewarding activities of everyday life, such as laughing with friends or winning a game, raise dopamine levels in the brain. Many psychoactive drugs "hijack" this natural process—the drugs synthetically boost dopamine concentration to unnaturally high levels, causing intense euphoria and the desire for more. Consequently, over time, other previously pleasurable activities like hobbies and athletics can lose their appeal. People who are addicted to drugs organize their lives around the drug use because their brains have been tricked into valuing drugs more than anything else.

25. From the context of this passage, what is the best synonym for euphoria?
    A confusion
    B aggression
    C hallucination
    D pleasure

26. According to this passage,
    F drug addiction releases a toxic chemical into the brain.
    G drugs are the only way to feel pleasure.
    H drug addicts can make a full recovery.
    J drugs interfere with a natural process in an unhealthy way.

Constructed Response

27. Addiction has been called a "disease of the brain." How does this passage support this view? Explain.

> **Test-Taking Tip**
>
> **Plan to study for your test well ahead of time. Avoid "cramming" for a test the night before. Your brain is more likely to retain and synthesize information if you study over a longer period of time.**

Standardized Test Prep

Math Practice
22. D
23. F
24. A

Reading and Writing Practice
25. D
26. J
27. Drug abuse causes changes in the brain that lead the drug user to want more of the drug. Once the brain changes, it is very difficult for the abuser to stop craving the drug.

Building Health Skills

18. *Sample answer:* Drug abuse may take time away from going to class and studying, lead to loss of motivation to do well in school, and cause changes in the brain that make it harder to learn.

19. *Sample answers:* I might print the story, but only if it was written in a way that played up the dangers of doing drugs.

20. Answers will vary but should follow the steps outlined on page 439: express your concern, help your friend face facts, describe your feelings, don't criticize or argue, and offer specific help.

21. Answers will vary but should reflect an understanding of factors that help protect against drug abuse.

Health and Community

Club Drugs Warning Students should address older teens and young adults who go to clubs, because these are the people who are most exposed to and likely to use club drugs. Images and words should appeal to this audience. For example, students might show a group of young adults having fun in the evening in the absence of drugs.

Focus on ISSUES

Should Students Be Tested for Alcohol Use Before School Events?

Teaching Strategies

- Ask students to describe their school's alcohol-testing policy. Is testing required before certain events? If so, which events, and what are the consequences of testing positive? (Students may or may not know their school's policy. Share it with them if they do not.) Call on a few volunteers to state their personal opinions about their school's alcohol-testing policy.

- Have students read pages 456–457. You may want to have students answer the questions on page 457 as a homework assignment so they will have more time to think about the issue.

- After students answer the questions on page 457, discuss the issue in class. Start the discussion by calling on a few volunteers on each side of the issue to read their answers to question 3. Encourage other students to offer additional reasons. Add any other reasons students fail to mention.

- After the discussion, take a class vote on the issue. Call on a few students to state their opinions and whether the discussion changed how they feel about the issue.

Focus on ISSUES

Should Students Be Tested for Alcohol Use Before School Events?

Even though underage drinking is illegal, alcohol is the most commonly abused drug among high school students. Drinking before school events, such as dances and sporting events, is a growing problem.

Some schools now require students to take a breath-alcohol test before they can enter school events. This gives school administrators an unbiased and consistent procedure for screening all students. Penalties range from contacting parents to suspension. Is a breath-alcohol test an effective way to reduce student drinking?

For Your INFORMATION!

Alcohol Testing in High Schools

Some high schools have tested students for alcohol before proms and similar school events for years. Testing generally reduces drinking by attendees to near zero. However, several programs have been challenged in courts, and the results of the challenges have been mixed. For example, the Pennsylvania Supreme Court ruled that alcohol testing at school events is not legal unless there is some reason to suspect that students have been drinking. The New Jersey Supreme Court ruled that alcohol testing at school events is legal if there is a documented alcohol problem at the school. As more schools adopt alcohol testing, it is likely that more legal challenges will be made.

456

The Case for Alcohol Testing

School districts that test for alcohol use have seen significant reductions in student drinking before school events. Alcohol testing clearly reinforces the school's "zero tolerance policy" for underage drinking. Testing might not stop every student from drinking. However, a strict testing policy significantly reduces the number of injuries and behavior problems that result from drinking.

" I think it's a great idea to test everyone. Last year, I worked for months to earn enough money for the prom. That night, a few kids showed up drunk and got rowdy. It was horrible. This year, my school plans to test everyone at the entrance to the prom. Anyone testing positive will have to wait outside with a teacher for their parents to pick them up. I'm sure everyone will have a much better time this year. And I'll feel safer on the roads driving home. "

The Case Against Alcohol Testing

Alcohol testing may prevent students from drinking before school events, but it doesn't address the core problem. Schools should spend their time and money educating and counseling students about the dangers of underage drinking in general. If students know the facts, they will be able to make smarter decisions.

" Alcohol-testing policies punish all of us for the actions of a few. Just because some students may make bad decisions, it's not fair to treat all of us like criminals. Testing makes me feel that my privacy is being invaded and that school officials have no trust in us. Who will want to attend a school event knowing that you'll have to wait in a long line? Besides, testing won't stop those who want to drink from doing so. They just won't show up at school events. "

What do **YOU** think?

Use these steps to analyze and express your opinion about alcohol testing.

1. Analyze the Issue Carefully consider both sides of the issue. Make a table listing the pros and cons of alcohol testing at school events.

2. Consider Your Values Suppose your friend tested positive and was refused entrance to a school event. How would you feel? How would you react?

3. Take a Stand Write a paragraph expressing your opinion about alcohol testing at school events. Make sure you state your opinion clearly and offer several strong supporting reasons. **WRITING**

457

What do **YOU** think?

1. Students' tables will vary. Pros might include reducing alcohol-related behavior problems at school events and decreasing the risk of alcohol-related injuries. Cons might include invading students' privacy and creating an atmosphere of distrust between students and school officials.
2. *Sample answer:* I would feel sorry for my friend and disappointed that she had been drinking. I would react by making sure she got home safely and trying to convince her not to drink again.
3. Students may take a stand on either side of the issue, as long as they provide adequate support for their position. For example, students who favor testing might argue that it prevents disruptive behavior at school events or that students should expect to give up some of their rights at school events. Students who are opposed to testing might argue that it unfairly targets all students, not just those who are suspected of drinking, or that testing is an unconstitutional invasion of privacy.

GO ONLINE

PearsonSuccessNet.com

Visit Pearson SuccessNet to access more on alcohol testing at school events.

Section Objectives	Standards Correlation	Instructional Resources (L3)	SE eTEXT	TE eTEXT	PRINT
1 **The Endocrine System** ⏱ 1 period; 1/2 block **18.1.1** **Describe** the general roles of the endocrine system. **18.1.2** **Identify** the glands of the endocrine system.	NHES: 1.12.2, 3.12.2	SE Warm-Up, p. 460	•	•	•
		RN Note Taking Guide 18-1	•	•	•
		IB Image Bank 18-2		•	
		TR Practice 18-1		•	
		TR Section 18-1 Quiz		•	
2 **The Male Reproductive System** ⏱ 1 period; 1/2 block **18.2.1** **Describe** three functions of the male reproductive system. **18.2.2** **Identify** five ways to keep the male reproductive system healthy.	NHES: 1.12.5, 3.12.1, 3.12.4, 7.12.2, 8.12.2	SE Warm-Up, p. 464	•	•	•
		RN Note Taking Guide 18-2	•	•	•
		IB Image Bank 18-3, 18-4		•	
		TR Practice 18-2		•	
		TR Section 18-2 Quiz		•	
3 **The Female Reproductive System** ⏱ 2 periods; 1 block **18.3.1** **Describe** three functions of the female reproductive system. **18.3.2** **Summarize** the stages of the menstrual cycle. **18.3.3** **Identify** five ways to keep the female reproductive system healthy.	NHES: 1.12.5, 2.12.5, 2.12.6, 3.12.2, 3.12.4, 7.12.2	SE Warm-Up, p. 469	•	•	•
		SE Media Wise Sexuality in Music Videos, p. 471	•	•	•
		RN Note Taking Guide 18-3	•	•	•
		IB Image Bank 18-7, 18-8		•	
		TR Practice 18-3		•	
		TR Section 18-3 Quiz		•	
Breast and Testicular Self-Exams ⏱ 1 period; 1/2 block **BHS.18** **Demonstrate** healthful behaviors by doing breast or testicular self-exams to detect cancer.	NHES: 1.12.4, 7.12.1, 7.12.2, 7.12.3	SE Practice the Skill, p. 477	•	•	•
		RN Building Health Skills 18	•	•	•
4 **Heredity** ⏱ 1 period; 1/2 block **18.4.1** **Explain** how genetic information passes from one generation to the next. **18.4.2** **Identify** the causes of genetic disorders. **18.4.3** **Compare** the role of genes, environment, and behavior in affecting a person's risk for disease.	NHES: 1.12.1, 1.12.3, 1.12.4, 2.12.6, 7.12.1, 8.12.4	SE Warm-Up, p. 478	•	•	•
		RN Note Taking Guide 18-4	•	•	•
		IB Image Bank 18-13		•	
		TR Practice 18-4		•	
		TR Section 18-4 Quiz		•	

Chapter Review and Assessment

SE Chapter 18 Review, p. 483 (L3)

CTB Chapter 18 Test (L2) (L3) (L4)

SE Standardized Test Prep, p. 485 (L3)

PROGRAM COMPONENTS

SE	Student Edition	CTB	Computer Test Bank
TE	Teacher Edition	AUD	Audio Section Summaries
TR	Teaching Resources		
RN	Reading and Note Taking Guide	DVD	Teens Talk Video Series
ARN	Adapted Reading and Note Taking Guide	VVG	Video Viewing Guide
		PPT	Presentation
IB	Image Bank		

Differentiated Instruction

L1 L2 L4 EL

		SE eTEXT	TE eTEXT	PRINT
ARN	Note Taking Guide 18-1 L2	•	•	
RN	Note Taking Guide 18-1 EL	•	•	•
AUD	Audio Summary 18-1 L1 L2 EL	•	•	
TE	Reteach Strategy, p. 463 L2		•	•
TR	Enrich 18-1 L4		•	
ARN	Note Taking Guide 18-2 L2	•	•	
RN	Note Taking Guide 18-2 EL	•	•	•
AUD	Audio Summary 18-2 L1 L2 EL	•	•	
TE	Reteach Strategy, p. 468 L2		•	•
TR	Enrich 18-2 L4		•	
ARN	Note Taking Guide 18-3 L2	•	•	
RN	Note Taking Guide 18-3 EL	•	•	•
AUD	Audio Summary 18-3 L1 L2 EL	•	•	
TE	Reteach Strategy, p. 475 L2		•	•
TR	Enrich 18-3 L4		•	
ARN	Building Health Skills 18 L2	•	•	
RN	Building Health Skills 18 EL	•	•	•
ARN	Note Taking Guide 18-4 L2	•	•	
RN	Note Taking Guide 18-4 EL	•	•	•
AUD	Audio Summary 18-4 L1 L2 EL	•	•	
TE	Reteach Strategy, p. 482 L2		•	•
TR	Enrich 18-4 L4		•	

ABILITY LEVELS

L1 For students with special needs
L2 For less proficient readers
L3 For all students
L4 For gifted and talented students
EL For English language learners

Chapter 18 Digital/Video Pathway

This alternative pathway allows you to teach this chapter's content using only the video and online materials.

Preview

DVD Video #18 Preview
SE Video #18 Preview Activity
VVG Video #18 Worksheet

Hormones in the Balance

1
DVD Video #18 Explore/Wrap-Up
VVG Video #18 Worksheet
PPT 18-1 Presentation
RN/ARN 18-1 Note Taking
PPT 18-1 Section Quiz

Hormones in the Balance

2
PPT 18-2 Presentation
RN/ARN 18-2 Note Taking
PPT 18-2 Section Quiz

3
PPT 18-3 Presentation
RN/ARN 18-3 Note Taking
PPT 18-3 Section Quiz

4
PPT 18-4 Presentation
RN/ARN 18-4 Note Taking
PPT 18-4 Section Quiz

Chapter Preview

Section 1 The Endocrine System
The endocrine system consists of glands such as the pituitary and thyroid glands. Endocrine glands control many of the body's long-term changes and daily activities.

Section 2 The Male Reproductive System
Functions of the male reproductive system are to produce sex hormones, produce and store sperm, and deliver sperm to the female reproductive system. Caring for the system includes cleanliness, self-exams, and regular medical checkups.

Section 3 The Female Reproductive System
Functions of the female reproductive system are to produce sex hormones, produce eggs, and nourish a developing baby. Eggs are released during the menstrual cycle. Caring for the system includes cleanliness, self-exams, and regular medical checkups.

 Practicing Healthful Behaviors
Breast and Testicular Self-Exams
Doing regular breast or testicular self-exams can help detect cancer early when it is easier to treat.

Section 4 Heredity
Heredity is the passing of biological traits from parent to child. Genetic disorders are caused by the inheritance of abnormal genes or chromosomes. The environment and behavior, more than genes, affect the risk of most other diseases.

GO ONLINE
PearsonSuccessNet.com
For resources and activities for this chapter.

Reproduction and Heredity

GO ONLINE PearsonSuccessNet.com

TEENS Talk

VIDEO 18

Hormones in the Balance

Preview **Activity**

What Are Hormones?

Complete this activity before you watch the video.

1. When you hear the word *hormone*, what things do you think about? Jot down your impressions of what hormones are and what they do.
2. Based on what you know, write a definition for *hormone*.
3. Compare your answers with a partner. Then revise your definition. **WRITING**

458

🚩 **Sensitive Issues**
- Reproduction is likely to be a sensitive issue for many students because of its association with sexual activity. Some students may hide their own sensitivity—or exploit that of others—by making crude comments or laughing inappropriately. Try to stem this behavior to make the issue less sensitive for other students.

- You should also be aware of cultural differences that might make the issue especially sensitive for some students. For example, students from certain cultural backgrounds may feel very uncomfortable discussing reproduction in class, because in their culture, adults do not typically talk to young people about issues related to sex.

Video Objectives

Use this video to help students

Recognize that changes in hormone levels are responsible for many of the body's changes during puberty.

Describe two kinds of hormone disorders.

Avoid behaviors that can negatively impact hormone balance and lifelong health.

Preview **Activity**

What Are Hormones?

Assign the Preview Activity in class before showing the video. After students complete the activity, ask three or four of the teams to share their revised definitions with the class. Then ask students what they know about the roles hormones play in the body. If students have trouble understanding the basics of hormones, it might be helpful to preview Section 1 before showing the video.

459

From the Authors

Students may be more willing to discuss issues related to human reproduction and sexuality if they know appropriate terminology. One challenge in teaching these topics is the existence of multiple words to refer to structures of the male and female reproductive systems. The words include scientific terms, euphemisms learned in childhood, and slang words that are used "on the street."

This chapter is most appropriately taught using scientific terms. Discourage the use of euphemistic or "street" words by students. Encouraging the use of scientific terms will help students show respect for each other. It will also help them view the reproductive anatomy and processes more like they do other biological processes in the body.

1. Focus

Warm-Up Health Stats

Call on students to describe in words the trends in growth rates shown in the graph. Ask students to stand to facilitate comparison of heights of boys and girls in the class. Class gender differences are likely to be similar to the gender differences in the graph. Ask students what might explain the gender differences.

Presentation 18-1

> **Sensitive Issues**
> This section introduces puberty, which may be a sensitive issue to students who are at or near puberty. These students may be self-conscious about the obvious physical changes they are experiencing. Take care in asking students to relate the content to personal experience. They may not be comfortable doing this.

Section 1

The Endocrine System

Objectives
► **Describe** the general roles of the endocrine system.
► **Identify** the glands of the endocrine system.

Vocabulary
• endocrine gland
• hormone
• hypothalamus
• pituitary gland
• puberty

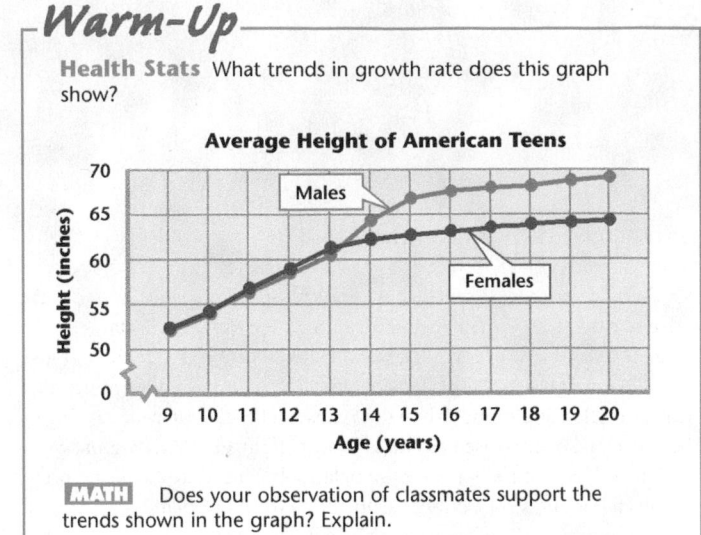

Warm-Up

Health Stats What trends in growth rate does this graph show?

Average Height of American Teens

MATH Does your observation of classmates support the trends shown in the graph? Explain.

What Is the Endocrine System?

How much have you grown in the past year? When will you reach your adult height? Your growth rate is one of the many functions controlled by your body's endocrine system. **The endocrine system regulates long-term changes in the body such as growth and development. It also controls many of your body's daily activities.** Two examples of daily activities include your body's use of energy from a meal and its response to stress.

Endocrine Glands Your endocrine system is made up of a group of organs, called endocrine glands (EN duh krin). An **endocrine gland** produces and releases chemical substances that signal changes in other parts of the body. Some of your body's glands, such as sweat glands, release their chemicals into tiny tubes called ducts. The ducts carry the chemicals to the place where they will be used. Endocrine glands, on the other hand, do not have ducts. Instead, they release substances directly into the bloodstream. The blood then carries those substances throughout the body.

MATH and Health

L3 Calculating Rates
You can use the data in the Warm-Up graph to give students a chance to practice calculating rates. Have them use the average heights of boys and girls at ages 12, 13, 14, and 15 years to calculate average annual rates of growth in height. (*For boys, the rates are 3 in/yr from ages 12 to* 13 yr, 4 in/yr from ages 13 to 14 yr, and 3 in/yr from ages 14 to 15 yr. For girls, the corresponding rates are 4 in/yr, 2 in/yr, and 1 in/yr, respectively.) Discuss how the rates give a different perspective on gender differences in growth by showing how fast growth occurs, rather than how much growth occurs.

Adrenaline directs your response to sudden stress or fear.

Testosterone controls beard growth in males.

Growth hormone regulates your growth to adult height.

FIGURE 1 Hormones play many roles in the body.

Hormones A chemical substance produced by an endocrine gland is known as a **hormone.** You can think of a hormone as a chemical messenger. Each hormone has a specific function and specific "targets" in the body. Once released into the bloodstream, a hormone travels to its target cells, where it turns on, turns off, speeds up, or slows down the activities of those cells. For example, targets of the hormone adrenaline include cells in your heart, muscles, and brain. Adrenaline causes a faster heartbeat, tensing of the muscles, and increased alertness—your "fight-or-flight" response.

The endocrine system is kept in balance by the coordinated action of various hormones. For example, a hormone from one gland may turn on the production of a different hormone by a second gland. In turn, the hormone from the second gland signals the first gland to stop releasing its hormone. By this system of checks and balances, the endocrine system keeps the body's activities functioning smoothly.

 **Connect to Your Life** Describe a time when you experienced a surge of adrenaline.

Functions of Endocrine Glands

Each of your endocrine glands plays a specific, important role in your body. **The endocrine glands include the hypothalamus, pituitary gland, thyroid gland, parathyroid glands, thymus gland, adrenal glands, pancreas, and reproductive glands.**

Hypothalamus The **hypothalamus** (hy poh THAL uh mus), an endocrine gland located in the brain, is actually part of both the nervous and the endocrine systems. For example, nerve signals from the hypothalamus control body temperature and feelings of sleep and hunger, and hormones from the hypothalamus control the body's water levels. The hypothalamus also produces a class of hormones called "releasing hormones" that signal the release of hormones from another region of the brain.

Reproduction and Heredity **461**

---

2. Teach

L3 EL Reading/Note Taking 18-1
L2 Adapted Reading/Note Taking 18-1

What Is the Endocrine System?

L2 Active Learning

Demonstrate with a simple role-play how an endocrine hormone acts as a chemical messenger. Explain that you will play the role of an endocrine gland. Select a nearby student to play the role of a hormone and a student across the room the role of a target cell. Write a note that reads, "When you get this note, raise your hand." Hand the note to the "hormone," and tell the "hormone" to carry it to the "target cell," who should respond by raising his or her hand. After the demonstration, call on volunteers to describe the role of an endocrine hormone, based on what they observed.

EL Class Discussion

For students who are having trouble understanding the role of endocrine glands, use an analogy. Have students describe the relationship between a conductor and an orchestra. *(The conductor signals the orchestra how to play.)* Discuss how endocrine glands regulate body functions in a similar way.

 **Connect to Your Life** *Sample answer:* I experienced a surge of adrenaline when I rode on a roller coaster.

Functions of Endocrine Glands

L2 Active Learning

Have students create an eight-column, 3-row table. Along the first row, have them fill in the names of eight different endocrine glands (listed in the bold-faced sentence in their text). Tell them to fill in details about each of the glands in the next two rows—gland locations and functions—as they continue reading this section.

L2 Visual Learning: Figure 2

Image Bank Figure 18-2

Have pairs of students write the names of the endocrine glands on one set of index cards and the functions of the glands on another set of index cards, using information in the figure. Then have partners try to match the two sets of cards. Students should repeat the activity until they have learned the functions of all the endocrine glands. **Caption Answer** The adrenal glands are located on top of the kidneys. They release hormones that trigger the body's response to sudden stress, affect salt and water balance in the kidneys, and influence general metabolism.

L3 Building Health Skills

Accessing Information Have students assume they have been feeling unusually tired for no apparent reason. As a homework assignment, ask them to use a library reference book (e.g., medical encyclopedia) to find out (1) whether tiredness can be a symptom of a thyroid problem, and (2) what type of doctor treats thyroid problems. During the next class, call on volunteers to share what they learned. *(Tiredness can be a symptom of hypothyroidism, or inadequate thyroid hormone. Endocrinologists treat thyroid problems and problems of other endocrine glands.)* Ask: **How could you locate an endocrinologist in your community?** *(Sample answers: Look in the yellow pages of the local telephone directory; ask your family doctor.)*

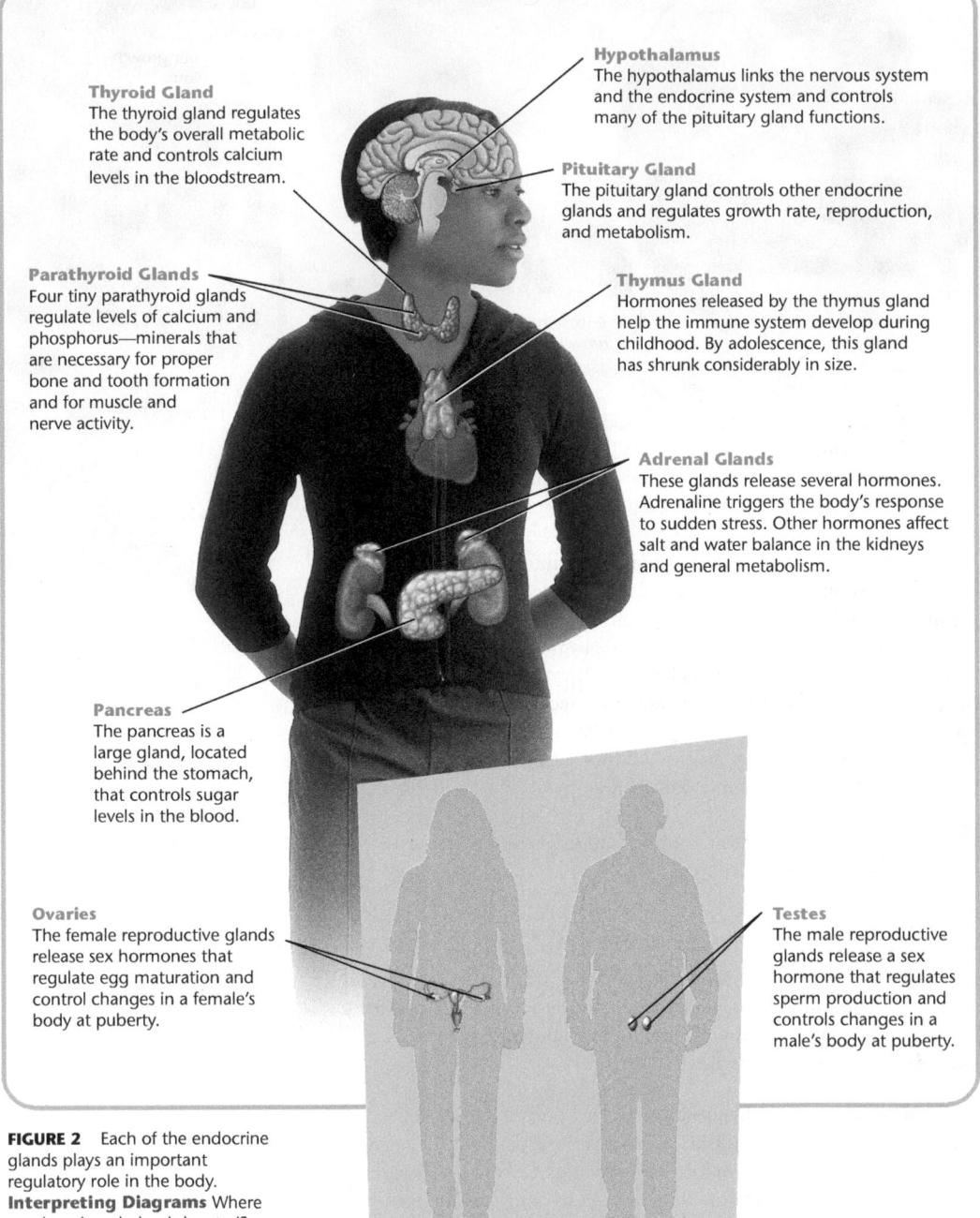

The Endocrine System

Hypothalamus
The hypothalamus links the nervous system and the endocrine system and controls many of the pituitary gland functions.

Thyroid Gland
The thyroid gland regulates the body's overall metabolic rate and controls calcium levels in the bloodstream.

Pituitary Gland
The pituitary gland controls other endocrine glands and regulates growth rate, reproduction, and metabolism.

Parathyroid Glands
Four tiny parathyroid glands regulate levels of calcium and phosphorus—minerals that are necessary for proper bone and tooth formation and for muscle and nerve activity.

Thymus Gland
Hormones released by the thymus gland help the immune system develop during childhood. By adolescence, this gland has shrunk considerably in size.

Adrenal Glands
These glands release several hormones. Adrenaline triggers the body's response to sudden stress. Other hormones affect salt and water balance in the kidneys and general metabolism.

Pancreas
The pancreas is a large gland, located behind the stomach, that controls sugar levels in the blood.

Ovaries
The female reproductive glands release sex hormones that regulate egg maturation and control changes in a female's body at puberty.

Testes
The male reproductive glands release a sex hormone that regulates sperm production and controls changes in a male's body at puberty.

FIGURE 2 Each of the endocrine glands plays an important regulatory role in the body. **Interpreting Diagrams** Where are the adrenal glands located? What is their function?

Female   **Male**

462 *Chapter 18*

TEENS *Are Asking . . .*

Q: I'm the youngest boy in my class. I always used to be about as tall as my friends, but now they are all at least three inches taller. Will I always be shorter than my friends?

A: If you were as tall as your friends throughout childhood, most likely you will be as tall as they are by the time you are an adult. At your age, you probably are about to begin a period of very rapid growth. You are likely to grow six or seven inches over the next couple of years. Most likely, your friends, who are older, have already begun this period of very rapid growth. Try to be patient—you will probably catch up with your friends soon. If you are still worried about your height, you should talk with a doctor about your concerns.

Pituitary Gland "Releasing hormones" from the hypothalamus signal the release of hormones from a pea-sized endocrine gland in the brain, called the **pituitary gland** (pih TOO ih tehr ee). The pituitary controls many of your body's functions. These functions include growth, reproduction, and metabolism. Metabolism is the process by which you obtain energy from food.

Some pituitary hormones act as "on" switches for other endocrine glands. For example, one pituitary hormone signals the thyroid gland to release hormones essential for normal metabolism. Other pituitary hormones control body activities directly. For example, growth hormone released by the pituitary gland regulates growth throughout your body from infancy to adulthood.

Other Endocrine Glands Endocrine glands are found throughout the body, as shown in Figure 2. Notice the range of body functions that your endocrine system controls—from your blood sugar level over the course of a day to the long-term changes in your body that you experience as a teen.

The reproductive glands are an important part of the endocrine system. In males, the reproductive glands consist of two testes, and in females, two ovaries. The reproductive glands work at low levels in both boys and girls until about the age of ten, when puberty typically begins. **Puberty** is the period of sexual development during which a person becomes sexually mature and physically able to reproduce.

Puberty starts when the hypothalamus signals the pituitary gland to begin producing two hormones. Those hormones in turn signal the reproductive glands to produce sex hormones. Sex hormones activate several changes in your outward appearance during puberty. Sex hormones also control reproductive functions inside your body. You will learn more about the reproductive glands and their hormones in the next two sections.

> **GO ONLINE**
> PearsonSuccessNet.com
> **For:** More on endocrine glands

Section 1 Review

Key Ideas and Vocabulary

1. What roles does the endocrine system play in the body?
2. What is a **hormone**? Explain how hormones reach the cells where they have their effect.
3. List the glands of the endocrine system.
4. What is the **hypothalamus**? How does it interact with the **pituitary gland**?

Critical Thinking

5. **Relating Cause and Effect** How is the onset of puberty related to the endocrine system?

Health at School

Adrenaline in Action Interview a musician or an athlete at your school about the role that adrenaline might play during a performance or game. Find out the conditions under which they have noticed this response and whether it helped their performance. Write a transcript of your interview. **WRITING**

---

6. **Applying Concepts** A driver brakes suddenly when a dog darts out in front of her car. How did the endocrine system aid her quick response?

 GO ONLINE PearsonSuccessNet.com   Audio Summary Section 18.1

Reproduction and Heredity **463**

Online Activity  GO ONLINE
Visit Pearson SuccessNet to access more information about coping with stress. Have students complete the Web activity.

3. Assess

Evaluate
These assignments can help you assess students' mastery of the section content.

Section 1 Review
Answers appear below.

Teaching Resources
• Practice 18-1
• Section 18-1 Quiz

Reteach
Play a quiz game in which you describe the functions of the endocrine glands and students try to name the glands. Go around the room, calling on one student after another, until most students show mastery of the information.

Enrich

Teaching Resources
• Enrich 18-1

Health at School

Adrenaline in Action Students can interview anyone who has ever had "butterflies" in the stomach or a racing heart because of an upcoming performance. Such a reaction can either help or hinder a performance, depending on the individual. Students can record the interview (with the interviewee's permission) and play it back later to transcribe it.

Section 1 Review

1. It regulates long-term changes in the body, such as growth and development, and controls many of the body's daily activities.

2. A hormone is a chemical substance produced by an endocrine gland. Hormones travel through the bloodstream to reach target cells.

3. hypothalamus, pituitary gland, thymus gland, adrenal glands, thyroid gland, parathyroid glands, pancreas, and ovaries or testes

4. The hypothalamus is an endocrine gland located in the brain. It produces hormones called "releasing hormones" that signal the pituitary gland to release its hormones.

5. Puberty starts when the hypothalamus signals the pituitary gland to begin producing two hormones. Those hormones in turn signal the reproductive glands to produce sex hormones. Sex hormones activate several changes in outward appearance and inside the body.

6. The adrenal glands released adrenaline, which increased alertness.

Section 2

The Male Reproductive System

Objectives
Before class begins, write the objectives on the board. Have students copy the objectives into their notebooks at the start of class.

1. Focus

Warm-Up Myth/Fact

After students do the writing assignment, ask a few volunteers to share what they wrote. Some reasons you might discuss if the students don't bring them up include: family or cultural attitudes that discourage frank discussion of reproductive functions, embarrassment that keeps them from asking questions regarding "private" areas of their bodies, and false information given by peers and the media. Discuss how the myths could affect the health of teenagers.

Presentation 18-2

Section 2

The Male Reproductive System

Objectives
▶ **Describe** three functions of the male reproductive system.
▶ **Identify** five ways to keep the male reproductive system healthy.

Vocabulary
- sperm
- fertilization
- testes
- testosterone
- scrotum
- penis
- semen
- ejaculation
- infertility

Warm-Up

Myth Cancers of the male reproductive system only affect older men.

Fact Cancer of the testes (testicular cancer) most often occurs in teens and young men.

WRITING Why do you think that teens may have a number of misconceptions about the reproductive system?

Structure and Function

One essential function of all living things is reproduction, the process by which organisms produce offspring. In humans, the process begins with the development of reproductive cells in the bodies of males and females. In males, the reproductive cells are called **sperm**. **The functions of the male reproductive system are to produce sex hormones, to produce and store sperm, and to deliver sperm to the female reproductive system.** There, a sperm cell may join with an egg in a process called **fertilization**. Under the right conditions, a fertilized egg develops into a baby.

Testes Look at Figure 3 to see the organs of the male reproductive system. Locate the two oval-shaped **testes** (TES teez), the male reproductive glands. The testes (singular, *testis*) have two major functions—the production of testosterone and the production of sperm. The sex hormone **testosterone** affects the production of sperm and signals certain physical changes at puberty, such as the growth of facial hair.

The testes, also called testicles, hang outside the main body cavity, within a sac of skin called the **scrotum**. Because they are located outside the body, the temperature of the testes is a few degrees lower than the temperature inside the body. Sperm need this lower temperature to develop properly and survive.

In some males, one or both of the testes may not descend into the scrotum before birth, a condition called *undescended testis*. Sperm will not develop properly in an undescended testis because the temperature is too high. The condition is also a risk factor for testicular cancer. Surgery is usually performed before age two to correct this condition.

464 *Chapter 18*

WRITING and Health

L3 Descriptive Writing
Have students describe male reproductive structures and their functions as though they are writing to inform an extraterrestrial alien—that is, someone who has no prior knowledge of human biology or reproduction. Students' descriptions should be clear, detailed, and complete, leaving nothing for readers to infer or imagine. This activity requires students to describe the male reproductive system so thoroughly that any gaps or misconceptions in their knowledge should be revealed to them as they write. Let students use their textbooks as needed to fill any gaps and correct any errors.

Penis The **penis** is the external sexual organ through which sperm leave the body. The tip of the penis is covered with loose skin, called the foreskin. In some males the foreskin is removed shortly after birth. This surgical procedure is known as circumcision. The decision to circumcise an infant is usually based on cultural or religious reasons.

Other Structures Besides the external structures of the male reproductive system, there are internal ducts and accessory glands that play an important role in storing and releasing sperm.

Sperm Production Once a male reaches puberty, millions of sperm are produced in his testes each day. Sperm production begins when the hypothalamus signals the pituitary gland to release two hormones—luteinizing hormone (LH) and follicle-stimulating hormone (FSH). LH signals the testes to begin making testosterone. Testosterone and FSH then signal the production of sperm. Sperm production continues throughout adulthood.

 **Why do you think some people are uncomfortable using the proper terms for reproductive structures?**

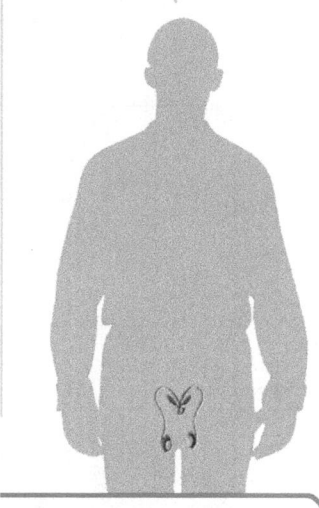

Male Reproductive System

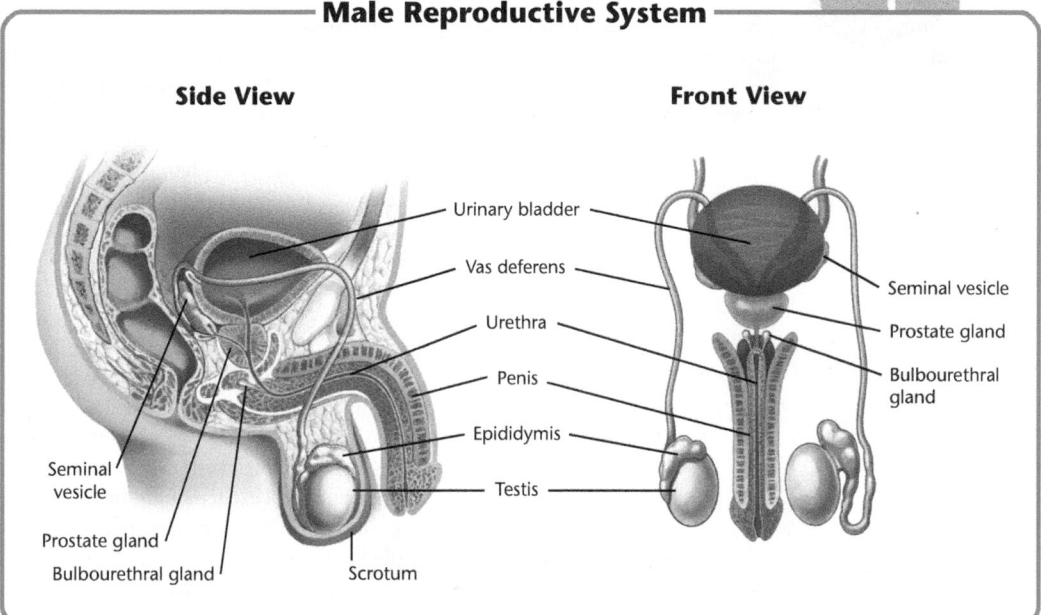

Side View

Front View

Urinary bladder

Vas deferens

Urethra

Penis

Epididymis

Testis

Seminal vesicle

Prostate gland

Bulbourethral gland

Seminal vesicle

Prostate gland

Bulbourethral gland

Scrotum

FIGURE 3 The male reproductive system produces, stores, and releases sperm.

Reproduction and Heredity **465**

---

2. Teach

L3 **EL** Reading/Note Taking 18-2

L2 Adapted Reading/Note Taking 18-2

Structure and Function

L2 **Class Discussion**

On the board, draw a flowchart entitled, "How Hormones Control Sperm Production." Draw three boxes labeled *Hypothalamus, Pituitary Gland,* and *Testis.* Remind students that the testis produces sperm. Draw an arrow from *Hypothalamus* to *Pituitary Gland,* and label it "Signal." Draw an arrow from *Pituitary Gland* to *Testis* and another from *Testis* back to itself. Ask students what hormones these two arrows represent. *(LH and FSH for the first arrow, testosterone for the second arrow)* Label the arrows, and call on students to describe the completed flowchart in their own words.

L3 **Visual Learning: Figure 3**

Image Bank Figure 18-3

Ask students to examine the figure and read the caption. Have them find the structures described in the text. *(testis, scrotum, penis)* Ask students to recall from Chapter 10 the functions of the urinary bladder and urethra. *(storing urine, carrying urine out of body)* Explain that the urethra also carries semen out of the body. Challenge students to predict the roles of remaining structures before they read about them. *(transporting, storing, and/or adding fluid to sperm)*

Connect to Your Life *Sample answer:* They are embarrassed to talk about the "private" parts of the body using proper terms, which are often unfamiliar and formal sounding. Using slang terms may be more comfortable because such terms are used more often by peers and in popular culture (in books, on TV, and so on) than the proper terms.

Differentiated Instruction

L2 **Less Proficient Readers**

Create a simple two-column table on the board to show students how to organize information about the male reproductive system. Explain that the table will help them sort the main ideas in a reading passage from the details. Label the columns *Structure* and *Function.* Fill in the first column with structures described in the text. Have students use the text to find the functions of these structures Add this information to the table. Urge students to use a similar strategy whenever they are reading a passage with many details.

⚫ Visual Learning: Figure 4
Image Bank Figure 18-4

Pair students of the same gender, and have partners work together to create a flowchart of the pathway of sperm, as described in the figure. Flowcharts should show all the structures that sperm pass through or near and what happens to the sperm at each structure. *(Sperm are produced in the testes; mature in the epididymis; travel through the vas deferens; combine with fluids from the seminal vesicles, bulbourethral glands, and prostate gland; and leave the body through the urethra in the penis.)* Set aside class time for pairs to work on the activity. Display their flowcharts in the classroom.
Caption Answer in the epididymis

⚫ Addressing Misconceptions

Sperm and Semen Students may have the misconception that semen contains only or mostly sperm. Explain that sperm cells are extremely tiny and contribute only a small amount to the total volume of semen. Instead, semen is made up mostly of fluids from the seminal vesicles, prostate gland, and bulbourethral glands. Ask: **Why are the fluids in semen important?** *(The fluids protect the sperm, provide them with energy, and help them pass through the urethra.)*

⚫ Teacher Demo

Borrow from a biology teacher a microscope and slide showing human sperm. Set up the slide for viewing by students with special needs to help concretize their understanding of sperm structure.

The Pathway of Sperm

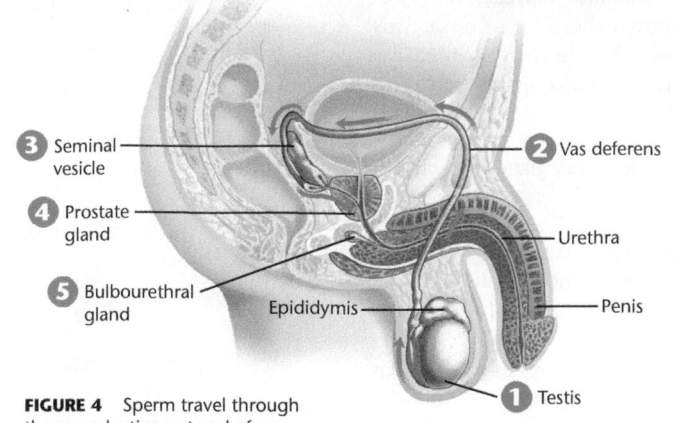

❸ Seminal vesicle
❹ Prostate gland
❺ Bulbourethral gland
❷ Vas deferens
Urethra
Epididymis
Penis
❶ Testis

FIGURE 4 Sperm travel through the reproductive system before they are released.
Interpreting Diagrams Where do sperm complete their maturation?

❶ Sperm are produced in the **testes**. They mature and are stored in the **epididymis**.

❷ Sperm travel through the **vas deferens** to the seminal vesicles.

❸ **Seminal vesicles** add a fluid that provides a source of energy for the active sperm.

❹ The **prostate gland** adds a fluid that protects the sperm.

❺ The **bulbourethral glands** add a fluid that protects sperm from acidic conditions in the **urethra**.

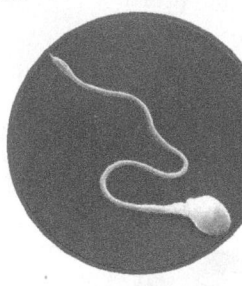

▲ **A sperm cell**

The Pathway of Sperm Look at Figure 4 to track the pathway of sperm through the male reproductive system. Note that during their passage through the male reproductive system, sperm cells mix with fluids produced by the prostate and two other glands. The mixture of sperm cells and these fluids is called **semen** (SEE mun).

Release of Sperm The ejection of semen from the penis is called **ejaculation.** Ejaculation occurs when muscles in the male reproductive system and at the base of the bladder contract, forcing semen through the urethra. The urethra—a tube that passes through the penis to the outside of the body—carries urine as well as sperm, but not at the same time. A valve within the urethra prevents the two fluids from mixing.

Several million sperm cells are released during one ejaculation. What happens to sperm that are not ejaculated? Sperm stored in the male reproductive system eventually degenerate, meaning they break down, and are disposed of.

Ejaculation can occur when the penis is in an erect state. An erection is a condition in which the penis becomes larger and stiffer as blood chambers in the penis become filled with blood. An erection does not need to result in ejaculation—in fact, most do not. Erections can be caused by different factors, including sexual excitement or tight clothing. Sometimes an erection may occur for no apparent reason at all. This is especially common during puberty.

It is also common for a teenage male to experience a nocturnal emission, or "wet dream," which is erection and ejaculation during sleep. Nocturnal emissions occur for various reasons, including sexually arousing dreams. They are a normal occurrence and may happen frequently. It is also normal not to experience nocturnal emissions.

466 *Chapter 18*

For Your INFORMATION!

Sperm Facts

• Humans have some of the smallest sperm cells among mammals. For example, human sperm are much smaller than the sperm of rats or mice.

• Sperm remain alive inside the female reproductive tract for an average of 24 to 48 hours. Some sperm may live longer, but older sperm are less likely to be able to fertilize an egg.

• Researchers recently discovered that the tails of sperm contain odor receptors. The receptors cause sperm to swim toward certain chemicals. Their ability to "smell" may explain how sperm can find their way to an egg through the maze of the female reproductive tract.

Keeping Healthy

A number of medical conditions can affect the male reproductive system. However, teens who adopt healthy habits can reduce their risk of problems. **Caring for the male reproductive system involves cleanliness, sexual abstinence, protection from trauma, self-exams, and regular medical checkups.**

Cleanliness Healthy habits start with cleanliness. It is important to thoroughly clean the external organs—the penis and scrotum—daily, preferably during a shower or bath. Each day, an uncircumcised male should gently pull the foreskin back to clean the head of the penis. Drying the groin area well after showering can prevent fungal infections that can cause jock itch.

Sexual Abstinence A number of serious infections of the reproductive system and other body systems can result from sexual contact. Healthy choices regarding sexual behavior can prevent such infections. The only way to eliminate your risk of sexually transmitted infections is to abstain—or refrain from—sexual activity. In other words, practice sexual abstinence. Sexually transmitted infections will be discussed further in Chapter 22.

Protection From Trauma Good health also requires protection and prevention. During athletic activities, males should wear a protector, also called a "cup," or supporter. Tight clothing should be avoided, since tight pants or underwear can irritate or cause pain in the groin area.

Males should also be careful when lifting heavy objects. Pressure in the abdomen during lifting can push a loop of intestine out of the area that usually contains it, causing a hernia. An inguinal (ING gwuh nul) hernia results if part of the intestine pushes into the scrotum. Surgery is almost always necessary to correct an inguinal hernia.

Self-Exams It is important for males to monitor their own bodies for any signs of possible medical problems. Pain when urinating, unusual discharges, or sores on the genitals require a medical examination. Such conditions should not be self-treated.

Males, especially teens and young men, should also examine their testes for signs of testicular cancer. Almost a third of testicular cancer cases occur in young men in their teens and twenties. The Building Health Skills on pages 476–477 includes instructions on how to perform a self-examination. As with all cancers, treatment is most effective when the cancer is caught in its early stages.

Connect to Your Life Why is it important for males in their teens to know the symptoms of testicular cancer?

GO ONLINE
PearsonSuccessNet.com
For: More on male reproductive health

FIGURE 5 This catcher protects himself with a helmet, face guard, body padding, and a "cup" that protects his reproductive organs from injury.

Reproduction and Heredity **467**

Keeping Healthy

L3 Content Update GO ONLINE

Use the Web Code to access up-to-date information about male reproductive health. Have students complete the Web activity.

L3 Building Media Literacy

Ask each student to bring to class a print media article on keeping the male reproductive system healthy. Students can use magazines, newspapers, or pamphlets. Ask several students to report on the relevance of their articles. Make sure several different types of print media are represented. Based on their reports, discuss whether certain types of print media seem more appropriate for this kind of information.

L2 Cooperative Learning

Ask students to work in groups to create brochures explaining how and why to care for the male reproductive system. Brochures should cover cleanliness, sexual abstinence, protection from trauma, self-exams, and regular medical checkups. Brochures should also describe health problems that can occur without good care of the male reproductive system. Suggest to students that they share their brochures with male family members or friends. **WRITING**

Connect to Your Life It is important because almost a third of testicular cancer cases occur in young men in their teens and twenties.

Differentiated Instruction

L4 Gifted and Talented

Challenge interested students to do online research about environmental estrogens and their link to male infertility. Students should find out the nature of the chemicals, how and why their environmental levels have changed since the early 1900s, and how they cause infertility in males. Ask students to summarize what they learn in an oral report. Suggest that they include visuals, such as graphs showing concentrations of the estrogens in the environment or average human sperm counts during different time periods.

3. Assess

Evaluate
These assignments can help you assess students' mastery of the section content.

Section 2 Review
Answers appear below.

Teaching Resources
• Practice 18-2
• Section 18-2 Quiz

L2 Reteach

List each of the section vocabulary terms on the board. Then point to each word and have students brainstorm facts about that term. Record the most important, accurate facts on the board. Do not move on to the next term until students can no longer think of additional facts. For any terms students know little about, have them reread relevant passages in the section. Suggest that students record the facts for each term in their notebooks.

L4 Enrich

Teaching Resources
• Enrich 18-2

Health at Home

Reminder Card E-mails will vary but should give persuasive reasons for regular medical checkups and self-exams. For example, students might stress the importance of self-exams in finding cancer early while it is still curable. Acting as advocates in this way may help persuade students to take good care of their own reproductive system.

FIGURE 6 Your doctor can answer any questions you have about your reproductive health.

Medical Checkups Medical exams throughout life can help ensure reproductive health. The prostate gland is of particular concern after middle age. In many older men, the prostate becomes enlarged or develops cancer. An enlarged prostate does not necessarily indicate either disease or illness, but it can cause discomfort. Since the prostate gland surrounds the urethra, an enlarged prostate may make urination painful or difficult. If that happens, surgery is usually required. Furthermore, starting at age 50, men are encouraged to get screened for prostate cancer during their regular medical exams. Prostate cancer is the second most common cause of cancer death of older men.

Another condition a doctor can diagnose is **infertility** —the condition of being unable to reproduce. Infertility can affect both males and females. In males, infertility is marked by the inability to produce healthy sperm or the production of too few sperm. Three causes of infertility are exposure to certain chemicals, having mumps after puberty, and having an undescended testis. Scientists are learning more about the causes of infertility and how to prevent or treat it.

Section 2 Review

Key Ideas and Vocabulary

1. What are three main functions of the male reproductive system?
2. What is the name of the sac in which the **testes** are located?
3. What is **semen**, and how is it formed?
4. List five things that males should do to maintain reproductive health.
5. What are two kinds of problems with sperm that lead to **infertility** in males?

Health at Home

Reminder Card Write an e-mail to a male family member reminding him of the importance of regular medical checkups and self-exams. **WRITING**

Critical Thinking

6. **Sequencing** Arrange the following structures in the order in which sperm pass by or travel through them: epididymis; vas deferens; testes; prostate gland; seminal vesicles
7. **Applying Concepts** How could more young men be convinced to follow the recommendations for reproductive health? **WRITING**

GO ONLINE PearsonSuccessNet.com Audio Summary Section 18.2

Section 2 Review

1. to produce sex hormones, to produce and store sperm, and to deliver sperm to the female reproductive system
2. scrotum
3. Semen is a mixture of sperm cells and fluids. It forms when sperm from the testes mix with fluids from the seminal vesicles, prostate gland, and bulbourethral glands.
4. Clean external organs daily, abstain from sexual activity, wear a protector during athletic activities, examine testes for signs of cancer, and get regular medical exams.
5. unhealthy sperm, too few sperm
6. testes, epididymis, vas deferens, seminal vesicles, prostate gland
7. *Sample answer:* You could make young men aware of how often testicular cancer occurs in their age group by sharing statistics on the disease in teens.

The Female Reproductive System

Warm-Up

Dear Advice Line,
I've been going to the same male doctor since I was a little kid. My doctor is really nice, but since my body started developing, I just don't feel comfortable having my checkups with him anymore. I'd like to see a female doctor. Is it OK to feel this way? What should I do?

WRITING Do you think this girl's feelings are normal? Write back with your advice.

Objectives
▶ **Describe** three functions of the female reproductive system.
▶ **Summarize** the stages of the menstrual cycle.
▶ **Identify** five ways to keep the female reproductive system healthy.

Vocabulary
- ova
- ovaries
- estrogen
- progesterone
- ovulation
- fallopian tubes
- uterus
- vagina
- menstrual cycle
- menopause
- Pap smear
- mammogram

Structure and Function

You learned that the reproductive cells in males are called sperm. In females, they are called eggs, or **ova** (singular, *ovum*). **The functions of the female reproductive system are to produce sex hormones, to produce eggs, and to provide a nourishing environment in which a fertilized egg can develop into a baby.**

Ovaries The reproductive glands in which eggs are produced are called **ovaries.** The ovaries are located a few inches below the waist, one on each side of the body. Each ovary is about the size of an almond. The ovaries have two important functions: they produce the female sex hormones estrogen and progesterone, and they release mature egg cells. The sex hormone **estrogen** activates certain physical changes at puberty, such as breast development, and controls the maturation of eggs. **Progesterone** activates changes to a woman's reproductive system before and during pregnancy.

When a girl is born, each ovary contains hundreds of thousands of immature eggs. The eggs begin to mature, or ripen, when the girl reaches puberty. Once puberty begins, one of the ovaries releases a ripened egg about once every month in a process called **ovulation.** The tiny egg that is released is no larger than the period at the end of this sentence.

Differentiated Instruction

EL English Language Learners
Guide students in using the diagrams in the section to learn the structures and functions of the female reproductive system. Make and distribute copies of Figures 7 and 8. In Figure 7, have students write the function of each structure under its label. They can find the functions in the text on pages 469 and 470.

In Figure 8, have students label the small drawings with the structures that are involved in each stage of the menstrual cycle. They can refer back to Figure 7 if they need help identifying the structures in the small drawings.

Objectives
Before class begins, write the objectives on the board. Have students copy the objectives into their notebooks at the start of class.

1. Focus

Warm-Up Advice Line

After students finish writing, call on a few volunteers to share what they wrote. Try to use their answers to make the point that such feelings are normal for both males and females after puberty. Tell students they will learn in this section why females should see a doctor for regular reproductive system checkups after reaching puberty.

Presentation 18-3

2. Teach

L3 **EL** Reading/Note Taking 18-3
L2 Adapted Reading/Note Taking 18-3

Structure and Function

L3 **Journal Writing**

Ask students to write a journal entry in which they explain why it is important for a person of their gender to know about the female reproductive system. Tell students they may keep their journal entries confidential. If male students have trouble thinking of reasons, point out that most males have female loved ones whose health concerns them. Thinking of reasons for learning about a topic may help motivate students to learn about it and relate it to their own lives. **WRITING**

EL **Building Vocabulary**

Write the following words on the board: ovary, fallopian tubes, testes, uterus, cervix, vagina. Call on a student to circle the word that does not belong. (*testes*) Then, ask students to write definitions for the uncircled words and explain how they are related. **WRITING**

L2 **Visual Learning: Figure 7**

Image Bank Figure 18-7

Have students use the figure to trace the path of an egg from an ovary through a fallopian tube to the uterus. Make sure they understand how the two views of the female reproductive system are related.

Connect to Your Life Possible sources of reliable information include encyclopedias, medical reference books, Web sites of universities and hospitals, and medical professionals such as doctors and nurses.

Fallopian Tubes Look at Figure 7 to locate the two **fallopian tubes** (fuh LOH pee un)—passageways that carry eggs away from the ovaries. When the ovary releases an egg during ovulation, the fingerlike ends of the fallopian tube draw the egg into the tube. Eggs, unlike sperm, cannot swim. Tiny hairlike extensions called cilia line the fallopian tube and sweep the egg toward the uterus. If sperm are present around the egg, it may be fertilized. The fallopian tubes are where fertilization usually occurs.

Uterus The **uterus** is a hollow, muscular, pear-shaped organ. In the uterus, a fertilized egg can develop and grow. The uterus has several layers of tissue and a rich supply of blood that protect and nourish the developing baby. The narrow base of the uterus is called the cervix. When a baby is ready to be born, the cervix expands to allow the baby to pass through.

Vagina The **vagina,** or birth canal, is a hollow, muscular passage leading from the uterus to the outside of the body. Sperm enter a female's body through the vagina. During childbirth, the baby passes out of the mother's body through the vagina. The walls of the vagina are very elastic, which allows it to expand dramatically during childbirth.

Connect to Your Life Where could you find reliable information about the female reproductive system?

Female Reproductive System

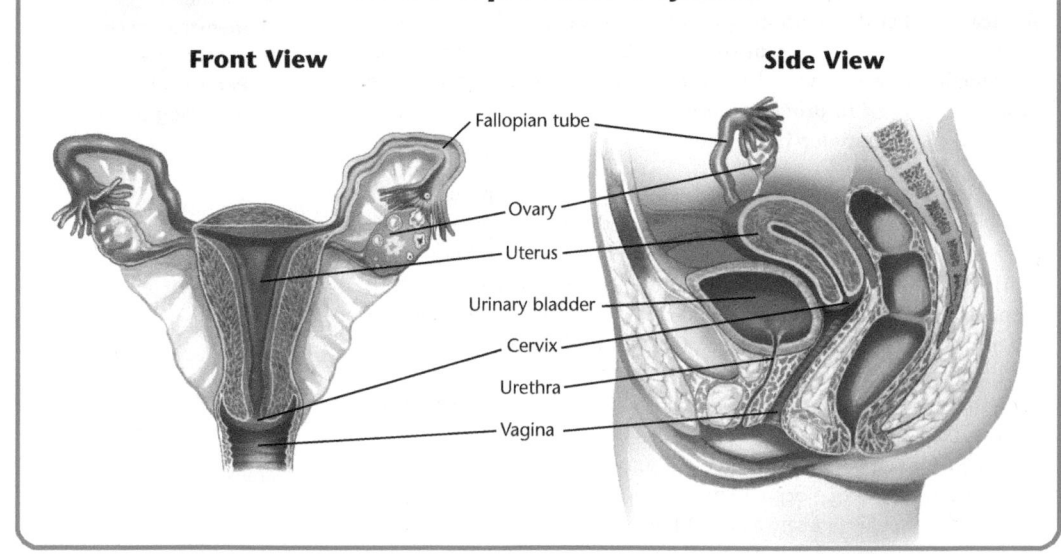

Front View **Side View**

- Fallopian tube
- Ovary
- Uterus
- Urinary bladder
- Cervix
- Urethra
- Vagina

FIGURE 7 The female reproductive system produces eggs and provides a nourishing environment for a fertilized egg to develop.

Sensitive Issues

The issue of menstruation may be sensitive to some students because of cultural attitudes about it. Encourage students to think about it as they would any other normal biological function, such as digestion.

TEENS *Are Asking . . .*

Q: I get my period only once every 6 weeks or so, but then it usually lasts about 7 days. Is that normal, or should I be worried?

A: Generally, having shorter- or longer-than average menstrual cycles or menstrual periods is nothing to worry about, because there is a lot of normal variation in these events. Variation is especially common during adolescence. However, if your periods change from what is typical for you or you are still concerned, talk with your doctor. It probably means nothing, but it could be a sign that you are under too much stress or have an underlying health problem.

Media Wise

Sexuality in Music Videos

When watching your favorite music videos, you may not think about the hidden, or not-so-hidden, meanings they contain. What messages are conveyed about sex? Consider these questions as they relate to music videos.

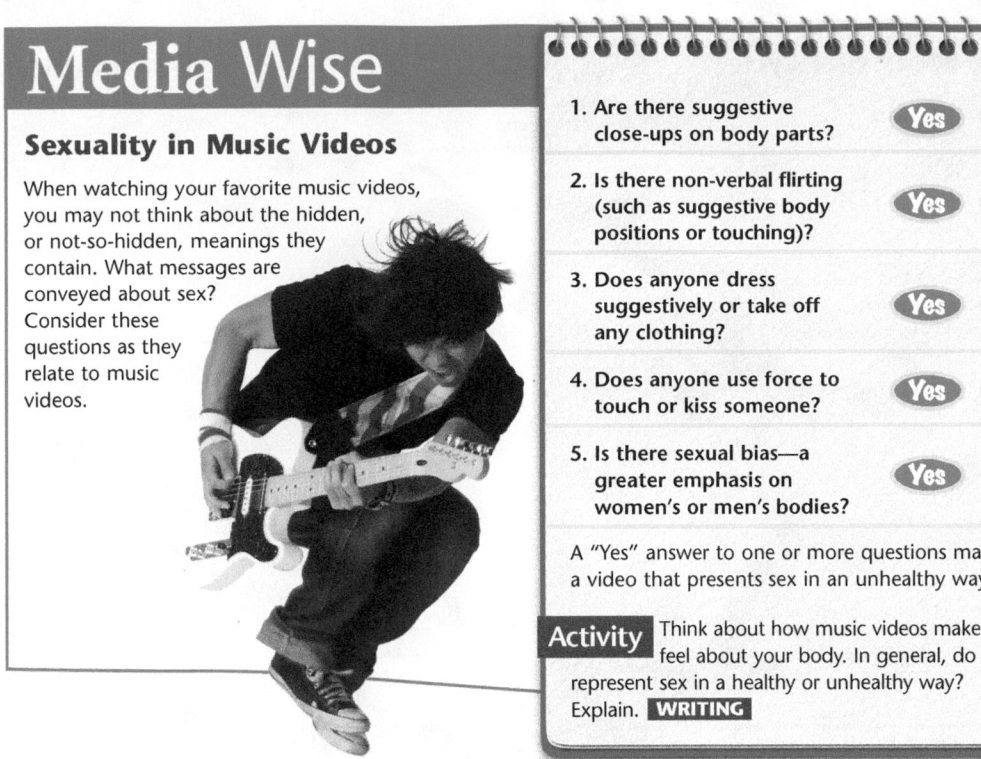

1. Are there suggestive close-ups on body parts?   **Yes**   **No**

2. Is there non-verbal flirting (such as suggestive body positions or touching)?   **Yes**   **No**

3. Does anyone dress suggestively or take off any clothing?   **Yes**   **No**

4. Does anyone use force to touch or kiss someone?   **Yes**   **No**

5. Is there sexual bias—a greater emphasis on women's or men's bodies?   **Yes**   **No**

A "Yes" answer to one or more questions may indicate a video that presents sex in an unhealthy way.

Activity Think about how music videos make you feel about your body. In general, do they represent sex in a healthy or unhealthy way? Explain. **WRITING**

The Menstrual Cycle

As you learned, males typically produce millions of sperm cells every day after reaching puberty. Females, on the other hand, usually produce only one mature egg cell each month during a process called the **menstrual cycle** (MEN stroo ul). **During the menstrual cycle, an ovary releases a mature egg. The egg travels to the uterus. If the egg is not fertilized, the uterine lining is shed and a new cycle begins.**

Factors Affecting the Menstrual Cycle On average, a menstrual cycle lasts 28 days. However, cycles as short as 21 days or as long as 35 days can be normal for some individuals. The endocrine system controls the menstrual cycle. The hormones involved include FSH and LH, which are released by the pituitary gland, and estrogen and progesterone, which are released from the ovaries. Factors such as diet, stress, exercise, and weight gain or loss also affect the menstrual cycle. The menstrual cycle may be irregular at times, especially during puberty.

Except during pregnancy, menstrual cycles occur each month from puberty until about the age of 45 to 55. At that time of life, called **menopause,** the ovaries slow down their hormone production and no longer release mature eggs. Gradually, the menstrual cycle stops, and the woman is no longer able to become pregnant.

Reproduction and Heredity **471**

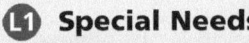

L2 **Visual Learning: Figure 8**

Image Bank Figure 18-8

Have pairs of same-gender students work together to learn the information in the figure. Give each pair five index cards. On the front of the cards, students should write the ranges of days from the figure (days 1–4, 5–13, and so on). On the back of the cards, they should list the menstrual cycle events that occur during those days of the cycle. Have partners shuffle the cards and try to put them in the correct order without looking at the days on the front. They should keep trying until they can do it correctly.

Caption Answer a fallopian tube

L2 **Active Learning**

Ask students to make a different kind of visual representation of the menstrual cycle that may be easier for some students to understand. The exercise may also help female students learn how to keep track of their own menstrual cycles. Make and distribute copies of a monthly calendar page for February (because it has the same number of days as the average menstrual cycle). Have students block out the five stages of the menstrual cycle on the calendar and write in specific menstrual cycle events (e.g., ovulation) on the appropriate days of the month. Display the calendars in the classroom.

L3 **Addressing Misconceptions**

The Menstrual Cycle and Conception
Many students will have misconceptions about pregnancy, such as believing that women can become pregnant *only* on the day of ovulation. Remind students that fertilization usually occurs in a fallopian tube. Have students use Figure 8 to find out on which days of the cycle an egg is in a fallopian tube. *(days 16–22)* Then have them infer on which days of the menstrual cycle conception is most likely. *(days 16–22)* Remind them that while a woman is most likely to get pregnant during the week surrounding ovulation, it is still *possible* for her to get pregnant at any time.

The Menstrual Cycle

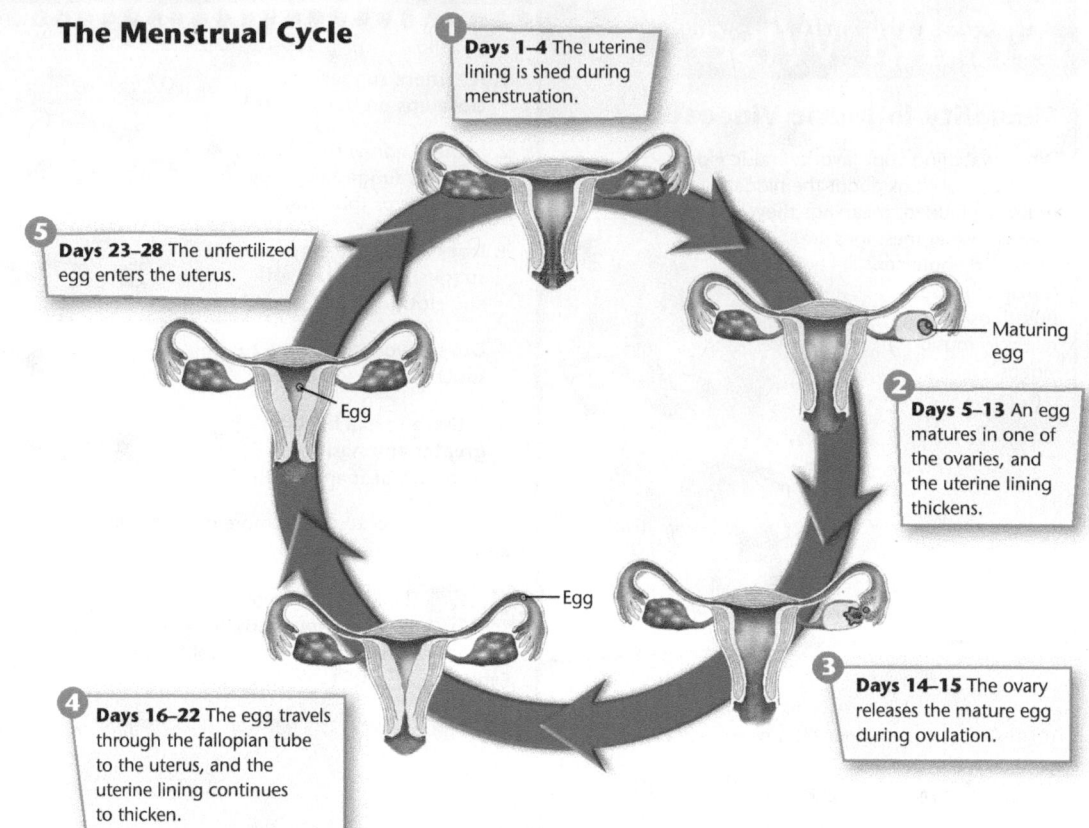

1 **Days 1–4** The uterine lining is shed during menstruation.

5 **Days 23–28** The unfertilized egg enters the uterus.

Maturing egg

Egg

2 **Days 5–13** An egg matures in one of the ovaries, and the uterine lining thickens.

Egg

3 **Days 14–15** The ovary releases the mature egg during ovulation.

4 **Days 16–22** The egg travels through the fallopian tube to the uterus, and the uterine lining continues to thicken.

FIGURE 8 The thickening of the lining of the uterus, ovulation, and menstruation are key events of the menstrual cycle.
Interpreting Diagrams
Through which structure does an egg travel before reaching the uterus?

Stages of the Menstrual Cycle Follow the stages of a typical menstrual cycle in Figure 8. During the first half of the cycle, an egg matures inside one of the ovaries. Meanwhile, the lining of the uterus thickens. At about the middle of the cycle—typically on day 14—ovulation occurs. The mature egg is released by the ovary and travels into the fallopian tube. A female is most fertile, or able to become pregnant, around the time of ovulation.

It takes about seven days for the egg to travel through the fallopian tube into the uterus. During this time the uterine lining continues to thicken, and the blood supply to it increases. If the egg has not been fertilized by the time it reaches the uterus, the uterine lining breaks down.

The blood and tissue of the thickened lining pass out of the body through the vagina in a process called menstruation, or the menstrual period. As menstruation is taking place, another egg begins to mature in one of the ovaries. Thus menstruation marks the end of one cycle and the beginning of another. In general, a menstrual period lasts about 3 to 5 days. Most women wear either a sanitary pad or a tampon to absorb the menstrual flow.

472 *Chapter 18*

Focus on **ISSUES**

L3 **Females and Medical Research**
Until recently, medical research projects rarely included female subjects. Most researchers reasoned that the monthly changes of the menstrual cycle would interfere with study controls. As a result, doctors were forced to assume whatever was learned from medical research on males applied to females as well. We now know that this assumption is not always true. Recently, federal laws were passed requiring females to be included as subjects in federally funded medical research. Hold a class discussion about the issue of female subjects in medical research. Start the discussion by asking students whether they agree with the legislation and why or why not.

Menstrual Discomfort During the menstrual period, some women may experience abdominal cramps or other discomfort. Cramps are caused by contractions of the uterus. See Figure 9 for some ways to relieve menstrual cramps. For severe cramps or for any other menstrual concerns, women should see a medical professional.

Some women experience discomfort some time before the menstrual period. This condition, known as premenstrual syndrome, or PMS, is marked by nervous tension, mood swings, headaches, bloating, and irritability. The dramatic change in hormone levels that occurs before menstruation begins may cause PMS. Some doctors recommend that PMS sufferers reduce their intake of salt, sugar, and caffeine, get regular exercise, and try other stress-reduction techniques.

Toxic Shock Syndrome A rare but serious medical condition associated with tampon use is toxic shock syndrome. This syndrome is caused by a bacterial infection. Symptoms of toxic shock syndrome include a sudden high fever, a rash, vomiting, diarrhea, and dizziness. Because toxic shock syndrome can lead to death, a woman with any of these symptoms during her period should seek medical attention immediately. To decrease the risk of toxic shock syndrome, women should use tampons with the lowest possible absorbency for their needs and change tampons often.

 **Connect to Your Life** What misconceptions did you hold about menstruation before reading this section?

GO ONLINE
PearsonSuccessNet.com
For: More on the menstrual cycle

Menstrual cramps ? Try this . . .
- Engage in moderate exercise.
- Take a warm bath.
- Apply a heating pad to the abdomen.
- Take aspirin or ibuprofen with doctor's approval.

FIGURE 9 Following these simple tips can help relieve menstrual cramps.

Reproduction and Heredity **473**

L3 Online Activity  GO ONLINE

Visit Pearson SuccessNet to access an online activity about the menstrual cycle. Have students complete the Web activity.

L2 Cooperative Learning

Ask groups of several students each to brainstorm three lists: factors that can influence menstruation *(stress, illness, change in weight)*; discomforts that may accompany menstruation *(cramps, mood swings, bloating)*; and possible ways to treat the discomforts *(heating pads, pain medication, exercise)*. Give groups a chance to share their lists.

L3 Building Media Literacy

Have students find examples of television, print, or Internet ads for products that claim to relieve menstrual discomforts. Ask students to write a paragraph examining the claims made in the ads. Do they think the claims are reliable or misleading? Why? **WRITING**

Connect to Your Life Allow students to answer this question in their private journals.

Differentiated Instruction

EL English Language Learners

Help students develop the skill of using context clues to determine the meanings of new words. First, work through an example to show students how. Point out the word *period* in the first sentence on this page. Read aloud from a dictionary at least two definitions of *period,* including the correct one. Ask students to select the correct definition, based on the word's context. Ask: **What other word in the sentence is a clue to the correct meaning of *period*?** *(menstrual)* Have students write down words on this page that they do not recognize. Have them look up the words in a dictionary and try to choose the correct definitions based on the context.

Keeping Healthy

⑫ Building Health Skills

Advocacy Have groups of students make posters conveying to other teens how and why to care for the female reproductive system. Students should illustrate each healthy habit listed in the text with a tasteful cartoon, sketch, or magazine photo to make the posters interesting and eye-catching. Arrange to display the posters at school in the girls' locker rooms and restrooms.

⑪ Cooperative Learning

Divide the class into same-gender groups, and have members of each group work together to express the five healthy habits as lists of "Do's" and "Don'ts." *(For example, for cleanliness, students might list: "Do shower daily;" and "don't use deodorant tampons.")* Give groups a chance to share their lists. Select one "Do" and one "Don't" statement about each habit. Call on students to explain how following the "Do's" and "Don'ts" contributes to good health.

⑬ Active Learning

Have interested students contact a medical professional in their community to find out at what age females should start having Pap smears to detect cervical cancer. Appropriate medical professionals might include a school nurse, a nurse in a gynecologist's office, or the director of a local chapter of the American Cancer Society. Ask students to share what they learn with the class. Discuss how detecting cancer early with Pap smears improves chances of survival.

Keeping Healthy

A number of medical conditions can affect the female reproductive system. Teens who adopt healthy habits can reduce their risk of problems. **Caring for the female reproductive system involves cleanliness, sexual abstinence, prompt treatment for infections, self-exams, and regular medical checkups.**

Cleanliness One important health habit is cleanliness, including daily washing of the external vaginal area. Cleanliness is especially important during menstruation, as is the regular changing of sanitary pads or tampons. Feminine hygiene sprays, douches, and deodorant tampons are not necessary. In fact, they may be harmful if they cover up signs of an infection or cause irritation. If washing does not get rid of normal body odors, or if any unusual discharge is noted, seek medical attention.

Sexual Abstinence A number of serious infections can result from sexual contact. Healthy choices regarding sexual behavior can prevent such infections. The only way to eliminate your risk of sexually transmitted infections is to abstain from sexual activity.

Prompt Treatment for Infections Some infections of the reproductive system are not related to sexual behavior. Many women experience vaginitis, a vaginal infection caused by yeast, bacteria, or other microorganisms. Symptoms include a thick discharge, odors, vaginal itching, and a burning sensation during urination. Only a doctor can diagnose the specific cause of vaginitis and provide appropriate treatment.

Self-Exams It is important for women to monitor their own bodies for signs of possible medical problems. Symptoms of vaginitis, sores on the genitals, or any unusual pain in the abdomen require a medical exam. A woman should also consult a doctor if she notices heavier bleeding than normal during menstruation, if her periods stop completely, or if she notices bleeding at times between her regular periods.

For the early detection of breast cancer, all women, including teens, should perform a monthly breast self-examination. Instructions can be found in the Building Health Skills on pages 476–477.

FIGURE 10 Daily washing is an important part of keeping the reproductive system healthy.

TEENS *Are Asking . . .*

Q: What is the difference between a Pap smear and a gynecologic exam? When should I start having them? I'm a 15-year-old girl.

A: You are not alone if you are confused about Pap smears and gynecologic exams. A recent study found that many teenaged girls and young women think that a Pap smear is the same thing as a gynecologic exam. Only 2 percent of girls in the study knew the difference. Experts fear this misconception may lead young women to delay their first gynecologic exam until after they become sexually active. A Pap smear is a test only for cervical cancer. A gynecologic exam is a more general checkup of the reproductive system. It may or may not include a Pap smear. According to new recommendations from the Centers for Disease Control, girls should have their first gynecologic exam between the ages of 13 and 15 and their first Pap smear at age 21.

Medical Checkups A yearly checkup of the reproductive system is recommended for all females who have reached puberty. During the exam, the doctor will examine the breasts and genitals and may perform a pelvic exam and a Pap smear. In a **Pap smear,** a sample of cells is taken from the cervix and examined under a microscope. Pap smears can detect cancer of the cervix.

Starting at about age 40, women may get a **mammogram,** an X-ray of the breast that can help detect breast cancer. A woman with a family history of breast cancer or other risk factors may have her first mammogram at a younger age. A mammogram may detect cancers that are too small for a woman or her doctor to feel in a breast exam.

A doctor can also detect and treat other reproductive problems, including cancers of the ovary or uterus, and

▶ **Ovarian cysts** Ovarian cysts are growths on the ovary. Large ones may be painful and need to be surgically removed.

▶ **Endometriosis** This is a condition in which tissue from the lining of the uterus—the endometrium—grows outside the uterus, in the pelvic cavity. This condition can be very painful and is usually treated with hormones or surgery.

▶ **Infertility** Causes of infertility in women include blocked fallopian tubes and problems with ovulation.

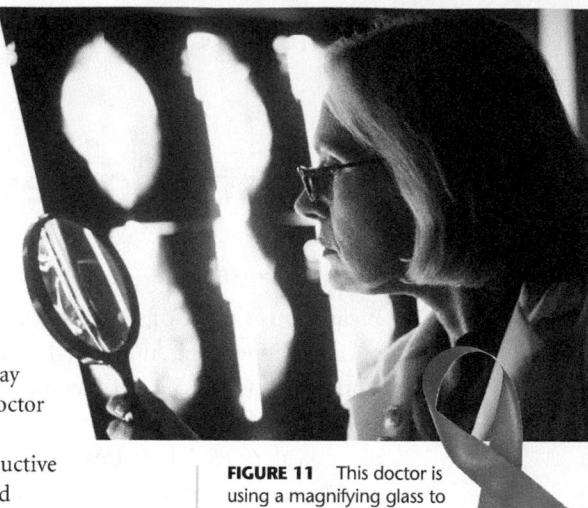

FIGURE 11 This doctor is using a magnifying glass to more closely examine a mammogram.

Section 3 Review

Key Ideas and Vocabulary

1. What are three main functions of the female reproductive system?
2. What is **ovulation**?
3. Where are the **fallopian tubes** located? What is their function?
4. What event marks the end of one menstrual cycle and the beginning of another?
5. List five things that females should do to maintain reproductive health.

Health at School

Medication Regulations Many girls suffer from menstrual cramps, sometimes during school hours. Ask your school nurse or an administrator what the policies are for taking pain medications on school grounds to treat menstrual cramps and other common aches and pains. Write a memo detailing your findings. **WRITING**

Critical Thinking

6. **Calculating** If a woman's ovaries release one egg per month for 30 years, how many eggs in total will she have released? **MATH**
7. **Applying Concepts** How could more young women be convinced of the importance of regular breast exams? **WRITING**

Section 3 Review

1. to produce sex hormones, to produce eggs, and to provide a nourishing environment in which a fertilized egg can develop into a baby
2. the release of a ripened egg by an ovary
3. The fallopian tubes are located between the ovaries and uterus. Their function is to carry eggs from the ovaries to the uterus.
4. menstruation
5. Keep clean, abstain from sexual activity, get prompt treatment for infections, do regular self-exams, and get yearly checkups.
6. 360 eggs
7. *Sample answer:* They could be convinced by information about the risk of breast cancer and how early detection saves lives.

Breast and Testicular Self-Exams

Objective

Demonstrate healthful behaviors by doing breast or testicular self-exams to detect cancer.

Teaching Strategies

- Many physicians have models of the breasts and testes with lumps. If possible, borrow the models and let students experience what a lump feels like before they do the self-exams.

- Try to convince students of the importance of self-exams by presenting the following statistics to the class:

   Breast cancer is the second most common cancer in women as well as the second most common cause of cancer deaths in women. In 2012 in the U.S., almost 227,000 new cases of breast cancer were diagnosed, and about 40,000 women died of breast cancer.

   Breast cancer is rare in males, but it can occur.

   Testicular cancer is the most common cancer found in young men between the ages of 15 and 34. In 2012 in the U.S., about 8,600 new cases of testicular cancer were diagnosed, and almost 400 men died of testicular cancer.

- Point out that self-exams save lives by detecting cancer early, before it has a chance to spread. However, many people have a hard time remembering to do self-exams. Challenge students to think of ways they could remember to do regular self-exams. *(Possible ways might include noting when to do self-exams on a calendar, asking a friend or family member to remind them, or posting a reminder on the bathroom mirror or in the shower.)*

Breast and Testicular Self-Exams

Breast Self-Exam

Breast cancer is one of the most common forms of cancer in women. Although it is rare in young women, breast cancer becomes more common as women age. If breast cancer is found early, the disease can be effectively treated and often cured.

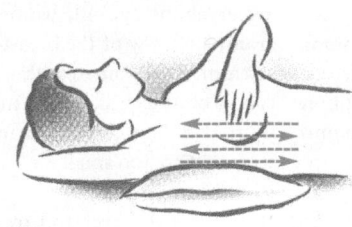

The teenage years are a good time to establish the habit of regular self-exams. The best time to do a breast self-exam is the week after a menstrual period, when the breasts are least swollen. For women who have reached menopause or have irregular periods, the exam should be done on the same day each month. If you forget a month, don't worry. Start the routine exams again once you remember.

❶ Check your breasts while lying down.

- Lie down and place your right arm behind your head.

- Use the finger pads of the three middle fingers on your left hand to feel for lumps in the right breast. Use overlapping dime-sized circular motions of the finger pads.

- Use three different levels of pressure. Use light pressure to feel the tissue closest to the skin. Use medium pressure to feel a little deeper. Use firm pressure to feel the tissue closest to the chest and ribs.

- Feel the breast in an up-and-down pattern starting at an imaginary line drawn straight down your side from the underarm, and move inward until you reach the bone in the middle of your chest, your sternum (See diagram above).

- Check the entire breast area, moving down until you can feel only ribs and up to the neck or collar bone.

- Repeat the exam on your left breast, using the fingers of the right hand.

❷ Look at your breasts while standing in front of the mirror.

- While pressing your hands down firmly on your hips, look for any change in breast shape or appearance, such as dimpling of skin, redness or swelling, or changes to the nipples.

- Slightly raise your right arm and feel your underarm with your lefthand fingers. Repeat on the left side.

❸ Report any abnormalities to your doctor immediately.

Many lumps are cysts or harmless tumors that are not cancerous. But only a doctor can make a diagnosis.

Sensitive Issues

Students may be uncomfortable discussing or asking questions about breast or testicular self-exams. Keep the discussion objective, and focus on the role of self-exams in detecting cancer early and saving lives.

Suggest to students that they ask for a demonstration from a nurse or doctor the next time they have a medical appointment if they are uncertain how to do the self-exam correctly.

Testicular Self-Exam

Cancer of the testes, or testicular cancer, is the most common cancer found in young men between 15 and 34 years of age. Testicular cancer can be cured if it is detected early and treated promptly. Most testicular cancers are noticed by men themselves, not by their doctors. The American Cancer Society recommends discussing with your doctor how frequently you should perform the exam. Unlike the breast self exam, it is generally not recommended as often as once a month.

The best time to do a testicular self-exam is after a hot shower or bath, when the scrotum is relaxed and the testes can be felt more easily.

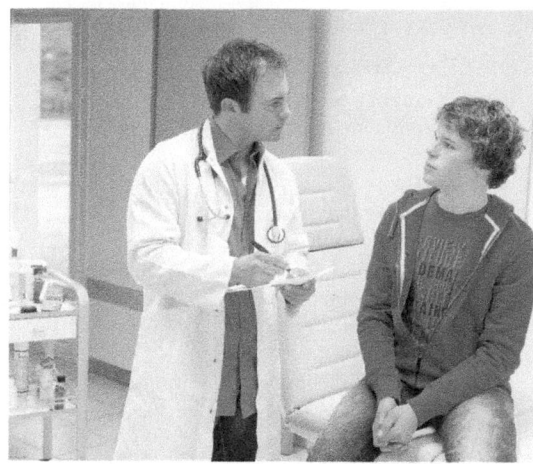

❶ Examine each testis separately with both hands.

- ► Roll each testis between the thumbs and fingers of both hands, feeling for lumps or hard places about the size of a pea. If a lump is present, it is usually found in the front or on the sides of a testis.

- ► Look and feel for any hard lumps or smooth, rounded masses, or any change in the size, shape, or texture of the testes.

- ► Learn to recognize what the epididymis feels like so you won't confuse it with a lump. The epididymis appears as a small "bump" on the back side of the testis.

❷ Report any abnormalities to your doctor immediately.

Lumps may not be cancerous, but only a doctor can make a diagnosis. Other signs of testicular cancer are enlargement of a testis, a dull aching in the genital area, or a feeling of heaviness in the scrotum. However, testicular cancer is not typically painful when it first develops.

Practice the Skill

Breast Self-Exam

1. Do the breast self-exam lying down and standing in front of the mirror, and again one week after your next menstrual period (or in one month if you haven't started your menstrual periods).

2. Describe the steps of the self-exam to a female family member. Find out if you have any history of breast cancer in your family.

Testicular Self-Exam

1. After a shower or hot bath, practice the testicular self-exam.

2. Describe the steps of the self-exam to a male family member. Find out if you have any history of testicular cancer in your family.

Reproduction and Heredity **477**

Breast Self-Exam

1. Female students should do the breast self-exam at home, following the directions in the activity.

2. Students might describe the steps of the self-exam to their mother, a sister, or an aunt. They should ask adult family members if they know of any biological relatives who have had breast cancer. If they do, it may increase their own risk of breast cancer, making regular self-exams even more important.

Testicular Self-Exam

1. Male students should do the testicular self-exam at home, following the directions in the activity.

2. Students might describe the steps of the self-exam to their father, a brother, or an uncle. They should ask adult family members if they know of any biological relatives who have had testicular cancer. A family history of testicular cancer may increase their risk of testicular cancer and make self-exams more important.

Health and Community

L4 Diagnosing Cancer

Explain that self-exams are just the beginning of the process of diagnosing cancer, because a lump in a breast or testicle may not be cancerous. Medical tests usually are required to make a firm diagnosis. Ask a few volunteers to find out how cancer is diagnosed in a hospital or clinic in their community. Have them report to the class what they learn.

Objectives

Before class begins, write the objectives on the board. Have students copy the objectives into their notebooks at the start of class.

1. Focus

Warm-Up **Quick Quiz**

Use the Warm-Up Presentation slide to survey student responses.

Call on a few volunteers to share their answers to the writing activity. Reiterate any correct ideas they state about dominant traits. Then ask: **Why do different people have different forms of the same trait?** *(They inherit different forms from their parents.)* Have the class brainstorm other physical traits that people inherit from their parents. *(Sample answers: hair color, eye color, nose shape, body shape)*

Presentation 18-4

Section 4

Heredity

Objectives

▶ **Explain** how genetic information passes from one generation to the next.

▶ **Identify** the causes of genetic disorders.

▶ **Compare** the role of genes, environment, and behavior in affecting a person's risk for disease.

Vocabulary

- heredity
- chromosome
- gene
- genetic disorder

Warm-Up

Quick Quiz Take a brief self-inventory of some of your physical traits, or characteristics.

① Do you have a widow's peak or a smooth hairline?

 **Widow's Peak**

 **Smooth**

② Do you have free or attached earlobes?

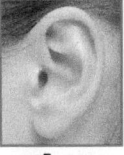 **Free**

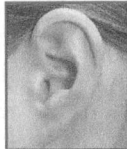 **Attached**

WRITING A widow's peak and free earlobes are examples of dominant traits. What do you think a "dominant trait" is?

The Basic Rules of Heredity

When a baby is born, people may say, "She looks just like her father," or "He has his grandmother's ears." Think about how children resemble their parents, grandparents, and other relatives. Their eye color, the shape of their ears, their height—these traits are determined in part from the genetic information they inherit from their parents. **Heredity** is the passing on, or transmission, of biological traits from parent to child. People are similar to each of their parents in some ways but different from their parents in other ways. What determines the combination of traits that are passed on?

Chromosomes To answer these questions, you must first learn about chromosomes. **Chromosomes** (KROH muh sohmz) are tiny structures found within cells that carry information about the characteristics you will inherit. Most of the cells in your body contain 23 pairs of chromosomes— 46 chromosomes in all. However, sex cells—sperm or eggs—contain half this number, or 23 chromosomes. When a sperm and egg unite, the fertilized egg ends up with 46 chromosomes—23 from each parent.

Sensitive Issues

Heredity may be a sensitive issue for students who live with adoptive or foster parents. Avoid asking students to talk about traits they share with their biological parents or other biological relatives. Give them the option of using hypothetical examples or other families they know.

For Your **INFORMATION!**

Cellular Differentiation

All the cells in the human body, except sex cells, are the result of repeated mitotic divisions that began with the single cell that was produced at fertilization. Thus, all the body's cells contain the same genes. As development proceeds, cells become specialized in structure and function. Cells become different, despite having the same genes, because only certain genes are "turned on" in each cell. Which genes are turned on is due to a complex combination of genetic and environmental factors.

Genes Every chromosome in your body is made up of many genes. A **gene** is a section of a chromosome that determines or affects a characteristic, or trait. Like the chromosomes that contain them, genes come in pairs. Since a sex cell contains only one half of each chromosome pair, it also has only one half of each gene pair. Once a sperm fertilizes an egg, however, the fertilized egg contains two copies of the gene for each trait—one from the father and one from the mother. **Hereditary information passes from one generation to the next through genes contained on the two sets of chromosomes that a person receives from their parents.**

Dominant and Recessive Traits Suppose a father has one trait and the mother has another. Which trait will their child have? The answer depends on the makeup of the pair of genes that the child inherits.

Consider earlobe shape. Earlobes can be either free or attached. There are two forms, or versions, of the gene for earlobe shape. One form of the gene carries information for free earlobes—the dominant trait. A dominant trait is one that appears in an offspring whenever its gene is present. The other form of the gene carries information for attached earlobes—the recessive trait. A recessive trait appears in an offspring only when the dominant form of the gene is *not* present.

You need two copies of the recessive form of the gene to have attached earlobes. You need just one dominant form of the gene to have free earlobes. Receiving a dominant form of the gene from both parents will also result in free earlobes.

Note that the rules of heredity for most traits, such as height and eye color, are more complex than those for earlobe shape. This is because many different genes plus factors other than genetics affect most traits.

 **Do you get dimples in your cheeks when you smile? Smile dimples are a dominant trait.**

FIGURE 12 Your looks are determined in part by the traits you inherit.

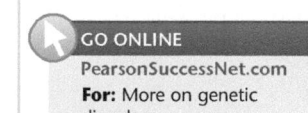
GO ONLINE
PearsonSuccessNet.com
For: More on genetic disorders

Reproduction and Heredity **479**

---

2. Teach

The Basic Rules of Heredity

L2 Teacher Demo
On the board, sketch a sperm and an egg, with 23 chromosomes each, and a cell with 23 pairs of chromosomes, or 46 chromosomes in all. (You can use tick marks to represent the chromosomes.) Use the sketches to explain how fertilization results in a cell with 23 pairs of chromosomes.

EL Building Vocabulary
Have students find the terms *dominant* and *recessive* in an English language dictionary. Ask students to explain the different meanings (in both general usage and in a genetics context) of each term. Then, have them use the terms in sentences that reflect the different meanings.

L3 Cooperative Learning
Ask students who know about Punnett squares to make and explain a Punnett square for a cross between an *Ee* mother and an *Ee* father (*Ee × Ee*), where *E* represents the dominant gene for free earlobes and *e* represents the recessive gene for attached earlobes. Ask: **What kind of earlobes do the parents have?** *(free)* **What possible genetic combinations can the offspring have?** *(EE, Ee, and ee)* **Which offspring will have free earlobes?** *(EE and Ee)* **Which offspring will have attached earlobes?** *(ee)*

 Students may answer "yes" or "no." If students are unsure whether they have dimples when they smile, they can ask a classmate.

L3 Content Update  **GO ONLINE**
Visit Pearson SuccessNet to access more information about genetic disorders. Have students complete the Web activity.

Heredity and Disease

L2 **Visual Learning: Figure 13**

Image Bank Figure 18-13

Guide students in comparing and contrasting the genetic disorders listed in the figure. Ask: **Which disorder is the only one listed in the table that is controlled by a dominant gene?** *(Huntington's disease)* **Which disorder is the only one caused by abnormal chromosomes?** *(Down syndrome)* **Which disorders cause problems with the blood?** *(sickle cell disease and hemophilia)* **Which disorders cause brain damage or mental retardation?** *(Tay-Sachs disease, PKU, and Down syndrome)* Call on a student to answer the caption question.

Caption Answer Duchenne muscular dystrophy and hemophilia

L3 **Cultural Connection**

Point out that several genetic disorders tend to be more common among certain cultures. For example, sickle cell disease occurs more commonly in people with African ancestry. Tay-Sachs is more common among people with Ashkenazi Jewish ancestry. Cystic fibrosis and PKU occur more frequently in people of Northern European ancestry.

Genetic Disorders

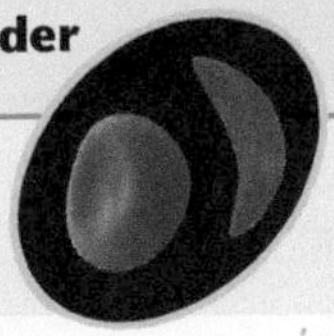

Disorder	Type of Disorder	Effect on the Body
Sickle cell disease	Recessive disorder	High number of red blood cells have an abnormal sickle shape; blood cells clump and block small blood vessels, causing severe pain and weakness
Tay-Sachs disease	Recessive disorder	Lack of important chemical in the brain results in brain damage and death in childhood
Cystic fibrosis	Recessive disorder	Mucus in lungs becomes thick and sticky, trapping bacteria that cause infections and lung damage; mucus also affects pancreas
Phenylketonuria (PKU)	Recessive disorder	Body cannot break down phenylalanine, a chemical found in food; causes brain damage if not diagnosed and treated early
Duchenne muscular dystrophy	Recessive disorder that primarily affects males	Lack of important protein needed for muscle function leads to loss of muscle control
Hemophilia	Recessive disorder that primarily affects males	Blood does not clot properly, leading to internal bleeding that can damage the joints
Huntington's disease	Dominant disorder	Cells in brain start to die in middle age; mental abilities decline and movements become uncontrollable, resulting in early death
Down syndrome	Chromosomal disorder	Mental retardation and heart defects; characteristic facial features; severity of disease ranges from mild to severe

FIGURE 13 Genetic disorders may be dominant or recessive, or caused by errors in chromosome inheritance.
Reading Tables Name two disorders that are more common in males.

Heredity and Disease

Just like earlobe shape, eye color, and other inherited traits, an abnormal condition known as a **genetic disorder** can be passed from parent to child. **Genetic disorders are caused by the inheritance of an abnormal gene or chromosome.**

Genetic Disorders Figure 13 provides information about some of the more common genetic disorders. Many genetic disorders, such as cystic fibrosis and hemophilia, are recessive traits. A child must receive two abnormal copies of the gene—one from each parent—in order for the disorder to develop. A few disorders, such as Huntington's disease, are dominant traits. Such disorders require just one abnormal copy of the gene. Other genetic disorders, such as Down syndrome, are the result of too few or too many chromosomes.

480 *Chapter 18*

For Your INFORMATION!

Sun Exposure in Teens

Skin cancer is caused mainly by sun exposure during childhood and adolescence. Sunburns at a young age are especially likely to increase the risk of skin cancer. According to a recent survey of more than 10,000 teens nationwide, most teens know that too much sun exposure causes skin cancer, but many continue to deliberately expose themselves to the sun, mainly because of a simple preference for tanned skin. In the same survey, only three in ten teens said they regularly use sunscreen, and eight in ten said they got a sunburn during the past year.

Family Medical History You have probably heard that certain diseases run in families. What does that mean? Scientists know that a person's risk for many diseases increases when close relatives have the disease. Therefore, it is important to develop a family medical history—a record of diseases and disorders that your parents, siblings, or grandparents experienced. Some diseases for which a genetic link is suspected or has been identified are breast cancer, colon cancer, high blood pressure, diabetes, and some forms of Alzheimer's disease. In addition, some genes do not typically cause disease, but they do increase a person's risk.

 **Connect to Your Life** What diseases run in your family? How can you decrease your risk for these diseases?

The Effect of Environment and Behavior Even if you have genes that increase your risk for certain diseases, many other factors also affect your risk. **For most diseases, your environment and your behavior affect your risk as much as or even more than your genes.** Environmental factors include such things as exposure to air pollution and certain chemicals. The typical climate where you live may be an environmental risk factor. Suppose, for example, that skin cancer runs in your family. Living in a warm, sunny climate would further increase your risk for developing the disease.

Exposure to environmental risk factors is sometimes not in your control, especially as a child. Other risk factors, however, are. Among the factors you can control are your habits or behaviors. For example, using sunscreen can reduce your risk of skin cancer. Regular physical activity can lower your risk of high blood pressure, diabetes, and breast cancer. Eating more fruits and vegetables can reduce your risk of colon cancer. Making wise choices now will greatly decrease your risk for disease later on in life.

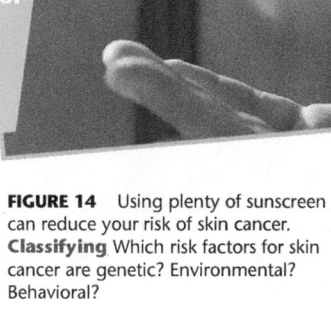

Risk Factors You Can Control
- Unprotected or excessive exposure to the sun
- Use of tanning beds
- Sunburns

Risk Factors You Can't Control
- Fair complexion
- Multiple or abnormal moles
- Family history of skin cancer
- Climate in which you live

FIGURE 14 Using plenty of sunscreen can reduce your risk of skin cancer. **Classifying** Which risk factors for skin cancer are genetic? Environmental? Behavioral?

Reproduction and Heredity **481**

L4 **Building Health Skills**

Analyzing Influences Have some students go online to research risk factors for diseases listed in the text for which a genetic link is suspected—breast cancer, colon cancer, high blood pressure, diabetes, some forms of Alzheimer's disease. Ask students to share what they learn with the class. Use what they report to start a class discussion of the relative influences of heredity, environment, and behavior on the risk of developing diseases with a genetic link.

L3 **Class Discussion**

Point out that genetic testing saves lives but may have drawbacks. Ask: **What might be some drawbacks of genetic testing?** *(Sample answer: high cost; misuse of the information by employers or insurance companies; coping with the knowledge that you will probably develop a particular disease later in life)* Ask students whether they think the drawbacks outweigh the benefits.

 Connect to Your Life Allow students to answer this question in their private journals.

L3 **Visual Learning: Figure 14**

Caption Answer: Fair complexion, multiple or abnormal moles, and a family history of skin cancer are genetic risk factors. Living in a warm, sunny climate is an environmental risk factor. Unprotected or excessive exposure to the sun, use of tanning beds, and sunburns are behavioral risk factors.

L1 **Active Learning**

To give special needs students a hands-on experience to reinforce concepts of sun protection, bring in several items for them to handle, compare, and evaluate. For example, you might bring in a baseball cap and wide-brimmed hat, or hats made of tightly woven and loosely woven fabrics. Also bring in sun lotions and creams with different SPF values. Have students handle the items and discuss how they protect the body. You may want to encourage students to add their own items from home.

Differentiated Instruction

L1 **Special Needs**

Students may not understand the distinction between genetic disorders and diseases with a genetic link. Make two spider diagrams on the board to show students the difference. Inside one of two large circles write *Genetic Disorders,* and inside the other write *Diseases With a Genetic Link.* Draw an arrow, labeled "Genes," to the first circle, and draw three arrows, labeled "Genes," "Behavior," and "Environment," to the second circle. Explain the diagrams to the class. Make sure students understand that they can change their behavior and sometimes their environment to reduce their chances of getting diseases with a genetic link. As you make this point, draw X's through the arrows labeled "Behavior" and "Environment."

Reproduction and Heredity **481**

3. Assess

Evaluate

These assignments can help you assess students' mastery of the section content.

Section 4 Review

Answers appear below.

Teaching Resources

- Practice 18-4
- Section 18-4 Quiz

 L2

Divide the class into small groups, and have members of each group demonstrate their knowledge of section objectives to one another. Group members should reread passages relating to any objectives for which they have disagreements or uncertainties.

 **Enrich**

Teaching Resources

- Enrich 18-4

Health and Community

Supporting a Cause Possible organizations students might contact include the Sickle Cell Disease Association of America and the Cystic Fibrosis Foundation. Web sites for the organizations generally give contact information and information about how people can help. Students' e-mails should be factually correct and persuasive.

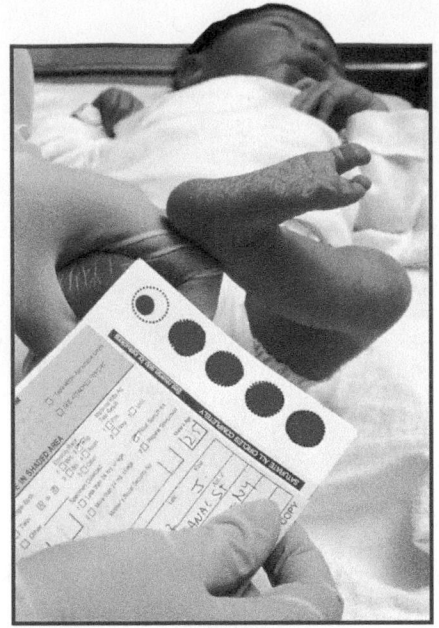

FIGURE 15 In the future, blood samples from newborns may routinely undergo genetic testing for both rare disorders and common diseases.

Medical Advances Today, scientists are working hard to develop new ways to identify and treat genetic disorders and diseases with a genetic link. Areas of research include genetic testing and gene therapy.

▶ **Genetic Testing** Genetic testing involves the analysis of a blood sample for the presence of abnormalities in specific genes. Genetic testing has become more common in recent years. The symptoms of some genetic disorders and most diseases don't show up early in life. By knowing someone has the defective gene as early as possible—in some cases, even before birth— doctors may be able to start therapies that can prevent or reduce future symptoms.

▶ **Gene Therapy** Scientists are currently researching a technique in which healthy copies of a gene are delivered to the cells of a person who has a defective copy of the gene. This therapy would ideally restore normal function to people with a genetic disorder. Unfortunately, gene therapy has yet to be proven as an effective treatment, but the research effort continues.

Section 4 Review

Key Ideas and Vocabulary

1. How is genetic information passed from one generation to the next?
2. What are **genes**? How are they related to **chromosomes**?
3. What are the causes of genetic disorders? Give two examples of genetic disorders.
4. What three factors influence your risk for disease? Which factors are under your control?

Critical Thinking

5. **Predicting** A man with free earlobes—who has two dominant forms of the gene—marries a woman with attached earlobes. What kind of earlobes will their children have? Explain.

Health and Community

Supporting a Cause Contact an organization that supports research for a genetic disorder. Find out how you can help support the cause. Write an e-mail to your friends telling them about the disease, its causes and treatment, and how people can help. **WRITING**

6. **Making Judgments** Government funding for research of some genetic disorders is very low because the disorders are so rare. Is that reasonable? Explain your position.
7. **Evaluating** Research shows that proper use of sunscreen can reduce the risk of skin cancer. However, nearly one third of Americans report never using sunscreen. Write a paragraph evaluating this statistic. Why might people choose not to use sunscreen despite the risk? **WRITING**

GO ONLINE PearsonSuccessNet.com   Audio Summary Section 18.4

Section 4 Review

1. through genes contained on the chromosomes that a person receives from his or her parents
2. Genes are sections of chromosomes that determine characteristics. Each chromosome contains many genes.
3. Genetic disorders are caused by the inheritance of an abnormal gene or chromosome. Accept any two genetic disorders from Figure 13 on page 480.
4. Genes, environment, and behavior influence your risk. Behavior and sometimes environment are under your control.
5. All of their children will have free earlobes because they will inherit the dominant gene for free earlobes from their father.
6. Students may or may not think it is reasonable. Their explanations should provide logical arguments and show a correct understanding of genetic disorders.
7. *Sample answer:* Some people do not use sunscreen because they prefer tanned skin. Others do not use it because they do not like how it feels on their skin.

Chapter 18
At a Glance

 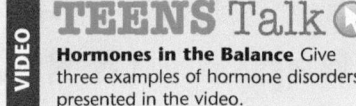
Section 1 The Endocrine System

Key Ideas

▶ The endocrine system regulates long-term changes in the body such as growth and development. It also controls many of your body's daily activities.

▶ The endocrine glands include the hypothalamus, pituitary gland, thyroid gland, parathyroid glands, thymus gland, adrenal glands, pancreas, and reproductive glands.

Vocabulary
- endocrine gland (460)
- hormone (461)
- hypothalamus (461)
- pituitary gland (463)
- puberty (463)

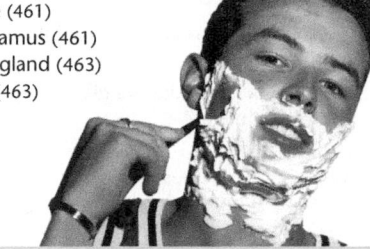

Section 2 The Male Reproductive System

Key Ideas

▶ The functions of the male reproductive system are to produce sex hormones, to produce and store sperm, and to deliver sperm to the female reproductive system.

▶ Caring for the male reproductive system involves cleanliness, sexual abstinence, protection from trauma, self-exams, and regular medical checkups.

Vocabulary
- sperm (464) • fertilization (464) • testes (464)
- testosterone (464) • scrotum (464) • penis (465)
- semen (466) • ejaculation (466) • infertility (468)

Section 3 The Female Reproductive System

Key Ideas

▶ The functions of the female reproductive system are to produce sex hormones, to produce eggs, and to provide a nourishing environment in which a fertilized egg can develop into a baby.

▶ During the menstrual cycle, an ovary releases a mature egg. The egg travels to the uterus. If the egg is not fertilized, the uterine lining is shed and a new cycle begins.

▶ Caring for the female reproductive system involves cleanliness, sexual abstinence, prompt treatment for infections, self-exams, and regular medical checkups.

Vocabulary
- ova (469) • ovaries (469) • estrogen (469)
- progesterone (469) • ovulation (469)
- fallopian tubes (470) • uterus (470) • vagina (470)
- menstrual cycle (471) • menopause (471)
- Pap smear (475) • mammogram (475)

Section 4 Heredity

Key Ideas

▶ Hereditary information passes from one generation to the next through genes contained on the two sets of chromosomes that a person receives from their parents.

▶ Genetic disorders are caused by the inheritance of an abnormal gene or chromosome.

▶ For most diseases, your environment and your behavior affect your risk as much as or even more than your genes.

Vocabulary
- heredity (478) • chromosome (478) • gene (479)
- genetic disorder (480)

Reproduction and Heredity **483**

Chapter 18
At a Glance

VIDEO **Hormones in the Balance** Ask volunteers to share their answers. Use examples from the video to review the endocrine system.

Key Ideas Review

L2 Have pairs of students copy the key ideas listed on this page, leaving one or two important words blank in each key idea. Then have partners exchange key ideas and try to fill in the blanks. They should review passages in the text about any key ideas they cannot complete.

L3 Play a quiz game by restating the boldfaced sentences as questions and having teams take turns answering them. If one team cannot answer a question, give other teams a chance. Award points for correct answers, and give members of the winning team token prizes.

Vocabulary Review

L2 Ask each student to make a crossword puzzle incorporating ten vocabulary terms. Have pairs of students exchange and try to solve one another's puzzle.

EL Have students write sentences in which they correctly use the vocabulary terms. For each term, call on a student to read his or her sentence. Ask other students whether the term was used correctly. If not, call on a volunteer to read his or her sentence for the term.

Chapter 18 Review

GO ONLINE

PearsonSuccessNet.com

Students can go online for a review activity on Chapter 18.

Reviewing Key Ideas

Section 1

1. c

2. adrenaline

3. ovaries in females and testes in males

4. *Sample answer:* Steroids might interfere with the proper development and functioning of the reproductive system, especially in teens, because steroids are similar to sex hormones, which normally regulate the reproductive system and trigger the changes of puberty.

Section 2

5. a

6. production of sperm and physical changes in males at puberty

7. The hypothalamus signals the pituitary gland to release LH and FSH. LH signals the testes to make testosterone. Testosterone and FSH then signal the testes to produce sperm.

8. *Any two:* exposure to certain chemicals, developing mumps after puberty, and undescended testis

9. A large number of sperm increases the chances of successful fertilization and increases the chance of a healthy sperm fertilizing the egg.

Section 3

10. d   11. c

12. LH, FSH, estrogen, and progesterone

13. cancer of the cervix

14. *Sample answer:* She should not be concerned, because menstruation often is irregular during puberty.

Section 4

15. b   16. b

17. A dominant trait appears whenever its gene is present. A recessive trait appears only when the dominant form of the gene is not present. Examples of dominant traits: free earlobes, widow's peak. Examples of recessive traits: attached earlobes, smooth hairline.

Chapter 18 Review

Reviewing Key Ideas

Section 1

1. Which of the following is *not* an endocrine gland?
   a. pituitary gland   b. adrenal gland
   c. prostate gland   d. ovary

2. Which hormone regulates the "fight-or-flight" response?

3. What are the reproductive glands called in females? In males?

4. **Critical Thinking** Steroids abused by some athletes to build muscle contain chemicals similar to sex hormones. Why do you think steroid use can have a harmful effect on the reproductive system, especially in teens?

Section 2

5. In males, straining to lift heavy objects may result in
   a. an inguinal hernia. b. an enlarged prostate.
   c. testicular cancer.   d. infertility.

6. What are two effects of testosterone?

7. Describe the roles played by hormones during sperm production.

8. List two causes of infertility in men.

9. **Critical Thinking** If only one sperm is needed to fertilize an egg, why do you think many sperm are released during ejaculation?

Section 3

10. Which organ releases mature eggs?
    a. uterus   b. pituitary gland
    c. vagina   d. ovary

11. How long is the average menstrual cycle?
    a. 3 to 5 days   b. 14 days
    c. 28 days   d. 9 months

12. Which four hormones play a role in the menstrual cycle?

13. Which kind of cancer may be detected by a Pap smear?

14. **Critical Thinking** Your 13-year-old sister does not mentruate regularly. Should she be concerned? Explain.

Section 4

15. How many chromosomes are contained in each of your sex cells?
    a. 2   b. 23
    c. 46   d. 92

16. Which of the following is *not* a genetic disorder?
    a. sickle cell disease b. breast cancer
    c. cystic fibrosis   d. hemophilia

17. Explain the difference between dominant and recessive traits. Give one example of each.

18. Identify two diseases that may be affected by genetics. What other factors influence the onset of these diseases?

19. **Critical Thinking** Explain how two parents without a genetic disorder could have a child that has the disorder.

 **Building Health Skills**

20. **Accessing Information** Suppose that your younger brother is worried because he's been hearing a lot of myths about puberty from his classmates. How could you help him find accurate information?

21. **Advocacy** Suppose that a friend has confided in you that during a breast self-exam, she detected a lump. She is reluctant to see a doctor. Write an e-mail to your friend with advice. **WRITING**

22. **Setting Goals** Set a personal goal to decrease your risk of skin cancer. Describe a specific change to your behavior that will help you reach your goal. Monitor your progress over the next year.

> ## Health and Community
>
> **Cancer Awareness** Write a script for a public service announcement to raise awareness about prostate or breast cancer. Think about the age of the people you want to target with your message. Develop your message to best reach that audience. **WRITING**

---

18. Any two of the following: breast cancer, colon cancer, high blood pressure, diabetes, Alzheimer's disease. Environment and behavior also influence the onset of these diseases.

19. If two parents each carry one gene for a recessive genetic disorder, their child could inherit two copies of the gene (one from each parent) and have the disorder.

Building Health Skills

20. Answers should include at least one reliable source of accurate information, such as a medical reference book.

21. Students should try to persuade the friend to see a doctor. They might stress how early treatment improves chances of survival. They might say that the lump may not be cancer, in which case finding out would be a relief.

Standardized Test Prep

Math Practice

The graph shows the approximate breakdown of new reproductive cancers diagnosed each year. Use the graph to answer Questions 23–25.

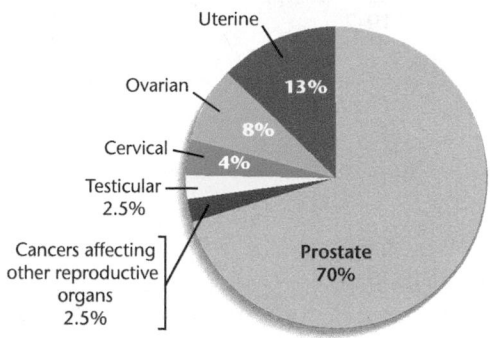

23. Which type of reproductive cancer is most common?
  A ovarian cancer
  B testicular cancer
  C prostate cancer
  D cervical cancer

24. About how much more common is ovarian cancer than cervical cancer?
  F half as common
  G equally common
  H twice as common
  J four times as common

25. What percentage of the total do prostate and testicular cancers represent?
  A 50%   **B** 70.25%
  C 72.5%   **D** 85%

Test-Taking Tip

On test day, be sure to bring along a sweater or sweatshirt. You want to be comfortable no matter how warm or cool it is in the test room.

Reading and Writing Practice

Read the passage. Then answer Questions 26–29.

Two hormones regulate calcium concentration in the bloodstream: calcitonin from the thyroid glands and parathyroid hormone (PTH) from the parathyroid glands. When blood calcium levels are too high, the thyroids release calcitonin. Calcitonin signals cells in the intestine to absorb less calcium from food and signals calcium deposition by bone tissue. If calcium levels drop too low, the parathyroids release PTH. PTH signals the intestine to absorb more calcium from food and signals bone cells to release some of the calcium stored in bone tissue into the bloodstream.

26. After the release of PTH,
  A blood calcium levels decrease.
  B bone tissue deposits calcium.
  C thyroid glands release calcitonin.
  D the intestine absorbs more calcium from food.

27. In this passage, the word *deposition* means
  F reduction.
  G storage.
  H destruction.
  J release.

28. What can you summarize from this passage?
  A Calcitonin and PTH have similar effects.
  B Calcium levels in the body are controlled by hormones.
  C Bones manufacture calcium.
  D Each hormone released by the body targets only one location.

Constructed Response

29. In a paragraph, explain how the body's regulation of blood calcium level is an example of "checks and balances."

Standardized Test Prep

Math Practice
23. C
24. H
25. C

Reading and Writing Practice
26. D
27. G
28. B
29. Paragraphs will vary but should show that students have a correct understanding of how endocrine hormones keep blood calcium levels in balance by controlling processes that increase the calcium level when it is too low and decrease the calcium level when it is too high.

22. Goals will vary but should include ways to reduce exposure to UV light. For example, students might set the goal of always applying sunscreen before going out in the sun.

Health and Community

Cancer Awareness Students' PSAs should be informative and convincing, and they should incorporate accurate information relevant to the age group they are targeting. For example, scripts might include statistics on breast or prostate cancer in the target age group. Students might target people over age 40 or 50, because breast and prostate cancer are more common in older adults.

CHAPTER 19 Pregnancy, Birth, and Childhood

Section Objectives	Standards Correlation	Instructional Resources L_3	SE eTEXT	TE eTEXT	PRINT
1 Development Before Birth ⏱ 1 period; 1/2 block **19.1.1 Summarize** the events that occur during the first week after fertilization. **19.1.2 Describe** the structures that protect and nourish the embryo and fetus.	NHES: 1.12.2, 2.12.8, 3.12.2, 5.12.6, 8.12.4	SE Warm-Up, p. 488	•	•	•
		RN Note Taking Guide 19-1	•	•	•
		IB Image Bank 19-2		•	
		TR Practice 19-1		•	
		TR Section 19-1 Quiz		•	
2 A Healthy Pregnancy ⏱ 2 periods; 1 block **19.2.1 Identify** four behaviors that are essential for a healthy pregnancy. **19.2.2 Explain** the importance of prenatal care throughout pregnancy.	NHES: 1.12.1, 1.12.3, 1.12.6, 1.12.9, 2.12.6, 3.12.1, 3.12.4, 7.12.3	SE Warm-Up, p. 492	•	•	•
		SE Technology & Health Surgery Before Birth, p. 497	•	•	•
		RN Note Taking Guide 19-2	•	•	•
		TR Practice 19-2		•	
		TR Section 19-2 Quiz		•	
3 Childbirth ⏱ 2 periods; 1 block **19.3.1 Identify** the three stages of the birth process. **19.3.2 Describe** four complicating factors that may arise at birth.	NHES: 1.12.1, 1.12.9, 5.12.6	SE Warm-Up, p. 498	•	•	•
		SE Hands-On Activity Be a Parent for a Day, p. 500	•	•	•
		RN Note Taking Guide 19-3	•	•	•
		IB Image Bank 19-6, 19-9		•	
		TR Practice 19-3		•	
		TR Section 19-3 Quiz		•	
Coping With Change ⏱ 1 period; 1/2 block **BHS.19 Implement** a plan to cope with transition times in life.	NHES: 1.12.5, 3.12.2, 6.12.2, 6.12.3	SE Practice the Skill, p. 505	•	•	•
		RN Building Health Skills 19	•	•	•
4 Childhood ⏱ 1 period; 1/2 block **19.4.1 Describe** the changes that children undergo during early childhood. **19.4.2 Identify** key areas of development that occur during middle and late childhood.	NHES: 2.12.1, 2.12.3, 8.12.1, 8.12.4	SE Warm-Up, p. 506	•	•	•
		RN Note Taking Guide 19-4	•	•	•
		TR Practice 19-4		•	
		TR Section 19-4 Quiz		•	

Chapter Review and Assessment

SE Chapter 19 Review, p. 510 L3

CTB Chapter 19 Test L2 L3 L4

SE Standardized Test Prep, p. 511 L3

PROGRAM COMPONENTS

SE	Student Edition	**CTB**	Computer Test Bank
TE	Teacher Edition	**AUD**	Audio Section Summaries
TR	Teaching Resources		
RN	Reading and Note Taking Guide	**DVD**	Teens Talk Video Series
		VVG	Video Viewing Guide
ARN	Adapted Reading and Note Taking Guide	**PPT**	Presentation
IB	Image Bank		

Differentiated Instruction
L1 L2 L4 EL

		SE eTEXT	TE eTEXT	PRINT
ARN	Note Taking Guide 19-1 L2	•	•	
RN	Note Taking Guide 19-1 EL	•	•	•
AUD	Audio Summary 19-1 L1 L2 EL	•	•	
TE	Reteach Strategy, p. 491 L2		•	•
TR	Enrich 19-1 L4		•	
ARN	Note Taking Guide 19-2 L2	•	•	
RN	Note Taking Guide 19-2 EL	•	•	•
AUD	Audio Summary 19-2 L1 L2 EL	•	•	
TE	Reteach Strategy, p. 496 L2		•	•
TR	Enrich 19-2 L4		•	
ARN	Note Taking Guide 19-3 L2	•	•	
RN	Note Taking Guide 19-3 EL	•	•	•
AUD	Audio Summary 19-3 L1 L2 EL	•	•	
TE	Reteach Strategy, p. 503 L2		•	•
TR	Enrich 19-3 L4		•	
ARN	Building Health Skills 19 L2	•	•	
RN	Building Health Skills 19 EL	•	•	•
ARN	Note Taking Guide 19-4 L2	•	•	
RN	Note Taking Guide 19-4 EL	•	•	•
AUD	Audio Summary 19-4 L1 L2 EL	•	•	
TE	Reteach Strategy, p. 508 L2		•	•
TR	Enrich 19-4 L4		•	

ABILITY LEVELS
- L1 **For students with special needs**
- L2 **For less proficient readers**
- L3 **For all students**
- L4 **For gifted and talented students**
- EL **For English language learners**

Chapter 19 Digital/Video Pathway

This alternative pathway allows you to teach this chapter's content using only the video and online materials.

Preview
DVD	Video #19 Preview
SE	Video #19 Preview Activity
VVG	Video #19 Worksheet

Teen Pregnancy

1
PPT	19-1 Presentation
RN/ARN	19-1 Note Taking
PPT	19-1 Section Quiz

2
DVD	Video #19 Explore/Wrap-Up
VVG	Video #19 Worksheet
PPT	19-2 Presentation
RN/ARN	19-2 Note Taking
PPT	19-2 Section Quiz

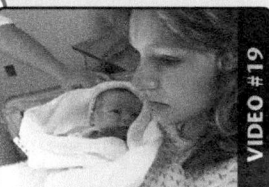
Teen Pregnancy

3
PPT	19-3 Presentation
RN/ARN	19-3 Note Taking
PPT	19-3 Section Quiz

4
PPT	19-4 Presentation
RN/ARN	19-4 Note Taking
PPT	19-4 Section Quiz

Chapter Preview

Section 1 Development Before Birth
Immediately after fertilization, the fertilized egg undergoes many cell divisions as it travels to the uterus. After the embryo implants in the uterus, it grows into a fetus and is protected and nourished by the amniotic sac, placenta, and umbilical cord.

Section 2 A Healthy Pregnancy
Getting proper nutrition and exercise and avoiding drugs and environmental hazards are especially important before and during pregnancy. Regular doctor visits throughout pregnancy help ensure the birth of a healthy baby.

Section 3 Childbirth
The birth process begins when the uterine muscles start contracting. Birth occurs in three stages—labor, delivery of the baby, and delivery of the after-birth. Complications at birth include premature birth, the need for a cesarean section, low birthweight, and multiple births.

 Setting Goals

Coping With Change
Students learn to effectively cope with change by building support systems and working through setbacks.

Section 4 Childhood
As babies grow into pre-adolescent children, they undergo many physical, mental, and social changes. Newborns, who are completely dependent on their parents, develop independence and the ability for higher-level thinking as they grow up.

GO ONLINE

PearsonSuccessNet.com

For resources and activities for this chapter.

Pregnancy, Birth, and Childhood

1 Development Before Birth

2 A Healthy Pregnancy
- **Technology & Health** Surgery Before Birth

3 Childbirth
- **Hands-On Activity** Be a Parent for a Day

 Building Health Skills
- **Setting Goals** Coping With Change

4 Childhood

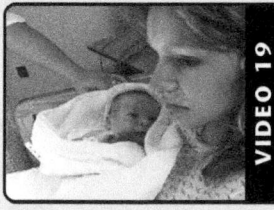

GO ONLINE PearsonSuccessNet.com

TEENS Talk

VIDEO 19

Teen Pregnancy

Preview **Activity**

How Would Your Plans Change?

Complete this activity before you watch the video.

1. Make a list of your plans for the weekend. Make a second list of your plans for after graduation.
2. Now suppose that you were a teen parent. Describe all the ways you think your weekend plans and your long-term plans would need to change. **WRITING**

Sensitive Issues

- Many students may feel uncomfortable during discussions of pregnancy and childbirth because of their association with sexual activity as well as their intimate involvement with female anatomy. To help students feel comfortable, maintain a matter-of-fact tone in all discussions about these concepts. Make it known that inappropriate laughter and crude comments will not be tolerated.

- Keep in mind that some students in the class may be or have been pregnant. Pay close attention to signs of student discomfort when discussing these concepts.

Video Objectives

Use the video to help students

Describe the extra challenges that teen parents face.

Explain why prenatal care is especially important for teen mothers.

Evaluate the sacrifices and setbacks to life goals experienced by teen parents.

Preview **Activity**

How Would Your Plans Change?

Assign the Preview Activity in class before showing the video. After students complete the activity, ask for volunteers to share their conclusions about how parenthood would affect both their weekend plans and their long-term plans. Summarize the themes that emerge from the discussion.

487

From the Authors

Any discussion about pregnancy and childbirth can cause a normally responsive class to sink into an embarrassed silence. Not only is the whole birth process scary, it also involves the female reproductive system. When teaching this chapter, connect the growth and development of the fetus to that of the child. Expand on students' experiences of their own childhood or family stories told of them. For discussions about pregnancy and prenatal care and the birth process, shift the focus to a hypothetical married couple.

The activities and questions in this chapter are designed to help students see the impact of pregnancy and a newborn on the life of a married couple. See, for example, the Health and Community activity on page 491, the Hands-On Activity on page 500, and the Building Health Skills activity on pages 504–505.

Objectives
Before class begins, write the objectives on the board. Have students copy the objectives into their notebooks at the start of class.

1. Focus

Warm-Up Quick Quiz

Use the Warm-Up Presentation slide to survey student responses.

After students finish writing, ask them to share the factors they thought married couples should consider before having children. List their responses on the board. Discuss the problems with reasons 1, 3, and 4. Also discuss whether 2 and 5 are good enough reasons on their own, or if prospective parents should consider other factors as well.

Presentation 19-1

Objectives
▶ **Summarize** the events that occur during the first week after fertilization.
▶ **Describe** the structures that protect and nourish the embryo and fetus.

Vocabulary
- zygote
- embryo
- blastocyst
- implantation
- amniotic sac
- placenta
- umbilical cord
- fetus

Warm-Up

Quick Quiz Which of the following statements made by a married couple do you think are good reasons for having a baby? Choose one or more.

1. "It's now or never. We're almost 40."
2. "We have lots of love to give a child."
3. "If we have one more, maybe it will be a girl."
4. "Our marriage will improve if we have a baby."
5. "With our new jobs, we've finally saved enough money to start a family."

WRITING In a paragraph, describe the factors that a married couple should consider before they have children.

The Beginning of the Life Cycle

Parenthood has many joys and satisfactions, but it is also stressful and involves a lot of hard work. The responsibilities of parenthood go far beyond those of most other occupations. Babies are demanding and totally helpless.

Along with the loving feelings, smiles, and cuddles, new parents face sleepless nights, worries about illness, and the loss of many freedoms they used to enjoy. Parents must also be prepared to give their child love and guidance throughout his or her life, not just as a baby.

Once a couple has decided to start a family, they may try to conceive, or get pregnant. Recall from Chapter 18 that, in a fertile woman's body, about once a month an egg enters one of the fallopian tubes and begins its journey to the uterus. During sexual intercourse, sperm from the man are deposited into the vagina. Some of these sperm swim through the uterus to the fallopian tubes. If the egg is on its way to the uterus, a sperm may fertilize it. This moment of fertilization is also called conception.

488 *Chapter 19*

⚑ Sensitive Issues
Discussing the process of conception may be awkward for you and your students. As a strategy to minimize the awkwardness without skipping this important topic, briefly review with students how and where fertilization occurs, then shift the lesson's focus to the development of the fertilized egg.

WRITING and Health

L3 Firsthand Account

Have students write a fictional firsthand account that describes the growing embryo's journey from the fallopian tube to the uterus. Students should include all the events that occur as the embryo makes this journey, beginning with the formation of the embryo after the zygote divides and ending with the implantation of the blastocyst. Suggest that students use Figure 1 to guide them through their story. Remind students that because this is a firsthand account, they should describe this journey from the perspective of the growing embryo.

1 Fertilization   In Figure 1, you can track the events that occur in the first week after fertilization. Only a few hundred sperm of the hundreds of millions that enter the vagina usually make it to the egg, and only one can fertilize it. Within seconds of fertilization, the surface of the egg changes so that no more sperm can enter the egg. **In the first week after fertilization, the fertilized egg undergoes many cell divisions and travels to the uterus.**

2 The Zygote   The united egg and sperm is called a **zygote** (ZY goht). Within 36 hours, while the zygote is still traveling through the fallopian tube, it begins to divide.

3 Cell Division   The original cell divides to make two cells. From the two-cell stage until about nine weeks after fertilization, the growing structure is called an **embryo** (EM bree oh). The two-celled embryo divides into four cells, and so on.

4 The Blastocyst   About five days after fertilization, the embryo reaches the uterus, where it floats free for a few days. By this time, it is made up of about 50 to 100 cells. The structure, called a **blastocyst** (BLAS tuh sist), is no longer a solid mass of cells, but a sphere of cells surrounding a hollow center.

5 Implantation   Once the blastocyst forms, it begins to attach itself to the wall of the uterus. The process of attachment is called **implantation.**

FIGURE 1   The fertilized egg travels to the uterus in the first week of pregnancy.
Interpreting Diagrams Through which structure does the embryo travel before reaching the uterus?

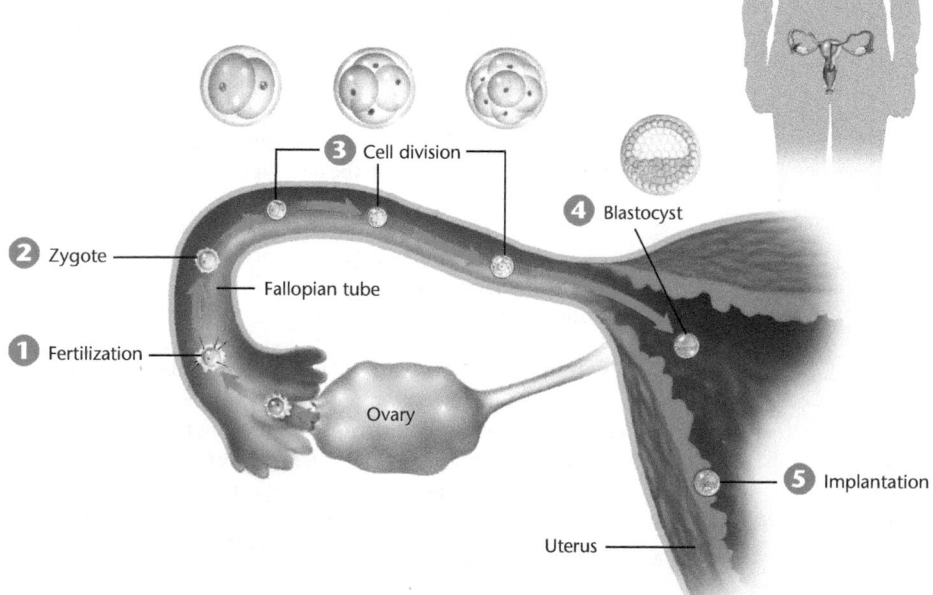

3 Cell division

4 Blastocyst

2 Zygote

Fallopian tube

1 Fertilization

Ovary

5 Implantation

Uterus

Pregnancy, Birth, and Childhood **489**

2. Teach

L3 EL Reading/Note Taking 19-1
L2 Adapted Reading/Note Taking 19-1

The Beginning of the Life Cycle

L3 Active Learning

Have students construct a time line on poster board that shows the stages and time frame of the development of an embryo during the first week. Students should begin the time line with fertilization and end it with implantation. They should also describe the location of the developing embryo through time. The time line should include these terms: zygote, cell division, embryo, blastocyst, and implantation.

L2 Visual Learning: Figure 1

Use Figure 1 to discuss the development of a fertilized egg. Begin with fertilization, pointing out that it occurs in a fallopian tube and that only one sperm fertilizes the egg. Then ask: **What is the fertilized egg called?** *(zygote)* **How long does it remain a zygote?** *(until it divides into two cells)* **About how long does it take the embryo to travel to the uterus?** *(about five days)* Point out the structure of the blastocyst. Explain that the outer group of cells will develop into a membrane that will nourish and protect the embryo. The inner group of cells forms the embryo.
Caption Answer fallopian tube

Differentiated Instruction

EL English Language Learners

Identify vocabulary terms for students to learn based on their level of understanding. For beginning English language learners, use the terms *embryo*, *placenta*, and *fetus*. Add *umbilical cord*, *implantation*, and *amniotic sac* to the list for intermediate students. Have students make flashcards for each term they are given. Students should include definitions, phonetic spellings if needed, and illustrations to help them with meaning.

Development in the Uterus

L2 Visual Learning: Figure 2
Image Bank Figure 19-2

Ask students to name the protective structures associated with the embryo. *(amniotic sac, placenta, umbilical cord)* Then ask: **What is the amniotic sac?** *(a fluid-filled bag of thin tissue around the embryo)* **How are the functions of the placenta and the umbilical cord similar?** *(Both carry nutrients and wastes between the mother and embryo.)*

L3 Teacher Demo

Demonstrate how amniotic fluid acts as a shock absorber. Attach a string with strong glue to each of two small balls. Suspend each ball in a separate jar or clear plastic container by tying the end of the string to a pencil that lies across the top of the container. Fill one container with water so that the ball is underwater. (Use balls that do not float, such as golf balls.) Then jiggle both containers with the same amount of force. Have students compare the movement of the balls. *(The ball in water will not swing as quickly as the ball in air.)* Then have students explain how amniotic fluid can cushion the embryo from shock. *(The amniotic fluid absorbs the force of the motion.)*

L1 Active Learning

To help students conceptualize the size of the fetus at various stages, have them use rulers to measure and mark off on a piece of paper one inch (eight-week embryo), 11 inches (average length of six-month fetus), and 20 inches (average length of a newborn). Show students pictures of the developing embryo at each of these stages. Then encourage students to find items in the classroom that are similar in size.

Connect to Your Life Fluids protect the brain and spinal cord, and lubricate some joints.

L3 Online Activity GO ONLINE

Visit Pearson SuccessNet to access an online activity about development before birth. Have students complete the Web activity.

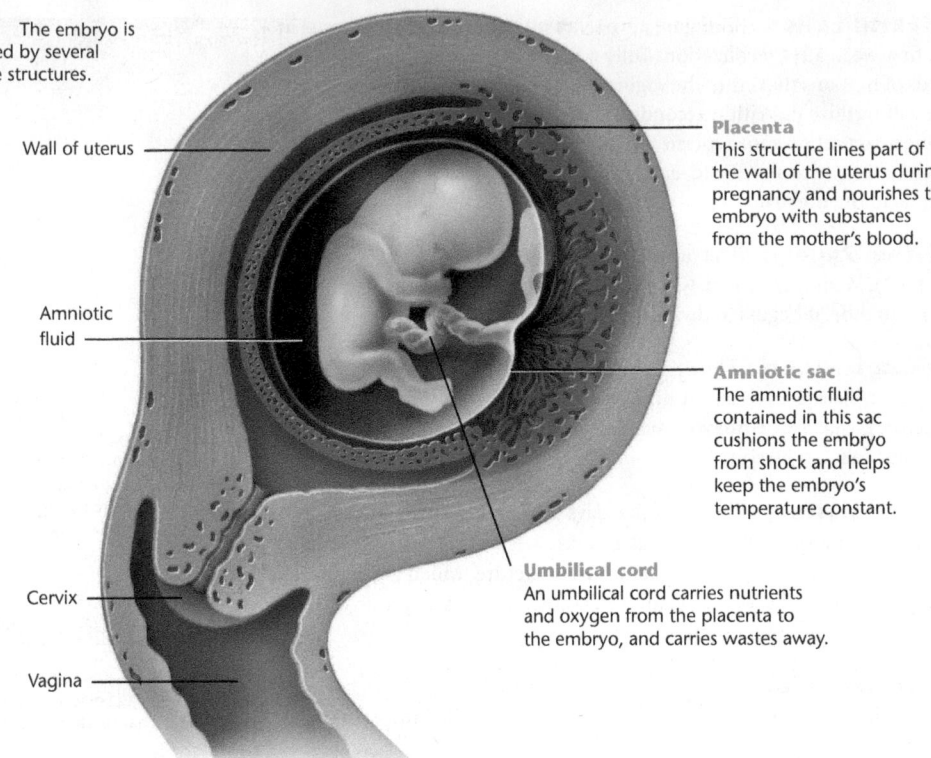

FIGURE 2 The embryo is surrounded by several protective structures.

Wall of uterus

Placenta
This structure lines part of the wall of the uterus during pregnancy and nourishes the embryo with substances from the mother's blood.

Amniotic fluid

Amniotic sac
The amniotic fluid contained in this sac cushions the embryo from shock and helps keep the embryo's temperature constant.

Cervix

Umbilical cord
An umbilical cord carries nutrients and oxygen from the placenta to the embryo, and carries wastes away.

Vagina

Development in the Uterus

After implantation, development continues in the uterus. While the embryo grows, several other structures that you can see in Figure 2 also develop. **These structures—the amniotic sac, placenta, and umbilical cord—protect and nourish the developing embryo, and later the fetus.**

Amniotic Sac Soon after implantation, a fluid-filled bag of thin tissue called the **amniotic sac** (am nee AHT ik) develops around the embryo. The sac continues to grow in size as the embryo grows. Inside the sac, the embryo floats in amniotic fluid.

Placenta The attachment holding the embryo to the wall of the uterus develops into a structure called the **placenta.** Within the placenta, oxygen and nutrients move from the mother's blood into tiny blood vessels that lead to the embryo. Dangerous substances can pass from mother to embryo, too, including alcohol, drugs, the chemicals in tobacco smoke, and some microscopic organisms that cause disease. Any of these substances can seriously harm the developing embryo.

 **GO ONLINE**
PearsonSuccessNet.com
For: More on development before birth

Connect to Your Life How do you think the fluid-filled sac helps protect a fetus during pregnancy?

TEENS *Are Asking . . .*

Q: Since a fetus doesn't breathe, how could the mother's smoking habit harm it?

A: Smoking increases the carbon monoxide levels in the mother's blood, which is shared with the fetus across the placenta. Blood that contains carbon monoxide cannot carry normal amounts of oxygen. Thus, the amount of oxygen available to the embryo or fetus is reduced. In addition, the nicotine in cigarette smoke causes blood vessels to narrow, reducing the amount of blood that can enter the placenta. With less blood entering the placenta, less oxygen and fewer nutrients are available to the fetus.

Together, these effects of smoking during pregnancy slow fetal growth, which may cause the newborn to be underweight and at greater risk for health problems and death.

Umbilical Cord About 25 days after fertilization, a ropelike structure called the **umbilical cord** (um BIL ih kul) develops between the embryo and the placenta. The umbilical cord is the embryo's lifeline. Blood vessels in the umbilical cord carry nutrients and oxygen from the placenta to the embryo and wastes from the embryo to the placenta.

The Growing Embryo During the first two months of development, the major body systems and organs start to form in the embryo. For example, a beating heart, major blood vessels, kidneys, and endocrine glands develop. By the end of eight weeks, the embryo is about an inch long and has recognizable external features such as eyes, ears, arms, and legs. The head is large in proportion to the body—it makes up nearly 50 percent of the length of the embryo.

The Fetus From the third month until birth, the developing human is called a **fetus.** During the third to sixth month, the fetus begins to move and kick, a sign that its skeleton and muscles are developing. As its nervous system matures, the sense organs begin to function. The fetus becomes sensitive to light and sound and alternates periods of activity with periods of sleep.

From the seventh to the ninth month, the fetus continues to grow and develop. The size of the body increases so that it is more in proportion to the size of the head, and body fat accumulates. The eyelids open and close. By the end of the ninth month, the fetus is ready to be born.

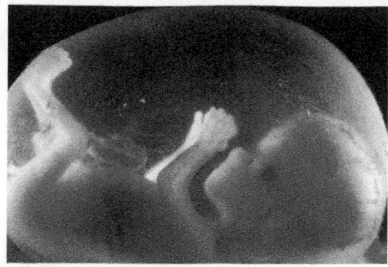

▲ **Fetus at 3 months**

▼ **Fetus at 8 months**

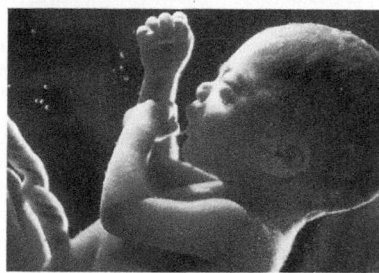

FIGURE 3 Between the third and eighth month of development, the facial features and limbs of a fetus change dramatically.

Section 1 Review

Key Ideas and Vocabulary

1. What happens during the first week of human development?
2. What happens during **implantation**?
3. What three structures protect and nourish the embryo, and later the fetus?
4. What is the **placenta**? What is its function?
5. How does a **fetus** change between the third and sixth months of pregnancy?

Critical Thinking

6. Calculating Suppose that only 200 sperm out of the original 400 million sperm deposited in the vagina survive the journey to the egg. What percentage is this? **MATH**

Health and Community

Support for New Parents Many communities offer free support groups for new parents. At the support group, parents can share the joys and frustrations of caring for their newborn. They may also learn new skills, such as how to bathe, diaper, and give first aid to their baby. Find out what services your community offers and make a pamphlet for new parents. **WRITING**

---

7. **Relating Cause and Effect** Why is it an unhealthy decision for a pregnant woman to drink alcohol?
8. **Sequencing** List in order the following steps of development: eyelids open and close, legs kick, embryo is about an inch long, amniotic sac develops.

Section 2

A Healthy Pregnancy

Objectives
Before class begins, write the objectives on the board. Have students copy the objectives into their notebooks at the start of class.

1. Focus

Warm-Up **Myth/Fact**

Ask students to share their do's and don'ts for pregnant women. List them on the board. Refer back to this list throughout the section, correcting any misconceptions that students might have had.

Presentation 19-2

Sensitive Issues

Discussing prenatal care may be distressing to girls in your class who are pregnant, have been pregnant, or think they could be pregnant. Boys who are fathers, or think they could be fathers, might also be concerned. Be aware of any student who is more self-conscious than usual. Take care not to draw attention to this student. Focus only on prenatal care from the perspective of a married couple, but do make yourself discreetly available to answer questions.

Section 2   A Healthy Pregnancy

Objectives
▶ **Identify** four behaviors that are essential for a healthy pregnancy.
▶ **Explain** the importance of prenatal care throughout pregnancy.

Vocabulary
• prenatal care
• obstetrician
• trimester
• ultrasound
• chorionic villus sampling
• amniocentesis
• ectopic pregnancy
• miscarriage
• preeclampsia
• gestational diabetes

Warm-Up

Myth A pregnant woman doesn't need to visit the doctor until she begins to show, or look pregnant.

Fact Regular doctor visits from the beginning of pregnancy until the birth are recommended to ensure health.

WRITING List some other do's and don'ts for pregnant women. Review and update your list when you complete this section.

Staying Healthy During Pregnancy

Amanda starts her day with a bowl of oatmeal. Later, she and her husband go out for a brisk walk. At night, she skips a party where people will be smoking.

Amanda and her husband are thinking about having a baby. Even before she becomes pregnant, Amanda started taking extra care to have a healthy pregnancy. **Getting proper nutrition and exercise and avoiding drugs and environmental hazards are especially important both before and throughout pregnancy.**

Proper Nutrition   "Now you're eating for two," people sometimes say to pregnant women. This is because a pregnant woman needs to eat more calories to support the growth of her own body and the developing embryo or fetus. During pregnancy, a woman needs to consume about 300 more calories than usual. The best way to obtain these extra calories is to eat a well-balanced diet rich in the key nutrients listed in Figure 4.

One vitamin that is especially important during pregnancy is folic acid, or folate. Folic acid is essential for proper development of an embryo's neural tube, which later develops into the spinal cord and brain. The neural tube forms early in an embryo's development, often before a woman knows she is pregnant. Therefore, a woman should not wait until she knows she is pregnant to get enough folic acid. Doctors recommend that all women of childbearing age consume at least 0.4 mg (400 micrograms) of folic acid every day.

For Your INFORMATION!

Changes During Pregnancy

Almost every organ and system in a woman's body is affected by pregnancy. The most important changes occur in the reproductive system. Ovulation and menstruation cease. The muscular walls of the uterus get stronger and more elastic. The cervix produces a mucus plug that prevents bacteria from entering the uterus.

A pregnant woman also experiences physiological changes that allow sufficient blood and oxygen to reach the growing embryo. Her heart beats slightly faster, and the volume of blood circulating in her body increases. The amount of oxygen her body uses increases by 15 to 20 percent.

Exercise Regular physical activity is also important for a healthy pregnancy. A fit woman will better meet the extra energy demands of carrying the fetus. She also reduces her risk for diabetes and other health problems during pregnancy. A woman should get her doctor's approval for her exercise program. Some forms of exercise should be avoided—for example, horseback riding, where there is a high risk of falling.

Avoiding Alcohol and Other Drugs As soon as she plans to become pregnant, a woman should abstain from all alcohol, tobacco, and any other drugs not prescribed or approved by her doctor. These substances, even in small amounts, can harm or kill the developing baby, decrease the newborn's chance to live, or cause lifelong problems. For example, women who drink alcohol during pregnancy risk having a baby with fetal alcohol syndrome. As you read in Chapter 15, symptoms of fetal alcohol syndrome may include mental retardation, minor to severe heart defects, and delayed growth.

Some drugs that are typically safe outside of pregnancy can cause harm to a fetus. A pregnant woman should talk to her doctor before using any prescription drugs or over-the-counter drugs, such as pain medications; creams and lotions; and vitamins. Likewise, a woman should get her doctor's approval before using herbal teas or herbal supplements.

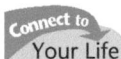

Connect to Your Life **Which recommendations for pregnant women are also good everyday advice for yourself?**

FIGURE 4 Proper nutrition contributes to the healthy development of a baby. **Reading Tables** Name three nutrients that play a role in the development of the nervous system.

Important Nutrients During Pregnancy

Nutrient	Needed For
Folic acid	Formation of neural tube; brain and spinal cord development
Protein	Muscle formation and growth
Calcium	Bone and tooth formation; nerve and muscle development
Iron	Oxygen delivery by blood cells
Vitamin A	Cell and bone growth; eye development
Vitamin B complex	Nervous system development

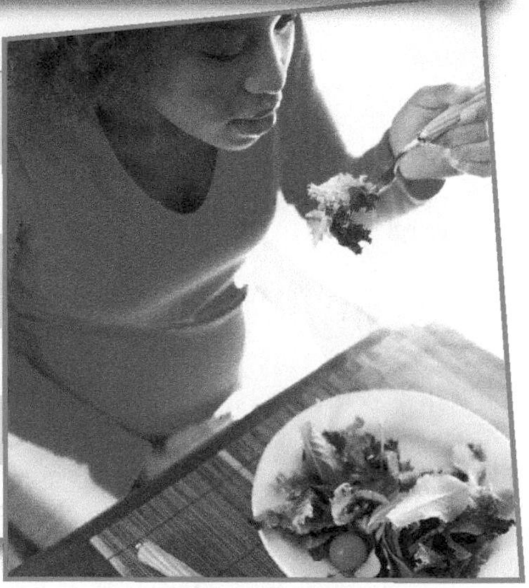

2. Teach

L3 EL **Reading/Note Taking** 19-2

L2 **Adapted Reading/Note Taking** 19-2

Staying Healthy During Pregnancy

L3 Active Learning

Explain that pregnant women can participate in many forms of exercise, but are cautioned against participating in others. Have students work in small groups to prepare an informational brochure about exercise for pregnant women. The brochure should help the women distinguish forms of exercise that are not appropriate from forms that are highly recommended. Students should divide up the task of collecting data. Some can search reliable Web sites. Others can interview an obstetrician and a fitness instructor who works with pregnant women. **WRITING**

L2 Visual Learning: Figure 4

Review the nutrients listed in Figure 4. Discuss food sources of these vitamins and minerals. If necessary, refer students to the charts in Chapter 8, Section 2. Explain that pregnant women are routinely given vitamin supplements as part of their prenatal care. Ask: **Why should women who are considering pregnancy get adequate amounts of these nutrients?** *(Critical embryonic development has already occurred before a woman realizes that she is pregnant.)*

Caption Answer folic acid, calcium, vitamin B complex

Connect to Your Life *Sample answer:* proper nutrition, exercise, and avoiding alcohol and other drugs

Differentiated Instruction

L2 Less Proficient Readers

After students read about the four behaviors that are essential for a healthy pregnancy, have them create a word web that summarizes the reading. Suggest that students use the title of the subsection, Staying Healthy During Pregnancy, in the center circle of the web. Students can use the run-in headings to name the behaviors that branch from the center circle. Finally, students should add details in circles that are attached to each behavior.

Pregnancy, Birth, and Childhood **493**

L3 Building Health Skills

Advocacy Have students write an e-mail to an imaginary older cousin or sister who is newly pregnant. In their e-mails, students should describe one environmental hazard their cousin or sister might inadvertently come into contact with. Students should explain how this substance or organism can harm the growing embryo and advocate for avoiding it. **WRITING**

Prenatal Care

L2 Building Vocabulary

Point out the meanings of the Latin roots of the word *trimester*. *Tri-* means "three;" *mensis* means "month." Ask students to list and define other words beginning with the prefix *tri-*. (Triangle, *a figure with three angles*; trilogy, *a story with three parts*; triplets, *three babies born at the same time*.) Then ask students to think of words that use the Latin root word *mensis*. (Semester, *originally a school term of six months*; menstruation, *bleeding that occurs each month in fertile women*)

L3 Cooperative Learning

Explain to students that during visits to her doctor, a pregnant woman has an opportunity to ask questions about her pregnancy, as well as how to care for her baby after it is born. Have student groups produce a list of questions that a woman might ask her doctor during a prenatal visit. Then ask groups to share their questions with the class.

Avoiding Environmental Hazards Some common substances found in the environment, including many chemicals and disease-causing organisms, can seriously harm a fetus. Pregnant women should take care to avoid exposure to these substances.

▶ **X-rays** The radiation from X-rays can harm a developing embryo or fetus. This is why doctors and dentists ask women if they could possibly be pregnant before taking an X-ray.

▶ **Lead** The main source of exposure to lead is from lead-based paint present in older homes. If a pregnant woman lives in a home built before 1978, she should contact her state health department for information on getting her home tested for lead.

▶ **Mercury** Most exposure to this dangerous metal comes from eating contaminated fish. Pregnant women should eat commercially caught fish only once a week, and should not eat swordfish or shark.

▶ **Cat litter** Cat feces can contain a parasite that is especially dangerous to a developing fetus. Pregnant women should avoid contacting soiled cat litter or garden soil.

Prenatal Care

Besides taking care of herself at home, a woman also needs to plan for **prenatal care,** or medical care during her pregnancy. Her doctor visits should be under the supervision of an **obstetrician,** a doctor specialized in pregnancy and childbirth. **The chances of having a healthy baby greatly increase if the mother visits her doctor or clinic for regular checkups throughout pregnancy.**

The Three Trimesters A pregnancy is divided into three periods of time—trimesters—each of which is approximately three months long. Figure 5 lists things the parents-to-be can expect at routine visits.

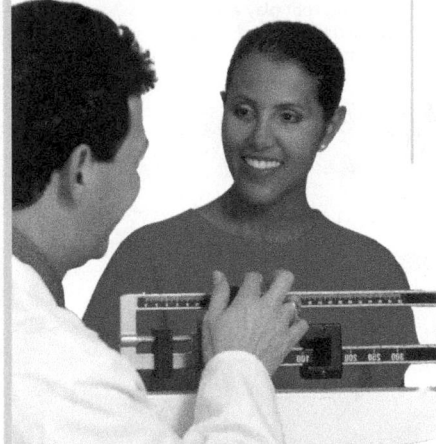

FIGURE 5 A doctor monitors the health of the mother-to-be and her fetus during regular prenatal visits.

First Trimester
- Record medical history and weight
- Note conditions that could affect the pregnancy
- Prescribe prenatal vitamins as needed

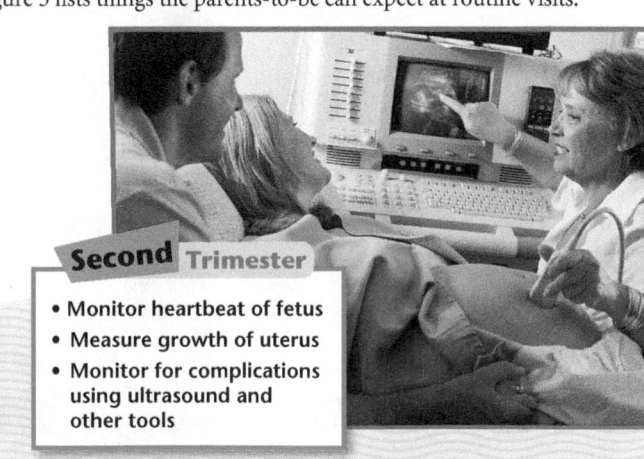

Second Trimester
- Monitor heartbeat of fetus
- Measure growth of uterus
- Monitor for complications using ultrasound and other tools

494 *Chapter 19*

WRITING and Health

L2 Summary

Have students write a summary about how to stay healthy during pregnancy. Students should base their summaries on the four behaviors that are essential for a healthy pregnancy described in the section.

Summaries should clearly differentiate between behaviors that should be practiced and behaviors that should be avoided. Challenge students to limit their summaries to one or two paragraphs.

Monitoring Tools Prenatal care gives a pregnant woman access to the latest medical tests and technologies.

▶ **Ultrasound** Did you know that your first pictures may have been taken months before you were born? High-frequency sound waves, or **ultrasound,** are used in most pregnancies to create an image of the developing fetus. Ultrasound may be used at any point during pregnancy, although it is typically used in the sixteenth to twentieth week. Using ultrasound, a doctor can tell the age of the fetus, whether it is a boy or girl, and if the heart, muscles, and bones are developing normally. Ultrasound may also detect the presence of more than one fetus or confirm the position of the fetus in the uterus.

▶ **Chorionic Villus Sampling** Around the eighth week of pregnancy, some women will undergo a test called **chorionic villus sampling,** or CVS. To perform the test, the doctor removes and tests a small piece of the developing placenta. CVS can detect inherited disorders in the embryo such as hemophilia or extra chromosomes. The test is only done when risk factors are present, such as a family history of genetic disorders or when the mother is over the age of 35. An older mother has an increased risk of having a baby with Down syndrome or other chromosomal abnormalities.

▶ **Amniocentesis** Another test that may be done around the fourteenth to sixteenth week of pregnancy is **amniocentesis** (am nee oh sen TEE sis). The procedure involves inserting a needle into the woman's abdomen and uterus to remove a small amount of amniotic fluid surrounding the fetus. The doctor then tests fetal cells naturally found in this fluid for abnormalities. Like CVS, amniocentesis is only performed when the fetus is at higher risk for a genetic disorder. CVS and amniocentesis are not routine tests because they slightly increase the risk of miscarriage, or death of the fetus.

Connect to Your Life **Have you ever seen an ultrasound picture of a fetus? What features could you recognize?**

Third Trimester
- Check position and size of fetus
- Check for warning signs of premature, or early, birth
- Continue to monitor for complications
- Discuss birth process

Pregnancy, Birth, and Childhood **495**

Differentiated Instruction

EL English Language Learners
The terms that describe the monitoring tools used during pregnancy and the possible complications of pregnancy might be difficult for students to say and comprehend. Work with students to create a notebook or bulletin board display of these terms. Include pictures or diagrams for terms that lend themselves to visuals (such as ultrasound and amniocentesis). Also include phonetic spellings and simple definitions. Have students practice saying the terms by pairing them with students who can pronounce the terms correctly.

L2 Visual Learning: Figure 5
Use the charts in Figure 5 showing typical events during prenatal checkups to begin a discussion on the importance of prenatal care. Ask: **What kinds of issues are addressed by the doctor during the first trimester?** *(preparing for future changes during the pregnancy, helping the mother change her behaviors to ensure a healthy baby)* **What is the focus of prenatal care during the second trimester?** *(the health of the mother and the developing fetus and the presence of complications)* **The third trimester?** *(getting ready for delivery and monitoring the fetus and mother for any health issues)* Explain that fathers are encouraged to accompany the mother during prenatal visits to give support, share in the joy of monitoring the growth of the fetus, and help make decisions about complications that might arise.

L1 Active Learning
Share pictures of ultrasound images of your own children or those of fellow teachers, friends, or family. Pass around the photos, or alternatively, make them into slides to project, and have students name any structures they can identify. Point out that internal structures, such as the brain, heart, stomach, and skeleton, are also imaged by ultrasound and may be visible in your pictures. Help students locate any internal parts that show up in your pictures. Remind students that ultrasound is a very useful, low-risk tool for doctors to check on the health of a fetus.

L3 Building Health Skills
Making Decisions Explain that it is possible for parents to learn the sex of their baby during pregnancy. Discuss the advantages and disadvantages of learning this information. Then ask students to write a paragraph explaining whether or not they would want to know the baby's sex if they had to make this decision. **WRITING**

Connect to Your Life Recognizable features include arms, legs, head, eyes, fingers, and toes.

 **Content Update** GO ONLINE

Visit Pearson SuccessNet to access more information about pregnancy care. Have students complete the Web activity.

3. Assess

Evaluate
These assignments can help you assess students' mastery of the section content.

Section 2 Review
Answers appear below.

Teaching Resources
- Practice 19-2
- Section 19-2 Quiz

 **Reteach**

Have students work in groups to create a poster that describes the four behaviors that are essential to a healthy pregnancy. Students should also add prenatal doctor visits and their importance.

Enrich

Teaching Resources
- Enrich 19-2

Health at Home

Ultrasound Pictures Students' paragraphs should describe their impressions of the ultrasound pictures and the parts of the fetus they were able to discern. Students should also describe how the parents were feeling and how the ultrasound pictures affected those feelings.

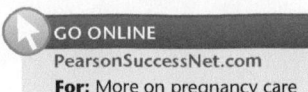 **GO ONLINE**
PearsonSuccessNet.com
For: More on pregnancy care

Complications Problems can occur at any time during pregnancy. For some of these complications, timely treatment can reduce negative consequences or even save the life of the woman or fetus.

▶ **Ectopic pregnancy** In the very rare case of an **ectopic pregnancy,** the blastocyst implants in the fallopian tube or elsewhere in the abdomen, instead of in the uterus. It cannot develop normally and may put the mother's life at risk. Surgery is necessary to remove the embryo and repair the damaged fallopian tube.

▶ **Miscarriage** The death of an embryo or fetus in the first 20 weeks of pregnancy is called a **miscarriage.** Almost all miscarriages take place during the first trimester. They can occur before or after a woman knows she is pregnant. At least 15 percent of recognized pregnancies end in miscarriages. Miscarriage is usually caused by a serious genetic defect, but it is sometimes due to illness or a drug the mother has taken. In other cases, there is no apparent reason for a miscarriage.

▶ **Preeclampsia** Preeclampsia (pree ih KLAMP see uh), which is also called toxemia, is characterized by high blood pressure, swelling of the wrists and ankles, and high levels of protein in the urine. Its onset is usually in the second or third trimester. Preeclampsia prevents the fetus from getting enough oxygen. This serious condition is treated with bed rest or medication.

▶ **Gestational Diabetes** Diabetes that develops in pregnant women is called **gestational diabetes** and is marked by high blood sugar levels. It usually develops later in pregnancy. If untreated, excess blood sugar can pass through the placenta to the fetus. The fetus may grow too large, which increases the risk of a difficult birth. The birth may also occur early, resulting in breathing problems for the newborn.

Section 2 Review

Key Ideas and Vocabulary

1. List four healthy habits that a pregnant woman should adopt before and during pregnancy.

2. Why is prenatal care so important throughout pregnancy?

3. About how long is each **trimester** of a pregnancy?

4. What is **chorionic villus sampling**? Under what conditions is it sometimes recommended?

5. Describe three symptoms of **preeclampsia**. How is it treated?

Health at Home

Ultrasound Pictures Ask your mother or other relative with children if she saved any ultrasound pictures from her pregnancy. Ask permission to see the pictures. Ask about her emotions during the ultrasound—were she and the father scared, happy, excited? Write a paragraph about the pictures and the parents' experience. **WRITING**

Critical Thinking

6. **Evaluating** From the following list, which food choice is generally recommended for pregnant women: swordfish, spinach, wine, herbal tea?

7. **Comparing and Contrasting** How are chorionic villus sampling and amniocentesis alike? How are they different?

 GO ONLINE PearsonSuccessNet.com Audio Summary Section 19.2

Section 2 Review

1. get proper nutrition, exercise, avoid alcohol and other drugs, avoid environmental hazards

2. Prenatal care greatly increases the chances of having a healthy baby.

3. three months

4. A small piece of the placenta is removed and tested; when there is a family history of a genetic disorder or when the mother is over the age of 35.

5. high blood pressure, swelling of the wrists and ankles, high levels of protein in the urine; bed rest or medication

6. spinach

7. Similarity: Both are tests performed when the fetus is at risk for a genetic disorder. Difference: Fetal cells in the amniotic fluid are tested in amniocentesis. A piece of the placenta is tested in chorionic villus sampling.

Technology & Health

Surgery Before Birth

What can be done if prenatal tests reveal a life-threatening condition in a fetus? In some cases, doctors can perform prenatal surgery—that is, surgery before birth. Prenatal surgery has been performed successfully on fetuses with heart conditions and neural tube defects. It has also been used to correct unbalanced blood flow between identical twins.

WRITING Any surgery has risks. What questions must parents consider with a doctor as they weigh the risks of prenatal surgery?

❶ Diagnosis

Doctors can diagnose an unbalanced blood flow between identical twins using tests that produce images of the fetuses. The imaging would show that a shared blood vessel between the fetuses is depleting blood from one twin—the donor. The other twin—the recipient—is getting too much blood. Without intervention, both twins would likely die.

❷ Surgery

The doctor makes a small incision in the mother's abdomen and uterus. Using a tiny instrument called an endoscope, the doctor locates the shared blood vessel and closes it off. Now each twin will have a separate blood supply.

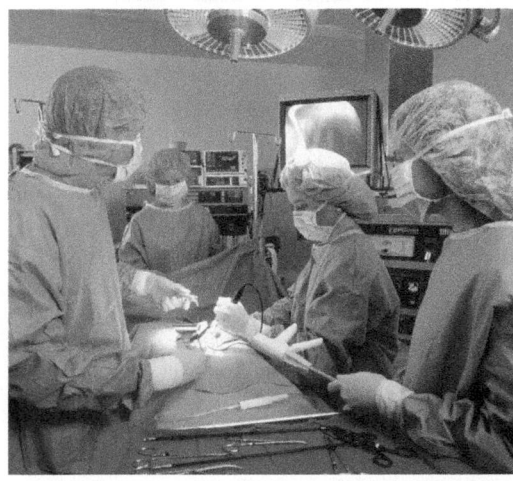

❸ A Successful Outcome

The surgery is successful. Here, the twins are 5 months old.

Technology & Health
Surgery Before Birth

Teaching Strategies

- Explain that MRI, or Magnetic Resonance Imaging, is a procedure that produces fairly clear images of soft tissues in the body, such as muscle tissue. This procedure is different from X-rays in that X-rays show only bones. Direct students to page 606 to read more about MRI.

- Tell students that blood imbalances between identical twins most often occur when the twin fetuses are growing inside the same placenta. Blood imbalances are potentially lethal because the twin getting too much blood will develop stressed kidneys and an enlarged heart. The twin not getting enough blood will become much smaller in size because it is not getting enough nutrition and its heart is pumping faster to keep the blood flowing.

WRITING Some questions that students might think parents should consider include: What will happen if the surgery is not performed? How many times has the doctor successfully performed the surgery? If something goes wrong during the surgery, what might happen to the fetuses and to the mother? Will the baby develop normally after the surgery? Will the surgery cause the baby to be born early?

For Your INFORMATION!

Prenatal Surgery

Prenatal, or fetal, surgery is most often performed to correct spinal cord malformations in fetuses with spina bifida or to relieve blockages in the urinary tract. Prenatal surgery has been particularly successful (a 75-80% survival rate) in correcting the balance of blood flow between twin fetuses. This particular syndrome, called Twin-Twin Transfusion Syndrome (TTTS), is the result of one twin receiving more blood flow than the other. The dangers of prenatal surgery include an increased chance of miscarriage or premature labor and delivery, as well as the chance of permanent organ damage or brain damage. The procedure also puts the mother at risk for infection or other serious complications.

Objectives
Before class begins, write the objectives on the board. Have students copy the objectives into their notebooks at the start of class.

1. Focus

Warm-Up **Health Stats**

Direct students to compare the two pie charts. Ask: **What effect does cigarette smoking during pregnancy have on a baby's weight?** *(The baby is more likely to have a low birthweight.)* Point out that low birthweight can be harmful to the newborn, and that they will learn more about the health risks to low birthweight babies in this section. After students finish writing, invite them to share their ideas for convincing women to stop smoking during pregnancy.

Presentation 19-3

 *Sample answer:* excitement and anxiety

---

Section 3
Childbirth

Objectives
▶ **Identify** the three stages of the birth process.
▶ **Describe** four complicating factors that may arise at birth.

Vocabulary
• certified nurse-midwife
• labor
• postpartum period
• stillbirth
• cesarean section
• premature birth
• low birthweight
• multiple birth

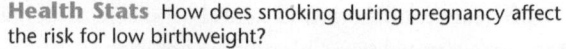

Health Stats How does smoking during pregnancy affect the risk for low birthweight?

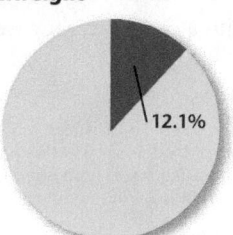

Percentage of Babies With Low Birthweight

7.5%   12.1%

When Mothers Didn't Smoke   **When Mothers Smoked**

WRITING Propose a plan that could help decrease the number of pregnant women who smoke.

The Birth Process

As the baby's due date approaches, the mother and father prepare. Most couples choose to have their baby in a hospital, where obstetricians, specially trained nurses, and medical equipment are available should something go wrong. If the pregnancy has gone well and the mother is in good health, a couple may choose to have the baby at home or at a home-like setting with the help of a certified nurse-midwife. A **certified nurse-midwife** is a nurse who is trained to deliver babies.

Near the end of the ninth month of pregnancy, the head of the fetus moves lower in the uterus. The birth process begins when the muscular walls of the uterus begin a series of contractions that will push the fetus out of the mother. **Birth takes place in three stages—labor, delivery of the baby, and delivery of the afterbirth.** Refer to Figure 6 to see what happens during each stage.

What mix of emotions might expectant parents feel during the birth process?

⚑ Sensitive Issues
The childbirth process is a sensitive subject to many students because of its association with female reproductive anatomy. Focus on the processes of childbirth. Maintain a clinical tone throughout all discussions of the birth process.

MATH and Health
⚫ Graphing
Instruct students to make a pie graph that shows the relative time each stage of childbirth typically lasts. Students can use the approximate times for each stage given in the text. Suggest that students calculate an average time based on the time ranges given to determine a total time for the process. Then students can use these averages to calculate the percent of total time that each stage requires.

1 **Labor** The work performed by the mother's body to push the fetus out is called **labor.** Labor for a first child may last from about 2 to 24 hours or longer. During this stage, strong contractions of the muscles of the uterus cause the cervix to increase in width, or dilate.

Each contraction typically lasts from 30 to 90 seconds. At first, the contractions may be minutes apart, but by the end of labor, they are usually only a few seconds apart. Near the end of this first stage, the amniotic sac breaks, and the cervix becomes softer and wide enough for the fetus to pass through.

2 **Delivery of Baby** Stage two involves the actual birth, or delivery, of the baby. This stage can take from half an hour to more than two hours. Contractions of the uterus continue, and the baby is pushed out, usually head first, through the cervix and vagina.

Once the baby is out, the doctor clamps and cuts the umbilical cord. There are no nerve endings in the cord, so this does not hurt the baby or the mother. The baby's nose and mouth are suctioned to remove mucus and make breathing easier. Eye drops are put in the baby's eyes to prevent infection, and an injection of vitamin K is given to prevent excessive bleeding from the cut umbilical cord. The doctor may also prick the baby's heel for a blood sample, which will be tested for abnormal protein levels. Abnormal test results may indicate a genetic disorder.

3 **Delivery of Afterbirth** Even though the baby is born, the birth process is not complete. The third stage involves contractions of the uterus that push out the placenta, also called the afterbirth. This stage typically takes about 15 to 30 minutes.

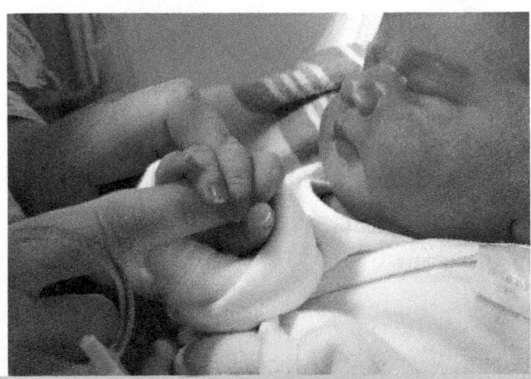

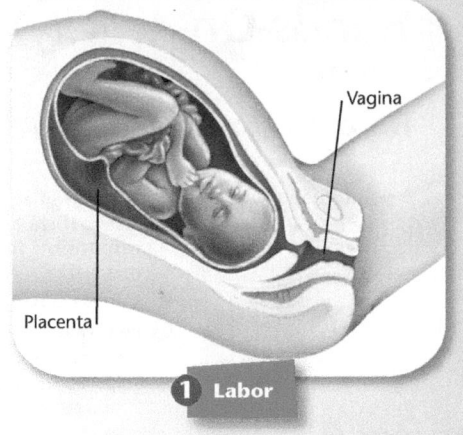

Vagina

Placenta

1 Labor

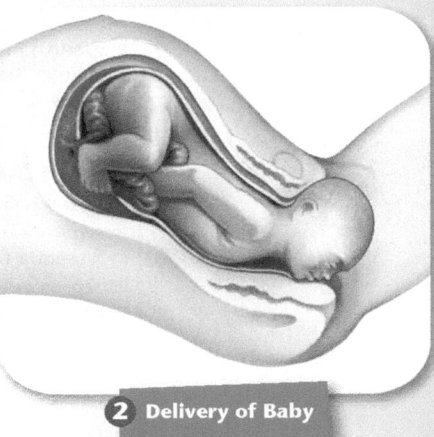

2 Delivery of Baby

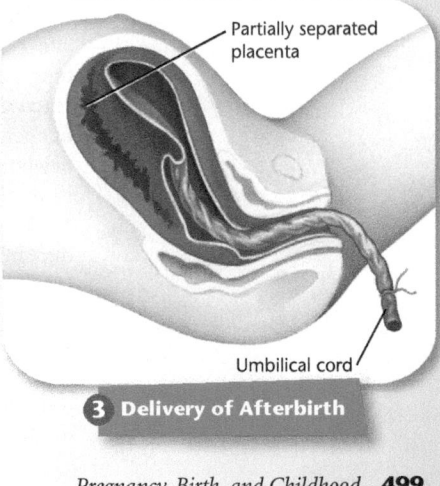

Partially separated placenta

Umbilical cord

3 Delivery of Afterbirth

Pregnancy, Birth, and Childhood **499**

Differentiated Instruction

L2 **Less Proficient Readers**

Have students make a flowchart that details the three stages in the birth process. Students should include the time frame for each stage as well as a brief description of what occurs, including the names of structures involved in the process.

---

2. Teach

L3 **EL** Reading/Note Taking 19-3

L2 Adapted Reading/Note Taking 19-3

The Birth Process

L2 **Visual Learning: Figure 6**

Image Bank Figure 19-6

Use the illustrations in Figure 6 to discuss the three stages of the birth process. Ask: **What happens during labor?** (*Contractions of muscles in the uterus cause the cervix to increase in width.*) **What happens during the second stage of birth?** (*the delivery of the baby*) Point out how the cervix has opened up, allowing the baby to be pushed out of the body. Then ask: **Why does the birth process not end after the birth of the baby?** (*The uterus pushes out the placenta, or afterbirth, in the third stage of the birth process.*)

L4 **Building Health Skills**

Accessing Information Have students find out the types of birthing facilities available in their community. (Some communities have both hospitals and birthing centers for women to choose from.) Students should find out how these facilities address the medical and comfort needs of both the parents and their newborns during the birth process. Students should learn how long mothers and their newborns stay in the facility after birth, as well as whether the infant and father can stay in the mother's room. Students can create a brochure or poster summarizing what they learned.

L3 **Addressing Misconceptions**

Childbirth Pain Some students may not realize that childbirth is painful. Explain that pain is caused by the strong contractions of the uterine muscles, as well as the pressure from the baby pushing on the cervix. Show students brochures describing childbirth classes given by local hospitals, birthing centers, or medical clinics. Point out how many give instruction on relaxation techniques to help women deal with the pain. Medications developed specifically for women in labor may also be used.

Hands-On *Activity*

Be a Parent for a Day

Suggest that students keep a written log or diary in which they record their thoughts and feelings as they take care of their "baby." Also have students record any lapses they had, the book they chose to read to the "baby," and the person who took care of the "baby" when they had to go out.

Think and Discuss

1. *Sample answers:* My free time was limited; I found myself worrying about the baby; I resented not being able to do what I wanted.

2. It is about the same size and weight as a baby.

3. The best time is when a couple is emotionally and financially ready to have a baby and has planned for the baby.

L2 Class Discussion

Make a chart on the board to summarize the changes that a newborn and mother undergo during the postpartum period. Ask: **What changes occur in the newborn?** *(Lungs begin to function, circulatory system and heart change, nervous system reacts to new stimuli, infant bonds with parents.)* Point out that these changes are due to the newborn's change in environment. **What changes does the mother go through?** *(Breasts produce milk, uterus shrinks in size, hormonal changes, fatigue, may become depressed.)* Explain that the mother's body is healing from the pregnancy and birth, as well as preparing to nourish the baby.

L3 Cultural Connection

During the pregnancy or postpartum period, parents choose a name for their newborn. Names often have cultural or family significance. Ask volunteers to find out how and why their names were chosen. Have them share their findings with the class.

Hands-On *Activity*

Be a Parent for a Day

Materials
5-pound bag of flour
plastic bag with tie

Try This

1. Place the bag of flour inside the plastic bag and fasten it shut. For the next 24 hours, you will be responsible for your bag of flour as if it were a real baby.

2. Choose a name for your "baby."

3. Follow these rules for taking care of your "baby."
   - Every 5 hours, including night, feed your "baby" for 20 minutes. During this time, you must remain seated in one place and devote your full attention to your "baby."
   - Every 3 hours during the time that you are awake, allow 5 minutes for changing your "baby's" diaper.
   - Spend 15 minutes in the evening talking or reading to your "baby."
   - Never leave your "baby" alone. If necessary, arrange for someone to babysit.

Think and Discuss

1. How did being a parent of a bag of flour affect your lifestyle?

2. In what ways is a bag of flour an appropriate object to use to represent a baby?

3. When do you think is the best time for a person to become a parent? Explain.

The Postpartum Period After the birth, a period of adjustment for the parents and their newborn begins. During the first six weeks, called the **postpartum period,** many changes take place. Immediately after the birth, the newborn's lungs begin to function for the first time. The circulatory system and heart undergo changes that send more blood to the lungs, where the baby now gets oxygen from the air. The nervous system reacts to new sensations: light, air against the skin, a parent's touch, hunger, and pain. While its organs adjust to life outside the uterus, the newborn is learning to get what it needs by forming a strong bond with its mother and father.

For the mother, changing hormone levels signal the breasts to produce milk and cause the uterus to gradually shrink back to its normal size. Hormonal changes and fatigue may cause the mother to feel overwhelmed, or even very sad, during the postpartum period. Usually, these "baby blues" pass within a few days. If, however, the sadness lasts longer or causes the mother to withdraw from the baby and other people, she should seek prompt medical attention. She may need to be treated for a serious condition called postpartum depression.

For Your INFORMATION!

Benefits of Breast Milk

In most cases, breast milk is the ideal food for newborns. It contains antibodies to disease, and it is nonallergenic. The act of breast-feeding requires close physical contact, which benefits both mother and child.

Prolactin is present throughout pregnancy. With estrogen, it prepares the breasts to produce milk. Little milk is produced until after the baby is born, because estrogen and progesterone released by the placenta before birth inhibit the actions of prolactin. Estrogen and progesterone levels drop sharply after delivery of the placenta. So the effects of prolactin are no longer inhibited and milk is formed.

Complications at Birth

Although the birth process usually proceeds smoothly, problems can sometimes occur. **Some complications result in a surgical delivery or premature birth. Low birthweight and the birth of more than one baby also may cause complications.** In addition, very rarely, a pregnancy may end with a stillbirth. A **stillbirth** occurs when a fetus dies and is expelled from the body after the twentieth week of pregnancy.

Surgical Delivery   Sometimes delivery through the cervix and vagina is not possible because of the position of the fetus in the uterus or the narrowness of the mother's hips. Other times, illness or other conditions may make labor and vaginal delivery dangerous for the mother or the fetus.

In these circumstances, the obstetrician will perform a cesarean section. A **cesarean section** (suh ZEHR ee un) is a surgical method of birth. The operation takes about one hour to complete, and the mother may be awake or asleep during the procedure. First the doctor makes an incision in the lower abdomen into the uterus. Then he or she removes the baby and placenta. About 30 percent of all babies born in the United States are delivered by cesarean section.

Premature Birth   Sometimes a baby is born before it has developed fully. Delivery of a live baby before the 37th week of pregnancy is called **premature birth.** The earlier the birth, the more problems the baby tends to have. The lungs of a premature baby are usually not fully developed, and in some cases, the baby cannot breathe by itself. The baby may also have additional problems if other organs aren't fully developed. A premature baby may receive care in an incubator, a chamber designed to protect the baby until it has developed more.

 **Connect to Your Life**   What misconceptions about premature babies did you hold before reading this section?

 **GO ONLINE**
PearsonSuccessNet.com
For: More on the birth process

FIGURE 7   A premature baby may need extended hospital care until it becomes more fully developed.

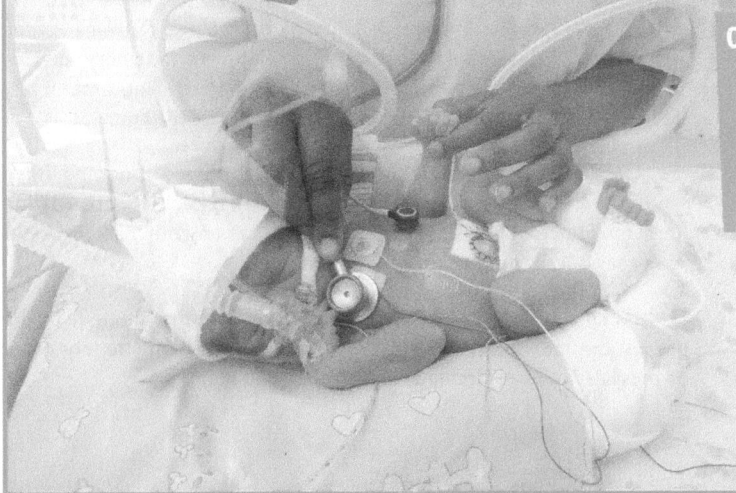

On average, hospital costs for premature babies are 14 times as high as costs for healthy newborns.

501

Complications at Birth

🔵 **Online Activity**   🔵 GO ONLINE

Visit Pearson SuccessNet to access an online activity about the birth process. Have students complete the Web activity.

🔵 **Cooperative Learning**

Divide the class into groups of four or five, and assign each group one of the following birth complications: stillbirth, premature birth, and low birthweight. For each complication, ask students to learn more about what it is and its possible causes, if known. Then challenge students to think of ways in which the complication might be prevented. Instruct students to make a poster that displays this information about the complication and present it to the class.

🔵 **Building Vocabulary**

Explain that the term *cesarean section* is derived from the Latin phrase *a caeso matris utere,* which means "from the cut womb of his mother." Then have students write a paragraph relating the Latin phrase to the current meaning and summarizing the information they learned about the procedure from the text. **WRITING**

🔵 **Visual Learning: Figure 7**

Invite students to compare the size of the baby in the photograph with the size of the adult's hand. Then ask: **Why do you think the hospital costs for premature babies are so much higher than the costs for healthy newborns?** *(Sample answer: Premature babies are in the hospital for a longer period of time and require more specialized care.)* Explain that in some cases, premature babies continue growing and developing in incubators where they receive only intravenous feedings until their digestive system is able to digest breast milk.

Connect to Your Life   *Sample answer:* that premature babies were fully developed, only smaller

Differentiated Instruction

🔵 **Gifted and Talented**

Have students research other complications that occur at birth and how these complications are handled. (Complications that students might choose include fetal aspiration of meconium during birth, unproductive labor, breech fetus, or an umbilical cord that is expelled before the fetus is delivered.) Students should prepare a presentation to the class on their findings using a poster, presentation software, or other visuals.

L3 Building Health Skills

Advocacy Have student groups prepare a brochure advocating ways to prevent low birthweight babies. Students should include preventive measures pregnant women can take such as not smoking, eating well, exercising, and making regular prenatal doctor visits. Teenage pregnancy also carries the risk of low birthweight. Encourage students to produce brochures that are suitable for distribution in public places, such as libraries, schools, and doctor's offices. **WRITING**

Multiple Births

L2 Visual Learning: Figure 9

Image Bank Figure 19-9

Use Figure 9 to compare the formation of fraternal and identical twins. Point out that fraternal twins develop when an ovary releases two eggs. This event can be due to an inherited tendency or to hormone therapy, which is used to improve fertility. Ask: **Can fraternal twins be the same sex? Explain.** *(Yes, the two sperm cells fertilizing the eggs carry the same type of sex chromosome.)* **Can identical twins be different sexes? Explain.** *(No, identical twins form when one embryo splits, so both embryos are identical.)*

Caption Answer Two different sperm fertilize two different eggs with fraternal twins, so each fertilized egg has a different genetic makeup. Identical twins develop from identical embryos.

L4 Active Learning

Invite students to research current findings about the personality traits of identical twins, especially those that were separated at birth. Encourage students to present their findings to the class.

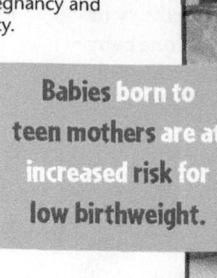

FIGURE 8 Risk factors for having a baby with low birthweight include smoking or dieting during pregnancy and teenage pregnancy.

Babies born to teen mothers are at increased risk for low birthweight.

Low Birthweight A newborn that weighs less than 5.5 pounds at birth is considered to have **low birthweight.** Some low-birthweight babies are also premature. Others are full-term, but they just didn't grow enough before birth.

Premature and low-birthweight babies face an increased risk of health problems as newborns, chronic lifelong health problems, and even death. Not all cases are preventable. However, the number of premature and low-birthweight babies could dramatically decrease if more women adopted healthy habits during pregnancy. For example, a woman reduces her risk of having a baby with low birthweight by about 40 percent by not smoking during pregnancy.

Multiple Births

The delivery of more than one baby—for example, twins, triplets, or quadruplets—is called a **multiple birth.** These births carry greater risk to the mother and babies, and are closely monitored by doctors. Delivery by cesarean section is more likely for a multiple birth than for a single birth.

What causes more than one fetus to develop? Figure 9 shows how the two types of twins develop.

Identical Twins Twins that develop from a single fertilized egg, or zygote, are called identical twins. Early in development, the embryo divides into two identical embryos. Because they develop from identical embryos, identical twins have the same inherited traits and are the same sex.

Fraternal Twins Sometimes two eggs are released from the ovary and are fertilized by two sperm. When this happens, fraternal twins develop. Fraternal twins are no more alike than any other siblings, and they may or may not be the same sex.

Triplets or More Triplets, quadruplets, and other multiple births are less common than twins. But the number of births with three or more babies has increased dramatically in the last 30 years.

502 *Chapter 19*

MATH and Health

L3 Percentages

Divide the class into groups and assign each group a grade (9th, 10th, and so on). Ask each group to determine how many twins are in its assigned grade. Ask students to report both the number of twins and the percentage of twins. Then pool the data and calculate the percent-age of twins in the school population. Have students compare their percentage with the national percentage, which was 3.31% in 2010. If students differentiated between identical and fraternal twins, ask them to calculate a percentage for each category.

Identical Twins

A sperm fertilizes a single egg.

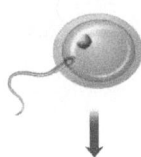

Early in development, the embryo splits and forms two identical embryos.

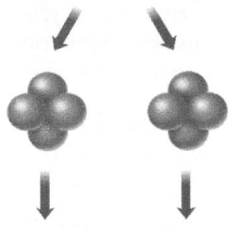

Identical twins result.

Fraternal Twins

Two different sperm fertilize two eggs.

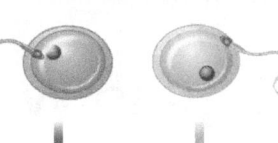

Each of the fertilized eggs develops into an embryo.

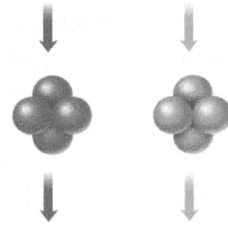

Fraternal twins result.

FIGURE 9 Identical twins inherit identical traits, whereas fraternal twins do not. **Applying Concepts** Why can fraternal twins be different sexes while identical twins cannot?

Section 3 Review

Key Ideas and Vocabulary

1. What are the three stages of birth?
2. Describe what happens during **labor**.
3. What is the **postpartum period**? List two changes that happen in the newborn and two changes that happen in the mother during this period.
4. What are four complicating factors that may arise at birth?
5. What is a **cesarean section**? Give two reasons why a cesarean section may be performed.

Health at School

Twins Interview Interview twins you know at your school or in your community. Ask them how they think being twins affects their relationship as siblings. Write a transcript of your interview. **WRITING**

Critical Thinking

6. **Relating Cause and Effect** Describe two risk factors for low birthweight.
7. **Comparing and Contrasting** How do fraternal twins differ from identical twins?

GO ONLINE PearsonSuccessNet.com   Audio Summary Section 19.3   *Pregnancy, Birth, and Childhood* **503**

3. Assess

Evaluate
These assignments can help you assess students' mastery of the section content.

Section 3 Review
Answers appear below.

Teaching Resources
- Practice 19-3
- Section 19-3 Quiz

L2 Reteach
Have student pairs work together to construct a concept map for the section. Students should include the stages in the birth process, complications in childbirth, and the different kinds of multiple births. Challenge students to include all the vocabulary terms from the section.

L4 Enrich
Teaching Resources
- Enrich 19-3

Health at School

Twins Interview Have students prepare a list of questions before interviewing the twins. For the transcript, students should write their questions followed by the twins' responses. If students wish, they may record the interview (with the twins' permission) and play it back later to transcribe it.

Section 3 Review

1. labor, delivery of the baby, delivery of the afterbirth
2. Strong contractions of the muscles of the uterus cause the cervix to dilate. Then the amniotic sac breaks, and the cervix becomes softer and wide enough for the fetus to pass through.
3. the first six weeks after birth; *any two newborn changes:* lungs function, circulatory system sends blood to lungs, nervous system reacts to new sensations, forms bond with parents; *any two mother changes:* breasts produce milk, uterus shrinks, hormonal changes, fatigue
4. cesarean section, premature birth, low birthweight, multiple births
5. a surgical method of birth in which the doctor makes an incision in the lower abdomen and removes the baby and placenta; position of fetus or hips too narrow
6. *any two:* smoking or dieting during pregnancy, teenage pregnancy
7. Fraternal twins develop from two different eggs that are fertilized by two different sperm. Identical twins develop from a single embryo that divides into two embryos.

Pregnancy, Birth, and Childhood **503**

Setting Goals

Coping With Change

Objective

Implement a plan to cope with transition times in life.

Teaching Strategies

- You may choose to use the example of Dolores and Miguel as you work through the steps of coping with change, the example of moving to a new school, or an example of your own choosing, whichever you think students can best relate to. Use the example to illustrate each step for coping with change.

- When teaching students to understand their resistance to change, emphasize that having a positive attitude about change will help them overcome the disadvantages. Point out that by eliminating and letting go of disadvantages, the advantages become clearer and easier to accept. This makes change easier.

- Emphasize that setbacks are normal and are an essential part of the change process. Encourage students to prepare for setbacks by planning who they will turn to for support and what actions they will take to get back on track.

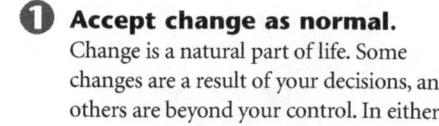 **Setting Goals**

Coping With Change

Dolores and Miguel brought their first baby home from the hospital last week. They had been planning for the birth of their first child for months, but now they are feeling overwhelmed.

Dolores has been up every night, feeding and comforting the baby. Miguel is also feeling stress because of all his new responsibilities. How can they cope with all these changes in their lives?

The period between the old and new ways of life, called the transition time, can be difficult. The following guidelines can help you deal with transition times in your life, no matter what type of change you are facing.

1 Accept change as normal. Change is a natural part of life. Some changes are a result of your decisions, and others are beyond your control. In either case, the transition is often stressful.

2 Expect mixed feelings. Because some fear and loss accompany even the most desirable new experience, change usually brings mixed feelings—both positive and negative.

When you are faced with a significant change, make a chart listing the advantages and disadvantages the change will bring into your life. This "change chart" can help you understand your mixed feelings.

3 Understand your resistance. Moving on to "unexplored territory" is stressful, and resistance is common. There are a couple things you can do to reduce your resistance to change.

▶ Review your "change chart" to identify those disadvantages that are the immediate, or short-term, stresses associated with the change. Cross those out. They will disappear as soon as you integrate the new situation into your life.

▶ Now circle the disadvantages over which you have no control. Remind yourself that you often must "let go" of things you cannot control.

504

Sensitive Issues

Some students may not feel comfortable sharing information about the change they have chosen to work on. Do not ask students to discuss their change or share their change chart, and use discretion even if they volunteer to do so.

Change Chart

Change: Moving to a new school

Advantages
- Academics are better
- School is safer
- Can make new friends
- Walking distance to home
- Soccer team

Disadvantages
- Won't see old friends every day
- Won't know anyone
- Can't find my way to class
- Have to memorize new schedule
- Lunch costs more

4 **Build an inside support system.**

▶ Use lessons from the past to help you get through the current situation. Think about how you coped with past changes. How can you build on your past successes and apply them to your current situation?

▶ Focus on the positive aspects of the change you are now facing. Jot down the most important benefits of the change and add a reassuring message, such as "I can handle . . . and feel good!" Place your list where you will see it often.

5 **Build an outside support system.**

▶ Enlist the support of friends and family members who were helpful to you in the past. Let them know you would appreciate their support again.

▶ Seek new sources of support. You may want to join organized groups that are working on similar issues.

6 **Start with small steps.**

Even a small step can make you feel confident that you can handle the change in your life.

▶ Decide on a goal and put it in words, such as "to feel more a part of my new school."

▶ Take a small, positive step toward that goal, such as attending a meeting of one after-school club.

7 **Work through setbacks.**

It is not unusual to feel scared, even as you are making progress. Your natural tendency may be to go back to what was safe and comfortable. Instead, remind yourself of your successes and the steps you have already taken toward your goal. Tell yourself that you can do it . . . and you can!

1. Think back to a major change you faced in the recent past. List the positive and negative reactions you felt about the change. Did you use any of the strategies above in coping with the change? Explain.

2. Think about a change you are currently facing or are about to face.
   a. Make a "change chart" that lists the advantages and disadvantages of the change.
   b. Cross out the short-term disadvantages that will go away after a short time. Circle those disadvantages that are out of your control so you can "let them go."
   c. List the people that you could ask to be your outside support system.
   d. Decide on a first small step toward making the change a part of your life. Explain your choice.

1. Possible answers: moving to another state, going to a new school, parents divorcing or remarrying, death of a loved one; accept any reasonable responses

2. Students may choose any change they are currently facing or about to face. Some examples include changing schools, taking a part-time job after school, trying out for a sports team or joining a school activity, having a parent who remarries and sharing a home with step-brothers or sisters, having a parent return to work

   a. Students should list the advantages and disadvantages of the change in a chart similar to the one shown.

   b. Students should cross out disadvantages that will disappear after the change is no longer new. They should circle disadvantages that they cannot control.

   c. People that students might list include parents, friends, and relatives.

   d. Students should write a goal that will help them become comfortable with the change, then write an action that will help them meet that goal. For example, to meet the coworkers at my new job, I will smile, say hello, and introduce myself.

Health and Community

L3 **Support Groups**

Most communities have support groups to help people who have lost a loved one, who are living with a terminally ill family member, or who are living with an alcoholic. Have students find out which support groups are active in their community. Instruct them to list several of these groups along with their meeting place and time and contact information.

Section 4

Childhood

Objectives

Before class begins, write the objectives on the board. Have students copy the objectives into their notebooks at the start of class.

1. Focus

Objectives
► **Describe** the changes that children undergo during early childhood.
► **Identify** key areas of development that occur during middle and late childhood.

Vocabulary
• pre-adolescence

Warm-Up **Advice Line**

After students write, invite them to share any experiences they have had with two-year-olds. Lead students to conclude that two-year-olds want to be independent, even though they do not yet have all the skills they need. By allowing the two-year-old to have some control (like picking which pajamas to put on) or some independence (like getting her own snack while you pour the milk), she will be more willing to accept your help.

Presentation 19-4

Warm-Up

Dear Advice Line,

I babysit a 2-year-old. She can't do things by herself like pour milk into her cup or put on her pajamas, but she gets mad at me when I try to help and insists on doing it herself. What should I do?

WRITING Explain what factors might be contributing to this two-year-old's behavior. What advice can you give the babysitter?

Early Childhood

Do you have younger siblings or cousins? Do you babysit for young children? If so, you have probably noticed that they do not behave or think the way that older children or adults do. Babies and young children are not miniature adults. Their bodies and brains are still growing and developing rapidly. **From birth to age six, children change from helpless babies into confident individuals who can do many things for themselves.**

Birth to Eighteen Months Have you ever seen or held a newborn baby? A newborn is born with some physical skills. It can nurse, cry, and direct its gaze right at you. However, it will not learn to smile until it is about one month old. At birth, many of the baby's organs and systems are not yet fully developed. A newborn's bones are still soft and flexible.

FIGURE 10 Children change dramatically during childhood.

Birth to 18 Months
• Cries for help
• Learns to sit, crawl, stand, and walk

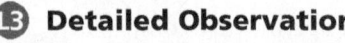

WRITING and Health

L3 Detailed Observation

Have students observe the behaviors of a child under 6 years of age for at least 30 minutes. Tell students to watch how the child interacts with other children, gets attention from adults, and solves problems. Students should also observe how physically coordinated the child is and how well the child can talk. Then have students write several paragraphs in which they describe in detail the physical, mental, and social behaviors of the child during the time of their observation.

By the time a baby is 3 or 4 months old, the brain, nerves, and muscles are ready for more coordinated movement. The baby recognizes its parents and siblings, cries to get what it needs, and responds to attention with smiles. By 18 months of age, the baby has probably learned to sit, crawl, stand, and walk. He or she now has some "baby" teeth and can chew solid food.

Eighteen Months to Three Years Most children learn to talk sometime between 18 months and 3 years of age. This is also the age when children lose their babylike appearances—baby fat is lost and the arms and legs get longer. Appetite decreases as growth slows down. Physical coordination improves.

During this time, most children gain abilities to do things for themselves. They may show off around family and friends but be shy around strangers. When they are with others their age, toddlers tend to play alongside, but not with, each other. They are not ready to share or to play together because they are busy learning to do things for themselves. With encouragement from parents and caregivers, the child's confidence grows.

Three to Six Years Between the ages of 3 and 6, most children lose all traces of babyhood. They become more independent and active. Muscles grow, energy is high, and the curious child is "into everything." Communication skills advance rapidly. Most 4-year-olds talk in sentences.

During this stage, children learn to play together and to make friends. They begin school and learn how to behave in a group. They also start to develop a sense of right and wrong.

Connect to Your Life Think back to when you were in first grade. How did you look and act?

GO ONLINE
PearsonSuccessNet.com
For: More on growth and development

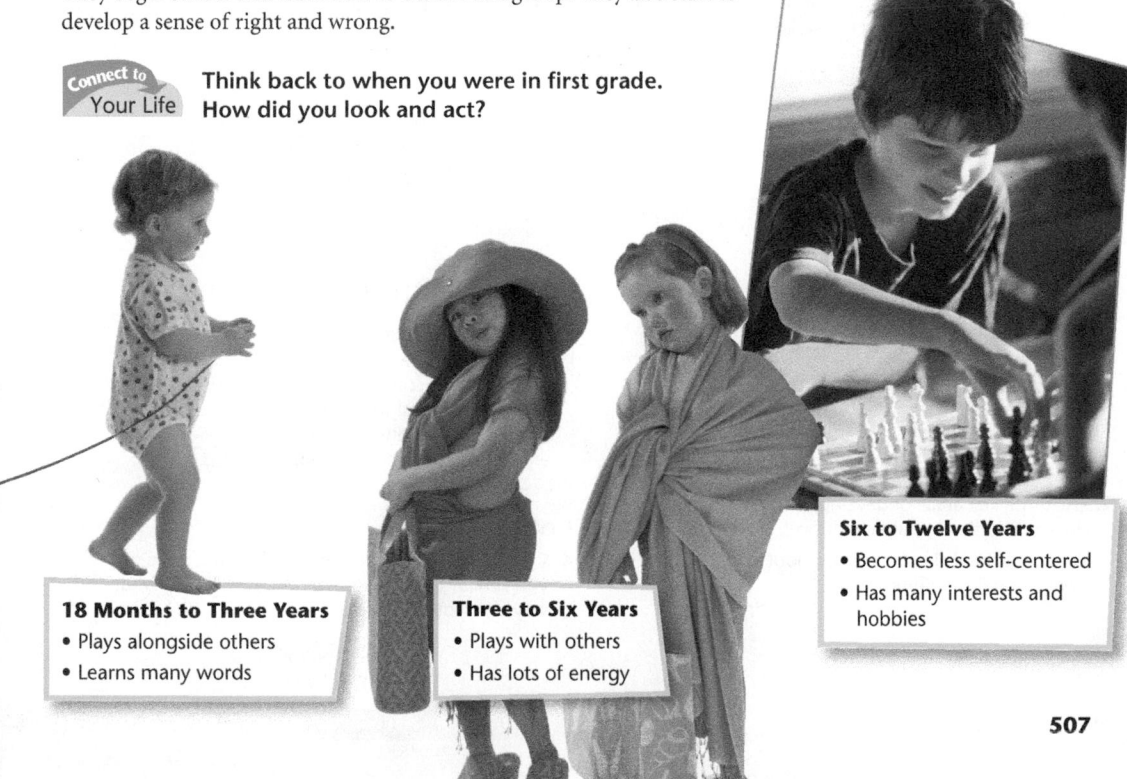

18 Months to Three Years
• Plays alongside others
• Learns many words

Three to Six Years
• Plays with others
• Has lots of energy

Six to Twelve Years
• Becomes less self-centered
• Has many interests and hobbies

507

Differentiated Instruction

L1 Special Needs
Provide parenting and childhood magazines for students to cut out pictures of children at various ages. Have groups of mixed abilities work together to sort the pictures in order from birth to age 6. Have students point out which children are walking and which have achieved other milestones.

2. Teach

L3 EL **Reading/Note Taking** 19-4

L2 **Adapted Reading/Note Taking** 19-4

Early Childhood

L3 Content Update GO ONLINE
Use the Web Code to access up-to-date information about growth and development. Have students complete the Web activity.

L3 Cultural Connection
Tell students that by the time children are 1 or 2 years old, they use one- or two-word utterances to convey meaning. For example, *da* often means "dad" and *baba* might mean "bottle," "mom," or "pacifier." Have students find out what words they first uttered and the meaning of those words. Pool the class findings to find any similarities. Explain that these first words are a baby's attempt at communicating with his or her family and form the foundation of speech. As such, these words are often based on the family's native language or "family talk."

L2 Visual Learning: Figure 10
Use the photos and charts in Figure 10 to begin a discussion on the changes that children undergo during early childhood. Ask such questions as: **When do children typically learn to walk?** *(by the time they are 18 months old)* **When do children begin playing with each other?** *(from three to six years)*

L4 Active Learning
Have students research and estimate approximatley how much it would cost to support a child for one month. Assume the child is 2 years old and stays in a day-care center from 8 a.m. until 5 p.m., Monday through Friday. The child needs food, diapers, and a new pair of shoes during the month. Instruct students to make an itemized list of expenses and compute the cost. MATH

Connect to Your Life *Sample answer:* I was much smaller, and I liked to play dress-up with my friends.

Middle and Late Childhood

L3 Cooperative Learning

Assign groups one of the key areas of development that occurs during middle and late childhood: physical growth, mental development, and making friends. Have each group describe the changes that children during middle and late childhood experience in their assigned area of development. Groups should make a poster using pictures from magazines or from their own childhood to show examples of these changes.

3. Assess

Evaluate

These assignments can help you assess students' mastery of the section content.

Section 4 Review

Answers appear below.

Teaching Resources
• Practice 19-4
• Section 19-4 Quiz

L2 Reteach

Have student pairs make a table in which they summarize the physical, mental, and social changes that children undergo from birth to late childhood.

L4 Enrich

Teaching Resources
• Enrich 19-4

Health and Community

Babysitter's Guide Brochures should be targeted to one age range. Suggestions and tips should be appropriate for that age group based on their physical and mental abilities.

FIGURE 11 Having a best friend is important during pre-adolescence.

Middle and Late Childhood

Think about some of the things you did between the ages of 6 and 12. Maybe you learned to play a sport, developed a hobby, or made a best friend. **Physical growth, mastering new skills, and making friends are key areas of development during middle and late childhood.** Middle childhood is defined as the period between age 6 and 8, and late childhood as ages 9 through 12. Late childhood is also called **pre-adolescence** or the "tween" years. It is the stage of development before adolescence.

Physical Growth Many changes occur during middle and late childhood. For example, at around age 6 or 7, a child's facial structure changes with the appearance of permanent teeth. Muscles and bones continue to grow, and coordination develops further. As children enter pre-adolescence, their bones begin to grow faster, mostly in the legs. Their appetite also increases.

Mental Development Mental development continues during these years, as children learn higher-level thinking skills. Children will feel pride in accomplishing tasks and attempting new challenges. Praise from teachers and parents helps increase their self-confidence.

During middle and late childhood, the self-centeredness of early childhood lessens, and children continue to learn values, such as honesty and fairness. They may start taking on responsibilities at home, such as chores, during this stage.

Importance of Friends When did the approval of friends and the need to fit in with a social group become very important to you? Often, this occurs at about age 10. These feelings help children learn to work well in group situations. Having a best friend also becomes important in pre-adolescence and will remain so into the teen years.

Section 4 Review

Key Ideas and Vocabulary

1. In a sentence, describe a typical newborn. Then describe a typical 18-month-old, a 3-year-old, and a 6-year-old.

2. List three key areas of development that occur during middle and late childhood.

3. What is **pre-adolescence**? At about what ages does it begin and end?

Health and Community

Babysitter's Guide Choose one age range of children described in this section. Create a brochure that contains information and tips for babysitters of children in that age range. Be sure to include suggestions for keeping the children both entertained and safe from injury. **WRITING**

Critical Thinking

4. **Comparing and Contrasting** In what ways are you similar to how you were at age 10? In what ways are you different?

 GO ONLINE PearsonSuccessNet.com   Audio Summary Section 19.4

Section 4 Review

1. A newborn can nurse, cry, and direct its gaze right at you. An eighteen-month-old is learning to talk, can walk, and plays alongside other toddlers. A three-year-old is active and independent and is learning to communicate and make friends. A six-year-old can work in groups, have a best friend, and has many interests.

2. physical growth, mental development, and making friends

3. the stage of development before adolescence that occurs between the ages of 9 and 12

4. *Sample answer:* I have many of the same interests, but I look much different physically and I have different friends.

Section 1   Development Before Birth

Key Ideas

▶ In the first week after fertilization, the fertilized egg undergoes many cell divisions and travels to the uterus.

▶ The amniotic sac, placenta, and umbilical cord protect and nourish the developing embryo and later the fetus.

Vocabulary

- zygote (489)
- embryo (489)
- blastocyst (489)
- implantation (489)
- amniotic sac (490)
- placenta (490)
- umbilical cord (491)
- fetus (491)

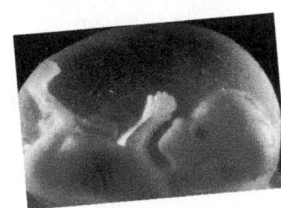

Section 2   A Healthy Pregnancy

Key Ideas

▶ Getting proper nutrition and exercise and avoiding drugs and environmental hazards are especially important both before and throughout pregnancy.

▶ The chances of having a healthy baby greatly increase if the mother visits her doctor or clinic for regular checkups throughout pregnancy.

Vocabulary

- prenatal care (494)
- obstetrician (494)
- trimester (494)
- ultrasound (495)
- chorionic villus sampling (495)

- amniocentesis (495)
- ectopic pregnancy (496)
- miscarriage (496)
- preeclampsia (496)
- gestational diabetes (496)

Section 3   Childbirth

Key Ideas

▶ Birth takes place in three stages—labor, delivery of the baby, and delivery of the afterbirth.

▶ Some complications at birth result in a surgical delivery or premature birth. Low birthweight and the birth of more than one baby also may cause complications.

Vocabulary

- certified nurse-midwife (498)
- labor (499)
- postpartum period (500)
- stillbirth (501)

- cesarean section (501)
- premature birth (501)
- low birthweight (502)
- multiple birth (502)

Section 4   Childhood

Key Ideas

▶ From birth to age six, children change from helpless babies into confident individuals who can do many things for themselves.

▶ Physical growth, mastering new skills, and making friends are key areas of development during middle and late childhood.

Vocabulary

- pre-adolescence (508)

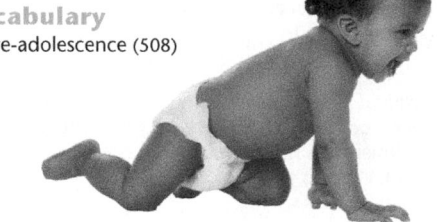

Pregnancy, Birth, and Childhood   **509**

Key Ideas Review

L2 Have each student write one question about each key idea for the chapter. Pool the class questions, and play a game show in which student teams try to correctly answer the most questions.

L3 Have students make a time line in which they chronologically list the events of pregnancy, childbirth, and childhood. Students should begin the time line with the fertilization of an egg and end it with a 12-year-old child. In between, students should identify the key points in the development of the embryo and the child, as well as the childbirth process.

Vocabulary Review

L1 Choose to test students on only the vocabulary terms that are most important to their understanding of the key chapter concepts. These terms might include *embryo, umbilical cord, placenta, fetus, prenatal care,* and *labor.* Use the figures from the chapter to help make these terms as concrete to students as possible. Encourage students to describe the meaning of each term using their own words.

L2 Invite students to make a word puzzle using as many terms from the chapter as they can. Students can exchange puzzles with a partner and solve them.

Chapter 19 Review

 GO ONLINE

PearsonSuccessNet.com

Students can go online for a review activity on Chapter 19.

Reviewing Key Ideas

Section 1

1. c

2. Blood vessels in the umbilical cord carry nutrients from the placenta to the embryo and wastes from the embryo to the placenta.

3. The body size of the fetus increases so that it is more in proportion to the head, body fat accumulates, and the eyelids open and close.

4. *Sample answer:* Because the risk of miscarriage is highest in the first trimester, many parents choose to wait until the pregnancy is further along.

Section 2

5. b

6. X-rays, lead, mercury, and cat litter

7. the first trimester

8. *Sample answer:* go to childbirth classes at a local hospital or talk with other parents about their experiences

Section 3

9. d

10. overwhelming feelings of sadness that last for a long time or cause the mother to withdraw from the baby and other people

11. *Sample answer:* Most newborns who are bonded to their parents have all their needs met and are content. They do not expend extra energy being fussy or crying.

Section 4

12. c

13. between the ages of 18 months to three years

14. *Sample answer:* Two-year-olds think they can do many things for themselves, even if they do not have the coordination, and they are very curious. They may get into something that can cause them harm.

Chapter 19 Review

Reviewing Key Ideas

 GO ONLINE

PearsonSuccessNet.com

For: Chapter 19 review activity

Reviewing Key Ideas

Section 1

1. During implantation
  a. the egg is fertilized.
  b. the blastocyst travels to the uterus.
  c. the blastocyst attaches to the wall of the uterus.
  d. the embryo grows to about an inch in length.

2. Describe how a fetus obtains nutrients and gets rid of wastes.

3. What changes occur in a fetus between the 7th and 9th month of development?

4. **Critical Thinking** Why do you think many expectant parents keep pregnancy a secret until after the first trimester?

Section 2

5. Which nutrient is critical for proper neural tube development?
  a. iron   **b.** folic acid
  c. sodium   **d.** vitamin A

6. List four environmental hazards of particular concern to pregnant women.

7. During which trimester of a pregnancy should a woman start prenatal care?

8. **Critical Thinking** Besides prenatal care, how can expectant parents prepare for the experience of birth?

Section 3

9. All of the following happen during a typical labor *except*
  a. the uterus contracts.
  b. the cervix dilates.
  c. the amniotic sac breaks.
  d. the umbilical cord breaks.

10. What are some warning signs of postpartum depression?

11. **Critical Thinking** Newborns who form a close, loving bond with their parents grow faster and are healthier than newborns who do not form this bond. Why do you think this is so?

Section 4

12. During what stage does a child typically begin to get his or her permanent teeth?
  a. newborn
  b. early childhood
  c. middle childhood
  d. late childhood

13. Between which ages do children typically learn to dress themselves?

14. **Critical Thinking** Explain why parents of 2-year-olds must "keep an eye on them" all the time.

 **Building Health Skills**

15. **Advocacy** How could you help an older cousin stop smoking before she decides to have a baby?

16. **Accessing Information** How would someone go about choosing an obstetrician or certified nurse-midwife? What resources could they use?

17. **Making Decisions** A 26-year-old pregnant woman with no genetic disorders in her family says she wants an amniocentesis done so that she "gets all that medical science has to offer." Do you agree with her reasoning? Explain. **WRITING**

18. **Setting Goals** Identify one habit you could change that would help you be a better parent in your 20s or 30s. It may seem a long way off, but changing habits is easiest when you are young. Write down the habit you would like to change, and monitor your progress over the school year.

Health and Community

Folic Acid Awareness Many health organizations recommend that all women increase their folic acid consumption, starting in their teen years. Create a public service announcement to deliver this important message to teenaged girls. In it, describe the importance of folic acid and offer tips for adding more of it to one's diet. **WRITING**

Building Health Skills

15. *Sample answer:* Share statistics about low birthweight, stillbirths, and newborn deaths associated with women who smoke during their pregnancy.

16. *Sample answer:* Interview doctors or certified nurse-midwives who accept your insurance or have privileges at a hospital or birthing center you wish to use. Make sure the person you choose has a personality that suits you, and the skills and experience to meet your medical needs.

17. *Sample answer:* I disagree because her young age and family history indicate low risk for genetic disorders. The risks of the amniocentesis procedure are probably greater.

18. Students can pick any habit that might interfere with being a good parent or having a healthy pregnancy later on.

Standardized Test Prep

Math Practice

The graphs below display data on multiple births in the U.S. between 1980 and 2010. The first graph shows births of triplets or more. The second graph shows births of twins. Use the graphs to answer Questions 19–21.

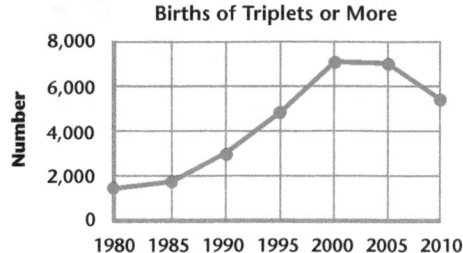

Births of Triplets or More

19. About how many more births of triplets or more were there in 2000 compared with 1980?
    A 4,000   **B** 2,000
    C 5,500   **D** 7,000

20. Which of the following best describes the change in the number of births of triplets or more between 1980 and 2005?
    F They increased slightly.
    G They increased by 50 percent.
    H They doubled.
    J They nearly quadrupled.

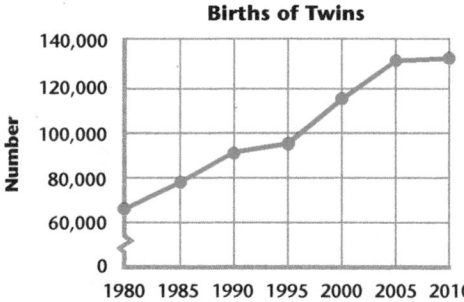

Births of Twins

21. Approximately how much greater was the number of twin births compared with births of triplets or more in the year 2005?
    A 2 times   **B** 4 times
    C 8 times   **D** 18 times

Reading and Writing Practice

Read the passage. Then answer Questions 22–25.

In the United States, more than 20 percent of women smoke. More than half of these women smoke while they are pregnant. This is a major public health problem because, not only can smoking harm a woman's health, but smoking during pregnancy can lead to pregnancy complications and serious health problems in newborns. The statistics are compelling. If all pregnant women in the United States stopped smoking, there would be an estimated 11 percent reduction in stillbirths and a 5 percent reduction in deaths of newborns.

22. In this passage, the word *compelling* means
    A interesting.   **B** doubtful.
    C convincing.   **D** reliable.

23. According to the passage, which of these statements is true?
    F There is no correlation between smoking and newborn deaths.
    G More than 20 percent of women smoke during pregnancy.
    H If more women chose not to smoke during pregnancy, more newborns would survive.
    J Smoking during pregnancy does not affect the number of stillbirths.

24. What word best describes the tone of this passage?
    A poetic   **B** angry
    C sarcastic   **D** persuasive

Constructed Response

25. Write a sentence summarizing the viewpoint of the author of this reading passage. Then, in a paragraph, explain how the author uses statistics to defend this viewpoint.

> **Test-Taking Tip**
>
> Skip difficult questions. You can return to them later. Don't get stuck on them and waste time.

Standardized Test Prep
Math Practice
19. C
20. J
21. D

Reading and Writing Practice
22. C
23. H
24. D
25. Sentences should explain that the author thinks that women should not smoke during pregnancy. Paragraphs should describe how the author uses statistics about the higher rates of stillbirths and newborn deaths that occur when pregnant women smoke.

Health and Community

Folic Acid Awareness In their public service announcements, students should explain that folic acid aids in the formation of the neural tube. The neural tube forms very early in a pregnancy, often before a woman knows she is pregnant. Students should also identify sources of folic acid, such as a multivitamin, or in foods such as green, leafy vegetables and legumes.

Section Objectives	Standards Correlation	Instructional Resources L3	SE eTEXT	TE eTEXT	PRINT
1 **Adolescence: A Time of Change** ⏱ 2 periods; 1 block	NHES: 1.12.4, 2.12.5, 2.12.8, 8.12.4	SE Warm-Up, p. 514	•	•	•
		RN Note Taking Guide 20-1	•	•	•
20.1.1 **List** three main categories of physical changes that occur during adolescence.		IB Image Bank 20-5		•	
20.1.2 **Describe** three mental changes that adolescents experience.		TR Practice 20-1		•	
20.1.3 **Summarize** the emotional changes of adolescence.		TR Section 20-1 Quiz		•	
Setting a Goal ⏱ 1 period; 1/2 block	NHES: 5.12.7, 6.12.2, 6.12.3, 6.12.4, 7.12.1	SE Practice the Skill, p. 523	•	•	•
		RN Building Health Skills 20	•	•	•
BHS.20 **Set** a personal goal and develop a plan for achieving the goal.					
2 **Adolescence and Responsibility** ⏱ 2 periods; 1 block	NHES: 2.12.1, 2.12.3, 2.12.8, 5.12.1, 5.12.2, 7.12.1, 8.12.2, 8.12.3	SE Warm-Up, p. 524	•	•	•
		SE Hands-On Activity Living on a Budget, p. 527	•	•	•
20.2.1 **Identify** the responsibilities that adolescents have to themselves and others.		RN Note Taking Guide 20-2	•	•	•
		TR Practice 20-2		•	
		TR Section 20-2 Quiz		•	
3 **Adulthood and Marriage** ⏱ 2 periods; 1 block	NHES: 1.12.1, 1.12.5, 6.12.4, 8.12.3	SE Warm-Up, p. 529	•	•	•
		RN Note Taking Guide 20-3	•	•	•
20.3.1 **Summarize** the changes that people undergo during adulthood.		TR Practice 20-3		•	
20.3.2 **List** three keys to a successful marriage.		TR Section 20-3 Quiz		•	
20.3.3 **Analyze** how decisions made in youth can affect the aging process.					
4 **Death and Dying** ⏱ 1 period; 1/2 block	NHES: 2.12.2, 3.12.1, 3.12.3, 3.12.4, 4.12.1, 4.12.4	SE Warm-Up, p. 537	•	•	•
		RN Note Taking Guide 20-4	•	•	•
20.4.1 **List** the five stages of dying that some people experience.		IB Image Bank 20-17		•	
		TR Practice 20-4		•	
20.4.2 **Summarize** healthy strategies for coping with a dying loved one and coping after a death.		TR Section 20-4 Quiz		•	

Chapter Review and Assessment

SE Chapter 20 Review, p. 542 L3
CTB Chapter 20 Test L2 L3 L4
SE Standardized Test Prep, p. 543 L3

PROGRAM COMPONENTS

SE	Student Edition	**CTB**	Computer Test Bank
TE	Teacher Edition	**AUD**	Audio Section Summaries
TR	Teaching Resources		
RN	Reading and Note Taking Guide	**DVD**	Teens Talk Video Series
		VVG	Video Viewing Guide
ARN	Adapted Reading and Note Taking Guide	**PPT**	Presentation
IB	Image Bank		

Differentiated Instruction
L1 L2 L4 EL

		SE eTEXT	TE eTEXT	PRINT
ARN	Note Taking Guide 20-1 L2	•	•	
RN	Note Taking Guide 20-1 EL	•	•	•
AUD	Audio Summary 20-1 L1 L2 EL	•	•	
TE	Reteach Strategy, p. 521 L2		•	•
TR	Enrich 20-1 L4		•	
ARN	Building Health Skills 20 L2	•	•	
RN	Building Health Skills 20 EL	•	•	•
ARN	Note Taking Guide 20-2 L2	•	•	
RN	Note Taking Guide 20-2 EL	•	•	•
AUD	Audio Summary 20-2 L1 L2 EL	•	•	
TE	Reteach Strategy, p. 528 L2		•	•
TR	Enrich 20-2 L4		•	
ARN	Note Taking Guide 20-3 L2	•	•	
RN	Note Taking Guide 20-3 EL	•	•	•
AUD	Audio Summary 20-3 L1 L2 EL	•	•	
TE	Reteach Strategy, p. 536 L2		•	•
TR	Enrich 20-3 L4		•	
ARN	Note Taking Guide 20-4 L2	•	•	
RN	Note Taking Guide 20-4 EL	•	•	•
AUD	Audio Summary 20-4 L1 L2 EL	•	•	
TE	Reteach Strategy, p. 540 L2		•	•
TR	Enrich 20-4 L4		•	

ABILITY LEVELS

L1 **For students with special needs**
L2 **For less proficient readers**
L3 **For all students**
L4 **For gifted and talented students**
EL **For English language learners**

Chapter 20 Digital/Video Pathway

This alternative pathway allows you to teach this chapter's content using only the video and online materials.

Preview
- **DVD** Video #20 Preview
- **SE** Video #20 Preview Activity
- **VVG** Video #20 Worksheet

Pictures of "Perfection"

1
- **DVD** Video #20 Explore/Wrap-Up
- **VVG** Video #20 Worksheet
- **PPT** 20-2 Presentation
- **RN/ARN** 20-2 Note Taking
- **PPT** 20-2 Section Quiz

Pictures of "Perfection"

2
- **PPT** 15-1 Presentation
- **RN/ARN** 15-1 Note Taking
- **PPT** 15-1 Section Quiz

3
- **PPT** 20-3 Presentation
- **RN/ARN** 20-3 Note Taking
- **PPT** 20-3 Section Quiz

4
- **PPT** 20-4 Presentation
- **RN/ARN** 20-4 Note Taking
- **PPT** 20-4 Section Quiz

Chapter Preview

Section 1 Adolescence: A Time of Change
Adolescence is a time of physical, mental, and emotional changes. These changes can have positive results, such as an increased ability to use reasoning to solve problems. At other times, the changes of adolescence can be a source of stress.

 Setting Goals
Setting a Goal
Setting realistic and achievable goals can help adolescents transition into adulthood.

Section 2 Adolescence and Responsibility
Adolescents have responsibilities to themselves that include making healthy decisions, resisting negative influences, and planning for the future. Adolescents also have responsibilities to their families, friends, and community.

Section 3 Adulthood and Marriage
Adulthood is characterized by physical and emotional maturity. Marriage is a part of many adults' lives. Aging involves physical, emotional, and social changes. Some of the physical signs of aging can be reduced or delayed by the early establishment of healthy habits.

Section 4 Death and Dying
Death is a normal part of life. Those who are dying and their family members often experience five stages of grief. Emotional support can be a comfort to those who are grieving for a loved one.

Adolescence and Adulthood

⊙ GO ONLINE PearsonSuccessNet.com

TEENS Talk
VIDEO 20
Pictures of "Perfection"

Preview **Activity**

What's Important to You?

Complete this activity before you watch the video.

1. Rank the following qualities by how important you think they are to *your* overall attractiveness (with 1 being most important).
   ____ body shape
   ____ facial features
   ____ mature appearance
   ____ personality
   ____ intelligence
2. Now rank the list by how important you think each quality is to *other* people's attractiveness. How do your two rankings differ?
3. Now reflect. Do you think that your rankings for yourself and others are as they *should* be? Explain. **WRITING**

512

⊙ **GO ONLINE**
PearsonSuccessNet.com
For resources and activities for this chapter.

 Sensitive Issues

- Many students are uncomfortable discussing the changes that occur during adolescence. Permitting students to submit anonymous written questions will allow them to ask questions about this topic without risking embarrassment.
- Some students may be reluctant to discuss topics such as mid-life crisis or divorce if these situations are currently occurring in their families. Avoid making judgments about those who divorce or undergo negative changes during a mid-life crisis.
- The topic of death and dying may be difficult for those who have a terminally ill loved one or have experienced a loss.

VIDEO 20

TEENS Talk 🔘

Pictures of "Perfection"

Video Objectives

Use this video to help students

Identify some of the reasons why teens have a negative body image.

Analyze why media images of "perfect" bodies are not realistic.

Apply some techniques to become more accepting of their own bodies.

Preview **Activity**

What's Important to You?

Assign the Preview Activity for homework a few days before you plan to show the video. After students complete the activity, discuss how their rankings for "self" differed from their rankings for "others." You may also want to compile the rankings for the class and compare the class averages. Ask students if their rankings for "self" and "others" seem fair. After the discussion, ask students if they would change any of their rankings, and why.

From the Authors

What is adolescence really like? Why not ask the experts? The students in your class can provide insight about adolescence. Ask students to share their ideas about ways that adolescence has changed over time.

After students have shared their ideas, have them consider the following facts: The period of time called adolescence is expanding. This is because the age at which girls reach puberty is younger than it used to be (about 12.6 years now as compared to around age 14 in the year 1900). At the same time, the age when young adults leave home is increasing. Also, brain research suggests that the brain continues to develop into the early twenties. Challenge students to consider what these facts suggest about today's adolescents.

Objectives
Before class begins, write the objectives on the board. Have students copy the objectives into their notebooks at the start of class.

1. Focus

Warm-Up Advice Line

After students have completed their writing, ask volunteers to share their responses with the class. Then explain that the changes of adolescence often bring stress. Tell students that learning about the physical, emotional, and social changes that occur during adolescence can help reduce this stress.

Presentation 20-1

Section 1

Adolescence: A Time of Change

Objectives

▶ **List** three main categories of physical changes that occur during adolescence.

▶ **Describe** three mental changes that adolescents experience.

▶ **Summarize** the emotional changes of adolescence.

Vocabulary

- adolescence
- reproductive maturity
- secondary sex characteristics

Warm-Up

Dear Advice Line,

I'm very self-conscious because I look more grown up than all of my friends. I'm tired of people staring at me and making comments about my body. What can I do?

WRITING What advice and reassurances would you offer this teen?

Changes in Your Body

If you were to compare a recent photograph of yourself to one taken three years ago, you would notice many changes. From about the ages of 12 to 19, you gradually change from a child into an adult. This period of gradual change is called **adolescence.** During adolescence, a person undergoes many physical, mental, and emotional changes.

As photographs reveal, adolescence is a period of rapid physical growth. However, photos show only some of the physical changes taking place. Important physical changes are also occurring inside the body during this time. **During adolescence, the reproductive system matures, adult features appear, and height and muscle mass increase.**

Reproductive System Puberty usually begins before you reach adolescence and ends during mid-adolescence. As you learned from Chapter 18, puberty is the period of sexual development when a person becomes sexually mature and able to reproduce. You may have heard the term *puberty* used in many different ways. Some people use the term to refer to all of the changes of adolescence. However, the term refers specifically to the changes that happen to your reproductive system.

Sensitive Issues

Students may feel uncomfortable discussing the changes of adolescence. Take steps to create a classroom environment in which students are encouraged, but not required, to join classroom discussions of these sensitive topics. Remind students that showing respect to others is particularly important during these discussions.

WRITING and Health

L3 Comparison

Ask students to write a paragraph that compares and contrasts puberty and adolescence. Encourage students to use a graphic organizer, such as a Venn diagram, to organize their thoughts before they write. Remind students that a paragraph should include a topic sentence and supporting details. After students have completed their writing, ask volunteers to share their paragraphs with the class. Use the students' writing to reinforce the correct usage of the terms *puberty* and *adolescence*.

Also recall from Chapter 18 that sex hormones control the changes that occur during puberty. At some point between the ages of 9 and 16, the pituitary gland in the brain signals a girl's ovaries or a boy's testes to begin producing sex hormones. The ovaries produce estrogen and progesterone while the testes produce testosterone.

The release of sex hormones causes girls to begin to ovulate and menstruate, and boys to begin to produce sperm. Ovulation in girls and sperm production in boys signal **reproductive maturity,** or the ability to produce children. Early in puberty, the body does not produce sex hormones consistently. In girls, this affects the regularity of the menstrual cycle. Many girls begin to ovulate before their menstrual cycles become regular. In fact, in some girls, menstrual cycles do not become regular for many years. As the glands mature, hormone production becomes more regular.

Appearance The sex hormones also cause the development of **secondary sex characteristics,** which are physical changes that develop during puberty, but are not directly involved in reproduction. Secondary sex characteristics are listed in Figure 1.

The physical changes at puberty can be overwhelming at times. Some adolescents have difficulty adjusting to their changing body shape, or may be embarrassed or confused about the sexual changes occurring to their bodies. Having someone to talk to, especially a trusted adult, can help adolescents understand and accept their feelings.

FIGURE 1 At puberty, sex hormones cause the development of secondary sex characteristics.

Connect to Your Life Whom can you talk to when you feel concerned about the changes in your body?

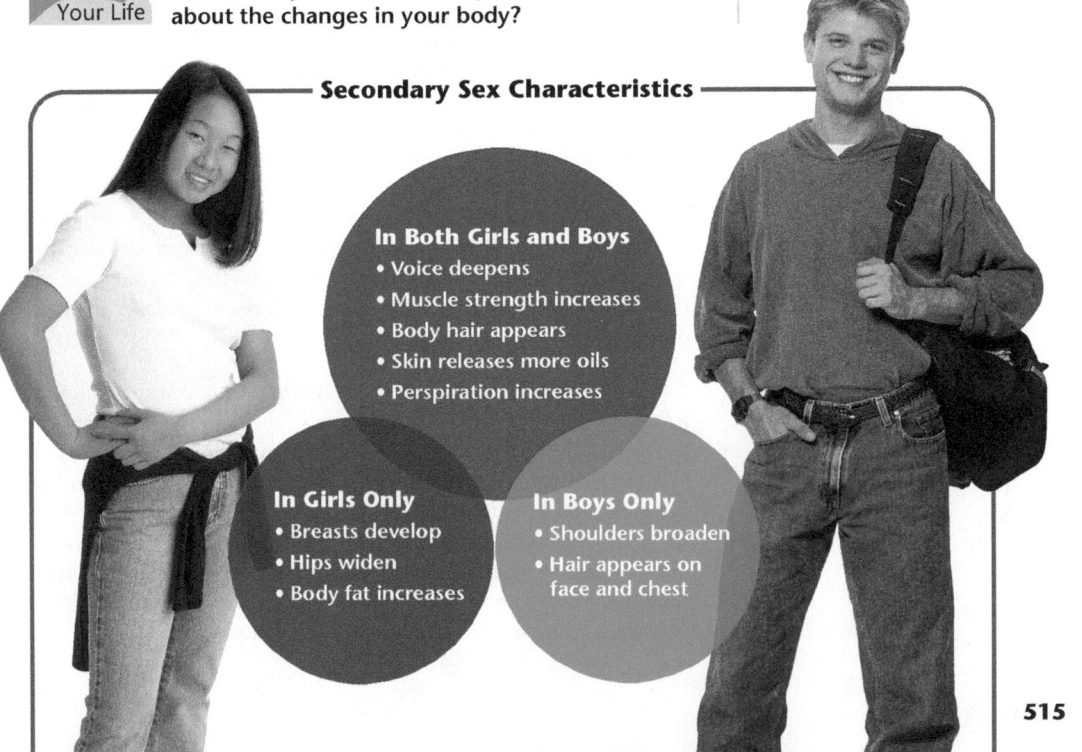

Secondary Sex Characteristics

In Both Girls and Boys
- Voice deepens
- Muscle strength increases
- Body hair appears
- Skin releases more oils
- Perspiration increases

In Girls Only
- Breasts develop
- Hips widen
- Body fat increases

In Boys Only
- Shoulders broaden
- Hair appears on face and chest

515

2. Teach

(L3) (EL) **Reading/Note Taking** 20-1

(L2) **Adapted Reading/Note Taking** 20-1

Changes in Your Body

(EL) Building Vocabulary

Ask students to recall the definition of the word *hormone*, which they learned in Chapter 18. *(a chemical substance produced by an endocrine gland)* Tell students that the word *hormone* comes from a Greek word meaning "to stir up." Ask students to give examples of ways in which hormones can "stir up" one's life. *(Hormones stir up changes in physical appearance, leading to feelings of awkwardness and uncertainty.)*

(L3) Building Health Skills

Accessing Information Point out that the physical changes of puberty can be stressful and confusing. Have students identify possible sources of information about puberty (for example, the Internet, books, friends, school nurse, parents or guardians). Record their responses on the board. Then, review the list and have students explain how they would assess the reliability of each source of information.

(L2) Visual Learning: Figure 1

Have students examine Figure 1, which describes the secondary sex characteristics that develop during puberty. Ask: **Why are the changes described in the figure classified as secondary sex characteristics?** *(These changes are not directly related to reproduction.)* Point out that the text mentions that these changes can be overwhelming. Ask: **What other adjectives might be used to describe the emotional impact of these physical changes?** *(Sample answers: scary, confusing, exciting, frustrating)*

Connect to Your Life *Sample answer:* I can talk to my parents when I have a concern about the changes in my body.

Differentiated Instruction

(L2) Less Proficient Readers

Pair less proficient readers with advanced readers. Have each pair of students organize the information in this section using a chart or a graphic organizer. Provide several completed graphic organizers for students to use as models as they organize the section content. Remind students to include physical, mental, and emotional changes of adolescence in their graphic organizers. Circulate among the students to offer guidance and to correct any errors or omissions. Remind students that their graphic organizers can be used as a guide to reading and as a study aid as they prepare for the Section Review and the Chapter Review.

L3 **Cooperative Learning**

Explain that many adolescents experience frustration with the rate at which they get taller and build muscle mass. This frustration leads a small minority of teens to illegally use anabolic steroids with the hope of becoming more muscular or toned. Divide the class into small groups. Ask each group to find an article about the negative health aspects of anabolic steroids, using library or internet resources. Have each group prepare and present a short lesson based on its article. Follow up with a discussion of influences, such as the media, that can lead teens to experience frustration with their rates of growth.

L2 **Active Learning**

Ask students to work with a partner to create a print, radio, or television advertisement that informs teens about changes in height and muscle mass that occur in adolescence. The advertisement should also describe ways to cope with the awkwardness brought on by these changes. Ask each pair of students to share its advertisement with the class. **WRITING**

8th Grade Dance

Senior Prom

FIGURE 2 Girls typically begin their growth spurt earlier than boys, but don't grow as much overall.

Height and Muscle Mass Around the same time that puberty starts, the pituitary gland also increases its production of growth hormone. Growth hormone is a chemical messenger that activates growth. First your hands and feet grow, then your arms and legs.

Growth does not occur in a regular fashion, but in spurts. Some months little growth hormone is produced, and you do not seem to grow at all. Other months there is a surge of growth hormone, and you seem to jump shoe sizes in a very short time.

If you were to look at a group of young adolescents, you would notice that, for the most part, the girls are taller than the boys. Girls tend to begin their growth spurt earlier than boys. If you looked at the same adolescents at the end of high school, however, the boys would be taller than the girls, for the most part. Boys start their growth spurt later, but they grow for a longer period of time—eventually becoming taller than girls, on average.

Growing Pains Adjusting to changes in your body proportions can be difficult at times. Rapid lengthening of the bones in your arms and legs can cause aches and cramps. It can also make you feel awkward. You may feel as if you are tripping over your own feet, or you may find that you are no longer comfortable in your favorite chair.

If you challenge your growing body with a variety of physical activities, you will adjust more rapidly to your new size and shape. Physical activity will also help to develop your muscles and your coordination. As unlikely as it may seem, your feelings of discomfort and awkwardness will soon disappear.

516 *Chapter 20*

For Your INFORMATION!

Bone Growth

Bone growth occurs at the regions of bones called the growth, or epiphyseal, plates. These plates consist of cartilage rather than bone. Rapid bone growth occurs during the adolescent growth spurt, and bones continue to grow slowly for some time after the growth spurt. By the end of adolescence, the growth plates ossify, or change to hardened bone. Once ossification is complete, bones can no longer increase in length, however they can still become denser. Until ossification occurs, the growth plates are susceptible to fracture because they are the weakest portion of the bone. Bone growth and ossification of the growth plates require a supply of calcium, other minerals, and vitamins.

Energy Demands You may also notice another effect that growth has on your body—it makes you hungry. Your family may remark that your stomach seems to be a "bottomless pit." This is normal during adolescence because you need extra energy to fuel your growing body. It is important, however, to eat nutritious meals and snacks to supply your body with the nutrients it needs. You should not gain excessive weight.

Early Bloomers and Late Bloomers If you are like most adolescents, you have probably compared your own physical development to that of your peers. Some of your classmates may already look like adults, while others may be just starting to show signs of puberty. You can see in Figure 4 that the age range for the "normal" onset of puberty is wide. Some people start puberty before middle school, some start puberty toward the end of high school, and others start somewhere in between.

Adolescents who develop at an early age, before most other adolescents, are sometimes called early bloomers. Those who develop at a late age, after most other adolescents, are called late bloomers. Although they may not think so, most early bloomers and late bloomers are developing at a normal rate.

What accounts for the wide range of ages at which puberty and the growth spurt begin? The ages at which people mature sexually and grow to their adult height are determined in large part by heredity. You are probably maturing at about the same age and speed as your parents did. Another factor that influences your unique timetable of development is your overall state of health.

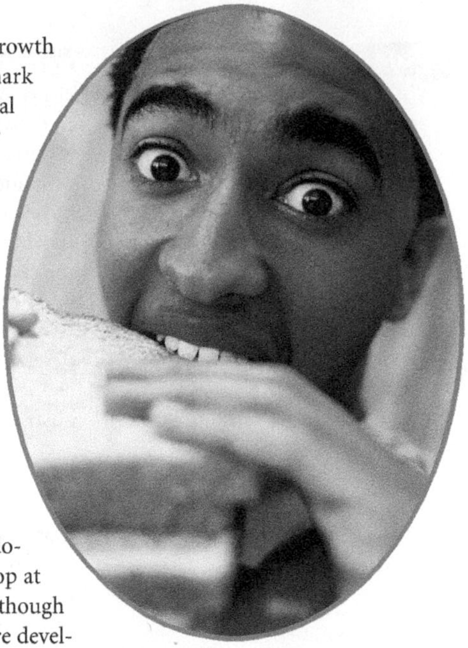

 **Connect to Your Life** Do you consider yourself an early bloomer, late bloomer, or somewhere in between? Why?

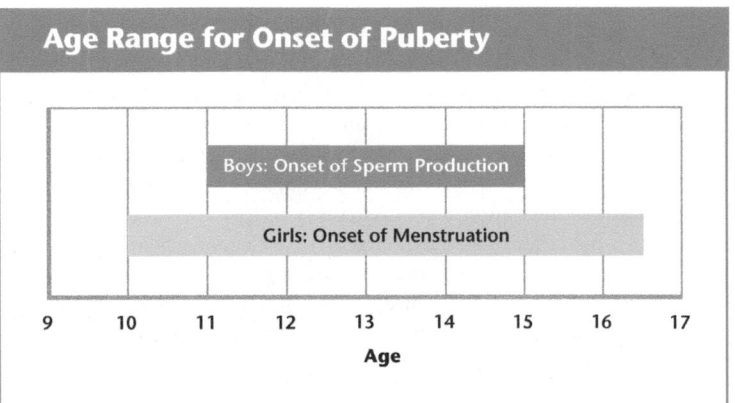

Age Range for Onset of Puberty

Boys: Onset of Sperm Production

Girls: Onset of Menstruation

9 10 11 12 13 14 15 16 17
Age

FIGURE 3 It's normal to feel an increase in your appetite during adolescence—your body needs extra fuel for growth.

FIGURE 4 There is no "typical" age at which puberty begins. This timeline shows that the age range for onset of puberty is wide. **Calculating** What is the range in years between the earliest and latest onset of menstruation in girls? **MATH**

Adolescence and Adulthood **517**

Mental Changes

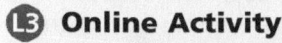 **Online Activity**  GO ONLINE

Visit Pearson SuccessNet to access an online activity about adolescence. Have students complete the Web activity.

L2 Class Discussion

Write on the board the three categories of mental changes that occur in adolescence (abstract thinking, reasoning skills, and impulse control). Ask the class to provide everyday examples of each of these changes and list their responses under the appropriate category on the board. Discuss each of the examples with the class. Use these everyday examples to help students understand the mental changes of adolescence.

Connect to Your Life *Sample answer:* Today in history class, I used abstract thinking skills to compare three different forms of government.

L3 Building Health Skills

Making Decisions Point out that the increased reasoning skills associated with brain development during adolescence allow teens to make thoughtful decisions. Remind students of the importance of examining pros and cons when making decisions. Divide the class into small groups. Have each group identify one common, everyday decision faced by teens. Ask each group to develop a written list of pros and cons associated with its identified decision. Have each group share its responses with the class. Follow up with a class discussion of the positive impact that good decision making can have on overall health and wellness.

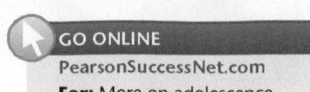
GO ONLINE
PearsonSuccessNet.com
For: More on adolescence

Mental Changes

Hormones control most of the outward physical changes of adolescence. But changes in the way you think and feel have more to do with changes occurring in your brain. In your first few years of life, millions of brain cells and the pathways connecting them formed. Then, when you were between 10 and 13 years old, a second dramatic wave of growth and development took place. In fact, your brain grew a bit too much! During the rest of your adolescence, your brain will be "pruned back." Only the brain cells and connections that you use will survive and flourish.

Scientists are discovering how changes in the brain affect teenage development. Figure 5 shows four regions of the brain in which significant changes occur. **Mental changes during adolescence include improved abstract thinking, reasoning skills, and impulse control.**

Abstract Thinking When you were a child, your thoughts and feelings were tied directly to your physical experiences at each moment. For example, you thought about hunger only when your stomach was empty. Now, however, it is easier for you to think abstractly—to consider ideas that are not concrete or visible. For example, you can now think about the problem of chronic hunger in communities around the world. Your growing ability to think abstractly is partly due to the dramatic growth in your brain's frontal cortex, shown in Figure 5.

 **Connect to Your Life** How have you used abstract thinking skills today at school? Explain.

Reasoning Skills During adolescence, changes to your brain also help to expand your reasoning abilities—including the way you solve problems and make decisions. You are becoming increasingly able to see more than one side of a question and to think through the pros and cons of decisions you face. As you gain experience making wise choices in simple everyday dilemmas, you find it easier to make wise choices when more difficult situations arise.

Impulse Control Some teenagers find that their impulses, or tendencies to act rapidly based on emotional reactions, are sometimes clouding their decision-making abilities. Maybe a friend dares them to do something dangerous, and before they consider the consequences, they go ahead and do it. As described in Figure 5, the emotional region of an adolescent's brain is more active than the same region in an adult's brain. Scientists hypothesize that greater activity in the amygdala may be one reason why it is harder for teens to ignore impulses.

You may not like the consequences of acting on your impulses. Removing yourself from an intense situation and taking some time to think things through can help you stay in control. As you mature, your impulse control will improve.

518 *Chapter 20*

Focus on **ISSUES**

 Debate: Teens Tried as Adults

Explain to students that teens charged with crimes are sometimes tried as adults. Divide the class into two teams. Have one team support the position that, for certain crimes, teens should be tried as adults. Have the other team support the position that, due to the incomplete development of the teen brain, there are no circumstances under which a teen should be tried as an adult. Encourage students to do further research to support their team's position.

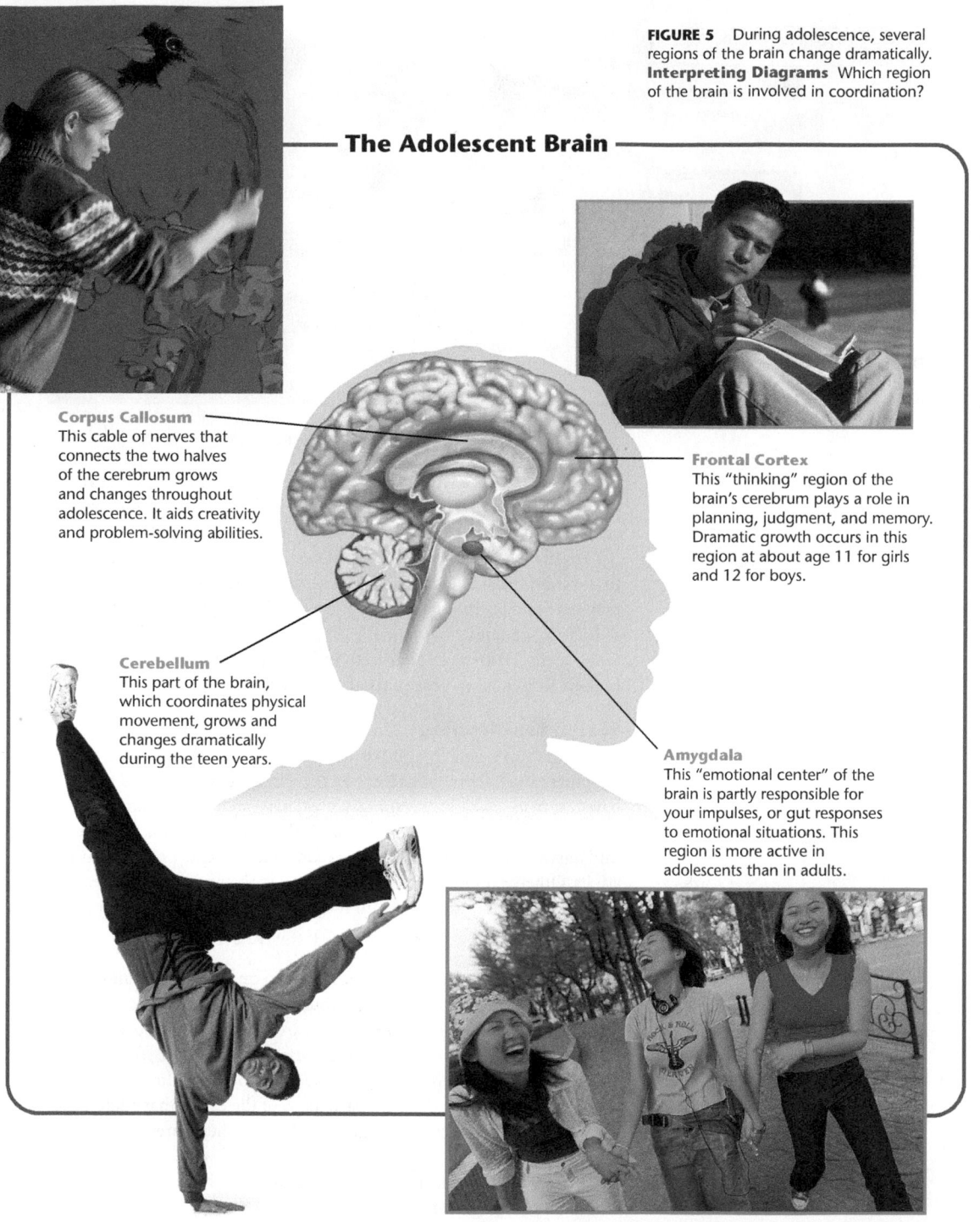

The Adolescent Brain

Corpus Callosum
This cable of nerves that connects the two halves of the cerebrum grows and changes throughout adolescence. It aids creativity and problem-solving abilities.

Cerebellum
This part of the brain, which coordinates physical movement, grows and changes dramatically during the teen years.

Frontal Cortex
This "thinking" region of the brain's cerebrum plays a role in planning, judgment, and memory. Dramatic growth occurs in this region at about age 11 for girls and 12 for boys.

Amygdala
This "emotional center" of the brain is partly responsible for your impulses, or gut responses to emotional situations. This region is more active in adolescents than in adults.

Adolescence and Adulthood **519**

ⓛ2 Visual Learning: Figure 5

Image Bank Figure 20-5

Have students read about each of the changes highlighted in Figure 5. Ask students to discuss how each of these changes impacts the way teens think or behave. Ask: **Which region of the brain is involved in thinking, judgment, and memory?** *(the frontal cortex)* **What is one way that growth and development of the frontal cortex could impact a teen's life?** *(Sample answer: Development of the frontal cortex allows teens to more easily complete school work that involves memorization.)*
Caption Answer The cerebellum is the region of the brain involved in coordination.

ⓔⓛ Building Vocabulary

Pair English language learners with students who are proficient in English. Have each pair use a dictionary to find the meaning of the word *impulsive*. Then, have students write sentences that use the word *impulsive* in the context of teen emotions. Call on several pairs of students to share their sentences with the class.

ⓛ3 Journal Writing

Have students write an entry in their personal journals that describes one way they feel their behavior or thought processes have changed during adolescence. Remind students that their journal entries will remain confidential. **WRITING**

Differentiated Instruction

ⓛ1 Special Needs

Have visually impaired students work with a partner to discuss the photographs, diagrams, and text presented in Figure 5. If possible, provide visually-impaired students with a three-dimensional model of the human brain. Have a partner guide the visually impaired student as he or she identifies and explores the regions of the brain that change during adolescence. Have the partners work together to review this information before the Chapter Review is assigned.

Emotional Changes

L1 Active Learning

Ask students to bring in a magazine photo that they think represents an important emotional aspect of adolescence. Have each student present his or her photograph and describe what emotional aspect of adolescence it illustrates. List each idea on the board. Have students use the ideas on the board to develop a description of emotional changes that accompany adolescence.

L3 Building Media Literacy

Have students evaluate the representation of teens as portrayed in TV shows. For example, students might transcribe several quotes from teen characters that reflect strong negative and positive emotions. In class, have students share the quotes and talk about how the characters worked through their strong emotions. Did they do so in a healthy way? Do students think that story lines on TV accurately represent teen life? If not, how is real life different?

L2 Class Discussion

Provide students with several examples of statements that describe personal beliefs, such as "I believe that people should conserve resources." Ask students to write five "I believe..." statements that describe their personal values. Then have students discuss their statements with a parent or guardian. Ask students to find out if their values are similar to their parent's or guardian's values. Have students write a statement that summarizes their results.

 Allow students to answer this question in their private journals.

"She thought I was in college!"

"I don't have a date for the prom!"

"I made the team!"

"Oh no! Not another pimple!"

FIGURE 6 Most teenagers experience many strong feelings, both positive and negative.

Emotional Changes

During adolescence, you may feel like you are on an emotional roller coaster—very happy one moment, and miserable the next. You are not alone in having these strong feelings—all teens experience them.

For many teens, adolescence is a time for questioning. You may begin to question many things that you have simply accepted until now. You may start to question the actions and values of people around you, such as friends and family members. Most important, you may start to question yourself. **During adolescence, individuals start to define meaning in their lives, a set of personal values, and a sense of self.**

Search for Meaning During adolescence, it is not unusual to suddenly question whether your friends are really true friends and whether happiness and love are possible to attain. These questions signal that you have begun to search for meaning in life. This search is important because you are beginning to choose a way of life that is right for you. Some teens find answers to these questions by talking with parents or other trusted adults. Others explore these questions through their own experiences. For example, some teens volunteer in hospitals or food pantries. Such experiences often help them figure out what is important to them.

Search for Values Have you started to question the opinions and beliefs of others, especially those of your parents? This process helps you discover your values—those beliefs that are important to you. Although you may disagree with your parents at times, they can offer you guidance and serve as role models. Parents, teachers, and other adults can help you clarify your values. For the most part, many of the values that adolescents eventually come to accept are similar to those of their parents.

 **What important values do you share with your parents?**

WRITING and Health

L3 E-mail

Have students imagine that they have received an e-mail from a friend who is searching for meaning in his or her life. Have students generate a response to the e-mail that gives several positive examples of ways that their friend can explore what is important in his or her life. Students' e-mails should also assure their friend that this search for meaning is normal. After students have completed their writing, ask volunteers to share their responses with the class. Ask students to note and describe similarities and differences in the responses.

Search for Self Some of the most difficult questions that adolescents ask concern themselves and their place in the world. These questions are signs of a search for who you are—your identity. This search for identity may take many forms. You might discuss the question of identity with others, or you might compare yourself to people you admire. Exploring your racial and ethnic traditions can be an important part of your search for identity. You may experiment with new hairstyles, different clothing, and even new behaviors.

As you explore ways to express your identity, think about the long-term social consequences of your actions. Some changes are difficult to reverse. What will the person in Figure 7 think about her tattoo when she is 50?

If you are like many adolescents, your self-esteem may not be as high today as it was a few years ago. Right now your feelings about yourself are strongly influenced by the opinions of others, particularly your peers. You may worry whether your peers approve of your clothing, your looks, your personality, and your interests. It is normal to have these worries. In time, these feelings will lessen.

It is not always easy to keep a clear and consistent picture of yourself, or to feel positive about who you are. Try writing about your accomplishments and talents in a journal. When the question "Who am I?" comes up, you can find some good answers in your journal.

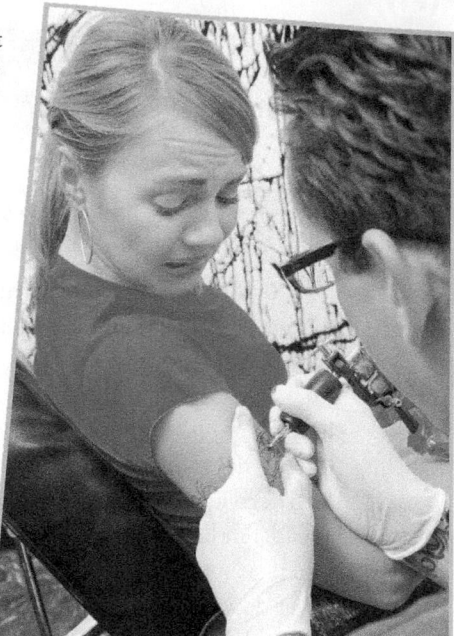

FIGURE 7 Sometimes people use a tattoo to express their identity.
Evaluating Could having a tattoo affect a person's ability to get a job?

Section 1 Review

Key Ideas and Vocabulary

1. What are three categories of physical changes that occur during adolescence?
2. What is **reproductive maturity**? How is it related to puberty?
3. What are **secondary sex characteristics**? List two for males and two for females.
4. Describe three mental changes that occur during adolescence.
5. How do teens develop emotionally during adolescence? Give three examples of questions teens may ask themselves.

Health at Home

Advertising Appeal Choose two magazine or television advertisements that target adolescents. Make a list of the products being advertised and answer these questions for each: How does the ad take advantage of a teen's search for self? Do the ad's images promote a particular identity? Is the identity related to the product or not? Explain your answers. **WRITING**

Critical Thinking

6. **Making Judgments** In your opinion, is it more difficult to be an early bloomer or a late bloomer? Explain.
7. **Predicting** How have your values changed since you were young? How do you think your values might change as you get older? Explain. **WRITING**

GO ONLINE PearsonSuccessNet.com Audio Summary Section 20.1 *Adolescence and Adulthood* **521**

Section 1 Review

1. The reproductive system matures, adult features appear, and height and muscle mass increase.
2. Reproductive maturity is the ability to produce children. Puberty is the period of sexual development that results in reproductive maturity.
3. Secondary sex characteristics are physical changes that develop during puberty, but are not directly involved in reproduction. males: shoulders broaden and hair appears on face and chest; females: breasts develop and hips widen
4. a growing ability to think abstractly, increased reasoning skills, difficulties with impulse control

3. Assess

Evaluate
These assignments can help you assess students' mastery of the section content.

Section 1 Review
Answers appear below.

Teaching Resources
• Practice 20-1
• Section 20-1 Quiz

L2 Reteach

Have students review the physical, mental, and emotional changes of adolescence by reviewing each figure in the section. Have students write one sentence for each figure, summarizing the information it presents.

L4 Enrich

Teaching Resources
• Enrich 20-1

Health at Home

Advertising Appeal Provide students with magazines to use for this activity. Remind students to select advertisements that specifically target teens. After students have completed their work, ask volunteers to share their responses with the class. Follow up with a class discussion of the common methods advertisers use to market products to teens.

5. Teens develop emotionally by defining meaning in their lives, setting personal goals, and developing a sense of self. Examples of questions teens ask themselves: Who are my true friends? What is important to me? Who am I?
6. *Sample answer:* It is more difficult to be an early bloomer, because your peers cannot relate to the changes you are experiencing.
7. *Sample answer:* My values have moved away from my parents' values, but will probably become more like theirs as I get older.

Adolescence and Adulthood **521**

Setting a Goal

Objective

Set a personal goal and develop a plan for achieving the goal.

Teaching Strategies

- Have students work in small groups to discuss goals that they have previously set and achieved. Have students work with their group to develop a list of factors that they feel helped them achieve their goals. Ask each group to share its list of factors with the class. Record the responses on the board. Then have students compare the list on the board to the numbered guidelines in the activity (knowing yourself; making goals clear, specific, and positive; including deadlines; breaking long-term goals into small steps; keeping written goals visible; and evaluating progress).

- Remind students that teens' long-term goals often change, as interests and priorities change. Explain that this is normal. By focusing on achieving positive short-term goals (such as maintaining good grades); a wide range of long-term goals can be achieved (attending a four-year college, attending a two-year college, finding a good job).

- Point out the first guideline: know yourself. Ask students to relate this to the search for identity that occurs during adolescence. Point out that clarifying personal values is an important part of setting achievable goals.

Setting a Goal

Now that Diego is a senior in high school, everyone is asking him about his goals. When his uncle tells him to consider "where he'll be in ten years," his father complains that Diego doesn't know where he'll be next week.

Diego knows he should start looking ahead, but how far ahead? He's always said he wants to be an architect, but he's never done anything about it. His attention and energies seem to skip from one thing to another. The following guidelines could help Diego focus his energies on achievable goals. You can use them, too, to help set your own realistic and reachable goals.

1 Know yourself.

Before deciding on specific goals, jot down what you know about yourself. What are your long-term interests? What activities do you enjoy? What are your abilities? What are the most important things in your life? Goals that correspond to your interests and values will be more desirable. Goals tied to your abilities will be easier to reach.

2 Make goals clear, specific, and positive.

A clear, specific, positive goal accurately describes what you want to be doing when you achieve it. An example of a well-written goal is: "I want to get all Bs this term." This is clearer and more specific than "I want to do better in school." It allows you to measure your success by counting the number of Bs you receive. In contrast, you cannot measure "doing better."

Getting all Bs is also more positive than "I don't want any Fs this term." Making progress toward a positive goal will give you a sense of pride and inspire you to keep going.

522

Sensitive Issues

- Students may be uncomfortable stating their personal goals if those goals are different from the expectations of their family or their community. Allow students to keep their goals confidential if they wish.

- Remind students that there are a wide range of positive and healthy long-term goals. Remind students that struggling to make long-term goals is normal and common among teens.

❸ Include deadlines.

Set a reasonable time limit for your goals. Deadlines make goals more specific, add a sense of urgency, and provide a good way to measure success. If you cannot meet the deadline, you may need to consider a more realistic time limit. For example, if you were able to raise four out of five grades to Bs this term, this would be good progress, not failure. The goal of earning all Bs can be rescheduled for next term.

❹ Break long-term goals into small steps.

Long-term goals, such as running a marathon, should be broken into smaller, more manageable, measurable steps. Future marathoners begin their training with short distances. Only when they have built the speed and endurance necessary for long distances do they go on to run the full marathon course.

❺ Keep written goals visible.

Write your goals down. Then tape them to your closet door, mirror, notebook, or other place you look at frequently. This repeated reinforcement of a goal will keep you focused on achieving it.

> Review class notes every day.
>
> Ask teacher for extra help.
>
> Study in library before track practice.

❻ Evaluate your progress.

At times, stop and ask yourself if you are making progress toward your goal. If so, good. If not, how can you get on track?

Practice the Skill

1. Review Diego's situation. How could Diego use the steps given here to help set some long-term and short-term goals? How could he use a career goal to focus his energies during his senior year?

2. Evaluate each of the goals below. Is each one as clear, specific, and positive as it could be? Revise each goal to increase its chances of being met. Break up the goal into smaller steps if necessary. Also include realistic deadlines.
   a. I don't want to gain any more weight.
   b. I want to be a professional tennis player.
   c. I want to stop fighting with my parents so much.
   d. I want to eat better.
   e. I want to be happy.

3. Think about a time when you set a goal and tried to reach it. Did you use any of the steps described here? Explain. Did you reach your goal? Why or why not?

4. Get to know yourself better by listing your interests, abilities, and values. Keeping that list in mind, write three clear, specific, positive goals you want to achieve by
   a. the end of the school year.
   b. the end of high school.
   c. the end of ten years.

   Then break each goal down into manageable steps, or short-term goals, that will allow you to measure your progress toward the overall goal.

5. Review the list of your interests from question 4. Using the guidelines described here, set a goal with a realistic deadline of two weeks or less. After two weeks, evaluate your success. How did the guidelines help make your goal achievable?

Practice the Skill

1. Diego could spend some time evaluating and listing his interests and abilities. Based on that list, he could set a long-term goal, such as pursuing a career in architecture. He could then break down the long-term goal into smaller goals, such as achieving good grades in his senior year. His long-term goal of being an architect can be used to guide and direct his short-term goals as he completes his senior year and moves toward college.

2. *Sample revised goals:*
   a. I would like to eat healthy foods and maintain my current weight.
   b. I want to make the varsity tennis team this year.
   c. I want to practice effective communication skills with my parents for the next week.
   d. For the next week, I will choose fruits and vegetables instead of fatty snack foods.
   e. I want to pursue ceramics, a hobby that I enjoy.

3. *Sample answer:* Recently I set a goal to improve my math grades. I included a deadline (the end of the grading period), I broke the goal down into smaller steps (achieving good grades on each weekly quiz), I kept my goal visible (on a note above my desk), and I evaluated my progress by checking with my math teacher each week.

4. Lists of interest, abilities, and values will vary. *Sample goals:*
   a. By the end of the school year, I would like to play first trombone in the band.
   b. By the end of high school, I would like to play trombone in the state youth orchestra.
   c. At the end of ten years, I would like to be teaching music to high school students.

5. *Sample answers:* At the end of 2 weeks, I would like to have mastered a difficult part of a trombone solo piece. The guidelines helped keep me on track for working toward my goal.

Health at School

⓭ Planning Your Future

Setting goals for the future is an important task for high school students. However, making choices about a future career or continuing education can seem overwhelming. Invite the school guidance counselor to visit the class to discuss the resources available to students who are struggling with their long-term plans. Encourage students to make an appointment with the guidance counselor to have a specific discussion of their individual goals.

Objectives

Before class begins, write the objectives on the board. Have students copy the objectives into their notebooks at the start of class.

1. Focus

Warm-Up Quick Quiz

Use the Warm-Up Presentation slide to survey student responses.

Give students several minutes to take the quiz. Then ask students to complete their written paragraph. Ask volunteers to describe some of the steps they identified in their paragraph. Explain that the steps they identified are similar to an action plan used to achieve a goal.

Presentation 20-2

⚑ Sensitive Issues

Your students will probably exhibit a wide range of levels of responsibility. Point out to the class that just as physical growth occurs at different rates, responsibility also develops at different rates. While responsibility is certainly a desirable trait, avoid casting a negative light on students who are still developing their sense of responsibility. Use the section material to highlight the steps that all students can take to improve their level of responsibility.

Section 2

Adolescence and Responsibility

Objective

▶ **Identify** the responsibilities that adolescents have to themselves and others.

Vocabulary

- autonomy

Warm-Up

Quick Quiz See how many of these questions you can answer "yes" to.

1. Do you do what is best for you even if friends urge you to do otherwise?

2. Are your decisions consistent with your values?

3. Do you think about how your behavior impacts others?

4. Do you accept responsibility for your actions?

WRITING In a paragraph, describe some steps teens can take to be able to answer "yes" to all the questions.

Responsibilities to Yourself

With adolescence comes increased privileges. You are treated more like an adult, and you make decisions that direct your life. However, the flip side of privilege is responsibility. You are expected to behave consistently and to assume responsibility for yourself and others. Often the move to this new status is not a smooth one. You may be anxious for the privileges but not so anxious for the responsibilities. Some days you may want to make all your own decisions. Other days you may wish you could hide your head under your pillow and let someone else take charge. **Your pathway to adulthood will be marked by a growing responsibility for your own decisions and actions.**

Making Everyday Decisions During adolescence you become responsible for taking care of yourself. Adults may still remind you, but ultimately, it's up to you to eat nutritious meals, exercise, and visit the dentist. You are responsible for other decisions, too, such as what to wear. If you pay for some or all of your clothes and other personal items, you also become responsible for managing a budget.

For Your INFORMATION!

Making Healthy Decisions

According to the Centers for Disease Control and Prevention, 72% percent of deaths during adolescence are due to unintentional injuries, homicide, and suicide. These causes of death are often linked to risky behaviors, poor impulse control, or negative peer pressure. The tendency to take part in risky behaviors during adolescence is in part due to the development of the teen brain, which students learned about in Section 20-1. Explain that developing responsibility during adolescence includes making everyday decisions that impact their health and safety. Remind students that with practice the process of healthy decision making becomes easier.

Resisting Negative Influences While following the clothing styles of your peers may be harmless, following all of their behaviors may have more serious consequences. Many decisions you will face can affect your health and safety, including decisions about smoking, drinking, drugs, and sexual activity. Parents and other adults may make rules for you early in your teens. Eventually, however, you make these decisions on your own and take responsibility for the results.

Thinking About Your Future Adolescence is also a time to begin looking toward the future. During these years, you make many decisions that can affect your future career opportunities. You now know that you have to plan and work for what you want—these things do not just happen on their own. There is plenty of time to figure out what you want to do, or to change your mind. However, making responsible decisions now can help keep your options open.

 **Connect to Your Life** What are you doing now to take responsibility for your future?

Responsibilities to Others

Your responsibilities to your family, friends, and community increase greatly during adolescence. At the same time that you are gaining more independence, others may be relying more on you for help.

Your Role in the Family How does your status as an adolescent affect your relationships with your family? In many families, the family unit and family rules are valued more highly than a teenager's **autonomy,** or independence. This may lead to friction between generations. Parents may expect their teens to stick to the older ways. At the same time, teens may be pulled in other directions by their peers.

GO ONLINE
PearsonSuccessNet.com
For: More on responsibility

FIGURE 8 Teens want more autonomy, but they are also expected to take on more responsibilities around the house. **Evaluating** How could this teen and his dad work out a solution to their conflict?

2. Teach

L3 **EL** Reading/Note Taking 20-2

L2 Adapted Reading/Note Taking 20-2

Responsibilities to Yourself

L3 **Content Update**  GO ONLINE

Visit Pearson SuccessNet to access more information about responsibility. Have students complete the Web activity.

L2 **Cooperative Learning**

Have students work in small groups to discuss ways in which teens can take a growing responsibility for their own decisions and actions. Ask each group to generate a bulleted list of responses. Have each group share its list with the class. Follow up with a class discussion of the positive results that are associated with becoming more responsible.

Connect to Your Life *Sample answer:* I work hard to achieve good grades in order to be accepted to college.

Responsibilities to Others

L3 **Visual Learning: Figure 8**

Ask students to describe the conflict presented in the cartoon. Have them analyze what makes the cartoon funny. Ask students who they think is overreacting—the dad, the son, or both? Why?

Caption Answer *Sample answer:* This teen could start folding and putting away his own laundry. This would take some of the burden off his dad, and give the teen more privacy, too.

Differentiated Instruction

EL **English Language Learners**

Write the term *autonomy* on the board. Underline the word part *auto-* and explain that *auto-* means "self." Ask how this prefix relates to the meaning of the term *autonomy.* (*Autonomy* means "taking care of yourself" or "independence.") Have students use the word *autonomy* in a spoken sentence.

Then help students identify other words that contain the prefix *auto-* (for example, autograph, autobiography, automatic). Ask students to look up the definitions of these words and relate their meanings to the meaning of the prefix *auto-.*

L3 Cultural Connection

Have students identify common ways in which teens show responsibility to their families. Point out that cultural background has an impact on the individual's role and responsibilities in the family. Explain that some cultures emphasize individual achievement and independence. This cultural norm is called individualism. In other cultures, called collectivist cultures, the emphasis is on the success of the entire family. Teens in families from collectivist cultures may be expected to work in a family business or provide childcare while other members of the family work. Ask students to reflect on and discuss ways in which cultural background can impact a teen's responsibilities to his or her family.

L2 Cooperative Learning

Divide the class into small groups, and ask each group to identify and discuss common problems related to the division of household chores and other family responsibilities. *(Examples may include dishes piling up in the sink or the car running out of gas because no one refilled the tank.)* Ask students to identify one way to solve or alleviate each identified problem. Have each group share its responses with the class.

FIGURE 9 Helping out more around the house and looking after a younger sibling are just two of the new responsibilities you may encounter at home.

Responsibility to Family   Despite images in the media that show teenagers as angry, rude, and rebellious, most teenagers are happy, healthy people who value their families. Research shows that most families are able to work out the conflicts that normally arise as teenagers strive for more autonomy.

Working out these conflicts involves some give and take on the part of both parents and teens. It helps to show respect for the feelings, tastes, and values of family members on minor issues, such as clothing styles. This sets the stage for increased independence on bigger issues, such as borrowing the family car.

With increased independence at home comes increased responsibilities. What are your responsibilities to your family?

▶ **Helping Out** You may now be responsible for more of the physical work needed to maintain your household. You may need to learn new skills, such as house painting, grocery shopping, or laundering. You may be responsible for taking care of a younger brother or sister after school. Perhaps you are contributing to the family finances with money you bring home from an after-school job.

▶ **Giving Back** You are responsible for becoming more of a "giver" in your family relationships. You are now mature enough to offer understanding and support to other family members. You can participate more fully in the emotional life of your family. For example, if your sister is studying for a test, you can offer encouraging words and help her study.

▶ **Playing by the Rules** Another responsibility is to follow your family guidelines about clothing, curfews, and other activities. This does not mean that your parents make all of the rules all of the time. You can help your parents establish guidelines that are right for you.

526   *Chapter 20*

TEENS *Are Asking . . .*

Q: **Between school, athletic practice, and my part-time job, I don't have time to do housework. Why does my family insist that I help out?**

A: It can be frustrating to have household chores added to an already busy schedule, but you need to remember that you aren't the only one with a hectic life. Your parents or guardians probably feel just as overwhelmed as you do, and they need your help. Rather than say you don't have time to help, why don't you take a minute to sit down with your parents or guardians and discuss your schedule? Find times during the week that you could schedule for housework, and then ask what chores your family needs to have completed during that time. By contributing to the household, you will demonstrate increased responsibility.

Hands-On *Activity*

Living on a Budget

Materials
employment ad section of newspaper
apartment ad section of newspaper
sample utility bills
supermarket circulars

Try This

❶ Look through the employment ads and find a job for which you think you are qualified. Calculate an average monthly salary. Subtract 30 percent for taxes and other deductions—this amount is your spendable monthly income.

❷ Use the apartment ads to find out how much it costs to rent a one-bedroom apartment.

❸ Use sample utility bills to estimate the monthly costs of electricity, gas, heat, and telephone.

❹ Use supermarket circulars to estimate your total food costs for a month.

❺ Estimate how much it costs to operate a car for a week, and multiply by four. Include gas, insurance, and repairs. Alternatively, calculate the cost of public transportation.

❻ Estimate how often you like to go out for entertainment, such as movies and restaurants, and how much these would cost for a month.

❼ Calculate how much you spend on clothing during a month.

Think and Discuss

❶ Total the monthly amounts in items 2 through 7. Is it more or less than your monthly spendable income?

❷ If your expenses are more than your income, what could you do to either increase your monthly income or to decrease your monthly expenses?

❸ What did you learn by doing this activity?

Responsibility to Friends During adolescence, you may realize that your friends are more than just people with whom to have fun. Friends are people who really listen when you talk and who support you when you have a problem. You have similar responsibilities toward them. You should be willing to take time away from your activities to help out a friend, to be a good listener, and to offer comfort and encouragement when needed.

You may also witness some friends engaging in destructive or dangerous behaviors. When you have a concern about a friend's health, safety, or well-being, you have a responsibility to try to help. Peer pressure—in spite of the way the term is often used—can be a positive force. You can use peer pressure to influence your friends in positive directions and to provide a network of support in times of stress or crisis.

Connect to Your Life When did you last help out a friend? What did you do?

Hands-On *Activity*

Living on a Budget

Provide students with the listed materials. Be certain to remove any personal information from the sample utility bills that you provide to students. Ask students to follow the numbered steps to determine their monthly income and expenses. Guide students to make realistic choices of jobs and apartments.

Think and Discuss Answers

1. Explain that items 2 through 7 represent monthly expenses. Some students will indicate that their expenses are greater than their monthly spendable income. Other students will indicate that their expenses are less than their monthly spendable income.

2. Answers will vary, but should indicate that students understand that expenses can not exceed income. Have a class discussion of expenses, such as entertainment, that can easily be reduced.

3. Answers will vary. Students may indicate that they did not realize how difficult it is to become self-supporting.

L3 Addressing Misconceptions

Peer Pressure Peer pressure is often mistakenly seen only in a negative light by both teens and adults. Challenge students to identify reasons for this misconception. *(The results of negative peer pressure are often more visible or startling.)* Then have students identify ways in which peer pressure can be constructive and positive. *(Teens forming study groups, teens encouraging others to join a team or club.)*

Connect to Your Life Allow students to answer this question in their private journals.

Differentiated Instruction

L1 Special Needs

Help students plan and carry out a project that will benefit their community. Possible projects include a bake sale or penny drive to raise money for a good cause within the community or a poster campaign to promote a positive community environment. Involve students in all aspects of planning and carrying out the project. After the project is completed, ask students to explain why it is important to show responsibility in the community. Ask students to identify the emotions they experienced as they planned, worked on, and completed the project.

3. Assess

Evaluate

These assignments can help you assess students' mastery of the section content.

Section 2 Review

Answers appear below.

Teaching Resources

- Practice 20-2
- Section 20-2 Quiz

 **Reteach**

Have students make a three-column table. In the table, instruct students to list bullet points of the responsibilities that adolescents have to themselves, their families, and their communities.

L4 Enrich

Teaching Resources

- Enrich 20-2

FIGURE 10 During adolescence, you take on more responsibility to your community.

Responsibility to Community As you continue through your teen years, you will begin to see yourself as an important part of your larger community. You may also recognize that your actions directly affect community life. For example, you probably appreciate clean streets and parks, and you like knowing that cars will stop at red lights when you are crossing the street. Now you are mature enough to see that these benefits depend on you and people like you.

Littering, vandalism, or reckless driving endanger the quality of life in a community. Some of these irresponsible behaviors are also dangerous, and many of them are against the law. During your teen years, you become responsible for knowing the laws of your community and for obeying them. You are expected to think about the effect that your actions will have, not only on yourself and your friends but on the community as a whole. Acting responsibly is a way of showing your new maturity.

You may even want to go further in helping to improve your community. Participating in cleanup or fund-raising activities or giving aid directly to less fortunate community members can be satisfying. During adolescence, many teens become more interested in public issues, and they find that their actions can have a noticeable positive effect on their community.

Health at School

School Responsibility To introduce the activity, have a brief class discussion of problems that exist at your school. Ask leading questions to help students distinguish problems that could be solved by increased student responsibility and those that could not. After students have completed their action plans, ask volunteers to share their plans with the class. Have students work as a class to select three action plans to be submitted to the school newspaper or presented to the principal and administrators.

Section 2 Review

Key Ideas and Vocabulary

1. What responsibilities do adolescents have to themselves?
2. What is **autonomy**? How might it lead to conflicts with family members during adolescence?
3. List one example each of increasing responsibilities that teens may have to their family, their friends, and their community.

Critical Thinking

4. **Relating Cause and Effect** A teen who often breaks her parents' rules may feel she has less autonomy than her friends who follow family rules. Explain why this might be the case. **WRITING**

Health at School

School Responsibility Identify a problem at your school—for example, littering or tardiness—that could be solved by an increase in responsibility by the student body. What strategies would you propose to increase the student body's sense of responsibility for the problem? Write a one-page action plan. **WRITING**

5. **Evaluating** A teen decides not to use his cell phone while driving. To whom is he being responsible? Explain.
6. **Applying Concepts** Describe one way you "give back" to your community. How has this experience affected you? **WRITING**

GO ONLINE PearsonSuccessNet.com   Audio Summary Section 20.2

Section 2 Review

1. making everyday decisions, resisting negative influences, thinking about the future
2. Autonomy is independence. It can lead to conflicts as teens become independent and move away from family rules and ways of doing things.
3. *Sample answer:* Responsibilities to family include helping out, responsibilities to friends include being a good listener, and responsibilities to community include obeying laws.
4. A teen who frequently breaks family rules may lose privileges; a teen who follows the family rules may be granted more freedom.
5. This teen is showing responsibility for himself by making a decision that enhances his safety and responsibility to the community by acting in a way that keeps others safe.
6. *Sample answer:* I help coach little league. I have developed many friendships as a result of this work.

Adulthood and Marriage

Warm-Up

Health Stats What trend does this graph show?

Number of Older Americans

[Graph showing Population (in millions) on y-axis from 0 to 100, and Year on x-axis from 1900 to 2050 (Projected). Two lines labeled "65 or older" and "85 or older"]

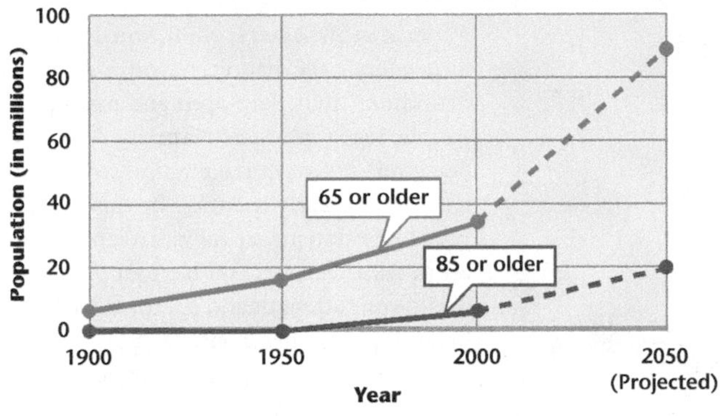

WRITING How might this trend affect communities and the need for health services?

Young Adulthood

At what point do you become an adult? On a certain birthday? When you are financially independent? When you marry? When you have physically matured? From a legal standpoint, Americans are considered to be adults at the age of 18 for some activities and at the age of 21 for others. From a physical and emotional standpoint, however, it is difficult to say when adulthood begins.

During the next few years, you will begin the transition from adolescence to adulthood. **You will change physically and emotionally during the transition from adolescence into young adulthood. In fact, changes continue throughout your life as an adult.**

 **Connect to Your Life** At what age do you think adulthood begins? Explain your answer.

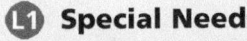 **Differentiated Instruction**

L1 Special Needs

Ask students to complete the sentence "When I am an adult, I plan to..." Discuss students' responses. Then ask students to describe ways they think they will change as they move into adulthood. Be sensitive to students who may not be able to achieve complete independence as an adult. Tell students that this section of the text tells more about adult life and the ways that adults continue to change.

Objectives

▶ **Summarize** the changes that people undergo during adulthood.

▶ **List** three keys to a successful marriage.

▶ **Analyze** how decisions made in youth can affect the aging process.

Vocabulary

- physical maturity
- emotional maturity
- dementia
- Alzheimer's disease

Objectives

Before class begins, write the objectives on the board. Have students copy the objectives into their notebooks at the start of class.

1. Focus

Warm-Up Health Stats

After students have completed their writing, ask several volunteers to share their responses with the class. Students' responses should note that the trends shown in the graph indicate that the need for health care services will increase as the number of older Americans increases. Students' responses about the ways that this trend will affect communities will vary. Lead a class discussion of positive ways older adults impact the community.

Presentation 20-3

2. Teach

L3 EL Reading/Note Taking 20-3

L2 Adapted Reading/Note Taking 20-3

Young Adulthood

L2 Cooperative Learning

Have students work in small groups to generate a list of adjectives that describe adults. Have each group share its list with the class. Ask students to classify the responses into three categories: those that describe the physical attributes of adults, those that describe the emotional attributes of adults, and those that describe the mental attributes of adults.

Connect to Your Life *Sample answer:* I think adulthood begins after college graduation, because that is when I plan to be self-supporting.

L3 Building Health Skills

Setting Goals Ask students to review the suggestions for staying at your physical peak that are listed in Figure 11. Challenge students to set a goal to make these suggestions part of their everyday life. Ask students to write an action plan that describes the specific steps they could use to incorporate these suggestions into their lives. Remind students to periodically monitor their progress toward their goal.

L1 Active Learning

Have students work in pairs to make a comic strip that illustrates a person's journey to emotional maturity. Challenge students to add an element of humor to their comic strip. Have student pairs share their completed comic strips with the class.

L3 Active Learning

Have students prepare a brief presentation about a career of interest to them. The presentation should include a thorough description of the career, as well as a description of the training or education required for that career. Encourage students to interview an adult employed in the field to gather more information. Ask each student to share his or her presentation with the class.

To Stay at Your Physical Peak
- Maintain a healthy diet.
- Avoid tobacco and other drugs.
- Exercise regularly.
- Get adequate rest.
- Have regular medical and dental checkups.

FIGURE 11 It's not all downhill after reaching your physical peak. You can adopt the habits listed above to keep your physical strengths for many years.

Physical Maturity If you look up the term *adult* in the dictionary, you might find this definition: "fully developed and mature." Most people reach **physical maturity,** the state of being full-grown in the physical sense, by their late teens or early twenties. By this time, all of your body systems are fully developed, and you are as tall as you will ever be. Your physical abilities—your strength and speed, as well as your breathing and heart efficiencies—will reach their peak during young adulthood.

Emotional Maturity Unlike physical maturity, adults reach **emotional maturity,** or full development in the emotional sense, over their lifetime. There are three major factors that contribute to emotional maturity—developing close relationships with others, giving back to society, and learning to accept yourself for who you are.

In young adulthood, an important emotional milestone is the establishment of close relationships with individuals outside your family. As an adult, you are more likely to form long-lasting friendships than you are forming now as an adolescent. Why? You will have a better sense of who you are, and be better able to choose friends with interests and values similar to your own. Having a clear idea of who you are and trusting others will also give you the foundation for emotional intimacy. Emotional intimacy is the openness, sharing, affection, and trust that can develop in a close relationship.

Your Career One major concern of young adults is finding a career in which they feel productive and satisfied. During adolescence, you need to think, plan, and prepare for your life's work. During young adulthood, you make decisions and take action towards your career goals. You need to know what skills, education, and training are necessary to achieve your goal. You also should consider the income you will need to earn to be self-supporting. If you get married and have children, you will have to juggle your work responsibilities with the needs of your family.

530 *Chapter 20*

TEENS *Are Asking . . .*

Q: How can I prepare for a career if I keep changing my mind about what career I want to pursue?

A: Many teens have a difficult time making a decision about a career. The first step is to think about your favorite classes, clubs, and activities. This should give you some ideas about your general areas of interest. Talk to as many adults in different careers as possible. Ask these adults to describe the best and worst parts of their job. Consider taking a summer or after-school job in a field that seems interesting. Your guidance counselor is also an excellent resource as you consider various career choices. Remember that many adults change careers, so you will not be stuck if you find your original choice is not right for you.

Marriage

More than 70 percent of all Americans marry at some time during their lives. Therefore, it is likely that you will marry someday. If you do choose to marry, it will probably be one of the most important decisions you will make. It will affect you, your spouse, your family, your friends, and future generations.

Why People Marry   People marry for a variety of reasons. Some people marry because they desire another person's love and companionship. Others marry for financial, social, or cultural reasons. Some couples marry in order to start a family of their own.

You need to know yourself fairly well before you select a marriage partner. You need to know what your goals are and how you are going to achieve them. You need to know what is important to you. When it comes time to marry, people usually select marriage partners who have similar interests, values, level of education, and social background to themselves. People who are quite different from each other can also have successful marriages, but they may have to work harder to overcome their differences.

Successful Marriages   You probably feel, as most people do, that successful marriages are based on love. But what is love? Often young people mistake sexual attraction or short-lived crushes for love. Real love is part of a long-lasting relationship in which people really know, like, and accept each other as they are. People who are truly in love appreciate the things they like about each other and accept the things they dislike. When you love someone, his or her well-being becomes as important to you as your own.

Although love is a basic element in a successful marriage, it is not the only one. **Love, compatibility, and commitment are key factors in a successful marriage.** Compatibility is the ability to live together in harmony. Couples who share many qualities tend to be more compatible. Commitment is the strong determination by the couple to make their marriage a fulfilling lifelong relationship, despite the challenges. Other important factors to consider when thinking about marriage are listed in Figure 12.

 **What do you think is most important in a successful marriage?**

> **What Qualities Make a Marriage Successful?**
> • Love
> • Friendship
> • Commitment
> • Compatibility
> • Communication
> • Mutual respect
> • Physical attraction
> • Ability to compromise

FIGURE 12   There are many elements of a successful marriage besides love.

531

Marriage

 Cultural Connection

Many cultures have customs related to weddings and marriages. Ask students to describe any of these customs with which they are familiar. Then ask students to identify common elements of marriage and wedding customs from the different cultures.

L2 Visual Learning: Figure 12

Ask students to examine the list of qualities that make a marriage successful, which are shown in Figure 12. Ask students to discuss reasons why each of these factors is important to a marriage. Ask: **Why is the ability to compromise an important part of a successful marriage?** *(Sample answer: In a marriage, you cannot always get your own way. Compromise is necessary to resolve conflicts as they arise.)*

L4 Active Learning

Have students prepare a ten-question survey on how responsibilities in a marriage are shared. Have each student ask five husbands and five wives to respond to the survey. Ask students to compile the class results and create graphics or visuals to summarize the results. **MATH**

Connect to Your Life   *Sample answer:* I think that friendship is the most important factor in a successful marriage.

Differentiated Instruction

EL English Language Learners

Ask students to work with a partner to review the list of qualities that contribute to a successful marriage, which is found in Figure 12. Ask students to identify any unfamiliar terms on the list. Then, have students work with their partner to use a standard dictionary to find the meanings of these terms. Have students use index cards to record the definitions of the terms. Ask students to work with their partner to practice pronouncing these terms and using them in spoken sentences.

L3 Building Health Skills

Communicating Explain that stresses and conflicts are a part of all marriages. Marriages are successful when partners are able to use good communication skills to manage their differences. Remind students that good communication skills allow people to resolve conflicts while showing care and respect for others. Divide the class into small groups. Assign each group a potential source of marital conflict related to division of household chores (for example, who is going to do the dishes?). Have the members of each group write a dialogue showing how this conflict could be resolved in a positive way by using good communication skills. Ask each group to share its dialogue with the class.

L2 Active Learning

Divide the class into groups of five students. Give each group a poster board with the following categories written across the top: Family, Friends, Co-Workers, Spouse, Children. Assign one member of each group to each category. Have students list on separate index cards the positive aspects of forming these different kinds of relationships. Students should then tape or paste their index cards to the correct column of the poster board. Have each group identify aspects that appear in more than one column and use marking pens to circle them. The groups should then compare their finished poster boards.

FIGURE 13 Many married couples share responsibilities both inside and outside the home.

Stresses in Marriage Throughout marriage, a couple must be willing to make adjustments to meet each other's needs. The changes in attitudes and expectations that these adjustments require can produce stress.

One difficult adjustment in marriage can be determining the responsibilities that each spouse will have. Some couples decide early in their marriage how each person will contribute financially and who will do certain household tasks. Who will do the cooking? Who will pay the bills?

By compromising and accepting tasks that fit their abilities and schedules, a couple usually can develop a comfortable give-and-take relationship. When changes occur, such as the birth of a child or a new job, the couple may need to redefine their responsibilities.

Marriages can become strained when unexpected problems arise. One spouse may lose his or her job. A spouse or child may become seriously ill. There may be an unplanned pregnancy. Effective communication can be an important tool in helping a couple get through a crisis. Sometimes a couple may need to seek help from community agencies that provide financial or counseling services. Turning to family or friends for emotional support is another way to get through hard times.

Parenthood For some people, young adulthood is not only a time for marriage but also a time to become parents. The relationship between parent and child is critical to the child's healthy development. As you read in Chapter 19, parents need to be able to commit a lifetime of love, guidance, and attention to their children.

At least one part of making the decision to become parents is purely practical. A couple should review their budget to find out whether or not they can afford to provide food, clothing, and medical care for a child. They need to discuss who will care for the child if both spouses continue to work. They need to find out if their employers grant maternity or paternity leave, so that at least one of them can stay home with the baby for a few months and still return to the same job. They may also need to investigate the costs and availability of child care.

532 *Chapter 20*

MATH and Health

L3 Percentages

According to the United States Department of Agriculture, a two-parent family with an annual income at or below $59,410 will spend an average of $169,080 to raise one child to the age of 17. (This figure does not include any college costs.)

The cost is broken down as follows:
Housing: $53,820
Food: $31,050
Transportation: $24,630
Clothing: $11,130
Health Care: $14,070
Child care and education: $23,640
Miscellaneous: $10,740
Have students determine the percentage of the total cost that is represented by each of these categories and make a pie graph that displays the information. (*Answers rounded to the nearest whole number: Housing 32%, Food 18%, Transportation 15%, Clothing 7%, Health Care 8%, Child Care/Education 14%, and Miscellaneous 6%*)

Teens and Marriage When teens marry, they often face additional challenges compared with those who marry later. Adjusting to a new relationship, earning a living, and completing an education can feel overwhelming. Many married teens drop out of school. Without a high-school diploma, it can be difficult to find a good job. Even if both teens work, they may have difficulty earning enough money for rent and food. The couple may end up living with parents or other relatives. Such an arrangement can limit a couple's opportunities to get to know each other, to make decisions, and to develop as a couple.

Teens who marry may experience changes in their friendships. Friends who are not married often do not have the same interests and goals as a married couple, especially if the couple has a baby. A married couple may be concerned about stretching a small income. Single friends may be more concerned about school or dating.

It is difficult to know when you are 17 or 18 just how you will feel when you are 25 or 30. People change a great deal during their teens and early twenties. For this reason, many teenagers choose to wait before making a long-term commitment. They want to find out more about themselves, to meet people, and to have other experiences.

In spite of all the obstacles, some teenage marriages are successful. The couple must be willing to put in the effort needed to make their marriage work. They need to learn to communicate, to compromise, and to develop the qualities that are important for a fulfilling relationship.

 **Connect to Your Life** What would you say to a friend who is thinking about getting married?

FIGURE 14 Divorce rates are higher for couples who marry in their teens.
Reading Graphs What percentage of teens who marry under age 18 will divorce in the first five years of marriage?

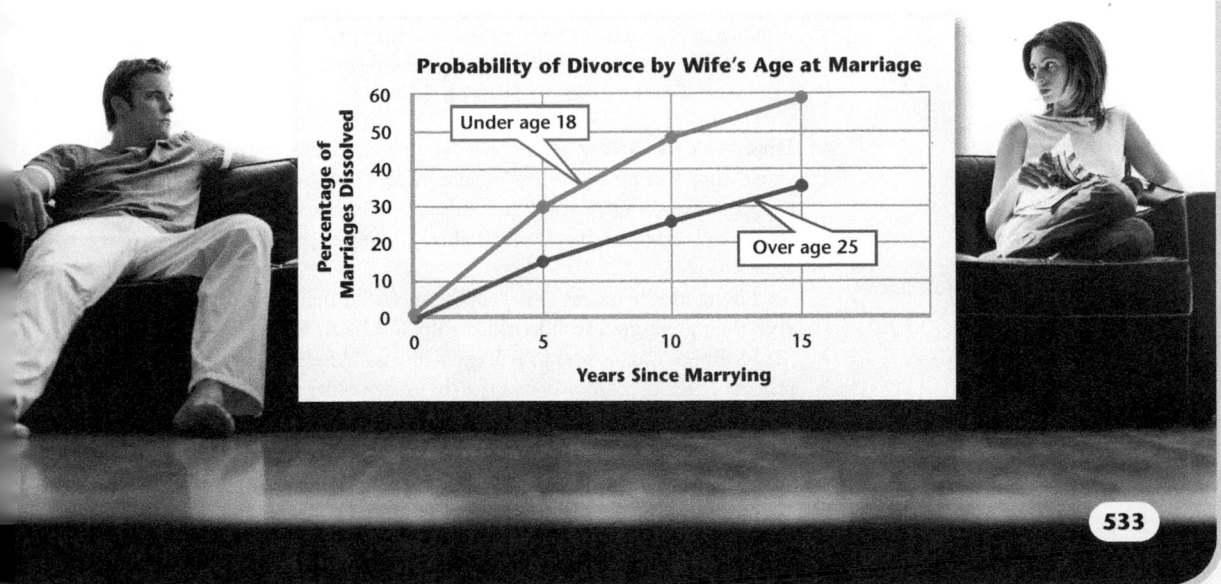

Probability of Divorce by Wife's Age at Marriage

Percentage of Marriages Dissolved

Under age 18

Over age 25

Years Since Marrying

L2 Visual Learning: Figure 14

Have students examine the graph that shows the relationship between a woman's age at marriage and the probability of divorce. Ask: **How do divorce rates for women who marry as teens compare to divorce rates for women who marry after age 25?** *(The divorce rate for women who marry as teens is consistently higher than that of women who marry after age 25.)*
Caption Answer 30 percent of those who marry under age 18 will divorce in the first five years of marriage.

L3 Journal Writing

Have each student write a journal entry that lists goals that he or she hopes to achieve between the ages of 17 and 25. In their journal entry, have students write a few sentences that summarize how teen marriage could impact these goals. Remind students that they will not be required to share their journal entries. **WRITING**

L3 Class Discussion

Ask students to identify reasons why married teens face more stress than couples who marry later. *(adjusting to a new relationship, difficulty earning a living, stress of completing their educations, changes in friendships)* List each reason on the chalkboard.

Connect to Your Life *Sample answer:* I would explain to my friend that it takes extra effort for teens to succeed at marriage.

Differentiated Instruction

L2 Less Proficient Readers

Point out to students that the information about marriage on pages 531–533 is further divided by boldface headings. Point out the first heading, "Why People Marry," on page 531. Ask students to copy each heading onto a separate index card. For each heading, ask students to add a few words or pictures to the index card to summarize the main ideas presented in that section of the text. Model this activity for students by completing an index card for the text on pages 529–530 and showing it to students. Have students use their index cards as a study aid to prepare for the Chapter Review.

Healthy Aging

L4 Building Health Skills

Accessing Information Have students perform library or Internet research to find information about healthy behaviors that teens can practice to reduce or delay the physical signs of aging. Have them find out what specific diseases, disorders, or conditions the healthy behaviors protect against and why. To help students get started, have them brainstorm a list of potential topics, and record their responses on the board. (Some examples include use of sunscreen, consumption of adequate amounts of calcium, taking part in regular physical activity, and consuming a healthy diet.) Give each student an opportunity to share his or her results with the class.

L3 Addressing Misconceptions

The Abilities of Older Adults Explain that many teens and young adults have the misconception that most older adults are frail, hard-of-hearing, and forgetful. Ask students to identify examples from television or movies that promote this misconception. Tell students that most older adults are actually healthy and active, and challenge students to find examples in the media that support this fact.

Sample answer: I plan to swim and play golf in order to stay active as I age.

L3 Online Activity GO ONLINE

Visit Pearson SuccessNet to access an online activity about perceptions of aging. Have students complete the Web activity.

FIGURE 15 Aging affects many of the body systems. Exercising in water can help maintain joint flexibility.

GO ONLINE
PearsonSuccessNet.com
For: More on perceptions of aging

Healthy Aging

After about the age of 30, adults begin to experience changes associated with the aging process. Aging is a normal biological process that you cannot avoid. However, there are many things you can do over your lifetime to slow the effects of aging. **People tend to reduce or delay the physical signs of aging when they establish healthy behaviors during their youth.**

Connect to Your Life What hobbies will you engage in to stay active as you age?

Physical Changes What physical changes occur as people age? Adults may notice that their hair starts to turn gray, facial wrinkles begin to appear, and their vision and hearing become less sharp. Figure 15 identifies several of the effects of aging on the body.

Diseases of Older Adulthood For someone born in 1900, life expectancy was only about 47 years. In contrast, boys born today can expect to live about 75 years, and girls about 80 years. The population of the United States is aging. By 2030, about 20 percent of Americans will be age 65 or older.

Living longer means that people can watch their grandchildren, or even their great-grandchildren, grow up. But living longer also increases the likelihood that a person will get a disease associated with the aging process. The most common diseases that strike older adults include heart disease, cancer, and lung disease. Other common diseases of older adulthood are listed on the next page.

534 Chapter 20

WRITING and Health

L3 Public Service Announcement

Explain to students that a public service announcement is a short message that gives information about an important topic. Ask students to describe any public service announcements with which they are familiar. Then, divide the class into small groups. Ask each group to develop a public service announcement that mentions at least one specific health behavior that can help to delay or reduce one of the physical signs of aging. Ask each group to share its announcement with the class. Evaluate the public service announcements based on the accuracy of the message and the creativity with which the message is presented.

As You Age . . .
- Bones shrink in size and become more brittle.
- The heart has to work harder to pump blood through the body.
- Memory becomes less sharp.
- Reflexes slow down.
- Skin becomes drier and less elastic.

▶ **Arthritis** This disease attacks the body's joints. It can make simple tasks, such as holding a pencil or climbing stairs, very painful. Arthritis can be managed with pain medication and physical activities that are gentle on the joints, such as exercising in water.

▶ **Osteoporosis** The bones of older people tend to break easily and heal slowly. This is due to osteoporosis, a condition caused by a loss of bone calcium. Medications can help slow calcium loss. In addition, railings installed along stairs and in bathtubs can help prevent falls that could fracture bones.

▶ **Parkinson's disease** This disease of the nervous and muscular systems causes the muscles to become stiff. A person experiences shaky movements and progressive loss of muscle function. Medications can slow the progression of this disease.

▶ **Dementia** Approximately 14 percent of adults over 70 and 37 percent of adults over 90 suffer from **dementia** (dih MEN shuh). This disorder is characterized by loss of mental abilities, abnormal behaviors, and personality changes. Dementia has several causes, some of which can be treated.

▶ **Alzheimer's disease** About two thirds of people with dementia have **Alzheimer's disease** (AHLTS hy murz). This disease causes brain cells to die, resulting in the gradual loss of mental and physical function. There is no cure, but some medications may slow the progression of the disease.

L2 Building Vocabulary

Write the term *arthritis* on the board. Point out the word parts *arthr-*, which means "joint," and *-itis*, which means "inflammation." Ask students to identify the names of other diseases or disorders that include the word part *-itis* (tonsillitis, bronchitis, appendicitis).

L3 Building Health Skills

Advocacy Many communities offer services and programs for older adults. Challenge students to find the names and phone numbers of community organizations and groups that advocate for older adults. Ask students to find out more about the services that these groups provide to older adults who are dealing with health issues related to aging. Have students write a letter to the editor of a local newspaper encouraging the community to support these programs and organizations. Challenge students to work as a class to develop a list of volunteer opportunities that are available through these organizations. **WRITING**

L4 Cultural Connection

In many cultures older adults are revered and treated with great respect. Have students research how older adults are perceived in one of these cultures: Native American, Korean American, Japanese American, Mexican American, or another culture of their choosing. Ask students to share their findings with the class. Follow up with a class discussion of similarities and differences in the ways that older adults are perceived and treated in various cultures.

Adolescence and Adulthood **535**

Differentiated Instruction

L1 Special Needs

When discussing the physical signs of aging, focus more on the general signs of aging listed in Figure 15, rather than requiring students to memorize and define specific diseases. Whenever possible, provide a concrete example to help students understand the physical effects of aging.

For example, use a pencil (strong) and a pretzel rod (brittle) to demonstrate the way that bones change with age. Remind students that the physical signs of aging are not disabling for most older adults. Tell students that many older adults are healthy and active.

3. Assess

Evaluate

These assignments can help you assess students' mastery of the section content.

Section 3 Review

Answers appear below.

Teaching Resources
- Practice 20-3
- Section 20-3 Quiz

L2 Reteach

Ask students to review the boldface headings and the figures in the section. Then have students make a concept web showing the changes that individuals undergo during adulthood.

L4 Enrich

Teaching Resources
- Enrich 20-3

Health and Community

Reaching Across Generations Describe positive interactions that can occur between people of different age groups. Help students brainstorm a list of projects that would benefit their community. Then, have students determine ways young people and senior citizens could contribute to their chosen projects. Ask students to share their completed proposals with the class.

Emotional and Social Changes Maintaining emotional and social health during adulthood is also important for healthy aging. For many people, adulthood is a time of contribution to their family and community. For example, adults in midlife may help take care of their grandchildren or their aging parents, or may serve as volunteers in their community. They must find a healthy balance between meeting their own needs and helping others.

You may have heard the phrase "midlife crisis" used to describe the emotions that some adults experience. Many adults do undergo a period of self-evaluation—comparing the dreams they had in young adulthood with their actual accomplishments. But despite the phrase, this period of self-evaluation does not usually have a bad outcome. A midlife crisis can lead to positive change—a different career, a return to school, or travel.

Older adults may begin to reflect on their lives. Accepting the good and the bad in their past without regrets helps them enjoy the time they have left. Older adults can best maintain their emotional health if they continue to stay psychologically connected to others. It also helps if they stay committed to something that gives meaning to their lives, such as family, friends, religion, or community activities.

FIGURE 16 Many adults in middle adulthood enjoy spending time with their grandchildren.

Section 3 Review

Key Ideas and Vocabulary

1. How do people continue to change in adulthood?
2. Define **physical maturity**. When is it reached?
3. What are three keys to a successful marriage?
4. How do healthy behaviors during youth affect aging?
5. What is **dementia**? How is it similar to **Alzheimer's disease**?

Critical Thinking

6. **Applying Concepts** How can you help your grandparents or other older adults stay connected to others?

GO ONLINE PearsonSuccessNet.com   Audio Summary Section 20.3

Health and Community

Reaching Across Generations Write a proposal to the officials in your city or town for a project in which young people can work side by side with senior citizens. Focus on something that will beautify or in some other way improve the quality of life in your town. **WRITING**

7. **Predicting** Two 17-year-olds marry in their senior year of high school and start living in their own apartment. How could the marriage affect their academic goals?
8. **Evaluating** How might a midlife crisis contribute to an adult's emotional maturity?

Section 3 Review

1. During adulthood, individuals continue to change physically and emotionally.
2. Physical maturity is full development in the physical sense. Most people reach physical maturity by their late teens or early twenties.
3. love, compatibility, commitment
4. Healthy behaviors by young people can reduce or delay some signs of aging.

5. Dementia is a disorder characterized by loss of mental abilities, abnormal behaviors, and personality changes. It is similar to Alzheimer's disease, which also causes a decline in mental functioning.
6. By visiting and interacting with older adults, young people can help them stay connected to others.

7. These teens might be too busy supporting themselves to have time to study or even to attend school.
8. A midlife crisis is a period of self-evaluation that can lead to positive changes and increased emotional maturity.

Death and Dying

Warot-Up

Myth When visiting a dying person, you should never talk about the person's condition or about death.

Fact Many dying people want to talk about what is happening to them, but you should let them raise the subject.

WRITING Is this myth common around the world? Write about your knowledge of different cultural attitudes towards death.

Dying With Dignity

Death is part of the normal cycle that all living things go through. No amount of fame, money, or love prevents death. As strange as it sounds, dying is a part of living. Still, it is never easy to face death, whether one's own or that of a loved one. However, understanding the process and learning some strategies for coping can help.

End of Life Care The process of dying has changed in the last few decades. In the past, most people died in their homes, surrounded by family and friends. The medical advances that have lengthened the average life span have also given doctors the ability to prolong the life of a dying person. Today, a person is more likely to die in a nursing home or hospital than at home.

Some people who are dying choose to be cared for in a **hospice** (HAHS pis). A hospice is a facility or program that provides physical, emotional, and spiritual care for dying people and support for their families. Some hospice programs have their own facilities where dying patients can be given round-the-clock care by hospice workers. Other hospice workers visit the dying person at home or in the hospital. Hospice workers help patients and their families to accept death and to enjoy whatever time is left. To make hospice affordable, most of the workers, except for medical personnel, are trained volunteers.

Adolescence and Adulthood **537**

Objectives

► **List** the five stages of dying that some people experience.

► **Summarize** healthy strategies for coping with a dying loved one and coping after a death.

Vocabulary

- hospice
- terminal illness

Differentiated Instruction

L2 Less Proficient Readers

Have less proficient readers work in small groups to make a flowchart showing the stages of dying. Ask students to include a brief description of each stage in their flowcharts. Have students post their completed flowcharts in the classroom. Remind students that some people do not experience all five stages of grief, and some people experience the stages of grief in a different order. Refer to the flowcharts as students read the information in this section about the stages of dying.

Objectives

Before class begins, write the objectives on the board. Have students copy the objectives into their notebooks at the start of class.

1. Focus

Warm-Up Myth/Fact

After students have completed their writing, ask several volunteers to share their responses with the class. Then ask them to reflect on similarities and differences in cultural attitudes toward death.

Presentation 20-4

2. Teach

L3 EL Reading/Note Taking 20-4
L2 Adapted Reading/Note Taking 20-4

Dying With Dignity

EL Building Vocabulary

Write the word *hospice* on the board. Explain that the word *hospice* is derived from the Latin word *hospes,* which can mean "guest" or "host." Ask students if they can identify other English words that might be based on the Latin word *hospes.* (hospital, hostel, hospitality, hotel) Also ask students if they know words in other Latin-influenced languages that use this word root, and to explain what these foreign words mean in English. Record their responses on the board.

L2 **Visual Learning: Figure 17**

Image Bank Figure 20-17

Have students review Figure 17, which shows the five stages of dying. Ask: **In what ways are the stages experienced by a dying person and their loved ones similar?** *(Sample answer: At each stage, the person who is dying and their loved ones experience the same predominant emotion.)* **Do you think people who are dying and their loved ones always progress through these stages at the same time?** *(Sample answer: No, grief is an individual process. Not everyone will progress through these stages in the same order or at the same pace.)*

Coping Skills

L3 **Content Update**  GO ONLINE

Visit Pearson SuccessNet to access more information on the grieving process. Have students complete the Web activity.

Stages of Dying

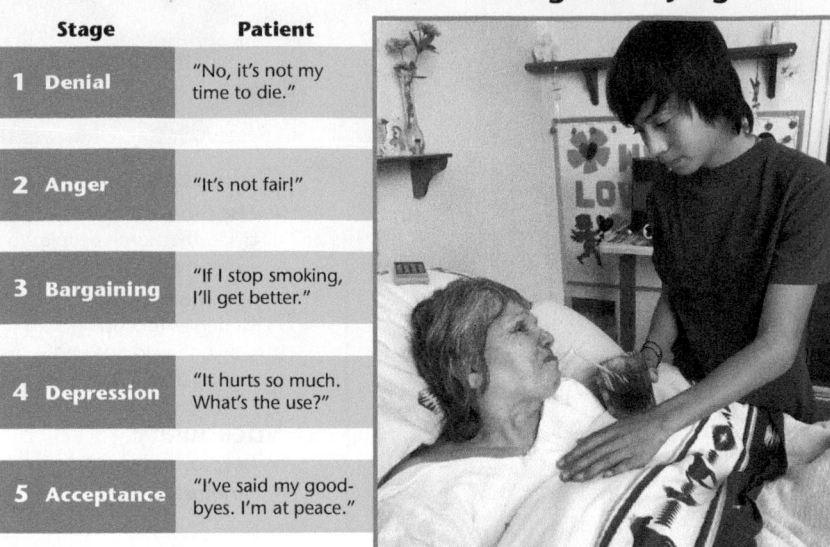

Stage	Patient		Family Member
1 Denial	"No, it's not my time to die."		"The doctor can't be right."
2 Anger	"It's not fair!"		"Why not somebody else?"
3 Bargaining	"If I stop smoking, I'll get better."		"I'd do anything to keep her here."
4 Depression	"It hurts so much. What's the use?"		"I can't stand to lose her."
5 Acceptance	"I've said my good-byes. I'm at peace."		"Soon she won't be in pain anymore."

FIGURE 17 The dying person and their loved ones may go through similar stages of emotion as death draws near.

GO ONLINE

PearsonSuccessNet.com

For: More on the grieving process

Stages of Dying When you think about death and grief, you may first think about the feelings of family and friends left behind when a loved one dies. But people who know they are dying also experience grief.

Consider the case of a person who has been diagnosed with a terminal illness. A **terminal illness** is an illness for which there is no chance of recovery. When the American psychiatrist Elisabeth Kübler-Ross studied the reactions of terminally ill people and their families, she discovered that they typically go through five emotional stages. **The five stages of dying are denial, anger, bargaining, depression, and acceptance.** These stages may be experienced by both the dying person and their loved ones, as shown in Figure 17.

It is important to note that not everyone reacts in the same way. The way people deal with an approaching death depends on their expectations, their emotional strengths, and the reactions of loved ones. Some people do not experience all five stages, and others may experience them in a different order.

Coping Skills

Suppose your grandparent, parent, or friend is dying. Like most people, you may find it very uncomfortable to deal with death and dying. Some people try to cover up their grief by false cheer—they pretend that everything is fine and that they are happy. Others may refuse to talk about their grief. Some keep away from the dying person. These are generally not healthy strategies. What should you do if a person close to you is dying?

538 *Chapter 20*

Sensitive Issues

Students who have recently experienced a loss or have a terminally ill family member may have a difficult time participating in discussions of death and dying. Monitor students closely for signs of discomfort, and privately offer support to students who seem upset.

WRITING and Health

L3 **Summary**

Have students write a paragraph that summarizes the stages of dying and how those stages are experienced by both the person who is dying and their loved ones. Remind students to include a topic sentence and supporting details in their paragraphs. Invite several volunteers to share their summaries with the class. Follow up with a short discussion of individual differences in the grief process. Ask students to brainstorm ways that individual differences in temperament and circumstances could affect the way in which a person experiences grief.

Emotional Support Staying silent or absent doesn't help either the dying person or your grieving process. **Staying actively involved in a dying loved one's life will help both you and the dying person cope.**

▶ Visit the person as often as you can. Make dying a time for loving and sharing, not loneliness and despair.

▶ Listen to what the dying person has to say. Let the dying person direct the conversation. Let him or her talk about the past. Others may want to talk about what is happening to them.

▶ Try not to be shy about discussing death. If death frightens you, think of the dying person as someone who is about to set out on a long journey. Try to share your feelings of loss before a loved one goes.

▶ Talk about your plans and hopes. Even though the person will not be there to share the future with you, it will cheer the person to think about things other than the present.

Grieving After Death Dealing with your grief after a loved one dies is not easy. It may be even more difficult if the death is sudden—for example, if a loved one dies in a car crash. **After the death of a loved one, it is important not to deny your feelings. However, don't become so overwhelmed with emotion that you forget to take care of yourself.**

▶ Try to talk about your loss. Discuss your feelings with family and friends or write them in a journal. Talk about how you miss the person. Think of how you would like to remember the person.

▶ Continue your usual routine as much as possible. This will help you focus your mind on something other than the death. It will also help get you out of the house and interacting with other people.

▶ Allow yourself some time to grieve. However, if your feelings of grief do not lessen or pass after a time, seek the help of a parent, counselor, or other trusted adult.

FIGURE 18 Different families and cultures honor the memories of dead loved ones in different ways.

▼ **Jewish funeral**

◀ **Honoring Chinese ancestors** ▶

▼ **Jazz funeral procession**

Adolescence and Adulthood **539**

L3 Cultural Connection

Discuss with the class the traditions shown in each of the pictures on this page. Explain that Jewish traditions include a seven-day formal mourning period observed by the deceased's family. Chinese ancestors are honored by the placement of food on graves on Tomb Sweeping Day, a traditional Chinese celebration. Jazz funeral processions are a New Orleans tradition. Ask students to describe other cultural traditions that honor the memories of loved ones.

L3 Cooperative Learning

Divide the class into small groups. Provide each group with a printed copy of W.H. Auden's poem "Funeral Blues." Ask one member of each group to read the poem aloud to the remainder of the group. Within each group, have students discuss the emotions expressed by the grieving person portrayed in the poem. Call on each group to share some of its responses with the class.

L2 Class Discussion

In a discussion format, review and expand on each of the steps on page 540 for helping others through their grief. For each bulleted suggestion in the text, ask students to identify specific ways to carry out that suggestion. Record students' responses on the board. Then, encourage students to think of additional suggestions for supporting a grieving friend, and add these suggestions to the list.

Differentiated Instruction

L4 Gifted and Talented

Ask students to research musical compositions and works of art that portray grief. Have students choose one composition or work of art to analyze. Instruct students to write a summary that includes a brief background about the artist or composer and an analysis of the emotions expressed in the piece. Allow students to share their results with the class. If possible, have students also display a copy of the artwork or play a portion of the musical composition.

3. Assess

Evaluate

These assignments can help you assess students' mastery of the section content.

Section 4 Review

Answers appear below.

Teaching Resources

• Practice 20-4
• Section 20-4 Quiz

L2 Reteach

Have students work in groups to generate a bulleted list of specific ways to help someone who has experienced a loss. Ask students to include original ideas in addition to those supplied in the text. Have each group share its responses with the class.

L4 Enrich

Teaching Resources

• Enrich 20-4

Health at Home

Note of Sympathy Remind students that a sympathy note should express caring and concern without dictating how the grieving person should be feeling. Ask volunteers to share their letters with the class. Ask students to point out the characteristics of particularly effective letters.

FIGURE 19 Supporting your friends through their grief shows that you care about them.

Helping Others Through Their Grief How can you support your friends when they have lost a loved one?

▶ **Be a good listener.** Your grieving friend may want to sort through some emotions by talking to you.

▶ **Write a sympathy note.** Remember that your friend will be feeling his or her loss in a unique and personal way. Don't say things like "I know how you must feel," or "You'll get over it soon." Instead, say "I'm thinking of you," or "I'm here if you want to talk."

▶ **Help with everyday errands.** Offer to bring homework assignments home for your friend, bring the family a meal, or run other errands.

▶ **If necessary, help your friend get counseling.** If your friend doesn't seem to be making any progress after time, ask a trusted adult to help you get your friend in touch with a grief counselor.

Section 4 Review

Key Ideas and Vocabulary

1. What is **hospice**? What are the benefits of a hospice program?
2. What is a **terminal illness**?
3. Describe the five stages of dying as defined by Elisabeth Kübler-Ross.
4. What is one healthy strategy for coping with a dying loved one? What is one strategy for grieving after a death?

Health at Home

Note of Sympathy Suppose a close friend's grandparent has died. Write an imaginary letter to your friend, expressing your sympathy and offering your help. **WRITING**

Critical Thinking

5. **Classifying** Into which stages of dying would you classify the following reactions:
   a. "It must be a mistake. I don't really have cancer."
   b. "I just don't care about anything anymore."
6. **Applying Concepts** Suppose your neighbors experience a death in the family. How could you offer support?

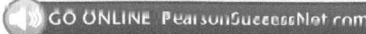
GO ONLINE PearsonSuccessNet.com   Audio Summary Section 20.4

Section 4 Review

1. A hospice is a facility or program that provides care for dying people and their families. A benefit of a hospice program is that hospice workers help patients and their families accept death and enjoy what time is left.

2. an illness for which there is no chance of recovery

3. denial (not believing that death is near), anger (getting mad about the situation), bargaining (believing there is someway to reverse the situation), depression (giving up and feeling miserable), acceptance (being at peace)

4. *Sample answer:* listening to what the dying person has to say; talking about the loss

5. a. denial   b. depression

6. *Sample answer:* Some strategies for helping a neighbor who has experienced a loss include being a good listener, writing a sympathy note, and helping with everyday errands and tasks.

Chapter 20
At a Glance

 **VIDEO**

TEENS Talk

Pictures of "Perfection" How did the video change your perception of models? Of yourself?

Section 1   Adolescence: A Time of Change

Key Ideas

▶ During adolescence, the reproductive system matures, adult features appear, and height and muscle mass increase.

▶ Mental changes during adolescence include improved abstract thinking, reasoning skills, and impulse control.

▶ During adolescence, individuals start to define meaning in their lives, a set of personal values, and a sense of self.

Vocabulary

• adolescence (514) • reproductive maturity (515)
• secondary sex characteristics (515)

Section 2   Adolescence and Responsibility

Key Ideas

▶ Your pathway to adulthood will be marked by a growing responsibility for your own decisions and actions.

▶ Your responsibilities to your family, friends, and community increase greatly during adolescence.

Vocabulary

• autonomy (525)

Section 3   Adulthood and Marriage

Key Ideas

▶ You will change physically and emotionally during adulthood.

▶ Love, compatibility, and commitment are key factors in a successful marriage.

▶ People tend to reduce or delay the physical signs of aging when they establish healthy behaviors during their youth.

Vocabulary

• physical maturity (530)
• emotional maturity (530)
• dementia (535)
• Alzheimer's disease (535)

Section 4   Death and Dying

Key Ideas

▶ The five stages of dying are denial, anger, bargaining, depression, and acceptance.

▶ Staying actively involved in a dying loved one's life will help both you and the dying person cope.

▶ After the death of a loved one, it is important not to deny your feelings. However, don't become so overwhelmed with emotion that you forget to take care of yourself.

Vocabulary

• hospice (537) • terminal illness (538)

Adolescence and Adulthood   **541**

Chapter 20
At a Glance

VIDEO

Pictures of "Perfection" Ask for volunteers to share their answers. Use examples from the video to review what influences perceptions of attractiveness in self and in others.

Key Ideas Review

L3 Ask students to write a paragraph that summarizes the physical, mental, and emotional changes that occur during adolescence.

L2 Have students restate each of the chapter Key Ideas using their own words. Call on students to share their responses with the class.

Vocabulary Review

EL Ask English lanuage learners to write three sentences that show the relationship between two or more of the chapter vocabulary terms.

L2 Have students develop a ten-question quiz that tests knowledge of each of the chapter vocabulary terms. Have students exchange quizzes with a partner. After students have completed the quizzes, have them grade each other's papers.

Chapter 20 Review

 GO ONLINE

PearsonSuccessNet.com

Students can go online for a review activity on Chapter 20.

Reviewing Key Ideas

Section 1
1. b   **2.** c

3. At the start of adolescence, girls are generally taller than boys.

4. The parent should convey the message that he or she loves the teenager even if he or she does not love the identity that is being tried. If the identity is harmless, the parent should try to tolerate it until the adolescent tires of it.

Section 2
5. a

6. Teens show responsibility to their families by helping out, giving back, and playing by the rules.

7. *Sample answer:* A teen could exert positive peer pressure on a friend by inviting the friend to study together before a big test.

Section 3
8. c

9. Commitment is the determination to make a marriage work in spite of challenges. Commitment is important because all marriages face challenges that must be worked through.

10. *Sample answer:* earning a living and completing their educations

11. Physical maturity is reached during adolescence; emotional maturity is achieved by adults over a lifetime.

Section 4
12. a

13. Four ways to give emotional support to a dying person are by visiting as often as you can, listening to what the person has to say, trying not to be shy about discussing death, and talking about your hopes and plans.

14. Three healthy ways to cope with grief are by talking about your loss, continuing your usual routine, and allowing yourself time to grieve.

Chapter 20 Review

Reviewing Key Ideas

 GO ONLINE

PearsonSuccessNet.com

For: Chapter 20 review activity

Section 1

1. Secondary sex characteristics
   a. occur in girls, but not boys.
   b. are associated with puberty.
   c. are directly involved in reproduction.
   d. cause a growth spurt.

2. One mental characteristic that develops over the course of adolescence is
   a. a reduction in memory.
   b. decision-making based on immediate physical experiences.
   c. improved reasoning skills.
   d. stronger impulses.

3. Contrast height trends in girls versus boys at the start of adolescence.

4. **Critical Thinking** You are the parent of a teenager who "tries on" an identity you dislike. How could you show disapproval without destroying your child's self-confidence?

Section 2

5. Autonomy is
   a. independence.   **b.** a value or belief.
   c. emotional maturity.   **d.** a curfew.

6. List three ways teens show responsibility to their families.

7. **Critical Thinking** How could a teen use peer pressure to help be responsible to his friends? Give a specific example.

Section 3

8. When you are full-grown in the emotional sense, you will reach
   a. emotional intimacy.   **b.** your physical peak.
   c. emotional maturity.   **d.** a midlife crisis.

9. Explain the importance of commitment to a successful marriage.

10. Describe two big challenges most married teenagers face.

11. **Critical Thinking** Compare and contrast physical and emotional maturity. When in life are they reached? Explain. **WRITING**

Section 4

12. According to Elisabeth Kübler-Ross, the final stage of dying is
   a. acceptance.   **b.** denial.
   c. bargaining.   **d.** depression.

13. Describe four ways you can give emotional support to a dying loved one.

14. Name three healthy ways to cope with grief after a death.

15. **Critical Thinking** Why do you think some people are more afraid of the process of dying than of dying itself?

 ## Building Health Skills

16. **Communicating** Your 14-year-old friend is worried because he is shorter than other guys and still looks the same as he did in seventh grade. Write him with your advice. **WRITING**

17. **Making Decisions** You really want to play on the softball team, but you worry that your grades will suffer if you do. How would you decide what to do?

18. **Advocacy** Since her mother died, your friend has dropped out of all social activities and barely talks to anyone. It's been a month now and you are very concerned. What could you do to help your friend?

19. **Setting Goals** What daily habits could you adopt to reduce the aging of your bones and skin? Explain the specific steps you will take. Monitor your progress over the school year.

Health and Community

An Interview With Adults Interview three adults—a young adult, a middle-aged adult, and an older adult. Ask them what advice they would offer to teenagers who are trying to set goals for the future. Compare the responses of the people you interviewed. What did you learn about planning for the future? **WRITING**

---

15. The process of dying often includes pain and suffering, which many people find more frightening than death itself.

 ## Building Health Skills

16. *Sample letter:* People experience growth spurts and other physical changes of puberty at different ages. Your growth spurt probably hasn't happened yet, but it will in a year or two. If you are still concerned about the way your body is developing, you should discuss the topic with a parent, guardian, or medical professional.

17. Answers should reflect the use of reasoning skills and the ability to weigh the pros and cons of a situation.

Standardized Test Prep

Math Practice

The graph shows the average age at which people in the United States first marry. Use the graph to answer Questions 20–22.

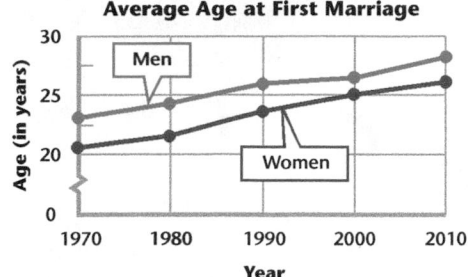

Average Age at First Marriage

20. For men, by about how much did the average age at marriage increase from 1970 to 1990?
    A 0.5 year
    B 3 years
    C 5 years
    D 6 years

21. About how much younger were women than men at first marriage in 2000?
    F 1 year   G 3 years
    H 4 years   J 6 years

22. What trend does the graph show?
    A Men marry at a younger age than women.
    B People were more likely to get married in 1970 than today.
    C Age at first marriage has risen steadily since 1970.
    D Age at first marriage rose until 1990, then declined.

Reading and Writing Practice

Read the passage. Then answer Questions 23–26.

Grief takes a toll on the body as well as the mind. Physical symptoms of grief include sagging energy levels, loss of appetite, and too much or too little sleep. Disrupted sleep patterns make the immune system less effective, sometimes leading to illness. In fact, individuals experience more sick days and hospital admissions in the year following their loss than do non-grieving individuals.

Pre-existing stress and depression are significant contributors to disrupted sleep after bereavement. On the other hand, people who have worked out effective coping strategies, have good social support networks, and maintain a healthy sleep profile are the most physiologically resilient.

23. From the context of this passage, the best definition for the word *bereavement* is
    A depression brought on by grief.
    B a coping strategy.
    C the death of a loved one.
    D lack of sleep.

24. What does the author suggest is the link between depression and physical illness in grieving people?
    F It disrupts sleep patterns.
    G It increases resiliency.
    H It reduces appetite.
    J It is a bad coping strategy.

25. According to this passage, who is most resilient after experiencing a loss?
    A Those who spend time alone
    B Those who maintain a healthy sleep profile
    C Those who take time off from work
    D Those who go to the hospital

Constructed Response
26. In a paragraph, summarize the main point of this passage in your own words.

Standardized Test Prep

Math Practice
20. B
21. F
22. C

Reading and Writing Practice
23. C
24. F
25. B
26. Students' paragraphs should identify factors affecting grief's physical toll on the body and physical health as the main idea of the passage.

---

18. Supporting a grieving friend can include listening, expressing sympathy, and if necessary, helping the friend get counseling.

19. Students' responses should identify habits, such as increasing calcium intake and using sunscreen regularly, which will help them to reduce aging of bones and skin. They should also list specific steps they will follow to reach these goals.

Health and Community

An Interview With Adults *Sample answer:* The responses to my interview questions indicate that adults in all three age groups would encourage teens to continue with their education as a part of achieving goals. I also learned that planning for the future is valuable, but I must be able to adapt to unexpected changes in my plans.

Human Development

Teaching Strategies

- Call on students to name the major stages of life, from birth through old age. Ask: **What needs or problems are associated with each of these stages of life?** *(Accept all reasonable responses. Sample answer: In old age, people may need help walking or caring for themselves.)* Challenge students to think of at least one career related to each need or problem that they mention. *(e.g., home health aide for house-bound elders)*

- Have students read about the human development careers. Ask them to identify the training typically required for each career. Ask: **Which career requires an associate's (two-year) degree?** *(ultrasound technician)* **Which career requires a master's degree?** *(guidance counselor)*

- Have students read the Career Focus. Challenge them to think of traits and skills that might be needed by a hospice caregiver. Have students describe what they think might be some of the rewards and challenges of this career.

CAREERS

Human Development

Careers in human development focus on the needs of people at all life stages—from babies to adults to people facing terminal illnesses.

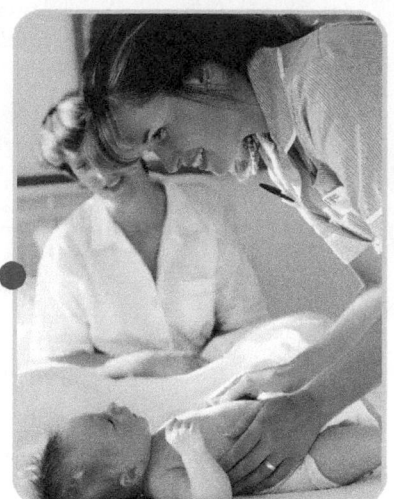

Certified Nurse-Midwife

Certified nurse-midwives care for women during pregnancy, supervise labor, and perform deliveries. They also teach new mothers about breastfeeding, nutrition, and child care. This career requires a bachelor's degree as a registered nurse, a minimum of one year of training in midwifery, and certification by the American College of Nurse Midwives.

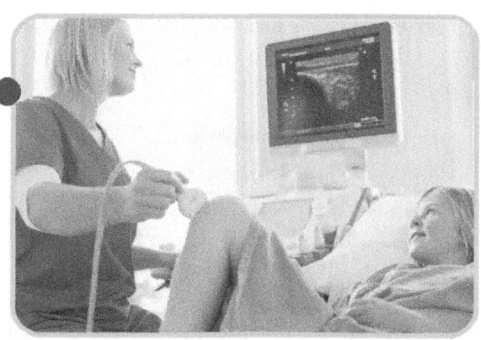

Guidance Counselor

Guidance counselors help students with behavioral, social, and personal problems. They also advocate for at-risk students and for those with special needs. Guidance counselors in high schools assist students with college planning and job-search skills. A career as a guidance counselor usually requires a master's degree in school counseling as well as state certification.

Ultrasound Technician

Ultrasound technicians operate machines that use high frequency sound waves—ultrasound—to create images of internal parts of the body. The images help doctors diagnose diseases in various organs, including the heart and brain. Ultrasound is also used during pregnancy to determine the size and health of the fetus. To pursue this career, an associate's degree in ultrasound technology is typically required.

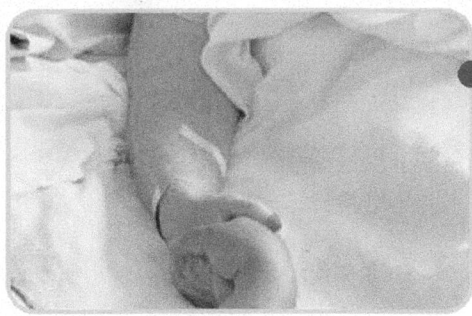

Hospice Caregiver

Hospice caregivers care for terminally ill patients. Their primary concern is to ensure that the patient is as pain-free as possible. Hospice caregivers also provide psychological and social support to help make the patient's final days comfortable. A career as a hospice caregiver requires a bachelor's degree in nursing or social work.

Career Focus

John Williams, Hospice Caregiver

What is the most important part of your job?

"People at the end of life, for the most part, know how they want their final days to play out. We help them by honoring their wishes. Most people want to be at home with their families when they die—most of our patients do just that."

How do you help your patients deal with their physical and emotional pain?

"Physical and emotional pain are often tied together. Managing pain with the most beneficial medication is only part of the picture. Actively listening to the patient and their loved ones is as important. Sometimes listening to what people are saying 'between the lines' and validating their fears and concerns can bring a large measure of relief."

Are the patients' families involved with their care?

"Family members are really on the 'front line' of care. We do a lot of teaching with family members, such as how to care for a bed-bound patient, how to follow a medication schedule, and anything else that can make the home environment more comfortable for their loved one. Ongoing teaching empowers family members and helps make the process of seeing their loved one approaching death less frightening."

Health and Careers

Careers in Human Development Research other careers in human development. Think about what stage of life and what skills you would like to focus on if you pursued a career in this field. Which career would best fit your preferences? Explain your choice. **WRITING**

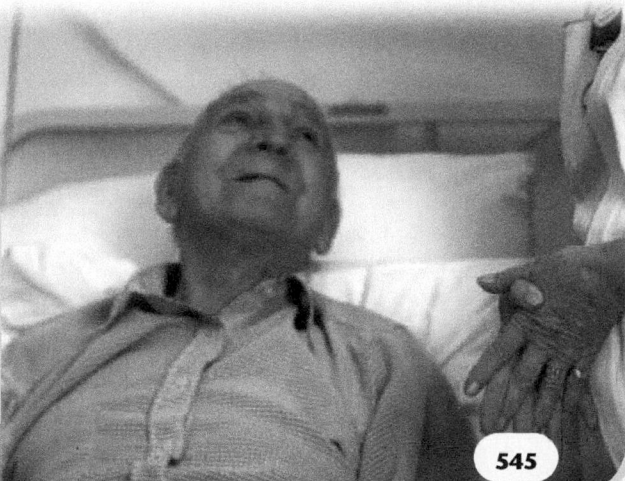

545

Health and Careers

Careers in Human Development Before students start to search particular human development careers, you may want to have them list their preferences by answering these two questions: (1) What skills do you want to develop? *(Students should choose skills for which they have an aptitude.)* (2) What stage of life most interests you? After answering these questions, students can search for a human development career that matches their preferences. For example, for a student who wants to develop childcare and teaching skills and is interested in early childhood, a good career match might be preschool teacher.

Section Objectives	Standards Correlation	Instructional Resources ⑬	SE eTEXT	TE eTEXT	PRINT
1 **Understanding Infectious Diseases** ⏱ 1 period; 1/2 block **21.1.1** **Identify** the causes of infectious diseases. **21.1.2** **Describe** four ways in which infectious diseases are spread.	NHES: 1.12.3, 1.12.5, 2.12.1, 7.12.3, 8.12.2	**SE** Warm-Up, p. 548	•	•	•
		RN Note Taking Guide 21-1	•	•	•
		TR Practice 21-1		•	
		TR Section 21-1 Quiz		•	
2 **Defenses Against Disease** ⏱ 1 period; 1/2 block **21.2.1** **Identify** the body's physical and chemical defenses against infectious disease. **21.2.2** **Describe** the inflammatory response. **21.2.3** **Summarize** how the immune system works. **21.2.4** **Compare** passive and active immunity.	NHES: 1.12.1, 1.12.3, 2.12.10, 7.12.3	**SE** Warm-Up, p. 552	•	•	•
		RN Note Taking Guide 21-2	•	•	•
		IB Image Bank 21-3, 21-5, 21-7		•	
		TR Practice 21-2		•	
		TR Section 21-2 Quiz		•	
3 **Common Infectious Diseases** ⏱ 2 periods; 1 block **21.3.1** **Identify** some diseases caused by bacteria and by viruses. **21.3.2** **Describe** behaviors that can help you get healthy and stay healthy.	NHES: 1.12.1, 1.12.3, 1.12.8, 3.12.4	**SE** Warm-Up, p. 558	•	•	•
		SE Media Wise Evaluating Antibacterial Products, p. 562	•	•	•
		RN Note Taking Guide 21-3	•	•	•
		IB Image Bank 21-9		•	
		TR Practice 21-3		•	
		TR Section 21-3 Quiz		•	
Using Medicines Correctly ⏱ 1 period; 1/2 block **BHS.21** **Demonstrate** the ability to use a medicine correctly by reading the directions on the medicine label.	NHES: 2.12.10, 3.12.5, 7.12.3	**SE** Practice the Skill, p. 565	•	•	•
		RN Building Health Skills 21	•	•	•
		IB Image Bank Page 564		•	
4 **Emerging Infectious Diseases** ⏱ 1 period; 1/2 block **21.4.1** **Define** the term *emerging disease*. **21.4.2** **Identify** five reasons why diseases emerge.	NHES: 1.12.3, 3.12.3	**SE** Warm-Up, p. 566	•	•	•
		RN Note Taking Guide 21-4	•	•	•
		TR Practice 21-4		•	
		TR Section 21-4 Quiz		•	

Chapter Review and Assessment

SE Chapter 21 Review, p. 570 ⑬
CTB Chapter 21 Test ⑫ ⑬ ⑭
SE Standardized Test Prep, p. 571 ⑬

PROGRAM COMPONENTS

SE	Student Edition	**CTB**	Computer Test Bank
TE	Teacher Edition	**AUD**	Audio Section Summaries
TR	Teaching Resources		
RN	Reading and Note Taking Guide	**DVD**	Teens Talk Video Series
		VVG	Video Viewing Guide
ARN	Adapted Reading and Note Taking Guide	**PPT**	Presentation
IB	Image Bank		

Differentiated Instruction

		SE eTEXT	TE eTEXT	PRINT
ARN	Note Taking Guide 21-1 L2	•	•	
RN	Note Taking Guide 21-1 EL	•	•	•
AUD	Audio Summary 21-1 L1 L2 EL	•	•	
TE	Reteach Strategy, p. 551 L2		•	•
TR	Enrich 21-1 L4		•	
ARN	Note Taking Guide 21-2 L2	•	•	
RN	Note Taking Guide 21-2 EL	•	•	•
AUD	Audio Summary 21-2 L1 L2 EL	•	•	
TE	Reteach Strategy, p. 557 L2		•	•
TR	Enrich 21-2 L4		•	
ARN	Note Taking Guide 21-3 L2	•	•	
RN	Note Taking Guide 21-3 EL	•	•	•
AUD	Audio Summary 21-3 L1 L2 EL	•	•	
TE	Reteach Strategy, p. 563 L2		•	•
TR	Enrich 21-3 L4		•	
ARN	Building Health Skills 21 L2	•	•	
RN	Building Health Skills 21 EL	•	•	•
ARN	Note Taking Guide 21-4 L2	•	•	
RN	Note Taking Guide 21-4 EL	•	•	•
AUD	Audio Summary 21-4 L1 L2 EL	•	•	
TE	Reteach Strategy, p. 568 L2		•	•
TR	Enrich 21-4 L4		•	

ABILITY LEVELS

- L1 For students with special needs
- L2 For less proficient readers
- L3 For all students
- L4 For gifted and talented students
- EL For English language learners

Chapter 21 Digital/Video Pathway

This alternative pathway allows you to teach this chapter's content using only the video and online materials.

Preview

DVD	Video #21 Preview
SE	Video #21 Preview Activity
VVG	Video #21 Worksheet

Protection From Infection

1
PPT	21-1 Presentation
RN/ARN	21-1 Note Taking
PPT	21-1 Quiz

2
PPT	21-2 Presentation
RN/ARN	21-2 Note Taking
PPT	21-2 Quiz

3
DVD	Video #21 Explore/Wrap-Up
VVG	Video #21 Worksheet
PPT	21-3 Presentation
RN/ARN	21-3 Note Taking
PPT	21-3 Quiz

Protection From Infection

4
PPT	21-4 Presentation
RN/ARN	21-4 Note Taking
PPT	21-4 Quiz

Chapter Preview

Section 1 Understanding Infectious Diseases
Infectious diseases are caused by pathogens that enter and multiply within the human body. Pathogens can spread through contact with an infected person, an infected animal, contaminated objects, and contaminated food, soil, or water.

Section 2 Defenses Against Disease
The human body has a number of defenses against disease. The first defense includes both physical and chemical defenses that prevent pathogens from entering the body. The second defense is inflammation, the body's general response to injury. The third defense is the body's immune system.

Section 3 Common Infectious Diseases
Common bacterial diseases include strep throat, Lyme disease, meningitis, and tuberculosis. Common viral diseases include the common cold, influenza, pneumonia, and hepatitis. Ways to prevent infectious diseases include avoiding contact with pathogens, making sure that immunizations are current, and choosing healthful behaviors.

 Practicing Healthful Behaviors

Using Medicines Correctly
Learning how to use a medicine correctly is essential for the medicine to be safe and effective.

Section 4 Emerging Infectious Diseases
An emerging disease is an infectious disease that has become increasingly common or threatens to become more common. Factors that may enable diseases to emerge include human contact with infected animals, drug resistance, lack of immunization, international travel, and the global food supply.

 GO ONLINE

PearsonSuccessNet.com

For resources and activities for this chapter.

Infectious Diseases

1 Understanding Infectious Diseases

2 Defenses Against Disease

3 Common Infectious Diseases
 • **MediaWise** Evaluating Antibacterial Products

Building Health Skills
 • **Practicing Healthful Behaviors** Using Medicines Correctly

4 Emerging Infectious Diseases

GO ONLINE PearsonSuccessNet.com

TEENS Talk

VIDEO 21

Protection From Infection

Preview **Activity**

What Behaviors Put You at Risk for Infectious Diseases?

Complete this activity before you watch the video.

1. With a partner, prepare a list of five behaviors that might put you at risk for an infectious disease.

2. On your own, rank the five behaviors from most risky to least risky.

3. Get together with your partner and compare your rankings. Discuss why you ranked the behaviors as you did.

Sensitive Issues
Disease may be a sensitive issue for students who are ill or whose family members are ill. Never ask students to disclose information they would rather keep confidential, and always give students other options for activities in which they are asked to apply what they have learned to their own lives.

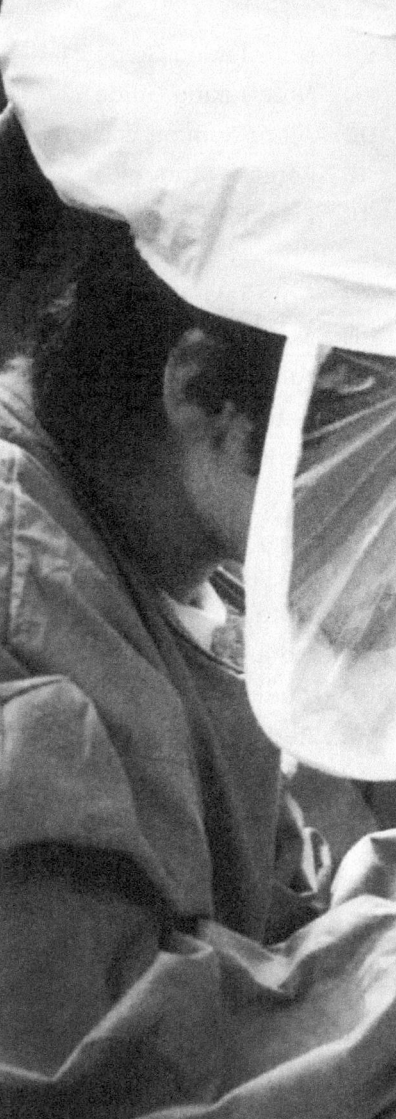

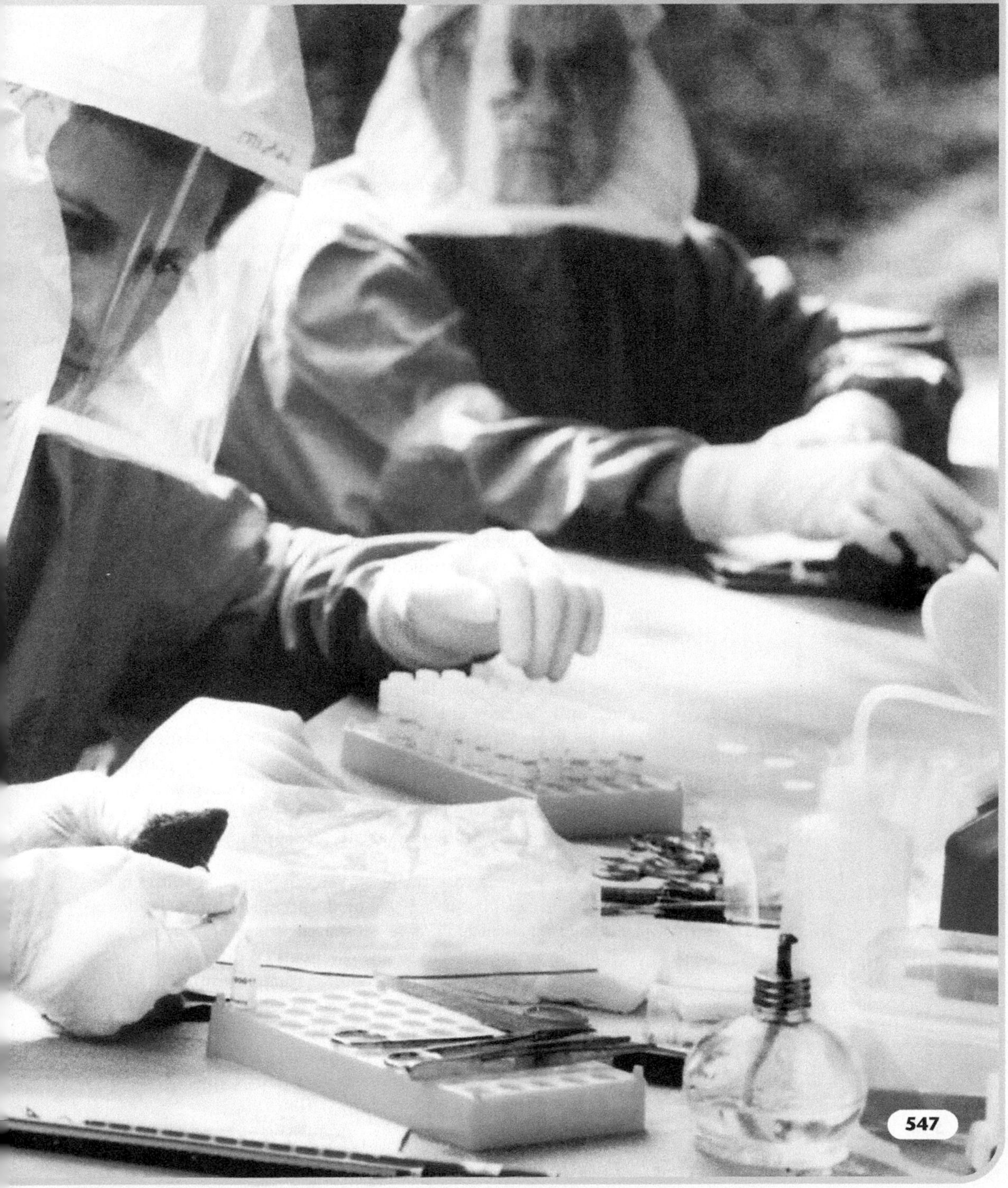

VIDEO 21

TEENS Talk

Protection From Infection

Video Objectives

Use this video to help students

Identify behaviors that may put them at risk for infectious diseases.

Practice healthful behaviors that minimize their risk of infection.

Preview **Activity**

What Behaviors Put You at Risk for Infectious Diseases?

Just before watching the video, have students complete the Preview Activity. After students complete the assignment, ask them to share the behaviors they listed as most risky. Write those behaviors on the board so students can see them while watching the video. After showing the video, ask students if they still think those behaviors are the most risky.

From the Authors

Learning about infectious diseases is interesting for many students because they have had experiences with common diseases. To help make the topic even more relevant, you might take advantage of recent news stories about epidemics—actual and projected—as well as about the development of new vaccines. Be aware, though, that some students may become unduly anxious about the threat of an epidemic, especially as they learn about emerging diseases in Section 4.

One way to allay student fears is to point out the major differences between the United States and developing countries in terms of the risk of epidemics. Infectious diseases are no longer leading causes of death in the United States because of advances in such areas as clean drinking water, sewage treatment, and the availability of vaccines. You may want to use the Section 3 Warm-Up activity on page 558 to drive home this point.

You can also focus attention on the table of recommended immunizations in Figure 7 on page 557 to emphasize one factor in reducing the risk of epidemics in the United States.

Section 1
Understanding Infectious Diseases

Objectives

Before class begins, write the objectives on the board. Have students copy the objectives into their notebooks at the start of class.

1. Focus

Warm-Up Myth/Fact

After students complete the writing assignment, call on a few volunteers to read their ideas to the class. Most students will be able to think of some ways to encourage more frequent hand washing among teens. Ask students to reread the myth, and discuss why the myth is believed by many people.

Presentation 21-1

2. Teach

L3 **EL** Reading/Note Taking 21-1

L2 Adapted Reading/Note Taking 21-1

Causes of Infectious Diseases

L2 **Class Discussion**

Ask students to brainstorm a list of every disease they think humans can catch. Write the list on the board. Then ask students what it means to "catch" a disease. *(Students should refer to coming into contact with pathogens and pathogens multiplying within the body.)* If students list diseases that are not infectious, be sure to explain that not all diseases are caused by pathogens and therefore cannot be "caught." Chronic diseases are discussed in Chapter 23.

Objectives

▶ **Identify** the causes of infectious diseases.

▶ **Describe** four ways in which infectious diseases are spread.

Vocabulary

- infectious disease
- microorganism
- pathogen
- bacteria
- toxin
- virus
- fungi
- protozoan

─*Warm-Up*───────────────

Myth There isn't much a person can do to avoid spreading or catching a cold or the flu.

Fact About 80% of infectious diseases are spread by hand contact. Washing your hands with soap and water is a simple and effective way to prevent the spread of colds and the flu.

WRITING Do you think most teens wash their hands as much as they should? What do you think are some ways to encourage more frequent hand washing?

Causes of Infectious Diseases

For as long as there have been humans, there have been infectious diseases. Also known as communicable diseases, **infectious diseases** (in FEK shus) are caused by organisms or viruses that enter and multiply within the human body. Most disease-causing organisms and viruses are so small that they can be seen only through a microscope. Organisms this small are called **microorganisms** (my kroh AWR guh niz ums).

Not all microorganisms that enter and live in your body cause disease. In fact, many are present in your body all the time. Billions of microorganisms live in your mouth, on your skin, and in your digestive tract.

Microorganisms and viruses that cause disease are called **pathogens** (PATH uh junz). Pathogens do not belong in your body. **Pathogens can cause an infectious disease when they enter your body and multiply.** There are many kinds of pathogens. Some examples are shown in Figure 1.

Bacteria **Bacteria** (bak TEER ee uh) are simple, single-celled microorganisms. Bacteria live in air, soil, food, and in and on the bodies of plants and animals, including you. Most bacteria are not pathogens.

Some bacteria injure cells by giving off poisons called **toxins** (TAHK sinz). Certain bacteria that grow on food, for example, give off toxins that can cause food poisoning. A type of bacteria found in soil produces a toxin that causes tetanus (TET n us). These bacteria can also grow inside deep wounds. In the body, tetanus toxin damages the nervous system, causing uncontrollable muscle contractions, paralysis, and even death.

For Your **INFORMATION!**

Nonliving Pathogens

Most biologists do not consider viruses to be living things. First, viruses are not cells, and a fundamental concept of biology is that all living things are composed of cells. In addition, unlike living things, viruses have no growth and development, and they do not obtain and use energy. Finally, viruses can multiply only within a host cell. Viruses are like living things in that they do reproduce themselves—even if only within a cell—and they do change over time, or evolve.

There are other nonliving pathogens. A prion is a type of protein that is infectious. The pathogen that causes the so-called mad cow disease, for example, is a prion.

Viruses The smallest pathogens are **viruses.** They are about 100 times smaller than most bacteria. Unlike most bacteria, a virus can multiply only after entering a living cell. The virus then takes over the cell's reproductive mechanisms, resulting in cell damage or death.

Some viruses, such as those that cause the common cold, invade the cells of the respiratory tract. Other viruses invade other regions of the body. The virus that causes chickenpox, for example, invades skin cells.

Fungi Organisms such as yeasts, molds, and mushrooms are known as **fungi** (FUN jy). Fungi grow best in warm, dark, moist areas. Two examples of disease caused by fungi are athlete's foot and ringworm, a skin infection that forms a reddish circle on the skin.

Protozoans Single-celled organisms that are much larger and more complex than bacteria are known as **protozoans** (proh tuh ZOH unz). Protozoans have the ability to move through fluids in search of food. Malaria, a disease that is common in tropical areas, is caused by a protozoan that infects red blood cells, causing weakness and nausea. Amebic dysentery is caused by a different protozoan. Dysentery is characterized by stomach pain and diarrhea.

Other Pathogens Some infectious diseases are caused by animals such as mites, lice, and certain worms. For example, the trichina worm can live in the muscle tissue of some animals, such as pigs. If the meat of an infected animal is not thoroughly cooked, a person who eats the meat can become infected.

What types of pathogens do you think you commonly encounter?

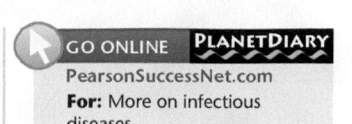
GO ONLINE **PLANETDIARY**

PearsonSuccessNet.com
For: More on infectious diseases

FIGURE 1 Different types of pathogens cause different infectious diseases. **Classifying** What type of pathogen causes tuberculosis? Polio?

Infectious Diseases by Type of Pathogen

Bacteria	Viruses	Fungi	Protozoans
strep throat, Lyme disease, anthrax, tuberculosis, cholera, diphtheria, pertussis, tetanus, typhoid fever, staph infection, **food poisoning** ▼	common cold, hepatitis, chickenpox, measles, mononucleosis, mumps, polio, rabies, rubella, West Nile virus, **influenza** ▼	athlete's foot, **ringworm** ▼	malaria, amebic dysentery, **African sleeping sickness** ▼

 GO ONLINE PLANETDIARY

L3 Online Activity

Visit Pearson SuccessNet to access an online activity about infectious diseases. Have students complete the Web activity.

L3 Visual Learning: Figure 1

Have students read the list of diseases associated with each type of pathogen. Explain that the representative photos of each type of pathogen are not reproduced to the same scale. Ask: **Which of these pathogens are the smallest?** *(Viruses are about 100 times smaller than most bacteria.)* **Which of these pathogens are not classified as living things?** *(viruses)*

Caption Answer A type of bacteria causes tuberculosis. A virus causes polio.

Connect to Your Life Answers will vary, though most students will say that they commonly encounter bacteria, viruses, and fungi.

Differentiated Instruction

L2 Less Proficient Readers

Help students create a detailed concept map to organize and record the most important information in Section 1. Use the headings and subheadings to start the concept map, leaving room where needed for additional information. Tell students to finish the concept map by adding details as they read. For example, students can add details about each of the different types of pathogens. Check completed concept maps for errors and omissions. Suggest that students use their concept maps when they review the section.

How Pathogens Are Spread

L1 Active Learning

Divide the class into several large groups. Choose one member of each group, and use a bottle of talcum powder to cover the student's right hand with powder. Tell the student whose hand has been powdered to shake the hand of one other student in the group. Have the second student shake a third student's hand, and so on until all members of a group have shaken hands with another student. Ask all students to examine their hands for evidence of the talcum powder. (All should have some talcum powder on the right hand, even those last in the series of hand shaking.) Ask: **How is the transfer of talcum powder from person to person similar to a way that pathogens are spread?** *(The transfer of talcum powder is like the spread of a pathogen by direct contact with an infected person.)*

L2 Addressing Misconceptions

Infectious Bites Some students who learn about the spread of pathogens by infected animals may think that it is the bite itself that causes the disease. Point out that a person can be bitten many times by mosquitoes without catching a disease. Only when a mosquito is infected with a pathogen can the person be infected. Ask: **How can the bite of a mosquito transmit a pathogen into a person's body?** *(Sample answer: The bite penetrates the skin, and a pathogen inside the mosquito moves into the person's blood.)*

L3 Building Health Skills

Making Decisions Describe a situation in which a teen orders a hamburger in a restaurant. The waitperson asks how she wants the hamburger cooked—rare, medium, or well-done. The teen answers that she loves a hamburger when it is red inside, and so she wants it cooked rare. Ask: **Why might her decision not be a wise one?** *(A hamburger that is cooked rare may not be cooked long enough to kill pathogens in the meat.)*

Connect to Your Life *Sample answer:* limit physical contact with people infected with a disease, never use cups or utensils used by other people

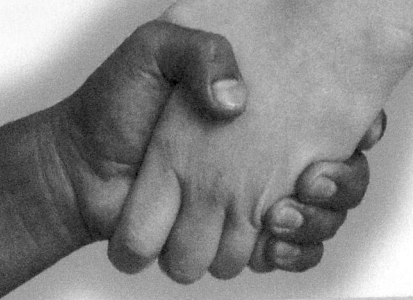

Infected Person
Pathogens can be spread when you shake hands with someone.

Infected Animal
A raccoon can transmit pathogens when it bites you.

Contaminated Object
You can pick up pathogens from an object that an infected person has touched, coughed on, or sneezed on.

550 *Chapter 21*

How Pathogens Are Spread

How does a person come in contact with pathogens? **Pathogens can spread through contact with an infected person; an infected animal; contaminated objects; or contaminated food, soil, or water.** The pathogens can then enter the body through breaks in the skin or through the moist linings of the eyes, ears, nose, mouth, or other openings.

Infected People Many infectious diseases are spread through some form of contact with a person who has the disease. The contact may be direct physical contact, such as shaking hands or kissing. If you kiss someone with a cold sore, for example, the cold sore viruses could enter your body. Sexually transmitted infections are transmitted through direct physical contact.

Infectious diseases can also spread through indirect contact. For example, if an infected person coughs or sneezes, you can inhale the pathogens in tiny droplets of moisture in the air. Influenza, measles, mumps, and chickenpox can spread by droplet inhalation. Contact with an infected person's blood, such as when needles are shared to inject illegal drugs, is another form of indirect contact that can spread disease.

Infected Animals Some infectious diseases are transmitted to humans through the bites of animals. For example, rabies, a deadly disease of the nervous system, can be transmitted by bites from infected dogs, bats, or raccoons. People contract malaria through mosquito bites. Lyme disease and Rocky Mountain spotted fever are spread through tick bites.

Contaminated Objects Some pathogens can survive for a period of time outside a person's body. These pathogens can be spread from person to person on objects such as doorknobs, eating utensils, towels, and needles used for body piercings and tattoos. If you drink from a cup used by an infected person, you can become infected as well. If you touch a desktop or money that has been sneezed or coughed on, or contaminated in some other way, you can become infected when you touch your eyes, your mouth, or your food. This is why it is always a good idea to wash your hands often, especially before eating.

FIGURE 2 Infectious diseases can be spread in several different ways.

WRITING and Health

L3 Firsthand Account

Ask students to write a firsthand account of a pathogen spreading from one person to another. Tell students that they should pretend to be a pathogen and use the pronoun *I* in telling the story of moving from an infected person to another person through a break in the skin, through the nose, through the bite of an insect, or through the mouth in contaminated food or water. Tell students that although this should be a fanciful account of a journey, they should use accurate information they've learned about pathogens and how pathogens spread.

Contaminated Food, Soil, or Water Some pathogens are naturally present in food and soil. One common type of food poisoning is caused by *Salmonella* bacteria, which can live in poultry and eggs. Another type of food poisoning is caused by *E. coli* bacteria, which can live in beef. It is important to cook foods thoroughly to kill these bacteria. It is also important to refrigerate food promptly to prevent the growth of harmful bacteria.

Other bacteria can live in foods that have been improperly canned. These bacteria cause botulism (BAHCH uh liz im), a very serious and often deadly type of food poisoning. The bacteria that cause tetanus are naturally present in soil. These bacteria can enter your body through cuts on your skin.

Sometimes, water and food become contaminated with pathogens from infected people. Drinking water contaminated by sewage is a common source of disease in many areas of the world. Cholera, for example, is a bacterial disease of the digestive system that causes severe diarrhea. Cholera outbreaks can occur after floods and earthquakes, when water and sanitation systems are disrupted.

 **Connect to Your Life** List some things you can do to avoid contact with pathogens.

Contaminated Food
Some foods have bacteria that can make you sick if the food isn't cooked or stored properly.

Section 1 Review

Key Ideas and Vocabulary

1. What is a **pathogen**? Name four types of pathogens.
2. How do pathogens cause infectious diseases?
3. What is a **virus**? How are viruses different from bacteria?
4. What are four ways that infectious diseases can spread?

Critical Thinking

5. **Applying Concepts** If you were traveling to a country where mosquito-borne diseases were common, how would you protect yourself from getting infected?

Health at Home

Food Safety Evaluate the way your family handles food at home. Do you wash fruits and vegetables thoroughly before eating or cooking them? Do you cook meats thoroughly? Do you promptly clean countertops and wash your hands after handling raw meat? Create a checklist to hang in your kitchen to remind yourself of practices that prevent the spread of infectious diseases. **WRITING**

6. **Relating Cause and Effect** Why do you think that communities boil their drinking water after a water line break?

 **GO ONLINE** PearsonSuccessNet.com Audio Summary Section 21.1

Infectious Diseases **551**

Objectives
Before class begins, write the objectives on the board. Have students copy the objectives into their notebooks at the start of class.

1. Focus

Warm-Up **Quick Quiz**

Use the Warm-Up Presentation slide to survey student responses.

Give students a few minutes to do the quiz. Then explain that each of the behaviors described in the statements concern ways to avoid pathogens. For example, thoroughly washing fruits and vegetables washes off pathogens from contaminated objects. Ask students to brainstorm other healthful behaviors that reduce the risk of being infected by pathogens.

Presentation 21-2

Connect to Your Life *Sample answer:* A cut on my skin once did become infected because the cut skin allowed pathogens to enter my body.

Objectives
▶ **Identify** the body's physical and chemical defenses against infectious disease.
▶ **Describe** the inflammatory response.
▶ **Summarize** how the immune system works.
▶ **Compare** passive and active immunity.

Vocabulary
• mucous membrane
• inflammation
• phagocyte
• immune system
• lymphocyte
• immunity
• T cell
• B cell
• antibody
• lymphatic system
• immunization
• vaccine

Warm-Up

Quick Quiz Complete each of these statements with *always, sometimes,* or *never.*

1. I __?__ wash my hands before meals.

2. When preparing fruits and vegetables, I __?__ wash them thoroughly.

3. I am __?__ careful to use only my own eating utensils, drinking cups, towels, toothbrush, and grooming items.

4. I __?__ cover my mouth when I cough or sneeze.

5. If I spend time in wooded areas, I __?__ wear insect repellent.

WRITING For each of your responses, explain how your behavior could affect your chances of getting or spreading an infectious disease.

Physical and Chemical Defenses

If pathogens are everywhere, why aren't you sick all the time? When you do get sick, what keeps the pathogens from multiplying until they take over your body? The answer to these questions is that your body has a number of defenses against infection. **Your body's first line of defense against infectious disease includes both physical and chemical defenses that prevent pathogens from entering your body.** Figure 3 shows the body's first line of defense.

Skin Your skin serves as both a physical and a chemical barrier against pathogens. The surface cells are hard and have no gaps between them. Sweat acts as a chemical barrier because it contains acids that kill many bacteria. Finally, old skin cells are shed constantly, and the pathogens on these cells are shed, too. In fact, microorganisms usually cannot get through your skin unless you have a cut, scrape, burn, or other injury.

Connect to Your Life Have you ever had a cut in your skin that became infected? Why did that happen?

For Your **INFORMATION!**

Mucous Membranes

The body's mucous membranes line all the tubes and cavities that lead to the outside, including the tubes of the respiratory, digestive, urinary, and reproductive systems. At several places in the body, mucous membranes meet the skin, including at the lips, ears, nostrils, anus, and genitals.

Normally, mucous membranes protect the walls of the stomach and lower intestine from the acids that break down foods. A stomach ulcer, which is caused by a bacterial pathogen in the great majority of cases, is the breakdown of the stomach's mucous membrane.

Mucous Membranes   The openings into your body, such as your mouth, eyes, and nose, are covered by protective linings called **mucous membranes** (MYOO kus). Mucous membranes secrete a liquid called mucus. The mucus traps many pathogens and washes them away. Mucus also contains chemicals that attack pathogens.

Cilia   Some of your body's mucous membranes are lined with tiny hair-like structures called cilia (SIL ee uh). Your air passages, for example, are lined with cilia. Together, cilia and mucus help trap and remove pathogens. When you inhale, dust and pathogens get trapped in the mucus of your air passages. The cilia beat rhythmically, moving the mucus up your windpipe toward your mouth and nose. When you cough, sneeze, or blow your nose, the pathogens are removed along with the mucus.

Saliva and Tears   Your saliva and tears can trap pathogens and wash them away. Like mucus, saliva and tears also contain chemicals that attack pathogens.

Digestive System   Chemicals in your digestive system, including acids in your stomach, kill many pathogens. In addition, the normal motions of the digestive system not only move food through your system but also move pathogens out. Finally, bacteria that normally live in your digestive system produce substances that can harm or kill invading bacteria.

Your Body's Physical and Chemical Defenses

FIGURE 3   Your body's physical and chemical defenses prevent many pathogens from entering your body and causing disease.

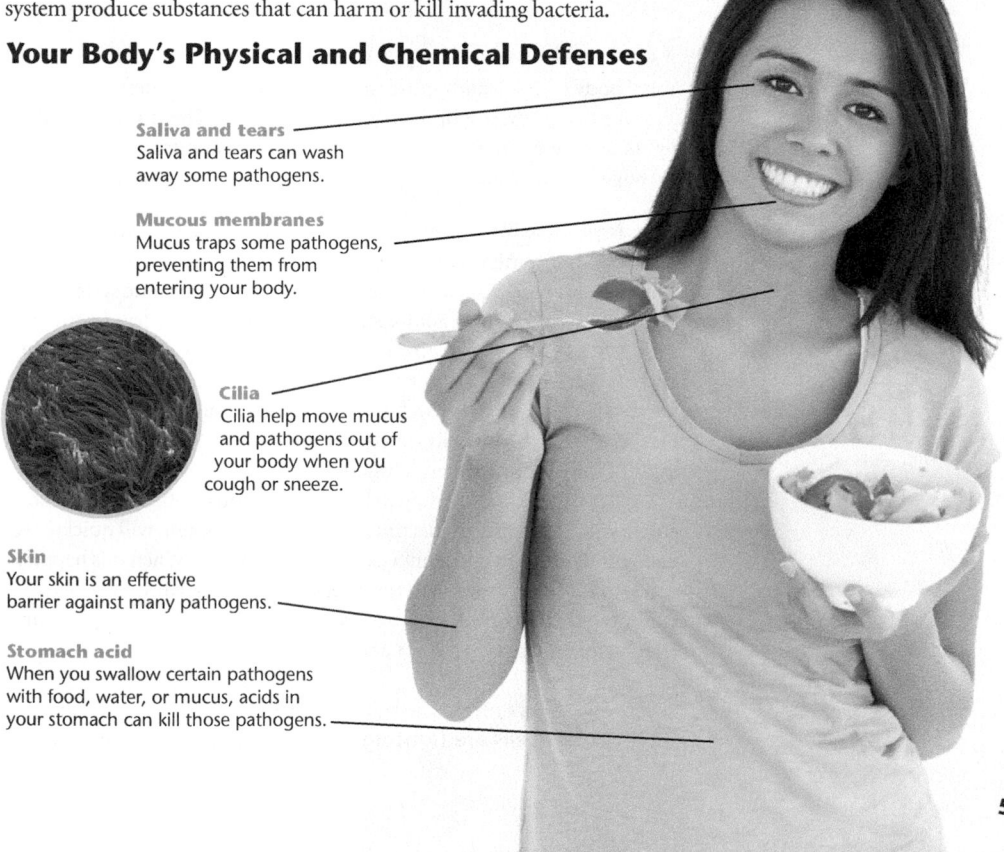

Saliva and tears
Saliva and tears can wash away some pathogens.

Mucous membranes
Mucus traps some pathogens, preventing them from entering your body.

Cilia
Cilia help move mucus and pathogens out of your body when you cough or sneeze.

Skin
Your skin is an effective barrier against many pathogens.

Stomach acid
When you swallow certain pathogens with food, water, or mucus, acids in your stomach can kill those pathogens.

553

2. Teach

L3 **EL** Reading/Note Taking 21-2

L2 Adapted Reading/Note Taking 21-2

Physical and Chemical Defenses

L3 **Visual Learning: Figure 3**
Image Bank Figure 21-3

Have students read about the body's defenses in Figure 3. Then ask students to classify defenses as either physical or chemical. Ask: **Based on this figure and what you've read in the text, what are the body's physical defenses against pathogens?** *(skin, the trapping of pathogens by mucous membranes, the moving of cilia, the washing away of pathogens by saliva and tears, and the motions of the digestive system that move pathogens out)* **What are the body's chemical defenses?** *(the chemicals in mucus that attack pathogens, the chemicals in saliva and tears that attack pathogens, and the chemicals in the digestive system that kill many pathogens)*

L2 **Teacher Demo**
Show students an apple. Then, use a knife to cut the apple in half. Place each half on a paper towel on a table, one with the cut side up and the other with the cut side down. Use a dropper to drop food coloring on each of the halves. Then, show students the effect the food coloring had on both halves. Ask: **How did the food coloring affect each of the halves?** *(The food coloring penetrated inside of the apple with the cut side up, but the coloring did not affect the apple with the cut side down.)* **Suppose that the food coloring is a pathogen. What part of the apple is the first line of defense?** *(the apple's skin)*

Differentiated Instruction

L1 **Special Needs**
Make sure students understand what is meant by the term *defense*. Provide students with an analogy for both physical defenses and chemical defenses. You might compare the body to a castle. The skin, a physical defense, is a wall surrounding the castle. The wall prevents invaders from getting into the castle. Chemical defenses can be compared to knights within the castle. The knights fight invaders who manage to penetrate the castle wall.

Inflammation

L3 Addressing Misconceptions

Inflammation Some students may think that inflammation is harmful by its very nature, because in their experience inflammation is a sign of pain, discomfort, and infection. Ask: **What is happening inside the body when a wounded area becomes inflamed?** *(Phagocytes are destroying pathogens and giving off substances that cause healing to begin.)* Point out that though the signs of inflammation include heat, swelling, pain, and redness, these are indications not of disease but of the body's second line of defense against pathogens.

EL Building Vocabulary

Analyze the word *phagocyte* so that students will have a better understanding of what this type of cell does. Explain that the word part *phago-* derives from a Greek word meaning "to eat," and explain that the word part *–cyte* means "cell." Ask students to use this information to define *phagocyte. (a cell that eats)* Point out that students may encounter other terms in studying health and biology that contain *-cyte*, including the vocabulary term *lymphocyte*. This word part is always an indication that the term refers to a type of cell.

The Immune System

L3 Class Discussion

Initiate a class discussion by writing the word *immunity* on the board. Ask students to brainstorm what it means to them. Emphasize that immunity means protection from being infected by a pathogen. The immune response is the body's most complex line of defense against pathogens. Ask: **What might happen if the immune system was not able to function properly in a person's body?** *(That person would not be able to fight off pathogens effectively.)* Explain that such is the case in people who have AIDS.

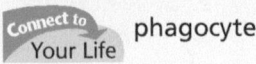
phagocytes

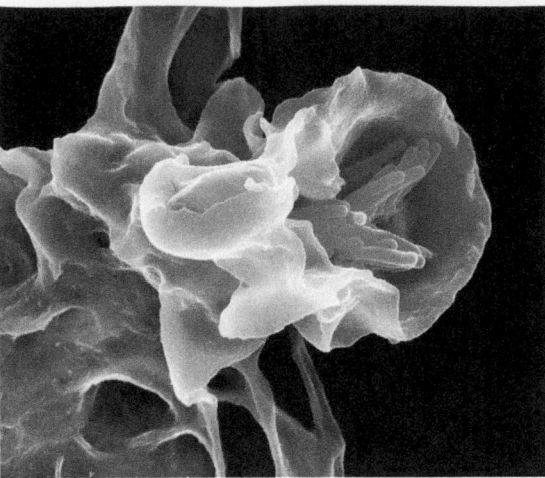

FIGURE 4 This micrograph shows a phagocyte (blue) attacking bacteria (pink). Phagocytes kill pathogens by engulfing and then digesting them.

Inflammation

If pathogens are able to get past the physical and chemical defenses and begin to injure cells, your body is ready with its second line of defense—**inflammation** (in fluh MAY shun). **Inflammation is your body's general response to all kinds of injury, from cuts and scrapes to internal damage.** Inflammation fights infection and promotes the healing process.

Phagocytes Within seconds after your body is injured, the damaged cells release chemicals that cause blood vessels in the injured area to enlarge. Blood, other fluids, and white blood cells called **phagocytes** (FAG uh syts) leak out of the enlarged vessels. The phagocytes engulf and destroy pathogens. Meanwhile, the infected area becomes red, swollen, and sore—in other words, inflamed.

Healing Phagocytes also give off substances that cause healing to begin. The fluids, phagocytes, and dead cells that accumulate at the injury site often result in the formation of a thick, white liquid called pus. Eventually, the inflammation process heals the damage, and the inflammation subsides.

The Immune System

Your body's third and most sophisticated line of defense against pathogens is your **immune system** (ih MYOON). **The immune system fights disease by producing a separate set of weapons for each kind of pathogen it encounters.**

The Immune Response When a pathogen enters your body for the first time, it often causes disease. If your immune system is working, why does this happen? The explanation is that your immune system must build up its arsenal of weapons against the newly encountered pathogen. This process takes time, during which the pathogen multiplies in your body and causes disease. Once the immune system's arsenal is built up, however, the immune system kills the pathogen, and your body gradually recovers. White blood cells called **lymphocytes** (LIM fuh syts) carry out most of the immune system's functions.

What happens if a pathogen that has previously attacked your body enters your body again? This time, your immune system will quickly recognize the pathogen and launch an immediate attack. When this happens, you are said to be immune to the disease. **Immunity** (ih MYOON ih tee) is your body's ability to destroy pathogens that it has previously encountered before the pathogens are able to cause disease.

 **When you experience inflammation, what blood cells are fighting the pathogens in your body?**

WRITING and Health

L2 Interview

Ask students to write an "interview" with a phagocyte. Tell students that they should take the role of a television war reporter interviewing one of the combatants after a series of battles against invading pathogens. Remind students that phagocytes are involved in both inflammation and the immune response. Tell students that the information they include in their interview should accurately reflect what they learned about the role of phagocytes in defenses against disease.

T Cells There are two types of lymphocytes—T lymphocytes, or T cells, and B lymphocytes, or B cells. **T cells** perform several functions.

▶ **Killer T cells** destroy any body cell that has been infected by a pathogen.

▶ **Helper T cells** produce chemicals that stimulate other T cells and B cells to fight off infection.

▶ **Suppressor T cells** produce chemicals that "turn off" other immune system cells when an infection has been brought under control.

T cells also help your immune system "remember" pathogens. This memory capacity, along with the memory capacity of B cells, is what causes you to develop immunity to a previously encountered pathogen.

B Cells The B lymphocytes, or **B cells,** produce antibodies. **Antibodies** (AN tih bahd eez) are proteins that attach to the surface of pathogens or to the toxins produced by pathogens. This binding action keeps the pathogen or toxin from harming the body. Each type of B cell produces antibodies that attack a specific pathogen or toxin. Figure 5 shows how T cells and B cells work together in destroying a pathogen.

Once an infection is overcome, your B cells stop producing antibodies, but they do not "forget" how to produce them. Those B cells continue to circulate in your body for years. They are ready to produce antibodies quickly if the same pathogen reenters your body. This memory capacity of B cells explains why you develop immunity to some diseases you've already had.

GO ONLINE

PearsonSuccessNet.com

For: More on the immune response

FIGURE 5 T cells and B cells work together when fighting pathogens, such as viruses.
Interpreting Diagrams Which type of lymphocyte destroys infected body cells?

The Immune Response

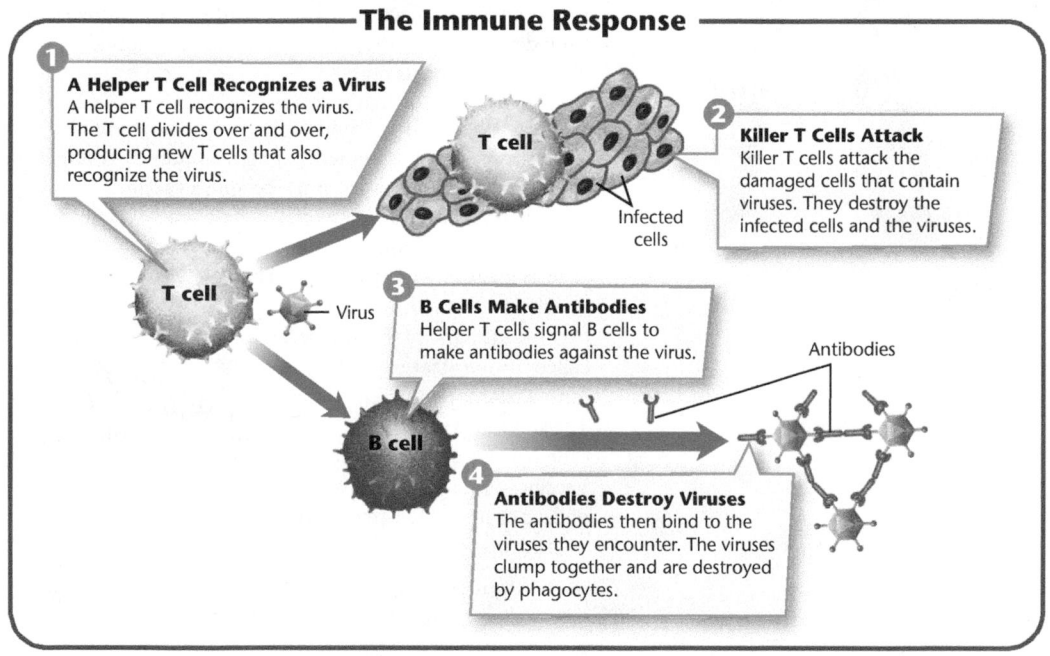

1 **A Helper T Cell Recognizes a Virus**
A helper T cell recognizes the virus. The T cell divides over and over, producing new T cells that also recognize the virus.

T cell

Infected cells

2 **Killer T Cells Attack**
Killer T cells attack the damaged cells that contain viruses. They destroy the infected cells and the viruses.

T cell

Virus

3 **B Cells Make Antibodies**
Helper T cells signal B cells to make antibodies against the virus.

Antibodies

B cell

4 **Antibodies Destroy Viruses**
The antibodies then bind to the viruses they encounter. The viruses clump together and are destroyed by phagocytes.

Infectious Diseases **555**

L3 Online Activity  GO ONLINE

Visit Pearson SuccessNet to access an online activity about the immune response. Have students complete the Web activity.

L3 Visual Learning: Figure 5

Image Bank Figure 21-5

Have students read through the steps in the immune response. Point out that the figure shows two paths after helper T cells recognize the virus. Focus students' attention on the lower path, and ask: **What stimulates the B cells to make antibodies?** *(helper T cells)* **How do the antibodies destroy viruses?** *(They bind to the viruses, and the viruses are destroyed by phagocytes.)* **After the viral infection is overcome, what happens to the B cells?** *(They continue to circulate in the body for years, ready to produce antibodies quickly if the same kind of pathogen reenters the body.)* **Would this process be different if the pathogens were bacteria instead of viruses?** *(The process would be the same.)*

Caption Answer killer T cells

L2 Addressing Misconceptions

Combating Teleology Some students may have the misconception that the different T cells and B cells react to pathogens in thoughtful ways, attacking pathogens or producing antibodies by assessing a situation and acting accordingly. Remind students that the functions of the immune system are all automatic. Different cells are stimulated to carry out functions as they come into contact with certain chemicals or objects. Point out that the "memory" capacity of B cells is not like a person's memory. Rather, it is more like the memory of a device that has been built to react to certain substances.

L3 Cooperative Learning

Divide the class into small groups, and challenge each group to create a skit that focuses on the body's immune response to invading pathogens. Explain that a skit may be dramatic or humorous, but it should also include accurate information about the body's third line of defense. Invite each group to perform its skit for the class.

🔵 L3 Visual Learning: Figure 6

Use Figure 6 to clarify the description in the text of the lymphatic system. Explain that the system is separate from the cardiovascular system, though the two systems are connected. Ask: **How is the lymphatic system connected to the cardiovascular system?** *(The lymphatic system collects fluid from body tissues and returns it to the bloodstream.)* Have students try to locate the lymph nodes on either side of their neck. Explain that these lymph nodes become swollen when the body is fighting an infection because phagocytes and lymphocytes accumulate at the lymph nodes.

Passive and Active Immunity

🔵 EL Building Vocabulary

The word *vaccinate* is derived from the Latin word *vacca*. Have students look up the meaning of *vacca*. *(cow)* Explain that the word *vaccinate* is derived from the Latin word for cow because of the successful use of vaccination in 1796 by Edward Jenner. Jenner was able to immunize people against the deadly viral disease smallpox by injecting them with a similar, but more benign, cowpox virus. Ask students to write the word for *vaccinate* in their native language.

🔵 L3 Cultural Connection

Some immunizations are recommended for travel to other countries. Have students choose a country they would like to visit and determine which vaccines they should get. The Centers for Disease Control and Prevention Web site provides this information.

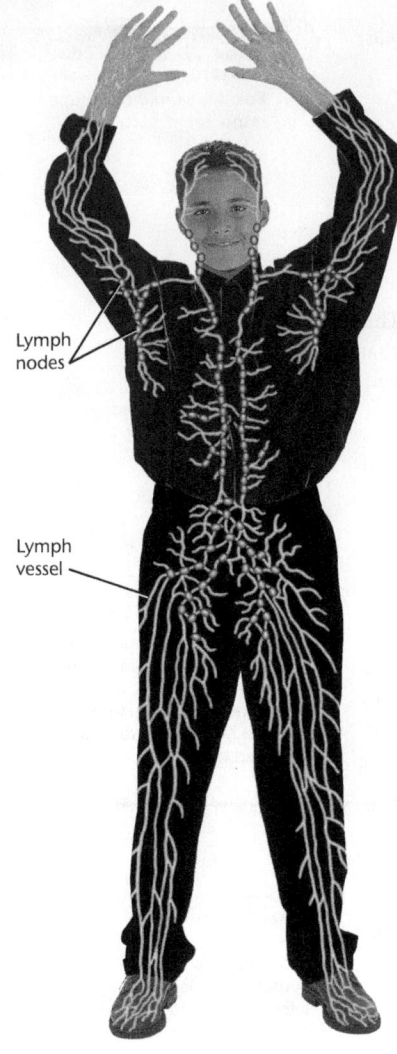

Lymph nodes

Lymph vessel

FIGURE 6 Your lymphatic system is a complex network of vessels and nodes.

The Lymphatic System Much of your immune system is contained within your lymphatic system. The **lymphatic system** (lim FAT ik) is a network of vessels that collects fluid from your tissues and returns it to the bloodstream. The fluid flowing through the lymphatic system is called lymph (limf).

As shown in Figure 6, the lymphatic vessels have hundreds of small stations, called lymph nodes. Each lymph node acts as a sort of filter. Phagocytes and lymphocytes are present in the lymph nodes and attack pathogens as they pass through.

Passive and Active Immunity

There are two types of immunity—passive and active. Both types are important in protecting your body against infections.

Passive Immunity People can develop immunity if they are given antibodies against a pathogen. **Immunity acquired by receiving antibodies from a source other than one's own immune system is called passive immunity.** This type of immunity is temporary, not lifelong. It occurs naturally in babies, who receive antibodies from their mothers before birth. After birth, antibodies also pass to an infant in the mother's breast milk. These antibodies protect newborns before their own immune systems have fully developed.

Passive immunity also can be artificially acquired. For example, suppose you were bitten by a dog with rabies. A doctor would give you injections of rabies antibodies to prevent you from developing the disease. Eventually these antibodies would disappear from your body.

Active Immunity Immunity that your own immune system creates is called active immunity. **Active immunity results from either having a disease or from receiving a vaccine.**

When you were a baby, you may have received injections to protect you from some common childhood infectious diseases, such as measles, mumps, and rubella. These injections, which caused you to become immune to the disease, are called **immunizations** (im yuh nih ZAY shunz), or vaccinations. The substance that is injected is called a **vaccine** (vak SEEN). Vaccines contain small amounts of dead or modified pathogens or their toxins.

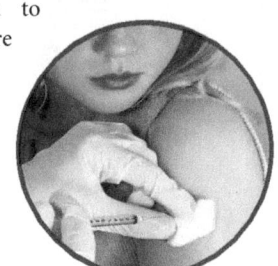

▲ **Immunization**

TEENS *Are Asking . . .*

Q: What immunizations should I get?

A: The American Academy of Pediatrics recommends that teens be vaccinated for varicella (chickenpox); hepatitis B; measles, mumps, and rubella; and tetanus, diphtheria, and pertussis (whooping cough). The immunization against pertussis is important because of the increasing incidence of that disease in the United States. In recent years, a new pertussis vaccine has been developed that causes fewer side effects in adolescents than the old vaccine. In addition, the Centers for Diseases Control and Prevention (CDC) recommends that all college students receive the meningococcus vaccine as a prevention against meningococcal meningitis. College students, particularly those living in dormitories, are at risk of contracting this bacterial meningitis.

Recommended Immunizations

Birth–4 months	6 months–18 months	4 years–12 years
• Diphtheria, Tetanus, Pertussis	• Diphtheria, Tetanus, Pertussis	• Diphtheria, Tetanus, Pertussis
• *Haemophilus influenzae* type b	• *Haemophilus influenzae* type b	• Polio
• Pneumococcal conjugate	• Pneumococcal conjugate	• Measles, Mumps, Rubella
• Hepatitis B	• Hepatitis A and B	• Meningococcal
• Polio	• Polio	• HPV
	• Varicella	
	• Influenza	
	• Measles, Mumps, Rubella	

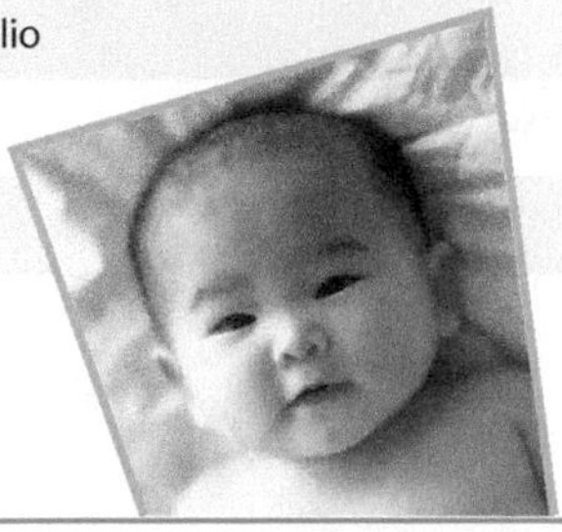

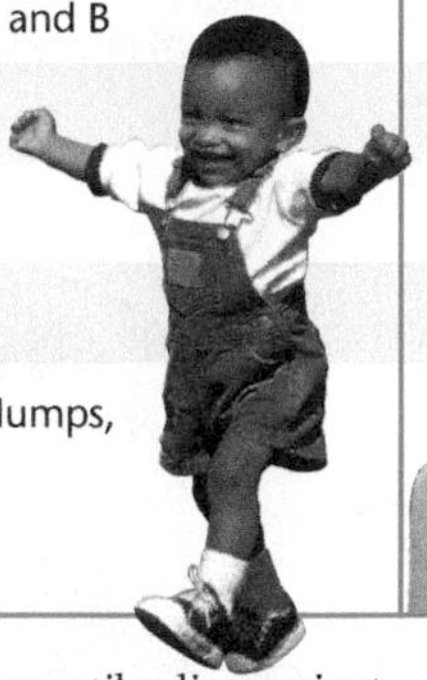

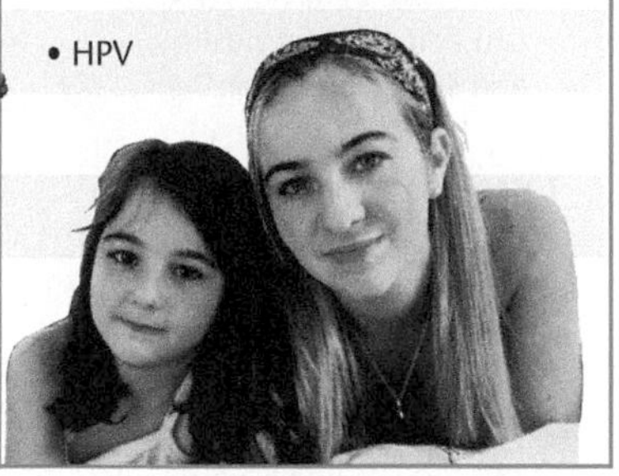

FIGURE 7 Different immunizations are given at different ages. If you missed any of the recommended immunizations, talk to your doctor about catch-up vaccines.

A vaccine causes your immune system to produce antibodies against the pathogen, as if you had actually been infected. You develop immunity without having to experience the disease. After a few years, you may receive a booster dose of some vaccines to "remind" your immune system to maintain your immunity.

Many people need additional immunizations because of the work they do, the places to which they travel, or their exposure to an unusual pathogen. Other people may need to be immunized because of risk factors such as age or poor health. Influenza vaccines, for example, are given to elderly people to protect them from the flu.

Section 2 Review

Key Ideas and Vocabulary

1. Name five physical and chemical defenses that prevent pathogens from entering your body.
2. How does the inflammation process fight an infection in the body?
3. What is a **lymphocyte**?
4. How do the T cells and B cells of your immune system respond to pathogens?
5. How are passive immunity and active immunity similar? How are they different?

Health at School

Immunizations Find out which immunizations are required in order for students to be allowed to attend your school. Your school nurse should have this information. Write a paragraph summarizing your findings. Why do you think these immunizations are required? **WRITING**

Critical Thinking

6. **Applying Concepts** Name two physical defenses that would protect your body against pathogens that might be found in a swimming pool.
7. **Classifying** What type of immunity—passive or active—does a polio vaccine trigger? Explain.

GO ONLINE PearsonSuccessNet.com Audio Summary Section 21.2

L3 Visual Learning: Figure 7

Image Bank Figure 21-7

3. Assess

Evaluate

These assignments can help you assess students' mastery of the section content.

Section 2 Review

Answers appear below.

Teaching Resources
- Practice 21-2
- Section 21-2 Quiz

L2 Reteach

Pair students with partners, and have them make a general outline of the section. They should work together to add vocabulary definitions, boldface key ideas, and examples to the outline. Ask partners to use their detailed outlines to quiz each other on section content.

L4 Enrich

Teaching Resources
- Enrich 21-2

Health at School

Immunizations You may want to collaborate with the school nurse in preparing a handout about which immunizations are required at your school. Introduce the activity by asking students whether they think most students in their school have had the immunizations listed in Figure 7. Then, have students pick up the handout at the nurse's office. After students have summarized their findings and explained why they think immunizations are required, ask volunteers to share their ideas with the class.

Section 2 Review

1. skin, mucous membranes, cilia, saliva and tears, digestive system
2. Within seconds after the body is injured, the damaged cells release chemicals that cause blood vessels to enlarge. Blood, other fluids, and white blood cells called phagocytes leak out of the enlarged vessels. The phagocytes engulf and destroy pathogens.
3. A lymphocyte is a white blood cell that carries out a function of the immune system.
4. Killer T cells destroy any body cell that has been infected by a pathogen. Helper T cells produce chemicals that stimulate other T cells and B cells to fight off infection. B cells produce antibodies.
5. Both involve antibodies that protect the body against infection. In passive immunity, the body receives antibodies from a source other than its own immune system. In active immunity, the body creates the antibodies as a result of having a disease or receiving a vaccine.
6. *Sample answer:* skin and mucous membranes
7. A polio vaccine triggers active immunity; the vaccine causes the body to create antibodies against the pathogen that causes polio.

Infectious Diseases 557

Objectives
Before class begins, write the objectives on the board. Have students copy the objectives into their notebooks at the start of class.

1. Focus

Warm-Up Health Stats

After students complete the writing assignment, call on a few volunteers to read their ideas to the class. Most students will recognize that none of the leading causes of death in 2000 were infectious diseases. The reasons for the change in the causes of death in the United States between 1900 and 2000 include the widespread prevalence of immunizations, better sanitary conditions in most places, and the development of effective medicines against infectious diseases, including antibiotics. You may want to revisit this Warm-Up after students read about treating bacterial diseases.

Presentation 21-3

Sensitive Issues
- Some students may have family members or friends with some of the diseases discussed in this section. Be sure not to imply that people who have any of these diseases have done anything wrong.
- For students whose religious beliefs preclude them from using medicines or seeking medical care, emphasize the importance of practicing healthful behaviors to help avoid getting infectious diseases.

Objectives
▶ **Identify** some diseases caused by bacteria and by viruses.
▶ **Describe** behaviors that can help you get healthy and stay healthy.

Vocabulary
- antibiotic

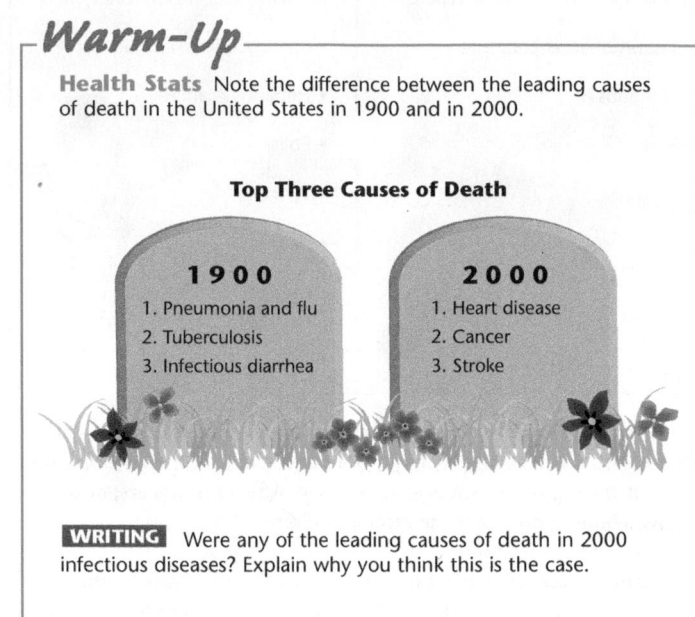

Warm-Up

Health Stats Note the difference between the leading causes of death in the United States in 1900 and in 2000.

Top Three Causes of Death

1900	2000
1. Pneumonia and flu	1. Heart disease
2. Tuberculosis	2. Cancer
3. Infectious diarrhea	3. Stroke

WRITING Were any of the leading causes of death in 2000 infectious diseases? Explain why you think this is the case.

Bacterial Diseases

Despite all your body's defenses, occasionally pathogens are able to enter your body and cause disease. In most cases, your immune system fights the infection and you gradually recover. There are thousands of infectious diseases, and over 40 kinds commonly occur in the United States. **Four infectious diseases caused by bacteria are strep throat, Lyme disease, meningitis, and tuberculosis.**

Strep Throat   A bacterial disease that is common among teens is strep throat. "Strep" is short for *Streptococcus*, the bacterium that causes the disease. Strep bacteria, which are usually found in the nose and throat, can be spread by contact with mucus from an infected person. Symptoms include sore throat, swollen lymph nodes on the sides of the neck, headache, and fever. A fever is a body temperature above 98.6°F and usually indicates that your body is fighting an infection. A doctor can diagnose strep throat by swabbing the back of your throat and identifying the bacteria in the sample.

For Your INFORMATION!

Tuberculosis
The bacterial pathogens that cause tuberculosis (TB) have been infecting humans since the Stone Age. The TB bacteria usually attack the lungs, though the bacteria can attack other parts of the body. Tuberculosis meningitis, for example, can be a deadly bacterial meningitis. Although a third of the world's population is infected with TB, that does not mean they will all become sick. The immune system protects most people who breathe in the bacteria. The bacteria become inactive and live within the body, perhaps becoming active later. Although TB is not as common in the United States as it once was, the disease is a major problem around the In 2011, tuberculosis caused 1.4 million deaths worldwide.

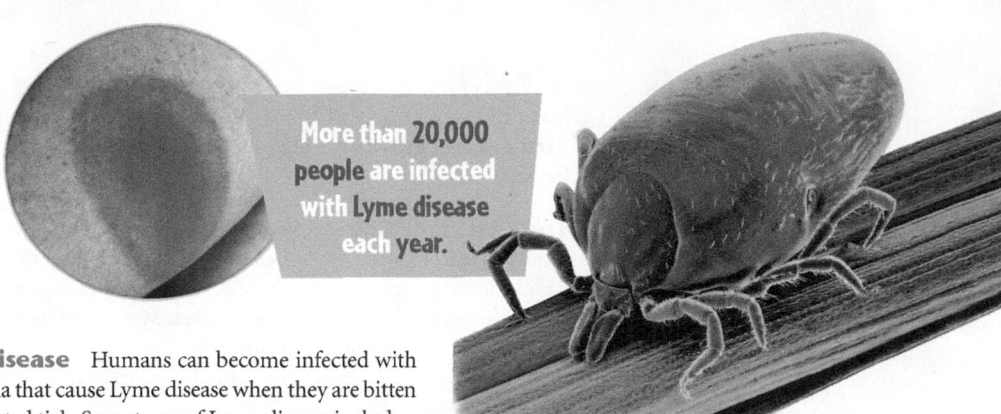

More than 20,000 people are infected with Lyme disease each year.

Lyme Disease   Humans can become infected with the bacteria that cause Lyme disease when they are bitten by an infected tick. Symptoms of Lyme disease include a red rash at the site of the tick bite, fever, chills, and body aches. The best way to protect yourself from Lyme disease is by avoiding tick bites. In wooded areas, wear long-sleeved shirts and long pants, and tuck your pants into your socks.

FIGURE 8   The deer tick can carry the bacteria that cause Lyme disease. One of the symptoms of Lyme disease is a bull's eye-shaped rash that forms at the site of the bite.

Bacterial Meningitis   An infection of the fluid in the spinal cord and the fluid that surrounds the brain is called meningitis. Symptoms of meningitis include high fever, headache, vomiting, and a stiff neck. Anyone who experiences these symptoms should seek medical attention immediately. There are two types of meningitis—one is caused by bacteria, the other by a virus. Bacterial meningitis tends to be more serious than the viral kind. Early treatment of bacterial meningitis is critical to prevent serious illness and death.

Tuberculosis   A highly contagious bacterial infection of the lungs is tuberculosis (too bur kyuh LOH sis), or TB. It is transmitted when droplets from an infected person's cough or sneeze are inhaled. Symptoms, which include fatigue, weight loss, a mild fever, and a constant cough, may not show up for many years after the initial infection. One-third of the world's population is infected with TB, and nearly two million people die of TB each year.

Treating Bacterial Diseases   If your doctor determines that you have a bacterial disease, he or she may treat your infection with an **antibiotic** (an tih by AHT ik), a drug that inhibits or kills bacteria. An antibiotic is a prescription medicine—a medicine that is available only with a written order from a qualified healthcare professional.

Using antibiotics exactly as they are prescribed is very important to prevent bacteria from developing resistance to the medicine. Antibiotic resistance can result if you don't finish your prescription and some of the bacterial pathogens in your body survive. For instance, some TB bacteria have developed antibiotic resistance, making them very difficult to treat.

 **Connect to Your Life**   When was the last time you took an antibiotic? What was it for?

Viral Diseases

L3 Visual Learning: Figure 9

Image Bank Figure 21-9

Have students read through the five stages of the flu. Call on a volunteer to answer the caption question. Ask: **Which days of having the flu are you contagious?** *(Days 4 though 10 you are definitely contagious. Days 11 through 15 you may still be contagious.)* **How many days does it take for symptoms to appear after the virus enters the body?** *(Symptoms appear around the fourth day the virus is in the body.)* **What occurs during the first three days that results in the appearance of flu symptoms?** *(The virus multiplies inside the body.)*

Caption Answer You would be likely to infect others because you are contagious during days 4 and 5.

L1 Cooperative Learning

Divide the class into small groups, and ask each group to create a comic strip that shows a person in the stages of the flu. The comic strip can impart information about each stage through a label at the bottom of each box or through "bubble thoughts" of the cartoon character. Post the completed cartoon strips in the classroom.

L2 Addressing Misconceptions

Causes of Colds Some students may have the misconception that cold weather causes people to get the common cold. The reason that colds are more prevalent in the winter months is because people spend more time indoors, and viruses can spread more easily from one person to another.

Viral Diseases

Some diseases are caused by viruses that enter the body and multiply. **Viral diseases include the common cold, influenza, pneumonia, and hepatitis.**

The Common Cold The common cold is really a group of symptoms caused by different viruses. Soon after exposure to a cold virus, people develop sneezing, sore throats, runny noses, coughing, chest congestion, fever, headaches, and muscle aches. Most colds last three to seven days. Colds spread when a person touches a contaminated object or inhales droplets from a sneeze or a cough. Unfortunately, there is no cure for the common cold.

Influenza The flu, or influenza, is a common viral infection of the upper respiratory system. Like the common cold, influenza is spread by airborne droplets and contact with contaminated objects. Typical symptoms are high fever, sore throat, headache, and a cough. When you have the flu, you will most likely go through the stages shown in Figure 9.

Influenza viruses can cause more serious illness than cold viruses, especially in infants, the elderly, and people with heart and lung diseases. During an average year in the United States, between 3,000 and 49,000 people die of the flu. Some types of influenza can be prevented by an immunization, commonly called a "flu shot." An annual flu shot is especially important for children aged 6 months to 4 years and adults aged 50 and over. Sometimes, antiviral medications can help reduce the severity of the illness for those already infected. Currently, such medications are given only to groups of people at high risk for complications from influenza.

Pneumonia In people who are elderly, or who have heart disease or breathing problems, flu may develop into pneumonia (noo MOHN yuh), a serious infection of the lungs. Many people die each year from pneumonia, which can be caused by viruses, bacteria, or even fungi.

FIGURE 9 The flu usually passes through five stages.
Predicting If you went to school during the fourth or fifth day of your illness, would you be likely to infect others? Explain.

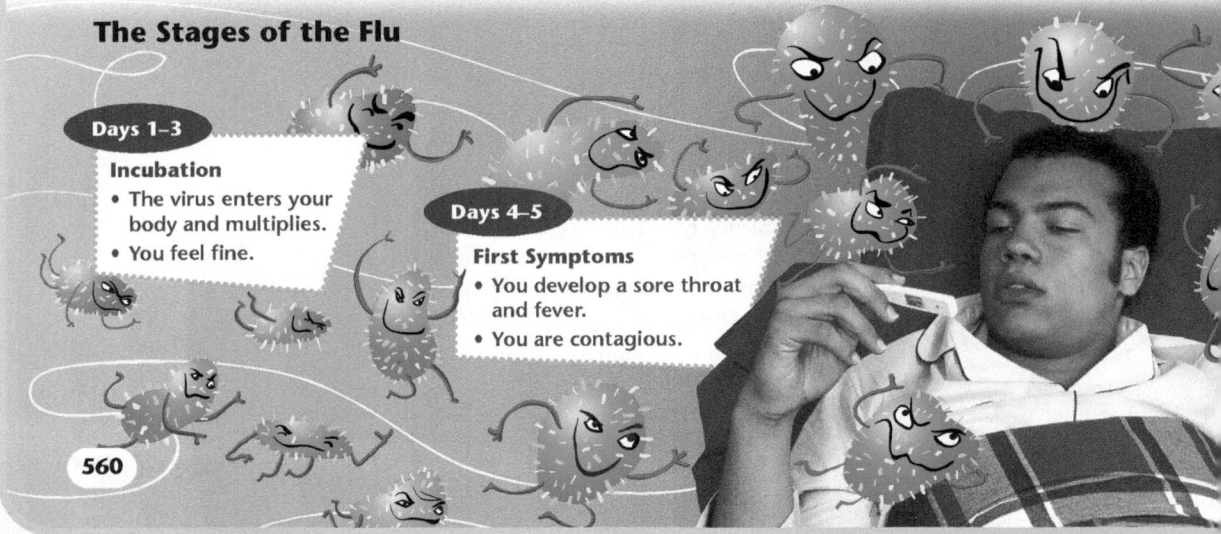

The Stages of the Flu

Days 1–3

Incubation
- The virus enters your body and multiplies.
- You feel fine.

Days 4–5

First Symptoms
- You develop a sore throat and fever.
- You are contagious.

560

Focus on ISSUES

L3 Stay Home or Go?

Have students consider what they would do if they developed symptoms of an infectious disease before an event, such as a big party or an important athletic match. Have students identify their values in relation to deciding whether to go or stay home. For example, it may be more important to some students to protect their health and the health of others than to attend the event. Other students may feel they would not want to miss the event and would go despite their illness. Divide the class into groups based on students' points of view, and have each group come up with a rationale for its position. Each group should present its rationale to the class.

Hepatitis A group of viruses that infect the liver can cause hepatitis (hep uh TY tis), or inflammation of the liver. Because the liver is important to so many bodily functions, hepatitis is a serious disease. Symptoms of hepatitis include fever, nausea, pain in the abdomen, and jaundice (JAWN dis), or yellowing of the skin. People with hepatitis need medical care. The most common types of hepatitis are identified as A, B, or C.

▶ **Hepatitis A** is transmitted in human wastes and in contaminated water and food. Illness begins about four weeks after exposure, and recovery takes several weeks. A vaccine for hepatitis A can effectively prevent the disease.

▶ **Hepatitis B** is more severe than type A. The virus can be transmitted in blood or during sexual contact. It can also be transmitted during tattooing or body piercing if tools are not properly sterilized. Over a million Americans carry hepatitis B, for which there is a vaccine.

▶ **Hepatitis C** is also more severe than type A. Like hepatitis B, it can be transmitted in blood, during sexual contact, or during tattooing or body piercing. Hepatitis C is the number one reason for liver transplants in the United States. Approximately three million Americans carry hepatitis C.

Treating Viral Diseases In most cases, there is no particular medicine that can cure a viral infection. Antibiotics, for instance, are only effective against bacteria—not viruses. Although antiviral medications may shorten the length of infection in some cases, the best treatments for viral infections are rest, a well-balanced diet, and plenty of fluids. In addition, many over-the-counter medicines—those available without a prescription—can treat the symptoms of viral infections. They may make you feel better, but they do not cure the infection.

 **Connect to Your Life** When you have a cold, how do you treat your illness?

 GO ONLINE
PearsonSuccessNet.com
For: More on infectious diseases

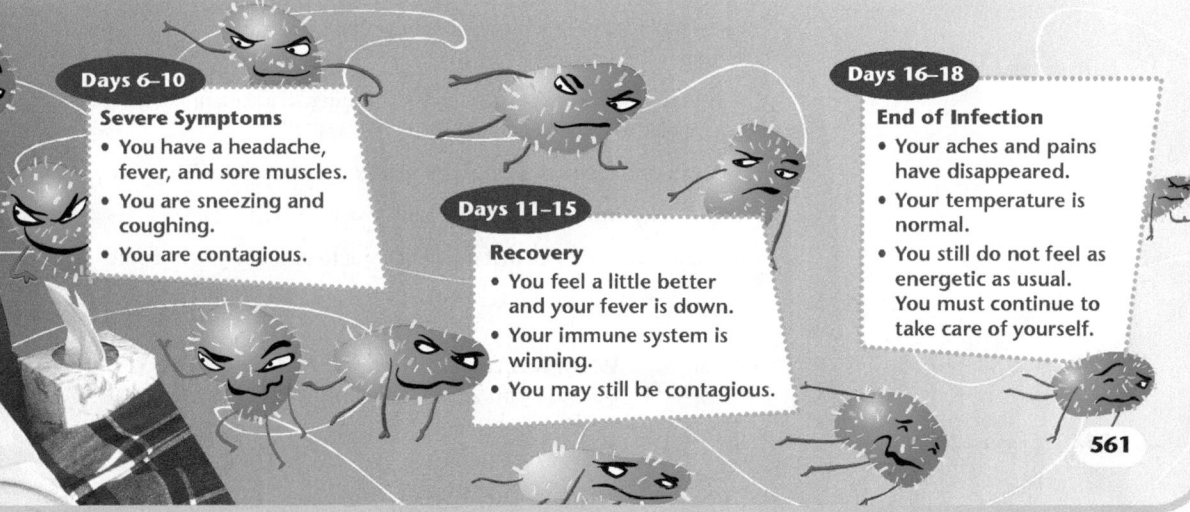

Days 6–10
Severe Symptoms
- You have a headache, fever, and sore muscles.
- You are sneezing and coughing.
- You are contagious.

Days 11–15
Recovery
- You feel a little better and your fever is down.
- Your immune system is winning.
- You may still be contagious.

Days 16–18
End of Infection
- Your aches and pains have disappeared.
- Your temperature is normal.
- You still do not feel as energetic as usual. You must continue to take care of yourself.

561

L3 Content Update GO ONLINE
Visit Pearson SuccessNet to access more information about infectious diseases. Have students complete the Web activity.

L3 Class Discussion
Focus students' attention on the way that hepatitis A is transmitted. Ask: **Which of the four ways that pathogens are spread accounts for the spread of the virus that causes hepatitis A?** *(The virus is spread through contaminated food or water.)* Point out that the virus is often transmitted by human wastes in water used for drinking and cooking. Ask: **What prevents such transmission in your community?** *(The community has a water treatment plant that eliminates most pathogens from the water people use.)* Explain that hepatitis A is a problem in countries where water treatment is lacking and human wastes find their way into the water resources that people use.

L2 Cooperative Learning
Pair students up and have them put together a role-play in which one student is sick and the other is healthy. Have them act out a situation in which the sick student is coughing or sneezing near the healthy student. How does the healthy student react? After all the pairs perform their role-plays, ask the class to evaluate the reactions of the healthy students. Which reactions are most effective for staying healthy?

Connect to Your Life *Sample answer:* I take an over-the-counter cold medicine and try to get a lot of rest.

Differentiated Instruction

L4 Gifted and Talented
Encourage interested students to learn more about the incubation period for each of the bacterial and viral diseases they learn about in Section 3. The incubation period of a disease is the time period between exposure to the pathogen and the onset of symptoms. Ask students to summarize what they learn in a table that they can share with the class.

Getting Healthy, Staying Healthy

Media Wise

Evaluating Antibacterial Products

Explain that many products claim to be antibacterial, including hand soaps, dish soaps, and bathroom cleaners. Advise students to look for such products at home. Make sure students understand that to answer the fifth question about a product they will need to read the label of a similar product that does not advertise itself as antibacterial.

Activity Students may assume that they have the use of sophisticated scientific equipment and can carry out the experiment over an extended period. Students' experiments might focus on testing for the presence of bacteria on hands or surfaces after using an antibacterial product, or they might focus on whether the number of bacterial diseases declines in a household over time if the product is used regularly.

L3 **Building Health Skills**

Setting Goals Have students choose one of the healthful behaviors that would help a person avoid disease, such as frequent hand washing or eating well-balanced meals. Ask each student to set a goal related to that behavior and then develop an action plan to achieve the goal.

L1 **Teacher Demo**

Tell students that washing their hands frequently is important for avoiding infectious disease. Then, demonstrate the proper way to wash hands.
- Wet your hands with warm water and apply soap.
- Rub your hands vigorously for 20 seconds.
- Rinse well and dry your hands with a paper towel.

Connect to Your Life Allow students to answer this question in their private journals.

Media Wise

Evaluating Antibacterial Products

Products claiming to rid your home of pathogens seem to be everywhere. Do you think these products stand up to their claims? Evaluate products claiming to have antibacterial action using this questionnaire.

Does the product claim to inhibit or destroy all pathogens?	Yes No
Does the product seem to be using scare tactics to get you to buy it?	Yes No
Does the product use non-scientific words, such as "germs" or "bugs"?	Yes No
Do the benefits sound too good to be true?	Yes No
Are the ingredients identical to those in non-antibacterial products?	Yes No

A "Yes" answer to one or more questions indicates that the product may not live up to its claims.

Activity Choose a product from a local store that claims to be antibacterial. Devise an experiment to test the effectiveness of the product. **WRITING**

Getting Healthy, Staying Healthy

Infectious diseases are unpleasant at best, but they are part of life. When you do get sick, you can help your body recover by going to bed and resting. This treatment and well-balanced meals are all that you need to recover from most mild infections. However, what if you have a more serious infection? Do you know when to see a doctor?

When to Seek Medical Care If you are worried about your health for any reason, see a doctor and discuss your concerns with him or her. You need to seek professional medical care if you have any of the conditions listed below:

▶ An extremely sore throat, earache, vomiting, diarrhea, or a temperature of 101°F that lasts more than two days

▶ Mucus from your nose or throat that is thick and yellowish green

▶ Difficulty breathing, or severe pain anywhere

▶ A cut, scrape, or sore that does not seem to be healing as it should

▶ An illness that lasts longer than usual

 **Connect to Your Life** When was the last time you had to see a doctor because you weren't feeling well?

MATH and Health

L3 **Converting Units**

Explain that medical professionals, including doctors and nurses, often use the metric temperature scale, Celsius, instead of the Fahrenheit scale. In this section, students learn that they should seek medical care when a temperature of 101°F lasts for more than two days. Have students convert that temperature into a Celsius reading. Explain that to convert Fahrenheit to Celsius, you subtract 32 from the Fahrenheit number, divide that answer by 9, and then multiply that answer by 5. *(101 − 32 = 69; 69 ÷ 9 = 7.7; 7.7 × 5 = 38.5)* Students should calculate that 101°F equals 38.5°C.

Preventing Infectious Diseases You can protect yourself from infectious diseases in three ways: avoiding contact with pathogens, making sure that your immunizations are current, and choosing healthful behaviors. But as you know, it is impossible to avoid all pathogens, and immunizations are not available for all infectious diseases. However, choosing healthful behaviors—the best long-term strategy for preventing disease—is something you can always do.

Here are some healthful behaviors you should practice to help you avoid disease.

▶ Wash your hands several times a day, especially before eating and after using the bathroom (or use hand sanitizer if running water is not available).

▶ Do not share items that can transfer pathogens, such as towels, eating utensils, cups, or hairbrushes.

▶ Cook and store foods properly. Meats should be cooked thoroughly. Keep hot foods hot, and cold foods cold.

▶ Avoid close contact with people who are ill. Stay home when you are not feeling well.

▶ Sneeze into your sleeve or elbow to prevent spraying germs onto others.

▶ Learn to manage stress in healthful ways, and get at least eight hours of sleep each night.

▶ Eat well-balanced meals, and do not skip meals. Exercise regularly, at least three or more times a week.

▶ Avoid unhealthful substances, such as tobacco, alcohol, and illegal drugs.

FIGURE 10 Never share your toothbrush with a friend.

Section 3 Review

Key Ideas and Vocabulary

1. List four bacterial diseases.

2. What is an **antibiotic**? What type of pathogen does it work against?

3. List four viral diseases. Describe how a mild viral infection might be treated.

4. Describe five symptoms that should prompt you to seek medical care.

5. Identify three healthful behaviors that can help you avoid infectious diseases.

Health at School

Good Hygiene Count the number of times you wash your hands at school in one day. Do you wash your hands before eating lunch? Where are sinks with soap and paper towels located? Create a poster to remind students of the importance of hand washing. **WRITING**

Critical Thinking

6. **Evaluating** If you had the flu, how would you try to reduce the chances of spreading it to other members of your family?

7. **Relating Cause and Effect** Children usually have more infectious diseases per year than adults. Why do you think this is so?

🔊 GO ONLINE PearsonSuccessNet.com Audio Summary Section 21.3

Infectious Diseases **563**

---

3. Assess

Evaluate

These assignments can help you assess students' mastery of the section content.

Section 3 Review

Answers appear below.

Teaching Resources
• Practice 21-3
• Section 21-3 Quiz

L2 Reteach

Have students make a compare/contrast table that lists the bacterial and viral diseases discussed in Section 3. The table could have four columns, with the column headings Disease, Type of Pathogen, Symptoms, and Treatment.

L4 Enrich

Teaching Resources
• Enrich 21-3

Health at School

Good Hygiene Introduce the activity by reminding students of how pathogens spread through contact with contaminated objects. Then call on volunteers to answer the question about where soap and paper towels are located. You may want to have pairs of students work together to create a poster that advocates hand washing. Ask students to present their posters to the class, and find places around the school where they can hang their posters.

Section 3 Review

1. strep throat, Lyme disease, meningitis, and tuberculosis

2. An antibiotic is a drug that inhibits or kills bacteria. It works against bacteria.

3. Viral diseases include the common cold, influenza, pneumonia, and hepatitis. The best treatments for a mild viral infection are rest, a well-balanced diet, and plenty of fluids. Over-the-counter medicines can treat the symptoms of a viral infection.

4. *Sample answer:* an extremely sore throat that lasts more than two days; mucus from the nose that is thick and yellowish green; difficulty breathing; a sore that does not seem to be healing as it should; an illness that lasts longer than usual

5. *Sample answer:* wash your hands several times a day; avoid close contact with people who are ill; eat well-balanced meals

6. *Sample answer:* I would wash my hands several times a day, cover my mouth and nose when coughing or sneezing, and avoid close contact with family members.

7. *Sample answer:* Children are usually around other children every day; children often do not practice good personal hygiene.

Infectious Diseases **563**

Using Medicines Correctly

Objective

Demonstrate the ability to use a medicine correctly by reading the directions on the medicine label.

Teaching Strategies

Image Bank Page 564

- Explain that as students begin to take charge of their own health, they need to be aware of the importance of using medicines correctly. Learning this skill can help students figure out what a medicine is supposed to do, what the directions for use are, and what the side effects are.

- Provide students with more practice in using the guidelines by bringing to class a variety of prescription labels on empty medicine bottles. (Before presenting bottles to students, mark out the names of the patients and the doctors.) For each label, have students complete question 1 in Practice the Skill. After students have examined the label, lead a class discussion about what students found interesting or surprising on the labels.

- Ask students when the side effects of a prescription medicine should be reported to a doctor. *(immediately)* Explain that some medicines have side effects for almost everyone who takes them. Point out that for serious conditions, putting up with minor side effects may be necessary in order to gain the benefits of the medicine. Explain that it is important to discuss any side effects with a doctor because the doctor may be able to change the dosage or change the medicine to one with fewer side effects.

- Suggest that students get permission from their parents or guardians to investigate the medicine cabinets at home. Encourage students to make a list of any medicines that have expired, are improperly stored, or are the remaining portions of old prescriptions. Ask students to discuss their findings with their parents or guardians and then—with permission—take any corrective actions that seem necessary.

Using Medicines Correctly

Felicia got home from her after-school job, ate dinner, and sat down to study. All of a sudden, she realized she had forgotten to take an antibiotic tablet earlier that day. Her doctor had prescribed the antibiotic for her strep throat. Should Felicia take two tablets now to make up for the one she missed? Or should she take just one tablet now?

To be safe and effective, medicines must be used according to their directions. When should you use a medicine, and how can you make sure that you use it correctly? These guidelines will help you decide.

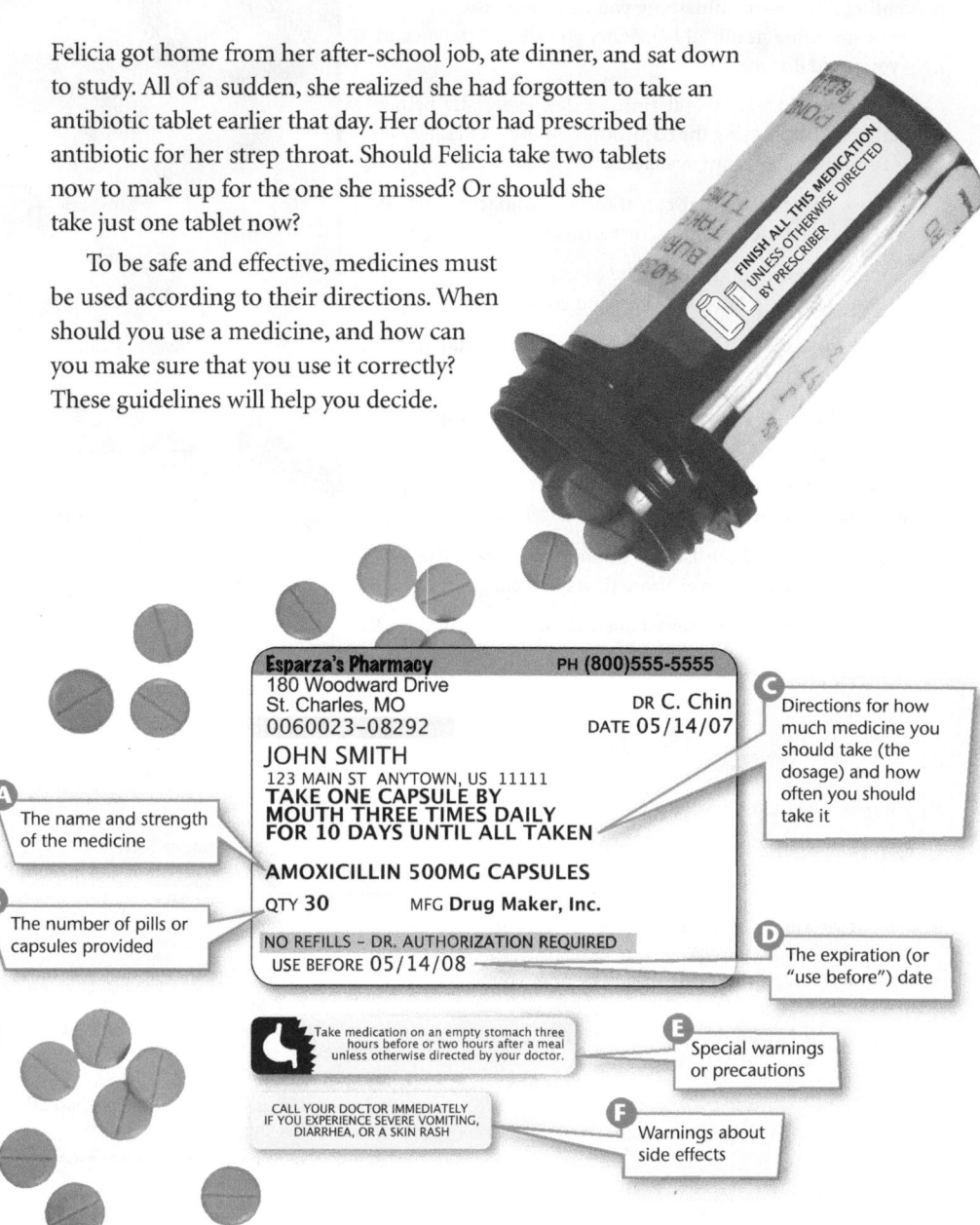

Esparza's Pharmacy   PH (800)555-5555
180 Woodward Drive
St. Charles, MO
0060023-08292   DR C. Chin   DATE 05/14/07
JOHN SMITH
123 MAIN ST ANYTOWN, US 11111
TAKE ONE CAPSULE BY MOUTH THREE TIMES DAILY FOR 10 DAYS UNTIL ALL TAKEN
AMOXICILLIN 500MG CAPSULES
QTY **30**   MFG **Drug Maker, Inc.**
NO REFILLS – DR. AUTHORIZATION REQUIRED
USE BEFORE 05/14/08

A The name and strength of the medicine

B The number of pills or capsules provided

C Directions for how much medicine you should take (the dosage) and how often you should take it

D The expiration (or "use before") date

Take medication on an empty stomach three hours before or two hours after a meal unless otherwise directed by your doctor.

E Special warnings or precautions

CALL YOUR DOCTOR IMMEDIATELY IF YOU EXPERIENCE SEVERE VOMITING, DIARRHEA, OR A SKIN RASH

F Warnings about side effects

564

Sensitive Issues

Make sure that students obtain permission from their parents or guardians before examining the contents of the home medicine cabinet. Some parents and guardians may object to the activity as an invasion of their privacy. Tell students that no action should be taken without a prior discussion with a responsible adult.

① Read all the information on the label and follow the directions.

▶ Be sure to take your medicine as prescribed. Keep a record of the times when you take your medicine.

▶ If you forget to take your medicine at a scheduled time, do not take a double dose to try to make up for it. Take a single dose and get back on the original schedule. If you miss more than one dose, consult with your doctor or pharmacist.

▶ With an antibiotic, continue taking it until you have used all of it. If you do not finish the entire prescription, your infection may return.

② Only take medicines prescribed for you.

Medicines are prescribed according to factors that are specific to each person, such as age, weight, health conditions, and other medicines being taken. It is dangerous to use medicines prescribed for another person.

③ Call your doctor if a medicine causes serious side effects.

All medicines have side effects, some more serious than others. Side effects might include headache, dizziness, drowsiness, and nausea. Common allergic reactions to medicines include a skin rash, runny nose, breathing difficulties, and rapid heartbeat. If you develop serious side effects, contact your doctor or a hospital emergency room immediately.

④ Never combine medicines without checking with your doctor.

Sometimes it is necessary to use different medicines at the same time to treat a single problem or to treat several problems. Not all medicines, however, can be used in combination with each other. Before you start using more than one medicine at a time, check with your doctor or pharmacist.

⑤ Never drink alcohol while taking medicines.

Alcohol and medicines can be a dangerous, or even deadly, combination. Anyone taking medicines should avoid alcohol.

⑥ Store medicines according to the label's instructions.

▶ Keep medicines in their original containers so that their directions for use, precautions, and expiration dates are always known. Keep medicines out of the reach of children.

▶ Many medicines lose their effectiveness over time and should not be used after their expiration date. Dispose of medicines properly so they are kept away from children and animals.

Practice the Skill

1. Study the prescription medicine label on the facing page and answer these questions.
   - What medicine has been prescribed?
   - What is the dosage?
   - How often should the person take the medicine?
   - Should this medicine be taken with meals?
   - Are there specific foods or fluids that should not be taken with this medicine?
   - Should the person stop taking the medicine as soon as symptoms of the illness disappear?

2. At your local drugstore, read the label of an over-the-counter medicine, such as aspirin or a cold-relief medicine. What is the medicine used for? What warnings or cautions are on the label? What is the recommended dosage? Under what conditions should you consult a doctor?

Practice the Skill

1. The medicine is amoxicillin 500-mg capsules. The dosage is one capsule. The person should take one capsule by mouth three times daily for 10 days until all are taken. The medicine should not be taken with meals. There are no specific foods or fluids that should not be taken with this medicine. The person should take the medicine for 10 days without regard to the symptoms.

2. Answers will vary depending on the medicine. Students will find that a typical over-the-counter medicine label will be divided into several sections, including Indications, Directions, Ingredients, and Warnings. The Indications section provides information about what the medicine is used for. The Warnings section often ends with the conditions for which a doctor should be consulted. Have students record the information on an aspirin or cold-medicine label. Call on volunteers in class to share what they found.

Health and Community

⑫ A Pharmacist's Advice

The role of a pharmacist is not only to fill prescriptions written by doctors but also to provide consumers with accurate information about medicines, including over-the-counter medicines. Encourage students to visit a local pharmacy—such as in a major drug store or grocery store—and ask a pharmacist for advice about over-the-counter cold medicines. A student might ask which over-the-counter medicine is most effective and has the fewest side effects. Students should write down the pharmacist's advice. In class, call on volunteers to share the advice they were given.

Objectives

Before class begins, write the objectives on the board. Have students copy the objectives into their notebooks at the start of class.

1. Focus

Warm-Up Health Stats

Explain that dengue fever is a serious disease that affects 50–100 million people each year. The disease causes death in about 2.5 percent of cases. After students answer the question, call on volunteers to read their explanations to the class. Many students may conclude that the United States should be concerned because the map shows that dengue fever has greatly spread throughout the world after 1960. Ask students to speculate about the reasons why dengue fever has emerged as a threat in the last several decades.

Presentation 21-4

2. Teach

L3 **EL** Reading/Note Taking 21-4

L2 Adapted Reading/Note Taking 21-4

What Is an Emerging Disease?

EL Building Vocabulary

Analyze the word *emerge* so that students will have a better understanding of the concept. Explain that the prefix *e-* comes from a Latin word meaning "out," and that the word part *merge* comes from a Latin word meaning "to plunge." The word *emerge,* then, literally means "to plunge out." In this context, *emerge* means "to crop up, or come into existence."

Objectives

▶ **Define** the term *emerging disease.*

▶ **Identify** five reasons why diseases emerge.

Vocabulary

• epidemic
• emerging disease

Warm-Up

Health Stats The map shows how dengue fever, a viral disease carried by mosquitoes, has spread since 1960.

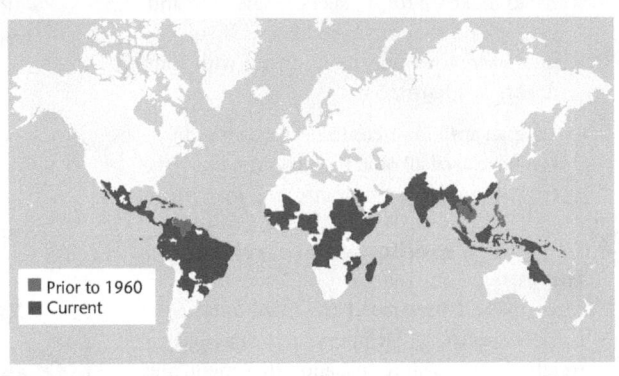

■ Prior to 1960
■ Current

WRITING Should the United States be concerned about dengue fever? Explain.

What Is an Emerging Disease?

In the winter of 1918, just as World War I was coming to an end, an influenza virus spread around the globe. Unlike previous flu viruses, this one was especially deadly. More than 20 million people died from the flu between 1918 and 1919, including almost 700,000 Americans.

The deadly flu outbreak of 1918 is an example of an epidemic. An **epidemic** (ep uh DEM ik) is an unusually high occurrence of a disease in a certain place during a certain time period. When an epidemic affects many areas of the world, as the 1918 flu outbreak did, it is sometimes called a *pandemic.*

You have probably heard news reports about epidemics of various diseases occurring today. Some of the diseases are known as **emerging diseases. An emerging disease is an infectious disease that has become increasingly common in humans within the last 20 years or threatens to become more common in the near future.** Figure 11 describes some emerging diseases that scientists are currently monitoring around the world.

For Your **INFORMATION!**

Avian Flu

Influenza viruses occur naturally in birds. Most avian (bird) flu viruses do not infect humans. The main route of human infection by bird flu is when domesticated poultry are infected and the humans who are in close contact with the poultry become infected. In the 1990s, the first human cases of a new type of avian flu (influenza A virus subtype H5N1) were reported in Hong Kong. By 2006, over 100 human cases had been reported in Asia and the Middle East, with some deaths. Scientists feared the virus would mutate enough to spread easily from human to human. If that happened, the flu could quickly become a pandemic, because no one would have immunity to the virus. This is what occurred in the 1918 flu pandemic, also caused by an avian flu virus.

Why Do Diseases Emerge?

Emerging diseases are a reminder that the human immune system is in a never-ending battle with pathogens. No matter how many medicines or vaccines are developed, certain pathogens will cause disease anyway.

A number of different factors are responsible for emerging diseases around the world. **Diseases can emerge when humans come into contact with infected animals; pathogens become resistant to existing drugs; or people lack appropriate immunizations.** In addition, the increased frequency of international travel and a global food supply can enable emerging diseases to spread very quickly.

Contact With Infected Animals Some diseases that are common in animals can spread to humans. For example, avian flu is caused by a virus that infects certain birds. There have been recent cases in Asia in which people have become sick after being exposed to infected birds. Even more worrisome is that a high percentage of those who got sick died. Some scientists fear that another deadly flu epidemic could result if the virus takes on a form that can spread easily between people.

GO ONLINE

PearsonSuccessNet.com
For: More on modern epidemics

FIGURE 11 Several viral diseases threaten to become more common. There are no specific treatments for these diseases.

Viral Diseases to Watch

Disease	How Spread	Where	Symptoms	Prevention
Avian flu	Close contact with an infected bird; person-to-person transmission may become possible	Asia	Severe, flu-like symptoms	Vaccines in development; avoiding close contact with birds and poultry farms
SARS (Severe Acute Respiratory Syndrome)	Droplet inhalation from an infected person's cough or sneeze	Currently contained in Asia	High fever, headache, body aches, dry cough, pneumonia	Frequent hand washing
Yellow fever	Bite from an infected mosquito	Africa, South America, Caribbean islands	Fever, muscle pain, headache, nausea, jaundice	Vaccine; avoiding mosquito bites; mosquito control
Dengue fever	Bite from an infected mosquito	Widespread throughout many tropical and sub-tropical regions (see map on facing page)	High fever, severe headache, joint and muscle pain, vomiting	Vaccines in development; avoiding mosquito bites; mosquito control
West Nile virus	Bite from an infected mosquito	United States, Africa, Australia, Europe, the Middle East, and West Asia	Fever, headache, body aches, nausea, vomiting, muscle weakness, vision loss	Avoiding mosquito bites; mosquito control

◀ **West Nile mosquito**

Infectious Diseases **567**

Differentiated Instruction

L2 Less Proficient Readers

To reinforce understanding of emerging diseases, divide the class into pairs, matching less proficient readers with students who have shown a grasp of the main concepts related to emerging diseases.

Ask the paired students to quiz each other on the details of emerging diseases, using both the text and Figure 11 as resources for questions.

Why Do Diseases Emerge?

L3 Content Update

Use the Web Code to access up-to-date information on modern epidemics. Have students complete the Web activity.

L2 Visual Learning: Figure 11

Have students read about the viral diseases to watch listed in the table. Ask: **Why do you think that several viral diseases are prominent among the emerging diseases?** *(Sample answer: In most cases, there is no particular medicine that can cure a viral disease.)* **Which of these diseases are spread by infected animals?** *(avian flu, yellow fever, dengue fever, and West Nile virus)* Focus students' attention on the information about dengue fever, and then have them think again about their answer to the Warm-Up question. Ask: **Given this information, do you think all of the United States should be concerned about dengue fever?** *(Sample answer: The disease is widespread throughout many tropical and subtropical regions. Therefore, only subtropical regions of the United States, such as Florida, need to be concerned about the disease.)*

L3 Cultural Connection

Point out that avian flu is spread by close contact with an infected bird. Ask: **Do most people in the United States normally have close contact with birds?** *(no)* Explain that in countries where people have a more traditional way of life, domesticated birds such as chickens are kept close to the household. In their daily lives, these people normally have much more contact with birds than do most Americans. Point out that this is one reason why avian flu has emerged in Asian countries.

L3 Building Media Literacy

Ask students to recall news reports they have heard recently about the spread of an infectious disease. How did the news media portray the threat? Was more than one point of view presented? Remind students that no one report should cause them to panic. Reading and listening to different news sources can help them gain a fuller understanding of how much of a threat an infectious disease poses to the United States.

3. Assess

Evaluate

These assignments can help you assess students' mastery of the section content.

Section 4 Review

Answers appear below.

Teaching Resources

- Practice 21-4
- Section 21-4 Quiz

 Reteach

Ask students to write a two- or three-paragraph newspaper article that would inform the public about what emerging diseases are, why diseases emerge, and which diseases threaten to become more common.

L4 Enrich

Teaching Resources

- Enrich 21-4

Health and Community

Flu Season Encourage students to contact the local health department or a doctor's office to find out where community flu shots are offered and for which groups flu shots are recommended. (Typically, flu shots are recommended for small children, the elderly, people with respiratory diseases, and people with compromised immune systems.) Call on volunteers to share what they have found with the class. Then, have individual students create a brief announcement that includes the relevant information written in a way that would catch a reader's attention.

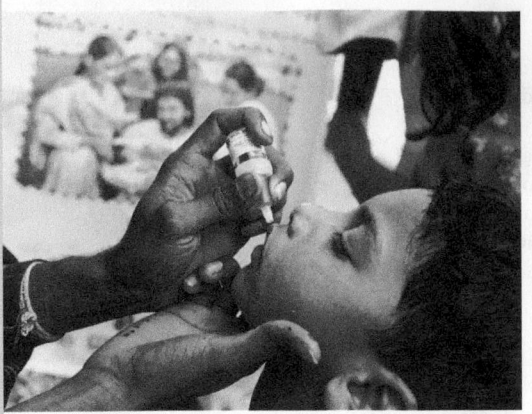

FIGURE 12 Health officials in India hope to eradicate polio by giving an oral vaccine to all children under age five.

Drug Resistance Some diseases are caused by pathogens that can mutate, or change, over time. Sometimes these mutations result in a strain, or type, of pathogen that no longer responds to medicine. As mentioned earlier, some strains of tuberculosis are antibiotic resistant. Thus, people who become infected with a resistant strain cannot be treated with existing antibiotics and can spread the disease to others.

Lack of Immunization Diseases that were common many years ago can pose a threat again if people don't get the proper immunizations. For example, polio was nearly eliminated 50 years ago by an effective vaccine. But the polio virus remains a threat in several Asian and African countries because many people in those countries have not received the vaccine.

International Travel You may have heard the term *globalization*. That term refers to the fact that people around the world are no longer geographically isolated from each other. In a 12-hour plane ride, you could be on the other side of the world. Not only can people travel much more easily, but so can any pathogens that live in their bodies. This is one reason that globalization is a concern when disease outbreaks occur. World travelers could spread the pathogen around the world in a short amount of time.

Global Food Supply Food also travels all over the world. For example, you may have eaten an apple from China or a mango from Mexico. If a pathogen is present in a food product, it can spread quickly.

An infectious disease known as mad cow disease caused a global food scare when contaminated beef was distributed to several countries. A number of people who ate the beef became very sick. Cattle and meat are closely monitored to make sure that mad cow disease does not enter the global food supply again.

Section 4 Review

Key Ideas and Vocabulary

1. What is an **epidemic**?
2. Explain what is meant by the term *emerging disease*. Give an example of an emerging disease.
3. List five factors that contribute to the development of emerging diseases.

Critical Thinking

4. **Relating Cause and Effect** Federal agencies closely monitor meats and produce that are brought into the United States from other countries. Why is this important?

Health and Community

Flu Season Find out where in your community flu shots are offered. For what groups of people are the flu shots recommended? Create an announcement for your local newspaper detailing the information about flu shots for people in your community. **WRITING**

5. **Predicting** If you were traveling from a country with high rates of yellow fever, you could not enter some other countries without proof of a yellow fever vaccination. Predict what might happen if vaccinations were not required.

🔊 **GO ONLINE** PearsonSuccessNet.com | Audio Summary Section 21.4

Section 4 Review

1. An epidemic is an unusually high occurrence of a disease in a certain place during a certain time period.
2. An emerging disease is an infectious disease that has become increasingly common in humans within the last 20 years or threatens to become more common in the near future. Avian flu is an example of an emerging disease.
3. contact with infected animals, drug resistance, lack of immunization, international travel, and global food supply
4. Pathogens may be present in meats and produce, and they could spread quickly in the United States.
5. *Sample answer:* If vaccinations were not required, people infected with yellow fever could enter another country, and the disease could spread to the people of that country.

Chapter 21
At a Glance

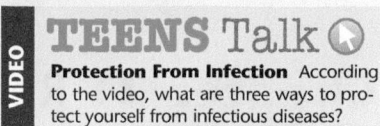

VIDEO **TEENS Talk**
Protection From Infection According to the video, what are three ways to protect yourself from infectious diseases?

Section 1   Understanding Infectious Diseases

Key Ideas

▶ Pathogens can cause an infectious disease when they enter your body and multiply.

▶ Pathogens can spread through contact with an infected person; an infected animal; contaminated objects; or contaminated food, soil, or water.

Vocabulary
- infectious disease (548)
- microorganism (548)
- pathogen (548)
- bacteria (548) • toxin (548)
- virus (549) • fungi (549)
- protozoan (549)

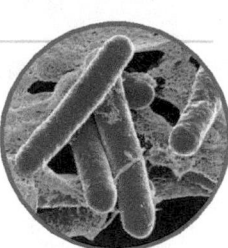

Section 2   Defenses Against Disease

Key Ideas

▶ Your body's first line of defense against infectious disease includes both physical and chemical defenses that prevent pathogens from entering your body.

▶ Inflammation is your body's general response to all kinds of injury.

▶ The immune system fights disease by producing a separate set of weapons for each kind of pathogen it encounters.

▶ Passive immunity is acquired by receiving antibodies from outside your own immune system. Active immunity results from having a disease or from receiving a vaccine.

Vocabulary
- mucous membrane (553) • inflammation (554)
- phagocyte (554) • immune system (554)
- lymphocyte (554) • immunity (554) • T cell (555)
- B cell (555) • antibody (555) • lymphatic system (556)
- immunization (556) • vaccine (556)

Section 3   Common Infectious Diseases

Key Ideas

▶ Bacterial diseases include strep throat, Lyme disease, meningitis, and tuberculosis.

▶ Viral diseases include the common cold, influenza, pneumonia, and hepatitis.

▶ You can protect yourself from infectious diseases in three ways: avoiding contact with pathogens, making sure that your immunizations are current, and choosing healthful behaviors.

Vocabulary
- antibiotic (559)

Section 4   Emerging Infectious Diseases

Key Ideas

▶ An emerging disease is an infectious disease that has recently become more common or could become more common in the near future.

▶ Diseases can emerge when humans come into contact with infected animals; pathogens become drug-resistant; or people lack immunizations.

▶ International travel and a global food supply also can enable emerging diseases to spread.

Vocabulary
- epidemic (566) • emerging disease (566)

Infectious Diseases **569**

Chapter 21
At a Glance

VIDEO **Protection From Infection** Ask for volunteers to share their answers. Use examples from the video to review strategies for avoiding infectious diseases.

Key Ideas Review

L2 Have students rewrite each of the major headings in each section into questions and then answer those questions. For example, the heading Causes of Infectious Diseases can be rewritten as What are the causes of infectious diseases? Students should find answers in the text for any questions they have trouble answering.

L3 Divide the class into small groups, and ask each group to brainstorm a list of challenging questions that cover each of the sections' objectives. Then, have members of each group work together to answer the questions devised by another group.

Vocabulary Review

EL Have students make flashcards to review chapter vocabulary. They should write each term on one side of an index card and the definition and an example of the term on the other side. Pair students, and have partners quiz each other using the flashcards.

L2 Ask each student to write two multiple-choice questions for each section in the chapter. Tell students the questions should focus on the vocabulary of each section. Then pair students, and have partners answer each other's questions.

Chapter 21 Review

 GO ONLINE

PearsonSuccessNet.com

Students can go online for a review activity on Chapter 21.

Reviewing Key Ideas

Section 1

1. c

2. *Sample answer:* malaria

3. Pathogens can be spread from person to person on objects. If you drink from a drinking glass used by an infected person, you can become infected too.

4. Not all microorganisms are pathogens. Most bacteria, for example, are not pathogens.

Section 2

5. b

6. Phagocytes engulf and destroy pathogens.

7. B cells

8. A vaccine causes the immune system to produce antibodies against a particular pathogen. A person develops immunity without having to experience the disease.

9. B cells continue to circulate through the body even after the infection is gone. When the same pathogen is encountered again, those B cells are ready to produce antibodies against the pathogen. T cells also have a memory capacity.

10. Normal T cells destroy only body cells that have been infected by a pathogen, not healthy body cells.

Section 3

11. d

12. Hepatitis affects the liver. A virus causes hepatitis.

13. If your immunizations are current, you have active immunity against many serious diseases.

14. *Sample answer:* During the winter, people often spend their days inside with other people. In such situations, influenza is spread more easily by airborne droplets and contact with contaminated objects.

Chapter 21 Review

Reviewing Key Ideas

 GO ONLINE

PearsonSuccessNet.com

For: Chapter 21 review activity

Section 1

1. Infectious diseases are caused by
   a. phagocytes.   b. cilia.
   c. pathogens.   d. vaccines.

2. Give an example of a disease caused by a protozoan.

3. Why is it not a good idea to share a drinking glass with someone?

4. **Critical Thinking** Do you think that all microorganisms are pathogens? Explain your answer.

Section 2

5. White blood cells that carry out most of the immune system's functions are called
   a. antibodies.   b. lymphocytes.
   c. vaccines.   d. antibiotics.

6. What role do phagocytes play in inflammation?

7. What types of cells produce antibodies?

8. Explain how a vaccine can make you immune to a particular infectious disease.

9. **Critical Thinking** How does your immune system "remember" a particular pathogen?

10. **Critical Thinking** Multiple sclerosis is a disease in which T cells attack parts of the central nervous system. How are these T cells acting differently from normal T cells?

Section 3

11. Antibiotics are usually prescribed for diseases caused by
    a. viruses.   b. protozoans.
    c. fungi.   d. bacteria.

12. What part of the body does hepatitis affect? What type of pathogen causes hepatitis?

13. Why is it important to make sure that your immunizations are current?

14. **Critical Thinking** More people get the flu during the winter months than at any other time of year. Why do you think this is true?

Section 4

15. An epidemic refers to a disease that
    a. affects very few people.
    b. affects many people in one area.
    c. is caused by bacteria.
    d. doesn't spread.

16. Explain how antibiotic resistance could lead to a bacterial disease epidemic.

17. **Critical Thinking** During the SARS outbreak of 2003, the World Health Organization issued a warning against traveling to countries where SARS was present. Explain why this warning was issued.

 ## Building Health Skills

18. **Practicing Healthful Behaviors** Sometimes, over-the-counter medicines that you might take for a cold or the flu can make you feel well enough to go about your usual routine even though your body is still fighting the infection. Why might this be a problem?

19. **Analyzing Risks and Benefits** Matt's doctor prescribed an antibiotic for his skin infection. One of his friends has a similar looking sore on his arm. Should Matt share his medicine with his friend? Why or why not?

20. **Accessing Information** A friend is going to the pharmacy to pick up a prescription medicine. Write down a list of questions that she should ask the pharmacist about the medicine. **WRITING**

21. **Setting Goals** Make a list of things you do that put you at risk for infectious diseases. Choose two items from your list and set goals for lessening your risk. Monitor your behavior over the next week to see how you did.

Health and Community

Prevention Poster Evaluate the risk of getting Lyme disease or West Nile virus in your community. Prepare a poster that warns people about the risk and offers tips about how to avoid getting bitten by ticks or mosquitoes. **WRITING**

Section 4

15. b

16. People infected with a resistant strain of a bacterial disease cannot be treated with antibiotics and can spread the disease to others. As more people become infected, an epidemic could occur.

17. *Sample answer:* SARS is spread by droplet inhalation from an infected person's cough or sneeze. A traveler to countries where SARS is present could contract the disease by inhaling the pathogens.

Building Health Skills

18. *Sample answer:* Going about your usual routine could use energy that the body needs to fight the infection. As a result, the infection could become worse.

19. *Sample answer:* Matt should not share his medicine with his friend because the friend's sore must be diagnosed by a doctor in order to be treated correctly.

Standardized Test Prep

Math Practice

The graph below compares the amount of time it takes the immune system to produce antibodies upon first exposure to a pathogen and upon second exposure to the same pathogen. Use the graph to answer Questions 22–25.

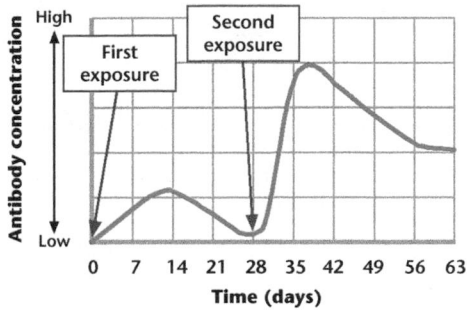

22. The first exposure to the pathogen generated
 A more antibodies than the second exposure.
 B fewer antibodies than the second exposure.
 C the same number of antibodies as the second exposure.
 D no antibodies.

23. The second exposure occurred how many days after the first?
 F 14 days
 G 21 days
 H 28 days
 J 30 days

24. The amount of time for the antibody concentration to reach its peak after the first exposure was
 A 4 days.
 B 6 days.
 C 8 days.
 D 12 days.

25. The amount of time for the antibody concentration to reach its peak after the second exposure was
 F 4 days.
 G 8 days.
 H 12 days.
 J 14 days.

Reading and Writing Practice

Read the passage. Then answer Questions 26–29.

The social, economic, and human toll exacted by malaria globally is widespread and profound. Each year, acute malaria occurs in more than 300 million people and results in more than one million deaths worldwide. Malaria is caused by one of four species of *Plasmodium,* a single-cell parasite transmitted by mosquitoes. Drug-resistant *Plasmodium* strains are widespread, as are insecticide-resistant strains of the mosquitoes that carry the parasites.

26. *Plasmodium* is
 A a type of mosquito.
 B a type of insecticide.
 C a parasite.
 D a malaria drug.

27. In this passage, the word *exacted* means
 F decreased.
 G preserved.
 H survived.
 J harmed.

28. According to the passage, which of these statements is true?
 A Malaria is decreasing worldwide.
 B About 0.33% of those who get malaria die from the disease.
 C Insecticide-resistant mosquitoes don't carry the *Plasmodium* parasite.
 D All types of malaria can be treated with drugs.

Constructed Response

29. In a paragraph, explain how drug resistance relates to the spread of malaria.

> ### Test-Taking Tip
>
> In the days leading up to a test, stay healthy by getting plenty of rest and eating balanced meals.

Standardized Test Prep

Math Practice
22. B
23. H
24. D
25. G

Reading and Writing Practice
26. C
27. J
28. B
29. Students' answers will vary. A good answer will explain what drug resistance is, identify *Plasmodium* as the pathogen that causes malaria, and point out that drug-resistant *Plasmodium* strains are widespread. Students should conclude that drug resistance contributes to the spread of malaria because those infected with a drug-resistant strain cannot be easily treated and thus are likely to spread the disease indirectly when they are bitten by mosquitoes and those mosquitoes then bite other people.

---

20. Students should list questions that focus on how the medicine should be used and what the side effects are.

21. Students should list several behaviors, such as sharing drinking containers and not eating well-balanced meals. Students should choose two behaviors for which to set goals and monitor over the next week.

Health and Community

Prevention Poster The risk of getting Lyme disease or West Nile virus will vary according to the students' region. Students may want to check with a local health department. You may want to have students work in small groups to make their posters.

CHAPTER 22 Sexually Transmitted Infections and AIDS

Section Objectives	Standards Correlation	Instructional Resources ⓛ₃	SE eTEXT	TE eTEXT	PRINT
1 **The Risks of Sexual Activity** ⏱ 1 period; 1/2 block **22.1.1 Identify** risky behaviors associated with the current epidemic of sexually transmitted infections. **22.1.2 Describe** behaviors that can help prevent the spread of sexually transmitted infections.	NHES: 1.12.8, 1.12.9, 2.12.3, 3.12.1, 4.12.2, 7.12.3, 8.12.1	SE Warm-Up, p. 574	•	•	•
		RN Note Taking Guide 22-1	•	•	•
		IB Image Bank 22-1		•	
		TR Practice 22-1		•	
		TR Section 22-1 Quiz		•	
2 **Kinds of STIs** ⏱ 2 periods; 1 block **22.2.1 Identify** three of the most common STIs, including their symptoms and treatments. **22.2.2 List** four other STIs and describe their symptoms. **22.2.3 Know** when a person should seek treatment for an STI.	NHES: 1.12.9, 3.12.1, 3.12.2, 3.12.3, 3.12.5, 8.12.1	SE Warm-Up, p. 578	•	•	•
		RN Note Taking Guide 22-2	•	•	•
		TR Practice 22-2		•	
		TR Section 22-2 Quiz		•	
3 **HIV and AIDS** ⏱ 2 periods; 1 block **22.3.1 Explain** how HIV infection leads to AIDS. **22.3.2 Describe** how HIV is transmitted from person to person. **22.3.3 Summarize** the state of HIV infection and AIDS throughout the world.	NHES: 1.12.8, 1.12.9, 2.12.10, 8.12.3, 8.12.4	SE Warm-Up, p. 584	•	•	•
		SE Hands-On Activity How Quickly Can HIV Spread?, p. 586	•	•	•
		RN Note Taking Guide 22-3	•	•	•
		IB Image Bank 22-9, 22-12		•	
		TR Practice 22-3		•	
		TR Section 22-3 Quiz		•	
(BUILDING HEALTH SKILLS) **Evaluating Internet Sources** ⏱ 1 period; 1/2 block **BHS.22 Evaluate** Internet sources to access reliable health information.	NHES: 2.12.6, 3.12.1, 3.12.5	SE Practice the Skill, p. 591	•	•	•
		RN Building Health Skills 22	•	•	•
4 **Protecting Yourself From HIV and AIDS** ⏱ 1 period; 1/2 block **22.4.1 Identify** three behaviors that can prevent the spread of HIV. **22.4.2 Describe** how a person gets tested for HIV. **22.4.3 Describe** the goal of HIV treatment.	NHES: 1.12.1, 1.12.8, 3.12.5, 5.12.7, 7.12.2, 7.12.3, 8.12.1, 8.12.4	SE Warm-Up, p. 592	•	•	•
		RN Note Taking Guide 22-4	•	•	•
		TR Practice 22-4		•	
		TR Section 22-4 Quiz		•	

Chapter Review and Assessment

SE Chapter 22 Review, p. 598 ⓛ₃

CTB Chapter 22 Test ⓛ₂ ⓛ₃ ⓛ₄

SE Standardized Test Prep, p. 599 ⓛ₃

PROGRAM COMPONENTS

SE Student Edition	**CTB** Computer Test Bank
TE Teacher Edition	**AUD** Audio Section Summaries
TR Teaching Resources	
RN Reading and Note Taking Guide	**DVD** Teens Talk Video Series
	VVG Video Viewing Guide
ARN Adapted Reading and Note Taking Guide	**PPT** Presentation
IB Image Bank	

Differentiated Instruction
(L1) (L2) (L4) (EL)

		SE eTEXT	TE eTEXT	PRINT
ARN	Note Taking Guide 22-1 (L2)	•	•	
RN	Note Taking Guide 22-1 (EL)	•	•	•
AUD	Audio Summary 22-1 (L1) (L2) (EL)	•	•	
TE	Reteach Strategy, p. 577 (L2)		•	•
TR	Enrich 22-1 (L4)		•	
ARN	Note Taking Guide 22-2 (L2)	•	•	
RN	Note Taking Guide 22-2 (EL)	•	•	•
AUD	Audio Summary 22-2 (L1) (L2) (EL)	•	•	
TE	Reteach Strategy, p. 583 (L2)		•	•
TR	Enrich 22-2 (L4)		•	
ARN	Note Taking Guide 22-3 (L2)	•	•	
RN	Note Taking Guide 22-3 (EL)	•	•	•
AUD	Audio Summary 22-3 (L1) (L2) (EL)	•	•	
TE	Reteach Strategy, p. 589 (L2)		•	•
TR	Enrich 22-3 (L4)		•	
ARN	Building Health Skills 22 (L2)	•	•	
RN	Building Health Skills 22 (EL)	•	•	•
ARN	Note Taking Guide 22-4 (L2)	•	•	
RN	Note Taking Guide 22-4 (EL)	•	•	•
AUD	Audio Summary 22-4 (L1) (L2) (EL)	•	•	
TE	Reteach Strategy, p. 596 (L2)		•	•
TR	Enrich 22-4 (L4)		•	

ABILITY LEVELS

(L1) **For students with special needs**
(L2) **For less proficient readers**
(L3) **For all students**
(L4) **For gifted and talented students**
(EL) **For English language learners**

Chapter 22 Digital/Video Pathway

This alternative pathway allows you to teach this chapter's content using only the video and online materials.

Preview

DVD Video #22 Preview
SE Video #22 Preview Activity
VVG Video #22 Worksheet

Risks and STIs

1
PPT 22-1 Presentation
RN/ARN 22-1 Note Taking
PPT 22-1 Section Quiz

2
DVD Video #22 Explore/Wrap-Up
VVG Video #22 Worksheet
PPT 22-2 Presentation
RN/ARN 22-2 Note Taking
PPT 22-2 Section Quiz

Risks and STIs

3
PPT 22-3 Presentation
RN/ARN 22-3 Note Taking
PPT 22-3 Section Quiz

4
PPT 22-4 Presentation
RN/ARN 22-4 Note Taking
PPT 22-4 Section Quiz

Chapter Preview

Section 1 The Risks of Sexual Activity
Several risky behaviors account for the current epidemic of sexually transmitted infections (STIs), including ignoring the risks of sexual activity. Practicing sexual abstinence is the best way to avoid STIs.

Section 2 Kinds of STIs
Three of the most common STIs in the United States are trichomoniasis, human papilloma virus, and chlamydia. Other STIs include hepatitis, gonorrhea, genital herpes, and syphilis. Individuals who think they may be infected with an STI should seek prompt medical attention.

Section 3 HIV and AIDS
HIV attacks specific cells of the immune system. When the immune system becomes severely disabled, the infected person has AIDS. Individuals infected with HIV can pass the virus on to someone else through the exchange of blood or other body fluids. HIV and AIDS are global health problems.

 **Accessing Information**
Evaluating Internet Sources
Knowing how to access reliable Internet sources about health topics can help students find the information they need to stay healthy.

Section 4 Protecting Yourself From HIV and AIDS
You can protect yourself from HIV by practicing abstinence, avoiding drugs, and avoiding contact with others' blood and body fluids. In an HIV test, a person's blood is tested for antibodies to HIV. The main goal of HIV treatment is to keep the person's immune system functioning as normally as possible.

Sexually Transmitted Infections and AIDS

1 The Risks of Sexual Activity

2 Kinds of STIs

3 HIV and AIDS
- **Hands-On Activity** How Quickly Can HIV Spread?

 **Building Health Skills**
- **Accessing Information** Evaluating Internet Sources

4 Protecting Yourself From HIV and AIDS

GO ONLINE PearsonSuccessNet.com

TEENS Talk

Risks and STIs

VIDEO 22

Preview **Activity**

How Risky Is Sexual Activity?

Complete this activity before you watch the video.

1. Complete each of the following statements by filling in the blank.
   a. Being sexually active as a teen is __?__ .
   b. There are __?__ risks that come with sexual activity.
   c. A person should not be sexually active until __?__ .
2. Look over your responses. In a paragraph, summarize what you learned about your self by completing the statements. **WRITING**

GO ONLINE

PearsonSuccessNet.com

For resources and activities for this chapter.

Sensitive Issues
- Sexually transmitted infections and AIDS are likely to be sensitive issues for many students because of their association with sexual activity, particularly early sexual activity, and sexual activity with multiple partners. Students may be hesitant to discuss or ask questions about the issues for fear of appearing either too naive or too experienced in front of their peers. Give students the option of doing written activities instead of participating in classroom discussions.
- Be sure to stress the seriousness of STIs to the class. Make sure students realize that some STIs can cause lifelong illness, permanent infertility, and death.

573

Video Objectives

Use this video to help students

Identify the risks associated with sexual activity.

Explain why abstinence is the most effective strategy for avoiding STIs.

Practice abstinence to protect themselves from STIs.

Preview **Activity**

How Risky Is Sexual Activity?

Before watching the video, have students complete the Preview Activity by writing their answers in their private journals. After showing all three portions of the video, ask students to revisit their responses and make any changes they feel are necessary.

From the Authors

You may be wondering why we, as well as most public health professionals, have replaced the term *sexually transmitted disease (STD)* with the term *sexually transmitted infection (STI)*. Using *STI* instead of *STD* allows inclusion of HIV infections (and not just AIDS, the disease) in the same category as sexually transmitted diseases. Using *STI* instead of *STD* also puts more emphasis on transmission and the fact that STIs are preventable. Prevention of STIs is the focus of many of the activities in this chapter. See, for example, the Health and Community activity on page 577 and the Connect to Your Life questions throughout the chapter.

Objectives
Before class begins, write the objectives on the board. Have students copy the objectives into their notebooks at the start of class.

1. Focus

Warm-Up Quick Quiz

Use Warm-Up Presentation slide to survey student responses.

Give students a few minutes to do the quiz. Then call on volunteers to read aloud their explanations. Make sure students understand that each statement is true. Discuss how thinking the statements are false might lead people to engage in risky behaviors.

Presentation 22-1

Section 1

The Risks of Sexual Activity

Objectives
- ▶ **Identify** risky behaviors associated with the current epidemic of sexually transmitted infections.
- ▶ **Describe** behaviors that can help prevent the spread of sexually transmitted infections.

Vocabulary
- sexually transmitted infection (STI)

Warm-Up

Quick Quiz Which of these statements do you think are true? Which are false?

1. It can take only one sexual contact with an infected person to get a sexually transmitted infection.

2. Even if you've been infected with a sexually transmitted infection before, you can get that same infection again.

3. You can have more than one sexually transmitted infection at a time.

4. You can get a sexually transmitted infection from sharing needles.

WRITING For each of your responses, explain why you gave the answer you did. Review your answers after reading this section.

The Silent Epidemic

Any pathogen that spreads from one person to another during sexual contact is called a **sexually transmitted infection,** or **STI.** (Such infections are sometimes called sexually transmitted diseases, or STDs.) There are approximately 20 million new cases of STIs in the United States each year. Of those cases, about half occur in people between the ages of 15 and 24.

Harmful Effects of STIs The STI epidemic is a serious concern for several reasons. STIs are harmful in terms of physical and emotional suffering. And yearly healthcare expenses related to STIs in the United States amount to well over $10 billion.

In the short term, STIs may cause pain, discomfort, and embarrassment. The long-term consequences of STIs may include an increased risk of certain cancers and an increased risk of infertility in both men and women. Infertility is the condition of being unable to have children.

Many STIs can be treated with medicines, but some are incurable. If left untreated, some STIs are fatal. Unlike many other infectious diseases, people do not develop immunity to STIs after being infected. A person can be cured and then reinfected with the same STI again.

⚑ Sensitive Issues

Students who feel uncomfortable asking questions about sexually transmitted infections need a way to ask questions anonymously. At the end of class, allow students to submit questions on slips of paper. During the next class, answer all serious, relevant questions.

MATH and Health

L3 Calculating Rates

Using Figure 1, have students calculate the average annual rate of increase in cases of chlamydia in 10- to 19-year-olds from 2006 to 2010. (Subtract the number of cases in 2006 from the number of cases in 2010, and divide the answer by 4 years; or, 90,000 cases ÷ 4 yr = 22,500 cases/yr.)

Challenge students to calculate the number of cases there would be in 2014. Assume the same rate of increase. (Add 22,500 cases per year, times 4 years, to the number of cases in 2010; or, 450000 cases + 90,000 cases = 540,000 cases.) Provide CDC data for recent years so students can test the assumption about the rate of increase.

Risky Behaviors and the STI Epidemic There are several risky behaviors that account for the current STI epidemic, including ignoring the risks of sexual activity, having sexual contact with multiple partners, and not getting proper treatment when necessary.

▶ **Ignoring Risks** Being sexually active puts a person at risk for STIs. Many people who are sexually active do not take precautions against infection. They often do not realize the risks of contracting STIs, or they choose to ignore the risks. Adolescents in particular tend to ignore the risks, thinking "It can't happen to me." But the reality is that it can, and it does happen to many teens.

▶ **Multiple Partners** Many people begin to engage in sexual activity at a young age, and some may have multiple sexual partners during their lifetimes. The more sexual partners a person has, the greater the chance of getting an STI.

▶ **Not Seeking Treatment** Some people who become infected do not seek immediate medical treatment. Sometimes people are too embarrassed to seek treatment. Others don't know that they have an STI because they do not recognize the symptoms. In some cases, STIs have no symptoms and can only be detected by laboratory tests. Sometimes the symptoms go away temporarily, leading the person to think the infection has been cured. In all of these situations, the infection may go untreated, increasing the chances that the person will spread it to others.

 **Connect to Your Life** What advice would you give a friend who seems to be ignoring the risks of sexual activity?

GO ONLINE
PearsonSuccessNet.com
For: More on sexually transmitted infections

FIGURE 1 This graph shows data for one STI, chlamydia, that is common among young people. **Evaluating** Why do you think young people are especially at risk for STIs?

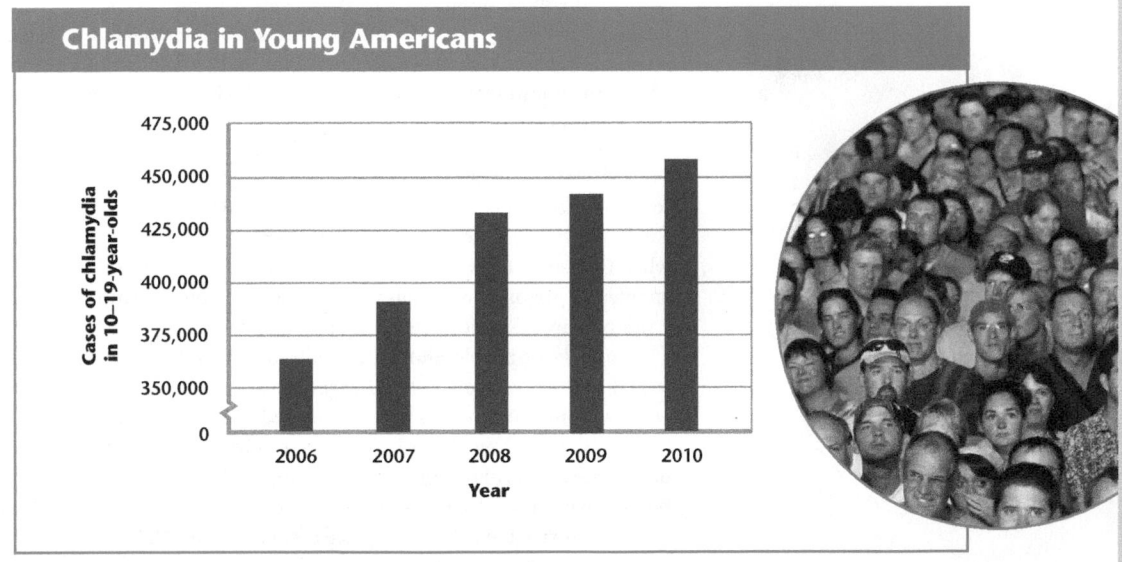

Chlamydia in Young Americans

Cases of chlamydia in 10–19-year-olds

- 475,000
- 450,000
- 425,000
- 400,000
- 375,000
- 350,000
- 0

Year: 2006, 2007, 2008, 2009, 2010

---

2. Teach

🔵 🔵 Reading/Note Taking 22-1
🔵 Adapted Reading/Note Taking 22-1

The Silent Epidemic

🔵 **Content Update**  **GO ONLINE**

Visit Pearson SuccessNet to access more information about sexually transmitted infections. Have students complete the Web activity.

🔵 **Active Learning**

Ask students to create posters about the harmful effects of STIs, using the information on page 574 as a starting point. Students' goal should be to impress observers with the seriousness of STIs. Arrange to display their posters throughout the school.

🔵 **Building Health Skills**

Analyzing Influences Have students read about the risky behaviors that account for the current STI epidemic. Ask: **What factors might influence some young people to adopt these risky behaviors?** *(Sample answers: seeing sexual activity without consequences in the media; feeling peer pressure to become sexually active)* **How could you resist these influences?** *(Sample answers: learn about the risks of sexual activity; choose friends who practice sexual abstinence)*

🔵 **Visual Learning: Figure 1**

Image Bank Figure 22-1

Introduce the graph in the figure by telling students that chlamydia is one of the most common STIs in the United States. Call on a volunteer to describe in words the trend shown in the graph. Discuss what young people should do if they think they have chlamydia. Call on students to answer the caption question. **Caption Answer** *Sample answer:* Young people may be especially likely to ignore the risks of sexual activity, to have multiple sexual partners, and to not get proper treatment.

Connect to Your Life *Sample answer:* I would advise the friend to avoid sexual activity because of the risk of getting STIs.

Avoiding STIs

L2 Building Health Skills

Advocacy Have small groups of students write public service announcements in which they advocate sexual abstinence as a way to avoid STIs. Give groups a chance to share their announcements with the class. Make sure students understand that sexual abstinence applies to any activity in which blood or body fluids could be exchanged, not just to sexual intercourse. **WRITING**

L1 Cooperative Learning

Divide the class into pairs, and have each pair write a dialogue in which a teen resists pressure from another teen to try intravenous drugs. Dialogues should focus on refusing these drugs in order to avoid STIs. Have several pairs present their dialogues to the class, and ask other students to evaluate them. Discuss attributes of convincing refusals.

L3 Addressing Misconceptions

Teen Sexual Activity Teens often think that "everybody" they know is sexually active. Call on volunteers to estimate the percentage of teens in their grade who they think is sexually active. (Students are likely to overestimate the percentage of sexually active peers.) Share with students that recent studies show the majority of high school students have not had sex and choose to remain abstinent. Discuss why teens might talk more about sex than actually participate in it.

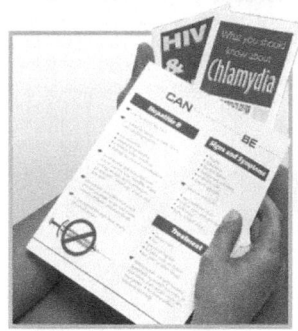

FIGURE 2 Educating yourself about STIs can help you make healthy decisions.

Avoiding STIs

STIs are transmitted mainly through sexual contact, but a few are also transmitted through contact with the blood of an infected person. The good news about STIs is that they are preventable. **Healthy behaviors such as practicing abstinence, avoiding drugs, and choosing responsible friends are ways to avoid STIs.**

Practice Abstinence Because STIs are spread mainly by sexual contact, the most certain way to avoid STIs is to practice sexual abstinence. Sexual abstinence means not having sexual intercourse, oral sex, or anal sex. Even teens who have not been abstinent up to this point can still choose to be abstinent now. However, teens who have been sexually active should be tested for STIs.

Avoid Drugs Some STIs can be transmitted from an infected person to an uninfected person by blood-to-blood contact. People who use illegal drugs or inject steroids run a high risk of contracting certain STIs when they share needles that have been contaminated with the blood of an infected person. Individuals who get body piercings or tattoos also run a risk of being infected with a contaminated needle.

Not only are people who share needles at risk for STIs, but so are their sexual partners. Anyone who engages in sexual activity with someone who has come into contact with an infected needle is at risk.

Drugs, including alcohol, also play an indirect role in the STI epidemic. Because alcohol and other drugs impair the ability to think clearly, people may make decisions they later regret. For example, they may engage in sexual behaviors that place them at risk for STIs.

576 Chapter 22

TEENS Are Asking . . .

Q: My boyfriend is pressuring me to have sex, but I want to wait until marriage. How can I resist the pressure?

A: Congratulations on your healthy decision to remain abstinent! These tips may help you resist the pressure.
- Set specific goals. Know the line you will not cross, and review it often. Ask a friend to hold you accountable.

- State your boundaries. Make sure your boyfriend knows your limits. State them clearly at the start of the relationship.
- Put it in writing. Write a journal entry explaining your decision. This will help strengthen your commitment.
- Find supportive friends. Hang out with other teens who want to remain abstinent. They will support your decision.

Choose Responsible Friends It might sound obvious, but the best way to ensure that you practice abstinence and avoid drugs is to choose friends who have also chosen those behaviors. Friends who support your healthy decisions can make it easier to resist the pressure to use drugs or engage in sexual behavior. Furthermore, going out in groups, rather than as couples, can make it easier to choose abstinence.

Parents, teachers, and other adults can also provide support for healthy behavior choices. It may feel uncomfortable at first to talk to a parent or other adult about the pressures to engage in sexual activity. But most adults can offer helpful advice about choosing abstinence as the responsible and healthy choice.

FIGURE 3 Choosing friends and activities that encourage abstinence can greatly reduce your risk of becoming infected with an STI.

Section 1 Review

Key Ideas and Vocabulary

1. What is a **sexually transmitted infection**?
2. What are three risky behaviors that contribute to the current STI epidemic?
3. Explain how practicing abstinence, avoiding drugs, and your choices of friends can help you avoid STIs.

Critical Thinking

4. **Relating Cause and Effect** How is the fact that some STIs have few or no symptoms related to the STI epidemic?

Health and Community

STI Education Create a poster or a web page to educate teens about the risks of sexual activity and STIs. Include statistics about the incidence of STIs in teens. Include other facts that you think teens should be aware of. **WRITING**

5. **Evaluating** Explain how refusal skills and effective communication are important skills that teens can use to avoid STIs.

3. Assess

Evaluate
These assignments can help you assess students' mastery of the section content.

Section 1 Review
Answers appear below.

Teaching Resources
• Practice 22-1
• Section 22-1 Quiz

L2 Reteach
Work with students to make an outline of section content. Begin the outline with the major headings in the section, and leave room for students to add subheadings and important details. Have students work with partners to complete the outline. Suggest that students use their completed outlines when they review section content.

L4 Enrich
Teaching Resources
• Enrich 22-1

Health and Community

STI Education Students can use just the facts in the text, or they can include additional facts from other sources. Check that any additional facts are reliable, up-to-date, and relevant to teens. Posters and Web pages should be attractive, informative, and persuasive.

Section 1 Review

1. any pathogen that spreads from one person to another during sexual contact

2. ignoring risks of being sexually active, engaging in sexual activity with multiple partners, not seeking treatment for STIs

3. Sexual abstinence is the best way to avoid STIs. Avoiding drugs helps one avoid STIs because some STIs can be transmitted by sharing drug needles and because alcohol and other drugs make people more likely to engage in risky behaviors. Friends who support your healthy decisions can help you avoid STIs by making it easier to resist pressure to use drugs or engage in sexual activity.

4. People who have few or no symptoms are unlikely to seek medical attention or protect partners from infection.

5. Refusal skills and effective communication are important skills for resisting peer pressure to be sexually active and use drugs.

Objectives
Before class begins, write the objectives on the board. Have students copy the objectives into their notebooks at the start of class.

1. Focus

Warm-Up Myth/Fact

Call on a few students to read their answers. Try to get a diversity of views. Some students might think that all STIs can be cured. Make sure students realize that some STIs infect people for life. Tell students they will learn about different kinds of STIs in this section, including those that can be cured and those that cannot.

Presentation 22-2

Section 2

Kinds of STIs

Objectives
▶ **Identify** three of the most common STIs, including their symptoms and treatments.
▶ **List** four other STIs and describe their symptoms.
▶ **Know** when a person should seek treatment for an STI.

Vocabulary
• trichomoniasis
• urethritis
• vaginitis
• human papilloma virus
• chlamydia
• pelvic inflammatory disease
• gonorrhea
• genital herpes
• syphilis
• chancre

Warm-Up

Myth All STIs can be treated with antibiotics.

Fact STIs caused by viruses cannot be treated with antibiotics. Antibiotics are only used to treat STIs caused by bacteria. Several STIs caused by viruses cannot be cured and can cause lifelong health problems.

WRITING Do you think most teens are aware that some STIs are not easily treated? And that some may persist for years? Explain your answer.

The Most Common STIs

Like other infectious diseases you have learned about, STIs are caused by pathogens, including bacteria, viruses, and protozoans. The pathogens that cause STIs live in the reproductive organs of males and females. Some also live in the blood. STIs can be spread from person to person through blood and body fluids such as semen, vaginal secretions, and breast milk.

Early diagnosis and treatment of STIs is essential in preventing long-term health problems. Although some STIs do not have obvious symptoms, many do have distinct symptoms. Anyone experiencing symptoms of an STI should see a doctor immediately.

Three of the most common STIs in the United States are trichomoniasis, human papilloma virus, and chlamydia. It is important to be able to recognize the symptoms of these infections.

Trichomoniasis The STI known as **trichomoniasis** (trik uh moh NY uh sis) is caused by a protozoan that infects the urinary tract or vagina. In males, symptoms include painful urination, a clear discharge from the penis, and some itching. Most males experience no symptoms at all. Symptoms in females include itching and burning in the vagina, an unpleasant-smelling, yellowish discharge, and pain when urinating.

A doctor can prescribe medicine to cure a trichomoniasis infection. In males, if trichomoniasis is not treated, it can lead to inflammation of the lining of the urethra, called **urethritis** (yoor uh THRY tis). In females, untreated trichomoniasis can lead to **vaginitis** (vaj uh NY tis), which is a vaginal infection or irritation.

578 *Chapter 22*

Sensitive Issues

Joking can be a defense mechanism for dealing with sensitive issues. Curb any joking behavior about STIs because joking can reinforce misconceptions and make issues seem less serious than they are. Stress that STIs are very serious and nothing to laugh about.

WRITING and Health

L3 Persuasive Letter

Have students suppose that a sexually active friend has developed painful urination and a clear discharge from the penis. He is reluctant to tell his parents about his problem and wants advice. Ask students to write a letter in which they try to persuade the friend to make the best choice for his health. (In their letters, students should try to convince the friend to see a doctor immediately because he might have an STI. They also might warn the friend to stop all sexual activity so as not to spread the infection.)

Human Papilloma Virus The most common viral STI in the U.S. is caused by a group of viruses called **human papilloma virus** (pap uh LOH muh), or HPV. Often, HPV causes no symptoms. So people may not know that they are infected. The body's immune system may destroy the virus. But in some people, HPV remains in the body for life.

Some forms of HPV cause genital warts, which may itch or burn. A doctor can remove the warts, but they may reappear. A more serious condition associated with HPV is cervical cancer in women. Regular pap tests help detect cervical cancer before it becomes life-threatening.

The FDA has licensed a vaccine for use in girls and young women ages 9 to 26. The vaccine protects against the four types of HPV virus that cause 70 percent of cervical cancers and 90 percent of genital warts. Research is ongoing to see if the HPV vaccine has benefits for males.

Chlamydia The most common STI caused by bacteria in the U.S. is **chlamydia** (kluh MID ee uh). People who are sexually active should be checked regularly for chlamydia, which can be cured with antibiotics.

Infected males often experience painful, frequent urination and discharge from the penis. If untreated, chlamydia may lead to urethritis.

In females, often the only symptom is a yellowish vaginal discharge. If untreated, chlamydia can cause a serious infection of the reproductive organs called **pelvic inflammatory disease,** or PID. PID can lead to infertility or an ectopic pregnancy, a potentially fatal condition where a fertilized egg implants somewhere other than in the uterus. Also, a pregnant woman can transmit chlamydia to her baby during birth. If an infected infant survives, it may suffer damage to the lungs or eyes.

GO ONLINE
PearsonSuccessNet.com
For: More on sexually transmitted infections

FIGURE 4 The micrographs show the pathogens that cause trichomoniasis, HPV, and chlamydia. These STIs affect millions of Americans every year.

Connect to Your Life For each STI, list the symptoms that a person needs to watch for.

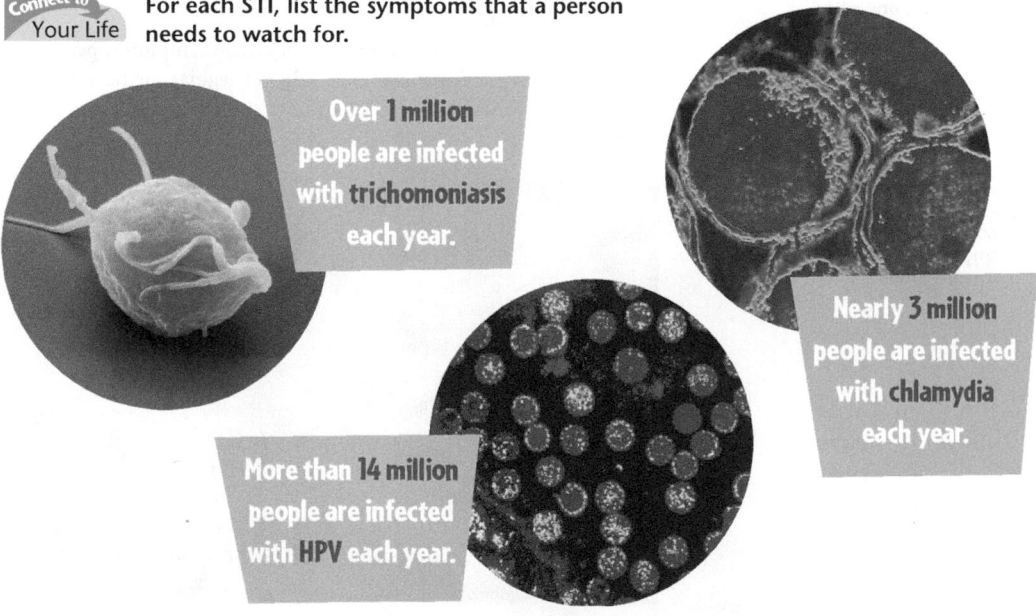

Over 1 million people are infected with trichomoniasis each year.

More than 14 million people are infected with HPV each year.

Nearly 3 million people are infected with chlamydia each year.

---

2. Teach

L3 EL Reading/Note Taking 22-2
L2 Adapted Reading/Note Taking 22-2

The Most Common STIs

L3 Online Activity
Visit Pearson SuccessNet to access an online activity about sexually transmitted infections. Have students complete the Web activity.

L3 Building Media Literacy
Ask students to come up with criteria to assess media sources for different types of STI information. Ask: **What would be important if you were looking for the most recent statistics on trichomoniasis?** (how up-to-date the source is) **If you wanted to know what genital warts look like?** (whether the source has illustrations) **If you wanted to know which antibiotic is used to treat chlamydia?** (whether the source was written or reviewed by a doctor)

L2 Building Vocabulary
Explain that the suffix -itis means "inflammation of" and that symptoms of inflammation can include itching, pain, and swelling. Ask: **What structures are inflamed in urethritis and vaginitis?** (urethra and vagina, respectively) **What are some other conditions that end in -itis?** (Sample answers: tonsillitis, appendicitis, tendonitis) In each condition, ask students to identify what structure is inflamed.

L3 Class Discussion
Explain that the HPV vaccine is most effective when it is given before a girl is sexually active. Doctors recommend that the vaccine be given to girls who are 11 or 12. Doctors do not think that most girls this age will soon be sexually active. But they know that some girls do become sexually active in their early teens, and they want to make sure that all girls are protected against HPV.

Connect to Your Life Answers should include symptoms that are described on pages 578–579.

Differentiated Instruction

EL English Language Learners
The names of STIs in this section may be difficult for English language learners to pronounce. Point out the phonetic spellings of these terms in the text. Read the terms aloud, being careful to pronounce them correctly. Ask students to say each term aloud a few times after you read it.

L4 Gifted and Talented
Challenge interested students to learn more about one of the three most common STIs from reliable online or library resources. Make sure all three STIs are covered by different students. Invite students to share what they learn with the class in an oral report.

Other STIs

ⓛ Class Discussion

Have students read about hepatitis in the text. Ask: **Why do you think people with hepatitis B or C are often unaware of their infection?** *(Most of the symptoms of hepatitis can also be caused by other illnesses, such as flu or food poisoning.)* **Why are new cases of hepatitis B, but not hepatitis C, likely to decline in the future?** *(Children are now routinely vaccinated against hepatitis B, but there is no vaccine for hepatitis C.)*

ⓛ Cultural Connection

Discuss how different cultures have different attitudes toward sex. However, most are somewhat reluctant to talk seriously about sex and its consequences. For example, some aspects of American culture are very open about sex, yet many Americans have limited knowledge about the risks of STIs. Challenge students to think of examples in American culture and other cultures that illustrate this dichotomy. Ask: **How might the reluctance to talk about the risks of sexual activity affect the STI epidemic?**

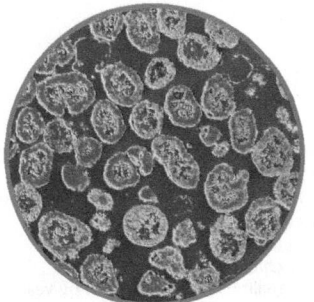

▲ **Gonorrhea**

FIGURE 5 Newborn babies are routinely given medicated eyedrops to prevent gonorrhea infection. The micrograph above shows the bacteria that cause gonorrhea.

Other STIs

Other STIs can also cause health problems and require medical treatment. Information about some of these STIs is summarized in Figure 6. **Other STIs include hepatitis, gonorrhea, genital herpes, and syphilis.**

Hepatitis   Hepatitis B and C, also called HBV and HCV, are sexually transmitted infections that attack the liver. They are also spread by blood-to-blood contact, such as when people share needles.

Individuals with HBV or HCV are often unaware of their infection. The most common symptoms are fatigue, abdominal pain, nausea, and jaundice. Both infections may lead to liver cancer or cirrhosis (sih ROH sis), a condition in which normal liver tissue is replaced by scar tissue.

Hepatitis B and C can be diagnosed by a blood test. Medications may relieve symptoms, but there is no cure for HBV or HCV. Children are now routinely vaccinated against HBV. Currently, there is no vaccine for HCV.

Gonorrhea   A bacterial STI that infects the urinary tract of males and females and the reproductive organs of females is **gonorrhea** (gahn uh REE uh). Researchers estimate that about 820,000 Americans are infected with gonorrhea each year. Males usually have a thick, puslike discharge from the penis and painful urination. Females sometimes experience painful urination and a puslike discharge from the vagina or urinary tract. More often, however, symptoms in a woman are very mild and may not be noticed. If left untreated, gonorrhea can lead to urethritis and infertility in males. In females it may lead to PID and infertility.

An infected woman can transmit gonorrhea to her baby during birth. In the United States, babies are given medicated eyedrops at birth to prevent infection of the eyes.

Because gonorrhea often has no noticeable symptoms, people participating in high-risk behaviors should get regular medical checkups. Treatment for gonorrhea requires antibiotics.

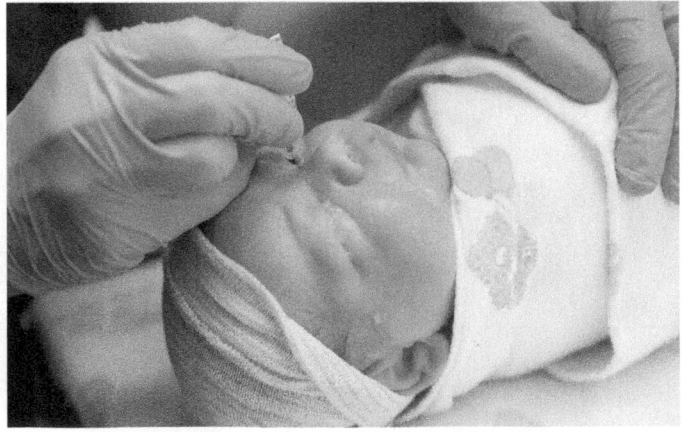

For Your INFORMATION!

STIs in Teens

In 2005, the American Social Health Association (ASHA) reported the following facts about STIs in American teens.
- Half of sexually active youth become infected with an STI by the age of 25.
- Half of all new HIV cases occur in teens.

- Less than half of teens talk about STIs with their doctor.

In the same report, ASHA made the following recommendations.
- There should be better communication about STIs between teens and parents and between teens and healthcare providers.

- Teens should be educated about STI risks and prevention.

As a health teacher, you can help implement both recommendations. You can give students opportunities to improve their communication skills and teach them about STI risks and prevention.

◀ Chancroid

FIGURE 6 Chancroid, bacterial vaginosis, pubic lice, and scabies are all treatable STIs. **Classifying** Which of these STIs can affect both males and females?

Other STIs

Infection	Pathogen	Symptoms	How Spread	Treatment
Chancroid	Bacteria	Painful sores around the genitals	Contact with sores	Antibiotics
Bacterial vaginosis	Bacteria	In women, discharge, pain, itching, or burning in or around the vagina	Role of sexual activity in the spread of bacterial vaginosis is unclear	Antibiotics
Pubic lice and Scabies	Insects and mites that infest the hair around the genitals	Itching around the genitals; a rash	Direct physical contact with an infested person or with infested clothing or bedding	Medicated shampoo; washing infested clothing or bedding in very hot water

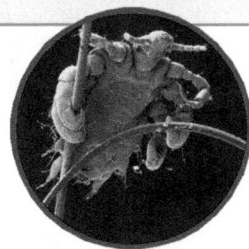

▲ Pubic louse

Genital Herpes Another STI caused by a virus is **genital herpes** (HUR peez). The virus that causes genital herpes is a herpes simplex virus. Researchers estimate that one out of six people aged 14 to 49 has had a genital herpes infection.

In some people, the symptoms may be hardly noticeable, and they may not realize they are infected. In other people, symptoms may be more severe, including painful blisters that appear on or around the genitals. A doctor can prescribe medicine to relieve the discomfort and dry up the blisters, but there is no cure for genital herpes. Infected people can experience periodic outbreaks of blisters throughout their lives.

An infected individual can pass the herpes simplex virus to a sexual partner whether blisters are present or not. A woman with genital herpes can infect her infant during childbirth, causing blindness and possibly death. A doctor may recommend that an infected woman have a cesarean section to prevent the baby from being infected.

Connect to Your Life If a friend were considering a body piercing, what would you say about the risk of hepatitis?

Sexually Transmitted Infections and AIDS **581**

L2 Visual Learning: Figure 6

Have students read about the other STIs in the table. Challenge students to brainstorm how each of the STIs could be prevented. (Students' responses should make it clear that abstinence is the only certain way to avoid infection with each STI.) Make sure students realize that avoiding infested clothing and bedding is also important for preventing infections of pubic lice and scabies.
Caption Answer: chancroid, pubic lice, and scabies

L3 Journal Writing

Ask students to imagine what it would be like to have genital herpes. Remind them that there is no cure for this viral STI and that infected people may have periodic outbreaks of painful blisters throughout their lives. Have students consider how this would affect their health, relationships, and happiness. Ask students to address these questions in a confidential journal entry. Writing about possible lifelong negative consequences of sexual activity should reinforce the importance of practicing abstinence now. **WRITING**

Connect to Your Life *Sample answer:* There is a risk of contracting hepatitis from contaminated piercing needles. Hepatitis is an incurable disease that can lead to liver cancer and cirrhosis.

Differentiated Instruction

L1 Special Needs

Pair special needs students with more proficient students, and ask pairs to make a table, modeled on Figure 6, comparing and contrasting hepatitis, gonorrhea, and genital herpes. For each STI, they should include the type of pathogen, symptoms, how the infection is spread, and treatment. Organizing what they read in a compare/contrast table will help students focus on the most important information in the passage.

L2 Cooperative Learning

Divide the class into small groups, and have students design a survey for other teens to see how familiar they are with each of the STIs described in the text. Students should design their surveys so as to determine how much teens know about each disease, such as how the disease is transmitted, what symptoms it causes, and whether it can be cured. If time allows, have students use their surveys to assess the knowledge of other students at their school. Ask students to share the results of their surveys. Ask: **How can lack of knowledge about STIs increase the risk of infection?**

L3 Building Health Skills

Accessing Information Ask students where they could learn about several different aspects of syphilis, including the origin of the term (e.g., dictionary), current statistics on the prevalence of the disease (e.g., government Web site), and usual treatment (e.g., medical reference book). Discuss how different types of information about the same topic may require accessing different kinds of sources.

Seeking Treatment

L3 Active Learning

Ask small groups of students to contact their state or local health department or the Centers for Disease Control and Prevention to learn about clinics in their community that test for STIs. They should find out about clinic costs, policies regarding patient confidentiality, and clinic contact information. Ask groups to compile what they learn in a pamphlet. Display their pamphlets in the classroom.

Syphilis Although far less common than it used to be, thousands of people in the United States become infected with syphilis each year. **Syphilis** (SIF uh lis) is a serious bacterial STI that progresses through three distinct stages.

▶ In the first stage, a painless sore called a **chancre** (SHANG kur) appears at the site of exposure. The bacteria may spread from the sore to different parts of the body.

▶ In the second stage, sores appear in the mouth and flulike symptoms develop. A nonitchy skin rash often appears on the hands and feet.

▶ In the third stage, symptoms may disappear for years. During this time, however, the bacteria attack internal parts of the body, such as the brain and heart. Eventually, untreated syphilis can cause brain damage, paralysis, and heart disease. This damage can lead to death.

In its early stages, syphilis can be treated and cured with antibiotics. Once it progresses beyond the second stage, the bacteria can be killed, but any damage that has already occurred is permanent.

A pregnant woman with syphilis will pass the disease to her developing baby. If the mother does not receive treatment during pregnancy, syphilis can damage the baby's skin, bones, eyes, teeth, and liver. A baby born with syphilis is said to have congenital syphilis.

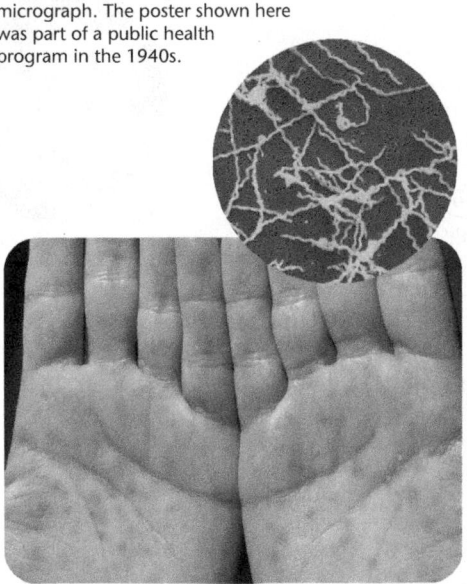

FIGURE 7 An itchless rash on the hands is one of the symptoms of syphilis. The bacteria that cause syphilis are spiral-shaped, as you can see in the micrograph. The poster shown here was part of a public health program in the 1940s.

WHOM HAVE YOU EXPOSED TO SYPHILIS

TELL YOUR PHYSICIAN THEY SHOULD BE EXAMINED THEY MAY NEED TREATMENT

N.Y. STATE DEPT. OF HEALTH

TEENS *Are Asking . . .*

Q: I'm abstinent now, but I was sexually active on one occasion in the past. I had a rash after that one time, and I was worried that I might have an STI. Then the rash went away, so I figured it was nothing. Was I right?

A: The fact that your rash went away is no guarantee that you are free of infection.

STIs may cause no symptoms or cause only temporary symptoms. For example, gonorrhea often causes no noticeable symptoms in females, and the initial symptoms of syphilis usually go away after a short time. There is significant risk of infection, especially for females, with even one exposure to an STI. For example, 60 to 90 percent of females become infected with gonorrhea after one exposure. You should tell your doctor about your situation and get tested. If you do have an STI, you should be treated as soon as possible.

Seeking Treatment

Being tested for STIs may be uncomfortable and embarrassing, but it is crucial for long-term health. **People who participate in high-risk behaviors should get medical checkups every six months. Individuals who suspect they may be infected should seek prompt medical attention.**

A person who suspects an STI infection should refrain from sexual activity and see a doctor. Depending on the symptoms, the doctor may need to do a physical exam or a blood test. If an infection is present and treatable, the person should start treatment immediately. It is important to finish all of the prescribed medicine, even if symptoms disappear.

If a person finds out that he or she has an STI, it is also important to notify any sexual partners, so they can seek treatment as well. If the STI is not curable, the doctor can offer advice about how to live with the disease and how to prevent passing it on to others.

Many states have clinics that test for STIs. The results of these tests are confidential. Information about clinics that test for STIs is available from state or local public health departments or from the Centers for Disease Control and Prevention.

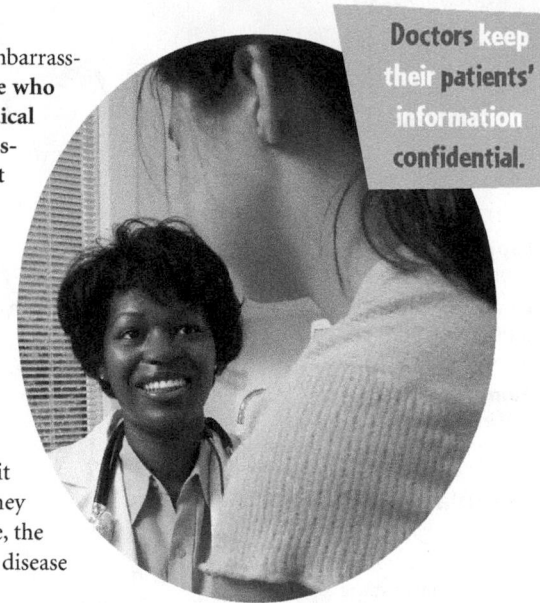

Doctors keep their patients' information confidential.

FIGURE 8 It is very important for long-term health to see a doctor if you think you might have an STI.

Section 2 Review

Key Ideas and Vocabulary

1. What are three of the most common STIs in the United States? What type of pathogen causes each STI?

2. Why is **pelvic inflammatory disease** a serious problem in women?

3. List the symptoms of hepatitis, gonorrhea, genital herpes, and syphilis.

4. Which stage of syphilis is characterized by the appearance of a **chancre**?

5. When should a person seek treatment for STIs?

Health at Home

Accessing STI Information Write down a list of questions that you have about STIs. Set up a time with a parent or other trusted adult to discuss your questions. If the person doesn't know the answers, ask for his or her help in finding the answers. **WRITING**

Critical Thinking

6. **Classifying** Which of the STIs that you learned about in this section can be treated but not cured? Which can be cured if treated early?

7. **Applying Concepts** Suppose a friend is worried about a possible STI. Write an e-mail to your friend, offering your advice about what to do. **WRITING**

3. Assess

Evaluate

These assignments can help you assess students' mastery of the section content.

Section 2 Review
Answers appear below.

Teaching Resources
• Practice 22-2
• Section 22-2 Quiz

L2 Reteach

Have pairs of students play a quiz game in which one student chooses an STI and the partner asks three "yes" or "no" questions (e.g., Is it caused by a virus? Does it cause symptoms?) to try to identify which STI it is. Have partners alternate roles. Partners should play the game until they have covered all the STIs in the section. The partner who correctly identifies more STIs is the winner.

L4 Enrich

Teaching Resources
• Enrich 22-2

Health at Home

Accessing STI Information Suggest that students discuss their questions with a school nurse if they feel uncomfortable discussing them with a parent. If students cannot find answers to some of their questions, suggest possible sources of relevant information.

5. A person who participates in high-risk behaviors should get medical checkups every six months. A person who suspects he or she may be infected should seek prompt medical attention.

6. HPV, hepatitis B and C, and genital herpes can be treated but not cured. Trichomoniasis, chlamydia, gonorrhea, chancroid, bacterial vaginosis, pubic lice, scabies, and syphilis can be cured if treated early.

7. E-mails should urge the friend to be tested for STIs as soon as possible so treatment, if needed, can be started early.

Section 2 Review

1. trichomoniasis (protozoan), human papilloma virus (virus), and chlamydia (bacteria)

2. PID can lead to infertility or an ectopic pregnancy, which is potentially fatal.

3. Hepatitis: fatigue, abdominal pain, nausea, and jaundice; gonorrhea: puslike discharge and painful urination; genital herpes: painful blisters on or around the genitals; syphilis: a painless sore at the site of exposure, sores in the mouth, flulike symptoms, a rash on the hands and feet, brain damage, paralysis, and heart disease.

4. the first stage

Objectives

Before class begins, write the objectives on the board. Have students copy the objectives into their notebooks at the start of class.

1. Focus

Warm-Up Health Stats

Call on volunteers to share what they wrote. Factors students identify might range from an increase in sexual activity in 13–24-year-olds to new drugs that help people with HIV and AIDS live longer. Tell students they will learn more about the trends in this section.

Presentation 22-3

Section 3

HIV and AIDS

Objectives

▶ **Explain** how HIV infection leads to AIDS.

▶ **Describe** how HIV is transmitted from person to person.

▶ **Summarize** the state of HIV infection and AIDS throughout the world.

Vocabulary

• HIV
• AIDS
• asymptomatic stage
• opportunistic infection

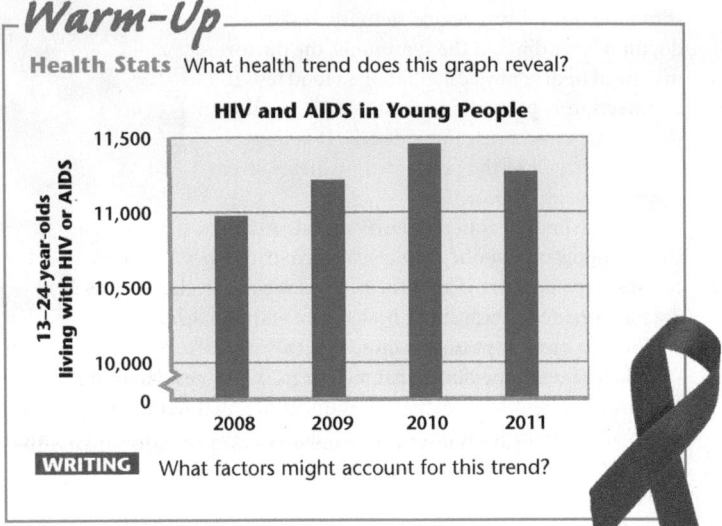

Warm-Up

Health Stats What health trend does this graph reveal?

HIV and AIDS in Young People

13–24-year-olds living with HIV or AIDS

11,500 / 11,000 / 10,500 / 10,000 / 0

2008 2009 2010 2011

WRITING What factors might account for this trend?

HIV Infection

The most serious incurable STI is caused by the human immunodeficiency virus, commonly called **HIV.** As of 2011, about 1.4 million people in North America were living with HIV. In the United States, 13- to 24-year-olds account for about 13 percent of HIV cases.

HIV infection can lead to **AIDS,** or acquired immunodeficiency syndrome, which is an often fatal disease of the immune system. **HIV attacks specific cells of the immune system, disabling the body's defenses against other pathogens. When the immune system becomes severely disabled, the infected person has AIDS.**

How HIV Attacks the Immune System Inside the body, HIV infects helper T cells, which stimulate other cells of the immune system to produce antibodies against invading pathogens. Inside a helper T cell, HIV reproduces, killing the cell in the process. The new viruses are released from the cell and move on to destroy other helper T cells.

Doctors can use the number of helper T cells that remain active in the body to monitor the progression of HIV infection. The fewer helper T cells, the more advanced the disease. Figure 9 shows how helper T cell counts can be used to monitor the progression of the disease.

584 *Chapter 22*

🚩 Sensitive Issues

HIV and AIDS may be sensitive issues for students who have personal experiences with them. Be careful in the language you use when discussing the issues. For example, refer to AIDS patients as "people with AIDS," rather than as "victims of AIDS."

WRITING and Health

L3 Persuasive Letter

Have students find a local organization that supports people with HIV and AIDS and that needs volunteers. Then have students write a letter in which they try to convince a friend to volunteer for the organization. Letters should be informative and persuasive and provide information that makes it easy for the friend to get involved. Urge students to mail their letters and to get involved themselves.

Stages of HIV Infection HIV slowly destroys the immune system. Doctors describe HIV infection as progressing through three stages.

▶ **Asymptomatic Stage** Soon after exposure to HIV, an infected person may experience flulike symptoms, which usually go away after a few weeks. Many months or years may follow during which the person shows no outward signs of disease. Because of the lack of symptoms, this period is called the **asymptomatic stage.** During this stage, the virus destroys helper T cells. People in the asymptomatic stage can infect others even though they feel fine.

▶ **Symptomatic Stage** When an HIV-infected person starts to experience symptoms, he or she has entered the symptomatic stage of infection. Symptoms may include weight loss, a persistent fever, diarrhea, or fungal infections. Such symptoms may not appear until 7 to 10 years after infection with HIV.

▶ **AIDS** The onset of AIDS is usually marked by a very low number of helper T cells in the blood, as shown in Figure 9. At this stage, HIV-infected people are usually experiencing even more severe symptoms than in the symptomatic stage. Because the body's ability to fight disease has been weakened by HIV, they are susceptible to infections that a healthy person's immune system could easily fight off.

 **Your Life** Can you assume that someone who looks healthy is not infected with HIV? Explain.

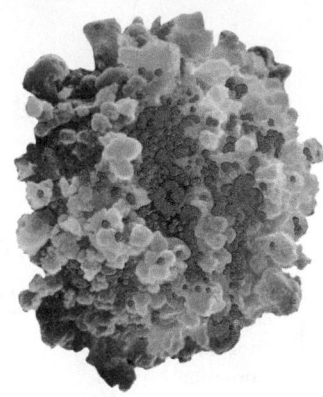

▲ **HIV viruses (red) emerging from a human helper T cell**

FIGURE 9 The number of helper T cells in the blood decreases as HIV infects and destroys more cells. **Reading Graphs** Describe how T cell counts change over time in a person infected with HIV.

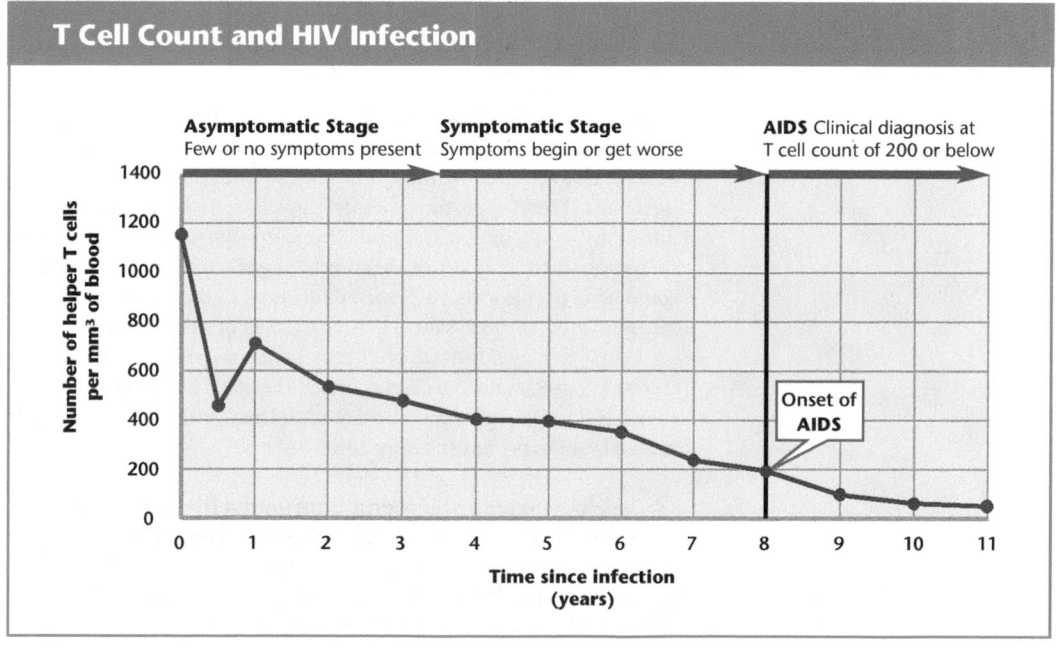

T Cell Count and HIV Infection

Asymptomatic Stage Few or no symptoms present

Symptomatic Stage Symptoms begin or get worse

AIDS Clinical diagnosis at T cell count of 200 or below

Onset of AIDS

(y-axis) Number of helper T cells per mm³ of blood — 0, 200, 400, 600, 800, 1000, 1200, 1400

(x-axis) Time since infection (years) — 0, 1, 2, 3, 4, 5, 6, 7, 8, 9, 10, 11

2. Teach

L3 **EL** Reading/Note Taking 22-3
L2 Adapted Reading/Note Taking 22-3

HIV Infection

L2 **Addressing Misconceptions**

HIV or AIDS? Many people are confused about the difference between HIV and AIDS. Make sure students understand that HIV refers to the virus that causes the infection and that AIDS is the disease caused by the virus. Ask: **How does HIV cause AIDS?** *(HIV attacks cells in the immune system so people cannot fight off infections.)* Point out that people may have HIV infections for many years before developing AIDS.

L3 **Visual Learning: Figure 9**
Image Bank Figure 22-9

Guide students in interpreting the graph. Ask: **At what level of helper T cells is AIDS diagnosed?** *(below 200 helper T cells per mL of blood)* **Based on the graph, about how long does it take AIDS to develop after infection with HIV?** *(about eight years)* Point out to students that this time can vary from person to person. Call on a volunteer to answer the caption question.

Caption Answer T cell counts decline sharply in the first six months after infection, rise somewhat in the second six months, and then show a steady, continuous decline for many years.

Connect to Your Life No, because the first stage of HIV infection is asymptomatic, meaning the person shows no outward signs of disease.

Differentiated Instruction

EL **English Language Learners**
There are many difficult terms in this lesson, including *immunodeficiency*, *asymptomatic*, and *opportunistic*. These and other terms may be obstacles for English language learners and discourage them from reading. In class, make sure that you correctly pronounce and clearly enunciate difficult terms. Have English language learners create flashcards of those terms, including pronunciations. Students should write the definitions of difficult terms in their own words on the flashcards.

Hands-On *Activity*

How Quickly Can HIV Spread?

You can use other items to represent HIV and non-HIV (such as two different types of dried beans), as long as they are distinct. At the start of the activity, fill one student's cup with only cinnamon candies to represent a single infected individual. Fill all the other students' cups with only chocolate candies to represent uninfected individuals.

Think and Discuss Answers

1. Answers will vary. The more partners students exchange candies with, the greater the number of students who will end up with cinnamon candy (HIV).

2. *Sample answer:* Having multiple sexual partners greatly increases the chances of getting infected with HIV or another STI.

L3 **Building Media Literacy**

Assign groups of students different types of health media (e.g., medical Web sites, health magazines, encyclopedias). Ask each group to search its type of media for a source about opportunistic infections and AIDS. Tell students to look for sources that are informative yet understandable by people without any special background knowledge. Ask groups to share their sources and discuss which type of health media seems most suitable for people without prior knowledge of a topic.

Connect to Your Life *Sample answer:* No, because a person who is HIV-positive might have a weakened immune system and be more susceptible to the flu.

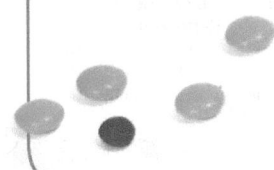

Hands-On *Activity*

How Quickly Can HIV Spread?

Materials
cups
chocolate candies
cinnamon candies

Try This

1. Your teacher will give you a cup filled with small candies. Do not look inside the cup.
2. Walk around the room until your teacher tells you to stop. At that point, pair up with the student closest to you.
3. Pour a few of the candies from your cup into your partner's cup. Your partner should also pour some candies into your cup.
4. Repeat steps 2 and 3 two more times.
5. Look at the candies in your cup. If you have a cinnamon candy, you have been "infected" with HIV.

Think and Discuss

1. How many people in your class ended up with a cinnamon candy (HIV) in their cup? Would it surprise you to learn that only one person was infected to begin with?
2. Suppose that each person you exchanged candies with represents a sexual partner. How many people other than you did each of your partners exchange candies with? What does this suggest about having multiple sexual partners and the chances of getting infected with HIV or another STI?

Opportunistic Infections The infections that attack a person with a weakened immune system are called **opportunistic infections.** AIDS is characterized by the appearance of one or more opportunistic infections. These opportunistic infections include tuberculosis, fungal infections, and a lung disease called pneumocystis carinii pneumonia (noo moh SIS tis kuh RY nee eye). Certain types of cancer are also more common in people with AIDS, including cancer of the cervix and Kaposi's sarcoma (kuh POH seez sahr KOH muh), a kind of skin cancer.

People living with AIDS often experience severe weight loss. As the disease progresses, the virus may attack the brain and nervous system, causing blindness, depression, and mental deterioration. Death is usually caused by an opportunistic infection.

 **Connect to Your Life** Would you spend time with a friend who is HIV-positive if you were sick with the flu? Explain.

For Your **INFORMATION!**

HIV Transmission Among Teens

HIV transmission is especially high among teens. One quarter of all new HIV cases in the United States is diagnosed in people age 20 or younger. The main modes of HIV transmission in teens are sexual contact and shared drug needles. The incidence of other STIs, such as chlamydia and genital herpes, is also high in teens, and this increases the risk of infection with HIV. This is because many STIs cause sores that provide portals through which HIV can enter the bloodstream.

Transmission of HIV

People with HIV are infectious whether or not they have any symptoms of disease. **Individuals infected with HIV can pass the virus on to someone else through the exchange of blood, semen, vaginal secretions, or breast milk.**

Risky Behaviors   There are four main ways that HIV spreads from person to person.

> ▶ **Sexual Contact** HIV can be transmitted through any form of sexual contact that involves contact with an infected person's body fluids, including vaginal, oral, and anal sex. Infected fluids can enter a person's bloodstream through sores or tiny cuts in the lining of the mouth, vagina, rectum, or opening of the penis.

> ▶ **Shared Needles** HIV can be transmitted through shared needles or syringes that are contaminated with the blood of an infected person. Therefore, sharing needles for tattoos or body piercings and injecting illegal drugs put you at risk for HIV infection.

> ▶ **Contact With Blood** HIV can be transmitted if a person has an open cut or sore that comes into contact with the blood or blood parts of an infected person. Avoid all contact with others' blood.

> ▶ **Mother to Baby** HIV can pass from an infected mother to her child, either during pregnancy, birth, or breast-feeding. Certain drugs can decrease the chances of transmission during pregnancy, and the doctor might deliver the baby by cesarean section to reduce the risk of transmission during birth. In addition, mothers infected with HIV should not breast-feed their babies.

GO ONLINE
PearsonSuccessNet.com
For: More on AIDS

FIGURE 10   It is safer for an HIV-positive mother to bottle-feed, rather than breast-feed, her baby.

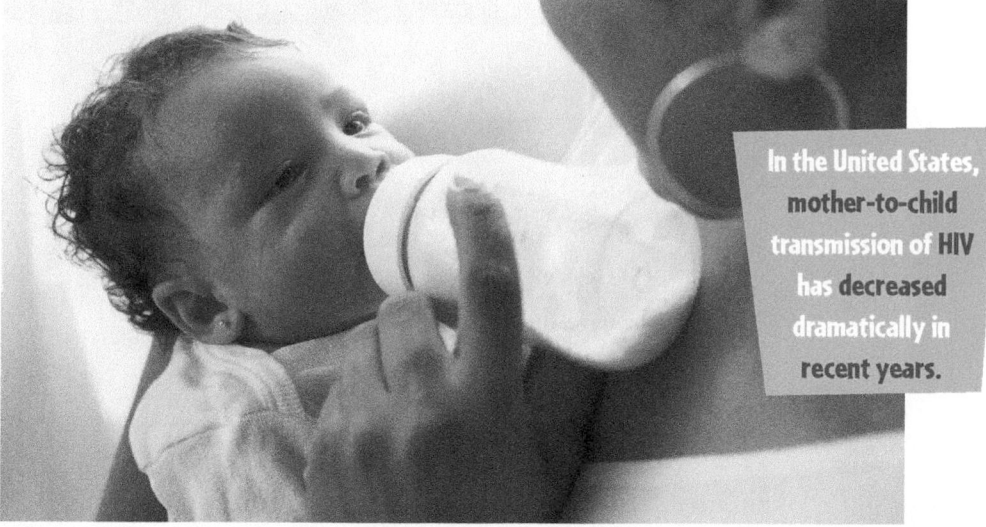

In the United States, mother-to-child transmission of HIV has decreased dramatically in recent years.

Transmission of HIV

L3 **Content Update**  GO ONLINE

Visit Pearson SuccessNet to access more information about AIDS. Have students complete the Web activity.

L3 **Building Health Skills**

Practicing Healthful Behaviors Ask: **What risky behaviors increase the risk of HIV infection in teens and adults?** *(sexual contact, shared drug needles, contact with others' blood)* Have the class brainstorm healthful behaviors they could practice to decrease the risk of HIV infection. *(Sample answers: Practice sexual abstinence; do not use drugs.)* Encourage students to put the healthful behaviors into practice.

L2 **Cooperative Learning**

Divide students into groups and ask them to create a warning to other teens about the potential risk of HIV infection from tattoos and body piercings. They may create a poster or a presentation. Suggest that students include statistics on risks of infection and visuals explaining how contaminated needles can spread HIV from one person to another.

L2 **Visual Learning: Figure 10**

Have students read about mother-to-child transmission of HIV in the figure. Ask: **When can HIV pass from an infected mother to her child?** *(during pregnancy, birth, and breast-feeding)* **What practices can decrease the chances of HIV passing from an infected mother to her child during these three times?** *(taking certain drugs during pregnancy, delivering the baby by cesarean section, and bottle-feeding, respectively)*

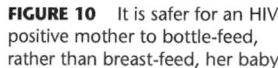

Differentiated Instruction

L4 **Gifted and Talented**

Ask interested students to interview a local public health official about HIV and AIDS. Students might ask which modes of transmission are most common locally, how local cases of HIV infection and AIDS are reported, and what progress is being made in developing an HIV vaccine. Have students share what they learn in an oral report to the class.

L1 Building Health Skills

Communicating Some students may still have fears about being infected with HIV through casual contact. Ask students to write their fears on anonymous slips of paper and give them to you at the end of class. At the next class, write the different fears on the board. Then pair up students and have each member of a pair choose one of the fears listed on the board. Students should explain to each other (or write an explanation) in understandable terms why that fear is unfounded and reinforce the safe behaviors discussed in the text.

L3 Active Learning

Have interested students contact their local chapter of the American Red Cross and find out how potential donors are screened for HIV risk factors and how donated blood is tested for HIV infection. If possible, students should obtain a copy of the questionnaire that potential donors must fill out to be considered as donors. Ask students to create a bulletin board to display what they learn.

A Global Problem

L2 Visual Learning: Figure 12

Image Bank Figure 22-12

Caption Answer From greatest to smallest, the list is: Sub-Saharan Africa (23.5 million), South and Southeast Asia (4 million), Latin America (1.4), Eastern Europe and Central Asia (1.4 million), North America (1.4 million), Western Europe (900,000), East Asia (830,000), North Africa and Middle East (300,000), Caribbean (230,000), Oceania (53,000). North America, along with Latin America and Eastern Europe and Central Asia, has the third highest number of people living with HIV.

FIGURE 11 Playing contact sports such as rugby does not put you at risk for HIV infection.

FIGURE 12 The global distribution of HIV infections is uneven. **Sequencing** List the areas of the world from greatest number of infected people to smallest number of infected people. What position does North America have on the list?

Safe Behaviors HIV is not transmitted by casual contact. You cannot get HIV by going to classes or eating lunch with an infected person. You cannot get HIV by holding hands or hugging an infected person. Families who live with an infected person are not at risk of contracting HIV unless they engage in high-risk behaviors. Small amounts of HIV occur in saliva, tears, and perspiration. However, the amounts are so small that infection from contact with these fluids is unlikely.

The Safety of Donated Blood The risk of getting HIV from blood transfusions is extremely small. Since 1985, all of the blood collected in the United States has been tested for the presence of HIV. Blood that tests positive for HIV antibodies is discarded. Potential donors are interviewed and are not allowed to give blood if they have engaged in behaviors that place them at risk for HIV infection.

A Global Problem

Figure 12 shows the global distribution of HIV infections. **With approximately 34 million people infected around the world, HIV and AIDS represent a global health problem.**

► **Africa** Sub-Saharan Africa accounts for 69% of all global infections. Some estimates indicate that, if infections continue to rise at the current rate, 80 million Africans may die from AIDS by 2025.

► **Asia** HIV infections are also increasing in certain parts of Asia. For example, researchers estimate that about 2.5 million people are living with HIV and AIDS in India.

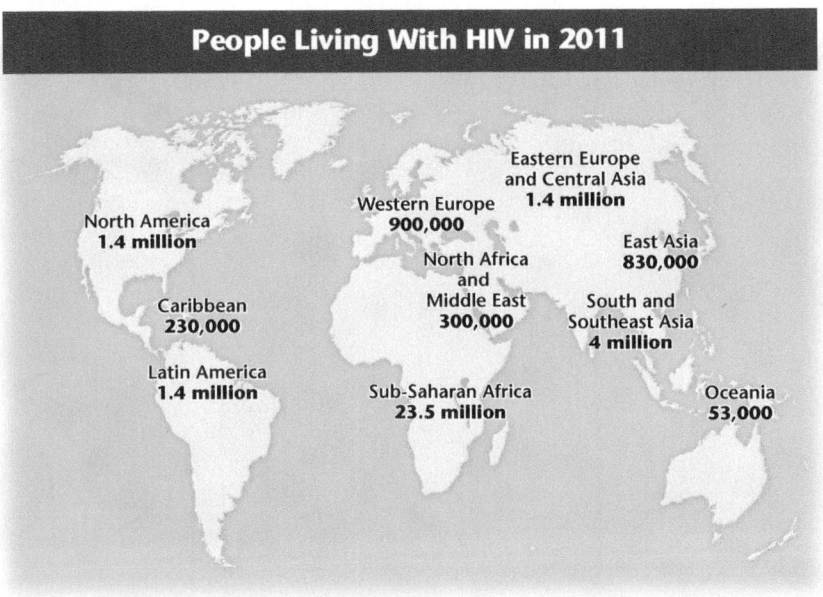

People Living With HIV in 2011

- North America **1.4 million**
- Western Europe **900,000**
- Eastern Europe and Central Asia **1.4 million**
- East Asia **830,000**
- Caribbean **230,000**
- North Africa and Middle East **300,000**
- South and Southeast Asia **4 million**
- Latin America **1.4 million**
- Sub-Saharan Africa **23.5 million**
- Oceania **53,000**

Focus on **ISSUES**

L3 Debate: AIDS Funding in Africa

Some people think the United States should contribute a significant amount to the billions of dollars a year needed to fight AIDS in Africa. Ask a few students to go online to learn more about the impact of AIDS in Africa, both on African nations and on the rest of the world. Then, have students choose sides and debate whether the United States should be expected to pay so much to help fight AIDS in Africa. After the debate, discuss why AIDS in Africa should concern people throughout the world.

High-Risk Groups In all areas of the world, HIV is spreading among people who share needles to inject drugs and people who engage in high-risk sexual behaviors. In many countries, young women represent the majority of new HIV infections. In sub-Saharan Africa, for example, 75% of young people infected with HIV are female. The higher infection rates in women are often due to a lack of information about how to protect themselves or, in some cases, a lack of power to protect themselves.

Education and Prevention Several international organizations are working to lessen the toll that HIV and AIDS are taking on populations all over the world. The World Health Organization and the Joint United Nations Programme on HIV/AIDS monitor the situation and recommend steps for stemming the epidemic in different countries.

The main goal of international organizations is HIV education. Making people in high-risk countries aware of how to protect themselves from HIV infection is a huge step toward prevention. Because treatment can be very expensive and inaccessible for the people at highest risk, much effort is put toward preventing HIV infection in the first place.

In addition to prevention education, international organizations coordinate treatment efforts for people already living with HIV and AIDS. Efforts are being made to provide medicine to millions of infected people in countries most affected by HIV and AIDS.

FIGURE 13 A girl from Zambia, a country in Africa, holds a sign she made for World AIDS Day.

3. Assess

Evaluate

These assignments can help you assess students' mastery of the section content.

Section 3 Review

Answers appear below.

Teaching Resources

• Practice 22-3
• Section 22-3 Quiz

L2 Reteach

Ask students to write a paragraph in which they correctly use each of the section vocabulary terms. Have pairs of students exchange and check for errors in one another's completed paragraphs. Partners should work together to rewrite any incorrect sentences.

L4 Enrich

Teaching Resources
• Enrich 22-3

Section 3 Review

Key Ideas and Vocabulary

1. Explain how HIV affects the immune system and how it eventually leads to AIDS.
2. What is meant by an **opportunistic infection**? Give an example.
3. What are four ways that HIV can be transmitted from an infected person to an uninfected person? List three ways HIV is *not* transmitted.
4. Which region of the world accounts for the majority of HIV infections?

Critical Thinking

5. **Making Judgments** Should teens in the United States be concerned about the global AIDS problem? Why or why not?

Health at School

AIDS Awareness Plan an AIDS Awareness Day at your school. Divide your class into groups to make posters about different aspects of HIV and AIDS. For example, one poster could focus on how HIV is transmitted. Another poster could focus on the status of the AIDS epidemic. Display your posters at school to help educate other students. **WRITING**

6. **Evaluating** HIV is more common in poorer countries than in wealthier countries. Why do you think this might be the case?

Health at School

AIDS Awareness Divide the class into groups, and assign a different aspect of HIV/AIDS to each group. After groups complete their posters, arrange for students to hold poster sessions in the cafeteria during lunch periods on AIDS Awareness Day. At the sessions, students can use their posters to educate other students about AIDS.

mitted through casual contact, such as going to classes, eating lunch, or holding hands with an infected person.

4. sub-Saharan Africa
5. Answers may vary, but they should be logical and show awareness of the dangers of a global HIV/AIDS problem.
6. *Sample answer:* because there is less money in poorer countries to educate people about how to prevent AIDS

Section 3 Review

1. HIV attacks specific cells of the immune system, disabling the body's defenses against other pathogens. When the immune system becomes severely disabled, the infected person has AIDS.
2. An opportunistic infection is an infection that attacks a person with a weakened immune system. Students may give any one of the following examples: tuberculosis, fungal infections, and pneumocystis carinii pneumonia.
3. HIV can be transmitted through sexual contact, shared needles, contact with blood, and from mother to baby. HIV is not trans-

Evaluating Internet Sources

Objective

Evaluate Internet sources to access reliable health information.

Teaching Strategies

- Make sure students are aware of search engines that are generally useful for academic research.

- If computer time is limited, you can have students work on this activity in pairs or small groups. You can also bookmark the SciLinks.org/health Web site so students can access it more quickly.

- Share with students names of government agencies that have some of the most useful and reliable Web sites for health information, including the Centers for Disease Control and Prevention (CDC) and the National Institutes of Health (NIH).

- Advise students not to rule out automatically all .com Web sites. Some major research hospitals, including the Mayo Clinic, have .com Web sites that provide the public with reliable, up-to-date medical information.

- Print copies of a Web page from an up-to-date, reliable Web site on HIV/AIDS. Show students where to look on the Web page for the agency or organization that operates the site, the author of the site, and when the site was last updated.

- Also print copies of a Web page from an out-of-date or unreliable Web site. Have students find evidence or clues that the information is dated or unreliable.

Accessing Information

Evaluating Internet Sources

The amount of health information available on the Internet can be overwhelming. For example, suppose you wanted to learn more about one of the sexually transmitted infections discussed in this chapter. If you typed the name of the STI into a search engine, you would likely come up with thousands of hits. You can't possibly visit every site, so how do you decide which sites have accurate information? The following guidelines will help you evaluate the reliability of Internet sources. These guidelines apply to Internet sources on all kinds of topics, not just health topics.

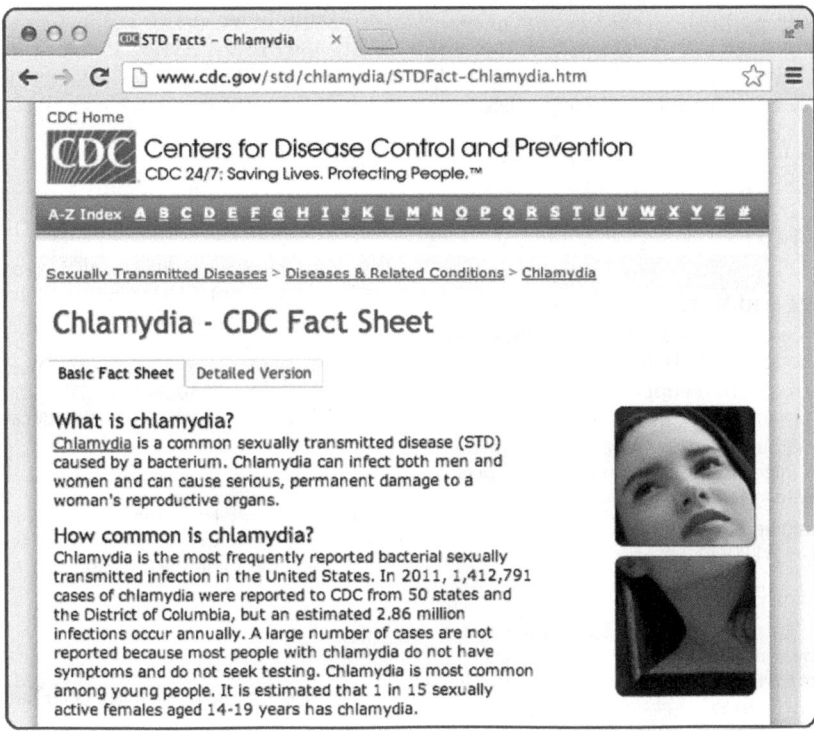

🚩 **Sensitive Issues**

Online research is a good alternative to class discussions of sensitive issues such as HIV/AIDS. Suggest that students follow the guidelines in this activity and do online searches to find answers to any questions they still have about HIV and other STIs. Make sure students use only reliable Web sites, because misinformation can be as dangerous as lack of information.

---

❶ Determine the type of Web site you are looking at and its purpose.

The Web address tells you what type of company or organization operates the site.

▶ A **.gov** in the address indicates that the site is run by a government organization. This type of site will usually provide reliable information. It may also represent the current administration's point of view.

▶ A **.com** or a **.net** indicates that it is a commercial site. A commercial site may provide information about products that are for sale. If the site is sponsored by the business that would profit from sales of those products, you probably will not find any negative information about the products on that site.

▶ A **.edu** indicates that an educational institution runs the site. Professors and students often post their own research on such sites.

▶ A **.org** indicates that a non-profit organization runs the site. Be aware of the organization's agenda as you consider its content.

❷ Identify the author(s) of the site.

The author(s) should be indicated clearly at the top or bottom of the page, or on a page that is linked to the page you are looking at. What are the author's credentials? Is there contact information for the author? If it is not clear who takes responsibility for the content, it may not be reliable.

❸ Determine if the information is current.

Many Web sites indicate when their content was last updated. Information on some topics may become out of date quickly. For example, if you are looking for the number of people who have been diagnosed with AIDS this year, you should look for a site that has been updated recently.

❹ Determine the quality of the site.

Does the site look organized and professional, or does it look like it was put together haphazardly? Is the information presented in a straightforward way, or does it ramble?

❺ Verify the information on the site with information from another source.

Does the site provide sources for the information it provides? If not, look elsewhere for information.

Practice the Skill

1. Go online and use a search engine to find a Web site on sexually transmitted infections and AIDS. See if you can answer the following questions based on the page you find:
   a. Who is the author of the site?
   b. What bias might the author have regarding the topic?
   c. When was the site last updated?
   d. What sources did the author use?

2. Based on your answers to the questions above, evaluate the reliability of the information on that Web site. Would you trust the information provided there? How would you verify that information?

Sexually Transmitted Infections and AIDS **591**

Practice the Skill

1. a. Students' answers should indicate the individual or group responsible for the site's content.

   b. Answers will vary depending on the site. For example, a medical researcher might be biased against research that contradicts his or her own research.

   c. Students should indicate the latest date shown on the page.

   d. Students' answers should list all sources cited on the page.

2. Answers will vary. Students should justify their evaluation of the site's content using the criteria listed in the numbered steps on this page.

Health and Community

 HIV/AIDS Task Force

Many communities have an HIV/AIDS Task Force, generally consisting of people from different professions who meet with the common aim of helping people with HIV and AIDS. A task force might include doctors, nurses, public health workers, clergy, lawyers, financial advisors, and social workers. Have students find out whether their community has an HIV/AIDS Task Force. If it does, ask students to arrange with the director to attend a meeting. Afterward, students should report what they observed to the class. Lead the class in a discussion on why people with HIV/AIDS might need help from people in a variety of professions.

Objectives
Before class begins, write the objectives on the board. Have students copy the objectives into their notebooks at the start of class.

1. Focus

Warm-Up Advice Line

After students finish writing, ask: **Why is abstinence the only sure way to avoid becoming infected with HIV and other STIs?** *(Accept all reasonable answers. Sample answers: You usually can't tell if your partner is infected. Condoms are not 100% effective against HIV and other STIs.)* Tell students they will learn additional ways to avoid HIV infection when they read this section.

Presentation 22-4

Connect to Your Life It is much easier to avoid risky behaviors if you choose friends who have also decided to avoid risky behaviors.

Sensitive Issues
Students may worry that they are infected with HIV but be reluctant to get tested for fear other people will find out. Tell students there are confidential testing centers for HIV. Stress the importance of getting tested so treatment can begin as soon as possible. Explain that the sooner treatment begins, the more effective it is likely to be.

Protecting Yourself From HIV and AIDS

Objectives
▶ **Identify** three behaviors that can prevent the spread of HIV.
▶ **Describe** how a person gets tested for HIV.
▶ **Describe** the goal of HIV treatment.

Vocabulary
• universal precautions
• HIV-positive
• viral load

Warm-Up

Dear Advice Line,

Lately my boyfriend has been asking me to have sex. I really like him, but I'm not ready for that. Plus I'm not sure he's telling me everything about his past. What should I do?

WRITING Write a response to this teen, encouraging her to choose abstinence. What would you tell her about the risk of becoming infected with HIV and other STIs?

Preventing HIV Infection

At present there is no cure for HIV or AIDS. But, the good news is that you can choose behaviors that will help you avoid this very serious disease. **You can protect yourself from HIV by practicing abstinence, avoiding drugs, and avoiding contact with others' blood and body fluids.**

Practice Abstinence Choosing sexual abstinence is the best way to avoid HIV and AIDS. Even if you have been sexually active, you can choose abstinence. It is much easier to be abstinent if you have friends who are also abstinent. Spending time with responsible friends can reduce the pressure you may feel to engage in sexual behavior.

Avoid Drugs Avoiding drug use is also extremely important for reducing the risk of HIV infection. People who share contaminated needles to inject themselves with drugs are at a high risk for contracting HIV. People who have sex with drug abusers are also at high risk. Do not inject illegal drugs, and avoid sexual contact with anyone who uses illegal drugs.

Using alcohol or other drugs can impair a person's judgment. People with impaired judgment are more likely to engage in behaviors that place them at risk. To guard against infection, you need to be able to think clearly so you can make healthy decisions.

Connect to Your Life **How can your choice of friends help you avoid risky behaviors?**

TEENS *Are Asking . . .*

Q: I heard that heterosexual people hardly ever get HIV infections or AIDS as long as they don't get involved in drugs. Is that a myth or a fact?

A: It's a myth, and a very dangerous one! In 2006, one quarter of new cases of HIV/AIDS in adolescents and adults were transmitted through heterosexual contact. All sexually active people are at risk of HIV infection, unless they are absolutely certain their partners are free of HIV. Otherwise, virtually any type of sexual contact can present a risk for transmission of HIV.

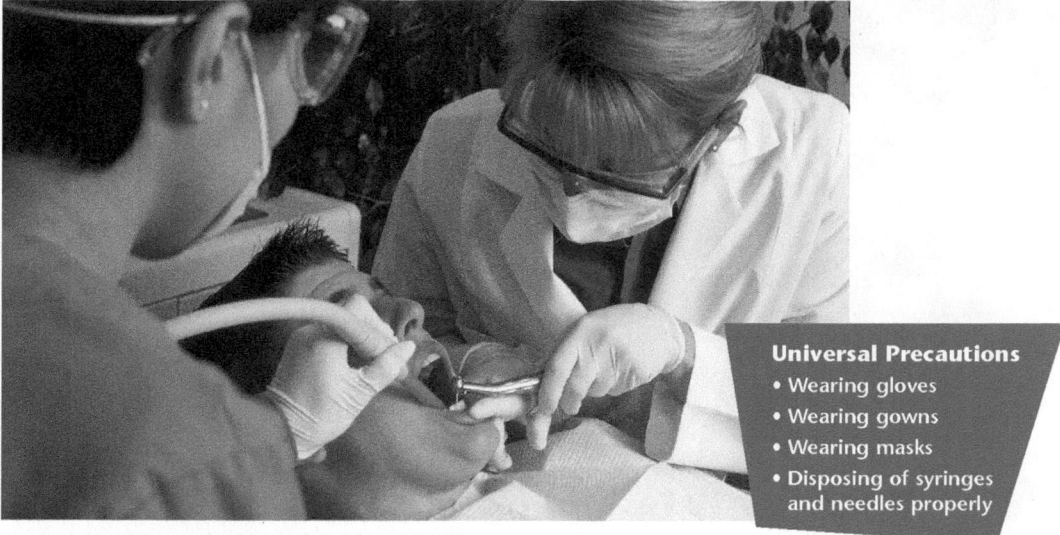

Universal Precautions
- Wearing gloves
- Wearing gowns
- Wearing masks
- Disposing of syringes and needles properly

FIGURE 14 Healthcare providers protect themselves and their patients by following universal precautions.

Avoid Contact With Blood or Body Fluids Never share any personal items that may have blood or other body fluids on them. For example, razors, syringes, and piercing or tattoo needles should never be shared. In addition, mothers who are infected with HIV should not breast-feed their babies because the virus can be transmitted through breast milk.

Healthcare providers often come into contact with the blood and body fluids of patients. To reduce the risk of HIV transmission, doctors, nurses, dentists, dental hygienists, and other healthcare providers practice **universal precautions,** as listed in Figure 14.

Sexual Fidelity For people in a sexual relationship it is important to practice sexual fidelity. Sexual fidelity is practiced when both partners agree to have sexual contact only with one another—to be monogamous. If both partners are uninfected, sexual fidelity eliminates the risk of getting HIV or another STI. If either partner has practiced risky behaviors in the past, he or she should be tested for HIV and other STIs.

Barrier Protection People in relationships may not be sure that their partners are faithful and uninfected. They can reduce the risk of HIV infection by using a condom during every sexual encounter. The condom must be made of latex or polyurethane, be free of tears, and be used in accordance with the directions on the package. Condoms serve as a physical barrier against HIV and some other pathogens that cause STIs. It is important to know that condoms are not 100 percent effective in preventing the transmission of HIV. Abstinence is the best way to protect yourself from HIV and other STIs.

2. Teach

L3 **EL** Reading/Note Taking 22-4
L2 Adapted Reading/Note Taking 22-4

Preventing HIV Infection

L2 Building Health Skills

Advocacy Have groups of students make posters advocating healthful behaviors that help prevent HIV infection. Posters should cover practicing abstinence, avoiding drugs, and the other behaviors described in the text. Posters should also be factually correct, attention-getting, and relevant to teens. Ask students to arrange to display their posters in places on and off campus where many teens will see them, such as the school cafeteria and local YMCA lobby.

L3 Journal Writing

Ask students to write a private journal entry describing ways they could respond to someone who pressures them to engage in sexual activity. Their responses should include reasons relating to HIV and other STIs. Encourage students to put their ideas into practice if they ever find themselves in such a situation. **WRITING**

L4 Active Learning

Have interested students interview dental hygienists or dental assistants about precautions they take to prevent contact with HIV and other infections. Ask the students to share what they learn with the class. Discuss how their reports relate to the universal precautions listed in Figure 14.

Differentiated Instruction

L2 Less Proficient Readers

As students read, tell them to look for information related to the section objectives that they copied into their notebooks earlier. Below or beside each objective, they should list relevant information. For example, for the first objective, they should list three behaviors that can prevent the spread of HIV. For the second objective, they should describe how a person gets tested for HIV. This exercise will help students focus on the most important points in the section.

Testing for HIV

L2 Addressing Misconceptions

HIV Testing Students may assume that HIV testing involves looking for the virus in blood. Tell them that HIV testing involves looking for antibodies to HIV in blood, not the virus itself, and it takes weeks or even months before there are enough antibodies to be detected. Explain that antibodies are proteins produced by an infected person's immune system in an (unsuccessful) attempt to fight the virus. People with antibodies to HIV in their blood are infected with HIV.

L3 Cultural Connection

Tell students that cultural beliefs make some people reluctant to be tested for HIV. For example, many Vietnamese and other Southeast Asian immigrants in the United States think that it is dangerous to have their blood drawn for testing, including HIV testing. This is because they believe that taking blood weakens the body. Ask students whether they know of similar beliefs in other cultures. Discuss how reluctance to be tested can adversely affect the health of people with HIV by delaying diagnosis and treatment.

L3 Class Discussion

Explain that most HIV testing centers provide counseling to people who test positive for HIV. Ask: **Why do you think it is important for people who test positive for HIV to receive counseling?** *(Sample answers: so they can learn how to avoid passing the virus to others; so they can get help coping with an incurable infection)*

Connect to Your Life *Sample answer:* by explaining that it could take months for antibodies to HIV to show up in the person's blood

FIGURE 15 A blood test can reveal if a person is infected with HIV. Getting an HIV-positive result can be frightening and depressing. Therefore, it is important that HIV-positive individuals receive counseling to help them deal with the emotional impacts of their infection.

Testing for HIV

The only way a person can know for certain whether or not he or she is infected with HIV is to have a blood test. People who engage in risky behaviors should have their blood tested at a clinic or by a private physician. The names of clinics that provide confidential HIV testing are available from each state's department of public health or from the Centers for Disease Control and Prevention. People who think they may have been exposed to HIV should practice abstinence to avoid spreading the virus.

In an HIV test, a person's blood is tested for antibodies to HIV. If antibodies are detected, a second test is done to verify the result. A person who is diagnosed as being infected with HIV is said to be **HIV-positive.**

An HIV-Positive Diagnosis If a person is diagnosed as HIV-positive, he or she needs to notify all previous sexual partners so that they can also be tested. Early diagnosis is important to prevent the spread of the disease and to start treatment as soon as possible.

It is difficult to cope with an HIV-positive diagnosis. For this reason, it is recommended that individuals receive counseling from a healthcare professional before being tested. People who learn they are HIV-positive should receive additional counseling.

Reasons for Follow-Up Testing If an HIV infection is recent, a blood test may not be accurate. This is because there is a lapse between the time of infection and the time when antibodies show up in a person's blood. Antibodies usually show up within three months after infection. So even if no antibodies are detected in the person's first blood test, he or she should avoid all high-risk behaviors and be tested again in three months.

Connect to Your Life How could you convince someone of the importance of follow-up testing?

MATH and Health

L3 Estimating

Remind students that about 1.2 million people in the United States had HIV infections in 2008. Point out in Figure 16 that the medical costs for a person with HIV may be about $25,000 per year. Ask students to use the data to estimate the total medical costs of HIV infections in the United States in 2006. (about $25,000 per person × 1.2 million people = about $30 billion in total costs) Discuss why the answer is just an estimate.

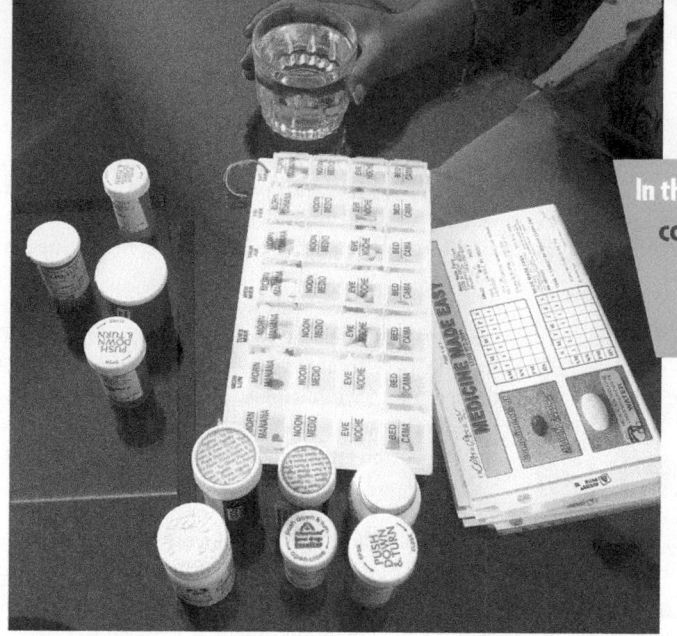

In the United States, medical costs for a person living with HIV are about $25,000 a year.

FIGURE 16 A common treatment regimen requires an HIV-positive person to take many pills each day. If the person misses too many doses, the virus may develop resistance to the medication.

Treatment for HIV and AIDS

Although there is no cure for HIV infection and AIDS, some treatments can add many years to a patient's life. The sooner a person begins treatment, the more effective it can be in slowing the progress of the disease.

The Goal of Treatment **The main goal of HIV treatment is to keep the person's immune system functioning as close to normal as possible.** To achieve this goal, the treatment must

- ▶ keep the person's **viral load**—the number of virus particles circulating in the body—as low as possible, and

- ▶ keep the person's T cell count as high as possible.

If both of these goals are achieved, the patient's immune system is more capable of fighting off opportunistic infections. Remember that current treatments do not rid the body of HIV. They try to stop HIV from destroying the immune system.

Combination Drug Therapy The most common treatment for HIV infection today is known as Highly Active AntiRetroviral Therapy, or HAART. HAART uses a combination of drugs to reduce the viral load in the blood. Multiple drugs are necessary to prevent the virus from reproducing inside helper T cells. A doctor prescribes a combination of drugs that is right for each individual patient.

Some drawbacks to HAART are its complicated dosage schedules, its cost, and its side effects, which can include liver and kidney damage. Furthermore, if a person is not consistent about taking the drugs exactly as prescribed, drug resistance can develop quickly.

GO ONLINE
PearsonSuccessNet.com
For: More on HIV/AIDS prevention

Sexually Transmitted Infections and AIDS **595**

3. Assess

Evaluate

These assignments can help you assess students' mastery of the section content.

Section 4 Review

Answers appear below.

Teaching Resources

- Practice 22-4
- Section 22-4 Quiz

L2 Reteach

Ask students to rewrite the section objectives as questions and then write answers to the questions. They can check their answers by rereading relevant passages in the text.

L4 Enrich

Teaching Resources
- Enrich 22-4

Health at School

HIV Prevention You may want to speak with teachers in grades six to eight about the program before students contact them. Check that students' outlines are accurate and complete. Ask students how they will convey the information covered in their outlines. Remind them that the material should be presented in ways that are suitable for younger students. Urge students to develop their programs and arrange to present them to classes in lower grades. You can ask the teachers of the classes to give you feedback on students' presentations.

FIGURE 17   Every year, thousands of people participate in walks to help raise money for AIDS research and education.

Living With HIV   People who are HIV-positive must take extra care to practice healthful behaviors. Eating right, exercising, and getting plenty of sleep are especially important for people who are HIV-positive. Regular visits to the doctor are also important for monitoring a patient's health and the effectiveness of HIV treatment.

When they are healthy, HIV-positive people can carry on with their careers and other activities. But they do have to avoid high-risk behaviors that put them at risk for infecting someone else. And because HIV compromises the immune system, they should stay away from anyone who has an infectious disease.

The Need for Support   As with any serious disease, people who are HIV-positive as well as their loved ones need a lot of support to help them deal with their distress and anxiety. Support may include counseling, healthcare services, and financial assistance.

HIV-positive individuals should be treated with compassion. They also should be allowed to live their lives with dignity. Because HIV cannot be transmitted by casual contact, such as hugging or shaking hands, no one needs to be fearful of working or going to school with someone who is HIV-positive.

Section 4   Review

Key Ideas and Vocabulary

1. What are three behaviors that can help you avoid HIV infection?

2. What does an HIV test involve?

3. What does **HIV-positive** mean?

4. What is the main goal of HIV treatment? How is that goal achieved?

Critical Thinking

5. Evaluating Depression can be a serious problem in people who are HIV-positive. What do you think are some ways to help people deal with the mental and emotional effects of this disease?

Health at School

HIV Prevention Some schools introduce HIV prevention education in grades six to eight. Find out if you or a group of classmates could prepare a program to help educate these younger students about protecting themselves from HIV infection. Then, develop an outline for your program. **WRITING**

6. Relating Cause and Effect Doctors recommend that people who are HIV-positive should stay as healthy as possible, eating well, getting enough sleep, and avoiding exposure to anyone with an infectious disease. Why do doctors recommend this?

GO ONLINE PearsonSuccessNet.com   Audio Summary Section 22.4

Section 4 Review

1. *Any three:* practice abstinence, avoid drugs, avoid contact with others' blood or body fluids, practice sexual fidelity in marriage, use barrier protection

2. It involves testing a person's blood for antibodies to HIV and retesting to verify the result if antibodies are detected.

3. It means a person is infected with HIV.

4. The main goal is to keep the person's immune system functioning as close to normal as possible. That goal is achieved by using a combination of drugs to reduce the viral load in the blood and prevent the virus from reproducing inside helper T cells.

5. *Sample answer:* reach out to loved ones for support, see a mental health professional

6. People who are HIV-positive have compromised immune systems. Healthy behaviors help to strengthen their immune systems and reduce their exposure to infections.

Chapter 22
At a Glance

VIDEO **TEENS Talk**

Risks and STIs List three things you learned from the video about the importance of sexual abstinence.

Section 1   The Risks of Sexual Activity

Key Ideas

▶ Risky behaviors that account for the current STI epidemic include ignoring the risks of sexual activity, having sexual contact with multiple partners, and not getting proper treatment.

▶ Practicing abstinence, avoiding drugs, and choosing responsible friends are ways to avoid STIs.

Vocabulary
• sexually transmitted infection (STI) (574)

Section 2   Kinds of STIs

Key Ideas

▶ Trichomoniasis, human papilloma virus, and chlamydia are common STIs in the United States.

▶ Other STIs include hepatitis, gonorrhea, genital herpes, and syphilis.

▶ People who participate in high-risk behaviors should get medical checkups every six months. Individuals who suspect they may be infected should seek prompt medical attention.

Vocabulary
• trichomoniasis (578)   • urethritis (578)
• vaginitis (578)   • human papilloma virus (579)
• chlamydia (579)   • pelvic inflammatory disease (579)
• gonorrhea (580)   • genital herpes (581)
• syphilis (582)   • chancre (582)

Section 3   HIV and AIDS

Key Ideas

▶ HIV attacks the immune system, disabling the body's defenses. When the immune system becomes severely disabled, the infected person has AIDS.

▶ Individuals infected with HIV can pass the virus on to someone else through the exchange of blood, semen, vaginal secretions, or breast milk.

▶ With 40 million people infected around the world, HIV and AIDS represent a global health problem.

Vocabulary
• HIV (584)   • AIDS (584)
• asymptomatic stage (585)
• opportunistic infection (586)

Section 4   Protecting Yourself From HIV and AIDS

Key Ideas

▶ You can protect yourself from HIV by practicing abstinence, avoiding drugs, and avoiding contact with others' blood and body fluids.

▶ In an HIV test, a person's blood is tested for antibodies to HIV. If antibodies are detected, a second test is done to verify the result.

▶ The main goal of HIV treatment is to keep the person's immune system functioning as close to normal as possible.

Vocabulary
• universal precautions (593)   • HIV-positive (594)
• viral load (595)

Sexually Transmitted Infections and AIDS   **597**

Chapter 22
At a Glance

VIDEO

Risks and STIs Ask for volunteers to share their answers. Use examples from the video to review risky behaviors and STIs.

Key Ideas Review

L1 Help small groups of students incorporate the key ideas on this page into a concept map summarizing chapter content.

L2 Have pairs of students make flashcards of chapter objectives. On the front of each card, they should write an objective, and on the back, the information that addresses the objective. Have partners use their flashcards to quiz each other on chapter content.

Vocabulary Review

EL Pair English language learners with proficient English speakers and ask each pair to make a crossword puzzle using at least ten terms from the chapter. Have pairs of students exchange and try to solve one another's puzzles.

L2 Play a quiz game in which you provide the answers and students respond with the correct questions. For answers, use definitions or descriptions of chapter vocabulary terms. For example, you might give the answer, "any pathogen that spreads from one person to another during sexual contact," for which the correct question would be, "What is an STI?"

Chapter 1 Review

 GO ONLINE

PearsonSuccessNet.com

Students can go online for a review activity on Chapter 22.

Reviewing Key Ideas

Section 1

1. c

2. *Any two:* practice sexual abstinence; avoid drugs, including alcohol; choose responsible friends

3. Answers will vary but should reveal knowledge that STIs can be spread by injecting illegal drugs.

Section 2

4. a   5. c

6. It can cause blindness and possibly death.

7. The person should refrain from sexual activity and see a doctor immediately.

8. so they can refrain from sexual activity and seek treatment

Section 3

9. d   10. d

11. because their immune system is weakened by HIV

12. through sexual contact that involves body fluids, via shared needles that are contaminated with infected blood, through direct contact with the blood of an infected person, and from an infected mother to her baby before, during, or after birth

13. Answers should reveal knowledge that STIs do not always cause symptoms and that treatment is important to prevent more serious health problems.

Section 4

14. c   15. b

16. Drug dosage schedules are complicated, the drugs are costly, and they can have serious side effects.

17. Yes, because it may take at least three months for HIV antibodies to show up in her blood.

18. Answers should show that students realize people need to know the risks in order to prevent HIV infection.

Chapter 22 Review

Reviewing Key Ideas

 GO ONLINE

PearsonSuccessNet.com

For: Chapter 22 review activity

Section 1

1. A reduced ability to have children is
   a. STI.
   b. epidemic.
   c. infertility.
   d. abstinence.

2. Describe two ways to avoid getting an STI.

3. **Critical Thinking** If you found out that the person you were dating had injected illegal drugs in the past, how would that affect your relationship?

Section 2

4. A serious infection of the female reproductive organs that can be caused by chlamydia is
   a. pelvic inflammatory disease.
   b. genital warts.
   c. syphilis.
   d. trichomoniasis.

5. An STI that cannot be treated with antibiotics is
   a. gonorrhea.   b. chlamydia.
   c. human papilloma virus.   d. syphilis.

6. How can genital herpes affect a newborn baby?

7. What steps should be taken by a person who suspects that he or she is infected with an STI?

8. **Critical Thinking** Why should someone who is diagnosed with an STI notify all of his or her sexual partners?

Section 3

9. The virus that causes AIDS is
   a. herpes.   b. HPV.
   c. PID.   d. HIV.

10. HIV destroys
    a. neurons.   b. antibodies.
    c. B cells.   d. T cells.

11. Why do people with AIDS fall victim to opportunistic infections?

12. Describe four ways that HIV is spread.

13. **Critical Thinking** Jason has engaged in high-risk sexual behavior, but he feels fine. He sees no reason to get tested for HIV or any other STI. What would you tell Jason about the importance of getting tested?

Section 4

14. Which of these behaviors is *not* a way to protect yourself from HIV?
    a. avoiding contact with blood
    b. practicing abstinence
    c. sharing needles
    d. avoiding alcohol

15. HIV-positive people receive treatments to keep
    a. their viral load as high as possible.
    b. their viral load as low as possible.
    c. their viral load equal to their T cell count.
    d. their T cell count as low as possible.

16. In what ways can HIV treatment be difficult?

17. **Critical Thinking** Alyssa has engaged in high-risk sexual behavior in the past three months. She had an HIV test a month ago that came back negative. Should she be tested again? Explain.

18. **Critical Thinking** Experts consider education critical in preventing HIV infection. Do you agree? Explain your answer.

 ## Building Health Skills

19. **Analyzing Influences** Do the media do a good job in educating people about HIV and other STIs? Give examples to support your answer.

20. **Advocacy** What could teens do to make abstinence an easier choice for their peers?

21. **Setting Goals** List some goals you have for the next ten years. How could practicing abstinence help you achieve those goals? **WRITING**

Health and Community

Public Service Announcement Some people behave in sexually risky ways. And in many cases, they don't get tested regularly for HIV or other STIs. Create a public service announcement that emphasizes the risks of certain behaviors and the importance of getting tested. Indicate where people in your community can go to get tested for HIV and other STIs. **WRITING**

Building Health Skills

19. Some students might say that the media do a poor job and cite examples from television or movies of people engaging in sexual contact, apparently without risk of STIs. Others might say that the media do a good job and cite examples of public service announcements warning people about the risks of HIV and other STIs.

20. *Sample answers:* Support peers' decisions to avoid risky behaviors. Set a good example for peers by avoiding risky behaviors themselves.

21. *Sample answer:* My goals are going to college and becoming a teacher. Practicing abstinence could help me achieve my goals by helping to keep me healthy and by preventing me from getting pregnant.

Standardized Test Prep

Math Practice

The graph shows the helper T cell counts recorded for a person who is HIV-positive. Use the graph to answer Questions 22–24.

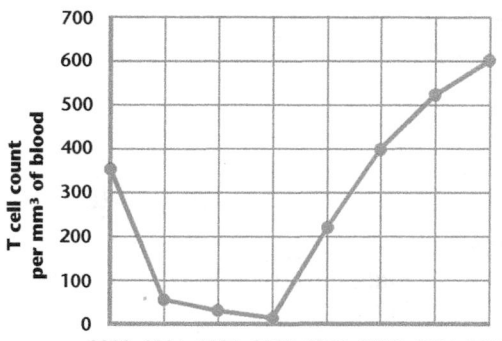

22. What is the lowest helper T cell count recorded for this patient?
  A 300 T cells per mm³ of blood
  B 100 T cells per mm³ of blood
  C 50 T cells per mm³ of blood
  D 10 T cells per mm³ of blood

23. During which year do you think this patient started treatment for HIV?
  F 1996   **G** 1998
  H 2000   **J** 2002

24. Between 2002 and 2006, the patient's T cell count
  A increased steadily.
  B decreased steadily.
  C fluctuated.
  D remained the same.

Test-Taking Tip

Underline important words and phrases as you read. Then when answering questions, you can access the important content quickly.

Reading and Writing Practice

Read the passage. Then answer Questions 25–28.

Researchers are working to develop preventive HIV vaccines to protect people who are HIV-negative and control the spread of HIV. Multiple HIV vaccines may be necessary to prevent infection in the same way that multiple drugs are needed to treat people who are already infected. Researchers are also evaluating therapeutic HIV vaccines to treat people who are HIV-positive. A therapeutic vaccine could theoretically be given during early infection to delay the need for antiretroviral therapy and reduce the risk of transmission.

25. A therapeutic vaccine would
  A prevent HIV infection.
  B treat people who are HIV-positive.
  C be given prior to HIV infection.
  D increase the need for antiretroviral therapy.

26. In this passage, the word *antiretroviral* refers to
  F drugs that treat HIV infection.
  G an HIV vaccine.
  H T cell count.
  J viral load.

27. According to the passage, which of these statements is true?
  A Only one vaccine will be needed to prevent HIV infection.
  B If a vaccine works to prevent HIV infection, it will also be able to treat someone who is HIV-positive.
  C Preventive vaccines will not control the spread of HIV.
  D A therapeutic vaccine should delay the need for antiretroviral therapy.

Constructed Response
28. In a paragraph, compare the two different types of HIV vaccines being developed.

Standardized Test Prep

Math Practice
22. D
23. G
24. A

Reading and Writing Practice
25. B
26. F
27. D
28. *Sample answer:* Preventive and therapeutic vaccines are the two different types of HIV vaccines being developed. Preventive vaccines would protect people who are HIV-negative. They would control the spread of HIV. Therapeutic vaccines would treat people who are HIV-positive. They would delay the need for treatment and reduce the risk of transmission.

Health and Community

Public Service Announcement Suggest that students contact the state department of public health, local hospitals, or health clinics. Much of the information students need is available online. The PSAs should include risk factors for infection and explain how testing helps people get the appropriate treatment for an STI and helps curb transmission of STIs.

CHAPTER 23 Chronic Diseases and Disabilities

Section Objectives	Standards Correlation	Instructional Resources L3	SE eTEXT	TE eTEXT	PRINT
1 Cardiovascular Diseases ⏱ 2 periods; 1 block **23.1.1 List** six types of cardiovascular disease. **23.1.2 Describe** the ways in which cardiovascular disease is detected and treated. **23.1.3 Identify** risk factors for cardiovascular disease and ways to lower your risk.	NHES: 1.12.4, 2.12.6, 6.12.1, 7.12.1, 7.12.2	SE Warm-Up, p. 602	•	•	•
		RN Note Taking Guide 23-1	•	•	•
		IB Image Bank 23-1		•	
		TR Practice 23-1		•	
		TR Section 23-1 Quiz		•	
2 Cancer ⏱ 2 periods; 1 block **23.2.1 Describe** how cancer affects the body. **23.2.2 Identify** the tests and treatments for cancer. **23.2.3 List** seven ways you can prevent cancer.	NHES: 1.12.3, 1.12.4, 3.12.5, 7.12.1, 7.12.3	SE Warm-Up, p. 609	•	•	•
		SE Media Wise Evaluating Tanning Products, p. 612	•	•	•
		RN Note Taking Guide 23-2	•	•	•
		TR Practice 23-2		•	
		TR Section 23-2 Quiz		•	
3 Other Chronic Diseases ⏱ 2 periods; 1 block **3.3.1 Distinguish** between the two types of diabetes. **3.3.2 Describe** how allergies and asthma affect the body. **3.3.3 Identify** the symptoms of arthritis.	NHES: 1.12.3, 2.12.4, 2.12.6, 7.12.1, 7.12.3	SE Warm-Up, p. 614	•	•	•
		SE Technology & Health Vital Signs on the Go, p. 622	•	•	•
		RN Note Taking Guide 23-3	•	•	•
		IB Image Bank 23-10		•	
		TR Practice 23-3		•	
		TR Section 23-3 Quiz		•	
Being Assertive ⏱ 1 period; 1/2 block **BHS.23 Communicate** assertively in difficult situations.	NHES: 4.12.1, 4.12.3, 4.12.4, 8.12.4	SE Practice the Skill, p. 621	•	•	•
		RN Building Health Skills 23	•	•	•
4 Disabilities ⏱ 1 period; 1/2 block **23.4.1 Identify** the three most common physical disabilities. **23.4.2 Explain** how the rights of people with disabilities are protected.	NHES: 2.12.4, 2.12.6, 2.12.10, 4.12.4, 8.12.3	SE Warm-Up, p. 623	•	•	•
		RN Note Taking Guide 23-4	•	•	•
		IB Image Bank 23-15		•	
		TR Practice 23-4		•	
		TR Section 23-4 Quiz		•	

Chapter Review and Assessment

SE Chapter 23 Review, p. 628 L3
CTB Chapter 23 Test L2 L3 L4
SE Standardized Test Prep, p. 629 L3

PROGRAM COMPONENTS

SE Student Edition	**CTB** Computer Test Bank
TE Teacher Edition	**AUD** Audio Section Summaries
TR Teaching Resources	
RN Reading and Note Taking Guide	**DVD** Teens Talk Video Series
	VVG Video Viewing Guide
ARN Adapted Reading and Note Taking Guide	**PPT** Presentation
IB Image Bank	

Differentiated Instruction

L1 L2 L4 EL

		SE eTEXT	TE eTEXT	PRINT
ARN	Note Taking Guide 23-1 L2	•	•	
RN	Note Taking Guide 23-1 EL	•	•	•
AUD	Audio Summary 23-1 L1 L2 EL	•	•	
TE	Reteach Strategy, p. 608 L2		•	•
TR	Enrich 23-1 L4		•	
ARN	Note Taking Guide 23-2 L2	•	•	
RN	Note Taking Guide 23-2 EL	•	•	•
AUD	Audio Summary 23-2 L1 L2 EL	•	•	
TE	Reteach Strategy, p. 613 L2		•	•
TR	Enrich 23-2 L4		•	
ARN	Note Taking Guide 23-3 L2	•	•	
RN	Note Taking Guide 23-3 EL	•	•	•
AUD	Audio Summary 23-3 L1 L2 EL	•	•	
TE	Reteach Strategy, p. 619 L2		•	•
TR	Enrich 23-3 L4		•	
ARN	Building Health Skills 23 L2	•	•	
RN	Building Health Skills 23 EL	•	•	•
ARN	Note Taking Guide 23-4 L2	•	•	
RN	Note Taking Guide 23-4 EL	•	•	•
AUD	Audio Summary 23-4 L1 L2 EL	•	•	
TE	Reteach Strategy, p. 626 L2		•	•
TR	Enrich 23-4 L4		•	

ABILITY LEVELS

L1 For students with special needs
L2 For less proficient readers
L3 For all students
L4 For gifted and talented students
EL For English language learners

Chapter 23 Digital/Video Pathway

This alternative pathway allows you to teach this chapter's content using only the video and online materials.

Preview

DVD Video #23 Preview
SE   Video #23 Preview Activity
VVG Video #23 Worksheet

Living With Disabilities

1
PPT   23-1 Presentation
RN/ARN   23-1 Note Taking
PPT   23-1 Section Quiz

2
PPT   23-2 Presentation
RN/ARN   23-2 Note Taking
PPT   23-2 Section Quiz

3
PPT   23-3 Presentation
RN/ARN   23-3 Note Taking
PPT   23-3 Section Quiz

4
DVD   Video #23 Explore/Wrap-Up
VVG   Video #23 Worksheet
PPT   23-4 Presentation
RN/ARN   23-4 Note Taking
PPT   23-4 Section Quiz

Living With Disabilities

Chapter Preview

Section 1 Cardiovascular Diseases
Cardiovascular diseases include hypertension, atherosclerosis, heart attack, arrhythmia, congestive heart failure, and stroke. Many medical technologies and surgical methods are available for detecting and treating cardiovascular disease. Healthful behaviors can lower the risk of cardiovascular disease.

Section 2 Cancer
Cancer harms the body by destroying healthy body tissues. The key to curing cancer is early detection and treatment. Certain behaviors have been shown to decrease the risk of cancer.

Section 3 Other Chronic Diseases
People with type 1 or type 2 diabetes have trouble using the glucose in their blood. Allergies occur when the immune system overreacts to a foreign substance. One type of allergic reaction can lead to asthma. Arthritis is a very common chronic disease in which joints become irritated or inflamed.

Communicating

Being Assertive
Communicating assertively in difficult situations can help people feel more self-confident and more in control of factors that affect their lives.

Section 4 Disabilities
The three most common disabilities are impaired vision, impaired hearing, and impaired mobility. The Americans with Disabilities Act (ADA) guarantees the civil rights of Americans who have physical or mental disabilities.

Chronic Diseases and Disabilities

1 Cardiovascular Diseases

2 Cancer
- **MediaWise** Evaluating Tanning Products

3 Other Chronic Diseases
- **Technology and Health** Vital Signs on the Go

Building Health Skills
- **Communicating** Being Assertive

4 Disabilities

GO ONLINE PearsonSuccessNet.com

TEENS Talk

VIDEO 23

Living With Disabilities

Preview **Activity**

What Does a Disability Mean to You?

Complete this activity before you watch the video.

1. Write down your own definition of the word *disability*.
2. Form a group with two of your classmates. Share and discuss the definitions you wrote.
3. As a group, write a new definition of *disability* that you all can agree on. **WRITING**

600

GO ONLINE
PearsonSuccessNet.com
For resources and activities for this chapter.

Sensitive Issues

- Chronic diseases are likely to be sensitive topics for students who have developed a chronic disease or have family members with a chronic disease. Never ask students to disclose information they would rather keep confidential.

- Learning about disabilities can be uncomfortable for disabled students or students who have disabled family members. Avoid asking students to share their experiences with the class, except when it is on their own initiative.

Video Objectives

Use the video to help students

Identify obstacles that people with disabilities face.

Describe the health skills that people with disabilities use to overcome obstacles.

Build resilience skills to help them deal with obstacles and setbacks in their lives.

Preview **Activity**

What Does a Disability Mean to You?

Before students watch the video, have them complete the Preview Activity. After students complete the assignment, review the definitions of the word *disability* asked for in step 3. Write a few of the definitions on the board so students can keep them in mind while watching the video. Be sure to revisit these definitions after showing the video, and have the class try to come to an agreement on one of the definitions.

601

From the Authors

Chronic diseases are not only among the leading causes of death in the United States, but they are also responsible for significant disease-related disability. In addition, physical disabilities due to impaired vision, hearing, and mobility constitute important causes of functional limitations that can reduce an individual's capacity for independent living. How do people react to a disability? Does a disability interfere with the things they want to do? When should others be ready to give assistance? Viewing and discussing the video *Living With Disabilities* should be helpful in exploring answers to such questions.

This chapter summarizes what is currently known about the causes, prevention, and treatment of chronic diseases and disabilities. Students should leave their study of this chapter with some practical knowledge. For example, they will learn about the warning signs of a heart attack in Figure 2 on page 604.

Objectives

Before class begins, write the objectives on the board. Have students copy the objectives into their notebooks at the start of class.

1. Focus

Warm-Up Quick Quiz

Use the Warm-Up Presentation slide to survey student responses.

Give students a few minutes to complete the quiz. Discuss how the behaviors represented by the four statements could affect a person's chances of developing a cardiovascular disease.

Presentation 23-1

Section 1

Cardiovascular Diseases

Objectives

▶ **List** six types of cardiovascular disease.

▶ **Describe** the ways in which cardiovascular disease is detected and treated.

▶ **Identify** risk factors for cardiovascular disease and ways to lower your risk.

Vocabulary

- chronic disease
- cardiovascular disease
- angina pectoris
- heart attack
- fibrillation
- stroke
- cerebral hemorrhage
- aneurysm

Warm-Up

Quick Quiz Complete each of these statements with *always, sometimes,* or *never.*

1️⃣ I __?__ eat foods rich in vitamins, minerals, and fiber, and I __?__ avoid foods high in saturated fats and salt.

2️⃣ I __?__ exercise on a regular basis.

3️⃣ I __?__ avoid tobacco products and alcohol.

4️⃣ I __?__ include relaxation time in my schedule.

WRITING Predict how your behavior may affect your chances of developing cardiovascular disease.

Types of Cardiovascular Disease

In the United States today, the leading causes of death are not infectious diseases. Instead they are **chronic diseases,** diseases that persist for a long period or recur throughout life. Chronic diseases are usually caused by risk factors that are behavioral, environmental, or hereditary—not by pathogens. The most common chronic diseases are **cardiovascular diseases** (KAHR dee oh VAS kyuh lur), which are diseases of the heart (cardio) and blood vessels (vascular). **Cardiovascular diseases include hypertension, atherosclerosis, heart attack, arrhythmia, congestive heart failure, and stroke.**

Hypertension A person whose blood pressure consistently measures 140/90 or higher has hypertension, or high blood pressure. Since many people experience no obvious symptoms, hypertension frequently goes undetected and is known as the "silent killer." The only way to know if you have hypertension is to have your blood pressure measured.

Over time, hypertension can lead to heart disease. This is because the increased blood pressure puts a strain on the heart and blood vessels. Hypertension can be controlled with behavior changes and medications.

Nearly one out of three American adults has hypertension, and the number of teens with hypertension is on the rise. You can reduce your risk of developing hypertension by exercising regularly, maintaining a healthy weight, reducing stress, and eating foods that are low in sodium.

Sensitive Issues

Students from families that are dealing with illness or death caused by cardiovascular disease may be uncomfortable during these discussions. There may also be students who are struggling with one of these diseases. Such students may choose to participate freely, or they may choose to be guarded about their condition.

For Your INFORMATION!

Cardiovascular Diseases

In 2005, the Centers for Disease Control and Prevention (CDC) reported the following facts about cardiovascular disease.

- About 1 American dies of cardiovascular disease every 33 seconds.
- About 1 in 5 Americans today have some form of cardiovascular disease.

- Heart disease is the leading cause of death in the United States; stroke is the third leading cause.
- The leading cause of premature, permanent disability in the United States is coronary heart disease.

Atherosclerosis Atherosclerosis (ath uh roh skluh ROH sis) is a disease in which fatty substances, including cholesterol (kuh LES tur awl), build up inside artery walls. These deposits, called plaque (plak), cause the artery walls to thicken and narrow, as shown in Figure 1. As it becomes more difficult for blood to flow in the narrowed vessels, blood pressure rises.

A diet high in saturated fats can increase your risk of developing atherosclerosis. This is because saturated fats tend to increase levels of cholesterol in the blood. Other major risk factors include a family history of heart disease, smoking, diabetes, obesity, and lack of exercise.

Atherosclerosis can also increase your risk of developing other cardiovascular conditions.

▸ **Arteriosclerosis** People who suffer from atherosclerosis often have arteriosclerosis (ahr teer ee oh skluh ROH sis) as well. Arteriosclerosis, or hardening of the arteries, develops when arteries lose their elasticity and become stiff.

▸ **Coronary Heart Disease** When atherosclerosis starts to develop in the arteries that supply blood to the heart, it can lead to coronary heart disease. As the coronary arteries narrow, blood flow to the heart decreases. **Angina pectoris** (an JY nuh PEK tur is) is the chest pain that occurs when an area of the heart does not get enough oxygen-rich blood. Coronary heart disease can lead to a heart attack.

 **Connect to Your Life** How do your exercise habits affect your chances of developing atherosclerosis?

FIGURE 1 An artery with atherosclerosis offers more resistance to blood flow than a healthy artery. This increases blood pressure and causes the heart to work harder.
Relating Cause and Effect What kind of eating habits could lead to atherosclerosis?

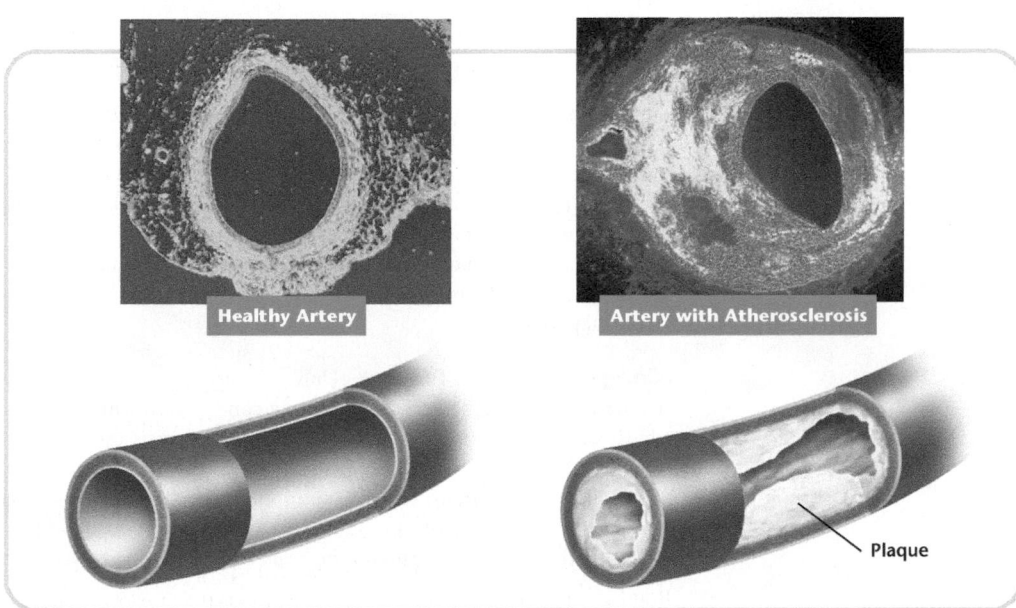

Healthy Artery

Artery with Atherosclerosis

Plaque

Chronic Diseases and Disabilities **603**

Differentiated Instruction

L2 Less Proficient Readers

The similarity of the terms *atherosclerosis* and *arteriosclerosis* may prove confusing for some students. Point out that the second part of both words is the same—*sclerosis,* which means "hardening." Students can remember that *arteriosclerosis* means hardening of the arteries by focusing on the first part of the term, *arterio-,* or artery. By contrast, the first part of

atherosclerosis—*athero*—comes from a Greek word for a pasty food (gruel). Atherosclerosis, then, indicates a hardening of a pastelike substance (plaque) on the inside of arteries. Emphasize that atherosclerosis is a disease and arteriosclerosis is a condition that can develop as part of the disease atherosclerosis.

---

2. Teach

L3 EL Reading/Note Taking 23-1
L2 Adapted Reading/Note Taking 23-1

Types of Cardiovascular Disease

L2 Class Discussion

Ask: **What are chronic diseases?** *(diseases that persist for a long period or recur throughout life)* **Would strep throat be considered a chronic disease? Why or why not?** *(It would not be considered a chronic disease because it is a disease that lasts for only a short period, and it is caused by a pathogen.)* **What are three types of risk factors that cause chronic diseases?** *(behavioral, environmental, and hereditary)* Remind students that they learned about genetic disorders in Chapter 18. Have students turn back to Figure 13 in Chapter 18 to refresh their memories about genetic disorders. Ask: **Why would hemophilia, for example, be considered a chronic disease?** *(It is a disease that persists throughout a person's life.)*

L3 Visual Learning: Figure 1
Image Bank Figure 23-1

Have students examine the photos of the two arteries, and ask: **What is the main difference you can observe between the two arteries?** *(The healthy artery has a larger hole, or inside diameter, than does the artery with atherosclerosis.)* **What caused the narrowing of the artery with atherosclerosis?** *(deposits of plaque)* **What are major risk factors for atherosclerosis?** *(a diet high in saturated fats, a family history of heart disease, smoking, diabetes, obesity, and lack of exercise)* **Caption Answer** A diet high in saturated fats can increase the risk of developing atherosclerosis.

Connect to Your Life Allow students to answer this question in their private journals.

Chronic Diseases and Disabilities **603**

L2 Teacher Demo

On the board, draw a flowchart to help students understand the connection between atherosclerosis and a heart attack. Begin with a box labeled *Risk Factors for Atherosclerosis*. Before labeling the following boxes, ask students to help you fill them in. Draw an arrow to a second box labeled *Atherosclerosis*. Draw an arrow to a third box labeled *Coronary Heart Disease*. Draw an arrow to a fourth box labeled *Blood Clot in Coronary Artery*. Draw an arrow to a fifth box labeled *Heart Attack*.

L1 Active Learning

Ask students to use the heart attack warning signs in Figure 2 to design and make a card that can be carried in a wallet or purse. With a card that lists the warning signs of a heart attack, a person experiencing a troubling symptom can quickly check to see if it is a symptom of a heart attack. Explain that a person having a heart attack might not have all the symptoms, and often a person doesn't know what they're experiencing. Tell students that they could include a warning at the bottom of the card that immediate medical attention is required for a heart attack. After students make their cards, suggest that they give them to friends or relatives who might appreciate having such a card.

EL Cooperative Learning

Make a set of cards with the name of a cardiovascular disease mentioned in the text written on each. Write the definition of each disease on another set of cards. Make multiple sets of cards so the class can do this activity in small groups. Divide the class into groups, and have them match the disease cards with the correct definitions.

▶ Uncomfortable pressure or pain in the center of the chest lasting for two minutes or longer

▶ Pain spreading to the shoulder, neck, or arms

▶ Severe pain, dizziness, fainting, sweating, extreme anxiety, nausea, or shortness of breath

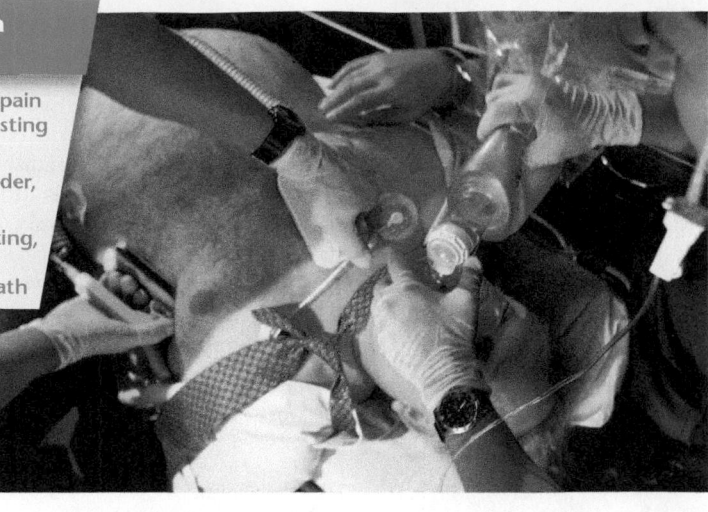

FIGURE 2 Learn to recognize the warning signs of a heart attack. Automated external defibrillators, located in public places such as malls and airports, can help save a heart attack victim's life.

Heart Attack A **heart attack** occurs when some of the tissue in the heart doesn't receive its normal blood supply and dies. The cause is usually a blood clot that forms in a coronary artery that has been narrowed by atherosclerosis. The clot blocks blood flow to the heart. The more heart tissue that dies due to lack of oxygen, the more severe the heart attack.

Each year, over a million people in the United States suffer a heart attack. Of those people, about 500,000 die. Figure 2 lists the warning signs of a heart attack. Immediate medical attention can mean the difference between life and death.

Four major risk factors for heart attacks are high blood pressure, high levels of cholesterol in the blood, physical inactivity, and smoking.

Arrhythmia Irregular heartbeats, or arrhythmias (uh RITH mee uhs), are another form of heart disease. The heart may beat too slowly or too quickly, or with an uneven rhythm. Arrhythmias may result from damage caused by a heart attack, or they may develop spontaneously. **Fibrillation** (fib ruh LAY shun) is a life-threatening arrhythmia in which the heart twitches rapidly in an uncoordinated fashion. Some abnormal heartbeats can be controlled by medications. Others require surgery to implant an artificial pacemaker.

Congestive Heart Failure Unlike a heart attack, congestive heart failure is not a single event. Instead it is a condition in which the heart slowly weakens over time. Usually, years of atherosclerosis and high blood pressure can lead to congestive heart failure. As the heart weakens, it is unable to pump as much blood as it once did. Swelling of the feet and lower legs is a symptom of congestive heart failure. Drugs that relax blood vessels and decrease the strain on the heart may be used to treat congestive heart failure.

604 *Chapter 23*

WRITING **and Health**

L3 Comparison of Diseases

Have students describe the conditions of two hypothetical heart patients. One patient just suffered a heart attack, and the other suffers from congestive heart failure. Students should write a paragraph that compares a heart attack to congestive heart failure. Students' descriptions should be clear and complete, with details about the similarities and differences between the two diseases and what causes them. As they write this comparison, any gaps or misconceptions in their knowledge should be revealed to them. Encourage students to use their textbooks as needed to fill in gaps and correct errors.

Stroke A **stroke** is a sudden disruption of blood flow to part of the brain. Strokes can occur when an artery that supplies blood to an area of the brain is blocked. The blockage may be caused by atherosclerosis or by a blood clot.

Strokes also can occur when a weakened artery in the brain bursts, flooding the area with blood. If the burst artery is located in the cerebrum, the main portion of the brain, the stroke is called a **cerebral hemorrhage** (suh REE brul HEM ur ij). Cerebral hemorrhage may also be caused by a head injury or by an aneurysm that bursts. An **aneurysm** (AN yuh riz um) is a blood-filled weak spot that balloons out from the artery wall.

Without a supply of blood, brain cells soon die from lack of oxygen. The effects of a stroke depend on its location and severity.

▶ Brain damage from a stroke can affect the senses, speech, comprehension, behavior, thought patterns, and memory.

▶ Paralysis on one side of the body is common. Many people who survive a stroke become severely disabled. Sometimes normal function can be regained with therapy.

▶ Over one third of stroke cases result in death.

Each year in the United States, more than 750,000 people experience a stroke. Risk factors for stroke include high blood pressure, high blood cholesterol, smoking, excessive use of alcohol, physical inactivity, and obesity. Figure 3 lists some of the warning signs of a stroke.

 **Connect to Your Life** List some ways you can lower your risk for a stroke.

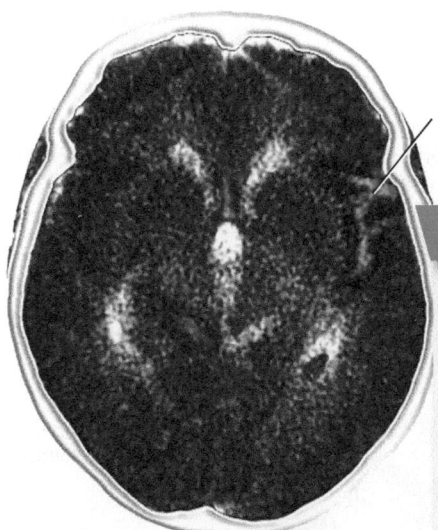

Top View of Brain

FIGURE 3 A blockage or break in an artery in the brain can cause a stroke. A person who experiences any of the warning signs of a stroke should seek prompt medical attention.

Cerebral hemorrhage

Warning Signs of a Stroke

▶ Sudden, severe headache with no apparent cause

▶ Sudden weakness or numbness of the face, arm, or leg on one side of the body

▶ Loss of speech, trouble talking, or trouble understanding speech

▶ Sudden dimness or loss of vision, particularly in one eye

▶ Unexplained dizziness, nausea, unsteadiness, or sudden falls

Chronic Diseases and Disabilities **605**

Treating Cardiovascular Disease

L3 Visual Learning: Figure 4

Have students read about the testing tools and treatment methods described in the figure. Challenge students to compare the kinds of information each tool can provide. For example, ask: **What information can an echocardiogram provide to a physician that an MRI cannot?** *(An echocardiogram shows the parts of a heart in movement, including the action of the valves, while an MRI provides a clear image of the heart.)* Explain that more than one of these testing tools may be used to diagnose a patient's disease. Which tool is used depends on what a physician needs to know in order to proceed with treatment.

L3 Building Media Literacy

Instruct each student to find and print one online source about treating cardiovascular disease. Divide the class into groups, and have group members pool their sources and rank them according to how reliable and informative they are. Before ranking the sources, each group should come up with a set of criteria with which to judge their sources. If they are having trouble, refer them to the Building Health Skills on pages 590–591. Students should rank each source separately on each criterion and then decide which is the best source overall. Call on a member of each group to explain the group's choice.

FIGURE 4 There are many testing and treatment options for patients with cardiovascular disease. New technologies are being developed that may replace these methods in the future.

Treating Cardiovascular Disease

Cardiovascular diseases cannot be cured, but they often can be controlled or prevented from getting worse. **There are many medical technologies and surgical methods available for detecting and treating cardiovascular diseases.** Some of these are described in Figure 4. In addition, medicines are often used to control cardiovascular diseases. Certain drugs may lower blood pressure, lower cholesterol levels in the blood, or lessen the chance of blood clots forming.

Testing and Treatment for Cardiovascular Disease

Testing Tools

Magnetic Resonance Imaging (MRI)
Magnetic energy is used to produce a clear image of the heart. Doctors can analyze the image for heart damage.

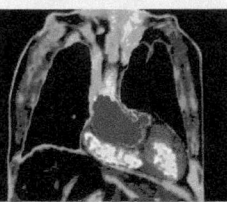

Electrocardiogram (ECG)
Electrodes attached to the skin detect the heart's electrical activity. Abnormalities in heart rhythm or other heart problems are revealed in the recorded pattern.

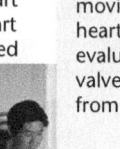

Echocardiogram
A device that generates sound waves is placed against the chest. The sound waves create a moving picture of the heart. A doctor can evaluate the heart's valves and chambers from the picture.

Arteriography
A flexible tube is threaded through an artery in an arm or leg until it reaches the heart. A dye is then released into the coronary arteries, and X-rays are taken. The X-rays can reveal blockages.

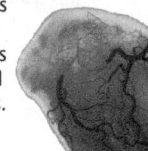

Treatment Methods

Balloon Angioplasty
A thin tube with an expandable tip is guided into a coronary artery. As the tip is inflated, it flattens fatty deposits in the artery wall, improving blood flow. Metal structures called stents are sometimes inserted to keep the artery open.

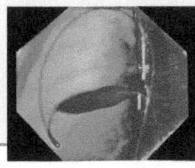

Coronary Bypass Surgery
Surgeons use a vein from the patient's leg or an artificial blood vessel to construct a detour around a blocked coronary artery. This procedure creates an alternate route for blood flow.

Artificial Pacemaker
An artificial pacemaker is a small, battery-operated device that is surgically implanted in the chest. It produces electrical impulses that regulate the heartbeat.

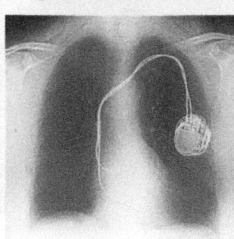

Heart Transplant
When a person's heart cannot function adequately, it may be replaced with a heart from an organ donor. This surgical procedure carries some risk because the immune system may reject the new heart. To lower rejection rates, doctors use drugs to suppress the immune system.

606   *Chapter 23*

For Your INFORMATION!

African Americans and Cardiovascular Disease

Studies have consistently shown that African Americans have higher rates of hypertension, stroke, and other cardiovascular diseases than do white Americans. Some scientists have long thought the main reason for the differences had to do with heredity—i.e., the genetic makeup of African Americans may put them at greater risk for these diseases.

But recent studies of Africans living in African countries and others of African heritage living around the world have conflicted with that idea. These studies claim that social factors, including stress, disparities in access to medical care, and poor health habits, are more likely to cause the differences between whites and African Americans.

FIGURE 5 Some people inherit a tendency to develop cardiovascular disease. Healthy behaviors are even more important for people with risk factors that they cannot control.

Preventing Cardiovascular Disease

Some risk factors for cardiovascular disease are out of your control. Others are within your control. **Choosing behaviors that lower your risk for cardiovascular disease is important for your health, both now and throughout your life.**

Risks You Cannot Control   Certain risk factors for cardiovascular disease are not within your control. If you have any of these risk factors, it is even more important that you practice healthy behaviors to combat cardiovascular disease.

▶ **Heredity** Having a family history of certain cardiovascular diseases, such as hypertension, may increase your risk of developing those diseases. It is important to be aware of your family's health history so that you can practice behaviors that may reduce your risk.

▶ **Ethnicity** Some diseases strike people of certain ethnicities disproportionately. For example, African Americans and Latinos tend to have higher rates of coronary heart disease.

▶ **Gender** Some cardiovascular diseases strike men and women at different rates. For example, men are more likely to suffer heart attacks than women. On the other hand, women are more likely to suffer strokes than men.

▶ **Age** As people age, their risk of cardiovascular disease increases. However, more young people today are being diagnosed with cardiovascular disease than ever before.

 Which of these factors increase your risk of cardiovascular disease?

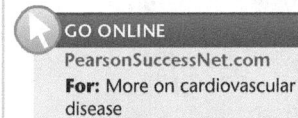
GO ONLINE
PearsonSuccessNet.com
For: More on cardiovascular disease

Chronic Diseases and Disabilities **607**

Preventing Cardiovascular Disease

L2 Building Health Skills

Accessing Information Have students determine the meanings of some frequently used terms on food labels, such as "low carb," "fat free," "reduced calorie," and "low sodium." Students should write a definition for each term based on their findings. As a class, discuss which terms are most helpful when deciding which foods to buy. **WRITING**

L2 Cultural Connection

Point out that people in different cultures eat different foods. For example, people of Asian heritage often eat more rice than people of European heritage. Ask students with different ethnic and cultural backgrounds to design a menu promoting cardiovascular health that includes traditional foods. Students may have to do some research to find out which foods are healthiest. Have students present their menus to the class. If possible, have students prepare some of the foods on their menus.

Connect to Your Life Allow students to answer this question in their private journals.

L3 Content Update  GO ONLINE

Visit Pearson SuccessNet to access an online activity for more on cardiovascular disease. Have students complete the Web activity.

L3 Journal Writing

Ask students to write a private journal entry in which they explain why it is important to practice healthy habits that may help them avoid cardiovascular disease. Also ask students to describe ways in which they can improve their habits, such as eating a healthier diet or becoming more physically active. Thinking of reasons why a topic is important may help motivate students to learn more about it and relate it to their own lives. **WRITING**

Differentiated Instruction

L4 Gifted and Talented

Challenge interested students to learn more from reliable online or library sources about one of the testing tools or treatment methods identified in Figure 4. Make sure all four testing tools and treatment methods are covered by different students. Invite students to share their findings with the class in an oral report.

3. Assess

Evaluate

These assignments can help you assess students' mastery of the section content.

Section 1 Review

Answers appear below.

Teaching Resources
- Practice 23-1
- Section 23-1 Quiz

 Reteach

Work with students to create a bulletin board illustrating the section content. Head the bulletin board with three labels, Types of Cardiovascular Disease, Treating Cardiovascular Disease, and Preventing Cardiovascular Disease. Ask students to add relevant examples, in writing or drawings, under the appropriate labels.

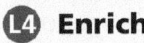 Enrich

Teaching Resources
- Enrich 23-1

Health at School

Heart Health Give students the option of which format—an ad, a song, or a skit—each wants to work on, and then form groups of like-minded students. A group might concentrate on only one or on several of the risks a person can control. Set a deadline for completion of the project, and provide time for presentations.

FIGURE 6 Healthy behavior patterns in your teen years can give you a head start in preventing cardiovascular disease.

Risks You Can Control There are many things you can do to avoid cardiovascular disease. Because the damage to your body can begin when you are young, it is important to develop healthy habits now.

▶ **Maintain a Healthy Weight** If you are overweight, your heart has to work harder than it should. Being overweight also raises blood pressure and blood cholesterol levels. Obese adults are more likely to develop diabetes, which is a major risk factor for cardiovascular disease.

▶ **Eat a Healthy Diet** Choose a diet that is high in plant products and low in saturated fat and cholesterol. Limit your intake of red meat, high-sodium snacks, and sugary foods, such as soda and candy.

▶ **Be Physically Active** Regular exercise strengthens your cardiovascular system and can lower blood pressure.

▶ **Manage Stress** Take time to relax each day. Feelings of stress and anxiety can raise blood pressure and contribute to cardiovascular disease.

▶ **Monitor Your Blood Pressure** Have your blood pressure checked regularly by a doctor or nurse. If your blood pressure is high, discuss ways to lower it.

▶ **Avoid Smoking and Drinking** Do not start smoking. And if you smoke, quit. Smokers have a higher risk of heart attack and stroke than nonsmokers. Excessive alcohol intake can also damage the heart.

Section 1 Review

Key Ideas and Vocabulary

1. Name six types of cardiovascular disease.
2. What is **fibrillation**?
3. What is an **aneurysm** and how can it lead to a stroke?
4. What medical test might be used to detect an arrhythmia? How might an arrhythmia be treated?
5. List four things you can do to lower your risk for cardiovascular disease.

Critical Thinking

6. **Comparing and Contrasting** Distinguish between a heart attack and a stroke.

Health at School

Heart Health Write an advertisement, song, or skit that informs teens about ways to prevent cardiovascular disease. Think about how you can motivate other students to practice healthy behaviors. Present your advertisement, song, or skit to the class. **WRITING**

7. **Applying Concepts** Suppose you have a friend who has a family history of cardiovascular disease. If you noticed your friend eating meals high in saturated fat and salt, what would you say?

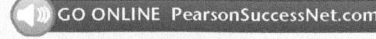 GO ONLINE PearsonSuccessNet.com Audio Summary Section 23.1

Section 1 Review

1. hypertension, atherosclerosis, heart attack, arrhythmia, congestive heart failure, stroke

2. a life-threatening arrhythmia in which the heart twitches rapidly in an uncoordinated fashion

3. An aneurysm is a blood-filled weak spot that balloons out from an artery wall. An aneurysm that bursts may lead to a cerebral hemorrhage.

4. electrocardiogram (ECG); can be treated with medications or an artificial pacemaker

5. *Sample answer:* maintain a healthy weight, eat a healthy diet, be physically active, and manage stress

6. A heart attack occurs when some of the tissue in the heart doesn't receive its normal blood supply and dies, while a stroke is a sudden disruption of blood flow to part of the brain.

7. *Sample answer:* Having a family history of cardiovascular disease may increase the risk of having cardiovascular disease. Although you cannot control that risk, you can control risks such as diet.

Cancer

Section 2

Warm-Up

Health Stats This graph shows the most common cancers in males and females in 2012.

Common Cancers in the United States

New cases (y-axis): 0, 50,000, 100,000, 150,000, 200,000, 250,000

Categories: Prostate, Lung, Colon & Rectum, Breast, Lung, Colon & Rectum

Legend: ■ Males ■ Females

WRITING Is lung cancer more common in males or females? Why do you think this is the case?

How Cancer Affects the Body

In the United States, cancer is the second leading cause of death in adults, just behind cardiovascular disease. **Cancer** is a group of diseases that involves the rapid, uncontrolled growth and spread of abnormal cells. **Cancer harms the body by destroying healthy body tissues.**

Cancer cells typically form a mass of tissue called a **tumor.** The word **malignant** (muh LIG nunt) is used to describe a cancerous tumor. A tumor that is not cancerous is called a benign tumor.

The cells of a malignant tumor grow into surrounding tissues and destroy them. In addition, some cancer cells may break away from the original tumor. The cells travel through blood vessels or lymph vessels to other parts of the body. There the cancer cells may start new tumors. The spread of cancer from where it first develops to other parts of the body is called **metastasis** (muh TAS tuh sis).

Many cancers can be cured if they are detected early and treated promptly. Because cancer cells eventually replace normal cells, death may result if the cancer is not treated.

 **Connect to Your Life** How much do you know about cancer? What questions do you have?

Section 2

Objectives

▶ **Describe** how cancer affects the body.

▶ **Identify** the tests and treatments for cancer.

▶ **List** seven ways you can prevent cancer.

Vocabulary

- cancer
- tumor
- malignant
- metastasis
- oncogene
- carcinogen
- biopsy

Section 2

Cancer

Objectives

Before class begins, write the objectives on the board. Have students copy the objectives into their notebooks at the start of class.

1. Focus

Warm-Up Health Stats

Give students time to write their answers, and then call on a volunteer for the answer to the first question. *(Lung cancer is more common in males.)* Ask for opinions about why there is a difference between males and females in lung cancer rates. Students might suggest that the main cause of lung cancer is smoking and that at one time, men smoked more than women. Then, ask whether students think this difference will remain the same in the future. Some students may predict that the rate for females will go up and may eventually equal the rate for males.

Presentation 23-2

Connect to Your Life Allow students to answer this question in their private journals.

⚑ Sensitive Issues

Cancer may be a sensitive issue for students who have experienced suffering or loss within the family because of cancer. Be sensitive to these feelings. Avoid asking about personal experiences or the experiences of family members. Always give students the option of using hypothetical examples or the experiences of people they know.

Differentiated Instruction

EL English Language Learners

There are many difficult terms in this lesson, including *malignant, metastasis,* and *carcinogen.* These and other terms may be obstacles for English language learners and discourage them from reading. In class, make sure that you correctly pronounce and clearly enunciate difficult terms. Have English language learners create flashcards of those terms, including pronunciations. Students should write the definitions of difficult terms in their own words on the flashcards.

2. Teach

Ⓛ3 ⒺⓁ **Reading/Note Taking** 23-2

Ⓛ2 **Adapted Reading/Note Taking** 23-2

How Cancer Affects the Body

Ⓛ3 **Building Vocabulary**

Explain that *metastasis* is derived from a Greek word meaning "removal from one place to another." Tell students that the verb form is *metastasize*. When a cancer spreads, it is said to metastasize, or move from one part of the body to another.

Ⓛ1 **Teacher Demo**

Use a large illustration of the human body to clarify how cancers metastasize. (If possible, use an illustration that displays the systems and organs of the body.) Begin by pointing to the lungs, the site of a common cancer. Explain that tumor cells of lung cancer can spread through either the cardiovascular system or the lymphatic system. Then point out locations where lung cancer spreads, including the liver, brain, and bone. Explain that one reason lung cancer is such a serious disease is because this cancer metastasizes early in its development, often before there are any symptoms.

 *Sample answer:* ultraviolet light; limit exposure to the sun

Ⓛ3 **Content Update**  GO ONLINE

Visit Pearson SuccessNet to access more information on cancer. Have students complete the Web activity.

FIGURE 7 This man is wearing a respiratory mask to protect himself from carcinogens such as asbestos.

Causes of Cancer In normal body cells, a control system keeps cell reproduction in check. In cancer cells, the control system has gone haywire, and cells reproduce more than they should. This damaged control system can result from hereditary and environmental factors.

▶ **Heredity** All human cells contain genes that control cell reproduction. But some people inherit genes that have a tendency to change, or mutate, into forms that allow cells to reproduce too rapidly. A normal gene that has changed into a cancer-causing gene is called an **oncogene** (AHN kuh jeen). People whose cells contain oncogenes may develop certain forms of cancer.

▶ **Environment** The environment contains cancer-causing agents known as **carcinogens** (kahr SIN uh junz). Carcinogens can cause mutations in genes that control cell reproduction. The range of possible carcinogens is broad. Ultraviolet light and X-rays can cause mutations. So can tobacco products, asbestos, arsenic, and some pesticides. Some types of viruses are also carcinogens.

Types of Cancer Cancer can occur in almost any part of the body. A cancer is named according to the part of the body where it first develops. Figure 8 surveys some different types of cancer.

Some cancers are rare. Others are more common. For example, one form of skin cancer—basal cell carcinoma—is the most common cancer that occurs in the United States. Fortunately, this common form of skin cancer is rarely life-threatening, especially if it is detected early. Another form of skin cancer, called melanoma (mel uh NOH muh), is less common but can be much more serious.

Many cancers are curable if they are caught early, including testicular cancer and breast cancer. Other cancers are hard to detect early in their development and pose a bigger challenge for treatment. Symptoms of lung cancer, for example, usually do not appear until the disease has spread.

GO ONLINE
PearsonSuccessNet.com
For: More on cancer

Connect to Your Life What carcinogens are you exposed to? How can you protect yourself from them?

For Your INFORMATION!

Skin Cancer

Skin cancers are classified as either nonmelanoma or melanoma. Nonmelanoma skin cancers include basal cell skin cancer and squamous cell skin cancer. There are more than 2 million nonmelanoma skin cancers diagnosed each year in the United States. These cancers rarely metastasize, though they can be disfiguring and even fatal if ignored. By contrast, melanoma accounts for only about 5 percent of skin cancers but 75 percent of skin cancer deaths. There are about 8,000 deaths from melanoma in the United States per year, and that figure is increasing. A history of one or more sunburns in childhood increases the risk of developing skin cancer as an adult.

Types of Cancers

Cancer	Symptoms	Screening	Prevention
Skin	A mole that changes size, shape, or color; tenderness, itching, or pain around a mole	• Check skin regularly for moles	• Avoid extended time in the sun • Wear sunblock • Do not use tanning salons
Prostate	If advanced, painful or burning urination, blood in the urine, or pain in the lower back or pelvis	• Regular checkups for men • Rectal examination • PSA (prostate-specific antigen) blood test	
Breast	Unusual lump in the breast	• Perform monthly breast self-exams • Mammogram	
Lung	Persistent cough; chest pain; recurrent pneumonia or bronchitis	• Chest X-ray	• Do not smoke
Colorectal	Bleeding from the rectum; blood in the feces; changes in bowel habits	• Colonoscopy	• Eat a diet low in saturated fat and high in fiber
Cervical	Abnormal vaginal bleeding	• Have regular Pap tests	• Avoid HPV infection by practicing abstinence
Oral	Lumps in the mouth; a sore in the mouth that bleeds easily; a red or white patch in the mouth	• Have regular dental checkups	• Do not smoke and do not use smokeless tobacco products • Do not drink alcohol
Non-Hodgkin's Lymphoma	Swollen lymph nodes	• X-ray • CT scan	
Ovarian	Usually no early symptoms	• Regular and thorough pelvic exams for women	
Leukemia	Weight loss; recurrent infections; fatigue; swollen lymph nodes	• Blood test	

▲ Mole

◄ Chest X-ray

Dental checkup ▼

Chronic Diseases and Disabilities **611**

L2 Building Health Skills

Making Decisions Have students suppose that they have received a free introductory membership to a tanning salon that would give them seven free sessions in a tanning booth. Ask students to consider the consequences of taking advantage of the free membership. (*They are increasing their exposure to ultraviolet light, a principal cause of skin cancer.*) Challenge students to identify their values in this situation. Is their appearance more important than a possible risk to their health?

Visual Learning: Figure 8

Caption Answer Prostate cancer affects only males; ovarian and cervical cancers affect only females. All other cancers listed in the table affect both males and females, though breast cancer predominantly affects females.

L3 Cooperative Learning

Divide the class into ten groups, and assign each group one type of cancer listed in Figure 8. Instruct students to use print or online resources to find out more about their assigned cancer. Explain that the table briefly lists the symptoms of each cancer, as well as some prevention and screening information. Ask groups to build on this information as they find out more about the disease. Have each group prepare a report that includes the probable cause, major symptoms, screening tests, preventative measures, primary treatments, and probable outcome of the assigned cancer. After groups have completed their reports, ask each group to make a brief presentation to the class about its type of cancer. **WRITING**

L2 Addressing Misconceptions

"Safe" Tobacco Some students may think that people are safe from cancer if they use smokeless tobacco products such as snuff and chewing tobacco. Explain that this is not true. Smokeless tobacco contains many of the same cancer-causing substances as tobacco that is smoked. Have students investigate the long-term effects of using snuff and chewing tobacco and identify the types of cancer that can result. (*Oral and throat cancer can develop.*)

Differentiated Instruction

EL English Language Learners

The names of some cancers in Figure 8 might be difficult for some students to pronounce or remember. Have students write the names of the different types of cancer on index cards. Then, for each type of cancer, read aloud the symptoms and call on a student to name the cancer.

Repeat the name, clearly pronouncing it. Students should then record the symptoms and the part of the body affected on the back of the appropriate index card. Continue with the process through all the cancers on the list.

Media Wise

Evaluating Tanning Products

Lead a discussion on the dangers of skin cancer. Tell students that skin cancer is caused by exposure to ultraviolet (UV) radiation in sunlight and other light, including the lights used at tanning salons. Ask: **What are prevention and screening strategies for skin cancer?** *(Avoid extended time in the sun. Wear sunblock. Do not use tanning salons that expose you to UV radiation. Check skin regularly for moles.)* Then, display a commercial sunblock lotion, and help students use the questionnaire to evaluate the product.

Activity Divide the class into two groups. Have one group look at tanning products and the other group look at tanning salons. Students who look at tanning products may either evaluate a product found in the home or one found on a store shelf. Those who evaluate tanning salons can begin by looking at Web sites or print ads for salons. They can follow up with phone calls or on-site interviews. After students have completed the writing assignment, ask volunteers to share what they learned.

Detecting and Treating Cancer

L3 Class Discussion

Lead a discussion on the treatments available for cancer. Ask: **What are four different types of cancer treatment?** *(surgery, radiation, chemotherapy, immunotherapy)* **What factors determine the type of treatments?** *(type of cancer, its location, and its stage of development)* Explain that the different types of treatment are not exclusive to one another. A woman who has breast cancer, for instance, may have surgery to remove a lump or a breast, then have radiation in the area to kill cancer cells that were missed by the surgery, and then have chemotherapy to attack cancer cells that metastasized to other parts of her body.

Media Wise

Evaluating Tanning Products

There is a lot of information available about the dangers of too much sun exposure. But, many young people still tan. Evaluate products that claim to give you a "healthy tan" using this questionnaire.

Does the product's labeling caution about the dangers of ultraviolet (UV) radiation? Yes No

Does the product provide SPF (sun protection factor) information? Yes No

Does the product encourage you to minimize your exposure to the sun or other UV radiation? Yes No

Does the product recommend other precautions—such as wearing sunglasses or a hat? Yes No

A "No" answer to one or more questions indicates that using the product may endanger your skin.

Activity Use the checklist to evaluate a tanning product. Then write a paragraph explaining why the tanning product you chose may or may not be healthy for your skin. **WRITING**

Detecting and Treating Cancer

Seven common warning signs of cancer are listed in Figure 9. If you experience any of these warning signs, you should seek medical attention. **The key to curing cancer is early detection and treatment.**

Tests   Screening tests, such as mammograms, chest X-rays, and endoscopies, can detect cancers before any symptoms appear. If cancer is suspected from screening test results, surgeons may remove a small piece of the tissue in question to examine it for signs of cancer. This procedure is called a **biopsy** (BY ahp see).

Treatments   Cancer treatments depend on the type of cancer, its location, and its stage of development.

▶ Surgery can remove part or all of a malignant tumor.

▶ Radiation therapy can kill cancer cells and slow tumor growth.

▶ Chemotherapy (kee moh THEHR uh pee) uses drugs to slow the reproduction of cancer cells. Immunotherapy (im yuh noh THEHR uh pee) uses drugs to stimulate the body's immune system to attack cancer cells.

When the signs or symptoms of cancer disappear, the cancer is said to be in remission. Most cancers that stay in remission for five years are considered cured. Sometimes, however, the cancer returns after five years. A second occurrence of the same cancer is usually more difficult to treat.

TEENS *Are Asking . . .*

Q: All the people I know who have gotten cancer are older. Are there any cancers that teenagers can get?

A: It's true that older people get cancer more than younger people. About 76 percent of all cancers are diagnosed in people 55 years or older. But teens can get cancer, too. Hodgkin's lymphoma, which is a cancer of the lymphatic system, accounts for about 16 percent of cancers in adolescents 15 to 19 years old. Leukemia, which is a cancer of the blood, accounts for another 11 percent of cancers in that age group. Among other cancers that teens 15 to 19 can get are brain cancer (10 percent), testicular cancer (9 percent), non-Hodgkin's lymphoma (8 percent), ovarian cancer (7 percent), and melanoma (7 percent).

Preventing Cancer

Early detection of cancer cannot prevent the disease, but it may prevent the cancer from killing you. Regularly examining your skin and breasts or testicles for abnormal lumps or growth is a good habit to start. Self-exams and seeing your doctor regularly can help you prevent the further development of a cancer—if one is present in your body—by catching it early.

Detecting cancer early is very important, but avoiding cancer altogether is ideal. **Although the specific cause of most cancers is unknown, certain behaviors have been shown to decrease the risk of cancer.**

▶ Do not use any form of tobacco. Tobacco and tobacco smoke contain carcinogens. Smokeless tobacco, or snuff, can cause oral cancer.

▶ Avoid alcohol. Drinking, especially along with smoking, greatly increases the risks of oral cancer and liver cancer.

▶ Avoid the sun's ultraviolet rays. Wear protective clothing and use sunscreen. Do not use tanning beds.

▶ Choose a diet low in saturated fat and cholesterol. Instead, eat plenty of vegetables, fruits, and whole grains. Such a diet is rich in vitamins and fiber, which may reduce the risks of some cancers.

▶ Exercise regularly and maintain a healthy weight.

▶ Avoid unnecessary X-rays, especially during pregnancy.

▶ Avoid known carcinogens. If you cannot avoid them, wear protective clothing or equipment.

Seven Warning Signs of Cancer

- **C**hange in bowel or bladder habits, such as constipation, diarrhea, or incomplete emptying of the bowel
- **A** sore throat that does not heal
- **U**nusual bleeding or discharge, particularly from the rectum or vagina
- **T**hickening or lump in the breast or elsewhere
- **I**ndigestion or difficulty in swallowing
- **O**bvious change in a wart or mole, such as growth, discharge, or unusual appearance
- **N**agging cough or hoarseness

FIGURE 9 If you experience any of these warning signs, see your doctor. Notice that the first letters of the warning signs spell "caution."

Section 2 Review

Key Ideas and Vocabulary

1. How does cancer harm the body? What changes in cells allow cancer to develop?
2. What is a **tumor?** When is a tumor considered **malignant?**
3. What is a **carcinogen?**
4. How does a doctor determine if a person has cancer? If cancer is present, what types of treatment might the patient receive?
5. Name four ways you can reduce your risk of developing cancer.

Critical Thinking

6. **Comparing and Contrasting** Distinguish between a normal gene and an oncogene.
7. **Applying Concepts** Some cancer cells live much longer than noncancerous cells. How might this play a role in the development of a tumor?

Health at Home

Cancer Prevention Many types of cancer can be prevented by practicing healthy behaviors. Discuss some cancer prevention tips with your family. Together, list some changes family members can make in their current behaviors. Post the list on your refrigerator or in another visible location. **WRITING**

GO ONLINE PearsonSuccessNet.com   Audio Summary Section 23.2   *Chronic Diseases and Disabilities* **613**

Preventing Cancer

L2 Building Health Skills

Advocacy Have student groups make a poster conveying to other teens behaviors that can reduce their risk of cancer. Students may illustrate each behavior with a cartoon, sketch, or magazine photo. Display the posters in the school.

3. Assess

Evaluate

These assignments can help you assess students' mastery of the section content.

Section 2 Review

Answers appear below.

Teaching Resources
• Practice 23-2
• Section 23-2 Quiz

L2 Reteach

Ask students to write a paragraph that could be used to inform the public about cancer. Have students describe how cancer affects the body, identify tests and treatments for cancer, and list ways a person can prevent cancer.

L4 Enrich

Teaching Resources
• Enrich 23-2

Health at Home

Cancer Prevention Emphasize that this is an opportunity to inform parents, siblings, and other family members of important information that can affect their lives. Assure students that they will not be required to report what occurred at home.

Section 2 Review

1. Cancer destroys healthy body tissues. The control system that keeps cell reproduction in check goes haywire, and cells reproduce more than they should.
2. a mass of tissue; when it becomes cancerous and grows into surrounding tissues
3. a cancer-causing agent
4. Screening tests can detect cancers before symptoms appear. If cancer is suspected, a surgeon may perform a biopsy. Treatments include surgery, radiation, chemotherapy, and immunotherapy.
5. *Sample answer:* by not using any form of tobacco; avoiding alcohol; wearing sunblock; choosing a diet low in saturated fat and cholesterol
6. An oncogene is a normal gene that has changed into a cancer-causing gene.
7. Instead of dying, cells live longer and reproduce. The result is an over-accumulation of cells in a tumor.

Section 3
Other Chronic Diseases

Objectives

Before class begins, write the objectives on the board. Have students copy the objectives into their notebooks at the start of class.

1. Focus

Warm-Up Advice Line

After students have written a response, call on volunteers to share their responses. Some students may know nothing about diabetes or may not differentiate between type 1 and type 2 diabetes. At this point, allow any misconceptions to go uncorrected. Give students a chance to rewrite their responses after reading about diabetes. Lead a discussion on what they changed or added to their responses.

Presentation 23-3

Objectives

▶ **Distinguish** between the two types of diabetes.

▶ **Describe** how allergies and asthma affect the body.

▶ **Identify** the symptoms of arthritis.

Vocabulary

- diabetes
- insulin
- allergy
- allergen
- histamine
- arthritis
- osteoarthritis
- rheumatoid arthritis

Warm-Up

Dear Advice Line,

My older brother was just diagnosed with diabetes. Is he going to be okay? Should I be worried about getting diabetes, too? What can I do to avoid it?

WRITING Write a draft of a response to this question. Revise your answer after reading this section.

Diabetes

About 26 million Americans are affected by diabetes. But some do not know that they have it. **Diabetes** (dy uh BEE teez) is a disease in which the body's ability to use glucose (blood sugar) is impaired. Diabetes involves **insulin** (IN suh lin), a hormone produced by the pancreas. Insulin stimulates body cells to take up and use blood sugar.

If not controlled, diabetes can be life-threatening. People with diabetes are also at risk for heart disease, stroke, kidney disease, blindness, infections requiring amputation, and complications during pregnancy. There are two common types of diabetes, type 1 and type 2.

Type 1 Diabetes About 5 to 10 percent of diabetics have insulin-dependent diabetes, or type 1 diabetes. **A person with type 1 diabetes produces little or no insulin. Without insulin, glucose levels in the blood remain high.** Symptoms include thirst, frequent urination, nausea, hunger, fatigue, and weight loss.

Although it can strike at any age, type 1 diabetes usually first appears in childhood. Type 1 diabetics must monitor their blood glucose levels and give themselves doses of insulin on a strict schedule. In addition, they need to eat the proper amounts of carbohydrates and other nutrients on a regular schedule.

Taking too much insulin, missing a meal, or exercising too much can result in low blood sugar levels. The opposite condition—high blood sugar—occurs when too little insulin is taken or too much food is eaten. If not treated promptly, both of these conditions can be life-threatening.

Sensitive Issues

Diabetes, asthma, and arthritis all may be sensitive subjects for some students. For example, a student with type 1 diabetes or rheumatoid arthritis may not want others to know about his or her condition. Avoid asking personal questions about students' experiences with these diseases, and always allow students to use hypothetical examples as legitimate responses.

MATH and Health

L3 Percentages

The text says about 26 million Americans are affected by diabetes and 5 to 10 percent of diabetics have type 1 diabetes. Ask: **How many Americans have type 1 diabetes?** *(0.05 × 26 million ≈ 1.3 million; 0.1 × 26 million = 2.6 million. Therefore,*

about 1.3 million to 2.6 million Americans have type 1 diabetes.) Ask: **How many Americans have type 2 diabetes?** *(26 million − 2.6 million = 23.4 million; 26 million − 1.3 million = 24.7 million. Therefore, about 23.4 million to 24.7 million Americans have type 2 diabetes.)*

Type 2 Diabetes   Also known as noninsulin-dependent diabetes, type 2 diabetes occurs mostly in people over the age of 30. However, it can strike children and teens, especially if they are overweight and do not get enough exercise. **People with type 2 diabetes produce sufficient insulin, but their body cells do not respond normally to insulin. As with type 1 diabetes, the result is a high level of glucose in the blood.**

Type 2 diabetes usually develops slowly and often goes undetected until symptoms become severe. Symptoms are the same as for type 1 diabetes, but also include drowsiness, itching, blurred vision, numbness in the hands or feet, and frequent, hard-to-heal infections. Risk factors for type 2 diabetes include a family history of diabetes, being overweight, and a lack of physical activity.

Fortunately, many people can prevent type 2 diabetes by maintaining a desirable body weight and by exercising regularly. Some people who develop the disease can control it if they follow a weight-loss and exercise program. In other cases, medications may be used. Excessive sugar consumption is not thought to be a direct cause of type 2 diabetes. However, a high-sugar diet can lead to obesity, which can increase the risk of developing type 2 diabetes.

 **Connect to Your Life**   **What can you do to lower your risk for type 2 diabetes?**

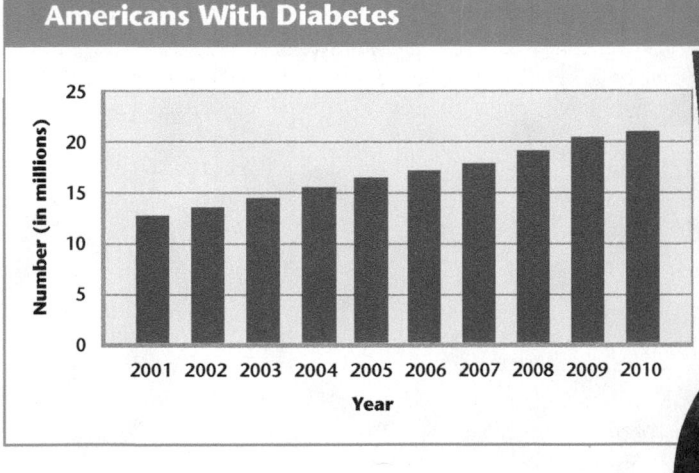

Americans With Diabetes

Tips for Preventing Type 2 Diabetes
- Maintain a healthy body weight.
- Eat nutritious meals low in sugar and saturated fats.
- Exercise for at least 30 minutes every day.

FIGURE 10   Diabetes is a major risk factor for cardiovascular disease. If you follow the guidelines for preventing type 2 diabetes, you can also reduce your risk of cardiovascular disease. **Predicting** How do you think the trend in diabetes will affect trends in other chronic diseases?

Chronic Diseases and Disabilities   **615**

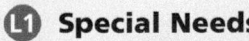
---

2. Teach

L3 EL Reading/Note Taking 23-3

L2 Adapted Reading/Note Taking 23-3

Diabetes

L3 Class Discussion

Tell students that type 1 diabetes used to be commonly called juvenile diabetes, to distinguish it from type 2 diabetes. That term is now rarely used by medical professionals. Point out that the causes of the two types of diabetes have not changed. Ask: **Why do you think the term *juvenile diabetes* has fallen out of favor?** *(Some students may correctly suggest that in the past very few young people developed type 2 diabetes, and so the designation of "juvenile" was enough to indicate a difference between the two types. But today, with so many overweight young people, type 2 diabetes is becoming more common in teenagers.)*

L2 Visual Learning: Figure 10
Image Bank Figure 23-10

After students have examined the graph, ask: **What trend can you infer from this graph about Americans with diabetes?** *(Every year, the number of Americans with diabetes increases.)* **Is this trend true about type 1 or type 2 diabetes?** *(The graph does not differentiate between the two types, but because 90 to 95 percent of diabetics have type 2 diabetes, the trend likely reflects an increase in the number of cases of type 2 diabetes more than type 1.)* **What could Americans do to reverse this trend?** *(Sample answer: maintain a healthy weight, eat nutritious meals, and exercise regularly)*

Caption Answer Because type 2 diabetes is a major risk factor for cardiovascular disease, the number of Americans with cardiovascular diseases will likely increase.

Connect to Your Life   Allow students to answer this question in their private journals.

Allergies and Asthma

⓵ Class Discussion

Have students recall from Chapter 21 the function of the immune system. Ask: **What is the immune system?** *(It is the body's most sophisticated line of defense against pathogens.)* Explain that the immune system may react against any foreign "invader," not just pathogens. Point out that plants produce pollen naturally, and most people breathe in pollen all the time with no particular reaction. Ask: **What is different about a person who is allergic to pollen?** *(The person has an immune system that is overly sensitive to pollen. As a result, the pollen causes an allergic reaction.)*

⓶ Teacher Demo

Bring to class an over-the-counter allergy medicine label, and show students that the label prominently identifies the medicine as an "antihistamine." Ask: **What is histamine?** *(a chemical responsible for the symptoms of an allergy)* **Does this antihistamine cure an allergy? If not, what does it do?** *(It does not cure an allergy. It relieves the symptoms of an allergy.)*

⓵ Building Health Skills

Communicating Describe this scenario for students: You are invited to spend time at a friend's house, and you would like to go. But the last time you were there, you began to sneeze and your eyes became very itchy. You noticed that your friend's family has several cats. Ask: **What do you think caused your symptoms?** *(I had an allergic reaction to my friend's cats.)* **If you did decide to visit your friend, what could you say or do to make your visit more comfortable?** *(Sample answer: I could explain the problem to my friend and suggest that we spend most of the time outside.)*

Allergies and Asthma

Some people's bodies overreact to harmless substances, and as a result, they may feel sick. An **allergy** is a disorder in which the immune system is overly sensitive to a particular substance not normally found in the body. One type of allergic reaction can lead to a condition called asthma, which you learned about in Chapter 12.

Causes of Allergies **Allergies develop when foreign substances enter the body and set off a series of reactions.** Any substance that causes an allergy is called an **allergen.** Common allergens include plant pollen, dust, molds, some foods, and even some medicines. Allergens may get into your body when you inhale them, eat them in food, or touch them with your skin.

The immune system's overly sensitive response to an allergen causes large quantities of a chemical called **histamine** (HIS tuh meen) to be released. Histamine is responsible for the symptoms of an allergy, such as sneezing and watery eyes. Antihistamines—medicines that interfere with the action of histamine—may relieve symptoms. However, the best strategy is to try to avoid any substance to which you are allergic.

Some allergic reactions can be very serious and require immediate medical attention. For example, people who are severely allergic to bee stings must carry medicine with them in case they get stung.

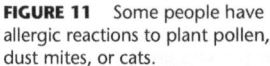

FIGURE 11 Some people have allergic reactions to plant pollen, dust mites, or cats.

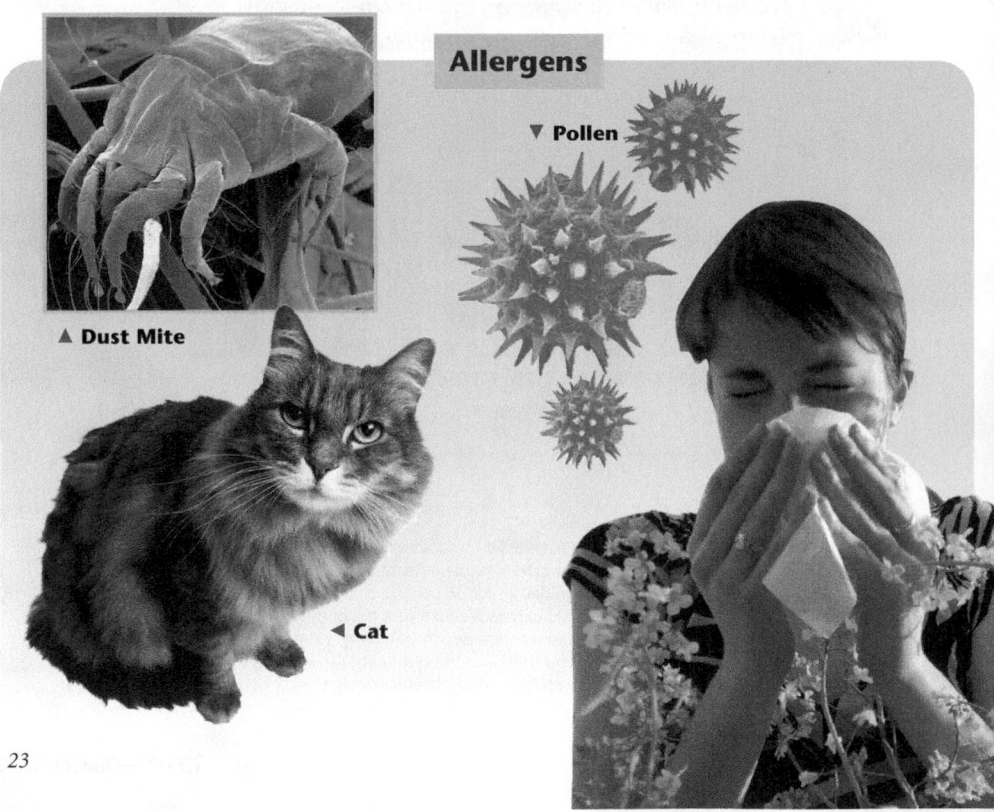

Allergens

▼ **Pollen**

▲ **Dust Mite**

◀ **Cat**

TEENS *Are Asking . . .*

Q: **I have terrible problems with sneezing and itchy eyes in the summer and fall. My family says I have hay fever. What is that?**

A: Hay fever is the common name of an allergic condition that affects 20 percent of Americans. The medical term for hay fever is *allergic rhinitis*, which is an allergic reaction to substances in the environment.

The symptoms include nasal congestion, sneezing, and eye irritation. Many outdoor allergens are pollens from trees, grasses, and weeds. The pollen of ragweed is often a problem. Indoor allergens include dust mites, pet dander, mold, and cockroaches. Hay fever symptoms can cause tiredness and irritability. Having hay fever increases your risk of developing asthma.

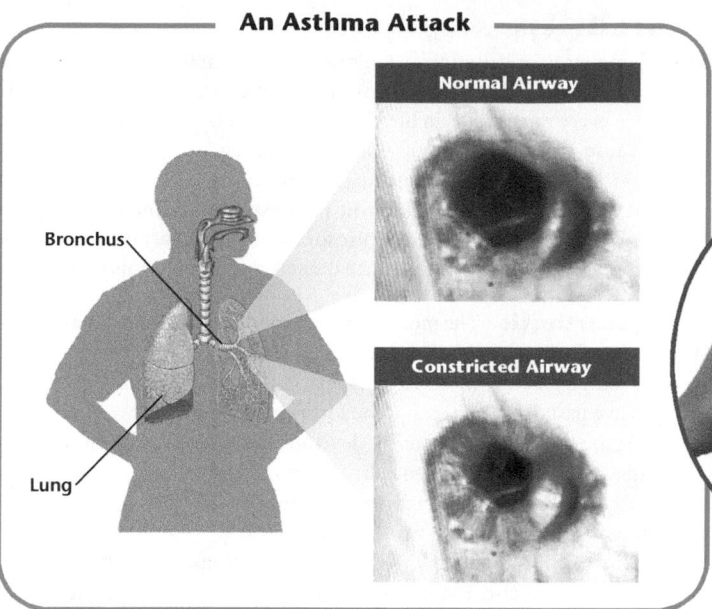

An Asthma Attack

Normal Airway

Bronchus

Lung

Constricted Airway

About 60% of children have missed school because of asthma.

FIGURE 12 During an asthma attack, the respiratory passages in the lungs become narrower and secrete extra mucus. Both responses make breathing difficult. Using an inhaler with medicine can stop an asthma attack.

Asthma Asthma is a disorder in which a person's respiratory passages become inflamed and narrow significantly in reaction to certain "triggers." Figure 12 shows a narrowed airway of a person having an asthma attack.

Asthma attacks can be triggered by many things, including certain allergens, stress, cold weather, tobacco smoke, or exercise. During an attack, a person may wheeze, cough, or become short of breath. Some people describe an asthma attack as trying to breathe through a straw.

Managing Asthma About 40 million people in the United States have asthma. Of these, about 10 million are children. Asthma can be serious, but it can be managed so that asthma sufferers can lead normal, active lives.

Managing asthma involves avoiding the triggers that bring on asthma attacks. It may also involve the use of medicines. Asthma medicines are either "controllers" or "rescue drugs." A person with asthma can use a controller each day to prevent asthma attacks from occurring. When the person has an attack, he or she uses a rescue drug to relieve the symptoms. Rescue drugs relax the muscles in the airways, making it easier to breathe.

 **Connect to Your Life** Do you know someone who has asthma? What does he or she do to manage it?

 **GO ONLINE**
PearsonSuccessNet.com
For: More on allergies

L2 Visual Learning: Figure 12

Have students examine the figure and read the caption. Ask: **How is a constricted airway different from a normal airway?** *(A constricted airway is narrower and contains extra mucus.)* **What causes an airway to constrict during an asthma attack?** *(An airway constricts in reaction to certain "triggers.")* **What are some asthma triggers?** *(certain allergens, stress, cold weather, tobacco smoke, exercise)* Point out that substances such as allergens and tobacco smoke can produce an asthma attack, but such things as stress and exercise can also trigger an attack. Explain that some people may experience an asthma attack when playing soccer or running. Doctors call this exercise-induced asthma.

EL Cooperative Learning

Pair up students, and have them create a cause and effect chart for asthma. They should include various triggers under the "Causes" heading and symptoms of asthma under the "Effects" heading. If students have trouble distinguishing between the terms *allergy* and *allergen*, review the meanings of those terms.

Connect to Your Life *Sample answer:* I have a cousin who has asthma, and she uses an inhaler to stop asthma attacks.

L3 Content Update  GO ONLINE

Visit Pearson SuccessNet to access more information on allergies. Have students complete the Web activity.

Differentiated Instruction

L1 Special Needs

For students who do not have asthma, it may be difficult to get a sense of what an asthma attack feels like. Have students breathe normally, first through the nose and then through the mouth. **CAUTION:** *Do not have students perform this activity if they have a medical condition that affects their breathing.* Then, give each student a drinking straw. They should put one end in their mouth and pinch their nostrils so they cannot breathe through their nose. Students should breathe in and out through the straw for 30 seconds. Ask them to compare their normal breathing pattern to their breathing pattern through the straw. Explain that the straw simulates the narrowed airways of a person having an asthma attack.

Arthritis

ⓛ Class Discussion

Have students compare and contrast osteoarthritis and rheumatoid arthritis. **In what way are the two types of arthritis similar?** *(Both involve inflammation of joints and joint pain.)* **How are the causes of the two types different?** *(The cause of osteoarthritis is wear and tear of a joint after years of use or repeated injuries to a joint. The probable cause of rheumatoid arthritis is a malfunction of the immune system.)* **If a young woman in her twenties has arthritis, which type would you expect her to have? Why?** *(Sample answer: She probably has rheumatoid arthritis. Osteoarthritis develops after years of wear and tear or repeated injuries, so she's probably not old enough to have osteoarthritis.)*

ⓛ Building Health Skills

Practicing Healthful Behaviors Use Figure 13 to initiate a discussion on behaviors that might prevent the development of osteoarthritis as students age. Point out that the inset photo shows a lack of cartilage at the knee joint, where leg bones meet. Explain that cartilage acts as a cushion between joints. Ask: **How might warming up and stretching before vigorous exercise protect joints?** *(Sample answer: If you stretch and warm up, you might not sprain or hurt a joint.)* **How might wearing proper gear when playing sports help prevent osteoarthritis?** *(Sample answer: Because osteoarthritis can develop due to repeated injuries to joints, wearing gear that prevents injuries can help prevent osteoarthritis.)*

ⓛ Building Vocabulary

Remind students what they learned in Chapter 21 about inflammation. Explain that the term *inflammation* is commonly used whenever swelling occurs somewhere in the body, such as when you sprain an ankle. In that case, the ankle may become inflamed. Certain common over-the-counter medicines are called anti-inflammatory medicines because they reduce swelling, or inflammation.

Arthritis

Inflammation or irritation of a joint is known as **arthritis** (ahr THRY tis). Arthritis is one of the most common chronic diseases, affecting nearly one in every three adults in the United States. In fact, arthritis is the leading cause of disability among Americans over age 15.

Arthritis is not life-threatening, but it can be extremely painful and disabling. **Arthritis results in joint stiffness, joint pain, or swelling in one or more joints.** There is no cure for most types of arthritis. However, treatments and exercise can reduce the severity of the symptoms.

Osteoarthritis The most common type of arthritis is **osteoarthritis** (ahs tee oh ahr THRY tis). This form of arthritis is caused by wear and tear on a joint after years of use or by repeated injuries to a joint. Most people who live past 60 will develop some form of osteoarthritis.

Symptoms of osteoarthritis develop slowly, usually beginning as a mild ache or soreness. Osteoarthritis can occur in almost any joint, but most commonly occurs in hips, knees, spine, and fingers. When it occurs at the finger joints, bony growths often appear.

Treatment for osteoarthritis may involve drugs, heat and cold treatments, and exercise. Exercise is important to maintain joint flexibility. Sometimes, weight loss is recommended to ease stress on the joints. In severe cases of osteoarthritis, surgery may be required to repair or replace affected joints.

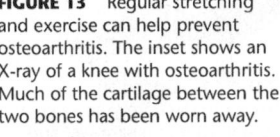

FIGURE 13 Regular stretching and exercise can help prevent osteoarthritis. The inset shows an X-ray of a knee with osteoarthritis. Much of the cartilage between the two bones has been worn away.

For Your INFORMATION!

Autoimmune Diseases

Both type 1 diabetes and rheumatoid arthritis are classified as autoimmune diseases. An autoimmune disease is a noninfectious, chronic disease in which the immune system malfunctions and attacks healthy tissues. Other well-known autoimmune diseases include systemic lupus erythematosus (SLE, or lupus), multiple sclerosis (MS), Grave's disease, and Crohn's disease. The cause of autoimmune diseases is unclear. Researchers think that heredity is probably a factor—a family history of an autoimmune disease increases a person's risk. Possibly, some kind of agent—such as bacteria or a virus—causes the immune system to begin to malfunction. None of these diseases can be cured at present.

Rheumatoid Arthritis In **rheumatoid arthritis** (ROO muh toyd), the membrane surrounding a joint becomes inflamed. The inflammation then spreads to other areas of the joint. An affected joint becomes hot, red, and swollen. Areas of the body other than joints may also become inflamed.

Rheumatoid arthritis affects both the young and the old. Over two million Americans suffer from rheumatoid arthritis. The exact cause of rheumatoid arthritis is still unclear. Much evidence suggests that the immune system malfunctions and attacks some of the body's own tissues. This "self-attack" leads to the inflammation that is characteristic of rheumatoid arthritis.

Any joint in the body may be affected by rheumatoid arthritis, although joints in the wrist and knuckles are most commonly affected. If not treated, rheumatoid arthritis can cause joints to stiffen in deformed positions. The damage can be so severe that it changes the shape of the joint, as you can see in Figure 14.

Treatment includes aspirin or other anti-inflammatory drugs, exercise, and rest. Early diagnosis and treatment by a doctor are the best ways to reduce the severity of the disease.

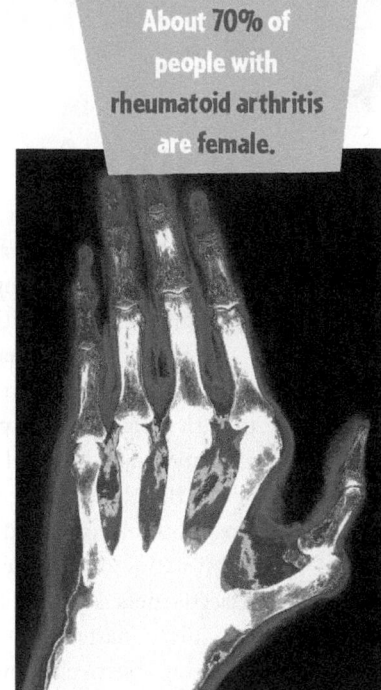

About 70% of people with rheumatoid arthritis are female.

FIGURE 14 In rheumatoid arthritis, joints become inflamed. Over time, the joints may become deformed, as shown in this X-ray.

Section 3 Review

Key Ideas and Vocabulary

1. Distinguish between type 1 and type 2 diabetes. How are their effects on the body similar?
2. Where is **insulin** produced, and what does it do?
3. How do allergies and asthma affect the body?
4. What is **histamine**?
5. What are the symptoms of arthritis?

Critical Thinking

6. **Comparing and Contrasting** How are osteoarthritis and rheumatoid arthritis similar? How do they differ?

Health at School

Reducing Asthma Triggers Asthma is one of the most common chronic diseases that occur in childhood. An important aspect of managing asthma is to reduce asthma triggers in the environment. Evaluate your school environment for asthma triggers. Write a paragraph summarizing your findings. **WRITING**

7. **Relating Cause and Effect** Why do you think that people with diabetes often feel tired?

GO ONLINE PearsonSuccessNet.com   Audio Summary Section 23.3   *Chronic Diseases and Disabilities* **619**

Section 3 Review

1. A person with type 1 diabetes produces little or no insulin, while a person with type 2 diabetes produces sufficient insulin but the body cells do not respond normally to insulin. For both, the result is a high level of glucose in the blood.

2. in the pancreas; stimulates body cells to take up and use blood sugar

3. In an allergy, the immune system's overly sensitive response to an allergen causes large quantities of histamine to be produced. In asthma, a person's respiratory passages become inflamed and narrow significantly in reaction to certain "triggers."

4. a chemical responsible for the symptoms of an allergy

---

3. Assess

Evaluate

These assignments can help you assess students' mastery of the section content.

Section 3 Review

Answers appear below.

Teaching Resources

- Practice 23-3
- Section 23-3 Quiz

L2 Reteach

Divide the class into small groups, and have members of each group demonstrate their knowledge of section objectives to one another. Group members should reread passages relating to any objectives for which they have disagreements or uncertainties.

L4 Enrich

Teaching Resources

- Enrich 23-3

Health at School

Reducing Asthma Triggers Give students a day to observe the school and evaluate the environment for asthma triggers. Mold, plant pollen, and dust mites might be problems. After students have completed the writing assignment, lead a discussion on their findings.

5. joint stiffness, joint pain, and swelling in one or more joints

6. Both involve damage to the body's joints, but they have different causes. Osteoarthritis is caused by years of wear and tear on joints, whereas rheumatoid arthritis is likely caused by a malfunction of the immune system. Osteoarthritis mostly strikes older people, but rheumatoid arthritis can strike both young and old.

7. In diabetes, the body cells have trouble taking up glucose from the blood. As a result, the cells do not get sufficient energy, and the person may feel tired.

Being Assertive

Objective

Communicate assertively in difficult situations.

Teaching Strategies

• Discuss with students the differences between assertiveness and aggressiveness. Aggressive behavior is self-expressive but indirect, denies the rights of others, and leaves them feeling hurt, humiliated, angry, or defensive.

• Discuss with students the idea that assertive behavior is a choice. Sometimes a person may choose not to assert himself or herself after determining that more would be lost than gained in a particular situation.

• Because so much of assertive behavior depends on nonverbal cues, it is important to have students observe one another as they role-play different situations to identify effective styles. You may want to call on volunteers to describe situations they listed to answer question 2. Choose a common or interesting situation, and have students take turns acting it out. Have students not involved in the role-play take careful notes so that they can give the actors feedback on both the verbal and nonverbal behavior displayed. If possible, videotape the role-plays so the actors can evaluate themselves.

• Lead a discussion on situations in which being assertive might be misinterpreted or may cause an aggressive response. For example, in the situation involving the car parked in a spot reserved for the disabled, Mark had every right to object assertively. Yet, a woman alone in a parking lot might become frightened if Mark seems at all threatening. In that case, she may even call the police. Or, for example, consider a situation when a car parked in the disabled spot contains several loud, threatening young men. In that case, it might be dangerous for an individual to say something.

▲ Communicating

Being Assertive

While walking to his car at the mall, Mark noticed a person parking in a spot reserved for people with disabilities. At first, Mark was going to ignore the situation. But he knew it wasn't right for someone who is not disabled to park there. So Mark politely informed the woman that she needed to move her car.

Mark behaved assertively in this situation. Do you think you could be assertive in a similar situation? If not, you are not alone. Assertiveness is a skill that many people find difficult to master.

Being assertive means expressing your feelings honestly in a way that respects your rights and the rights of others. Acting assertively can help you feel more self-confident and more in control of factors that affect your life. This step-by-step process can help you master the skill of assertiveness. The process is especially helpful in situations where you would like to act assertively but find it difficult to do so.

❶ Evaluate your current behavior.
To understand why you didn't act assertively in a situation, ask yourself these questions:

▶ What outcome did I desire?

▶ What outcome did I get?

▶ What negative thoughts kept me from acting assertively in this situation?

▶ What was I afraid might have happened if I had acted assertively?

❷ Observe a role model in action.

Identify a person who acts assertively in difficult situations. Observe the person as he or she handles a situation in an assertive manner. Pay attention to the words, tone of voice, and body language the person uses.

620 *Chapter 23*

⚑ Sensitive Issues

Being assertive may be much easier for some students than others. A shy, withdrawn student may have difficulty showing such behavior, even in a role-play. Be sensitive to such personality types, and avoid forcing a behavior or criticizing a student who cannot display assertiveness. Such students might benefit from writing what to say or do in a situation and watching more confident students role-play assertiveness.

❸ Conduct a mental rehearsal.
Imagine yourself being assertive in a situation you expect to be involved in. Mental rehearsal helps you think about how you will look, act, and feel in the actual situation.

❹ Use assertive verbal behavior.
When the situation you have rehearsed presents itself, put your plan into action.

▶ Ask for what you want by using "I" messages. Begin statements with "I feel" or "I want." Do not try to blame or demand things by saying "You should …" or "You did…."

▶ Be specific about what you want to say. Do not speak in terms that are too general.

▶ Be direct and unapologetic. For example, say "I believe I was ahead of you." Do not assume that the other person did something on purpose.

▶ Speak calmly and clearly. Take time to think things through. When listening, pay full attention to the other person.

❺ Use assertive nonverbal behavior.

▶ Pay attention to your body language. Be sure to use gestures and facial expressions that match what you are saying.

▶ Look directly at the other person when speaking. Make direct eye contact.

▶ Stand a comfortable distance from the person to whom you are speaking. Standing too close may seem uncomfortable or threatening to some people.

❻ Evaluate yourself.
After the encounter, ask yourself these questions:

▶ Did I say what I intended to say?

▶ Was I direct and unapologetic, yet still considerate?

▶ Did I stand up for myself without becoming defensive and without infringing on the other person's rights?

▶ Was my body language assertive?

▶ Did I feel good about myself after the encounter?

▶ Do I think the other person felt comfortable with my interaction?

Questions to which you answered *no* indicate areas you should work to improve for future encounters.

Practice the Skill

1. What would you have done in Mark's position? Would you have approached the person who parked illegally? Why or why not?

2. List some situations in which you need to be assertive. Some examples are saying *no* to a friend who asks for a favor, or returning a defective product to a store.

3. Mentally rehearse how you would act assertively in those situations. Write out what you would do and say. What verbal and nonverbal behavior would you use? Then, when the situations arise, use your assertiveness skills to take action.

1. Answers will vary. *Sample answer:* I probably would not have said anything because it can be frightening to say something to a stranger. Now that I've read how Mark handled the situation, I might speak out in the future. *Sample answer:* I probably would have said something to the woman who parked illegally. My aunt is disabled, and I know how hard it would be for her if she could not park close to the store.

2. Answers will vary. Students might describe situations such as when someone cuts in line, when a friend is driving too fast, or when someone nearby lights a cigarette in a restaurant or in the stands at a sports event.

3. Have students choose two of the situations they described in question 2. For each situation, ask them to write a paragraph that describes what they would do in that situation.

Health and Community

 Parking for the Disabled
Encourage interested students to find out the local regulations for disabled parking spots, including how many are required in a grocery store's lot and what disabled people need to do to be allowed to park in those spots. Students might interview a store manager, inquire at a local police station, or call local government offices. Have students prepare a brief oral report to the class on their findings.

Technology & Health
Vital Signs on the Go

Teaching Strategies

- Discuss with students how wearable monitoring technology could be helpful to a person with a disease such as asthma. Ask: **What data would a doctor receive from this technology that would not be available otherwise?** *(Sample answer: A doctor would be able to see if a patient with asthma has attacks in specific situations, such as during exercise or early in the morning.)*

- Focus students' attention on the photo of the firefighter. Point out that the wearable monitoring technology allows the firefighter's health status to be monitored in real time. Ask: **In the future, how could a similar technology be useful for a person who has had a heart attack?** *(Sample answer: The person could wear monitoring technology at home, and doctors at a medical center could monitor the person's heart in real time. If the person has another heart attack, an ambulance could be sent immediately.)*

WRITING A typical response might mention these three reasons why wearable technology is a good alternative: Wearable technology is more convenient for a patient than spending time undergoing tests at a doctor's office or a hospital. Wearable technology can provide data that are more realistic than the data collected when a person is in a doctor's office or a hospital. Wearable technology can provide data in real time for those, such as firefighters, who can find themselves in dangerous situations.

Technology & Health
Vital Signs on the Go

Suppose you could go about your normal activities while your doctor gathers data about your asthma or other health condition. That's the idea behind "wearable monitoring technology." These vests and shirts can record your every breath, as well as your heart rate, body temperature, oxygen levels, coughing, and even your posture. The data can then be downloaded and sent to your doctor over the Internet. With this new technology, your doctor can monitor your health without disrupting your life.

WRITING In a paragraph, give three reasons why wearable technology is a good alternative to monitoring patients in a hospital or doctor's office.

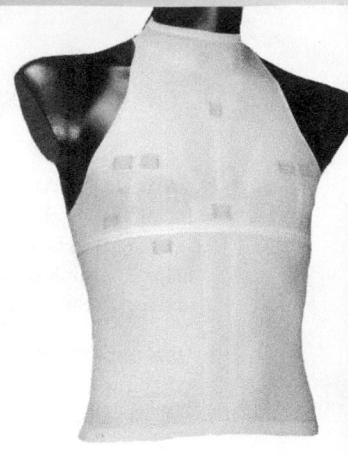

Monitoring Vest ▲
Leads from sensors woven into the fabric of this vest attach to the patient's body and record vital signs.

◄ Firefighter Safety
A firefighter's heart rate, oxygen levels, and breathing can be monitored in real time. A command center can alert the firefighter to any life-threatening conditions.

◄ Asthma
Doctors can monitor how things like activity level, temperature, stress, and medications affect asthma or other respiratory conditions.

◄ Sleep Apnea
Instead of going to a hospital sleep lab, patients can be monitored in their own beds for sleep apnea, a condition in which breathing stops for short periods of time during sleep.

622

For Your INFORMATION!
Wearable Monitoring Technology

Monitoring vests and shirts were made possible with the invention of fibers that are extremely strong, can conduct electricity, and can be woven into the ordinary fabric of clothes. Nanotechnology, which is microscopic, has also played a role in the development of wearable monitoring technology. In the future, a patient may be released from the hospital early because of wearable technology that monitors vital signs and sends them wirelessly to a data-storing network. If some irregularity is detected in the patient's condition, emergency responders could automatically be dispatched. In the near future, doctors will be able to wear connections to the data network and view patients' conditions with special eyeglasses that display the data.

Disabilities

Section 4

Warm-Up

Myth People with physical disabilities always need someone's help.

Fact Most people with physical disabilities can function independently. Allow a person with a physical disability to take the lead when performing a particular task. Wait for the person to perform the task independently or to ask you for help.

WRITING What other misconceptions do you think people hold about disabilities?

Objectives
▶ **Identify** the three most common physical disabilities.
▶ **Explain** how the rights of people with disabilities are protected.

Vocabulary
- disability
- macular degeneration
- tinnitus
- Americans with Disabilities Act

Types of Disabilities

A **disability** is any physical or mental impairment that limits or reduces normal activities, such as attending school or caring for oneself. **The three most common physical disabilities are impaired vision, impaired hearing, and impaired mobility.** The severity of a disability can vary, but in many cases, there are devices or ways to modify the physical environment to reduce a person's limitations.

Impaired Vision   Nearly 4 million Americans over age 40 are visually impaired, and a million of them are blind. Young people may also be visually impaired, often due to birth defects or eye injuries. The leading causes of vision impairment in the United States are diabetes, cataracts (cloudiness in the lens), glaucoma (pressure buildup in the eyeball), and macular degeneration. **Macular degeneration** is a condition affecting the retina and is the leading cause of vision loss in older Americans.

Technologies enable some people with vision impairment to see more clearly. For example, cornea transplants can restore vision in some people. Unfortunately, not every type of vision impairment can be treated at this time. In such cases, people usually depend on sound as a primary means of gathering information. Material written in Braille, a system that uses characters made up of raised dots, is also available. Canes may be used to detect obstacles, such as curbs, and trained guide dogs allow mobility for many vision-impaired people. Figure 15 on the next page lists some guidelines for interacting with someone who is visually impaired.

Chronic Diseases and Disabilities   **623**

Objectives
Before class begins, write the objectives on the board. Have students copy the objectives into their notebooks at the start of class.

1. Focus

Warm-Up Myth/Fact

Give students time to read the Myth/Fact and respond to the question. Then, ask students why they think many people believe the myth and act accordingly. Have students describe how they think a person with a physical disability feels when someone "helps" before asking if help is needed. Call on volunteers to identify other misconceptions people hold about disabilities. After students have read the section, revisit this topic to clear up other misconceptions.
Presentation 23-4

Differentiated Instruction

EL English Language Learners

Lead a discussion on the ways in which the English language has changed to reflect changing attitudes toward disabilities. Point out that terms such as *hearing impaired* are now preferred to *hard of hearing* or *deaf*. Similarly, the term *vision impaired* is preferred to *blind*. Explain that one reason a term such as *blind* is no longer preferred is because that term is commonly used in disparaging contexts, such as *He was* blind *to the consequences of his actions.* Today's preferred terms are more neutral and simply descriptive. Have students brainstorm other out-dated examples. *(physically disabled or impaired mobility rather than handicapped or crippled)* Have students who are learning English explain terms used for disabilities in their native languages.

Sensitive Issues
Issues of disability can be particularly sensitive for students with a disability or for students who have disabled family members. Do not use such students as "experts" (unless they volunteer) or allow other students to make examples of them.

2. Teach

L3 **EL** Reading/Note Taking 23-4

L2 Adapted Reading/Note Taking 23-4

Types of Disabilities

L1 Cooperative Learning

After students have read about people with impaired vision, divide the class into pairs and provide a blindfold to each pair. One partner should be blindfolded and given the task of placing several objects into a box, closing the box, and putting it away somewhere in the room. The other partner should assist the blindfolded student. When the task is completed, have pairs switch roles. After all students have performed the task while blindfolded, lead a discussion on what happened and how students felt as they performed the task, both as the blindfolded student and as the helper.

L3 Visual Learning: Figure 15

Image Bank Figure 23-15

Have students read the tips for interacting with a vision-impaired person and a hearing-impaired person. Ask: **Why should you place a vision-impaired person's hand on your arm instead of grabbing the person by the arm?** *(Sample answer: Grabbing the person by the arm is a way of controlling a person and shows disrespect for the person's independence.)* **Why should you make sure your mouth is visible when speaking to a hearing-impaired person?** *(Lip reading enables some people with severe hearing impairment to communicate. Keeping your mouth visible allows the person to read your lips.)*

Caption Answer *Sample answer:* By following the guidelines, you don't impose yourself on the disabled person, which shows respect for the disabled person's independence.

Interacting With a...

Vision-Impaired Person

▶ Speak right away so that the person knows you are there.

▶ If the person asks to be guided, extend your arm and place the person's hand on it. Do not grab the person by the arm.

▶ Ask for permission before touching or talking to a guide dog.

▶ Describe where things are and who is present.

Hearing-Impaired Person

▶ Touch the person gently to gain attention.

▶ Have the person look directly at you. Do not shout.

▶ Find out if the person hears better on one side and position yourself on the "good" side.

▶ Speak slowly and clearly and be sure your mouth is visible to the person.

▶ Use sign language if both of you know it.

FIGURE 15 Many people with physical disabilities can navigate their environment and communicate effectively.
Evaluating By following these guidelines, how are you showing respect for a disabled person's independence?

Impaired Hearing Hearing loss is more common in older people than in younger people. In fact, about 1 in 3 Americans over the age of 60 has some degree of hearing impairment. Nevertheless, some young people, including infants, may also experience hearing impairment and deafness. Some causes of hearing impairment include birth defects, genetic disorders, exposure to excessive noise, and ear infections.

Tinnitus is a condition in which ringing is heard in the ears, even when there is no external sound. Tinnitus can be so severe that it impairs a person's hearing. A major cause of tinnitus is prolonged exposure to loud sounds. You can protect your hearing by limiting your exposure to loud sounds, such as those at music concerts, car races, or sports events.

A variety of devices and techniques can help people with hearing impairments.

▶ Hearing aids increase the volume of sounds for people who are not completely deaf.

▶ Devices called cochlear implants can be surgically implanted to help people who are completely deaf to sense sounds.

▶ Sign language and lip reading enable people with severe hearing impairment to communicate. Signing is a language consisting of hand positions and movements.

▶ Special telephones and doorbells amplify sound or use lights.

▶ The Internet and e-mail allow people who are hearing impaired to gather information and communicate.

WRITING and Health

L1 Firsthand Account of a Disability

For students who do not have a disability, have them imagine what it would be like to have impaired vision, impaired hearing, or impaired mobility. Their lives might change dramatically. For example, a person with impaired vision would not spend time watching television or playing computer games. Ask students to write a firsthand account of what a day would be like if they had a disability.

For students who are disabled, have them write a first-hand account of what their typical day is like. If the disabled students feel comfortable doing so, they might share their accounts with the rest of the class.

Interacting With a...

Mobility-Impaired Person

► Be patient.
► Move only as quickly as the person can keep pace.
► Be ready to give assistance if asked.
► Sit down if the person is seated. Do not stand and "talk down" to the person.

Impaired Mobility The body's ability to move depends on the nervous, muscular, and skeletal systems functioning together in a coordinated fashion. Disease in, or injury to, any of these body systems may result in impaired mobility.

► **Diseases** In children, impaired mobility can be caused by diseases such as cerebral palsy and muscular dystrophy. Multiple sclerosis can develop in young people and may result in impaired mobility. In the elderly, arthritis, Alzheimer's disease, Parkinson's disease, and heart disease are common causes of impaired mobility.

► **Injuries** Paralysis of the arms or legs due to injuries to the brain or spinal cord is a major cause of impaired mobility. These kinds of injuries are frequently the result of unnecessary risk-taking, substance abuse, or violence. Nearly 80% of spinal cord injury victims are young males.

The loss of arms or legs due to injury is another cause of impaired mobility. Diseases such as diabetes and cancer can also require the surgical removal of a limb to save the person's life.

Individuals with impaired mobility can use canes, walkers, wheelchairs, crutches, braces, or artificial limbs to be mobile. Elevators, curb cuts, and ramps at building entrances allow people in wheelchairs access to places and services. For people who are paralyzed, research on nerve cell function holds some promise.

 **Connect to Your Life** In what ways is your school accessible to people with impaired mobility?

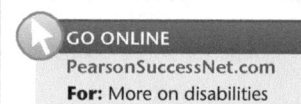 **GO ONLINE**
PearsonSuccessNet.com
For: More on disabilities

Chronic Diseases and Disabilities **625**

L2 Addressing Misconceptions

Impaired Mobility Some students may think that people with disabilities affecting muscular coordination, such as cerebral palsy, are also mentally disabled. Emphasize that in most cases this is not true. Ask: **What characteristics of a person with impaired mobility might lead to such a misconception?** *(Sample answer: A person with severe coordination impairment may not be able to control his or her body movements or speak clearly.)* Explain that when interacting with a mobility-impaired person, students must strive to see through such characteristics and recognize that the person has many of the same thoughts and feelings that they have.

L3 Cultural Connection

Students whose first language is not English may have had experiences similar to those of people with disabilities. Ask volunteers to share experiences and explain how they felt when someone treated them with a lack of respect.

Connect to Your Life Answers will vary depending on the school. Students might mention curb cuts around the school grounds, ramps leading into the school, and bathroom facilities built to allow wheelchair access.

L3 Online Activity  GO ONLINE

Visit Pearson SuccessNet to access an online activity for more on disabilities. Have students complete the Web activity.

Living With Disabilities

L2 Class Discussion

Lead a discussion on the purpose of the Americans with Disabilities Act. Ask: **What is the purpose of the ADA?** *(to guarantee the civil rights of Americans who have physical or mental disabilities)* **Why do you think the ADA is a necessary law?** *(Sample answer: Without the law, people with disabilities might still face discrimination and not be able to do anything about it.)*

3. Assess

Evaluate

These assignments can help you assess students' mastery of the section content.

Section 4 Review

Answers appear below.

Teaching Resources
• Practice 23-4
• Section 23-4 Quiz

L2 Reteach

For each of the three most common physical disabilities, call on students to identify the leading causes of the disability and describe technologies, devices, or techniques used to help a person with that disability.

L4 Enrich

Teaching Resources
• Enrich 23-4

Health and Community

Protecting Your Hearing Tell students that their PSAs can use different examples, such as the loud sound of a rock concert, a leaf blower, or a personal MP3 player. Each PSA should focus on how exposure to such sounds can affect hearing and what steps should be taken to avoid hearing impairment.

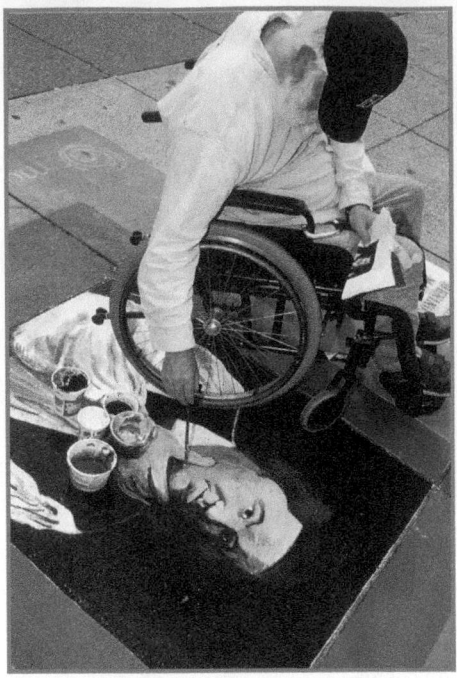

FIGURE 16 People with disabilities contribute in all areas of society.

Living With Disabilities

People adapt to physical disabilities in different ways, depending on the extent of the disability, their feelings about it, and the support they receive. Many organizations help people adapt to disabilities by providing equipment, education, and emotional support.

People with disabilities have the same life goals as people who do not have disabilities. And these goals require that they be integrated into school, the workplace, and the community. People with disabilities are capable of great things and should not be underestimated.

An important move toward integrating people with disabilities into the workplace and community came in 1990 when the Americans with Disabilities Act was signed into law. The **Americans with Disabilities Act** (ADA) guarantees the civil rights of Americans who have physical or mental disabilities. This includes people who are physically impaired or mentally retarded, as well as those who have cancer, epilepsy, and HIV or AIDS. It also protects people who are undergoing or have completed rehabilitation for alcoholism or drug abuse. The law guarantees that people with disabilities have access to the same employment opportunities, public services, public transportation, public accommodations, and communications capabilities as everyone else.

In addition, the Individuals with Disabilities Education Act (IDEA) of 1997 helps ensure that children with disabilities receive quality education alongside other students.

Section 4 Review

Key Ideas and Vocabulary

1. What is a **disability**?
2. What are the three most common physical disabilities?
3. What is **tinnitus** and how can it be prevented?
4. How are the rights of Americans with disabilities protected?

Critical Thinking

5. **Evaluating** If one of your friends were making fun of a person with a disability, how would you react?

Health and Community

Protecting Your Hearing Create a public service announcement informing people in your community about the dangers of prolonged exposure to loud noises. Include information about different types of noises and how they can affect your hearing. Describe ways you can protect your hearing at work and at play. **WRITING**

6. **Relating Cause and Effect** Some disabilities can be prevented. Choose a disability you read about in this section that is preventable. What behaviors could you practice now to avoid that disability?

GO ONLINE PearsonSuccessNet.com   Audio Summary Section 23.4

Section 4 Review

1. any physical or mental impairment that limits or reduces normal activities

2. impaired vision, impaired hearing, and impaired mobility

3. Tinnitus is a condition in which ringing is heard in the ears, even when there is no external sound. It can be prevented by limiting exposure to loud sounds.

4. The Americans with Disabilities Act guarantees the civil rights of Americans who have physical or mental disabilities.

5. A typical answer might suggest voicing objection to the person making fun and explaining why people with disabilities deserve respect.

6. *Sample answer:* Avoiding unnecessary risks, such as reckless driving, is a way to prevent impaired mobility.

Chapter 23
At a Glance

Section 1 Cardiovascular Diseases

Key Ideas

▶ Cardiovascular diseases include hypertension, atherosclerosis, heart attack, arrhythmia, congestive heart failure, and stroke.

▶ There are many medical technologies and surgical methods available for detecting and treating cardiovascular diseases.

▶ Choosing behaviors that lower your risk for cardiovascular disease is important for your health, both now and throughout your life.

Vocabulary
• chronic disease (602) • cardiovascular disease (602)
• angina pectoris (603) • heart attack (604)
• fibrillation (604) • stroke (605)
• cerebral hemorrhage (605) • aneurysm (605)

Section 2 Cancer

Key Ideas

▶ Cancer harms the body by destroying healthy body tissues. The key to curing cancer is early detection and treatment.

▶ Although the specific cause of most cancers is unknown, certain behaviors have been shown to decrease the risk of cancer.

Vocabulary
• cancer (609)
• tumor (609)
• malignant (609)
• metastasis (609)
• oncogene (610)
• carcinogen (610)
• biopsy (612)

Section 3 Other Chronic Diseases

Key Ideas

▶ People with type 1 diabetes produce little or no insulin, and blood glucose levels remain high.

▶ People with type 2 diabetes produce sufficient insulin, but their cells do not respond. Blood glucose levels remain high.

▶ Allergies develop when foreign substances enter the body and set off a series of reactions.

▶ With asthma, the respiratory passages become inflamed in reaction to certain "triggers."

▶ Arthritis results in joint stiffness, pain, or swelling.

Vocabulary
• diabetes (614) • insulin (614) • allergy (616)
• allergen (616) • histamine (616) • arthritis (618)
• osteoarthritis (618) • rheumatoid arthritis (619)

Section 4 Disabilties

Key Ideas

▶ The three most common physical disabilities are impaired vision, impaired hearing, and impaired mobility.

▶ An important move toward integrating people with disabilities into the workplace and community came in 1990 when the Americans with Disabilities Act was signed into law.

Vocabulary
• disability (623)
• macular degeneration (623)
• tinnitus (624)
• Americans with Disabilities Act (626)

Chronic Diseases and Disabilities **627**

Chapter 23
At a Glance

Living With Disabilities Ask for volunteers to share their answers. Use examples from the video to review strategies for dealing with obstacles and setbacks.
VIDEO

Key Ideas Review

L1 Have students copy the key ideas listed on this page, leaving one or two important words blank in each key idea. Then have partners exchange key ideas and try to fill in the blanks. Students should review passages in the text about any key ideas they cannot complete.

L2 Ask students to reword the section objectives as questions and then try to answer them. Students should find answers in the text for any questions they cannot answer.

Vocabulary Review

EL Have student pairs make flashcards of chapter vocabulary terms. On the front of each card, they should write a term, and on the back, the definition of the term. Have partners use their flashcards to quiz each other on chapter vocabulary.

L2 Ask students to write sentences in which they correctly use the vocabulary terms. For each term, call on a student to read his or her sentence. Ask other students whether the term was used correctly. If not, call on another volunteer to read his or her sentence for the term.

Chapter 23 Review

 GO ONLINE

PearsonSuccessNet.com

Students can go online for a review activity on Chapter 23.

Reviewing Key Ideas

Section 1

1. c   2. a

3. Hypertension can lead to other cardiovascular diseases, including congestive heart failure and stroke.

4. An excess of cholesterol in the blood can lead to atherosclerosis. Therefore, a drug that lowers cholesterol levels reduces the risk of atherosclerosis.

Section 2

5. a   6. b

7. If cancer is suspected from screening test results, surgeons may perform a biopsy to examine a small piece of tissue for signs of cancer.

8. *Sample answer:* Banning smoking in public places is justified because tobacco smoke contains carcinogens.

Section 3

9. c

10. family history of diabetes, being overweight, and a lack of physical activity

11. Osteoarthritis; wear and tear on a joint or repeated injuries to a joint

12. *Sample answer:* She could look around her grandmother's house for common allergens, such as dust, molds, or plant pollen. She could then try to eliminate that allergen from an area of the house.

Section 4

13. d

14. *Sample answer:* Hearing aids increase the volume of sounds for people who are not completely deaf. Cochlear implants are surgically implanted to help people who are completely deaf hear sounds. Special telephones and doorbells amplify sound or use lights.

15. canes, walkers, wheelchairs, crutches, braces, and artificial limbs

---

Chapter 23 Review

Reviewing Key Ideas

 GO ONLINE
PearsonSuccessNet.com
For: Chapter 23 review activity

Section 1

1. Hardening of the arteries is known as
   a. atherosclerosis.
   b. congestive heart failure.
   c. arteriosclerosis.
   d. angina pectoris.

2. An artificial pacemaker can help control
   a. arrhythmia.
   b. heart attack.
   c. cerebral hemorrhage.
   d. hypertension.

3. How is hypertension related to other forms of cardiovascular disease?

4. **Critical Thinking** How could a drug that lowers cholesterol levels in the blood affect the development of atherosclerosis?

Section 2

5. A mass of cancerous cells is called a(n)
   a. malignant tumor.   b. benign tumor.
   c. oncogene.   d. carcinogen.

6. A cancer-causing substance in the environment is
   a. a melanoma.   b. a carcinogen.
   c. a tumor.   d. an oncogene.

7. What role does a biopsy play in detecting cancer?

8. **Critical Thinking** Smoking is now banned in many public places. Do you think the health benefits to society justify this restriction? Explain.

Section 3

9. Which hormone regulates blood sugar levels?
   a. diabetes   b. histamine
   c. insulin   d. allergen

10. Name three risk factors for type 2 diabetes.

11. What is the most common form of arthritis? What is its cause?

12. **Critical Thinking** Whenever Julie visits her grandmother's house, she sneezes and sometimes has trouble breathing. How could Julie determine if she has an allergy to something there?

Section 4

13. A common cause of vision impairment in older people is
    a. eye injury.   b. spinal cord injury.
    c. tinnitus.   d. macular degeneration.

14. Describe three devices that may help people who are hearing impaired communicate effectively.

15. What devices are available to help mobility-impaired people be more mobile?

16. What needs are addressed by the Americans with Disabilities Act?

17. **Critical Thinking** What recommendations would you make to provide more job and other opportunities for disabled people in your community?

Building Health Skills

18. **Advocacy** What kinds of health programs would you want the government to support to help reduce type 2 diabetes in the United States? Would such programs save money? Explain.

19. **Making Decisions** After shoveling snow from his driveway, your elderly neighbor sits down suddenly, clutching his chest. What should you do?

20. **Setting Goals** Choose a disease from this chapter that you might be at risk for. List some behavior changes you can make to lower your risk. Monitor your behavior for a few weeks and evaluate your progress in a short report. **WRITING**

Health and Community

Disability Assistance Many communities have services that assist people with both physical and mental disabilities. Find out what services are available in your community for helping people with disabilities. You may look in the telephone directory, on the Internet, or on posting boards around your community. Share your findings with your class. **WRITING**

---

16. The law guarantees that people with disabilities have access to the same employment opportunities, public services, public transportation, public accommodations, and communications capabilities as everyone else.

17. *Sample answer:* Companies and public agencies should make all buildings and facilities accessible to people with disabilities.

Building Health Skills

18. *Sample answer:* Health programs that encourage people to control their weight and exercise regularly would help reduce cases of type 2 diabetes. Such programs would save money because the fewer people who develop type 2 diabetes, the lower the medical costs for treating the disease.

Standardized Test Prep

Math Practice

The graph shows the occurrence of cardiovascular diseases in men and women of different ages. Use the graph to answer Questions 21–23.

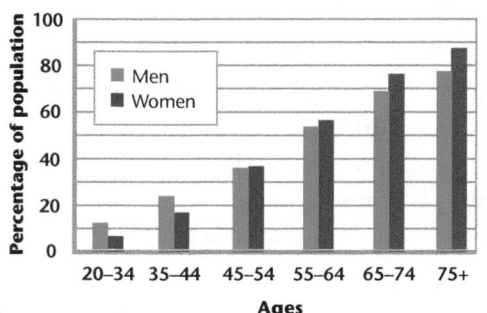

21. At what ages are more men than women affected by cardiovascular diseases?
  A 20–44
  B 35–44
  C 45–54
  D 65–75

22. What happens to the percentage of women with cardiovascular diseases between age 40 and age 60?
  F It stays the same.
  G It increases slightly.
  H It doubles.
  J It more than triples.

23. According to the graph, which of the following statements is true?
  A Men over 55 don't need to worry about cardiovascular disease.
  B Men are more at risk for cardiovascular disease than women.
  C As people age, the risk of cardiovascular disease decreases.
  D As people age, the risk of cardiovascular disease increases.

Reading and Writing Practice

Read the passage. Then answer Questions 24–27.

Scientists have been studying the link between the hormone leptin and breast cancer. Leptin helps regulate energy balance and weight. Leptin can increase the amount of estrogen in the breast tissue of obese women. Perhaps blocking leptin's activity could be a novel approach for treating some breast cancers. To test this idea, scientists designed non-toxic inhibitors of leptin, which they tested in mice. The inhibitors reduced both the number and size of mammary tumors in the mice. The incidence of metastasis to the liver was also reduced.

24. Leptin inhibitors may
  A increase the size of mammary tumors.
  B increase the number of mammary tumors.
  C decrease the number and size of mammary tumors.
  D increase estrogen in breast tissue.

25. In this passage, the word *novel* means
  F book-like.   G new.
  H beneficial.   J ill-timed.

26. According to the passage, which of these statements is true?
  A Leptin may contribute to tumor growth.
  B Leptin hasn't been linked to breast cancer.
  C Leptin inhibitors have been used for years to treat breast cancer.
  D Leptin inhibitors only work if they are toxic.

Constructed Response

27. In a paragraph, summarize the leptin inhibitor experiment and the results.

> ### Test-Taking Tip
>
> **When taking a test, be sure to read the directions first. Then start answering the questions.**

Standardized Test Prep

Math Practice
21. A
22. J
23. D

Reading and Writing Practice
24. C
25. G
26. A
27. Students' answers should mention that the leptin inhibitor experiment involved testing mice, that it reduced the number and size of mammary tumors in the mice, and that the incidence of metastasis to the liver was reduced.

---

19. Uncomfortable pressure or pain in the chest lasting for two minutes or longer is a sign of a heart attack. The best action to take is to call 911.

20. Responses will vary, though most students will choose either atherosclerosis or type 2 diabetes. In either case, behavior changes that would lower a person's risk would include a healthier diet and more physical activity.

Health and Community

Disability Assistance You might point students to the administrative offices of a local college or university, which may be able to provide a list of organizations that focus on services for the disabled. They can also look for Web sites of national organizations, such as the American Foundation for the Blind, the Alexander Graham Bell Association for the Deaf, and the National Spinal Cord Injury Association.

Focus on ISSUES

Should Experimental Medicines Be Available to the Terminally Ill?

Teaching Strategies

- Several days before discussing this issue, ask a few interested students to learn more about the topic. They can search online for additional arguments that have been made for and against the use of experimental medicines by terminally ill patients.

- On the day you discuss this issue, first have the class read about the issue. Then, provide students with a context. Explain that the federal Food and Drug Administration (FDA) is in charge of approving new drugs. The FDA requires pharmaceutical companies to do controlled studies to demonstrate that new drugs are both safe and effective. People with serious illnesses may be able to enroll in the drug studies (called clinical trials), and thus have access to experimental medicines before they are approved by the FDA. The number of people who can obtain experimental medicines in this way, however, is very limited.

- After students answer the questions on page 631, lead them in a discussion on the issue. Call on several volunteers to state their views and supporting reasons. Ask students who researched the topic in advance to add whatever additional arguments they learned from their research.

⚑ Sensitive Issues

This is likely to be a sensitive issue for students who have family members or friends with serious illnesses for which effective drugs are not available. These students may become upset or angry when the issue is discussed. Offer students other options, such as working independently on the questions or writing a report on a relevant topic (for example, the FDA drug-approval process).

Focus on ISSUES

Should Experimental Medicines Be Available to the Terminally Ill?

Over half a million Americans die every year from cancer. Some forms of cancer can be treated with medicines. But for other cancers, there are currently no effective treatments. A new cancer medicine takes an average of 12 years to go from discovery to approval for use in patients.

For patients with life-threatening illnesses, the drug discovery and approval process can feel too slow. Some diseases spread so quickly that a patient will likely die before a new drug is approved. Should terminally ill patients have the option of taking experimental medicines that show promise for treating their illness?

630

For Your INFORMATION!

Drug Approval: Historical Overview

From 1938 to 1962, the role of the FDA was to make sure drugs were safe. The FDA had 60 days to make this determination for each new drug. In 1962, the FDA was given the additional job of determining the efficacy, or effectiveness, of new drugs. This task greatly slowed the drug-approval process. In the 1980s, under pressure from AIDS patients, the FDA put several new AIDS drugs on a "fast track" for approval. The number of people who could receive experimental AIDS drugs was also increased. Today, some experts argue that fast-track approvals should be discontinued and the expanded use of experimental drugs should be curtailed. The issue is still under debate.

The Case for Experimental Medicines

Medicines should be made available to seriously ill patients as soon as the medicines show signs of promise and some degree of safety. It is not ethical to withhold these medicines from patients with very little time and hope left. If patients understand the risks of taking an experimental medicine, they should be allowed to make their own decision in consultation with their doctor.

" I lost a cousin last year to leukemia. While she was sick, we found out that there was a new medicine being tested. She was told that there was no way to get the new drug. I felt angry, like they were not giving her a chance to be cured. People should have the right to try anything that might slow or cure their disease. "

The Case Against Experimental Medicines

Using a medicine that is not yet approved may expose patients to serious side effects that might be worse than their disease. Approximately 1,000 possible cancer medicines, for example, are studied in the laboratory before one emerges as a candidate for testing in humans. The odds are too great that an experimental medicine might pose serious health risks to the patient.

" If I were terminally ill, I would only want treatments that have been proven to work and be safe. I wouldn't want to have false hope in a medicine that might even make me sicker. The testing process is in place to protect patients from harm. As slow as the process is, people need to let drug companies and the government thoroughly test new medicines. "

What do **YOU** think?

Use these steps to analyze and express your opinion about whether experimental medicines should be available to the terminally ill.

1. Analyze the Issue Carefully consider both sides of the issue. Make a table listing the pros and cons of making experimental medicines available to the terminally ill.

2. Consider Your Values Look at the different pros and cons you listed. Which of them are most important to you? Which are less important? Explain.

3. Take a Stand In a paragraph, express your opinion on whether experimental medicines should be available to the terminally ill. State your opinion clearly, and give several reasons that support your view. **WRITING**

631

What do **YOU** think?

1. Pros might include the possibility of experimental medicines saving people's lives and learning more about the medicine more quickly. Cons might include the risks of serious side effects and patients developing false hopes.
2. *Sample answer:* I think that the possibility of saving the lives of terminally ill patients is more important than the risks of serious side effects.
3. Students may take a stand on either side of the issue as long as they support their view with sound reasons. Students who favor experimental medicines might argue that patients and their doctors, rather than the government, should have the right to make such decisions. Students who oppose experimental medicines might argue that taking such medicines is too risky, especially when their benefits are unknown.

GO ONLINE

PearsonSuccessNet.com

Visit Pearson SuccessNet for more information on experimental medicines.

CHAPTER 24 Safeguarding the Public

Section Objectives	Standards Correlation	Instructional Resources L3	SE eTEXT	TE eTEXT	PRINT
1 The Healthcare System ⏲ 1 period; 1/2 block	NHES: 1.12.6, 2.12.5, 2.12.6, 3.12.2	SE Warm-Up, p. 634	•	•	•
		SE Media Wise Evaluating TV Doctors, p. 637	•	•	•
24.1.1 Identify the healthcare providers that work together to care for patients.		RN Note Taking Guide 24-1	•	•	•
24.1.2 Describe different types of healthcare facilities.		TR Practice 24-1		•	
24.1.3 Analyze how technology has affected healthcare.		TR Section 24-1 Quiz		•	
2 Participating in Your Healthcare ⏲ 2 periods; 1 block	NHES: 1.12.6, 2.12.10, 3.12.3, 3.12.5, 7.12.1	SE Warm-Up, p. 641	•	•	•
		RN Note Taking Guide 24-2	•	•	•
24.2.1 Decribe how to choose and participate fully in your healthcare.		IB Image Bank 24-6, 24-9		•	
		TR Practice 24-2		•	
24.2.2 Compare different options for paying for healthcare.		TR Section 24-2 Quiz		•	
3 Public Health ⏲ 2 periods; 1 block	NHES: 1.12.6, 1.12.7, 2.12.10, 3.12.1, 3.12.2, 3.12.3	SE Warm-Up, p. 648	•	•	•
		RN Note Taking Guide 24-3	•	•	•
24.3.1 Summarize the main goal of public health programs today.		TR Practice 24-3		•	
24.3.2 Describe how the United States' public health system is organized.		TR Section 24-3 Quiz		•	
Working in Groups ⏲ 1 period; 1/2 block	NHES: 4.12.1, 4.12.2, 4.12.3, 8.12.3	SE Practice the Skill, p. 655	•	•	•
		RN Building Health Skills 24	•	•	•
BHS.24 Develop the skills to work successfully in groups.					
4 Global Public Health ⏲ 1 period; 1/2 block	NHES: 1.12.3, 1.12.6, 1.12.7, 2.12.2, 8.12.3	SE Warm-Up, p. 656	•	•	•
		RN Note Taking Guide 24-4	•	•	•
24.4.1 Explain the importance of global public health efforts.		TR Practice 24-4		•	
24.4.2 Describe the types of public health problems that international health organizations work to overcome.		TR Section 24-4 Quiz		•	

Chapter Review and Assessment

SE Chapter 24 Review, p. 660 L3

CTB Chapter 24 Test L2 L3 L4

SE Standardized Test Prep, p. 661 L3

PROGRAM COMPONENTS

SE Student Edition	**CTB** Computer Test Bank
TE Teacher Edition	**AUD** Audio Section Summaries
TR Teaching Resources	
RN Reading and Note Taking Guide	**DVD** Teens Talk Video Series
	VVG Video Viewing Guide
ARN Adapted Reading and Note Taking Guide	**PPT** Presentation
IB Image Bank	

Differentiated Instruction
(L1) (L2) (L4) (EL)

		SE eTEXT	TE eTEXT	PRINT
ARN	Note Taking Guide 24-1 (L2)	•	•	
RN	Note Taking Guide 24-1 (EL)	•	•	•
AUD	Audio Summary 24-1 (L1) (L2) (EL)	•	•	
TE	Reteach Strategy, p. 640 (L2)		•	•
TR	Enrich 24-1 (L4)		•	
ARN	Note Taking Guide 24-2 (L2)	•	•	
RN	Note Taking Guide 24-2 (EL)	•	•	•
AUD	Audio Summary 24-2 (L1) (L2) (EL)	•	•	
TE	Reteach Strategy, p. 647 (L2)		•	•
TR	Enrich 24-2 (L4)		•	
ARN	Note Taking Guide 24-3 (L2)	•	•	
RN	Note Taking Guide 24-3 (EL)	•	•	•
AUD	Audio Summary 24-3 (L1) (L2) (EL)	•	•	
TE	Reteach Strategy, p. 653 (L2)		•	•
TR	Enrich 24-3 (L4)		•	
ARN	Building Health Skills 24 (L2)	•	•	
RN	Building Health Skills 24 (EL)	•	•	•
ARN	Note Taking Guide 24-4 (L2)	•	•	
RN	Note Taking Guide 24-4 (EL)	•	•	•
AUD	Audio Summary 24-4 (L1) (L2) (EL)	•	•	
TE	Reteach Strategy, p. 658 (L2)		•	•
TR	Enrich 24-4 (L4)		•	

ABILITY LEVELS
(L1) **For students with special needs**
(L2) **For less proficient readers**
(L3) **For all students**
(L4) **For gifted and talented students**
(EL) **For English language learners**

Chapter 24 Digital/Video Pathway

This alternative pathway allows you to teach this chapter's content using only the video and online materials.

Preview
DVD	Video #24 Preview
SE	Video #24 Preview Activity
VVG	Video #24 Worksheet

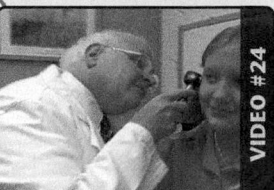
Taking Charge of Your Health

1
PPT	24-1 Presentation
RN/ARN	24-1 Note Taking
PPT	24-1 Section Quiz

2
DVD	Video #24 Explore/Wrap-Up
VVG	Video #24 Worksheet
PPT	24-2 Presentation
RN/ARN	24-2 Note Taking
PPT	24-2 Section Quiz

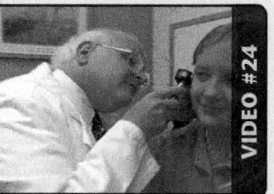
Taking Charge of Your Health

3
PPT	24-3 Presentation
RN/ARN	24-3 Note Taking
PPT	24-3 Section Quiz

4
PPT	24-4 Presentation
RN/ARN	24-4 Note Taking
PPT	24-4 Section Quiz

Chapter Preview

Section 1 The Healthcare System
Healthcare providers include doctors, nurses, and other professionals. These healthcare providers work in many different healthcare facilities. The Internet, e-mail, and other technologies can facilitate communication among providers and between providers and their patients.

Section 2 Participating in Your Healthcare
Choosing a doctor requires careful consideration. People who know what to expect at an office visit and are aware of their rights and responsibilities get the most benefit from each doctor visit. Good healthcare is made affordable with health insurance.

Section 3 Public Health
The public health system works to prevent disease and promote positive health behaviors. The public health system in the United States includes government agencies at the federal, state, and local levels, as well as private organizations.

Communicating
Working in Groups
Groups are successful when they have clear goals, a strong leader, scheduled tasks, and positive members.

Section 4 Global Public Health
Global public health efforts provide services and funding to help developing nations overcome problems such as malnutrition, lack of basic medical care, poor sanitation, and lack of clean water.

GO ONLINE
PearsonSuccessNet.com
For resources and activities for this chapter.

Safeguarding the Public

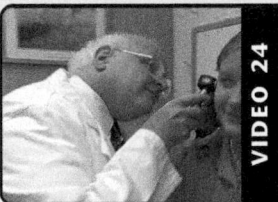

GO ONLINE PearsonSuccessNet.com

TEENS Talk
Taking Charge of Your Health

VIDEO 24

Preview **Activity**

Where Do You Get Your Health Information?

Complete this activity before you watch the video.

1. Choose a health topic you would like to know more about.
2. Write down a list of different sources that could provide you with more information on that topic. **WRITING**
3. Rank the sources you listed from most reliable to least reliable.
4. When you have looked for health information in the past, did you go to the most reliable source? Why or why not?

632

🚩 ### Sensitive Issues

- Students may hesitate to share personal health information for many different reasons. Some students might have inadequate healthcare or no health insurance. Others might go to free clinics rather than private hospitals.

- Selection of healthcare is often heavily influenced by family or community circumstances. Some communities may have limited healthcare facilities and services. Reassure students in smaller communities that healthcare services in larger communities are available to them if they require it.

TEENS Talk

Taking Charge of Your Health

Video Objectives

Use this video to help students

Understand the importance of getting regular medical checkups.

Identify reliable sources of health information.

Make responsible decisions regarding their own healthcare.

Preview **Activity**

Where Do You Get Your Health Information?

Before watching the video, have students complete the Preview Activity by writing their answers in their private journals. After showing all three portions of the video, ask students to revisit their list of sources and their reliability rankings. They should make a new list based on what they learned from the video.

From the Authors

This chapter is intended to help students understand the complexities of the healthcare system and how to navigate it when they or their families need services. In addition, the chapter describes the scope of the nation's public health system and some of the challenges we face in safeguarding the public as we contribute to global health.

You will find that the activities and questions in this chapter have been designed to get students to think critically about evaluating healthcare and how best to strengthen the current healthcare system. And because improving public health requires an informed and active citizenry, the Building Health Skills activity on page 654 focuses on fostering skills in working in groups.

Section 1

The Healthcare System

Objectives

Before class begins, write the objectives on the board. Have students copy the objectives into their notebooks at the start of class.

1. Focus

Warm-Up Quick Quiz

Use the Warm-Up Presentation slide to survey student responses.

After students take the quiz, tally students' responses for each statement. Then inform students that only statement 2 is true. From students' responses you will have an idea of which misconceptions to address as you teach the section.

Presentation 24-1

Section 1

The Healthcare System

Objectives

▶ **Identify** the healthcare providers who work together to care for patients.

▶ **Describe** different types of healthcare facilities.

▶ **Analyze** how technology has affected healthcare.

Vocabulary

- healthcare system
- primary care physician
- diagnosis
- medical specialist
- primary healthcare
- outpatient
- secondary healthcare
- inpatient
- tertiary healthcare

Warm-Up

Quick Quiz Only one of the following statements is true. Which statement do you think it is?

① You only need to see a doctor when you are sick.

② A doctor will keep your personal information confidential.

③ Health insurance covers 100% of your medical expenses.

④ Doctors know what's best for you, and you shouldn't question their opinions.

WRITING Explain why you gave the answer you did.

Healthcare Providers

When you go to a doctor for regular checkups and immunizations, you participate in the healthcare system. The **healthcare system** includes all available medical services, the ways in which individuals pay for medical care, and programs aimed at preventing disease and disability. **Within the healthcare system, doctors work with nurses and other healthcare providers to care for patients.**

Doctors **Primary care physicians** take care of most people's routine medical needs. Most primary care physicians are medical doctors who have specialized in one of three areas of medicine—family practice; internal medicine; or pediatrics, children's medical care.

After medical school and further training, a doctor must pass the medical licensing test of the state in which he or she intends to practice. Once licensed, a doctor can diagnose medical conditions, provide treatment, and write prescriptions for medication. A **diagnosis** (dy ug NOH sis) is a doctor's opinion of the nature or cause of a medical condition. A prescription is a written order to a pharmacist authorizing that a patient be given a particular medicine.

WRITING and Health

L2 **Summary**

Have students write a paragraph in which they summarize the responsibilities of a doctor. In their summaries, students should also explain what primary care physicians do and when people should see them.

Student paragraphs should contain a topic sentence and several supporting details. Emphasize that students should write the summary in their own words.

Medical Specialists If you have a condition that requires specialized treatment, a primary care physician will refer you to a medical specialist. A **medical specialist** is a doctor who has received additional training in a particular branch of medicine. Figure 1 describes some medical specialists.

FIGURE 1 If a doctor is not planning to become a primary care physician, he or she usually specializes in one area of medicine.

Neurologists treat nervous system disorders.

Dermatologists treat skin disorders.

Oncologists treat cancers.

Allergists treat allergies and other immune disorders.

Pediatricians provide primary care for children.

Orthopedic surgeons treat bone and joint disorders.

Ophthalmologists treat eye diseases.

Safeguarding the Public **635**

2. Teach

L3 EL Reading/Note Taking 24-1

L2 Adapted Reading/Note Taking 24-1

Healthcare Providers

L2 Class Discussion

Make a T-chart on the board to compare and contrast primary care physicians and medical specialists. Lead students in comparing these healthcare providers' education and their ability to diagnose medical conditions, provide treatment, and write prescriptions. Students should also identify medical conditions that would be treated by each type of medical provider.

L2 Visual Learning: Figure 1

Refer students to the photos of the medical specialists and ask questions such as: **What specialist would you see if you had a broken leg?** *(orthopedic surgeon)* **Which specialist treats cancer?** *(oncologist)* Then have students describe medical conditions that might be treated by one of the specialists shown. *(Sample answer: acne—dermatologist; poor eyesight—ophthalmologist; hay fever—allergist; concussion—neurologist)*

L3 Journal Writing

Have students write about their experiences in seeing a medical specialist. Students should identify what kind of specialist they saw, the purpose of their visit, and how the exam differed from the exam given by their primary care physician. Be aware that some students may still see a pediatrician as their primary care physician, while others will have never seen a medical specialist. Allow students to keep their journal entries private. **WRITING**

Differentiated Instruction

EL English Language Learners

Students can practice their language and communication skills by conducting an interview with a healthcare provider in their community. Students should write out their interview questions in advance and rehearse them with a classmate. Suggest that students get permission to record the interview so they can play it back later to help with comprehension.

L4 Building Health Skills

Accessing Information Challenge students to use library or online resources to find out about the educational requirements for at least three different healthcare professionals. Students may choose from the healthcare professionals described in the section or select different ones. Students can organize their findings in a table and present their table to the class.

L3 Active Learning

Have a few students bring in the employment sections of various local newspapers that list job openings in the medical field. List on the board the various medical careers that are advertised. Then ask students to determine from the employment ads which health professionals are in highest demand and create a poster that reflects this information.

L2 Visual Learning: Figure 2

Have students compare and contrast the responsibilities of the healthcare providers shown in Figure 2. Ask questions such as **What patient needs do nurses manage?** *(observe and assess symptoms, evaluate progress, counsel patients on how to stay healthy and avoid injury)* **How are a physical therapist's duties similar to a nurse's?** *(Both observe and assess symptoms, evaluate progress, and work to promote the recovery of a patient.)* **How are they different?** *(Sample answer: The physical therapist focuses on improving strength and mobility so the patient can easily perform the functions required for living. Nurses focus more on the general well-being of the patient.)*
Caption Answer *Sample answer:* laboratory technician; provides information about a patient's health by preparing and reading various medical tests.

Connect to Your Life Allow students to answer this question in their private journals.

Nurse ▶

FIGURE 2 A variety of providers care for patients' different needs. **Applying Concepts** What other types of healthcare providers have you heard of? What do they do?

◀ Registered dietitian

Nurses Nurses are licensed healthcare providers who work in collaboration with doctors to care for patients. There are several types of nurses that differ in their levels of training. Registered nurses (RNs) observe and assess patient symptoms, plan the best approach to promoting recovery, and evaluate progress. They also counsel patients of all ages about ways to stay healthy and prevent injury.

Registered nurses who have received additional training may become registered nurse practitioners. Nurse practitioners are trained to do many tasks that only doctors used to perform. For example, they may take medical histories, perform physical exams, order tests, treat routine medical problems, and prescribe medications. When nurse practitioners see patients for routine medical needs, they may be referred to as *primary care providers*. A nurse practitioner usually works with a doctor.

Other Providers A variety of healthcare professionals provide services that complement the work of doctors and nurses.

▶ **Physician assistants** Physician assistants perform many tasks previously done by doctors. These tasks may include taking medical histories, performing physical exams, and prescribing medications. Physician assistants work under the supervision of a doctor.

▶ **Physical therapists** Physical therapists help patients with arthritis, muscle pain, fractures, burns, strokes, or sports injuries. Physical therapists supervise exercise programs and may use heat and massage to relieve pain and improve strength and mobility.

▶ **Registered dietitians** Registered dietitians, sometimes called nutritionists, may set up and supervise food services for institutions such as hospitals. They may also provide nutritional counseling to patients in a healthcare facility or in private practice.

Connect to Your Life When was the last time you visited a healthcare provider?

◀ Physical therapist

Focus on ISSUES

L3 Minute Clinics

Escalating healthcare costs, difficulty in scheduling doctor's appointments, and declining insurance coverage combine to make it difficult for some people to get medical care for common ailments. To address these health needs, some communities are opening clinics in grocery stores and staffing them with nurse practitioners. No appointment is required, and most visits cost between $59 and $89. Nurse practitioners can diagnose and prescribe medicines for many common ailments. They refer complicated medical issues to doctors. Hold a class discussion on this new trend. Start by asking about the advantages and disadvantages of seeing a nurse practitioner for common illnesses in a place where you shop.

Media Wise

Evaluating TV Doctors

Many television shows are set in hospitals. How do different shows portray healthcare providers? What effect might these shows have on viewers' attitudes toward doctors? Evaluate a TV doctor using this questionnaire.

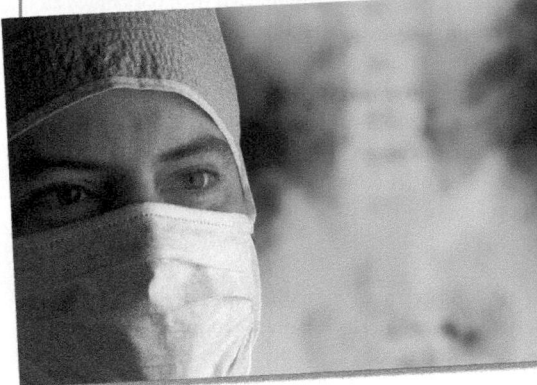

Does the doctor give each patient the time and attention he or she needs?	Yes No
Does the doctor make patients feel comfortable discussing personal information?	Yes No
Does the doctor explain each patient's condition in terms that are easy to understand?	Yes No
Is the doctor knowledgeable about patients' conditions and medical options?	Yes No
Does the doctor readily admit when he or she has made a mistake?	Yes No

"Yes" answers indicate positive qualities that patients should look for in a doctor.

Activity Use the checklist to evaluate a doctor from a television show. Then write a paragraph explaining whether you would be comfortable being treated by that doctor. Why or why not? **WRITING**

Healthcare Facilities

Healthcare facilities include doctors' offices, clinics, hospitals, and long-term care centers. These facilities offer different levels of care.

Doctors' Offices   Perhaps the most frequently used healthcare facility is the doctor's private office, which may be in a hospital or in a private building. Here doctors, nurse practitioners, or physician assistants do routine examinations and tests to diagnose and treat minor illnesses and injuries. Minor surgery, such as removing a wart, may also be done in a doctor's office. Routine healthcare provided in a doctor's office is called **primary healthcare.**

Clinics   When a medical test or procedure cannot be performed in a doctor's office, a person may go to an outpatient clinic. A clinic is a facility in which primary healthcare is provided by one or more doctors and other healthcare providers. An **outpatient** is a person admitted to a clinic for tests or treatments that do not require an overnight stay.

A variety of tests and surgical procedures can be performed at clinics. For example, cataract surgery, which involves removing a cloudy lens from an eye, can be performed at an outpatient clinic. Outpatient care is less costly than a hospital stay.

Media Wise

Evaluating TV Doctors

Invite students to name television shows that have a practicing doctor as a character. List these shows on the board. Elicit from students the day, time, and channel these shows are on television. Ask them to describe how they think each television doctor is portrayed. Then have students use the questionnaire to evaluate one or more of these television doctors.

Activity After students have written their paragraph, poll the class on which television doctors they would be comfortable with and which they would not. Encourage students to give reasons for their answers. Explain that it is typical for one person not to like the same doctor as another person; the relationship between a doctor and a patient is a very personal one.

Healthcare Facilities

L3 Building Health Skills

Advocacy Have students write a fictional e-mail to a friend who is experiencing a fever and a sore throat. In their e-mails, students should encourage their friend to visit a doctor's office to get treatment for his or her symptoms. Students should describe the type of care offered at a doctor's office. **WRITING**

L2 Cooperative Learning

Have small groups of students create a chart with the headings "Doctors' offices," "Clinics," "Hospitals," and "Long-term care facilities." Under each heading, they should list the types of care given at that type of facility.

Differentiated Instruction

L1 Special Needs

Use a map of your community to show students the locations of various doctors' offices, medical clinics, and hospitals. If possible, help students find the location of their own doctor's office. Then help students find routes from their home to their doctor's office and to the nearest hospital emergency room. Talk with students about the importance of knowing where to get emergency treatment. Emphasize that in life-threatening situations, immediate medical attention can save lives.

 **Content Update** GO ONLINE

Visit Pearson SuccessNet to access more information about healthcare professionals. Have students complete the Web activity.

Building Vocabulary

Have students make a concept map that distinguishes the terms *primary healthcare, secondary healthcare,* and *tertiary healthcare.* Students should describe where each kind of healthcare is administered.

Building Media Literacy

Explain that many hospitals, medical clinics, and doctors' offices have Web sites that give information about the doctors who work there and the services provided. Have students compare the Web sites for two of the same type of healthcare facility in their community. Students should compare and contrast the types of information given on each Web site and how useful that information would be to a patient. Then have students write a paragraph describing which Web site they think is better. **WRITING**

Building Health Skills

Making Decisions Have students imagine that their father is very ill with pneumonia. He needs to be hospitalized. Ask: **Should he go to a general hospital or to a teaching hospital?** *(Students should consider if the father's pneumonia is common or rare. If it is a common form, a general hospital would be adequate to treat him. However, if he has a rare form of pneumonia, he might get more advanced care at a teaching hospital.)* Students should describe as many scenarios and their possible outcomes as they can before making their decision. Remind students that the father's primary care physician would probably help with this decision.

Connect to Your Life Allow students to answer this question in their private journals.

GO ONLINE
PearsonSuccessNet.com
For: More on healthcare professionals

Hospitals Diagnosis and treatment of serious disorders require the services of a hospital. Hospitals are equipped to provide healthcare services requiring complicated procedures. Most hospitals also have emergency departments to treat sudden conditions or injuries.

Healthcare that is given to a patient in a hospital is known as **secondary healthcare.** Hospitals provide overnight accommodations for patients who need it. A patient who is required to stay in a hospital overnight or longer is called an **inpatient.** The patient's primary care physician and specialists, such as surgeons, visit the patient every day to note progress and adjust the patient's care.

Some hospitals are general hospitals, hospitals that treat patients of all ages and with all kinds of illnesses. Specialty hospitals, such as children's hospitals, specialize in treating one age group or one type of disorder. Hospitals located near medical schools may be "teaching hospitals." Doctors train medical students and other healthcare providers at these hospitals. Because many doctors at teaching hospitals carry out medical research, these hospitals often offer advanced and experimental medical care. Care provided in specialty hospitals and teaching hospitals is called **tertiary healthcare.**

Long-Term Care Long-term care facilities provide services for patients with a variety of medical needs. Figure 4 describes some long-term care facilities.

Connect to Your Life Have you ever stayed overnight in a hospital? If so, describe your experience.

FIGURE 3 Hospital emergency rooms provide care for people who are injured or who are suffering from a sudden onset of serious illness.

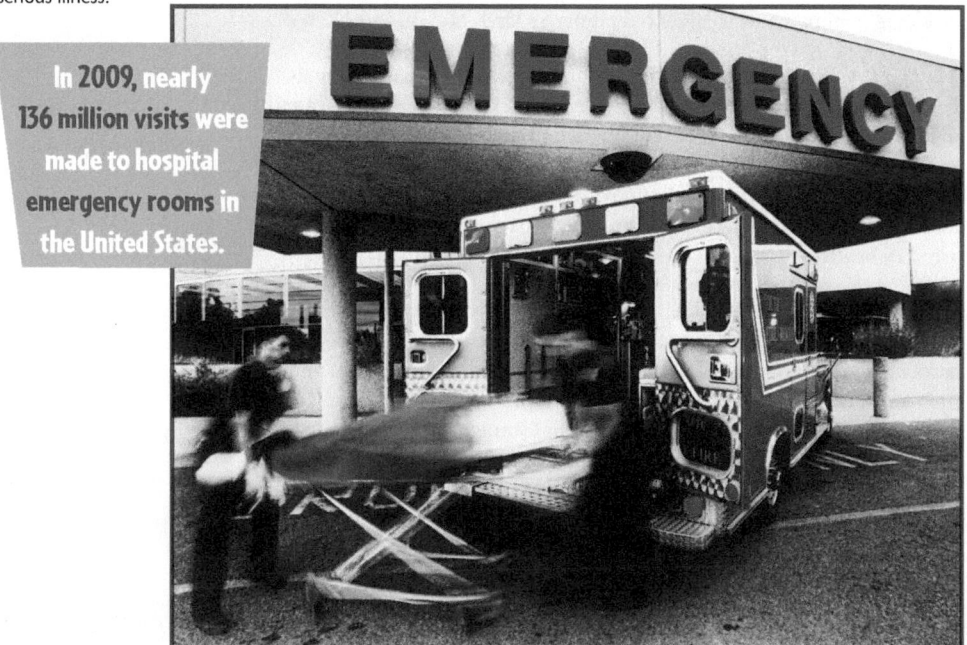

In 2009, nearly 136 million visits were made to hospital emergency rooms in the United States.

638

TEENS *Are Asking . . .*

Q: I have a friend who is in the hospital recovering from injuries she received in a car crash. Can I visit my friend? What can I do while I'm there?

A: Your friend will probably be very happy to see you. Call the hospital before you go to learn about visiting hours and whether your friend has any restrictions on visitors. Bring along cards, a game, or just hang out. It is okay to ask about your friend's experiences in the hospital; she probably needs to talk to someone about it. Depending on your friend's injuries or illness, she may be heavily bandaged, bruised, pale, or connected to beeping machines. Be prepared to give a big smile and tell your friend how much you have missed her.

Long-Term Care Facilities	
Skilled Nursing Facilities	Patients recovering from surgery, illness, or injury may require basic nursing care for an extended time before returning to their homes. A skilled nursing facility provides care for people in these situations.
Assisted Living Facilities	People who can no longer live by themselves, but do not require constant nursing care, may live in assisted living facilities. These facilities provide help with preparing meals, housekeeping, and taking medications.
Nursing Homes	Nursing homes provide long-term care for elderly or chronically ill people who cannot care for themselves.
Home-Health Care	Some patients who need long-term care are cared for in their own homes. The medical care is provided by nurses who visit the person's home.
Hospice	A special kind of nursing care is available for patients who are terminally ill. This care, called hospice, is usually given in the home. Hospice care focuses on helping a dying patient live as comfortably as possible.

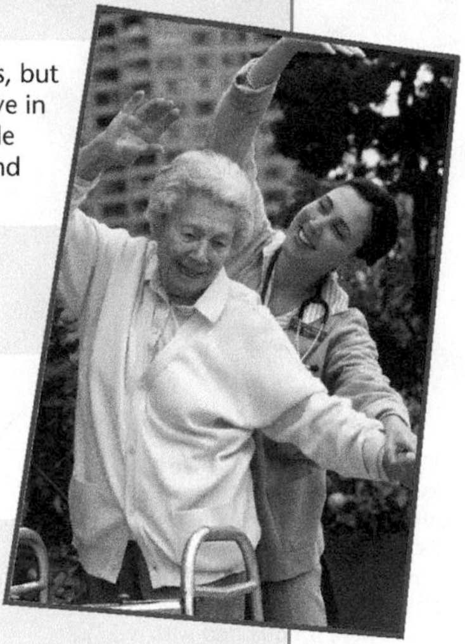

FIGURE 4 Long-term care facilites offer a variety of services depending on the level of care needed. **Classifying** Which type of facility provides nursing care for those recovering from surgery? For those who are chronically ill?

Technology and Healthcare

If you've been to a doctor's office or hospital lately, then you know that computers and other technology play a huge role in healthcare today. **The Internet, e-mail, and other technologies can make healthcare more efficient, and can make patients feel more involved in their care.**

The Internet and E-mail Many people today gather health information on the Internet. Some doctors appreciate that their patients are better informed. Others, however, worry that patients can get incorrect or biased information. Doctors often spend time with patients correcting misconceptions that stem from information the patients found on the Internet. This is why you should never rely on information you find on the Internet without first discussing it with your doctor.

Some doctors now use e-mail to communicate with their patients about non-emergency health issues. One benefit is that patients and doctors no longer need to be free at the same time to discuss things, as was the case with the telephone. There is also a written record of the communication, unlike with telephone calls. However, not everyone is comfortable communicating private health information via e-mail.

L2 Visual Learning: Figure 4

Have students use the chart in Figure 4 to compare and contrast long-term care facilities. Ask questions such as: **How does an assisted living facility differ from a nursing home?** *(People who need help with a few daily tasks may live in an assisted living facility. Elderly or chronically ill people who cannot care for themselves go to nursing homes.)* **What type of long-term care consists of nurses caring for patients in their own homes?** *(home-health care)*
Caption Answer skilled nursing facilities; nursing homes

Technology and Healthcare

L3 Building Health Skills

Accessing Information Have students find a Web site that gives health information for teens. They should evaluate the Web site to determine if it provides accurate and unbiased information. Students should prepare a short report about the Web site in which they describe the types of information given, who sponsors the site, and how they know the information is accurate. Consider sharing with the class a list of Web sites directed at teens that you judge to be accurate and unbiased.

L3 Class Discussion

Discuss each of the technologies described in the section that makes healthcare more efficient. Begin a list of pros and cons for each technology, eliciting answers from the class. For example, the Internet makes it easier for patients to gather information and become informed about their healthcare. However, many Web sites have incorrect or biased information. Write the pros and cons on the board, while students copy the information in their notebooks. Emphasize that as healthcare consumers, they need to be aware of both the pros and the cons to make good decisions about their healthcare.

Differentiated Instruction

L2 Less Proficient Readers

Provide students with a partial outline in which you have listed the five technologies described in this section: the Internet, e-mail, computerized imaging, telemedicine, and electronic health records. As students read about technology and healthcare, have them write details about each technology in the outline. Remind them to write only brief phrases and words so that the outline is easy to read. Review students' outlines, and help them add any pertinent details they missed and remove extraneous details.

3. Assess

Evaluate

These assignments can help you assess students' mastery of the section content.

Section 1 Review

Answers appear below.

Teaching Resources
• Practice 24-1
• Section 24-1 Quiz

 **Reteach**

Have students list the healthcare facilities described in this section. For each facility, have them list the kinds of healthcare providers who work there.

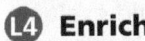 **Enrich**

Teaching Resources
• Enrich 24-1

Health at School

Provider Brochure Provide students with local telephone books to find healthcare providers and services in your school district. If your school district is large, consider dividing the class into groups and assigning each group a different type of provider or service.

Section 1 Review

1. *Sample answer:* Doctors diagnose and treat medical conditions. Medical specialists give specialized care in one area of medicine. Nurses work with doctors.

2. a doctor who takes care of most people's routine medical needs; primary healthcare

3. a doctor's opinion of the nature or cause of a medical condition

4. Routine examinations and tests are carried out in a doctor's office. More complex tests and procedures

---

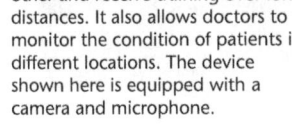

FIGURE 5 Telemedicine allows doctors to communicate with each other and receive training over long distances. It also allows doctors to monitor the condition of patients in different locations. The device shown here is equipped with a camera and microphone.

Computerized Imaging Many imaging techniques, including MRIs, CT scans, and X-rays, are performed with computerized equipment. Digital images allow doctors to share a patient's results more easily with other specialists. This can allow for quicker or more accurate diagnoses.

Telemedicine In a growing number of settings, healthcare providers may make "virtual visits" to their patients. Providers use two-way video, electronic monitoring, smart phones, and other electronic forms of communication to follow patients closely from distant locations. Telemedicine is useful for hospitals in which medical specialists are not always on site, in rural settings, or when one doctor rotates around to several hospitals in one region.

Electronic Health Records Patients benefit when their body scans, test results, or medical records can be shared efficiently between providers. For example, in an emergency situation, a doctor being able to access the patient's records quickly could save the patient's life. This type of file sharing, however, is not available everywhere. The Affordable Care Act requires providers and hospitals to completely convert from paper to electronic health records. Electronic health records cut down on medical mistakes that are sometimes made when a provider does not have access to a patient's medical history.

Section 1 Review

Key Ideas and Vocabulary

1. Describe the roles that three types of healthcare providers play in the healthcare system.

2. What is a **primary care physician?** What kind of care does a primary care physician provide?

3. What is a **diagnosis?**

4. Compare and contrast these healthcare facilities—doctors' offices, clinics, and hospitals.

5. How does an **inpatient** differ from an **outpatient?**

6. How has technology such as the Internet and e-mail affected the relationship between patients and doctors?

Health at School

Provider Brochure Find out what healthcare providers and services are available in your school district. Create a brochure for students that provides information about the different types of healthcare providers and services that are available to them. **WRITING**

Critical Thinking

7. **Comparing and Contrasting** Distinguish between an assisted living facility and a nursing home.

8. **Evaluating** Would you feel comfortable if a doctor handled some of your healthcare using telemedicine? What advantages and disadvantages might there be with that technology?

 GO ONLINE PearsonSuccessNet.com   Audio Summary Section 24.1

---

are carried out in a clinic. Hospitals can accommodate patients overnight for serious conditions and very complex treatments.

5. An inpatient stays overnight in a hospital; an outpatient receives care that does not require an overnight stay.

6. Patients feel more involved in their care because they are better informed, and they can communicate easily with their doctor.

Doctors may have to take more time to correct their patients' misconceptions.

7. A person in an assisted living facility does not require constant nursing care as do nursing home patients.

8. Answers will vary. Advantages: remote hospitals have better doctor coverage; disadvantages: doctor might miss a subtle symptom in a virtual visit.

Participating in Your Healthcare

Warm-Up

Dear Advice Line,

I just moved with my family to a new city, and I don't have a doctor here yet. How can I make sure that the doctor we choose is the right one for me?

WRITING Write a draft of a response to this question. Revise your answer after reading this section.

Your Healthcare

Up to now, adults have probably made most of the decisions about your healthcare. As you grow older, however, you will take on these responsibilities for yourself. Knowing some basics about your healthcare choices can help you choose what is best for you.

Choosing Healthcare Choosing your doctor is one healthcare responsibility that will eventually be yours. **Deciding what doctor to see for routine healthcare deserves careful consideration. After all, you want your healthcare delivered by qualified people with whom you feel comfortable.**

Some people prefer to see a doctor in a clinic. At some clinics you can arrange to see the doctor of your choice. At others, you may see the first available doctor. Some clinics also give you the option of seeing a nurse practitioner as your primary care provider.

Rather than seeing a doctor at a clinic, some people prefer to see a doctor who is in private practice. Often several doctors in private practice have their offices together in the same building and work together in a group practice.

Safeguarding the Public **641**

Objectives

▶ **Describe** how to choose and participate fully in your healthcare.

▶ **Compare** different options for paying for healthcare.

Vocabulary

- medical history
- physical examination
- premium
- copayment
- deductible

Participating in Your Healthcare

Objectives
Before class begins, write the objectives on the board. Have students copy the objectives into their notebooks at the start of class.

1. Focus

Warm-Up Advice Line

After students write their draft responses, explain that in this section they will learn how to choose a doctor. Further explain that students will learn about their rights and responsibilities as patients. After students read the section, give them time to revise their draft responses.

Presentation 24-2

Sensitive Issues

- The importance of having a medical history is described in this section. Be sensitive to the situation of students who are adopted. They may not have the benefit of a complete medical history.
- Insurance can be a sensitive issue for those students who do not have insurance or who receive government-sponsored insurance. Avoid asking students to talk about the kind of insurance their family has. Speak of people who use emergency rooms for their primary healthcare in a general, deferential way.

Differentiated Instruction

EL English Language Learners
Have students make a concept map about finding a doctor. Simplify the language of the boldfaced tips on page 642 to meet the level of understanding of your students. For example, use "Ask others" instead of "Ask for recommendations." Encourage students to illustrate each tip to improve their comprehension.

L2 Less Proficient Readers
As students read the text under Your Healthcare, instruct them to read only one subsection at a time. After reading each subsection, students should write several phrases that summarize the main ideas. For example for Choosing Healthcare, students might write "can choose a doctor in a clinic or in private practice."

2. Teach

L3 **EL** Reading/Note Taking 24-2

L2 Adapted Reading/Note Taking 24-2

Your Healthcare

L3 ## Building Media Literacy

Display several advertisements for doctors from local newspapers. Discuss with students the kinds of information found in the ads. Talk about whether these ads give enough information to determine whether these doctors would be a good choice. Ask: **What other kinds of information would you want to find a doctor that best suits your needs?** *(Sample answer: opinions of friends and family, educational background and certifications, personality)* Emphasize to students that they cannot choose a doctor based on advertisements alone.

L2 ## Building Health Skills

Practicing Healthful Behaviors Have students work in small groups of mixed abilities to develop an action plan for a friend who is looking for a doctor. Students should first create a list of key questions to identify the characteristics the friend thinks are important in a doctor. Students should then suggest how the friend could go about finding an appropriate doctor.

L2 ## Visual Learning: Figure 6

Image Bank Figure 24-6

Make a copy of Figure 6 for students, and distribute it to them. Encourage students to use the form to evaluate their own doctor. Instruct them to check the appropriate answer box for each question. Allow students to keep their evaluations private. Suggest that students talk with their parents about changing their doctor if many of their answers are "no."

Caption Answer Answers will vary.

 *Sample answer:* I look for a doctor who listens carefully to what I have to say and makes me feel comfortable during the exam.

Finding a Doctor   Here are some tips for finding a doctor who is suited to your needs.

▶ **Ask for recommendations.** The best way to begin your search for a doctor is to ask for recommendations from family members and friends. Also, you can ask the opinion of other healthcare providers you know, such as your school nurse.

▶ **Do your research.** When you have the names of some recommended doctors, you might go to your local library and check the *American Medical Directory*. This directory lists the names of doctors, the year they received their medical degrees, their areas of specialization, and whether or not they are board-certified. A board-certified physician has completed three or more years of additional training in a medical specialty and has passed a certification exam.

▶ **Identify your preferences.** Once you have the basic information, begin to think about your own preferences. Do you want a young doctor, or would you prefer an older one? Would you be more comfortable with a male or a female doctor? Do you want a doctor with an outgoing personality, or one who is more reserved?

The best time to make your first visit to a doctor is while you are well. Figure 6 lists some questions you might ask yourself about the doctor after your initial visit. These questions can help you decide if that doctor is right for you.

Connect to Your Life   What qualities do you look for in a doctor? Why are these qualities important to you?

FIGURE 6   It is very important that you feel comfortable with your doctor. **Evaluating** Use this checklist to evaluate your current doctor.

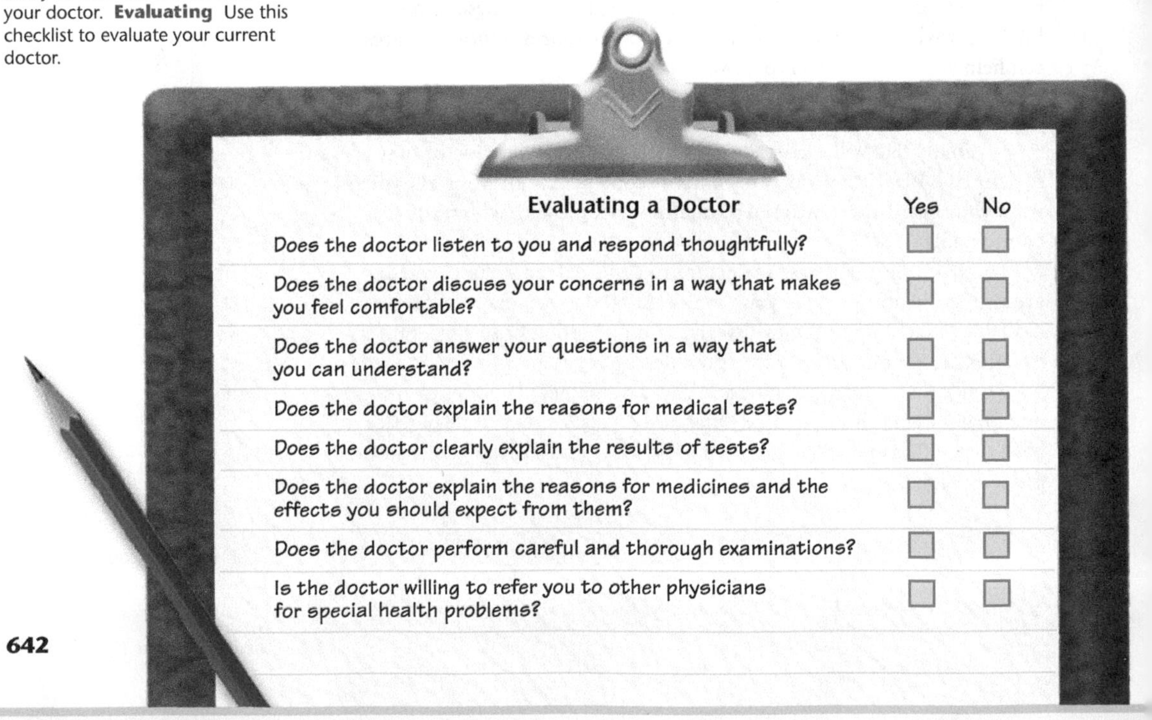

Evaluating a Doctor	Yes	No
Does the doctor listen to you and respond thoughtfully?	☐	☐
Does the doctor discuss your concerns in a way that makes you feel comfortable?	☐	☐
Does the doctor answer your questions in a way that you can understand?	☐	☐
Does the doctor explain the reasons for medical tests?	☐	☐
Does the doctor clearly explain the results of tests?	☐	☐
Does the doctor explain the reasons for medicines and the effects you should expect from them?	☐	☐
Does the doctor perform careful and thorough examinations?	☐	☐
Is the doctor willing to refer you to other physicians for special health problems?	☐	☐

642

WRITING and Health

L3 ## Advertisement

Have students write a doctor's advertisement in which they address as many potential patient concerns or questions as they can. Students can create a print advertisement in which they provide the layout with the copy and art. Students can also create the script for a radio or television advertisement. Suggest that students create a fictional doctor on which to base their advertisement.

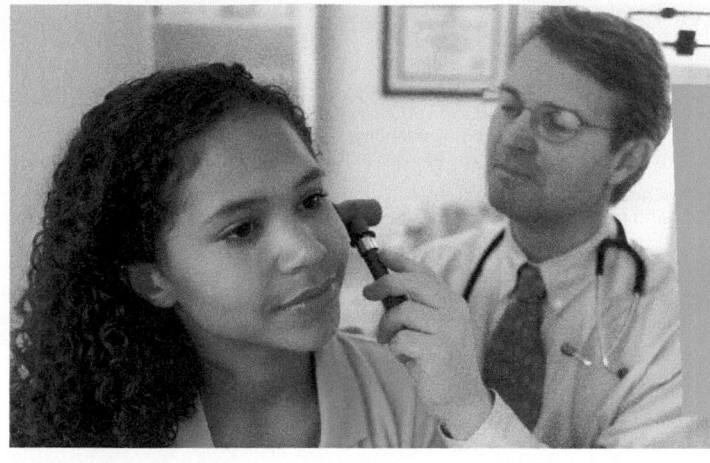

Reducing Anxiety at the Doctor's Office

• Write down your questions before going to the doctor.
• Bring along a family member or a friend for support.
• Share your questions and concerns with your doctor.
• Take notes during the visit.
• Ask for an explanation if you don't understand something.

The Doctor Appointment Have you ever put off seeing your doctor because you were afraid of getting a shot or dreaded getting undressed in the examining room? If so, you are like many other people. Instead, try thinking of a doctor's appointment as an opportunity. A visit to your doctor allows you to find out more about your body and prevent future health problems.

A doctor will usually first take your **medical history,** a record of your present and past health as well as the health of members of your family. You may have to fill out a medical history form, which the doctor will review with you.

Next, you will have a **physical examination,** a head-to-toe check of your body to identify any medical problems you may have. During the physical exam, the doctor may do some or all of the following:

► measure your height, weight, blood pressure, and body temperature

► check your skin, eyes, ears, nose, and throat

► listen to your lungs and heart

► check your muscles and bones, including your arms, legs, hands, and feet for signs of joint swelling or bone problems

► check your nervous system

► check your spine for abnormal curvature

► test your reflexes, balance, and coordination

If the doctor finds a medical condition requiring attention, he or she will discuss it with you. The doctor should explain what the condition means in terms of treatment, testing, and short-term and long-term effects.

Your medical examination should also include time for you to ask questions. Regardless of how foolish you think your questions are, keep asking them. Getting answers to questions about your body will help you participate more fully in your own healthcare.

FIGURE 7 It is normal to feel anxious about going to the doctor. The list of tips shown here can help you reduce your anxiety.

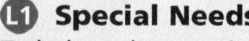

Journal Writing

Ask students to think about the doctors they have visited and write what they did and did not like about them. Then have students describe the qualities they consider important in a doctor. Allow students to keep their journal entries private. **WRITING**

Class Discussion

Begin a discussion on the importance of giving a complete medical history and talking with the doctor during the physical examination. Many doctors' offices have a medical history form to fill out before the first appointment. Obtain a copy of one, and show it to students so they know what kinds of questions to expect. Explain that some medical conditions tend to run in families. Point out that students who live in adoptive or foster families should tell their doctor.

Cooperative Learning

Divide the class into small groups of mixed abilities. Instruct groups to list questions to ask a doctor during a teen's routine medical examination. (Questions may concern nutritional information, skin problems and care, issues related to sports, worries about sexual development.) Invite groups to share their questions to create a class list. Stress to students that having a prepared list of questions is important because many people forget to ask their questions during the examination.

Differentiated Instruction

Special Needs

To help reduce anxiety about going to the doctor for a physical examination, review with students the steps in a routine physical exam. Invite the school nurse to demonstrate the various instruments used by the doctor or nurse during the exam. If possible, allow students to examine the instruments to see how they work. Emphasize the importance of having a friend or family member along for support. Point out that this person can take notes and ask questions on their behalf.

L2 Visual Learning: Figure 8

Ask volunteers to read aloud the patients' rights listed in Figure 8. Ask: **Why do you think these rights were adopted?** *(Sample answer: to give all health consumers the same rights to good healthcare)* **How does the Patients' Bill of Rights protect you?** *(Sample answer: by giving me the rights to file complaints about doctors, to keep my health information private, and to receive emergency care when needed)*

L3 Building Health Skills

Communicating Describe the following scenario to students: You dread going to the doctor; you never understand what the doctor means, and you feel like the doctor is in and out before you have a chance to ask any questions. But now you have a sore throat that is getting worse, and you need to see the doctor. Encourage students to write a plan to help them improve their communication with their doctor. Remind them of the Patients' Bill of Rights. Ask: **How can your rights influence your communication with your doctor?** *(Sample answer: They can give me the confidence to speak up when I think my doctor is not answering my questions to my satisfaction.)* Have students share their communication plans with the class. Ask: **What would you do if your communication plan did not work?** *(Sample answer: find a different doctor)*

 **Connect to Your Life** Allow students to answer this question in their private journals.

L3 Content Update GO ONLINE

Visit Pearson SuccessNet to access more information about participating in your healthcare. Have students complete the Web activity.

FIGURE 8 You and your doctor must work together as a team. If you feel that you and your doctor are not a good match, you have the right to choose another provider.

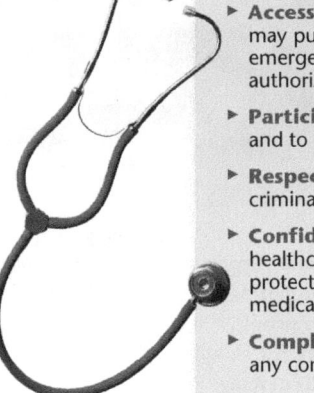

The Patients' Bill of Rights

▸ **Information** You have the right to accurate and easily understood information about your healthcare. If you speak another language, have a physical or mental disability, or just don't understand something, you will be provided with assistance.

▸ **Choice** You have the right to a choice of healthcare providers and to high-quality healthcare.

▸ **Access** If you have severe pain, an injury, or a sudden illness that may put your health in serious danger, you have the right to emergency care whenever and wherever needed, without prior authorization or financial penalty.

▸ **Participation** You have the right to know your treatment options and to participate in decisions about your care.

▸ **Respect** You have the right to considerate, respectful, and nondiscriminatory care from your healthcare providers.

▸ **Confidentiality** You have the right to talk in confidence with healthcare providers and to have your healthcare information protected. You also have the right to review and copy your own medical record.

▸ **Complaints** You have the right to a fair, fast, and objective review of any complaint you have against your healthcare providers or facilities.

Your Rights and Responsibilities You have certain rights as a patient. In 1998, the United States Advisory Commission on Consumer Protection and Quality in the Health Care Industry adopted the Patients' Bill of Rights. These rights are listed in Figure 8.

As a patient you also have certain responsibilities. You must fulfill these responsibilities in order to receive the best healthcare possible.

▸ Ask your doctor about anything that concerns your health. Most doctors expect questions. If a doctor seems annoyed by your questions, it would be wise to look for another doctor.

▸ Answer your doctor's questions honestly. Information about symptoms, medications you are taking, and any activities or behaviors that may affect your health or treatment are important for your doctor to know. The more information you can provide, the more likely your doctor can provide an accurate diagnosis.

Doctors and other healthcare providers vary in their attitudes, professional styles, and how they relate to people. If you are not satisfied with the services provided by a doctor or clinic, you do not have to continue there. Receiving good healthcare means being satisfied with the medical as well as the personal treatment you receive.

 **GO ONLINE** PearsonSuccessNet.com **For:** More on participating in your healthcare

Connect to Your Life How did you fulfill your patient responsibilities the last time you saw your doctor?

TEENS *Are Asking . . .*

Q: I am embarrassed to have a physical examination in front of my parents. Do my parents have to go with me to my doctor's appointment?

A: Most doctors will examine a teen without a parent if the parent calls ahead to give approval. You can also have your parent present at the beginning of the exam to help with your medical history, but leave during the physical exam. If you wish to have a confidential conversation with your doctor, ask beforehand. Doctors will keep your conversation confidential unless you are endangering your own life or the life of others; then the doctor must inform your parents.

Paying for Healthcare

One way to pay for healthcare is to pay for all of your own medical expenses out-of-pocket, which can be very expensive. Another way is through health insurance. **Health insurance pays for a major part of an individual's medical expenses.** Some companies offer health insurance options to their employees and their families. Individuals can also purchase their own health insurance.

Health Insurance Currently, the most commonly held health insurance plans in the United States are managed care insurance plans. Plan members pay a monthly or yearly fee called a **premium.** Whenever they visit the doctor, they may also be required to pay a small fee called a **copayment.** Managed care plans characteristically have a network of doctors who agree to provide healthcare at lower costs. Members are encouraged to see only doctors within the plan's network.

▶ **Health Maintenance Organizations** The most common managed care plans are health maintenance organizations, or HMOs. Members of an HMO choose a primary care physician who provides routine care and makes referrals to specialists within the network when necessary. HMOs usually only cover the costs of health services provided within the network.

▶ **Point of Service Plans** Like HMOs, point of service (POS) plans require you to choose a primary care physician. The difference is that your primary care physician may refer you to specialists outside the network. However, to see a doctor outside the network, you will have to pay a higher copayment.

▶ **Preferred Provider Organizations** A preferred provider organization (PPO) also has a network of doctors—the preferred providers—who charge reduced fees to plan members. Unlike HMOs and POS plans, however, you can see a specialist without a referral. In addition, a PPO covers services by out-of-network doctors, but at a higher cost to the patient. In general, PPOs are more expensive than HMOs and POS plans, but they allow members more flexibility.

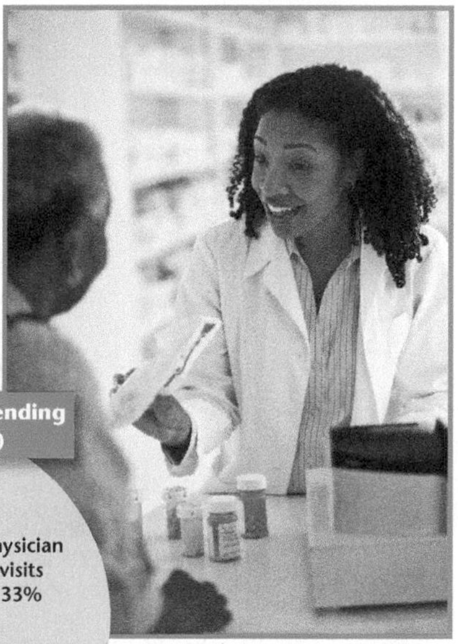

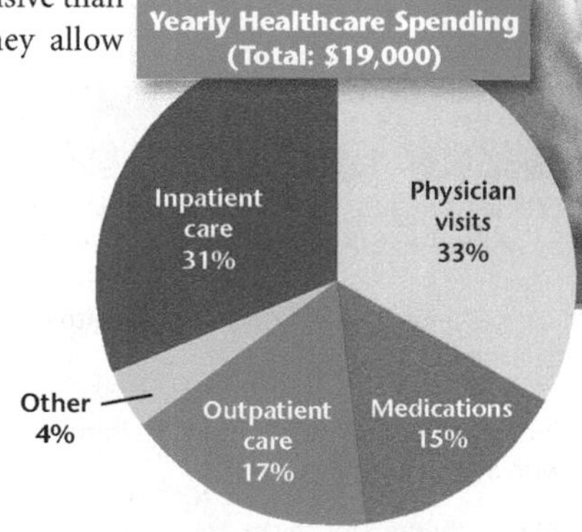

FIGURE 9 Average healthcare spending for an American family of four totals $19,000 per year. If the family has PPO insurance coverage through an employer, they pay about $3,280 every year out-of-pocket. The rest is covered by the employer and insurance.
Reading Graphs What percentage of the total healthcare spending is for medications?

Yearly Healthcare Spending (Total: $19,000)

- Physician visits 33%
- Inpatient care 31%
- Outpatient care 17%
- Medications 15%
- Other 4%

Paying for Healthcare

L3 Cultural Connection

The Canadian healthcare system differs significantly from the healthcare system of the United States. All Canadian citizens are automatically entitled to the entire range of medical care and hospital services. The federal and provincial governments of Canada provide the financial resources required to support this insurance system for all citizens. Supporters of this system point out that it ensures equal treatment for all. Ask students to compare the United States' healthcare system with that of Canada. They should list pros and cons for each country's system. If desired, students might look to the Internet for more details about Canada's system. Ask: **Which healthcare system do you think best serves patients? Why?** *(Students should provide logical explanations for their answers.)*

L2 Building Vocabulary

Help students create a Venn diagram in which they show how premiums and copayments are similar and different. First ask students for similarities. *(Both are fees that people pay for healthcare.)* Then help students identify differences by asking: **Who collects the premium?** *(insurance company)* **The copayment?** *(the doctor)* **Do all insurance plans have a premium?** *(Yes, plan members pay this premium or their employer pays it for them.)* **A copayment?** *(No, it depends on the plan.)*

L2 Visual Learning: Figure 9

Image Bank Figure 24-9

Have students study the graph in Figure 9. Ask: **What is most healthcare spending used for?** *(physician visits)* Remind students what they have learned about healthcare facilities. Then ask them to explain what is meant by "Inpatient care" and "Outpatient care" on the graph. *(Inpatient care is care that is given while staying in a hospital. Outpatient care includes tests and treatments performed in a medical clinic.)*
Caption Answer 15%

L2 Class Discussion

Make a chart on the board to compare and contrast traditional insurance with managed care insurance. Point out that both have premiums. Ask: **Which plan is usually more expensive? Why?** *(traditional plan; can see any doctor you wish)*

L3 Addressing Misconceptions

Insurance Coverage Some students may think that all medical procedures are covered by insurance. Explain that some procedures are not covered by insurance and must be paid for by the patient in full. Some of these procedures include cosmetic surgery and experimental procedures.

L4 Building Health Skills

Advocacy Have students write a letter to their congressional representative about the growing number of Americans who cannot afford health insurance and do not qualify for government-sponsored insurance. Challenge students to use Internet resources to find facts and figures to back up their claims. Students might even make suggestions for ways to address this problem. Encourage students to send letters that are thoughtful and meaningful. **WRITING**

L1 Active Learning

Some students may have grandparents or other older relatives who rely on Medicare. Have those students interview their older relatives about their experience with Medicare. Encourage them to ask questions such as, Are you satisfied with the medical care you receive? Are you able to see your choice of doctors? Do you feel your medical bills are manageable? How do you manage the cost of prescription medicines? Ask volunteers to share with the class what they learned about how Medicare works.

Traditional Insurance Historically, health insurance in the United States has been made available through an employer. Traditional health insurance plans offer more flexibility than managed healthcare plans by permitting you to use any doctor or facility you choose. In most cases, out-of-pocket expenses with these plans are more costly than those of managed care plans. Children up to 18 years of age and unemployed spouses are insured through a family plan purchased by an employed parent. Employers pay monthly premiums to a private insurance company. This premium or some part of it is usually deducted from the employee's salary. Individuals without a job or who work for an employer who does not offer health insurance may purchase insurance directly from an insurance company at a higher rate.

Not all adults are employed. Some people work in settings where health insurance is not offered, and others may have elected not to purchase insurance. For these reasons, the United States struggles with caring for its uninsured citizens. Many states have created models for covering the costs of care for uninsured adults and their children.

Because of the high cost of healthcare and health insurance, there have been many efforts to reduce premium costs. Employers may limit the number of options from which employees can choose. Employees may have to use only certain healthcare providers. Employees may be required to pay a co-payment or a deductible. A **deductible** is a fixed amount of money that employees must pay for medical expenses each year before the insurance company begins paying for procedures. Other methods to reduce premium costs include excluding some services from coverage and not covering care for pre-existing conditions.

Government-Sponsored Insurance Some people in the United States who cannot afford private health insurance are eligible for government health insurance programs. Medicare is the federally financed insurance program for people over age 65 and for younger people who are disabled or who have chronic kidney disease. Medicaid is a state program funded by both the state and federal governments. Medicaid pays for the healthcare of people whose incomes are below a certain level.

FIGURE 10 The Affordable Care Act puts in place comprehensive health insurance reforms outlined here.

The Affordable Care Act

- Creates a Health Insurance Marketplace that allows individuals and small businesses to buy affordable, qualified health benefit plans

- Creates a new type of non-profit health insurer called a Consumer Operated and Oriented Plan (CO-OP)

- Prohibits health insurers from charging more for, or denying coverage to, people with a pre-existing condition

- Allows children to stay on their parents' insurance plans until age 26

For Your INFORMATION!

Wellness Programs

One way companies are fighting back against the rising costs of healthcare is by initiating wellness programs. Most wellness programs are launched with blood pressure, cholesterol, and blood sugar checks of all employees. Everyone also completes a lifestyle inventory. From the results, employees receive health information targeted to their specific health needs. Additional health seminars, group activities, and health challenges enable employees to continue learning about healthy lifestyles. Employees are motivated by incentives that often include earning points to reduce their insurance premiums.

Rising Healthcare Costs There are many factors that contribute to the rising costs of healthcare in the United States.

▶ **An Aging Population** The growing population of elderly Americans is a major force in driving up costs. People live longer on average than they used to. The result is a growing number of people who are likely to need extensive medical services. Taxpayers of all ages contribute to federal programs such as Medicare that provide healthcare support for older Americans.

▶ **Chronic Diseases** The increasing incidence of chronic diseases such as cardiovascular disease and diabetes affects all Americans. When individuals require more and more medical care, health insurance companies must raise everybody's premiums to offset the extra costs.

▶ **Prescription Drug Costs** The research and development of prescription drugs is very expensive, and this cost is usually passed on to consumers. One way to relieve some of the burden is to use generic drugs. Generic drugs have the same active ingredients as brand-name drugs, but they usually cost significantly less. Unfortunately, there is not a generic version of every brand-name drug.

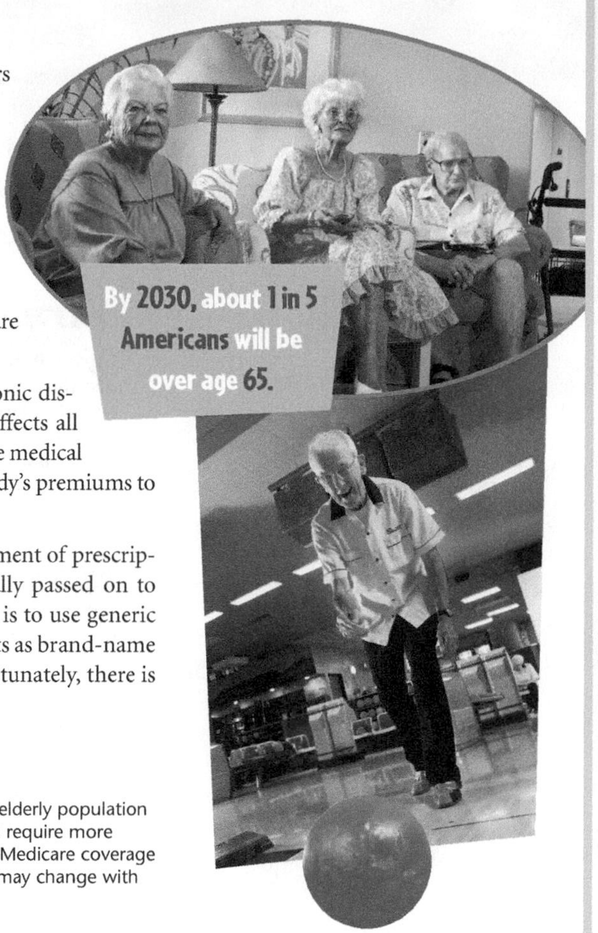

By 2030, about 1 in 5 Americans will be over age 65.

FIGURE 11 As the elderly population grows, Medicare will require more funding to keep up. Medicare coverage for older Americans may change with future legislation.

Section 2 Review

Key Ideas and Vocabulary

1. Why is it important to choose your doctor carefully? What are your responsibilities as a patient?

2. What is included in a **medical history**?

3. Briefly describe the three types of health insurance.

4. What is the difference between a **premium** and a **deductible**?

Critical Thinking

5. Evaluating Which of the patients' rights listed in Figure 8 is most important to you? Explain.

Health at Home

Family Health Talk to members of your family about your medical history. Is there a disease that is common in your family? Make a list of the information that is important to share with your doctor. **WRITING**

6. Making Judgments What, if anything, do you think should be done to help Americans deal with rising healthcare costs? Explain.

7. Calculating Suppose your family spends a total of $2,000 for healthcare in one year. If 40% of your healthcare spending is for visits to the doctor, what amount does your family spend on doctor visits in one year? **MATH**

3. Assess

Evaluate

These assignments can help you assess students' mastery of the section content.

Section 2 Review

Answers appear below.

Teaching Resources

• Practice 24-2
• Section 24-2 Quiz

L2 Reteach

Have student groups make a taped public service announcement that describes managed care insurance, traditional insurance, and government-sponsored insurance.

L4 Enrich

Teaching Resources

• Enrich 24-2

Health at Home

Family Health Allow students to keep their lists private. Be sensitive to those students who are adopted or living with guardians. Tell these students to focus on their personal medical history. Have them find out from their parents or guardians what is known about medical tests and procedures, vaccinations, and other treatments they have received.

Section 2 Review

1. to know that your healthcare is given by qualified people with whom you feel comfortable; to ask your doctor questions about your health and to honestly answer your doctor's questions

2. your present and past health and the health of family members

3. managed care insurance: have a network of doctors who agree to provide healthcare at lower costs; traditional insurance: able to see any doctor at any facility; government-sponsored insurance: available to people over the age of 65, people with certain disabilities, and people with incomes below a certain level

4. A premium is a monthly or yearly fee paid to the insurance company. A deductible is a fixed amount that must be paid for medical expenses before the insurance company begins paying.

5. Answers will vary but should include one of the patients' rights listed in Figure 8 with an explanation of the student's choice.

6. Answers will vary but should include an explanation that supports the student's opinion.

7. $2,000 \times 0.4 = 800

Objectives
Before class begins, write the objectives on the board. Have students copy the objectives into their notebooks at the start of class.

1. Focus

Warm-Up Myth/Fact

When students have written their responses, invite them to share their ideas, and list them on the board. Then tell students they will learn about the goals of public health programs. Return to this list as you teach the section to add or remove ideas.

Presentation 24-3

Objectives
▶ **Summarize** the main goal of public health programs today.
▶ **Describe** how the United States' public health system is organized.

Vocabulary
• public health
• quarantine
• epidemiology
• health code
• vital statistics

Warm-Up

Myth Public health officials only deal with natural disasters and infectious disease outbreaks that threaten large populations.

Fact Many public health efforts focus on preventing disease and injury in daily life, not just when catastrophes strike.

WRITING Why do you think prevention is a major focus in the field of public health?

What Is Public Health?

Suppose that you could find no clean drinking water. What if restaurants were not required to be clean and pest-free? What if children could attend school without being immunized against serious infectious diseases? These are all matters that would affect public health. **Public health** is the study and practice of protecting and improving the health of people in a group or community.

Fortunately, health-threatening conditions like those mentioned above rarely exist in the United States. That is because a public health system is in place to prevent them. The public health system includes all the government and private organizations that work with the public to prevent disease and promote positive health behaviors.

The History of Public Health   Throughout history, people associated disease with unclean or unsanitary conditions and took measures to promote cleanliness. The ancient Hebrews, for example, established rules for the sanitary preparation of foods. The ancient Romans built efficient systems to supply people with clean water and to remove wastes.

In Europe during the Middle Ages, however, cities became crowded with people and animals, and their wastes. Epidemics swept across Africa, Asia and Europe. One of the only ways people knew to combat these disease outbreaks was through quarantine. **Quarantine** (KWAWR un teen) is a period of isolation imposed on people who may have been exposed to an infectious disease. Quarantine prevents people who may be infected from spreading the disease.

⚑ Sensitive Issues
Be aware that some students may not have been vaccinated due to religious or personal beliefs. These students might feel uncomfortable during discussions about immunizations.

Focus on **ISSUES**

L3 Homelessness
Share with students the following statistics: Homeless people have the same health problems as people with homes, but at rates three to six times higher. When they get sick, homeless people tend to get worse instead of better because they do not have adequate shelter and they are unable to get to or pay for medical care. If they do finally get care, it is the most expensive care given at hospital emergency rooms. Many have addiction disorders, and about one-third also have mental illnesses.

Begin a discussion on why many consider homelessness to be a public health issue by asking students to explain how homelessness affects the health of the public.

New Understandings During the latter half of the 1800s, scientists began to understand that microorganisms cause many diseases. In 1850, London physician John Snow studied an outbreak of cholera (KAHL ur uh), an infectious disease that causes severe diarrhea and vomiting. Dr. Snow learned that all of the outbreak victims had drunk water from the same well. He was able to show that this well was contaminated with cholera-causing bacteria.

Starting in the early 1900s, vaccines against a variety of serious diseases became available. The United States government launched nationwide programs to immunize the public. As a result, the incidence of many infectious diseases, such as measles, was greatly reduced.

The field of epidemiology has also contributed to new understandings in the field of public health. **Epidemiology** (ep ih dee mee AHL uh jee) is the study of disease among populations. Epidemiologists look for patterns in the occurrence of infectious and chronic diseases. Their findings are used to develop policies and programs for disease control and prevention.

Public Health Goals Today The public health system continues to combat infectious diseases but also seeks to prevent a broad range of other health problems. **Public health programs today emphasize the need for prevention in order to avoid disease and other health problems.** Many public health problems today relate to people's behaviors. For example, drug and alcohol abuse, teenage pregnancy, obesity, violence, and child abuse are major public health problems related to people's behaviors.

The Department of Health and Human Services, or HHS, is the major public health agency in the United States. HHS developed an important public health document, *Healthy People 2020*, that identifies prevention as the key to improving the health of all Americans. Chapter 1 discusses the goals of *Healthy People 2020*.

 **Connect to Your Life** When did you last take part in a public health program, such as getting immunized?

FIGURE 12 In the 1950s, immunizing people against polio was a top public health priority. The photo above shows a drive-through polio vaccination clinic.

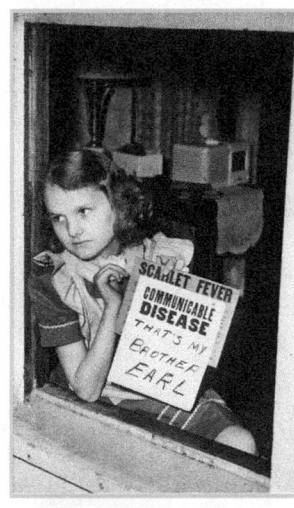

▲ **A Tennessee girl in quarantine for scarlet fever, 1949**

Safeguarding the Public **649**

2. Teach

(L3) (EL) Reading/Note Taking 24-3
(L2) Adapted Reading/Note Taking 24-3

What Is Public Health?

(L3) **Class Discussion**

Lead the class in a discussion on how the current goals of public health programs have changed. Ask: **How did epidemiology change the way infectious diseases are managed?** *(Epidemiologists use patterns in the occurrences of infectious diseases to set policies and programs to prevent and control the diseases. Before, public health officials could only react to outbreaks by quarantining sick individuals.)* **What is the nature of today's public health problems?** *(Many health problems are related to people's behavior.)* Discuss how treating infectious diseases differs from trying to change people's behaviors.

(L4) **Building Health Skills**

Advocacy Have students choose one of the public health problems related to people's behavior—drug and alcohol abuse, teenage pregnancy, obesity, violence, or child abuse. Then ask students to suppose that Congress is considering cuts to funding for programs related to their chosen issue. Challenge students to write a letter to their legislator advocating the benefits of the programs. Tell students when writing to legislators, they should identify themselves as constituents, use the legislator's correct title, be brief, clearly state their position, personalize the message, avoid ultimatums, avoid exaggerating, and thank the legislator. **WRITING**

Connect to Your Life Allow students to answer this question in their private journals.

Differentiated Instruction

(EL) **English Language Learners**

Remind students what it means to immunize against a disease. *(to give a person's body the ability to fight off an infectious disease)* Explain that the word *immune* comes from a Latin word meaning "to be exempt from." Show students other examples for uses of the words *immune* and *immunity*. For example, being immune to the effects of stress or the weather, or being granted immunity from criminal prosecution.

Public Health in the United States

L3 Online Activity GO ONLINE

Visit Pearson SuccessNet to access an online activity about public health. Have students complete the Web activity.

L2 Addressing Misconceptions

Public Health Issues Students might think that public health issues concern only disease prevention. Be sure to fully address public safety issues and environmental issues and their effects on health. Point out which federal agencies listed in Figure 14 deal with safety issues and the environment (OSHA and EPA). Give students scenarios of how laws enforced by these agencies improve their lives. For example, water is safe to drink because of laws enforced by the EPA.

L3 Class Discussion

Ask students: **Why might helping high-risk populations be more difficult than controlling an infectious disease?** *(Sample answer: Individuals' needs are highly variable; solutions often require behavior changes; help requires the best efforts of many public health workers doing many different tasks.)* Ask students why they think it may or may not be necessary to provide special help for high-risk populations.

L4 Cooperative Learning

Have students work in small groups to construct a fictional case history that describes a member of a high-risk population. Students should describe the person and identify the specific factor or factors that cause that person to be considered a member of a high-risk population. (for example, a drug abuser, a pregnant teen, an elderly person living alone, or a person waiting for subsidized housing) Groups should produce a brief written description of the person's current situation, the situation (including health status) six months from now, in a year, and in five years, assuming no assistance or health services are provided. Have the groups predict how assistance at each point might affect the person's status. Students should use library or Internet sources for background information. **WRITING**

GO ONLINE
PearsonSuccessNet.com
For: More on public health

Public Health in the United States

As the United States has grown and changed, so have its public health needs. The public health system today addresses many more problems than ever before. Most programs, however, fall into one of three main categories.

▶ **Fighting Chronic Diseases** As in most countries with high standards of living, deaths from chronic diseases exceed those from infectious diseases in the United States. Today, many public health programs emphasize the importance of behaviors such as regular exercise and proper nutrition to reduce people's risks of many chronic diseases.

▶ **Helping Populations at Risk** One of the greatest challenges in public health is to provide services to high-risk populations. High-risk populations are groups of people who, because of age, economic conditions, or some other factor, are more likely to contract a particular disease or disorder than the general population.

▶ **Safety and Environmental Health** Many public health regulations focus on safety issues in all areas of society. Safety standards, for example, must be met in the workplace, in the design and construction of buildings, in the transportation industry, and in many household and medical products. The public health system also addresses environmental concerns. For example, there are laws that limit pollution levels from industries and motor vehicles.

In the United States, public health is primarily a governmental responsibility that is managed at the federal, state, and local levels. A variety of private organizations also contribute significantly to the advancement of public health.

FIGURE 13 Workers from the federal Environmental Protection Agency monitor the environment for substances that could endanger public health.

The Federal Government As mentioned earlier, the federal agency with the widest range of responsibilities for public health is the Department of Health and Human Services (HHS). HHS provides many services, including:

▶ sponsoring health research and education

▶ compiling and analyzing health information

▶ setting health and safety standards

▶ supporting state and local health departments

▶ funding programs for people in need of public health services

Figure 14 summarizes the services provided by different federal agencies. The Centers for Disease Control and Prevention (CDC) and the National Institutes of Health (NIH) are particularly important research agencies that are reliable sources of health information.

WRITING and Health

L3 Public Service Announcement

Have students choose one of the federal agencies listed in Figure 14. Instruct them to prepare a public service announcement (PSA) to be aired on television or radio. The PSA should describe what the agency does and how it can specifically help the target audience. Students should identify the target audience, as well as any resources they use for background information.

FIGURE 14 Many federal agencies provide public health services for Americans. **Classifying** Which agencies provide services for all Americans? Which focus on specific populations?

Federal Public Health Agencies

Department of Health and Human Services	
Administration for Children and Families	Administers programs that improve the lives of children from low-income families and people with disabilities
Administration on Aging	Provides services to older persons and their caregivers
Agency for Healthcare Research and Quality	Promotes improvements in the practice of medicine, the organization and financing of healthcare, and access to quality care
Agency for Toxic Substances and Disease Registry	Investigates and assesses risks to human health from hazardous materials
Centers for Disease Control and Prevention (CDC)	Collects data and conducts research on nearly all types of diseases, disorders, and disabilities
Centers for Medicare and Medicaid Services	Supervises Medicare and Medicaid
Food and Drug Administration (FDA)	Inspects, tests, and assesses the safety of food, drugs, and a variety of consumer goods
Health Resources and Services Administration	Funds health services and resources for underserved populations such as migrant workers, people with AIDS, and homeless people
Indian Health Service	Provides comprehensive healthcare for Native Americans
National Institutes of Health (NIH)	Serves as the primary biomedical research facility of the federal government; provides grants to support medical research at institutions throughout the country
Substance Abuse and Mental Health Services Administration	Supports programs that prevent and treat substance abuse and mental illness. It assists states, communities, and healthcare facilities in substance-abuse and mental-health services
Other Federal Agencies	
Occupational Safety and Health Administration (OSHA)	In the Department of Labor, identifies occupational hazards and enforces laws requiring minimum safety standards in the workplace
Department of Agriculture (USDA)	Is responsible for inspecting and grading meat, poultry, and other agricultural products; manages nutrition programs such as school-lunch programs and food stamps
Environmental Protection Agency (EPA)	Protects the public from environmental hazards; enforces laws that regulate pollution and sets standards for safe levels of exposure to toxic substances and radiation

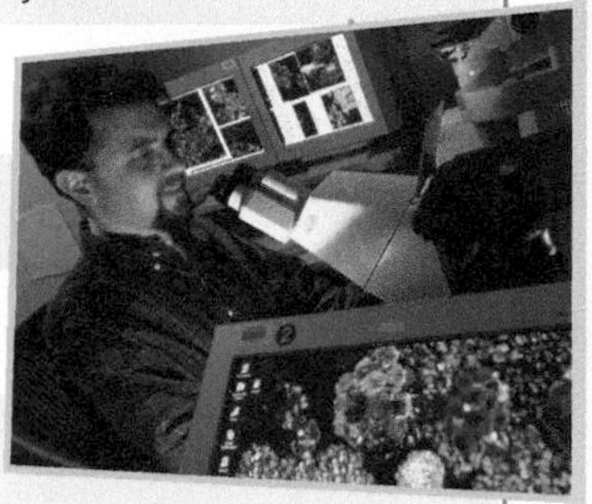

Differentiated Instruction

L1 Special Needs

Acquaint students with federal, state, or local agencies that they might actually use or be serviced by when they reach adulthood. Help students prepare an information card on which the name of the agency is listed, along with the contact information of a case worker who services their area. Also include the services provided by the agency and in what circumstances the student might need to use or contact the agency.

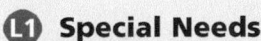

L3 Class Discussion

Ask students: **Why might a national health policy, developed and funded by the federal government, be more effective than separate policies made and enforced by state or local governments?** *(Sample answer: The federal government has more resources for research, more power to enforce compliance with regulations, and can mandate equal health benefits and treatment for all citizens.)* Then ask students to describe some disadvantages of federal public health agencies. *(Federal agencies cannot easily adapt to subtle differences unique to local needs and are farther away from the actual problems.)*

L2 Visual Learning: Figure 14

Help students digest the information in the table by guiding them in sorting the agencies into different categories. Then have students use the categories to make a table for these agencies that includes the services they provide and their acronyms.

Caption Answer service all Americans: Agency for Healthcare Research and Quality, Agency for Toxic Substances and Disease Registry, CDC, FDA, NIH, USDA, EPA; all other agencies service specific populations

L3 Building Health Skills

Accessing Information Explain to students that each of the agencies listed in Figure 14 maintains a Web site that may give information such as health statistics, health information, information about the agency, and how to use the agency's services. Instruct students to choose one agency and access its Web site. Have them explore the site to learn the kinds of information it provides. Then have students write a summary in which they describe the types of information provided by the Web site, who this information is targeted to, and whether or not they found any of the information useful. Display summaries on a bulletin board for all students' reference. **WRITING**

L2 Active Learning

Have students make a flowchart to show the flow of federal monies to state, local, and private health agencies. Explain that states also collect their own money (from tax revenues) to help fund their local public health agencies. Students should also include this information in their flowcharts.

L3 Building Health Skills

Making Decisions Pose the following scenario: A friend tells you that she became ill with nausea, vomiting, and diarrhea after eating at a local restaurant. She has not gone to the doctor. You later learn that six other people also became ill after eating at the same restaurant. You begin to suspect that your friend had food poisoning. Suggest that students use the DECIDE process to help them decide what action to take in this situation (see page 16). Students should identify the problem, outline how they will respond, and explain the reasons for their actions. *(Answers will vary but may focus on the friend's lack of response to her illness and the larger issue of public safety. Some students may urge the friend to notify her doctor, the restaurant, and the board of health, or do so themselves. These actions would reduce health risks to the friend, improve the restaurant, and remove a public health risk.)*

L2 Cooperative Learning

Have student groups choose one of the local health department services listed in Figure 15. Instruct groups to find out which local agency is responsible for providing that service and how the service protects the health of the public. Groups should summarize their findings on a large index card, including contact information for the agency. Have groups present their findings to the class and post their information cards on a classroom bulletin board.

Connect to Your Life *Sample answer:* The services help prevent me from getting an infectious or mosquito-borne disease.

State Government The federal government depends on the states to carry out programs to meet its public health objectives. States distribute federal funds to their local health departments or to private health-service providers. These agencies then carry out specific health programs, such as drug rehabilitation and prenatal care.

Most states have several departments or agencies involved in public health. State departments of public health, mental health, rehabilitation, environmental health, and social services are some common examples.

State health departments are also responsible for other services needed to maintain public health within the state. For example, they inspect healthcare and food-handling facilities; test water, food, and medical samples; compile health statistics; and monitor pollution levels.

Local Government In most states, public health services are provided directly by local health departments. Their services are usually free or have a fee based on a person's income. Figure 15 lists some of the services provided by local health departments.

Local health departments are also responsible for enforcing state health codes. **Health codes** are standards established by the state for certain factors that affect health, such as water quality, sanitation in restaurants, and sewage treatment facilities. Local health departments also collect **vital statistics**—the numbers of births and deaths and the numbers and kinds of diseases that occur within a population.

Connect to Your Life How do the services provided by your local health department protect your health?

FIGURE 15 Local health departments provide many health services directly to members of the community.

Local Health Department Services

- ▸ Insect control for prevention of mosquito-borne diseases
- ▸ Counseling for people with drug or alcohol problems
- ▸ Testing for and treatment of sexually transmitted infections
- ▸ Health education
- ▸ Prenatal care
- ▸ Immunizations
- ▸ Screening for tuberculosis, high blood pressure, cholesterol, and diabetes
- ▸ Home health services for people confined to their homes

TEENS *Are Asking . . .*

Q: I heard from an older friend that I will need more vaccinations before going to college. Is this really true? I thought only little kids need vaccinations.

A: Because of the close proximity of students on college campuses, infectious diseases can rapidly spread and outbreaks can occur. For this reason, most colleges require students to be immunized against polio, measles, mumps, rubella, tetanus, hepatitis, chickenpox, and bacterial meningitis. Each college has different vaccination requirements, based on state laws. Check with your prospective college to find out its requirements.

FIGURE 16 Volunteering at a soup kitchen is one way to help deliver public health services in your community.

Private Organizations   Many private organizations play important roles in providing public health services. Some of these are national organizations. Others exist only at the local level, in the communities they serve.

A number of national organizations raise funds to support specific health causes. You may be familiar with organizations such as the American Heart Association, American Cancer Society, and March of Dimes. Funds raised by these and other organizations pay for medical research, health services, and educational programs.

In most communities, churches and other community-based organizations offer public health services. These organizations may run programs such as food banks, counseling services, training programs, soup kitchens, and homeless shelters.

Section 3 Review

Key Ideas and Vocabulary

1. What is **epidemiology**?

2. What is the main goal of public health programs today? Why is this goal important?

3. Briefly describe how the public health system in the United States is organized.

4. What are **health codes**? What level of government is responsible for enforcing health codes?

Critical Thinking

5. **Evaluating** Which of the three major categories of public health challenges in the United States today do you feel should be given highest priority? Explain your answer.

Health and Community

Locating Community Resources Suppose that a family in your community was homeless and you wanted to help. Find out what services are available in your community to help homeless families. Summarize your findings in the form of a letter to your local newspaper. **WRITING**

6. **Applying Concepts** Many of today's public health problems result from people's behaviors. For example, obesity is a growing public health problem that results mainly from poor eating habits and lack of exercise. What public health approach would be most effective for combating obesity? Explain.

---

3. Assess

Evaluate

These assignments can help you assess students' mastery of the section content.

Section 3 Review

Answers appear below.

Teaching Resources
- Practice 24-3
- Section 24-3 Quiz

L2 Reteach

Instruct students to use the photos in the section to help them summarize the role of public health programs in the United States.

L4 Enrich

Teaching Resources
- Enrich 24-3

Health and Community

Locating Community Resources
Suggest that students contact local government agencies, churches, or homeless shelters for information. They can find contact information in a local telephone directory. Letters can be structured like a letter to the editor to inform the general public about local services available for homeless families. Tell students to include contact information in their letters.

Section 3 Review

1. the study of disease among populations

2. prevention; to avoid disease and other health problems

3. Public health is primarily a governmental responsibility that is managed at the federal, state, and local levels.

4. standards established by the state for certain factors that affect health; local government

5. Students may choose any one of the three categories—fighting chronic diseases, helping high-risk populations, or safety and environmental health—but should supply well-developed reasons for their choice.

6. *Sample answer:* health education about nutrition and exercise; this approach educates the public about caring for itself and preventing obesity.

Working in Groups

Objective

Develop the skills to work successfully in groups.

Teaching Strategies

- Divide the class into small groups, and lead the groups through each of the five guidelines for working in groups. Challenge groups to model each guideline as it is described. Give each group an identity, such as a family, charity group, sports group, or school club, to make it easier for them to set goals and priorities. Students in each group should take turns playing the positive and negative roles that people play in a group. (Make sure students know which roles are positive and which are negative.) As part of the evaluation process, ask students to describe the effects of each role on group dynamics.

- After students complete the Practice the Skill questions, invite them to share their ideas for improving the dynamics and productivity of groups. List their ideas on the board. For each idea, discuss how it could improve a group's performance.

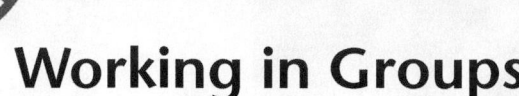

Communicating

Working in Groups

Sumiko sat listening as the other student council members argued about how they should raise money for the March of Dimes.

"We should have a walk-a-thon," said Sam.

"No, that's a bad idea," said Sylvia. "Let's have a…"

"I say we have a car wash," Tom interrupted.

Finally, Sumiko stood up and pointed out that no one was listening to anyone else's ideas. "If we're going to get anything accomplished," said Sumiko, "we have to start working together."

Have you ever wondered why some groups get a lot done and others do not? Group success often depends on group dynamics, how members work together. Since you participate in many groups—your family, friends, a sports team, this class—learning about group dynamics can be helpful. The following guidelines will help you work successfully in groups.

❶ Set goals and priorities.
As a group, set clear and realistic goals. If there are several goals, decide which ones are most important. All members should be involved in prioritizing the group's goals. Post your goals and priorities as a way to keep group members focused. Refer to them if you think the group is getting sidetracked.

❷ Choose a leader.
Groups work best when members select a leader who is respected by the group. A good leader has the time, interest, and patience to see that things run smoothly.

❸ Delegate tasks and make a schedule.
As a group, decide what steps are necessary to reach your goals. Which members have special skills or resources for these tasks? Divide activities so that everyone is involved. Finally, work together to come up with a realistic schedule for all tasks. Put the schedule in writing and distribute it to all group members.

654 *Chapter 24*

Sensitive Issues

Do not press students to divulge the group they have chosen to analyze. Some might have chosen to analyze their family or friends and are not comfortable sharing what they have observed.

Practice the Skill

4 **Monitor group dynamics.**
People play different roles in groups. Use the examples below to help you identify the roles that people are playing in your group. To improve group dynamics, urge everyone to adopt a positive role.

- ▶ **Starter:** Often begins discussions. Introduces new ideas.

- ▶ **Clarifier:** Requests additional information. Restates points so they are clear to all.

- ▶ **Peacemaker:** Suggests common ground and compromise when people disagree.

- ▶ **Supporter:** Is friendly and responsive to others and to their ideas.

- ▶ **Clown:** Uses jokes to attract attention. Disrupts group.

- ▶ **Blocker:** Always disagrees with others' ideas or focuses on trivial issues.

- ▶ **Dominator:** Tries to control group. Bullies other group members.

5 **Evaluate group progress.**
At different points, stop and consider the following questions.

- ▶ Are group members working together productively?

- ▶ Are tasks being completed on time? If not, the group should discuss why. Maybe the goals or schedule were unrealistic, or only a few people were doing all the work.

- ▶ Are there conflicts, and are they being handled well?

- ▶ Are there any communication problems within the group?

Remember that a group functions best when all members share in the process of helping the group meet its goals.

Practice the Skill

1. Choose a group that you belong to. Use the following questions to analyze how well the group works together.
   a. What are the goals of the group? How are the group's priorities decided?
   b. Who is the group leader? How was that person selected? Does the leader guide the group well? Explain.
   c. Does the group have a schedule for accomplishing its goals? Is the schedule realistic? Do all members have tasks that are suited to their own strengths?
   d. Identify the roles members play in the group. Who plays positive roles? Negative roles? What roles do you play?
   e. Is your group accomplishing its goals? Do members communicate well and meet deadlines?
   f. Is working with your group enjoyable? Why or why not?

2. Look over your answers to the questions above. For each, give your group an overall grade. Where does it do best? Worst?

3. List some suggestions for improving the dynamics and productivity of your group.

Safeguarding the Public **655**

Health and Community

 Community Groups

Suggest that students choose a group in their community, such as a charitable organization, social group, or government body, and attend one of its meetings. Tell students that not all meetings are open to the public, so they should get permission to attend any non-public meeting from the meeting organizer (usually the president of the organization). Students should use the guidelines described here to analyze how well the group works together. Students should prepare a summary in which they describe ways the group works well together and where group dynamics could be improved.

Global Public Health

Objectives
Before class begins, write the objectives on the board. Have students copy the objectives into their notebooks at the start of class.

1. Focus

Warm-Up Health Stats

As students read the statistics gathered by the WHO, share these statistics gathered by the Centers for Disease Control and Prevention: In 2010, a total of 28,902 children under 5 years of age died in the United States, and 825 women died during pregnancy or childbirth. Invite students to share their ideas about improving the lives of people in Africa. Then compare their ideas to programs currently in place as you teach the section.
Presentation 24-4

2. Teach

L3 **EL** Reading/Note Taking 24-4

L2 Adapted Reading/Note Taking 24-4

Why Are Global Efforts Important?

L2 **Class Discussion**

Discuss with students the need for global relief efforts. Identify several developing countries on a map, and discuss how people's lives in those countries differ from the lives of Americans. Ask students to consider what might happen to these countries if they did not receive help from global public health organizations.

Answers should reflect recent global events.

Section 4

Global Public Health

Objectives
▶ **Explain** the importance of global public health efforts.
▶ **Describe** the types of public health problems that international health organizations work to overcome.

Vocabulary
• developing nation
• World Health Organization (WHO)
• United Nations Children's Fund (UNICEF)

Warm-Up

Health Stats Here are some statistics gathered by the World Health Organization.

> Disease kills 3.5 million African children under 5 every year.

> HIV/AIDS affects more than 25 million Africans.

> Tuberculosis kills 1,500 Africans each day.

> Women in sub-Saharan Africa have a 1 in 16 chance of dying during pregnancy or childbirth.

WRITING How do you think the United States and other countries can help improve the lives of people in Africa?

Why Are Global Efforts Important?

In December 2004, a powerful tsunami struck South Asia. Because there was no warning of the tsunami, people did not know to evacuate coastal areas. As a result, hundreds of thousands of people in Indonesia, Thailand, India, and Sri Lanka died.

Threats of disease and a lack of clean drinking water were immediate concerns after the tsunami. Within days, governments and organizations from all over the world sent help in the form of money, supplies, and medical personnel.

In times of crisis, people around the world work together to combat public health problems in developing nations. **Developing nations** are countries with weak economies and low standards of living. Roughly 75 percent of the world's people live in developing nations. Many suffer from serious health problems. **Global efforts provide services and funding to developing nations that might not otherwise have the resources to make their public health programs succeed.**

What global public health efforts have you heard about recently?

WRITING and Health

L3 **Letter to the Editor**

Have students write a letter to the editor in which they address the need for global relief efforts. Students should use library or Internet resources to gather statistics about the needs of developing countries and use these statistics to show the real need for global efforts. Then students should give practical suggestions for ways in which ordinary citizens can help these global efforts.

International Health Organizations

In the aftermath of the tsunami, many international health organizations arrived on the scene to help. These organizations do work all over the world, in countries that have been devastated by natural disasters, wars, disease, or famine. Famine is a widespread lack of food. **International health organizations work in developing nations to overcome public health problems such as malnutrition, lack of basic medical care, poor sanitation, and lack of clean water.**

The United Nations A number of United Nations agencies are directly involved in improving the living conditions of people in developing countries.

▶ The **World Health Organization (WHO)** sends people trained in medicine, agriculture, water quality, engineering, and other health-related skills to countries in need. WHO workers seek to boost food production and prevent diseases through education and immunization programs. WHO also collects worldwide health statistics to evaluate and predict future health threats.

▶ The **United Nations Children's Fund (UNICEF)** focuses on programs that aid children, such as immunization programs, day-care and health centers, and school food programs. UNICEF also runs training programs for nurses and teachers.

International Committee of the Red Cross
The world's largest private international public health organization is the International Committee of the Red Cross, known in Muslim countries as the Red Crescent. This privately funded organization began in 1859 to aid victims on the battlefield. Today, its services have greatly expanded. The Red Cross organizes assistance anywhere in the world for victims of disasters. The organization provides medical care, food, water, clothing, and temporary shelter.

GO ONLINE
PearsonSuccessNet.com
For: More on global public health

FIGURE 17 The 2004 tsunami killed nearly 300,000 people and prompted millions of dollars of donations from countries around the world.

International organizations coordinated relief efforts for victims of the 2004 tsunami.

International Health Organizations

L3 Online Activity  **GO ONLINE**

Visit Pearson SuccessNet to access an online activity about global public health. Have students complete the Web activity.

EL Building Media Literacy

Ask students to compare the coverage of a current world health problem in at least two different newspapers or magazines. English language learners should look at one news source in their native language. Ask students to evaluate the coverage of the health problem and the international health organizations helping to solve it. Students should assess which sources have the more comprehensive and fair coverage. **WRITING**

L3 Cooperative Learning

Divide the class into small groups, and have each group create a fictional country with a public health crisis, such as famine, natural disaster, or a disease epidemic. Each group will play the role of government representatives who are seeking help from an international health organization for their fictional country. Other members of the class play the role of the health organization officials and determine how to help the country by asking questions to solicit information about the crisis.

L2 Visual Learning: Figure 17

Have students describe the types of services being provided to the tsunami victims shown in Figure 17. *(medical care, water, and supplies)* Ask: **Which international health organizations were probably involved in giving aid to tsunami victims?** *(Sample answer: UNICEF, WHO, Red Cross, Oxfam International, CARE)*

Differentiated Instruction

EL English Language Learners

Guide students in making a table for the international health organizations described in the section. Students should list the name of each organization and its acronym, if appropriate, and the functions of the organization.

L4 Gifted and Talented

Have students choose an international health organization and use Internet sources to find out how the organization is managed and where its funding comes from. Students should also learn what percentage of funds is used for healthcare or emergency assistance and what percentage is used for administrative expenses.

3. Assess

Evaluate

These assignments can help you assess students' mastery of the section content.

Section 4 Review

Answers appear below.

Teaching Resources

• Practice 24-4
• Section 24-4 Quiz

 Reteach

Have small student groups work together to make a list of global public health problems. Then have students write a statement that explains why global efforts are important for overcoming these problems. They should indicate which of the international health organizations discussed in the section can help with each problem they listed.

L4 Enrich

Teaching Resources

• Enrich 24-4

Health and Community

International Aid Suggest that students research their chosen health problem so they know what kind of help to ask for. In most cases, advertisements will ask for monetary donations. Students should prepare a script for a radio or television advertisement that has a well-developed idea for getting the audience's attention.

FIGURE 18 Peace Corps volunteers work with people in developing nations to improve all aspects of public health.

The Agency for International Development The United States Agency for International Development (USAID) was established to provide support for developing nations. A major focus of this support is the distribution of food to countries stricken by famine. USAID also funds programs for immunizations, medicines, sanitation, healthcare training, and treatment for dehydration. Dehydration occurs when the body suffers severe water loss. Dehydration resulting from diarrhea is the major cause of death among young children in developing nations.

The Peace Corps The Peace Corps is a United States government organization that trains volunteers for public health work in developing nations. The work that volunteers do depends both on their background and training and on the needs of the countries that invite them. Volunteers may help improve agricultural techniques, provide healthcare, construct shelters, or improve sanitation and water supply systems. In addition to health programs, some Peace Corps volunteers serve as advisors in the areas of education, technology, business, and industry.

Other Agencies The governments of many countries sponsor agencies that provide international public health assistance. Also, a number of privately supported organizations provide health services worldwide. For example, Oxfam International is known for its work in providing clean water and sanitation services in disaster areas. The Cooperative for Assistance and Relief Everywhere (CARE) provides healthcare, food, water, and emergency assistance to refugees and disaster victims. Many churches and missionary groups provide hospital, disease-prevention, and relief services.

Section 4 Review

Key Ideas and Vocabulary

1. What is a **developing nation?**
2. Explain why global public health efforts are important for helping developing nations.
3. What problems do international health organizations try to solve?
4. Describe the services provided by the **World Health Organization.**

Critical Thinking

5. **Evaluating** Sometimes, celebrities appeal to governments for aid on behalf of developing nations. Do you think this is an effective strategy? Why or why not?

Health and Community

International Aid Choose an international public health problem you are interested in, such as HIV/AIDS, childhood diseases, or famine. Create a 30-second public service advertisement for an organization that addresses the problem you chose. How will you command the attention of your audience? What kind of help will you ask for? **WRITING**

6. **Making Judgments** Many public health experts say that vaccinations were the greatest public health achievement of the 20th century. What do you think would be the greatest public health achievement so far this century? Explain your response.

GO ONLINE PearsonSuccessNet.com Audio Summary Section 24.4

Section 4 Review

1. a country with a weak economy and low standard of living
2. Developing nations do not have the resources or funds to make public health programs succeed. Global efforts can make these programs succeed by providing services and funding.
3. malnutrition, lack of basic medical care, poor sanitation, lack of clean water
4. WHO provides trained professionals to help boost food production and prevent disease. It also collects worldwide statistics to evaluate and predict health threats.
5. *Sample answers:* Yes, celebrities bring attention to the problem and help get results.

No, celebrities do not have the knowledge or expertise to negotiate effectively with other governments for aid.
6. Answers will vary, but students should support their answers with facts and logical arguments.

Chapter 24
At a Glance

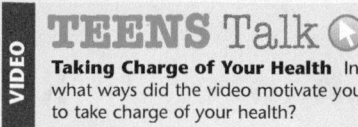

VIDEO

TEENS Talk

Taking Charge of Your Health In what ways did the video motivate you to take charge of your health?

Chapter 24
At a Glance

Section 1 The Healthcare System

Key Ideas

- Within the healthcare system, doctors work with nurses and other healthcare providers to care for patients.

- Healthcare facilities include doctors' offices, clinics, hospitals, and long-term care centers.

- The Internet, e-mail, and other technologies can make healthcare more efficient, and can make patients feel more involved in their care.

Vocabulary

- healthcare system (634)
- primary care physician (634)
- diagnosis (634)
- medical specialist (635)
- primary healthcare (637)
- outpatient (637)
- secondary healthcare (638)
- inpatient (638)
- tertiary healthcare (638)

Section 2 Participating in Your Healthcare

Key Ideas

- Deciding what doctor to see for routine healthcare deserves careful consideration.

- As a patient you also have certain responsibilities. You must fulfill these responsibilities in order to receive the best healthcare possible.

- Health insurance pays for a major part of medical expenses.

Vocabulary

- medical history (643)
- physical examination (643)
- premium (645) • copayment (645)
- deductible (646)

Section 3 Public Health

Key Ideas

- Public health programs today emphasize the need for prevention.

- In the United States, public health is primarily a governmental responsibility that is managed at the federal, state, and local levels.

Vocabulary

- public health (648)
- quarantine (648)
- epidemiology (649)
- health code (652)
- vital statistics (652)

Section 4 Global Public Health

Key Ideas

- Global efforts provide services and funding to developing nations that might not otherwise have the resources to make their public health programs succeed.

- International health organizations work in developing nations to overcome public health problems, such as malnutrition.

Vocabulary

- developing nation (656)
- World Health Organization (WHO) (657)
- United Nations Children's Fund (UNICEF) (657)

VIDEO

Taking Charge of Your Health Ask for volunteers to share their answers. Use examples from the video to review strategies for becoming more involved in one's own healthcare.

Key Ideas Review

L2 Have students use the Key Ideas as the framework for a chapter outline. Below each Key Idea, students should list relevant details from the chapter.

L1 Prepare an audio tape in which you convey the Key Ideas in simpler terms. Also provide additional supporting information in simpler terms as needed. Give students class time to listen to the recording. Then quiz the students orally on what they heard.

Vocabulary Review

L2 Have students divide all the vocabulary terms in the chapter into different categories of their own choosing. Then ask students to exchange their category titles with a partner and resort the terms into the new categories.

L3 Challenge students to write four paragraphs, one paragraph for each section of the chapter, in which they use as many of the vocabulary terms as possible. The meaning of each term used should be obvious from the context of the paragraph.

Chapter 24 Review

GO ONLINE

PearsonSuccessNet.com

Students can go online for a review activity on Chapter 24.

Reviewing Key Ideas

Section 1

1. c

2. b

3. diagnose medical conditions, provide treatment, and write prescriptions

4. Many doctors at teaching hospitals carry out medical research, making advanced medical care available.

Section 2

5. d

6. a

7. *Sample answer:* recommendations from family and friends, the doctor's education and certifications, personal preferences, and how well the doctor communicates

8. $200 \times 0.2 = $40

Section 3

9. c

10. the Department of Health and Human Services

11. *Sample answer:* Information about nutrition and symptoms of diabetes could be targeted to that ethnic population. Identifying that population as high-risk could make extra financial and medical help available.

Section 4

12. d

13. The World Health Organization (WHO) provides trained professionals to help boost food production and prevent disease; the United Nations Children's Fund (UNICEF) focuses on programs that aid children.

14. *Sample answer:* the 2004 tsunami; international groups provided medical care, food, water, clothing, living supplies, temporary shelter, clean-up, and rebuilding

15. Answers will vary. Students might desire to visit a certain part of the world or help people who are experiencing particular health problems.

Chapter 24 Review

Reviewing Key Ideas

GO ONLINE

PearsonSuccessNet.com

For: Chapter 24 review activity

Section 1

1. A doctor who has received additional training in a particular branch of medicine is called a
   a. physician assistant.   b. nurse practitioner.
   c. medical specialist.   d. physical therapist.

2. A person who receives treatment but does not stay overnight in a hospital is called a(n)
   a. inpatient.   b. outpatient.
   c. nurse.   d. primary care physician.

3. What three things is a doctor licensed to perform?

4. **Critical Thinking** Explain why a patient might receive more advanced care at a teaching hospital than at another type of hospital.

Section 2

5. A record of your health and of your family's health is called a
   a. premium.   b. deductible.
   c. physical examination. d. medical history.

6. The amount of money that a patient pays monthly for health insurance coverage is the
   a. premium.   b. deductible.
   c. copayment. d. HMO.

7. What are some things to consider when choosing a doctor?

8. **Critical Thinking** Suppose you have a traditional health insurance plan that pays for 80% of your medical bills. How much would your out-of-pocket costs be for a $200 bill? **MATH**

Section 3

9. The numbers of births, deaths, and diseases in a population are called
   a. quarantines.   b. health codes.
   c. vital statistics. d. deductibles.

10. What federal government agency has the major responsibility for public health?

11. **Critical Thinking** An epidemiologist studying diabetes finds that the disease is more common in people of a certain ethnicity than in the general population. How could this knowledge be used to help develop a public health policy for diabetes?

Section 4

12. A developing nation generally has
   a. a high standard of living.
   b. a strong public health system.
   c. excellent sanitation systems.
   d. a weak economy.

13. Describe two agencies of the United Nations that help people in developing nations.

14. Give an example of a public health crisis that required a global public health effort. What services did international groups provide?

15. **Critical Thinking** If you had the opportunity to join the Peace Corps, in what part of the world would you want to serve? Why?

 **Building Health Skills**

16. **Advocacy** Michelle has an unusual rash on her leg, but she hasn't seen a doctor because her family doesn't have health insurance. What advice would you give Michelle?

17. **Making Decisions** You notice the water in your school's water fountains has an unpleasant smell and taste. You are concerned about the possible cause. What would you do?

18. **Setting Goals** Identify one career in healthcare that you might be interested in pursuing. Write down specific steps you can take to learn more about that career and to determine if it is a good match for you. **WRITING**

Health and Community

Legislation Investigation Work with other students in your class to research the Health Insurance Portability and Accountability Act (HIPAA). What patient rights are granted by this law? How does this law protect patients' privacy? Present your findings to your class. **WRITING**

Building Health Skills

16. *Sample answer:* Have the school nurse look at the rash. If the rash looks worrisome, then ask the nurse to recommend a free or low-cost clinic to visit. Waiting could cause the problem to become worse and more costly to treat.

17. *Sample answer:* Inform a responsible adult in the school.

18. Some steps students might list include researching education requirements and job responsibilities using Internet or library resources, interviewing a person who is in that career, and job shadowing a person in that career.

Standardized Test Prep

Math Practice

The graph shows the number of people in the United States without any form of health insurance. Use the graph to answer Questions 19–21.

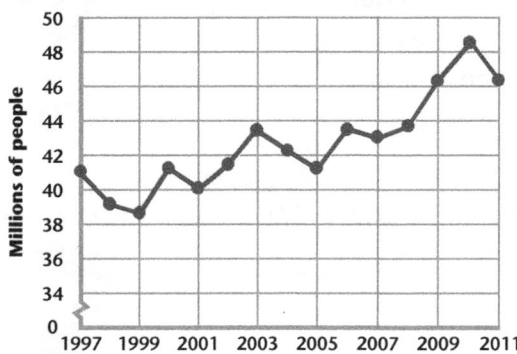

19. Approximately how many Americans were without health insurance in 1997?

A 38 million   B 39 million
C 40 million   D 41 million

20. By what percentage did the number of uninsured Americans increase from 2001 to 2011?

F 8 percent   G 10 percent
H 15 percent   J 18 percent

21. Which statement best describes the trend shown in this graph?

A The number of Americans without health insurance has decreased since 1997.
B The number of Americans without health insurance has increased steadily since 1997.
C The number of Americans without health insurance has remained the same since 1997.
D Overall, the number of Americans without health insurance increased between 1997 and 2011.

Test-Taking Tip

When taking a test, narrow down the possible answers by crossing out choices you know are wrong.

Reading and Writing Practice

Read the passage. Then answer Questions 22–25.

Prescription drug advertising and over-the-counter (OTC) drug advertisements that appear on television are among the most common forms of health communication reaching the U.S. public. The arrival of direct-to-consumer advertising has sparked both praise and criticism. Prescription drug advertising is regulated by the Food and Drug Administration, but questions remain regarding the most effective format for communicating benefit and risk information to consumers. Some health advocates fear that consumers are not well enough informed about the risks associated with certain drugs.

22. Prescription drug advertising directed at consumers is called

A OTC advertising.
B direct-to-consumer advertising.
C FDA regulation.
D risk and benefit analysis.

23. The Food and Drug Administration

F regulates prescription drug advertising.
G does not regulate prescription drug advertising.
H has nothing to do with advertising.
J is a television network.

24. According to the passage, which of these statements is true?

A Direct-to-consumer advertising of drugs is problem-free.
B Direct-to-consumer advertising of drugs is bad for the public.
C Direct-to-consumer advertising of drugs has drawn both praise and criticism.
D Drug advertisements on television do not reach many Americans.

Constructed Response

25. In a paragraph, summarize the main question that remains about direct-to-consumer drug advertising. Explain *your* opinion regarding direct-to-consumer drug advertising.

Standardized Test Prep

Math Practice

19. D
20. H
21. D

Reading and Writing Practice

22. B
23. F
24. C
25. Paragraphs should explain that communicating benefit and risk information to consumers is the main question that remains about direct-to-consumer drug advertising. Students should also describe their own opinions about prescription drug advertising.

Health and Community

Legislation Investigation Encourage students to check the Web site of the United States Department of Health and Human Services for information about the patient rights granted by HIPAA.

CHAPTER 25 A Healthy Community and Environment

Section Objectives	Standards Correlation	Instructional Resources L3	SE eTEXT	TE eTEXT	PRINT
1 Your Community, Your Health ⏲ 2 periods; 1 block	NHES: 1.12.3, 2.12.2, 2.12.4, 4.12.4, 8.12.4	SE Warm-Up, p. 664	•	•	•
25.1.1 Identify the different kinds of communities to which you belong.		RN Note Taking Guide 25-1	•	•	•
		TR Practice 25-1		•	
25.1.2 Describe how communities affect personal health.		TR Section 25-1 Quiz		•	
Locating Community Resources ⏲ 1 period; 1/2 block	NHES: 3.12.2, 3.12.3, 3.12.4, 3.12.5, 4.12.4, 5.12.4, 8.12.3	SE Practice the Skill, p. 671	•	•	•
BHS.25 Demonstrate an ability to locate community resources for help with problems.		RN Building Health Skills 25	•	•	•
2 Air Quality and Health ⏲ 1 period; 1/2 block	NHES: 1.12.3, 2.12.10, 3.12.2, 7.12.1	SE Warm-Up, p. 672	•	•	•
		RN Note Taking Guide 25-2	•	•	•
25.2.1 Summarize the potential health effects of air pollution.		IB Image Bank 25-6		•	
25.2.2 Evaluate factors that affect indoor air pollution.		TR Practice 25-2		•	
25.2.2 Analyze how government and personal actions can help improve air quality.		TR Section 25-2 Quiz		•	
3 Protecting Land and Water ⏲ 2 periods; 1 block	NHES: 1.12.3, 2.12.10, 3.12.1, 7.12.1	SE Warm-Up, p. 677	•	•	•
		SE Hands-On Activity Nontoxic Housecleaning, p. 681	•	•	•
25.3.1 Summarize the threats that hazardous wastes pose to human health.		RN Note Taking Guide 25-3	•	•	•
25.3.2 Identify three sources of water pollution.		TR Practice 25-3		•	
25.3.3 Describe three solutions for protecting land and water.		TR Section 25-3 Quiz		•	
4 Working for Community Health ⏲ 1 period; 1/2 block	NHES: 2.12.4, 7.12.1, 8.12.1, 8.12.2, 8.12.3, 8.12.4	SE Warm-Up, p. 684	•	•	•
		RN Note Taking Guide 25-4	•	•	•
25.4.1 Examine two keys to building a sense of community.		TR Practice 25-4		•	
25.4.2 Identify three steps to getting more involved in your community.		TR Section 25-4 Quiz		•	

Chapter Review and Assessment

SE Chapter 25 Review, p. 690 L3

CTB Chapter 25 Test L2 L3 L4

SE Standardized Test Prep, p. 691 L3

PROGRAM COMPONENTS

SE	Student Edition	**CTB**	Computer Test Bank
TE	Teacher Edition	**AUD**	Audio Section Summaries
TR	Teaching Resources		
RN	Reading and Note Taking Guide	**DVD**	Teens Talk Video Series
		VVG	Video Viewing Guide
ARN	Adapted Reading and Note Taking Guide	**PPT**	Presentation
IB	Image Bank		

Differentiated Instruction
L1 L2 L4 EL

		SE eTEXT	TE eTEXT	PRINT
ARN	Note Taking Guide 25-1 L2	•	•	
RN	Note Taking Guide 25-1 EL	•	•	•
AUD	Audio Summary 25-1 L1 L2 EL	•	•	
TE	Reteach Strategy, p. 669 L2		•	•
TR	Enrich 25-1 L4		•	
ARN	Building Health Skills 25 L2	•	•	
RN	Building Health Skills 25 EL	•	•	•
ARN	Note Taking Guide 25-2 L2	•	•	
RN	Note Taking Guide 25-2 EL	•	•	•
AUD	Audio Summary 25-2 L1 L2 EL	•	•	
TE	Reteach Strategy, p. 676 L2		•	•
TR	Enrich 25-2 L4		•	
ARN	Note Taking Guide 25-3 L2	•	•	
RN	Note Taking Guide 25-3 EL	•	•	•
AUD	Audio Summary 25-3 L1 L2 EL	•	•	
TE	Reteach Strategy, p. 683 L2		•	•
TR	Enrich 25-3 L4		•	
ARN	Note Taking Guide 25-4 L2	•	•	
RN	Note Taking Guide 25-4 EL	•	•	•
AUD	Audio Summary 25-4 L1 L2 EL	•	•	
TE	Reteach Strategy, p. 688 L2		•	•
TR	Enrich 25-4 L4		•	

ABILITY LEVELS
L1 For students with special needs
L2 For less proficient readers
L3 For all students
L4 For gifted and talented students
EL For English language learners

Chapter 25 Digital/Video Pathway

This alternative pathway allows you to teach this chapter's content using only the video and online materials.

Preview

DVD **Video #25 Preview**
SE Video #25 Preview Activity
VVG Video #25 Worksheet

Making a Difference

1
PPT 25-1 Presentation
RN/ARN 25-1 Note Taking
PPT 25-1 Section Quiz

2
PPT 25-2 Presentation
RN/ARN 25-2 Note Taking
PPT 25-2 Section Quiz

3
PPT 25-3 Presentation
RN/ARN 25-3 Note Taking
PPT 25-3 Section Quiz

4
DVD Video #25 Explore/Wrap-Up
VVG Video #25 Worksheet
PPT 25-4 Presentation
RN/ARN 25-4 Note Taking
PPT 25-4 Section Quiz

Making a Difference

Chapter Preview

Section 1 Your Community, Your Health
A person belongs to many different kinds of communities, including city or town, neighborhood, school community, and cultural community. Community factors contribute significantly to the physical and social health of community members.

 Accessing Information
Locating Community Resources
Knowing how to access community resources can provide students with help for health-related problems.

Section 2 Air Quality and Health
Air pollution can damage the respiratory system and harm other parts of the body, as well as reduce protection from the sun's radiation. Indoor air pollution is most severe in buildings that have been sealed against air leaks. Both government regulations and personal actions directly affect air quality.

Section 3 Protecting Land and Water
Hazardous wastes threaten the health of plants and animals, including humans. Wastes from household, industrial, and agricultural sources can cause pollution of water resources. The environmental damage to land and water is a serious problem, but there are solutions.

Section 4 Working for Community Health
Two keys to building a sense of community are civic engagement and a shared vision of the future. There are three steps to getting involved in a community: become informed, volunteer time, and be an advocate.

GO ONLINE
PearsonSuccessNet.com
For resources and activities for this chapter.

A Healthy Community and Environment

GO ONLINE PearsonSuccessNet.com

TEENS Talk

Making a Difference

VIDEO 25

Preview **Activity**

How Can You Make a Difference?

Complete this activity before you watch the video.

1. Think about this quote.
   You must be the change you wish to see in the world.
   Mahatma Gandhi
2. Explain what you think this quote means.
3. What changes would you like to see in your neighborhood, school, or larger community?
4. How could you help put these changes into effect? **WRITING**

662

⚑ Sensitive Issues

Teenagers cannot always influence or control their immediate environments. Some come from neighborhoods that are unclean and overlooked by the larger community. Some students may have parents who work in industries that are regarded by many as polluters, such as petrochemicals or computer manufacturing. Some students may themselves work in such an industry after school. When discussing ways to improve the environment, especially in the home, make suggestions rather than criticisms.

TEENS Talk

Making a Difference

Video Objectives

Use the video to help students

Explore different kinds of volunteer opportunities.

Evaluate the benefits of volunteering.

Become more actively involved in their own communities.

Preview **Activity**

How Can You Make a Difference?

Assign the Preview Activity in class before showing the video. After students complete the activity, ask volunteers to share their thoughts on what they think the quote means and what changes they would like to see in their community. Choose some of the more interesting ideas to further the discussion. Have students brainstorm ways they can promote their ideas. For example: Would they form a club? Write a newspaper editorial? Ask for help from school officials?

From the Authors

Health is more than the expression of biological, psychological, and behavioral factors. Health scientists increasingly see it as the product of the individual interacting with the physical and social environment in which he or she lives, works, and plays.

This chapter is intended to help students understand the important influence of community and environment on health. And because community health depends on collective action, the chapter is designed to get students thinking about civic engagement and what they can do to contribute to community health. See, for example, the Building Health Skills activity on pages 670–671, the Health and Community activity on page 676, and the Hands-On Activity on page 681.

Objectives
Before class begins, write the objectives on the board. Have students copy the objectives into their notebooks at the start of class.

1. Focus

Warm-Up Quick Quiz

Use the Warm-Up Presentation slide to survey student responses.

After students finish writing, read the first question in the quiz. Call on a volunteer to describe five adults who know the student by name, not counting adults at home. Also ask students to name community leaders and describe what each community leader does that influences health. Discuss why answering yes to these questions can be important to a person's overall health and well-being. Explain that in this section, students will learn how different kinds of communities affect personal health.

Presentation 25-1

Objectives
▶ **Identify** the different kinds of communities to which you belong.
▶ **Describe** how communities affect personal health.

Vocabulary
• social network
• community service organization
• mixed-use development
• urban sprawl

Warm-Up

Quick Quiz How connected are you to your community? See if you can answer "yes" to any of the following questions.

(1) Do at least five adults in your neighborhood know you by name?

(2) Can you name at least three of your community's leaders (e.g., the mayor, police chief, and the superintendent of schools)?

(3) Can you describe what each of the community leaders do that influences health?

WRITING How is being connected to your community important to your overall health and well-being?

What Is Community?

If someone were to ask you, "To what community do you belong?," what would you answer? You might answer by giving the name of the city or town in which you live. However, the complete answer is more complex.

There are, in fact, many different kinds of communities to which you belong. **Besides being a resident of your city or town and your neighborhood, you are a member of a particular school, a cultural community, and probably one or more clubs or organizations.** Being a member of each of these communities is important to your sense of identity.

The people with whom you interact and look to for friendship, information, and social support in all of these different communities make up your **social network.** The extent and quality of your social network can play a major role in helping to keep you healthy.

WRITING and Health

(L3) Magazine Article

Have students imagine that they have been hired by a travel magazine, and their first assignment is to write a description of the community in which they live. Tell students this article should be only a few paragraphs long, but they should include as much information as possible about their city, section of the city, or town. This information should include descriptions of various neighborhoods, cultural communities, schools, and prominent community organizations. Tell students to keep in mind that the readers of the magazine may live anywhere across the country, and therefore this article should not assume prior knowledge of their community.

Your City or Town The place where you live, whether it is a big city, small town, or rural village, has a number of specific features that shape your sense of community. Physical features include the weather and the natural environment. Social characteristics include the people who live there, the kinds of work these people do, and the local government.

Your Neighborhood Your neighborhood includes the people in the immediate vicinity of your home. The people in your neighborhood may know you and your family members by name. They are probably comfortable enough to ask you for a favor from time to time.

Your School Community Schools are not only responsible for your education, but they are also important communities in which you form friendships and develop leadership skills. At school, you are likely to belong to particular groups, such as clubs or teams in which you and others share the same interests.

Your Cultural Community Your cultural background is another factor that contributes to your sense of community. It determines what holidays you celebrate, what traditions you follow, and what kinds of foods you typically eat. What cultural traditions do you celebrate? How many people who share your cultural background live nearby? Answers to these kinds of questions help to define who you are and give you a sense of pride and belonging.

Other Communities In addition to the communities described so far, your involvement in clubs or other organizations may also be important in your life. **Community service organizations** are official groups whose members act or unite for a common purpose. For example, Boys and Girls Clubs of America and 4-H clubs provide teens with a supportive environment for recreation, learning, and service.

 **Connect to Your Life** Who are two or three adults in your community you could ask for help if you needed it?

FIGURE 1 You are a member of several communities.

Your Neighborhood

Your School

Your City or Town
Your Culture

665

2. Teach

L3 EL Reading/Note Taking 25-1

L2 Adapted Reading/Note Taking 25-1

What Is Community?

L2 Class Discussion

Call on students to describe the various political boundaries that are important in identifying their community. If students live in a large city, they might name the borough, the district, the ward, or the historical name for their area. If they live in a more rural area, they might name the county, the township, and the town or village that defines their community. Point out that people in different places may look to different political divisions as most important. A suburban student, for instance, may think of him- or herself as a member of both the suburban community and the nearby urban community. A rural student, by contrast, may think of the county as the primary definition of community.

L3 Cultural Connection

Ask volunteers to share with the class how cultural community contributes to their overall sense of community. Have students from different cultures describe holidays, traditions, foods, and other cultural markers that are important to them and their family. Explore how important the cultural community is for different students. For example, feeling a part of a cultural community might be extremely important for a first or second generation American but of less importance to a person whose ancestors arrived in this country long ago.

Connect to Your Life Allow students to answer this question in their private journals.

Differentiated Instruction

L4 Gifted and Talented

Encourage interested students to investigate community service organizations in their community, starting with those listed in the text, but including others as well. Ask students to prepare a table of their findings that can be handed out to others in the class. The table might have columns for the name of each organization, its main purpose, important activities it sponsors, and its contact information.

How Communities Affect Health

L4 Building Health Skills

Accessing Information Have students work together to learn about emergency medical services in their community. (In some cities these services are associated with the fire department, while in many towns and rural areas these services are largely staffed by volunteers.) Ask students to find out about the agency in charge of emergency medical services, how these services are paid for, and how the EMS system generally operates. Have students make a presentation to the class about their findings.

L4 Class Discussion

Lead a discussion on local regulations that protect the health of the community. Call on volunteers to explain what they know about local smoking regulations, noise regulations, and various zoning regulations that promote health. Call on volunteers to explain how such regulations protect the health of community members.

L3 Cooperative Learning

Prepare a basic map of the students' primary community, which may be a county, town, or section of a city. This map should show only major streets or thoroughfares and possibly landmarks, such as city hall or a prominent mall or shopping center. Divide the class into small groups, and provide each group with a copy of the map. Ask members of each group to work together to add places to the map that directly relate to the health of the citizens, such as parks, swimming pools, recreational facilities, bike paths, and hospitals. To gather this information, students can use their own knowledge of the community as well as area maps, online resources, and telephone books. After all groups have completed their maps, have groups compare maps and work together to make a class map.

FIGURE 2 Blood pressure screenings, no-smoking laws, and fitness courses in parks are just three ways a community can improve the health of its citizens.

How Communities Affect Health

Your health and quality of life are affected by the communities in which you live. **Community factors contribute significantly to the physical and social health of community members.**

Your City or Town Here are some of the ways that your city or town affects your health.

▶ **Basic health services** Your local government is responsible for providing water sewage treatment, clean drinking water, emergency medical services, road and highway maintenance, and other services that protect health. Restaurant inspections, infectious disease control, immunizations, and blood pressure screenings are other basic health services that your city or town may deliver.

▶ **Health legislation** Local governments also often approve and enforce regulations to protect the health of their citizens. For example, laws that limit noise levels or that ban cigarette smoking in restaurants and public buildings protect citizens from harm.

666 *Chapter 25*

MATH and Health

L3 Calculating With Percentages

You can use the percentage data in Figure 3 on page 667 to give students a more concrete understanding of the differences involved. Have students assume that a suburban community and a mixed-use community each have a population of 50,000. Ask: **How many people would walk to work in each community?** *(In the suburban community, $0.08 \times 50{,}000 = 4{,}000$ people. In the mixed-use community, $0.12 \times 50{,}000 = 6{,}000$ people.)* Give students a somewhat more realistic case: the suburban community has 120,000 people and the mixed-use community has 40,000 people. *(In the suburban community, $0.08 \times 120{,}000 = 9{,}600$ people. In the mixed-use community, $0.12 \times 40{,}000 = 4{,}800$ people.)* Point out that using percentages in this case gives a clearer picture of the difference.

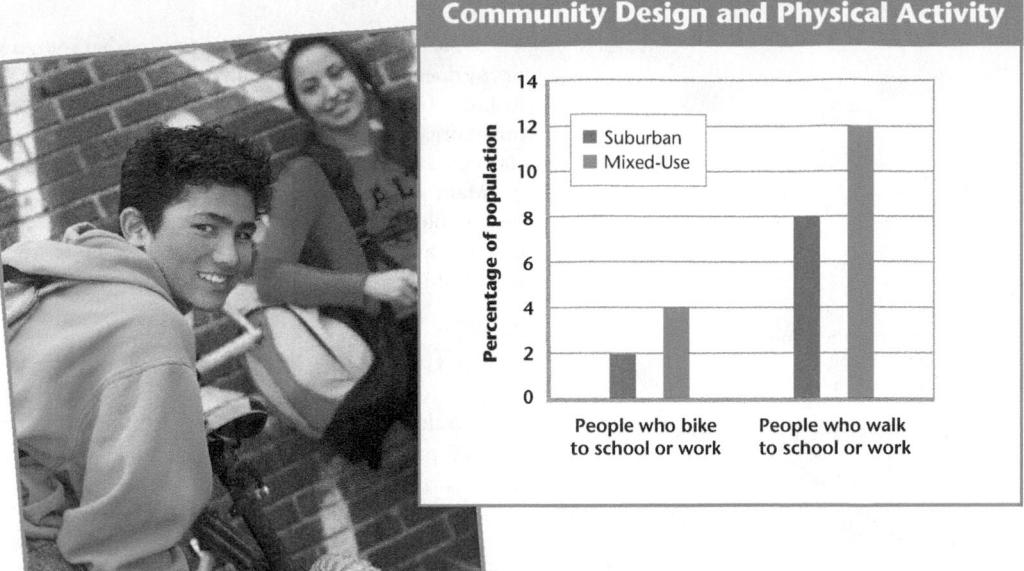

Community Design and Physical Activity

Legend: ■ Suburban ■ Mixed-Use

(Bar graph: Percentage of population, 0 to 14)

People who bike to school or work — Suburban: 2, Mixed-Use: 4
People who walk to school or work — Suburban: 8, Mixed-Use: 12

FIGURE 3 More people walk and bike in mixed-use communities.
Reading Graphs Compare the percent of people who walk to school or work in each type of community. How much greater is the percent in a mixed-used community? **MATH**

Community design

▶ **Promotion of healthy and active lifestyles** Your town or city may have recreational facilities and parks that encourage physical activity. Your community may also run blood drives, food pantries, nutritious school lunch programs, and weight-management groups.

▶ **Community design** Some communities plan new developments or redesign existing neighborhoods to promote walking, biking, and the use of public transportation. One way this is done is through **mixed-use development,** which means building homes closer to businesses and schools. In mixed-use neighborhoods, people can get to work or school and run errands easier by foot or by bike than by car.

Mixed-use development is a healthier alternative to the building of homes in suburbs away from business districts. This type of spread-out development is called **urban sprawl.** People who live in mixed-use neighborhoods rely less on cars and are more active. So they tend to suffer from fewer chronic health problems, including high blood pressure, obesity, and arthritis.

 **Connect to Your Life** How does your community's design promote health? What improvements could you suggest?

GO ONLINE
PearsonSuccessNet.com
For: More on community actions

L2 Visual Learning: Figure 3
After students have examined the data in the bar graph, ask: **From this data, can you make a general statement about the difference in physical activity between suburban communities and mixed-use communities?** (More people bike and walk to work in mixed-use communities than in suburban communities, and therefore physical activity is greater in mixed-use communities.) **What do you think accounts for this difference?** (In mixed-use communities, people can get to work or school and run errands easier by foot or by bike than by car.) Call on volunteers to support this conclusion by describing suburban and mixed-use communities they've lived in or visited.
Caption Answer In mixed-use communities, 12 percent of the population walks to work, while in suburban communities only 8 percent of the population walks to work, a difference of 4 percent.

Connect to Your Life Sample answer: My community has several recreational facilities and parks that promote an active lifestyle. One way to improve the community would be to build more sidewalks and fix existing sidewalks so that more people would walk to work and school.

L3 Content Update  **GO ONLINE**
Visit Pearson SuccessNet to access more information about community actions. Have students complete the Web activity.

Differentiated Instruction

L1 Special Needs

Provide visual aids to help students understand the difference between urban sprawl and mixed-use development. Display pictures from books or magazines that have aerial views of bedroom communities, with long stretches of roads with no sidewalks and few businesses. As students observe these pictures, emphasize the difficulty a person would have walking to stores and school. For contrast, display pictures that show small towns or city neighborhoods with shops at corners or small shopping centers interspersed with houses and apartment complexes. Point out that in such communities people can more easily get around on foot or by bicycle.

L2 Class Discussion

Lead a discussion on health-related activities that take place in the various neighborhoods represented in the class. Ask students to describe block parties, organized sports events, and clean-up efforts that have taken place in their neighborhoods. If some neighborhoods seem to lack such community-based events, ask students to infer why and suggest ways to build social relationships.

Connect to Your Life *Sample answer:* I could help clean up a local park, and I could talk to neighbors about having a block party.

L3 Building Health Skills

Analyzing Influences Remind students that in the DECIDE process for making decisions, one step involves thinking about your values and how those values affect the decisions you make. Ask students to write a paragraph describing the values they think are important in their own cultural tradition. After students have completed their paragraphs, call on volunteers to share their ideas with the class. **WRITING**

L3 Cultural Connection

Ask students to put together a booklet of recipes of traditional foods from cultural communities represented in the class. Ask a few volunteers to take responsibility for collecting and compiling the recipes into a booklet. After the booklet is completed, encourage students to try a recipe at home that is different from their own cultural tradition.

FIGURE 4 The traditional foods of your cultural community can contribute to a healthful diet.

Your Neighborhood In addition to what your town or city does, your neighborhood may also organize efforts to protect the health of its members. A neighborhood might organize safety patrols, sponsor a softball game, or clean up a local park.

Many neighborhood activities also promote social health. Block parties, carpools, and group gardening projects are some ways that neighbors build social relationships.

Connect to Your Life What could you do to improve the health of your neighborhood?

Your School Community Aside from your home, school is probably where you spend most of your time. It is not surprising, then, that your school's physical and social environment can significantly affect your health. For example, some older schools have problems with mold or crumbling ceilings and walls that expose toxic building materials. Such conditions can aggravate asthma and other respiratory conditions.

Many other factors at school can affect your health. These factors include

▶ Availability of nutritious foods for lunch and snacks

▶ Safe routes to school, including buses that are safe

▶ Policies that protect students from bullying and other types of violence

▶ Opportunities for physical activity for all students

▶ Access to school nurses and counselors

Your Cultural Community The cultural community in which you and your family live also influences your health. For example, a tightly-knit cultural community can serve as a "safety net" to support members who are in trouble or in need.

Family gatherings at which cultural traditions are celebrated also strengthen social health. In addition, foods that are important to your cultural group may enhance your health. For example, the soy proteins in tofu and other traditional Asian foods have been shown to help prevent certain cancers. The use of olive oil in Greek and Italian cooking may help prevent heart disease.

For Your **INFORMATION!**

Health Benefits of Soy and Olive Oil

Tofu, or soybean curd, is a soybean product that is widely used in Asian foods. Nutritionists have long recognized that soy products are good sources of protein. Recent studies of soy protein have suggested that it somehow cleans cholesterol out of the bloodstream, possibly by lowering the level of low-density lipoproteins (LDL).

Olive oil has traditionally been a staple in the diets of Greek and other Mediterranean cultures. There is evidence that olive oil is also beneficial to health, especially when it is used in place of foods high in saturated fats. Olive oil is high in monounsaturated fat, which has been shown to help raise the level of high-density lipoproteins (HDL), also called "good cholesterol."

Other Communities Community service organizations and other volunteer groups do many things to improve the health of community members. For example, Students Against Destructive Decisions (SADD) has helped to reduce the number of fatalities due to driving under the influence of alcohol in many communities through advocacy and education. Boy Scouts and Girl Scouts may organize food drives or maintain hiking trails. Other community groups may sponsor bicycle races or walk-a-thons to raise money for cancer research or other causes.

Religious organizations also have increasingly become involved in efforts to improve the health of their communities. For example, many churches, synagogues, and mosques now sponsor

▶ Programs that promote healthful eating

▶ Low-cost screenings for high blood pressure or cancer

▶ Youth groups that participate in community service projects to help people in need

FIGURE 5 This teen is a member of her local 4-H club, where she practices leadership and other life skills.

Section 1 Review

Key Ideas and Vocabulary

1. Identify five different types of communities to which people belong.
2. What is a **social network?** What people are most important to you in your social network?
3. What is a **community service organization?** Give an example.
4. Describe three ways that communities can affect a person's physical health and social health.
5. How is **mixed-use development** different from **urban sprawl?**

Critical Thinking

6. **Evaluating** Why do you think some communities are better at promoting health than others?

Health at School

Measuring School Health Make a list of things about your school that make it a healthy place to be. Then make a list of things about your school that need improvement. Write a letter to your school principal or school board detailing your findings. In your letter, emphasize the most important items that should be addressed to improve student health. **WRITING**

7. **Predicting** Many schools now restrict school buses from idling—leaving their engines running—outside of school buildings. In what ways do you think this change will improve student health?
8. **Applying Concepts** How do you think your cultural community improves your family's health?

Section 1 Review

1. city or town, neighborhood, school community, cultural community, clubs or other organizations
2. A social network is made up of the people a person interacts with and looks to for friendship, information, and social support in all the different communities. Students might identify parents, friends, coaches, and teachers.
3. an official group whose members act or unite for a common purpose; 4-H clubs
4. *Sample answer:* A city or town provides clean drinking water, a neighborhood provides safety patrols, and cultural traditions strengthen social health.

---

3. Assess

Evaluate
These assignments can help you assess students' mastery of the section content.

Section 1 Review
Answers appear below.

Teaching Resources
• Practice 25-1
• Section 25-1 Quiz

L2 Reteach
Divide the class into groups, and have each group create a concept map that ties together the main ideas of the section, including what *community* is and how communities affect health.

L4 Enrich

Teaching Resources
• Enrich 25-1

Health at School

Measuring School Health Call on volunteers to share items on their lists with the class. Write students' ideas on the board in two lists, one for items that promote health and another for items that need improvement. Invite volunteers to rank items on the board according to importance. Instruct students that, in writing their letters, they should address what they think are the most important things that promote health and need improvement. Send the best letters on to the principal and school board.

---

5. Mixed-use development has homes close to businesses and schools, while urban sprawl is the name for spread-out suburbs.
6. Answers will vary. Students might mention good leaders or cultural communities that place an emphasis on good health.
7. *Sample answer:* Restricting the idling of buses will result in less air pollution and less noise.
8. *Sample answer:* My cultural community provides a "safety net" for my family.

Locating Community Resources

Objective

Demonstrate an ability to locate community resources for help with problems.

Teaching Strategies

- Encourage students to think about who are the trusted adults in their lives. Have students make their own private list of trusted adults. Point out that though an adult may not be able to help a troubled person, he or she may be able to direct a teen to the proper resources.

- Make sure all students know how to access an Internet search engine and how to search with key words. Explain that if a search using a first set of words does not yield a useful Web site, students might change the wording and try again. Also make sure students know that they can recognize a U.S. government Web site because it has ".gov" in the Internet address.

- Have a number of local telephone books available for students. Point out that the yellow pages of telephone books have an index that students can check for a variety of headings. Have students explore as many different headings as they can think of, and then compile a list of headings on the board for students to copy.

- Have students brainstorm the kinds of questions a person might ask when calling to find out about the services a facility provides. Because cost is often an issue, explain that some community resources offer free or low-cost services.

- Advise students that before they visit a community resource, they should prepare for the visit by writing a list of questions or topics they want to discuss with the counselor or other professional.

 Accessing Information

Locating Community Resources

Dierdra has been feeling depressed since her parents told her they were getting a divorce. She hasn't been able to concentrate in school or fall asleep at night. Dierdra doesn't want to discuss her concerns with her parents because they both seem so upset already. But she doesn't know who else in her community to turn to for help.

Where do you think Dierdra could go for help with her problems? Below are some steps that Dierdra or you could take to help find resources that are available in your community.

1 Talk to a trusted adult.

When you have a problem or feel depressed, you may find it helpful to talk to an adult you know and trust. The person might be a parent, relative, friend of the family, trusted teacher, coach, school counselor, family doctor, or a religious leader.

2 Search the Internet.

Using search engines to search the Internet can identify countless sites for health-related information and services. Keep in mind, though, that not all sources of information are equally reliable.

Try to identify and read the advice of established organizations. Many county health departments have a listing on their Web sites of community-based health services and agencies. You may also want to check the Web sites of larger voluntary health organizations to see if they have a chapter in your area.

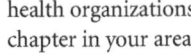

 Sensitive Issues

Many students may be sensitive about disclosing that they have personal issues for which they would need to talk to a counselor or other health professional. Although this activity will give all students some understanding about how to access community resources for personal problems, avoid singling out any student with the suggestion that he or she may need help. Discussion of problems should be couched in hypothetical terms.

③ Find local contact information.

Use the Internet or a telephone directory to find phone numbers for local resources. Include your location for Internet searches. Search for these terms online or in the phone book:

▶ "Self-Help" or "Health" (may be found at the front of white or yellow pages)

▶ "Community Health Services," "Human Health Services," or "Mental Health Services"

▶ "Government Services"

If you still can't find help, try calling people who are likely to keep "help" numbers handy. These include dialing 411 for directory assistance, your local library, or the police and fire departments. If you are in an emergency situation, dial 911.

④ Call to find out what services are provided.

After identifying what you believe to be an appropriate resource or service, call the service and briefly discuss your problem to find out whether the service can meet your needs. Be sure to ask about the location, the hours, and if there is a fee.

If the services do not meet your needs or are too costly, ask the person to whom you are speaking to suggest other places that you can call.

⑤ Select one resource and make an appointment to visit.

You may wish to ask a trusted person to accompany you to your first visit. You may want to have the person wait outside so you can talk privately with the counselor or other professional with whom you are meeting.

If you are not satisfied with the service you have selected, there may be other options. Discuss any concerns with the counselor or try a different service or organization.

 **Practice the Skill**

1. Make a list of some common problems that young people face today. Think about issues related to families, peers, academics, drugs, finances, illness, and others to include in your list.

2. Make a class directory of resources for each problem. List each organization's name, Web site, address, phone number, hours, fees, and services.

3. With permission, distribute the directory to people in your school community.

A Healthy Community and Environment **671**

Practice the Skill

1. Answers will vary. A typical list might include such problems as depression, divorce, child abuse, anorexia, pressure for grades, pressure to get into college, sexually transmitted infections, acquaintance rape, pressure to have sexual relationships, and pregnancy.

2. Divide the class into small groups, and have each group make a list of organizations. Then have a member of each group help in compiling a final class directory.

3. After the final directory is completed, ask a small group of volunteers to present the directory to a school counselor or administrator to get permission to distribute it throughout the school community.

Health at School

Talking to a School Counselor

Most schools have one or more counselors who not only provide help to individual students for a variety of personal problems but also can direct students to appropriate community resources. After students have used the Internet and local telephone directories to find resources in their community, invite a school counselor to make a presentation to the class about local agencies and organizations. Ask the counselor to describe what a student should expect when using the services of a community resource.

Objectives
Before class begins, write the objectives on the board. Have students copy the objectives into their notebooks at the start of class.

1. Focus

Warm-Up Advice Line

Remind students that an allergy is a disorder in which the immune system is overly sensitive to a particular substance not normally found in the body. After students complete the writing assignment, call on volunteers to share their answers with the class. As students list conditions that might affect indoor air quality, make a list on the board. Explain that they will learn in this chapter how air quality, including the quality of indoor air, affects health.

Presentation 25-2

Sensitive Issues

Students may become apprehensive about the quality of the air they breathe, especially if they have a respiratory condition such as asthma that can be exacerbated by polluted air. Assure students that though there may be some problems in some areas of the country, communities strive to protect the air from being polluted and great strides have been made in reducing air pollution in recent years.

Objectives
- ▶ **Summarize** the potential health effects of air pollution.
- ▶ **Evaluate** factors that affect indoor air pollution.
- ▶ **Analyze** how government and personal actions can help improve air quality.

Vocabulary
- pollution
- fossil fuels
- smog
- ozone layer
- asbestos
- radon

Warm-Up

Dear Advice Line,

My allergies always seem to be worse when I am indoors rather than outdoors. I thought flowers and other things found outdoors caused allergies. Is something wrong with me?

WRITING Make a list of indoor conditions that might affect indoor air quality. Then, write back with your answer and advice.

Air Pollution

One factor that is central to the health of communities is the quality of the air people breathe. As you read this sentence, you are breathing in air from your surroundings. Air is a mixture of gases and small particles. The one gas you need—oxygen—makes up about 20 percent of the air you breathe. The remaining 80 percent of the air consists mainly of nitrogen plus small amounts of other naturally occurring gases.

In addition to the natural gases a breath of air contains, harmful gases and particles that have been released into the air may also be present. **Pollution** is the presence or release of substances—called pollutants—into the environment in quantities that are harmful to living organisms. **Air pollutants can damage the respiratory system, enter the bloodstream and harm other parts of the body, and reduce your protection from the sun's radiation.**

How does air get polluted? Whenever substances such as wood and other fuels are burned, particles and harmful waste gases are produced. One of the biggest sources of air pollution is the burning of **fossil fuels,** energy-rich substances mined from deep in the earth. Fossil fuels include coal, oil, and natural gas.

Harmful gases also are released into the air when liquids such as gasoline or paint thinner evaporate, or when gases are released from natural sources such as volcanoes. Figure 6 lists five major air pollutants that affect health directly.

For Your INFORMATION!
Air Quality Index (AQI)

In hundreds of counties across the nation, scientists measure levels of air pollution daily. These measurements are used in coordination with the U.S. EPA to rank local pollution levels in a standard system called the Air Quality Index (AQI). The AQI is divided into six categories, each color coded: Good (green), Moderate (yellow), Unhealthy for Sensitive Groups (orange), Unhealthy (red), Very Unhealthy (purple), and Hazardous (maroon). Students can access the AQI for their area online through the EPA and local Web sites. Some newspapers and television stations also regularly report an area's AQI.

What Is Smog? If you live in or near a major city, you're familiar with smog. **Smog** is a brown haze that forms when air pollutants react in the presence of sunlight. It forms when there is little or no wind and a layer of air is trapped next to the ground. Without air circulation, pollutants can build up and become visible as smog. Local smog alerts warn people—especially those with respiratory conditions like asthma—to limit outdoor activity and physical exertion on days when smog levels are hazardous.

Air Pollutants and the Ozone Layer The gas ozone is a pollutant when it is near to the ground. But naturally occurring ozone located high up in earth's atmosphere—in the **ozone layer**—plays a protective role. The ozone layer absorbs most of the harmful ultraviolet light radiated by the sun, thus preventing it from reaching Earth's surface. Ultraviolet light is harmful to all living things. In people, it may cause skin cancer or cataracts, which is a cloudiness of the eye's lens. Ultraviolet light may also damage the immune system.

Some air pollutants destroy the ozone layer. Chemicals called CFCs, short for chlorofluorocarbons (klawr oh floor oh KAHR bunz) are especially damaging. CFCs have been widely used as cooling fluids in air conditioners and refrigeration units, as propellants in aerosol spray cans, and in foam insulating materials. CFCs are now banned in new products.

Connect to Your Life What physical activities do you enjoy outdoors that would be affected by a smog alert?

FIGURE 6 Air pollutants have a number of negative effects on health. **Predicting** If emissions of nitrogen oxides decrease, how are ozone levels likely to be affected?

Major Air Pollutants

Pollutant	Source	Health Effects
Carbon monoxide (CO)	Combustion of automobile engines; agricultural burning; tobacco smoke	Reduces ability of circulatory system to transport oxygen; causes headache, fatigue, nausea; reduces endurance
Sulfur dioxide (SO₂)	Combustion of fossil fuels; petroleum refining; smelting	Increases risk of chronic respiratory disease; causes shortness of breath; worsens narrowing of airways for people with asthma
Nitrogen oxides	Combustion of fossil fuels; fertilizers	May aggravate respiratory infections and symptoms; may increase risk of chest colds, bronchitis, and pneumonia in children
Ozone (O₃)	Reactions of nitrogen oxides with oxygen in presence of sunlight	Irritates upper respiratory tract and aggravates respiratory conditions such as asthma, bronchitis, and emphysema
Particulate matter	Forest fires; fuel combustion; incineration	Increases chronic and acute respiratory diseases; may irritate tissue of throat, nose, lungs, and eyes

A Healthy Community and Environment **673**

---

2. Teach

L3 **EL** Reading/Note Taking 25-2
L2 Adapted Reading/Note Taking 25-2

Air Pollution

L2 Building Vocabulary

Help students better understand the meaning of *smog* by describing the derivation of the word. Explain that *smog* comes from the combination of two other words, *smoke* and *fog*. The first two letters of the term come from *smoke,* and the last two letters come from *fog*. Ask: **Why do you think scientists named this kind of air pollution smog?** *(Sample answer: Smog has the appearance of smoky fog.)*

L2 Class Discussion

After students have read about the ozone layer, ask: **Why are CFCs considered harmful to Earth's atmosphere?** *(They destroy the ozone layer.)* Point out that ozone is listed in Figure 6 as a major air pollutant. Ask: **Why aren't CFCs doing a needed job by destroying ozone?** *(Ozone near the ground is a pollutant, but ozone in the ozone layer high up in Earth's atmosphere protects living things by absorbing ultraviolet light.)*

L3 Visual Learning: Figure 6

Image Bank Figure 25-6

Divide the class into five groups, and assign each group one of the pollutants in the table. Have students conduct research to find the current acceptable limits for the pollutant. Ask students to also find out who is responsible for measuring the levels of the pollutant, how often measurements are made, and how regulations are enforced. Ask each group to prepare a written report to share their findings.

Caption Answer If emissions of nitrogen oxides decrease, ozone levels would also decrease, because nitrogen oxides react with oxygen in sunlight to form ozone.

 *Sample answer:* bike riding, soccer, and swimming

Indoor Air Pollution

L3 Content Update  GO ONLINE

Visit Pearson SuccessNet to access more information about air pollution. Have students complete the Web activity.

L2 Visual Learning: Figure 7

After students have read the list of indoor air pollutants, ask: **How do pesticides get into homes and other buildings?** *(People use pesticides to kill roaches, ants, and other pests.)* **Where in a building would you find plywood glues?** *(in the walls or ceilings, where plywood is often used in construction)* **Foam insulation?** *(in the attic and crawl spaces)* **What is one way to reduce the level of all of these indoor pollutants?** *(by allowing for adequate ventilation year-round)*

L3 Building Media Literacy

Have students imagine the following scenario: Watching television one day, they see a commercial for a new household air filter that claims it "will remove all forms of air pollution from a house or apartment." Ask: **Would you believe this claim? Why or why not?** *(Sample answer: I probably would not believe it because it claims to remove "all" air pollution. This sounds like an exaggeration.)* **How would you find out if the claim were true?** *(Sample answer: I could check online to see if a product-testing agency has tested this claim.)*

L4 Active Learning

Encourage a few students to interview the school principal to find out what steps have been taken to reduce indoor air pollution in the school. Have students ask if all sources of asbestos have been eliminated from the school, if the school has been tested for radon, and what steps have been taken to reduce pollution caused by the various sources listed in Figure 7. Ask students to prepare a written report of their findings. **WRITING**

GO ONLINE
PearsonSuccessNet.com
For: More on air pollution

Indoor Air Pollution

Many people think that air pollution occurs only outdoors. In fact, the levels of some air pollutants can be higher indoors than outdoors. Some common sources of indoor air pollutants are listed in Figure 7.

Indoor air pollution is most severe in homes and other buildings that have been sealed against air leaks. A building with few air leaks uses less energy for heating and cooling. Unfortunately, inside such energy-efficient buildings, pollutants can build up to high levels if the air is not conditioned properly. To reduce pollutant levels, some houses and offices are now being designed to allow for adequate ventilation year-round.

Asbestos Many older buildings contain a dangerous indoor pollutant called asbestos. **Asbestos** (as BES tus) is a fibrous mineral that was used in fireproofing and other building materials. Unfortunately, bits of asbestos flake off easily. When asbestos fibers are inhaled into the lungs, they damage the cells of the lungs and can cause lung cancer. Today, the use of asbestos is banned entirely in construction. Asbestos removal programs for schools and other buildings have helped reduce exposure to this pollutant.

Radon A naturally occurring radioactive gas called **radon** is also a serious indoor air pollutant. Radon leaks from rocks in the ground through the foundations of buildings. In some buildings, radon can rise to dangerous levels. Radon is responsible for thousands of lung cancer deaths each year. Many experts recommend that people test their homes for radon. If a radon problem exists, people should improve ventilation and seal cracks in foundation walls and floors.

FIGURE 7 There are many sources of indoor air pollution.

Sources of Indoor Air Pollution

- ▶ Fumes from carpets and paint
- ▶ Pesticides
- ▶ Plywood glues
- ▶ Foam insulation
- ▶ Gas stoves
- ▶ Fuel-burning indoor heaters
- ▶ Air fresheners
- ▶ Mold
- ▶ Dust mites
- ▶ Asbestos
- ▶ Radon
- ▶ Tobacco smoke

674 *Chapter 25*

TEENS *Are Asking . . .*

Q: I hear that people should test their homes for radon. How can my family test for radon?

A: You can hire a certified radon tester, or you can test your home yourself. The EPA recommends that you begin with a short-term test that takes about two days. Kits for short-term tests are sold at hardware stores. You place the kit in the lowest lived-in level of your home and expose it to the air. After the time noted on the package, you reseal the package and mail it to a lab for testing. Depending on the results, you may need to do a second short-term test or use a detector that remains in the home for 90 days.

FIGURE 8 Electric buses help reduce air pollution.

Protecting Air Quality

Much progress has been made towards reducing air pollution. Decades ago, governments recognized that air pollutants harm people's health. They passed regulations to reduce emissions of harmful gases from motor vehicles and industries. **In addition to government regulations, personal actions, such as your day-to-day decisions about energy use, directly affect air quality.**

Government Regulations   The Clean Air Act of 1970 identified major air pollutants and set standards for air quality. Since 1970, Congress has made changes and additions to the Clean Air Act every few years. To comply with federal laws, some factories and power plants installed scrubbers, or filters, on smokestacks to remove some of the most toxic pollutants.

Some other federal and local government measures that help reduce air pollution include

▶ Funding for developing more efficient ways to use traditional fossil fuels or alternatives to these fuels, such as wind power and solar power

▶ Laws requiring vehicles to pass annual inspections of exhaust pollutants

▶ Tax breaks for drivers who purchase hybrid automobiles that save gasoline by running partly on electric power

Air Quality Ratings   Weather reports for cities and other areas with air pollution problems often include air quality ratings. The ratings, which are based on air quality standards set by the government, range from "good" to "unhealthy" to "very hazardous." In this way, communities can monitor their progress toward achieving cleaner, healthier air.

 Connect to Your Life   What measures taken by your community do you think are aimed at improving air quality? Explain.

A Healthy Community and Environment   **675**

Protecting Air Quality

 L3 Building Health Skills

Advocacy Divide the class into small groups, and have each group devise a strategy for making the general public more aware of what individuals can do to help reduce air pollution. Students might design a poster or brochure, write a public service announcement, or come up with some other kind of promotion. After all groups have a strategy, have the class evaluate all the strategies and choose the best one to implement as a class project.

L3 Journal Writing

Ask students to write a journal entry describing ways they could personally protect air quality. Explain that students should not just make general statements; rather, they should describe specific ways they could help reduce air pollution through their own actions. Students might describe walking or riding a bike to do errands and lowering the thermostat in winter. Encourage students to put their ideas into practice. **WRITING**

Connect to Your Life   *Sample answer:* The local government has provided special lanes on the highway that only cars with more than one passenger can use. This encourages car pooling, which can help reduce air pollution caused by combustion in car engines.

Differentiated Instruction

L2 Less Proficient Readers

Focus students' attention on the value of government regulations in protecting air quality by calling on students to read aloud the bulleted examples on page 675. For each bullet, call on other students to rephrase it in their own words.

Then ask for volunteers to describe a specific example of each concept. For the first sentence, for instance, a student might describe using a solar cell or a windmill to generate electricity instead of burning coal at a power plant.

3. Assess

Evaluate

These assignments can help you assess students' mastery of the section content.

Section 2 Review

Answers appear below.

Teaching Resources
• Practice 25-2
• Section 25-2 Quiz

L2 Reteach

Ask students to bring in pictures from magazines to create an air pollution collage on a bulletin board. Have students write a brief caption for each picture that includes one action that could be taken to reduce the problem of air pollution.

L4 Enrich

Teaching Resources
• Enrich 25-2

Health and Community

Local Air Pollution Students can find this information by using online resources or by contacting a local government agency that monitors air quality. In making this assignment, set a specific time period for students to research, such as during the previous month or the previous year. Explain that students will also have to research ways that individuals and specific industries can help reduce air pollution. You may want to instruct students to include in their reports three ways that individuals can reduce air pollution and three ways that an industry can reduce air pollution.

FIGURE 9 Using public transportation is one way you can help improve air quality.

What You Can Do Reducing air pollution depends on your actions as well as those of governments and industries. Here are some steps you and your family can take to help reduce air pollution.

▶ Walk, ride a bicycle, or use public transportation instead of an automobile.

▶ When driving, avoid unnecessary trips. For example, combine errands in one trip.

▶ Make sure your vehicle is well-maintained so it produces the least pollution.

▶ Turn off lights and appliances that are not being used. Saving energy saves fuel, which reduces air pollution.

▶ Clean the cooling fans or coils on refrigerators and air conditioners so they will work efficiently.

▶ In winter, set the thermostat lower and wear extra clothes to keep warm indoors.

▶ In the summer, if you have an air conditioner, set it at the highest comfortable temperature.

▶ Make sure that any fuel-burning appliances are vented and working properly.

Section 2 Review

Key Ideas and Vocabulary

1. What is **pollution**? Give examples of three sources of air pollution.
2. What health problems are caused by air pollution?
3. In what kind of building is indoor air pollution worst?
4. What is **asbestos**? How is it dangerous to health?
5. Give examples of one government action and one personal action that improve air quality.

Critical Thinking

6. **Predicting** On a cloudy, windy day, is a smog alert likely? Explain.

Health and Community

Local Air Pollution Find out how many days your community or the nearest large city reported "unhealthy" or worse air quality ratings. What efforts is your community making to reduce this number or keep it at zero? Write a report explaining your findings and describing what residents and industries can do to help reduce air pollution. **WRITING**

7. **Evaluating** What factors in a building's design and construction materials can affect indoor air pollution?

GO ONLINE PearsonSuccessNet.com   Audio Summary Section 25.2

Section 2 Review

1. the presence or release of substances into the environment in quantities that are harmful to living organisms; sources: burning of fossil fuels, evaporation of liquids such as gasoline or paint thinner, and gases released from natural sources

2. *Sample answer:* Air pollution can damage the respiratory system and reduce protection from the sun's radiation.

3. buildings that have been sealed against air leaks

4. A fibrous mineral that was used in fireproofing and other building materials; inhalation can cause lung cancer.

5. *Sample answer:* Government regulations can improve air quality. Walking instead of using an automobile can improve air quality.

6. No, smog forms when there is little or no wind and in presence of sunlight.

7. whether the design allows for adequate ventilation year-round and the construction materials are sources of indoor air pollution

Protecting Land and Water

Waste Disposal

As part of the normal processes of life, all organisms produce wastes. These wastes usually do not cause pollution because they are broken down by microorganisms and reused by other living things. Waste that can be broken down by microorganisms is called **biodegradable waste.**

In addition to biodegradable wastes, humans create wastes that are not, or are only partially, biodegradable. Some non-biodegradable wastes are not dangerous, but they do remain in the environment for a long time instead of being broken down into useful raw materials. Other non-biodegradable wastes, however, are hazardous.

Hazardous Wastes A **hazardous waste** is any waste that is either flammable, explosive, corrosive, or toxic to humans or other living things. Each year, millions of tons of hazardous wastes are produced in the United States alone. They include motor oil, pesticides, solvents, mercury, lead, and radioactive materials. **Hazardous wastes build up in the environment and threaten the health of plants and animals, including humans.** Some hazardous wastes are carcinogens, meaning they cause cancer. Others may cause birth defects, developmental problems, or diseases.

Differentiated Instruction

🔵 English Language Learners

The definition of *hazardous wastes* may be difficult for English language learners because of the terms used. Help the students grasp the concept of "hazardous waste" by restating the categories of materials considered hazardous in everyday terms. Also give an example of each. The word *flammable* means "burns easily." Flammable wastes include some paints and oils. The word *explosive* means "tending to explode." Firecrackers and reactive chemicals are examples. The word *corrosive* means "having the ability to eat away or destroy." Corrosive wastes include toilet bowl cleaners and drain cleaners. The word *toxic* means "poisonous." Toxic wastes include some household cleaners and pesticides.

Objectives
Before class begins, write the objectives on the board. Have students copy the objectives into their notebooks at the start of class.

1. Focus

Warm-Up Myth/Fact

After students finish writing, call on volunteers to share their ideas with the class. *(Students might suggest that bottled water tastes better than tap water and that companies that produce bottled water promote this myth through advertising.)* Point out that the plastic bottle often ends up in landfills. Tell students that in this section they will learn about sources of land and water pollution as well as what they can do to reduce these problems.

Presentation 25-3

2. Teach

🔵 🔵 **Reading/Note Taking** 25-3

🔵 **Adapted Reading/Note Taking** 25-3

Waste Disposal

🔵 **Class Discussion**
Display a piece of bread, a foam cup, a cotton towel, and a piece of metal. Ask: **Which of these materials are biodegradable, and which are non-biodegradable?** *(The bread and the cotton towel are biodegradable; the foam cup and the metal are not.)* Explain that biodegradable wastes generally come from materials made of plant or animal products. Non-biodegradable wastes generally come from mineral and artificially made products.

Section 3
Objectives
▶ **Summarize** the threats that hazardous wastes pose to human health.
▶ **Identify** three sources of water pollution.
▶ **Describe** three solutions for protecting land and water.

Vocabulary
- biodegradable waste
- hazardous waste
- landfill
- recycling
- sewage
- runoff
- conservation

L2 Visual Learning: Figure 10

As students compare the two circle graphs in the figure, emphasize that the data in these graphs show percentages and do not compare actual amounts of household trash. Explain that the actual amount of household trash disposed of in 2005 was much greater than that disposed of in 1960. The major difference shown in the graphs is not in the amounts landfilled but in the percent of total household trash recycled. Ask: **What sorts of materials are commonly recycled now?** *(newspaper, metals, plastics, and glass)* **Caption Answer** In 1960, only 6.4 percent of household trash was recycled, but by 2010, 34.1 percent was recycled, an increase of 27.7 percent.

L3 Cooperative Learning

Have students work in small groups to write a questionnaire to survey attitudes about hazardous waste disposal. Ask students to imagine they have been hired as consultants by the county commissioners and are using the questionnaire to help establish a hazardous waste collection center in the community. The questionnaire should assess the quantity and types of chemicals currently being used by citizens, as well as probing their willingness to participate in various waste-collection plans. Have groups share their questionnaires with the class for evaluation. **WRITING**

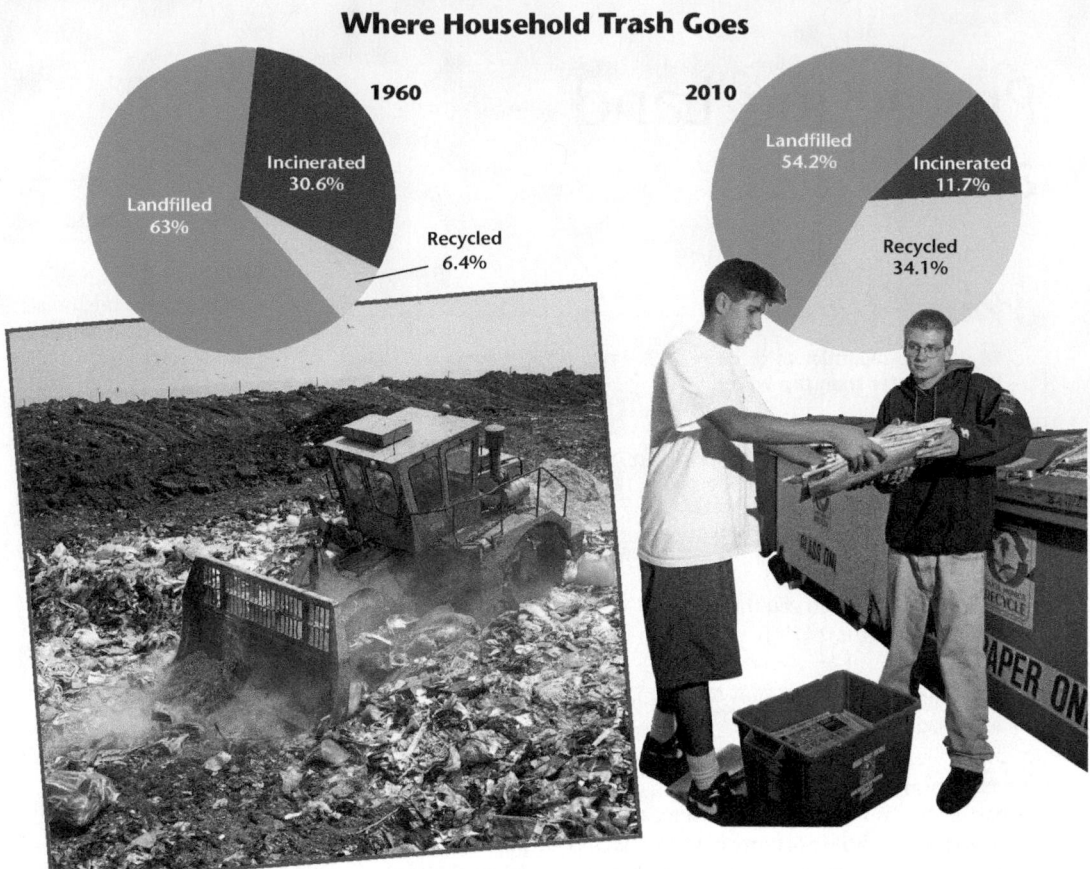

Where Household Trash Goes

1960
Landfilled 63%
Incinerated 30.6%
Recycled 6.4%

2010
Landfilled 54.2%
Incinerated 11.7%
Recycled 34.1%

FIGURE 10 The percentage of household trash that ends up in landfills has decreased in the last few decades.
Reading Graphs How much more trash was recycled in 2010 compared with 1960? **MATH**

Landfills A **landfill** is a permanent storage area where garbage and other wastes are deposited and covered with soil. Landfills are widely used for disposal of solid and liquid wastes. One problem with landfills is that many of them are at or near full capacity. Also, suitable space to build new landfills is running out.

Another more serious problem is that some landfills contain illegally dumped hazardous wastes that may leak into water supplies. However, many federal regulations are in place to prevent this from happening. These regulations include locating landfills away from wetlands, lining landfills to prevent seepage of chemicals, and monitoring water quality near landfills.

Another piece of good news is shown in Figure 10. Compared with the past, a greater percentage of household trash today is being recycled. A smaller percentage is being landfilled or incinerated, meaning burned. **Recycling** is the process of reclaiming raw materials from discarded products and using them to create new products. Many states and communities now require residents to recycle materials such as newspapers, metals, plastics, and glass.

TEENS *Are Asking . . .*

Q: There are a lot of landfills in my community with lots of space for trash. Why should I bother to recycle?

A: There are several reasons to recycle as much as you can. First, recycling saves energy. To mine and process the raw materials needed to make new products requires a great deal of energy. When you recycle, you eliminate this energy use. For example, recycling an aluminum can saves 95 percent of the energy it takes to make a new can. Second, your community might make money on recycled materials by selling them to industries that use them. Third, the recycling industry provides jobs for community members. Fourth, recycling conserves natural resources.

Sources of Water Pollution

Bodies of water such as lakes, rivers, and oceans have always been used to dispose of wastes. If the wastes are biodegradable and the amount is small, microorganisms can break them down. However, when both the amount and types of wastes increase, water pollution becomes more and more of a problem. **Wastes from household, industrial, and agricultural sources can cause pollution of water resources.**

Household Sewage The waste material carried from toilets and drains is referred to as **sewage.** If released into the environment too rapidly, sewage can make water foul-smelling and deadly to fish and other organisms. Sewage also contains bacteria and viruses that can cause disease. For example, in coastal areas, clams, oysters, and other shellfish exposed to sewage may become contaminated with the hepatitis A virus. People who eat raw shellfish may develop hepatitis A, a liver disease caused by this virus.

Up until the 1970s, many communities in the United States discharged raw, or untreated, sewage directly into lakes, rivers, or oceans. In 1972, the Clean Water Act required communities to treat their raw sewage before releasing it into the environment. Sewage treatment makes use of microorganisms to break down the wastes in the water. Treatment can occur in septic tanks, cesspools, or sewage treatment plants. Each provides conditions that allow microorganisms to break down wastes before they are released into the environment.

PROHIBITED SHELLFISH AREA
DO NOT HARVEST
OYSTERS, CLAMS,
OR MUSSELS
SHELLFISH NOT FIT FOR HUMAN CONSUMPTION

 **Connect to Your Life** Have pollutants ever caused a pool or beach in your community to close? Explain the circumstances.

FIGURE 11 If this beach had a sign like the one shown above, these men would not be able to harvest shellfish.

679

Sources of Water Pollution

L4 Active Learning

Encourage interested students to find out how and where sewage is treated in their community. Students might use online resources to gather information, or they can set up an interview with a representative of the local water treatment plant. Ask the students to share their findings with the class.

L1 Teacher Demo

Before class, partially fill three clear glasses with water. Add a few drops of food coloring to one, and crumble some soil into another. Keep the water in the third glass clear. In class, show students the three glasses of water, and ask: **Which of these glasses of water would you feel safe to drink?** *(Most students will reject the glass of colored water and the glass of dirty water as unsafe to drink. Most will say the glass of clear water is probably safe to drink.)* Point out that the glass of clear water may be safe to drink, though students really have no idea where that water came from. Explain that many pollutants dissolve into water and make no change in the water's appearance. For that reason, communities maintain water treatment plants that assure the quality of a community's water supply.

Connect to Your Life *Sample answer:* The beach was closed last year for a few days after an oil spill from an ocean tanker.

Differentiated Instruction

L2 Less Proficient Readers

Pair special needs students with more proficient students, and ask pairs to make a table that compares and contrasts the different sources for wastes that cause water pollution. The table could have three columns, with the headings Source of Water Pollution, Types of Pollutants, and Effects of Pollution. Organizing what they read in a compare/contrast table will help students focus on the most important information in the passage.

L2 Addressing Misconceptions

Water Pollution Some students may assume that water pollution is primarily a problem of urban areas. Explain that water pollution can be just as great a problem in rural areas because of the chemicals used for growing crops and the manure produced by large numbers of animals on "factory farms." Ask: **What chemicals are used on farm fields?** *(chemicals to control weeds and insect pests)* **How do farm chemicals get into the streams and rivers?** *(Runoff carries these pollutants into streams and rivers.)*

L3 Teacher Demo

Set up a demonstration to show how detergent phosphates can affect algae growth. Pour about 240 milliliters (8 ounces) of distilled water into each of three beakers labeled A, B, and C. Add about 60 milliliters (2 ounces) of water from a local pond to each beaker. Add 15 milliliters (1 tablespoon) of phosphate detergent to beaker A, 15 milliliters of nonphosphate detergent to beaker B, and no detergent to beaker C. Place the beakers in a warm, sunny place for two weeks, and have the students observe the results. (Beaker A should have the greatest algae growth.) Explain that greater rates of algae growth in ponds and lakes can cause a reduction in water-oxygen levels, making the water less hospitable to fish and other animals.

L3 Online Activity

Visit Pearson SuccessNet to access an online activity about the health effects of mercury. Have students complete the Web activity.

GO ONLINE **PLANETDIARY**
PearsonSuccessNet.com
For: More on health effects of mercury

Household Cleaners Household cleaners can be a source of pollution if they contain phosphates, which can harm water plants and animals, or harsh chemicals such as chlorine. Chlorine in high concentrations is toxic to all forms of life. Chlorine also can react with certain substances that are dissolved in water, forming carcinogens.

Industrial Wastes Waste products from industrial operations, such as mining and manufacturing, are some of the most dangerous types of water pollutants. Many industrial wastes are extremely hazardous or nonbiodegradable, or both. Industrial wastes include such things as dyes, acids, solvents, and heavy metals such as mercury, lead, and cadmium.

In the past, it was common for industrial wastes to be discharged into ground and surface waters, contaminating organisms that lived in or drank the water. Today, although there is much greater regulation to prevent such contamination, some of these pollutants are still a problem. The Environmental Protection Agency (EPA) estimates that one in six American women of childbearing age has a blood mercury level that would be considered dangerous to a developing fetus.

Agricultural Runoff The water that drains from land into streams is called **runoff.** Runoff can carry with it many kinds of substances that pollute water supplies. Runoff from agricultural land, for example, often contains chemicals applied to crops to control weeds and insect pests. Many of these chemicals are toxic if ingested in large enough quantities.

Even if polluted water is not used by humans directly, game animals may pass the contamination on to people who eat them. Most states now issue advisories to help protect people from consuming such pollutants. The advisory includes a list of recommendations to limit or avoid eating certain types of fish and other game animals.

FIGURE 12 Pesticides are sometimes sprayed onto crops from an airplane. Unfortunately, runoff from fields may contaminate local water supplies.

For Your INFORMATION!

Safe Ingredients for Household Use

These nontoxic ingredients recommended by the EPA can be used safely in homes.

- Baking soda, or sodium bicarbonate, can be used to scrub shiny materials without scratching, to deodorize, and to put out grease fires.
- Washing soda, or SAL, is used to cut grease in broiler pans and ovens.
- Cornstarch can be used to clean rugs, carpets, and windows. It also can be used to polish furniture and starch clothes.
- Borax is a mineral that can deodorize and stop the growth of molds. Borax can also be combined with sugar to make an effective poison for cockroaches.

Hands-On *Activity*

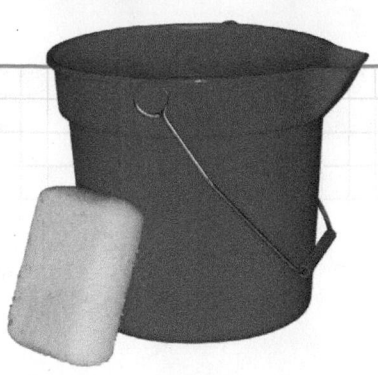

Nontoxic Housecleaning

Materials
bucket
hot water
baking soda
soap flakes
cornstarch
white vinegar
stirrer
sponge
rags or paper towels

Try This

1. In a bucket, make a nontoxic, all-purpose cleaner by adding 1/2 tablespoon of baking soda and 1/8 cup of soap flakes to 1/2 gallon of hot water. Stir until all ingredients are completely dissolved.

2. Moisten a sponge with the cleaning solution and clean your desktop or another surface that your teacher selects. Note how easily and effectively the cleaner works.

3. Make a nontoxic glass cleaner by adding 1 tablespoon of cornstarch and 1/4 cup of white vinegar to 1/2 gallon of warm water. Stir well.

4. Moisten a rag or paper towel with the glass cleaner. According to your teacher's instructions, try cleaning a window or mirror.

Think and Discuss

1. How well did the cleaners work? How do they compare with commercially prepared products you have used?

2. How do you think most people dispose of cleaning products? What effect do you think disposing of cleaning products has on the environment?

3. What are the benefits and drawbacks of making your own nontoxic cleaners? **WRITING**

Maintaining Environmental Health

The environmental damage to land and water—and in turn, the damage to human health—is a serious problem, but there are solutions. **Cleaning up waste sites, improving waste management, and conserving natural resources are three solutions for protecting land and water.**

Cleaning Up Waste Sites The EPA has placed over 1,000 of the most dangerous hazardous waste sites on a national priority list for cleanup. These so-called "Superfund" sites are found in every state. Thousands of other hazardous waste sites are being cleaned up by state governments or by private companies.

Some dump sites are identified only after citizens notify authorities. If you suspect hazardous chemicals have been dumped at a site, notify your local health department or state agency for environmental protection.

Do you know if there are any Superfund sites in your community? How could you find out?

Hands-On *Activity*

Nontoxic Housecleaning

Point out that many household cleaners contain chemicals such as ammonia, chlorine, phosphates, strong acids, or alkali. Such chemicals are not only a source of water pollution but can also be dangerous when used in combination. Bring in samples of common household cleaning products that clearly state the ingredients on the label. Show these labels to students, and also read aloud the Warning or Caution statement on each product.

Think and Discuss Answers

1. Answers may vary. Most students will find that their desktops and other surfaces were well cleaned, though certain kinds of ink, glue, and other marks may not have been completely removed. Students' comparisons to other products will vary with their experiences.

2. Answers may vary, though most students will respond that people generally pour cleaning products down the drain. Disposing of cleaning products in this way can have a harmful effect on the environment.

3. *Sample answer:* Benefits include reducing water pollution, being safer to use, and being less costly. Drawbacks include being less effective in some cases and less convenient.

L4 Building Health Skills

Accessing Information Encourage a few students to work together to find out if there are any Superfund sites near their community. Ask them to learn how the hazardous wastes came to be at the site, how long the wastes have been there, what threat the wastes pose to the public, and what is being done to clean up the site. Have students prepare a presentation of their findings to the class.

Connect to Your Life *Sample answer:* I don't know if there are any in this community. I could find out by searching online for the EPA list of Superfund sites.

Differentiated Instruction

L2 Less Proficient Readers

Show students how to use the subheadings under Maintaining Environmental Health to create a concept map that can help them identify the main ideas in the passage. The concept map should have the main heading in a top bubble, with each of the side headings in the next level of bubbles. Students should add details that describe how each action protects land and water. Suggest that students make concept maps whenever they need help identifying the main ideas in a passage.

L1 Active Learning

Make a display of packaging and other items from the school cafeteria that can be recycled. These might include plastic utensils and bottles, milk cartons, aluminum cans, and paperboard boxes. Have special needs students handle items in the display and discuss where they would deposit such items for recycling. You may wish to keep the display up for several days and ask students to continue to add new recycleable items as they encounter them.

L3 Building Health Skills

Advocacy Have students make a poster advocating for environmental health by following the "three Rs." Posters should include specific suggestions about how to reduce, reuse, and recycle and include illustrations and language to make them interesting and relevant to teens. Arrange for students to display their posters in places on and off campus where many teens will see them.

L3 Journal Writing

Ask students to write a private journal entry describing specific ways they could reduce, reuse, and recycle to help protect the environment. Encourage students to put these ideas into practice at home as well as in their community. **WRITING**

Sample answer: local chapters of the National Audubon Society and the Nature Conservancy

Proper Disposal of Wastes Laws now make it difficult for industries and individuals to dump wastes illegally. Today, legal dump sites for hazardous chemicals are designed to prevent the escape of wastes into the surrounding environment.

Many communities have collection centers where residents can turn in hazardous wastes, such as motor oil, pesticides, and car batteries, for proper disposal. Many companies have also developed ways to reduce the amount of wastes they generate in the first place or to recycle their wastes. Using new technologies, such as high-temperature incineration, has also helped eliminate large amounts of hazardous wastes.

Conservation Humans have been altering the land for thousands of years—for farming, settlement, and harvesting resources such as lumber. In most instances, the environment has been able to recover. In modern times, however, the demand for land development and the use of other natural resources has risen dramatically as the human population has grown rapidly.

Losing natural land areas can make pollution worse. For example, pavement cannot absorb rainwater. Therefore, paving an area may increase runoff of pollutants into streams and lakes.

Conservation is one key to slowing down the rate at which natural areas are lost. **Conservation** is the protection and preservation of the natural environment by managing natural resources wisely and developing land for new construction responsibly.

FIGURE 13 This community group has launched an effort to keep a local beach clean.

 **What conservation organizations are active in your community?**

WRITING and Health

L3 Editorial

Show students a few editorials from a local newspaper. Explain that editorials are written by the newspaper's editorial board, and unlike news articles, editorials take a position and provide reasons to back up that position. Ask students to write an editorial that advocates for a specific action individuals or the community should take on an issue related to maintaining environmental health. For example, the editorial might advocate for more community collection centers, regulations about the packaging of products, or the recycling of materials by individuals in the community.

What You Can Do You can help reduce the problems associated with land and water pollution by following the "three Rs"—reduce, reuse, and recycle.

▶ **Reduce** by creating less waste in the first place. For example, avoid using disposable, non-biodegradable products such as plastic cups. Purchase products that have a minimum of packaging, or that are packaged in recycled or recyclable materials. Finally, buy only as much of a product or material as you need.

▶ **Reuse** by finding other uses for objects or by donating them rather than discarding them. For example, reuse cardboard boxes and empty jars for storage. Pass magazines or catalogs on to friends after you are through with them. You might also donate old clothes, furniture, and sports equipment rather than throwing them out.

▶ **Recycle** by keeping separate from the trash any materials that can be reprocessed into new products. Glass, metal, most plastics, and many types of paper can be recycled. Check with your city or town for the recycling guidelines specific to your community.

FIGURE 14 To help remind others not to pollute, this teen is stenciling a warning message next to a storm drain.

Section 3 Review

Key Ideas and Vocabulary

1. What is a **hazardous waste?** Give three examples.
2. How do hazardous wastes affect human health?
3. What is a **landfill?** What serious problem do some landfills pose to the environment?
4. What are three sources of water pollution?
5. Identify three solutions that can help protect land and water resources.

Critical Thinking

6. **Applying Concepts** What are you doing to reduce the amount of waste you contribute to landfills? What else could you do?

Health at Home

Reducing Waste Make an inventory of products you buy that come with packaging. Put each package into one of three categories: "Reuse" means you will use it again; "Recycle" means you will recycle it; "Trash" means you can't recycle or reuse it. For each product in your "Trash" category, describe how you could "Reduce" instead by either going without the product or buying a less wasteful alternative. **WRITING**

7. **Relating Cause and Effect** What health concerns in your community have been caused by land or water pollution? Explain.

---

3. Assess

Evaluate

These assignments can help you assess students' mastery of the section content.

Section 3 Review
Answers appear below.

Teaching Resources
• Practice 25-3
• Section 25-3 Quiz

L2 Reteach

Write brief descriptions of problems that result from waste disposal and water pollution, and read the descriptions to the class *without* identifying the source of the problems. Include problems related to the improper disposal of hazardous wastes and the buildup of household waste in a landfill, as well as the pollution of water by sewage, household cleaners, industrial wastes, and agricultural runoff. Have students listen to each description. Then ask volunteers to identify the correct source and suggest what could be done to remedy the problem.

L4 Enrich

Teaching Resources
• Enrich 25-3

Health at Home

Reducing Waste Lead a discussion on products students commonly buy so that they have some ideas about what to look for at home. Ask students to survey products in their homes, placing a variety of products in each of the three categories. The next day, ask volunteers to share items from their lists with the class.

Section 3 Review

1. any waste that is either flammable, explosive, corrosive, or toxic to humans or other living things; *sample examples:* motor oil, pesticides, solvents

2. They can cause cancer, birth defects, developmental problems, or diseases.

3. A landfill is a permanent storage area where garbage and other wastes are deposited and covered with soil. Some landfills contain hazardous wastes that can leak into water supplies.

4. *Sample answer:* household sewage, industrial wastes, agricultural runoff

5. cleaning up waste sites, proper disposal of wastes, conservation

6. *Sample answer:* I recycle everything I can. I could try to produce less waste.

7. Answers will vary. Students should cite specific incidences of pollution that have occurred in their community.

A Healthy Community and Environment **683**

Objectives
Before class begins, write the objectives on the board. Have students copy the objectives into their notebooks at the start of class.

1. Focus

Warm-Up Health Stats

After students finish writing, call on volunteers to share their answers with the class. Ask if any students volunteer. If so, have these students briefly describe what they do and how it makes them feel. Discuss how volunteering benefits the community in which students live.

Presentation 25-4

Objectives
▶ **Examine** two keys to building a sense of community.
▶ **Identify** three steps to getting more involved in your community.

Vocabulary
• civic engagement
• consensus-building

Warm-Up

Health Stats What impact do teen volunteers make?

> **55% of teens do volunteer work.**

> Teens spend 1.3 billion hours volunteering each year.

> The typical teen volunteer contributes 29 hours per year.

WRITING Why do you think so many teens volunteer? What benefits do the volunteers get from doing so?

Volunteer

A Sense of Community
Building healthy communities requires that people work together. To do this, people need to have a sense of community. When people believe that they are part of a community, they have a stake in making their community function as well as it can. **Two keys to building a sense of community are civic engagement and a shared vision of the future.**

Civic Engagement How involved are people in your community? The level of involvement that average citizens have in the planning and decision-making that affects their community is called **civic engagement.** Some examples of civic engagement include

▶ Participating in community government

▶ Registering to vote when you turn 18

▶ Volunteering during a political campaign

▶ Attending public hearings or school board meetings

 **and Health**

L3 Calculating
You can use the data in the Warm-Up to give students practice calculating. Tell students that the U.S. population is about 315 million, and teens make up about 10 percent of that figure. Ask: **What is the U.S. teen population?** *(0.1 × 315,000,000 = 31,500,000 teens)* **How many teens do volunteer work?** *(31,500,000 × 0.55 =*

17,325,000 teens) **What is the average number of hours volunteered by each teen per year?** *(1,300,000,000 ÷ 17,325,000 = 75.04, or about 75 hours per year)* Discuss: **Why does this average differ from the number of hours a typical teen volunteers?** The average, or mean, accounts for teens who volunteer many more than 29 hours per year. In the statistic about *typical teens,* 29 hours per year is the median.

A Shared Vision For communities to make progress and bring about positive changes, members need to share common goals. How can citizens with very different views come to a consensus on important issues? **Consensus-building** is the process by which a community arrives at an agreed-upon vision for the future. Consensus-building requires strong leadership and give-and-take among citizens.

Achieving goals for the future often means that a community has to make sacrifices in the short term. For example, suppose that a city decides to expand its subway system. The project would be paid for by tax dollars today although its benefits will not be realized until several years later. In other words, one generation pays for a benefit that the next generation will receive.

If it were not for a shared vision, many communities might not make investments in their school systems, transportation systems, or public health programs.

 What sacrifices do you make in order to see a future benefit?

FIGURE 15 At a public hearing, people have the opportunity to express their opinions to the decision makers in their community.

A Healthy Community and Environment **685**

2. Teach

L3 **EL** Reading/Note Taking 25-4

L2 Adapted Reading/Note Taking 25-4

A Sense of Community

L2 Class Discussion

Ask a volunteer to read aloud the four examples of civic engagement listed in the text. Ask: **What are some ways you could participate in community government?** *(Sample answer: We could attend school board meetings, speak out at city council meetings, and volunteer to serve on committees set up to investigate a public issue.)*

L3 Active Learning

Have students find out the times and locations of upcoming school board meetings, city or town council meetings, county commissioner meetings, and any other local government meetings. Discuss what might be covered at each meeting and how long it might normally last. Then encourage students to attend one or more of these meetings and report their observations to the class.

EL Building Vocabulary

Explain that *consensus* comes from a Latin word meaning "to agree" or "to give consent." Ask: **What does it mean if I say that the consensus of the class is to take action on an issue?** *(It means that everyone in the class agrees to the idea of taking action on an issue.)* **What do you think would be involved in building consensus?** *(Sample answer: People would propose ideas and try to convince others to agree with those ideas. Everyone may have to compromise to come to a consensus.)*

 I recycle to help ensure future supplies of natural resources.

Differentiated Instruction

L4 Gifted and Talented

Have a group of students work together to write and perform a skit for the class that shows how members of a community can come to a consensus about action to take concerning a community problem. Ask students to focus on a problem faced by many communities, such as the collection of recyclables, and act out a community meeting in which members of a task force come to the meeting with very different ideas. The skit should show conflict and then resolution as the members of the task force talk about the differences in approach to the issue and come to a consensus about what action to take.

Getting Involved in Your Community

 Online Activity

Visit Pearson SuccessNet to access an online activity about getting involved. Have students complete the Web activity.

Visual Learning: Figure 16

After students have read the list of ways to become informed, ask: **How do you think most young people become informed about their local community?** *(Sample answer: Most young people probably are informed through a local television news program.)* **Do you think watching the local news provides you with more or less information than reading the local newspaper?** *(Most students will say that watching the news provides less information or more sensational information.)* Lead a discussion on why young people, including teens, generally don't read newspapers as much as older people do. Discuss the limitations of television news as a method for staying informed.

Caption Answer *Sample answer:* newspaper, local television station news, and comments of friends and family

Building Media Literacy

Gather as many newspapers as possible that are published in the students' community. These might include daily newspapers, weekly newspapers, alternative newspapers, advertisers, and newspapers associated with various cultural communities. Give small groups of students one or more of these newspapers, and ask them to look for articles or lists that inform the public about public meetings, community organizations, and volunteering opportunities. Have each group make a list of what they find and where they found each item. In class discussion, call on volunteers from each group to describe their results. Then ask students to decide which sources are best for such information.

Connect to Your Life My neighbors are concerned about a factory in the area that may be polluting the groundwater.

GO ONLINE
PearsonSuccessNet.com
For: More on getting involved

Getting Involved in Your Community

How can you get more involved in your community? **There are three steps to getting involved: become informed, volunteer your time, and be an advocate.** By following these steps, you can help bring about changes to improve the quality of life, or even save lives, in your community.

Become Informed What are some of the key health-related issues facing your community? What are people most concerned about? And what are the strengths and weaknesses of the community to address those issues? The first step in getting involved in your community is to become informed about questions like these.

By asking such questions, you can gain insight into what people are thinking about. Which concerns affect health? Maybe it's a dangerous traffic intersection, the quality of school lunches, or disease-carrying mosquitoes in the summer months. You can learn about the scope of a problem, how people view the problem, and any possible solutions that have been proposed. Several ways you can become informed are listed in Figure 16.

Connect to Your Life What community health concerns have your parents, friends, or neighbors expressed?

FIGURE 16 There are many ways to gather information about the concerns of your local community. **Applying Concepts** What sources do you rely on for information about your community?

How to Become Informed
• Read the local newspaper.
• Tune into the local radio or television stations.
• Attend a meeting of your town council, board of health, or school board.
• Interview community leaders.
• Survey your peers or other groups affected by your issue.

686

WRITING and Health

Persuasive Letter

Have students imagine a friend who spends most of his or her free time watching television or playing computer games. This person does well in school but does not participate at all in the community.

Ask students to write a letter to persuade this friend to consider volunteering for a community organization. Explain that the letter should provide reasons why volunteering would be of benefit to the teen as well as the community.

Volunteer Your Time Once you've become informed, the next step is to reach out, plan a strategy, and get more involved. Maybe your school has a stake in the issue and needs someone to serve as a student representative at key meetings. Or maybe you can volunteer with a community organization that has expressed concern about the issue.

Did you know that more than half of America's teenagers, ages 12 to 17, do some kind of volunteer community service work? On average, teenage volunteers devote almost four hours each week working with religious organizations, community service organizations, school groups, and other groups.

There are lots of ways that volunteering improves community health. Food drives and programs like "Meals on Wheels" help disadvantaged members of the community get food they might otherwise go without. School recycling programs can help improve your community's environment. And volunteering to coach disabled students can help improve the physical and mental health of the people you coach. It can also make you feel good about yourself simply because you've helped another person.

Volunteering helps the community at large, but it also helps the volunteers themselves. Figure 17 lists some of the many benefits of volunteering that teens report.

FIGURE 17 Volunteering benefits the community-at-large and also rewards the volunteer.

Benefits to Teen Volunteers
- Gain new perspective on community problems.
- Discover positive role models.
- Develop career goals and obtain job skills.
- Improve grades in school.
- Meet new people with shared values.

687

3. Assess

Evaluate

These assignments can help you assess students' mastery of the section content.

Section 4 Review

Answers appear below.

Teaching Resources

• Practice 25-4
• Section 25-4 Quiz

L2 Reteach

Ask students to rewrite the section objectives as questions and then answer the questions. They can check to see if their answers are correct by rereading relevant passages in the text.

L4 Enrich

Teaching Resources

• Enrich 25-4

FIGURE 18 These teens have organized a campaign for more resources for tobacco prevention in their school.

Be an Advocate Remember from Chapter 1 that advocacy means speaking or writing in support of a person or issue. There are several ways you can be an advocate and take a stand on issues in your community. All of these actions require good communication skills.

▶ Speak out about an issue at public meetings.

▶ Write a letter to the editor of your local or school newspaper.

▶ Recruit your peers to meet with a government official or other decision makers.

▶ Organize a "Teen Summit" to empower others to become advocates.

▶ Establish an electronic listserv, Web blog, or Web site where you can keep other concerned teens updated on developments.

▶ Work with some friends to provide information about an important health topic, such as organ donation, at a community event.

Whatever you do, by taking a stand as an advocate, you become an agent for change. But keep in mind, it takes courage to voice your opinion, especially when people may be reluctant to change. Enlist the support of peers, teachers, and other adults who support your ideas and can help you move your ideas forward.

Health and Community

Cell Phone Disposal Plan Explain to students that cell phones contain chemicals, such as antimony, arsenic, beryllium, cadmium, and lead, that are not biodegradable. The disposal of cell phones is a health concern because there are millions in use, and the average lifespan of a cell phone can be less than two years. Before students write a plan, encourage them to use the telephone book or online resources to find out where in their community cell phones are accepted for recycling. Then have each student use that information to develop a plan for a phone recycling program.

Section 4 Review

Key Ideas and Vocabulary

1. What are two keys to building a sense of community?

2. What is **civic engagement?** How does it apply to you?

3. Describe three steps you can take to get more involved in your community.

Critical Thinking

4. **Evaluating** What do you think are three health challenges facing the community in which you live? Explain.

Health and Community

Cell Phone Disposal Plan Disposing of cell phones—which often contain hazardous materials—in an environmentally and socially responsible manner is a growing health concern. Write a plan for organizing a phone recycling program for your community. You may want to first research organizations that accept old cell phones. Describe in your plan both the benefits and challenges of such a program. **WRITING**

5. **Applying Concepts** What more could be done to address the challenges you cited in Question 4? What role could you play as an advocate?

🔊 GO ONLINE PearsonSuccessNet.com   Audio Summary Section 25.4

Section 4 Review

1. civic engagement and a shared vision of the future

2. Civic engagement is the level of involvement that average citizens have in the planning and decision-making that affects their community. A community in which people get involved is a good place to live.

3. become informed, volunteer your time, be an advocate

4. Students should describe three specific health issues in their community. *Sample answer:* the use of illegal drugs, the number of people without health insurance, and air pollution caused by motor vehicles

5. Answers will vary depending on the problems described. Students might mention attending public meetings, joining an organization, and writing letters.

Chapter 25
At a Glance

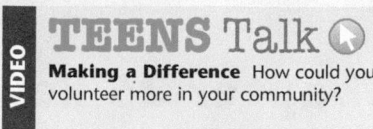

VIDEO **TEENS** Talk ▶
Making a Difference How could you volunteer more in your community?

Section 1   Your Community, Your Health

Key Ideas

▶ Besides being a resident of your city or town and neighborhood, you are a member of a particular school, a cultural community, and probably one or more clubs or organizations.

▶ Community factors contribute significantly to the physical and social health of community members.

Vocabulary
- social network (664)
- community service organization (665)
- mixed-use development (667)
- urban sprawl (667)

Section 2   Air Quality and Health

Key Ideas

▶ Air pollutants can damage the respiratory system, enter the bloodstream and harm other parts of the body, and reduce your protection from the sun's radiation.

▶ Indoor air pollution is most severe in homes and other buildings that have been sealed against air leaks.

▶ In addition to government regulations, personal actions, such as your day-to-day decisions about energy use, directly affect air quality.

Vocabulary
- pollution (672) • fossil fuels (672) • smog (673)
- ozone layer (673) • asbestos (674) • radon (674)

Section 3   Protecting Land and Water

Key Ideas

▶ Hazardous wastes accumulate in the environment and threaten the health of plants and animals, including humans.

▶ Wastes from household, industrial, and agricultural sources can cause pollution of water resources.

▶ Cleaning up waste sites, improving waste management, and conserving natural resources are three solutions for protecting land and water.

Vocabulary
- biodegradable waste (677) • hazardous waste (677)
- landfill (678) • recycling (678) • sewage (679)
- runoff (680) • conservation (682)

Section 4   Working for Community Health

Key Ideas

▶ Two keys to building a sense of community are civic engagement and a shared vision of the future.

▶ There are three steps to getting involved: become informed, volunteer your time, and be an advocate.

Vocabulary
- civic engagement (684)
- consensus-building (685)

A Healthy Community and Environment **689**

Chapter 25
At a Glance

 VIDEO **Making a Difference** Ask for volunteers to share their answers. Use examples from the video to review ways people can volunteer in their community.

Key Ideas Review

L2 Have students reword the section objectives as questions and then answer them. Students should find answers in the text for any questions they cannot answer.

L3 Divide the class into small groups, and have each group generate questions from the boldface sentences in the chapter. Ask groups to exchange questions. Then have students collaborate with other members of their group to answer the questions.

Vocabulary Review

EL Pair English language learners with English proficient students, and ask each pair to write sentences using at least ten terms from the chapter, leaving a blank in the sentence where a vocabulary term would be. Have pairs exchange and complete one another's sentences.

L2 Have students write sentences in which they correctly use the vocabulary terms. For each term, call on a student to read his or her sentence. Ask other students whether the term is used correctly. If not, call on a volunteer to read his or her sentence for the term.

Chapter 25 Review

GO ONLINE

PearsonSuccessNet.com

Students can go online for a review activity on Chapter 25.

Reviewing Key Ideas

Section 1
1. d
2. They provide teens with a supportive environment for recreation, learning, and service.
3. Because residents rely less on cars and are more active, they suffer from fewer chronic health problems.
4. *Sample answer:* The city has parks where I can play sports and be active.

Section 2
5. b
6. respiratory conditions like asthma
7. Radon is responsible for about 5,000 to 20,000 deaths from lung cancer each year.
8. *Sample answer:* Technology is used to measure air quality. With that information, communities can monitor their progress toward achieving cleaner, healthier air.

Section 3
9. c
10. They are broken down by microorganisms and reused by other living things.
11. *Sample answer:* Ocean organisms such as fish and shellfish could be contaminated by the toxic substances. Humans who eat those organisms could become ill.
12. *Sample answer:* An advantage is that the waste does not end up in a landfill. A disadvantage may be that the process causes air pollution.

Section 4
13. d
14. *Sample answer:* participating in community government, registering to vote when you turn 18, volunteering during a political campaign
15. Students should cite three of the ways listed in Figure 17.

Chapter 25 Review

Reviewing Key Ideas

Section 1
1. How is a social network important to health?
   a. It provides information
   b. It provides friendships
   c. It provides social support
   d. All of the above
2. What benefits do community service organizations provide for teens?
3. How can mixed-use developments improve the health of people living in a city?
4. **Critical Thinking** Describe how one condition of the town or city in which you live affects your health. **WRITING**

Section 2
5. Each of the following is an air pollutant *except*
   a. sulfur dioxide.
   b. nitrogen.
   c. carbon monoxide.
   d. particulate matter.
6. What health conditions are made worse by smog?
7. What is one health risk of excessive radon exposure?
8. **Critical Thinking** How do you think technology has helped to make people more aware of air pollution?

Section 3
9. A site where wastes are covered with soil is called a
   a. sewer.
   b. runoff.
   c. landfill.
   d. hazardous waste site.
10. What happens to most natural wastes in the environment?
11. **Critical Thinking** How could toxic substances dumped into oceans affect human health? Explain.
12. **Critical Thinking** What do you think are some of the advantages and disadvantages of burning trash?

GO ONLINE

PearsonSuccessNet.com

For: Chapter 25 review activity

Section 4
13. The process by which a community arrives at an agreed-upon vision for the future is called
    a. volunteerism   b. civic engagement
    c. advocacy   d. consensus-building
14. Give three examples of civic engagement.
15. Identify three ways that volunteering in their community benefits teen volunteers.
16. **Critical Thinking** Give three examples of community health programs that would require a short-term sacrifice for a long-term benefit. **WRITING**

Building Health Skills

17. **Advocacy** You recently learned that a neighbor has been changing her car's oil and dumping the used engine oil into the town sewer system. What would you do to try to discourage her from this behavior?
18. **Communicating** A friend of yours suggests that the actions of one person have little effect on the environment. What arguments could you use that might change his or her view? **WRITING**
19. **Setting Goals** Set a goal to become more active in your community on any issue by the end of the school year. Write out a stepwise plan that will help you achieve this goal. Monitor your progress along the way. **WRITING**

Health and Community

Community Cleanup Organize a community volunteer cleanup project. Select a lake, stream, road, park, or other area in your community to clean up. Submit your plan, including a list of necessary materials and safety precautions, to your teacher before beginning the project. After obtaining permission and carrying out your project, prepare a presentation about the experience. **WRITING**

---

16. Students should describe three specific examples. One example might be a city building a new park with exercise equipment that can be used by everyone. The short-term sacrifice is the cost to taxpayers. The long-term benefit is a healthier community.

Building Health Skills

17. *Sample answer:* I would research how dumping engine oil into the sewer system affects the environment and then tell her what I learned. If this did not persuade her to stop, I would inform local authorities.

Standardized Test Prep

Math Practice

The graph shows the distribution of causes for which teens volunteer. Use the graph to answer Questions 20–22.

Where Teens Volunteer

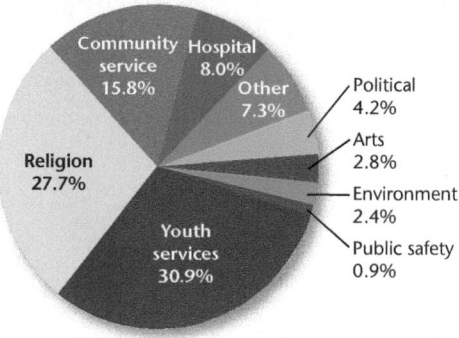

20. What percentage of teens volunteer for environmental causes?
    A 0.9%
    B 2.4%
    C 4.2%
    D 15.8%

21. In which two areas do teens volunteer the most?
    F hospital and religion
    G arts and environment
    H religion and youth services
    J political and community service

22. In a group of 1,000 teen volunteers, about how many would volunteer in youth services?
    A 16
    B 31
    C 158
    D 309

Test-Taking Tip

Take care to record your answers properly. For example, make sure you fill in the answer bubbles completely and don't make stray marks on the answer sheet.

Reading and Writing Practice

Read the passage describing a technology that is used to clean up the hazardous waste uranium. Then answer Questions 23–26.

One new development in cleaning up hazardous wastes is called bioremediation. Bioremediation uses microorganisms to convert wastes into substances that are either less toxic or easier to clean up. For uranium, the process involves pumping uranium-contaminated water into a reaction tank that contains a unique type of bacteria. These bacteria are able to convert uranium from a water-soluble form to a water-insoluble form. The water-insoluble uranium settles to the bottom of the tank. It is still radioactive, but because it is insoluble, it is much easier to separate and remove.

23. From the context of the passage, the best definition of *water-insoluble* is
    A not able to dissolve in water.
    B hazardous when in water.
    C hazardous when in air.
    D radioactive.

24. What role do bacteria play in the bioremediation of uranium?
    F They convert hazardous wastes into harmless substances.
    G They eat the uranium.
    H They convert the uranium to a form that is easier to clean up.
    J The bacteria die and sink to the bottom of the tank.

25. What is the best title for the passage?
    A Radioactive Waste
    B Insoluble Bioremediation
    C Uranium Bioremediation
    D Uranium and Bacteria

Constructed Response

26. What do you suppose the potential benefits of bioremediation are? On the other hand, what might be some of the disadvantages?

Standardized Test Prep

Math Practice
20. B
21. H
22. D

Reading and Writing Practice
23. A
24. H
25. C
26. The potential benefits include more efficient removal and storage of waste uranium and a cleaner environment. Disadvantages include that the waste remains radioactive and the waste still needs to be stored.

18. *Sample answer:* One person can harm the environment through such actions as producing unnecessary waste or polluting the air or water. One person can also help the environment by following the "three Rs" and advocating for government regulations that protect the environment.

19. Goals will vary. Each student should set a specific goal and identify specific steps that will help in achieving that goal.

Health and Community

Community Cleanup Start by discussing which areas in the community could benefit most from a cleanup. Suggest that students with similar areas of interest work together. After you review their plans, encourage students to carry out their projects. Remind them that they will need permission from the government agency that manages the park, stream, or other area of focus.

Section Objectives	Standards Correlation	Instructional Resources L3	SE eTEXT	TE eTEXT	PRINT
1 Safety at Home and in Your Community ⏱ 3 periods; 1 1/2 blocks	NHES: 1.12.5, 1.12.8, 7.12.3, 8.12.3	SE Warm-Up, p. 694	•	•	•
		SE Media Wise Internet Safety, p. 700	•	•	•
26.1.1 Describe five factors that can help you prevent unintentional injuries.		RN Note Taking Guide 26-1	•	•	•
		IB Image Bank 26-1		•	
26.1.2 Identify unintentional injuries that commonly occur in the home.		TR Practice 26-1		•	
		TR Section 26-1 Quiz		•	
26.1.3 Summarize ways to stay safe in natural disasters.					
26.1.4 Explain how to protect yourself from crime.					
2 Safety at Work and Play ⏱ 2 periods; 1 block	NHES: 1.12.5, 2.12.9, 2.12.10, 7.12.3, 8.12.2, 8.12.3, 8.12.4	SE Warm-Up, p. 702	•	•	•
		RN Note Taking Guide 26-2	•	•	•
26.2.1 Describe how occupational injuries and illnesses can be prevented.		IB Image Bank 26-6, 26-8		•	
		TR Practice 26-2		•	
26.2.2 Summarize the four basic guidelines for recreational safety.		TR Section 26-2 Quiz		•	
Analyzing Risks and Benefits ⏱ 1 period; 1/2 block	NHES: 1.12.7, 5.12.2, 5.12.5, 5.12.7	SE Practice the Skill, p. 711	•	•	•
		RN Building Health Skills 26	•	•	•
BHS.26 Demonstrate the ability to make decisions by analyzing the risks and benefits of an activity.					
3 Motor Vehicle Safety ⏱ 1 period; 1/2 block	NHES: 1.12.5, 2.12.6, 6.12.2, 6.12.3, 7.12.1, 7.12.3	SE Warm-Up, p. 712	•	•	•
		SE Technology & Health A Shocking Tool to the Rescue, p. 716	•	•	•
26.3.1 Identify the skills you need to be a safe driver.		RN Note Taking Guide 26-3	•	•	•
26.3.2 List safety rules you should follow when riding in a school bus.		TR Practice 26-3		•	
		TR Section 26-3 Quiz		•	

Chapter Review and Assessment

SE Chapter 26 Review, p. 718 L3
CTB Chapter 26 Test L2 L3 L4
SE Standardized Test Prep, p. 719 L3

PROGRAM COMPONENTS

SE Student Edition	**CTB** Computer Test Bank
TE Teacher Edition	**AUD** Audio Section Summaries
TR Teaching Resources	
RN Reading and Note Taking Guide	**DVD** Teens Talk Video Series
	VVG Video Viewing Guide
ARN Adapted Reading and Note Taking Guide	**PPT** Presentation
IB Image Bank	

Differentiated Instruction
L1 L2 L4 EL

		SE eTEXT	TE eTEXT	PRINT
ARN	Note Taking Guide 26-1 L2	•	•	
RN	Note Taking Guide 26-1 EL	•	•	•
AUD	Audio Summary 26-1 L1 L2 EL	•	•	
TE	Reteach Strategy, p. 701 L2		•	•
TR	Enrich 26-1 L4		•	
ARN	Note Taking Guide 26-2 L2	•	•	
RN	Note Taking Guide 26-2 EL	•	•	•
AUD	Audio Summary 26-2 L1 L2 EL	•	•	
TE	Reteach Strategy, p. 709 L2		•	•
TR	Enrich 26-2 L4		•	
ARN	Building Health Skills 26 L2	•	•	
RN	Building Health Skills 26 EL	•	•	•
ARN	Note Taking Guide 26-3 L2	•	•	
RN	Note Taking Guide 26-3 EL	•	•	•
AUD	Audio Summary 26-3 L1 L2 EL	•	•	
TE	Reteach Strategy, p. 715 L2		•	•
TR	Enrich 26-3 L4		•	

ABILITY LEVELS
- **L1** For students with special needs
- **L2** For less proficient readers
- **L3** For all students
- **L4** For gifted and talented students
- **EL** For English language learners

Chapter 26 Digital/Video Pathway

This alternative pathway allows you to teach this chapter's content using only the video and online materials.

Preview
DVD	Video #26 Preview
SE	Video #26 Preview Activity
VVG	Video #26 Worksheet

Playing It Safe

1
PPT	26-1 Presentation
RN/ARN	26-1 Note Taking
PPT	26-1 Section Quiz

2
PPT	26-2 Presentation
RN/ARN	26-2 Note Taking
PPT	26-2 Section Quiz

3
DVD	Video #26 Explore/Wrap-Up
VVG	Video #26 Worksheet
PPT	26-3 Presentation
RN/ARN	26-3 Note Taking
PPT	26-3 Section Quiz

Playing It Safe

Chapter Preview

Section 1 Safety at Home and in Your Community
Most events that are considered accidents can be prevented. Common unintentional injuries that occur in the home are due to falls, poisoning, suffocation, fires, electric shock, and firearms. People can prepare for or lessen the effects of natural disasters, including earthquakes, tornadoes, hurricanes, and floods. They can also prevent assault or reduce the likelihood of injury by following certain safety guidelines.

Section 2 Safety at Work and Play
Many occupational injuries and illnesses can either be prevented or made less serious by removing potential hazards from the workplace. Most recreational activities involve some degree of risk. People can protect themselves from injuries during recreational activities by following basic safety guidelines.

Making Decisions
Analyzing Risks and Benefits
Analyzing the risks and benefits of an activity can help a person determine whether an activity is worth the risk.

Section 3 Motor Vehicle Safety
To be a safe driver, a person needs to practice good driving skills and know how to respond to risky situations. When riding in a school bus or driving near a school bus, there are rules people should follow to ensure everybody's safety.

GO ONLINE
PearsonSuccessNet.com
For resources and activities for this chapter.

Preventing Injuries

1 Safety at Home and in Your Community
  • **MediaWise** Internet Safety

2 Safety at Work and Play

 Building Health Skills
  • **Making Decisions** Analyzing Risks and Benefits

3 Motor Vehicle Safety
  • **Technology & Health** A Shocking Tool to the Rescue

 GO ONLINE PearsonSuccessNet.com

TEENS Talk
VIDEO 26

Playing It Safe

Preview **Activity**

Which Activities Are Most Dangerous?

Complete this activity before you watch the video.

1. Pair up with another student. Together, list ten activities that teens do that you think carry a risk of injury.
2. On your own, rank the items in your list from most dangerous (1) to least dangerous (10).
3. Get together with your partner and compare your rankings.
4. Do you perceive the danger of certain activities differently from your partner? If so, why do you think that is the case? **WRITING**

Sensitive Issues
Some students may have had or caused a serious unintentional injury, or students may know someone who was seriously injured. Some students may have been assaulted or raped. As students learn about ways to reduce the risk of unintentional injuries, be sure to emphasize that despite taking precautions, unintentional injuries can still occur.

TEENS Talk

Playing It Safe

Video Objectives

Use this video to help students

Identify situations that pose a risk to their safety.

Describe ways to minimize their risk of injury when participating in different activities.

Practice safe behaviors in their everyday lives.

Preview **Activity**

Which Activities Are Most Dangerous?

Before watching the video, have students complete the Preview Activity. After students complete the assignment, discuss which activities students ranked as most dangerous and why. Revisit their rankings after showing the video.

693

From the Authors

Over the last decade, nonfatal injuries due to motor vehicle crashes, water and boating incidents, and poisonings have fallen steadily. Nevertheless, unintentional injuries are still the leading cause of premature death and disability among people ages 1 to 34. In addition, nonfatal assaults and rapes constitute an important cause of physical and emotional injury.

Because unintentional injuries are so common, this chapter covers safety at home and in the community, at work and at play, and on the road. The learning activities in the chapter are designed to get students thinking about how they can minimize their risk of unintentional injury. For example, the Safety Guidelines in Figure 11 on page 708 encourage students to ride recreational vehicles responsibly.

Objectives

Before class begins, write the objectives on the board. Have students copy the objectives into their notebooks at the start of class.

1. Focus

Warm-Up Myth/Fact

After students have completed the writing assignment, call on volunteers to share their ideas with the class. Then have students brainstorm a list of safe behaviors that could prevent common "accidents." Tell students that in this section they will learn about specific ways to reduce the risk of injuries that occur in the home, as a result of natural disasters, and as a result of crime.

Presentation 26-1

 *Sample answer:* I stopped my younger brother from running into a busy street to chase a ball.

⚑ Sensitive Issues

- Some students may have experienced or caused an injury at home or in the community. Explain that no matter what happened in the past, everyone can learn how to reduce the risk of unintentional injuries in the future.
- Be sensitive to the feelings of students who have experienced a natural disaster or had family members injured by a natural disaster. Stress that when a natural disaster occurs, injuries can occur through no fault of the victims.

Section 1

Objectives

- ▶ **Describe** five factors that can help you prevent unintentional injuries.
- ▶ **Identify** unintentional injuries that commonly occur in the home.
- ▶ **Summarize** ways to stay safe in natural disasters.
- ▶ **Explain** how to protect yourself from crime.

Vocabulary

- unintentional injury
- flammable material
- electrocution
- assault
- rape
- stalker

Safety at Home and in Your Community

Warm-Up

Myth Accidents just happen. There's nothing you can do to prevent them.

Fact Most "accidents" result from risky behaviors. They do not just happen. Many can be prevented by practicing safe behaviors or by removing hazards from the environment.

WRITING Do you think most people behave in ways to prevent injuries? Why or why not?

What Are Unintentional Injuries?

You are probably more familiar with the term *accident* than *unintentional injury*. To many people, the word *accident* refers to an event that cannot be predicted or prevented. In fact, most events that are considered accidents can be prevented.

This chapter uses the term *unintentional injury* instead of *accident* to make you aware that it is often possible to prevent injuries. An **unintentional injury** is an unplanned injury. **Five factors that can help prevent unintentional injuries or lessen their damage are awareness, knowledge, ability, state of mind, and environmental conditions.**

▶ **Awareness and Knowledge** Recognizing risks to your safety and knowing what actions to take can reduce the risk of unintentional injury.

▶ **Ability** Be realistic when you judge your abilities and those of others.

▶ **State of Mind** Be aware of your own condition and that of others. A person who is tired, rushed, distressed, or under the influence of drugs or alcohol is more likely to be injured or to cause injury to others.

▶ **Environmental Conditions** Consider the hazards in your environment that might cause an injury. For example, if the floor has just been mopped, do not run across it when the telephone rings.

Connect to Your Life Describe a situation in which you prevented an unintentional injury.

For Your INFORMATION!

Adolescent Risk Taking

Recent studies of the brain using magnetic resonance imaging (MRI) have shown that there are structural changes in the brain that occur during adolescence. In an adult, there is more activity in the part of the brain that controls emotions and impulses and makes decisions about right and wrong. In an adolescent, the part of the brain that influences emotions and gut reactions is more active. The result is that adolescents often have a more emotional response to situations than adults have.

Teens should be aware that their natural response to a situation may be more emotional than rational. They need to make sure to think clearly about the risks of an action in order to prevent injuries.

Injuries in the Home

One third of all unintentional injuries occur in the home. **Some common causes of unintentional injuries in the home are due to falls, poisoning, suffocation, fires, electric shock, and firearms.** Unfortunately, many of these injuries happen to young children. Figure 1 lists some guidelines for preventing injuries when you are caring for young children.

Falls Hazards in the home can cause anyone to fall. The main factor in avoiding falls is to consider environmental conditions.

► Make sure stairways have nonslip treads and strong railings. Keep stairs and walkways uncluttered and well lit.

► Make sure floors are not slippery, clear them of small objects, and anchor all carpets and rugs firmly.

► Equip bathtubs and showers with grab bars and nonskid rubber mats.

► Keep outdoor steps and sidewalks in good repair and free of ice, leaves, toys, and other obstacles.

Poisoning Most poisoning incidents involve children under the age of five. A local poison control center can tell you what household substances are poisonous and what to do in the event of a poisoning.

Another form of poisoning is carbon monoxide poisoning. Carbon monoxide is a colorless, odorless gas that is produced by vehicles and fuel-burning appliances. If garages or appliances are not vented or functioning properly, carbon monoxide can build up and cause severe illness or even death. It is recommended that people install carbon monoxide detectors near furnaces and in every sleeping area of a home.

FIGURE 1 When caring for a young child, it is important to take many precautions.

Caring for Young Children

Preventing Falls	Preventing Poisoning	Preventing Suffocation
► Never leave a baby alone on a table or other raised surface.	► Keep medications, household cleaners, cosmetics, and alcohol out of reach.	► Do not let children put small toys or other objects in their mouths.
► Use safety gates at the bottom and top of stairs.	► Keep hazardous substances in a locked cabinet.	► Cut food into small pieces.
► Do not allow children to sit on windowsills or lean against screens.	► Do not let children chew or swallow leaves from houseplants.	► Keep plastic bags, cords, and scarves away from children.
► Keep children away from decks or porches without railings.	► Carefully follow the directions for giving a child medication.	► Make sure bedding and clothing do not interfere with a child's breathing.
	► If you suspect a poisoning, call a poison control center immediately.	

Preventing Injuries **695**

---

2. Teach

L3 EL **Reading/Note Taking 26-1**

L2 **Adapted Reading/Note Taking 26-1**

What Are Unintentional Injuries?

L3 Class Discussion

Have students brainstorm a list of hazards that are common in the home. (They might mention loose carpeting, faulty electrical outlets, or poisonous substances within reach of children.) List students' ideas on the board. For each hazard, call on a volunteer to explain how one or more of the five factors—awareness, knowledge, ability, state of mind, and environmental conditions—could prevent unintentional injuries or lessen their damage.

Injuries in the Home

L2 Visual Learning: Figure 1

Image Bank Figure 26-1

After students have read the precautions for preventing falls, poisoning, and suffocation, make sure they understand the reasoning behind each precaution. For example, ask: **Why should you not let children chew leaves from houseplants?** *(The leaves might contain a poisonous substance that could make a child sick.)* **Why should you cut food into small pieces?** *(Large pieces of food might get stuck in the child's windpipe and cause suffocation.)* Call on volunteers to relate experiences that involved potential falls, poisonings, or suffocation.

L1 Building Health Skills

Accessing Information Before class, visit the Web site of the American Association of Poison Control Centers (AAPCC). This is a nationwide organization that maintains poison centers in every state. Using the Web site, find the location of the nearest poison center. In class, explain that the AAPCC has a phone number that operates 24 hours a day in all states: 1-800-222-1222. When a person calls this number, the call is routed to the nearest poison control center. An operator at that center can help in a poisoning emergency. Post the poison control number on a bulletin board, and advise students to post the number in a prominent place at home.

EL Building Vocabulary

Point out that the words *flammable* and *inflammable* have the same meaning—"able to catch fire." Explain that in formal writing, the word *inflammable* is preferred. There is a problem with that word, though. The prefix *in-* means "not" in most cases, and so some people might think that *inflammable* actually means "not able to catch fire." In this case, the prefix *in-* simply means "in" or "within." As a result of the confusion, the word *flammable* is often used to ensure clarity. The term for a material that does not catch fire is *nonflammable*.

L3 Cultural Connection

Tell students that the risk of death or injury from fire is not the same for everyone in the United States. Point out that the very old—people over 85—are almost five times more likely to die of fire than the general population. Ask: **Why would the very old have more of a risk?** *(Sample answer: Older people often cannot move quickly enough to escape a fire.)* Point out that African Americans and Native Americans have a much higher risk of dying in a fire than other Americans. Experts think the greater risk has to do with social factors such as poverty.

Suffocation When a person's supply of air is cut off, the result is suffocation. Suffocation can be caused by choking when an object gets caught in the breathing passages, by smothering, or by being trapped in an enclosed space. Suffocation can result in death.

Fires and Burns The seven most common causes of household fires are careless cooking, smoking, faulty or overloaded electrical wiring, unsafe heating units, improperly used fireplaces, children playing with matches, and improper storage of flammable materials. **Flammable materials** catch fire easily and burn quickly. Figure 2 lists some ways of reducing the risks of fire in your home. Most areas have 911 emergency calling, which you should use in case of a fire.

▶ If a small fire starts on the stove, put it out with a fire extinguisher.

▶ Never use water on a grease fire. Water causes the fire to spread.

▶ If a small fire begins to get out of control, leave immediately and alert other residents to the danger.

▶ If your home is on fire, leave immediately. If there is a lot of smoke, crawl along the floor to the nearest exit. Do not pause to collect any belongings. Your life is more important.

▶ Once you are outside, do not go back in. Go to a neighbor's house or to the nearest fire-alarm box and alert the fire department.

▶ If a person catches fire, roll the person on the ground, in a rug, or in a heavy coat to cut off the air the fire needs.

FIGURE 2 Fires can be prevented if you take the time to reduce the risks in your home.

Reducing Fire Risks

▶ Install smoke detectors on each floor of your home.
▶ Practice a fire escape plan.
▶ Keep fire extinguishers in the kitchen and garage.
▶ Make sure electrical outlets are not overloaded.
▶ Replace frayed or cracked appliance cords.
▶ Discourage smokers from smoking in bed.
▶ Keep matches and lighters out of reach of small children.
▶ Store flammable materials in fireproof containers.

696 *Chapter 26*

For Your INFORMATION!

Fire Facts

The U.S. Fire Administration (USFA) is the federal agency that coordinates fire protection throughout the country. The agency published these facts about fires in the United States in 2011.

• Fire killed more Americans than those killed by all natural disasters combined.

• 2,450 civilians (non-firefighters) died and 13,900 were injured as a result of fire.

• 76 percent of civilian fire-related injuries occurred in people's homes.

• 83 firefighters were killed while on duty.

• Direct property loss because of fires was estimated to be $6.7 billion.

Electric Shock   Electricity and faulty or misused equipment pose other risks. Make sure that your home is properly wired. Keep all home appliances in good repair, and know how to use them safely. Never try to repair an electric appliance when it is plugged in.

Death from direct contact with electricity is called **electrocution** (ih lek truh KYOO shun). To prevent electrocution, keep young children away from electrical outlets. Place safety covers over unused electrical outlets. Never use appliances when you are wet or near water.

Firearms   Each year about 600 people are unintentionally killed in the home by firearms. Many of the deaths occur among young people between the ages of 10 and 19. To prevent unintentional injuries and deaths, firearms should be kept unloaded and locked in a place where children cannot reach them. Ammunition should be locked in a separate place. Do not handle firearms if you have not been trained in their use.

Natural Disasters

Disasters are sudden, catastrophic events that affect many people. Disasters may result from human error or from a natural event. Oil spills and train derailments are examples of disasters caused by humans. **Earthquakes, tornadoes, hurricanes, floods, blizzards, and many forest fires are examples of natural disasters.**

How can you prepare for disasters or lessen their effects on you and your family? Figure 3 lists some questions that can help you evaluate how prepared your family is for a disaster. If a disaster occurs in your area, follow the instructions given over the Emergency Alert System (EAS) on your radio or television.

FIGURE 3 Being prepared for a disaster requires you to collect certain supplies. **Evaluating** What other supplies might be important to have in case of a natural disaster?

Connect to Your Life   What can your family do to be better prepared for a disaster?

Are You Prepared for a Disaster?

► Does your family have a first-aid kit?
► Do you have flashlights and fresh batteries?
► Do you have a battery-powered radio?
► Do you have a two-week supply of bottled water?
► Do you have a supply of canned foods?
► Do you know how to turn off your home's gas, electricity, and water?
► Is your vehicle's gas tank always at least half full?

Preventing Injuries   **697**

L3 Cooperative Learning

Divide the class into small groups. Ask students to imagine they have just been hired as home safety inspectors, and their supervisor has asked each group to develop a checklist of common hazards in the home. After all groups have created their checklists, allow students to review other groups' checklists and make changes to their own. Encourage students to take their checklists home and inspect their own living areas for potential hazards.

Natural Disasters

L2 Visual Learning: Figure 3

Call on students to read aloud the questions about being prepared for a disaster. Ask: **Why would you need flashlights and fresh batteries?** *(A disaster might disrupt electrical service, and a flashlight would be the only light the family has.)* **Why would you need a supply of canned goods?** *(If there is no electricity, the refrigerator won't work. Food in cans doesn't need to be refrigerated.)* **Why would you need to know how to turn off your home's gas, electricity, and water?** *(The disaster might cause breaks in gas lines, electrical lines, or water pipes. For safety, these utilities might need to be turned off.)*

Caption Answer *Sample answer:* a cell phone, proper clothing for the weather, and a portable camp stove

Connect to Your Life   *Sample answer:* We could collect supplies, such as a first-aid kit, flashlights and batteries, bottled water, and canned foods.

Differentiated Instruction

L1 Special Needs

Although some students may have experienced a natural disaster, few students will have experienced all the types of disasters discussed in the text. To help students comprehend each type of natural disaster, provide a variety of visual resources, including photographic books, nature magazines, news magazines, videotapes, and CD-ROMs.

L4 Gifted and Talented

Encourage interested students to research building codes and architectural designs for earthquake-proof buildings. Have them compare the damage done to non-earthquake-proof buildings in developing countries such as Pakistan to earthquake-proof buildings in San Francisco. Encourage students to write a report that can be shared with the class. **WRITING**

L2 **Visual Learning: Figure 4**

After students have read about hurricane facts and examined the photos, ask: **How are hurricanes rated?** (*on a scale of 1 to 5, from least severe to most severe*) Explain that this rating is based on how strong the winds are and that a hurricane rated 5 is called a category 5 hurricane. Point out that a hurricane's category can change from day to day. For example, hurricane Katrina was a category 5 hurricane, but its winds slowed down before it reached land, and then it was a category 4 hurricane. Ask: **Should people be fearful of only category 5 hurricanes?** (*no, because weaker hurricanes can also cause tremendous damage*)

L3 **Addressing Misconceptions**

Inland Flooding When most people think of hurricanes, they think about strong winds being the most threatening part. Hurricane winds are powerful and can do a great deal of damage. However, the greatest threat of a hurricane is inland flooding. Over the past 30 years, inland flooding has accounted for over half the deaths in the United States caused by hurricanes. Often, a hurricane contains a tremendous amount of water, and places far inland can be devastated by floods as the hurricane moves over land. According to the National Hurricane Center, when you hear *hurricane*, think "inland flooding." This kind of inland flooding from Hurricane Katrina is what caused the catastrophe in New Orleans in 2005, which resulted in large numbers of New Orleans neighborhoods being destroyed.

Hurricane Facts

▶ Hurricanes are rated on a scale of 1 (least severe) to 5 (most severe).

▶ Hurricanes develop from tropical storms over the ocean.

▶ A hurricane is named according to the tropical storm from which it developed. Tropical storms are named in alphabetical order and alternate between male and female names.

▶ In the Atlantic Ocean, hurricane season lasts from June 1 through November 30.

FIGURE 4 In 2005, hurricane Katrina caused damage in states along the Gulf Coast.

Satellite Image of Katrina

Fort Lauderdale, Florida

698 *Chapter 26*

Earthquakes An earthquake is a sudden shaking of the ground caused by the movement of rock beneath Earth's surface. If you are indoors during an earthquake, stand under the frame of an interior door or crawl under a table or desk. Stay away from windows, glass doors, heavy hanging objects, or furniture that might tip over. If you are outside, stay in the open, away from buildings, walls, and electrical wires. If you are driving, pull over and stop. After a major earthquake, turn off the gas and electricity in your home to prevent a gas leak or fire.

Tornadoes A tornado is a rapidly rotating column of air whirling at speeds of up to 500 miles per hour. Tornadoes are fairly common in the central and southern United States. If you are caught outdoors during a tornado, move away from the tornado at right angles to its path. If the tornado is too close for you to escape, find shelter or lie flat in a low place in the ground. If you are at home, go to the lowest floor of your home. Keep some windows open to equalize pressure, but stay away from them. If you live in a mobile home, go to a tornado shelter.

Hurricanes A hurricane is a powerful storm characterized by heavy rains and winds over 74 miles per hour. If you hear that a hurricane is coming, place tape across windows and board them up. Anchor or bring inside any furniture or other items outside your home. Hurricane-force winds can knock down power lines. Avoid contact with downed power lines. If local authorities tell you to evacuate, seek shelter elsewhere.

One of the most serious hurricanes to hit the United States in recent years was hurricane Katrina. Katrina struck the United States Gulf Coast in the summer of 2005. Figure 4 shows some of the devastation that Katrina caused, including severe flooding in New Orleans, Louisiana.

WRITING and Health

L3 **Firsthand Account**

Ask students to suppose that they are at home when a natural disaster is imminent or occurring. Allow students to choose any type of natural disaster, even if it is not common in their part of the country. Have them write a first-person story about the experience. Explain that the story should be creative and interesting and also contain accurate information about the natural disaster, how to prepare for it, and how to prevent injuries as it occurs. Encourage volunteers to share their completed stories with the class.

Floods In 2005, New Orleans, Louisiana, experienced some of the worst flooding ever to occur in the United States. The flooding resulted from levees that broke after hurricane Katrina struck the Gulf Coast. The city had to be evacuated because lack of food and clean water and contaminated floodwaters posed serious health threats to residents.

In the event of any flood, you should turn off your home's water, gas, and electricity and move your belongings to the highest floor before leaving home. When you are able to return home, discard any liquids or foods touched by floodwaters. Drink bottled water until local authorities tell you that the tap water is safe.

Most floods can be predicted, but a flash flood can occur suddenly, without warning, after a heavy rainfall or snowmelt. Check the history of your area to find out if there is a risk of flash flooding. If your area is at risk, find out where you should go if an evacuation is ordered.

Blizzards A blizzard is defined as a heavy snowstorm, with winds of at least 35 miles per hour, that lasts for three hours or more. These conditions usually result in very low visibility. Generally, the safest place to be during a blizzard is inside your home or other warm shelter. If you have a problem requiring special treatment, alert local authorities so that you can be evacuated safely from your home. Do not try to go out on your own.

Forest Fires Some forest fires are caused by humans, but others are the result of natural occurrences, such as lightning. Fire often serves an important "clean up" role in forests. But when fires spread near human communities, they can be very dangerous. It is important to pay attention to local authorities when they tell you to evacuate an area at risk for fire.

 **Connect to Your Life** Do you live in an area at high risk for certain natural disasters? Which ones?

Long Beach, Mississippi

New Orleans, Louisiana

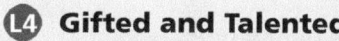

 **GO ONLINE** **PLANETDIARY**
PearsonSuccessNet.com
For: More on hurricanes

L3 **Online Activity**  **GO ONLINE** **PLANETDIARY**

Visit Pearson SuccessNet to access an online activity about hurricanes. Have students complete the Web activity.

L2 **Building Health Skills**

Practicing Healthful Behaviors Tell students that it is important for them to know how to react when a natural disaster occurs. Divide the class into small groups, and assign each group one of the natural disasters discussed in the text. Each group should put together a plan for what people should do in case their disaster occurs. Students may use the text and other online or library sources to put together a comprehensive plan. If one of the natural disasters could occur in your area, have that group include specific information about local radio and television stations that broadcast emergency information. Students in that group may also choose to contact local authorities for their recommendations about what to do in case of a disaster. Have groups make posters of their plans.

L2 **Cooperative Learning**

Ask students to determine which type of natural disaster is most common in their area. Then have small groups research and create a handbook that shows how the disaster is forecast, how the community is warned, what precautions people should take in advance of the natural disaster, and how a community can recover from the disaster. Have groups share their handbooks with other classes. **WRITING**

Connect to Your Life Students should list kinds of natural disasters that are common in their region of the country.

Differentiated Instruction

L4 **Gifted and Talented**

Hurricane Katrina was perhaps the most destructive natural disaster in the history of the United States. Ask interested students to use library and online resources to do research about the effects of Katrina in the states along the Gulf Coast. Encourage them to find out why Katrina was so devastating for New Orleans and how much damage the hurricane did to other areas of Louisiana as well as parts of Mississippi and Alabama. Also ask students to find out what the lasting effects have been for the people of the Gulf Coast in the years since the hurricane hit. Have students share their findings in a presentation to the class.

Protecting Yourself From Crime

Media Wise

Internet Safety

Have students take the survey about Internet safety, and ask: **Why is refusing to meet face-to-face with someone you've met on the Internet a wise practice?** *(Sample answer: The person might not be anything like what you think he or she will be, and you could be setting yourself up for an assault.)* Discuss with students how easy it is to misrepresent oneself online. A "nice guy" online could turn out to be just the opposite in person.

Activity Point out that a 30-second announcement is brief—maybe 30 to 40 words. A good PSA might have even fewer words, with time for pauses and music. Emphasize that the music must be appropriate in some way to the message. If possible, have students record their PSAs.

L3 Addressing Misconceptions

Rape Some people think that a women who has been raped "asked" for it. They may comment on what she was wearing or how she flirted with the assailant. Emphasize that no one "asks" to be raped, and that a victim's appearance, behavior, or history should not be used to excuse a rapist. Note that rapists often target people who appear vulnerable, not people who dress or act in a certain way.

L2 Journal Writing

Ask students to write an entry in their private journals in which they describe specific ways they can prevent being assaulted or raped. (They might list people they could tell before going out for an evening, or they could describe what to do if their car breaks down at night.) In addition to their own entries, encourage the boys in class to write a list of tips they could share with female family members or friends. **WRITING**

Media Wise

Internet Safety

The Internet can be a valuable resource for all kinds of information. Unfortunately, it can sometimes prove to be a dangerous place. Use this questionnaire to determine if you protect yourself adequately on the Internet.

Do you refuse to give out personal information, such as your address, phone number, or photos, on the Internet? **Yes** **No**

Do you refuse to meet face-to-face with anyone you have met on the Internet? **Yes** **No**

Do you send messages only to people you already know? **Yes** **No**

Do you stay away from sites that try to convince you to join or give money to questionable organizations? **Yes** **No**

Do you sign off if you feel uncomfortable in a chat room? **Yes** **No**

"Yes" answers indicate wise practices for protecting yourself on the Internet.

Activity Create a 30-second public service announcement about Internet safety for teens. Use a slogan or music to get your message across. **WRITING**

Protecting Yourself From Crime

Unfortunately, some injuries are intentional. Some, for example, are the result of crime. An **assault** is an unlawful attempt or threat to harm someone. An assault can lead to intentional injuries or death.

Rape and Stalking One type of assault that is both physically and psychologically painful is rape. **Rape** means that one person forces another to have sexual relations. Most rapes are acquaintance rapes—rapes carried out by someone the victim knows.

It is hard to tell if a person might be a potential rapist, but it is important to trust your judgment. If you feel that you might be in danger, you probably are. However, feeling "safe" with someone does not mean that you are safe. Always let a family member or friend know where you are going and when you will return home. If someone tries to rape you, do whatever you need to do to protect your life.

All rape victims should seek medical treatment immediately. Reporting a rape is not easy. Most police departments, however, have police officers who specialize in helping rape victims.

A **stalker** is someone who makes repeated, unwanted contact with a person and may threaten to kill or injure the person. If you are stalked, notify the police. Laws can help protect you from a stalker.

TEENS *Are Asking . . .*

Q: Is date rape the same thing as acquaintance rape? How can I prevent acquaintance rape?

A: Acquaintance rape is a rape in which the victim knows the attacker. Date rape is one type of acquaintance rape. The most likely victims of acquaintance rape are girls and women. But boys and men can be raped, too. Here are some tips to prevent acquaintance rape.

- Abstain from alcohol and drugs. Many acquaintance rapes involve alcohol or drugs.
- Avoid secluded places when you're with someone you don't know very well. This includes your room or a friend's room.
- Trust your own feelings. If something doesn't seem right, get away fast.

Avoiding Risky Situations You can prevent assault or reduce the likelihood of injury by following certain safety guidelines. The most basic guideline is to avoid risky situations.

▶ Lock all doors and windows when you are home alone. Never allow a stranger inside. Never let a caller know you are alone.

▶ Do not keep keys in an obvious place, such as under a doormat.

▶ Avoid deserted places, such as dark streets, parks, and garages. If you cannot avoid them, make sure you walk with a friend.

▶ Stay away from dark doorways and hedges where an attacker could hide. If someone follows you, step into the nearest business.

▶ When driving, keep the car doors locked. Always be sure to park in a well-lit place. Before getting back into your car, always check to make sure no one is hiding in the back seat or on the floor.

▶ Do not hitchhike or pick up hitchhikers.

▶ If your car breaks down, pull over, raise your hood, and turn on your emergency flashers. If a stranger stops to help, do not unlock your car door. Just ask the person to call the police.

▶ If someone tries to rob you, give up your possessions. They are not as important as your life.

▶ If you see a crime in progress, call the police immediately. Do not try to intervene, especially if weapons could be involved.

Protecting Yourself From Rape

Stay away from people who

• act strangely and make you uncomfortable.

• pay no attention to you when you say *no* or *stop*.

• try to touch you when you do not want to be touched.

• push you to do things you do not want to do.

FIGURE 5 Both males and females of all ages are potential victims of rape. Rapists look for people who appear vulnerable.

Section 1 Review

Key Ideas and Vocabulary

1. What is an **unintentional injury?**

2. Name five factors that can help you prevent unintentional injuries. Why is each factor important?

3. List six types of unintentional injuries that occur in the home.

4. What is **electrocution?**

5. How can you be prepared for earthquakes? For tornadoes?

6. What is the single best way to protect yourself from crime? Explain.

Critical Thinking

7. Applying Concepts What changes would you make in your home to ensure a one-year-old's safety during a visit?

Health and Community

Crime Prevention Programs Find out what kinds of crime prevention organizations are at work in your community. For example, some communities form Neighborhood Crime Watch groups that report suspicious activities to the police. Create a poster encouraging community members to get involved in one of the organizations you learned about. **WRITING**

8. Making Judgments Suppose you have a weekend job at a restaurant about three miles from your house. You need to drive home alone at night. What precautions should you take?

 GO ONLINE PearsonSuccessNet.com Audio Summary Section 26.1

Preventing Injuries **701**

3. Assess

Evaluate

These assignments can help you assess students' mastery of the section content.

Section 1 Review

Answers appear below.

Teaching Resources

• Practice 26-1
• Section 26-1 Quiz

L2 Reteach

Work with students to make an outline of section content. Begin the outline with the major headings, and leave room for students to add subheadings and important details. Have students work with a partner to complete the outline. Suggest that students use their completed outlines when they review section content.

L4 Enrich

Teaching Resources
• Enrich 26-1

Health and Community

Crime Prevention Programs
Encourage students to search for local crime prevention organizations and programs by using a local phone book or online resources. If none can be found through such searches, have volunteers contact the local police department and ask about the names and phone numbers of local organizations that sponsor crime prevention programs. After students have learned about local organizations, divide the class into small groups, and have each group create a poster.

Section 1 Review

1. an unplanned injury

2. Students should explain the importance of each of these factors: awareness, knowledge, ability, state of mind, and environmental conditions.

3. injuries due to falls, poisoning, suffocation, fires, electric shock, and firearms

4. death from direct contact with electricity

5. Being prepared requires a person to collect the supplies listed in Figure 3. Students should also demonstrate knowledge of the tips given in the text for what to do in case of an earthquake or tornado.

6. avoid risky situations; students' explanations should reflect an understanding of the importance of prevention.

7. Students should mention some of the precautions listed in Figure 1.

8. *Sample answer:* I would park in a well-lit place. Before getting into the car, I would check to make sure no one is hiding in the back seat or on the floor. When driving, I would keep the doors locked.

Objectives
Before class begins, write the objectives on the board. Have students copy the objectives into their notebooks at the start of class.

1. Focus

Warm-Up Quick Quiz

Use the Warm-Up Presentation slide to survey student responses.

After all students have finished writing, lead a discussion on how being prepared adequately for an activity can prevent unintentional injuries.

Presentation 26-2

Connect to Your Life *Sample answer:* I work in a fast-food restaurant where there are gas burners and hot grease.

Objectives

▶ **Describe** how occupational injuries and illnesses can be prevented.

▶ **Summarize** the four basic guidelines for recreational safety.

Vocabulary

• occupational injury
• occupational illness
• survival floating
• active supervision
• capsizing

Warm-Up

Quick Quiz Complete each of these statements with *always, sometimes,* or *never.*

① I __?__ bring plenty of drinking water when I go hiking or camping.

② I __?__ wear a personal flotation device when participating in water sports.

③ I __?__ wear appropriate protective gear when playing sports.

④ I __?__ wear a helmet when skateboarding or riding a bicycle.

WRITING For each of your responses, predict how your behavior may affect your risk of injury.

Occupational Safety

Many unintentional injuries occur at work. Although you are not working full time yet, you probably will be some day. You may already be working at an after-school job. You should know about the possible hazards of the workplace and what you can do to protect yourself.

The Occupational Safety and Health Administration (OSHA) is the federal agency that identifies workplace hazards and sets standards for safety. Both employers and workers are responsible for following OSHA regulations.

OSHA defines an **occupational injury** as any wound or damage to the body that results from an event in the work environment. OSHA defines an **occupational illness** as any abnormal condition or disorder caused by exposure to the work environment. **Many occupational injuries and illnesses can either be prevented or made less serious by removing potential hazards from the workplace.** Figure 6 gives information about some occupations that are especially hazardous.

Connect to Your Life Do you have an after-school job? What kinds of hazards are present in your work environment?

 and Health

L3 Averages

Point to the number of teens who get hurt on the job badly enough to require a hospital visit. Ask: **If 146,000 teens report occupational injuries each year, what is the average daily rate of teen occupational injury?** *(146,000 ÷ 365 = 400 teen occupational injuries a day, on average.)*

Teen Workers Many teens in the United States work after school and during the summer. Unfortunately, over 80 teens die each year from occupational injuries. These injuries often result from motor vehicle crashes, electrocution, or falls on the job. In a recent year over 146,000 teens reported occupational injuries. It is the responsibility of your employer to keep your workplace as safe as possible and to inform you of any on-the-job hazards. It is your responsibility to be well rested and alert, to be sober, and to follow all safety procedures.

Farm Safety Over a million teens in the United States work on farms. Farm jobs have the highest rate of injuries and deaths of all types of teen employment. When working on a farm, it is important to be properly trained on equipment and to use common sense.

▶ If you have to drive a truck or tractor, be sure that someone teaches you how it works and how to stop it and turn it off.

▶ Never drive a vehicle or operate a piece of machinery if you are not comfortable doing so.

▶ Never operate equipment under the influence of alcohol or other drugs.

▶ If you work around animals, approach them so that they can see you. A startled animal can be dangerous and may kick or charge.

▶ Avoid direct contact with pesticides and other chemicals. If you come into contact with a chemical, call a poison control center.

▶ Dress appropriately for farm work. Wear sturdy shoes, and avoid baggy clothing that could get caught in machinery. Tie back long hair.

▶ Wear goggles and earplugs to protect your eyes and ears. Wear sunscreen to protect your skin.

▲ A teen working on a farm

FIGURE 6 Some jobs carry a greater risk of fatal injury than others. **Reading Graphs** Which job shown here has the highest death rate? The lowest death rate?

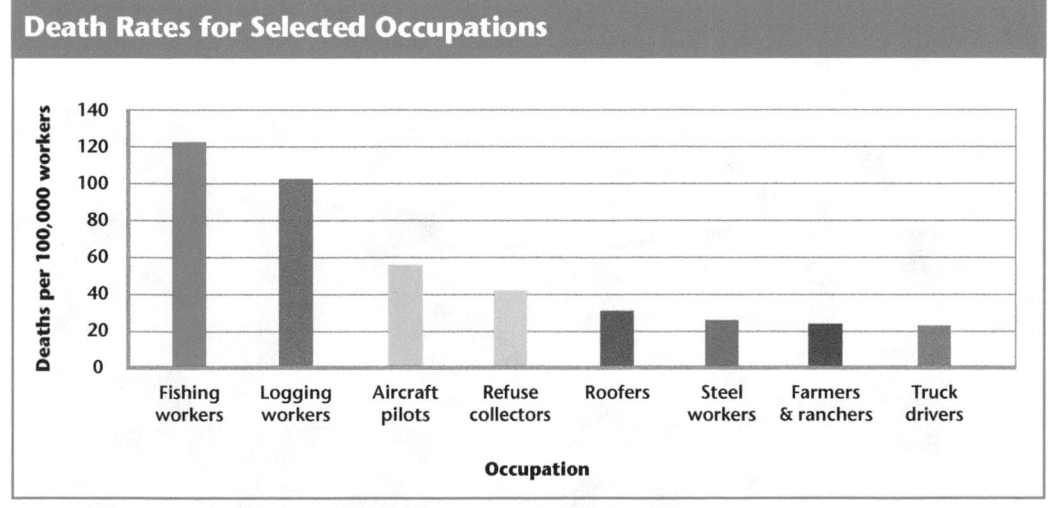

Death Rates for Selected Occupations

Deaths per 100,000 workers

Occupation: Fishing workers, Logging workers, Aircraft pilots, Refuse collectors, Roofers, Steel workers, Farmers & ranchers, Truck drivers

Preventing Injuries **703**

2. Teach

L3 EL Reading/Note Taking 26-2
L2 Adapted Reading/Note Taking 26-2

Occupational Safety

L2 Building Vocabulary
Explain that *occupational* is the adjective form of *occupation,* a word that comes from the Latin for "occupy." A person's occupation, then, is what occupies most of his or her time during a work day. A good synonym for *occupational* is *workplace.* Ask: **What could be another name for the Occupational Safety and Health Administration?** *(the Workplace Safety and Health Administration)*

L3 Visual Learning: Figure 6
Image Bank Figure 26-6
After students have examined the bar graph, ask: **What is the death rate for truck drivers?** *(about 24 deaths per 100,000 workers)* **What workplace hazards might cause the death of agricultural workers?** *(Sample answer: the operation of tractors and other machinery)* Point out that many jobs in today's work environment do not have the workplace hazards that hard-labor jobs such as logging and construction do. Yet, there are hazards that cause occupational injuries even in office jobs. Ask: **How could you get injured by working on a computer all day?** *(Sample answer: You could suffer from a repetitive motion injury such as carpal tunnel syndrome, or you could have eye strain.)*
Caption Answer Logging workers have the highest death rate; grounds workers have the lowest death rate.

L3 Active Learning
Have students interview an adult who works in a job they might like to do in the future. Tell students to ask the person about hazards on the job, including machinery hazards, stress, or repetitive motion injuries such as carpal tunnel syndrome. Ask the students to share their findings with the class.

Recreational Safety

L2 Class Discussion

Call on students to generate a list of favorite recreational activities. *(soccer, bike riding, dancing, and so on)* Write these activities on the board. Then, choose an activity such as soccer and call on volunteers to apply the four basic safety guidelines to that activity. Ask: **How can "learn and apply the proper skills" be applied to playing soccer?** *(Sample answer: You learn how to dribble, pass, and shoot the ball with your feet.)* Continue this process with each of the four basic guidelines, and then do the same with another activity.

L3 Cooperative Learning

After students have read the list of first-aid supplies for camping in Figure 7, ask volunteers to bring in items from home to make a first-aid kit. Coordinate what students contribute to avoid duplication. If no one has a first-aid manual, ask a volunteer to borrow one from the library. You may want to supply empty packages of the medications on the list. Gather the items for display in the classroom.

L2 Building Health Skills

Analyzing Influences Ask students if they think their friends are, in general, good influences when it comes to recreational safety. Ask volunteers to give examples (without mentioning names) of how their friends have influenced their behavior when camping, swimming, boating, or playing sports. Ask: **Did your friends encourage you to act more or less safely?** *(Sample answer: My friends made fun of me for wanting to wear a life vest when we went canoeing.)* Lead a discussion on how students can respond to friends who do not encourage safe behaviors. Write some effective strategies on the board.

Recreational Safety

Almost everyone enjoys some kind of recreational activity. And most recreational activities involve some degree of risk. **Whatever recreational activities you enjoy, you should follow four basic safety guidelines.**

▶ Learn and apply the proper skills.

▶ Have appropriate, well-maintained equipment.

▶ Know the safety rules specific to the activity.

▶ Prepare adequately for the activity.

Safety When Hiking and Camping Hiking and camping are great forms of exercise, but these activities also present safety risks.

▶ Always let someone know where you are going and when you expect to return home. Never hike or camp alone.

▶ Find out about any potential dangers, such as bears, ticks, or poisonous snakes and plants.

▶ Take along a first-aid kit. Figure 7 lists some supplies that should be included in a first-aid kit. Know how to respond to hazardous situations, such as snakebites or skin infections.

▶ Check the weather forecast, and dress appropriately. Layers are best when days are warm and nights are cool. Wear proper footwear.

▶ Wear sunscreen and a hat. Bring insect repellent if necessary.

▶ Be sure to take plenty of food and water. In your camp area, stow food and garbage in your car or up in a tree so as not to attract animals.

▶ Hike and camp only in approved areas. Follow campsite rules.

▶ Cook in a protected area so that sparks will not start a fire. Put a campfire out completely with water or dirt.

FIGURE 7 It is important to be prepared for outdoor conditions when hiking or camping.

First-Aid Supplies for Camping

- First-aid manual
- Sterile gloves
- Sterile bandages and gauze
- Antiseptic wipes and antibiotic ointment
- Burn ointment
- Calamine lotion
- Moleskin for blisters
- Pain reliever
- Anti-diarrhea medicine
- Scissors and tweezers
- Thermometer
- Instant cold pack
- Blanket

TEENS *Are Asking . . .*

Q: My family goes camping at least once a year. After reading about camping safety, I realize we haven't taken most of these safety precautions. What should I do?

A: The next time your family plans a camping trip, write down a few suggestions and present them to your parents. With your advice, they may decide to work with you in reducing safety risks. If not, take charge of some of the precautions yourself. For instance, you can put together a first-aid kit and check the weather forecast for the area where you'll be camping. At the campsite, you can teach your family how to store food and garbage in a way that does not attract animals.

FIGURE 8 Survival floating techniques allow a nonswimmer to stay afloat until help arrives. **Making Judgments** Should children be required to learn this technique? Why or why not?

Survival Floating

1. Inhale and Rest
- Take a breath and hold it.
- Put your face in the water.
- Let your arms and legs dangle.
- Rest.

2. Exhale
- Tilt your head back so your mouth clears the water.
- Press your arms and legs down to help raise your head out of the water.
- Exhale.
- Repeat step 1.

Water Safety Over 3,000 unintentional drownings occur ever year in the United States. Drownings can occur in bathtubs, hot tubs, swimming pools, lakes, rivers, and oceans. Most drownings are preventable if you follow certain precautions.

▶ Take swimming lessons. Even if you never learn how to swim, however, you should know how to protect yourself from drowning. Figure 8 shows **survival floating,** a lifesaving technique that allows you to float and breathe without using much energy.

▶ Never drink alcohol or use other drugs when you're going to be swimming.

▶ Never swim alone or in unsupervised areas.

▶ Never dive into water of unknown depth. Doing so could result in serious injuries, including spinal cord injuries.

▶ Pay attention to beach warning flags. If you are caught in a rip current, a current that pulls you away from shore, swim parallel to the shore.

▶ Use only battery-powered radios around a pool or hot tub to prevent electrocution. Never go in the water during a thunderstorm.

▶ If you are on an ice-covered body of water and the ice starts to crack, immediately lie down and crawl to shore.

Drowning is the second-leading cause of injury-related deaths among children ages 1 to 14. Pools should have fences around them with self-latching gates to keep children from getting in unsupervised. If you are watching children around water, you must actively supervise them. **Active supervision** means that you keep children in your view at all times when they are in or near the water. Do not engage in other distracting behaviors, and stay close to the water in case you are needed.

Connect to Your Life What would you tell someone who has never had swimming lessons?

Preventing Injuries **705**

L1 Teacher Demo

Bring a life jacket to class for students to examine. Ask: **What is this called?** *(a personal flotation device, or PFD)* **Why should you always wear a PFD when you're in a boat?** *(Sample answer: You may need a PFD if the boat capsizes.)* **Would you still need a PFD if you're a great swimmer?** *(Sample answer: Even a great swimmer may need a PFD if the weather is bad, if the boat capsizes far from shore, or if the swimmer is injured.)*

L3 Cooperative Learning

Have students work together in groups to create a brochure explaining how to operate a boat safely. Brochures should cover how to operate the boat, what to do if someone falls overboard or the boat capsizes, and how to avoid common causes of death in boating incidents. Groups might illustrate their brochures with drawings or pictures from magazines. Suggest that students share their brochures with family members or friends who enjoy boats and personal watercraft. **WRITING**

L2 Active Learning

Divide the class into small groups, and have each group create a skit that shows what to do if a boat capsizes or if someone falls overboard. Explain that the skit can be dramatic or comedic, but should reflect knowledge of the boating safety guidelines given in the text. Ask groups to perform their skits for the class.

L3 Content Update  GO ONLINE

Visit Pearson SuccessNet to access more information about recreational safety. Have students complete the Web activity.

Safe Boating Tips
- Always wear a personal flotation device.
- Never drink alcohol or use other drugs.
- Keep constant watch for other boats and personal watercraft.

FIGURE 9 Common causes of death in boating incidents are drowning, trauma, burns, and electrocution. Follow these safety tips to prevent injuries and death.

Boating Safety Millions of Americans enjoy boats and personal watercraft. Unfortunately, nearly 4,000 people each year are injured in boating incidents, and about 700 people die. Follow these safety guidelines when boating and operating personal watercraft.

▶ Take a boating safety class. Local Coast Guard branches, community boating facilities, the American Red Cross, and the United States Power Squadrons offer these classes.

▶ Make sure that your boat or watercraft is in good repair.

▶ Check the weather before you go out on the water. Never go out during a thunderstorm.

▶ Always wear a United States Coast Guard-approved personal flotation device (PFD), such as a life jacket, regardless of your swimming ability. Never allow a child to wear an air-filled swimming aid, such as "water wings," instead of a PFD.

▶ Never drink alcohol or use other drugs.

▶ If someone falls overboard, immediately toss a PFD and a towline to the person. Shut off the motor, and help the person into the boat.

▶ The overturning of a boat is called **capsizing.** If you are in a boat when it capsizes, grab your PFD and stay with the boat until help arrives and you are rescued.

▶ Keep the boat's signal lights on between dusk and dawn, and use a whistle or horn to signal when visibility is poor.

GO ONLINE
PearsonSuccessNet.com
For: More on recreational safety

WRITING and Health

L3 Article

Tell students they have just been hired as a writer for a teen magazine. Their first assignment is to write an article about ways to prevent injuries while participating in a favorite teen sport. They may choose any sport. The article should be written in a friendly voice and contain accurate details about the gear required and habits a participant should adopt to prevent injuries. Students may use information from the text, as well as information from library or online research.

Sports Safety Sports injuries may occur when you do not warm up properly before exercising or cool down properly afterward. Remember to stretch before and after exercise.

As you learned in Chapter 11, overuse injuries can result from playing one sport year-round or from doing the same movement over and over. The best way to prevent overuse injuries is to play several different sports, instead of specializing in just one. That way, the muscle groups you use in one sport have a chance to recover while you play another sport. However, you know your body best. If you feel pain, it is your responsibility to tell your coach and your parents, and to take a break.

Injuries can also occur if you use faulty or inappropriate equipment. Always wear protective gear when playing a contact sport. A forceful collision with an object or another person can cause a concussion, an injury that occurs when the brain hits the skull.

If you hunt, wear a bright-colored vest or hat so that you will not be mistaken for prey by another hunter. Hunt only in approved areas. Keep the safety on your gun until you are ready to shoot, and keep your trigger finger outside the trigger guard. Unload your gun as soon as you are done.

Here are some other tips you should follow when participating in any sport, including hunting.

▶ Drink lots of water to stay hydrated, even in cold weather.

▶ Do not participate in a sport if you are ill.

▶ Do not participate in a sport if you have been drinking or using drugs.

 **What sports do you participate in? How do you protect yourself from injuries?**

FIGURE 10 Always wear appropriate safety gear when playing contact sports, such as hockey.
Interpreting Photos What safety gear are these hockey players wearing? How does the gear protect the players?

L3 Building Health Skills

Accessing Information Ask students where they could find information on specific ways to avoid injuries in the sports they participate in. Discuss how different types of information about the same topic may require accessing different kinds of sources. Ask: **Who could you talk to about how to protect yourself from injury when you play a specific sport?** (the school's coach of that sport, the school nurse, a personal doctor) **Where else could you find information about how to avoid injuries in your sport?** (library books about the sport, library medical books about sports injuries, Web sites dedicated to the sport, medical Web sites)

L2 Visual Learning: Figure 10

Point out that the hockey players in the photo are well padded, and ask: **What kinds of injuries could these players suffer?** (They could break bones, break off teeth, break the nose, and have other sprains and bruises.) Emphasize that every sport requires appropriate, well-maintained equipment, which is one of the four basic guidelines for recreational safety.
Caption Answer The hockey players are wearing body pads, heavy gloves, high-top skates, and helmets. The gear protects the players from being injured by the sticks or skates of other players or by the hard ice when they fall.

Connect to Your Life Sample answer: I play soccer and basketball. For both, I try to warm up before playing and cool down properly afterward. When I play soccer, I wear shinguards to protect my legs from injury.

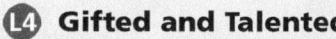

Differentiated Instruction

L4 Gifted and Talented

Encourage interested students to obtain information from the organizations listed in the text that offer boating safety courses (local Coast Guard branches, community boating facilities, the American Red Cross, and the United States Power Squadrons). Ask students to investigate questions such as: Are there beginning, intermediate, and advanced courses? Are the programs free? Are the courses offered at convenient times and places? Have students compare courses and choose one that best matches their background and needs.

L2 Visual Learning: Figure 11

Give students time to read through the safety guidelines shown in the figure. Ask: **What is one safety guideline that is the same for each type of vehicle?** *(wear a helmet)* **Why do you think wearing a helmet is so important?** *(Sample answer: A helmet protects the head and brain from injury. Because the brain is the controlling center of the body, any injury to the brain is serious.)* Then, review each set of guidelines, asking students to explain the reasoning behind each safety guideline.

L3 Building Health Skills

Accessing Information Encourage interested students to investigate recommended safety equipment for a sport such as skateboarding, bicycle riding, or snowmobiling, or any sport they choose. Have them find out why the equipment is recommended, where the equipment can be purchased, and how much it costs. Have students report to the class about what they learn.

L3 Journal Writing

Ask students to write a private journal entry analyzing how actively they practice sports safety. For example, they might note times when they have ridden a bicycle without a helmet. For each risk they have taken, students should write what the consequences could have been. Also ask students to list ways they can improve their sports safety habits in the future. **WRITING**

Safety Guidelines

FIGURE 11 To prevent injuries, be sure to ride bicycles, skateboards, motorcycles, and recreational vehicles responsibly.

ATV
- Wear a helmet, sturdy pants, boots, and gloves.
- Only ride in daylight.
- Do not ride on paved roads.
- Do not speed.
- Carry drinking water and a first-aid kit.

Snowmobile
- Wear a helmet, warm clothing, boots, and goggles.
- Only ride on designated trails.
- Go slowly over rough terrain.
- Never travel alone.
- Never venture out onto an ice-covered body of water.
- Always carry drinking water, a first-aid kit, and signal flares.

Skateboard
- Wear a helmet, wrist guards, elbow pads, and knee pads.
- Stay away from roads with heavy traffic.
- Skateboard in designated skate parks or only where skateboarding is permitted.

Bicycle
- Wear a helmet.
- Ride single file on the right, with the flow of traffic.
- Signal your intentions with hand signals before turning or stopping.
- If you have to pull over, get your bike well off the road.
- Wear reflective clothing.
- Be alert for oil spills, gravel, potholes, opening car doors, and other hazards.

Motorcycle
- Take a motorcycle safety training course.
- Wear a helmet and sturdy clothing, including pants, boots, and gloves.
- Follow the traffic rules that apply to larger vehicles.
- Make sure you have a working headlight, taillight, and brake light.
- Signal stops, turns, or changes in direction.
- Do not speed.

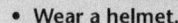

708 *Chapter 26*

For Your INFORMATION!

Skateboarding Injuries

According to the American Academy of Orthopaedic Surgeons, skateboarding injuries result in about 50,000 visits to U.S. emergency rooms each year. Every year, about 1,500 children and adolescents are hospitalized with skateboarding injuries. Most of those involve head injuries. Note that the result of a fall from a skateboard can be permanent disability, or even death, from a brain injury if the skateboarder is not wearing a helmet. A good helmet sits low on the forehead and does not move in any direction when the head is shaken. In 2003, California began requiring all children under 18 to wear a helmet when skateboarding, skating, or riding a scooter.

Bicycle and Recreational Vehicle Safety Many young people are killed or injured each year in incidents involving bicycles, motorcycles, all-terrain vehicles (ATVs), and snowmobiles. These incidents usually result from mechanical problems, poor judgment, or ignoring basic safety rules. Figure 11 lists some safety guidelines you should follow for bicycles, skateboards, motorcycles, snowmobiles, and ATVs. Motorcycle safety rules also apply to mopeds. These rules apply to all recreational vehicles.

▶ Never ride under the influence of alcohol or other drugs.

▶ Always wear appropriate clothing, a helmet, and other protective gear. Do not wear baggy clothing that could get caught in moving parts.

▶ Never allow someone else to ride with you unless the vehicle is intended for two people.

▶ Never ride while listening to headphones.

▶ Keep constant watch for possible hazards in your path. For some vehicles, you may need a rearview mirror.

▶ Never grab onto another moving vehicle.

▶ Make sure the vehicle is in good repair and can be seen easily by other riders. You will need reflectors or a headlight and a taillight.

Riding a motorcycle on a highway can present different challenges than riding on an ATV. On the motorcycle, you are sharing the highway with much larger vehicles. On the ATV, your trip must be limited by the hours of daylight. With both vehicles, you need to watch your speed.

Section 2 Review

Key Ideas and Vocabulary

1. What is an **occupational injury**?
2. How can many occupational injuries and illnesses be prevented?
3. List the four basic safety guidelines for recreational activities.
4. Briefly describe the steps of **survival floating**.
5. What does **active supervision** mean? How would you actively supervise a child in a pool?

Critical Thinking

6. **Predicting** If you worked on a farm that required you to operate a tractor, what kind of training would you expect to get? If you didn't receive training, what risks would you be taking?

Health at School

School Safety Survey teachers, coaches, and other school personnel to find out what kind of safety training they have had. Should further training be required? Write a letter to your principal summarizing your findings. **WRITING**

7. **Making Judgments** Suppose a friend tries to persuade you to go diving with him in a water-filled quarry at night. How would you talk your friend into doing something less hazardous?

8. **Applying Concepts** Suppose you and a group of friends wanted to go sledding after a heavy snow storm. What kinds of safety precautions would you take? Make a list of what you would wear and what you would bring. **WRITING**

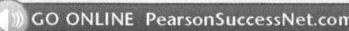 GO ONLINE PearsonSuccessNet.com   Audio Summary Section 26.2

Preventing Injuries **709**

Section 2 Review

1. any wound or damage to the body that results from an event at work
2. by removing potential hazards from the workplace
3. Learn and apply the proper skills. Have appropriate, well-maintained equipment. Know the safety rules specific to the activity. Prepare adequately for the activity.
4. Students should describe the steps shown in Figure 8.
5. Active supervision means that you keep children in your view at all times when they are in or near the water. Students should describe keeping a child in view at a pool, staying near the pool, and not engaging in distracting behavior.

3. Assess

Evaluate

These assignments can help you assess students' mastery of the section content.

Section 2 Review

Answers appear below.

Teaching Resources

- Practice 26-2
- Section 26-2 Quiz

L2 Reteach

Ask students to choose one of the recreational activities discussed in the section and write a paragraph explaining how the four basic safety guidelines can be applied to that activity. Ask volunteers to share their paragraphs with the class, and challenge other students to explain alternative ways the basic guidelines could be applied.

L4 Enrich

Teaching Resources

- Enrich 26-2

Health at School

School Safety Have students work in pairs, and assign each pair certain teachers, coaches, or other school personnel. Before students carry out the survey, discuss what are appropriate questions to ask. For example, students might ask whether teachers know how to prevent injuries in the recreational activities that students engage in at school. After students have completed the survey, organize the class into groups, and have each group discuss its results and compose a letter to the principal.

6. Students should describe being taught how the tractor works, how to stop it, and how to turn it off. Without training, a student would be risking injury or death.

7. Students should emphasize the risks of drowning and serious injuries when swimming in unsupervised areas.

8. Answers will vary. A good response should mention warm clothing, water, and a first-aid kit.

Analyzing Risks and Benefits

Objective

Demonstrate the ability to make decisions by analyzing the risks and benefits of an activity.

Teaching Strategies

- Tell students that learning this skill will help them make mature decisions that result from careful examination of likely outcomes rather than from short-term or emotional considerations.

- Ask students to think of specific actions or activities that have some degree of risk. *(Sample activities: playing indoor soccer, riding on an all-terrain vehicle, walking through an unfamiliar part of town at night, accepting a ride from a stranger)* List on the board three of the suggestions that represent different types of risks. Have students brainstorm the physical, emotional, legal, and social risks of each. Which activities could cause injury? Which action might delay the accomplishment of a goal? Have students rate the likelihood of various negative consequences that may arise from an activity, from 1 for highly likely to 5 for very unlikely.

- Have students make similar ratings for the possible benefits of each activity, from 1 for very important benefit to 5 for minimal benefit.

- After students have rated the risks and benefits of each action or activity, have them consider how knowledge, awareness, ability, state of mind, and environmental conditions might reduce the degree of risk or enhance the benefits of each of the suggested actions or activities.

- Tally the points for and against each action or activity. Ask: **Are there any other risks you might want to consider?** *(Sample answer: We might want to consider risks to other participants, parents, family members, or teammates.)* After all risks and benefits have been considered, ask students whether they should or should not take each action or do each activity, based on this risk-benefit analysis.

 **Making Decision**

Analyzing Risks and Benefits

LaToya's friends invited her to go inline skating with them in the city park. She had never done it before, but everyone said it was fun and that she would catch on quickly. LaToya wanted to go, but she worried about getting hurt just before basketball season started. Should she take the risk?

The risk may be worth taking if LaToya decides that the benefits are greater than the possible harm. For example, skiing is another activity that involves some risk of injury. Many people decide that skiing is worth the risk, however, because it is good exercise and fun. They also realize that there are ways they can reduce the risks involved.

Making responsible decisions is a sign of maturity. It shows that you are beginning to take control of your own well-being. How can you analyze the risks and benefits of an action you might take? The guidelines that follow will help you.

710

① Identify the possible risks involved in taking this action.

A risk is a possible harmful outcome or consequence of taking a certain action. These negative consequences may be physical, emotional, legal, or social.

▶ Identify all the possible negative consequences of taking this action. Write them down.

▶ Determine if any of the negative consequences are likely to cause a serious injury.

▶ Rate the likelihood of each negative consequence actually happening, from 1 for highly likely to 5 for very unlikely.

② Identify the possible benefits of taking this action.

▶ Identify all the possible positive consequences of taking this action. Write them down.

▶ Rate the importance of these benefits to you, from 1 for very important to 5 for not very important.

③ Determine what you could do to reduce the risk of injury.

Design a strategy to reduce the degree of risk involved and maximize the benefits. For example:

▶ **Knowledge and awareness:** LaToya could find out if she can rent or borrow protective equipment such as wrist, elbow, and knee guards. She could also find out what skating route has the fewest hills or pedestrians.

▶ **Ability:** LaToya could take a lesson in in-line skating before she goes with her friends.

▶ **State of mind:** LaToya could make sure she is well rested and not under the influence of alcohol or other drugs when she tries skating.

▶ **Environmental conditions:** LaToya could agree to go only if it had not been raining, so the paths wouldn't be slippery, or if her friends would stop skating before it got dark.

④ Determine if the benefits outweigh the risks.

▶ Analyze the risks and benefits you wrote down, including your ratings of the likelihood of negative consequences and the importance of the benefits to you. Also review your strategies for reducing the risk of injury.

▶ Ask yourself if the benefits outweigh the risks for you.

▶ Decide whether or not to take the action.

 Practice the Skill

1. Review LaToya's situation.
   a. What are all the possible risks involved in going inline skating?
   b. What are the possible benefits?
   c. What are some other ways she could reduce the risks and increase the benefits of doing this activity?
   d. What decision would you make after weighing the risks and benefits in this situation?

2. Consider a recent action you have taken or are considering taking. Analyze the action for risks and benefits following the steps described here. What strategies could minimize the possible risks and increase the benefits? Do the benefits outweigh the risks? Why or why not?

Preventing Injuries **711**

 Practice the Skill

1. a. Answers may vary, though the most important possible risk would be a serious physical injury, and an injury may jeopardize her basketball accomplishments.

b. Benefits might include having fun, getting exercise, having a good time with friends, and discovering a great sport.

c. Other ways might include taking skating lessons and talking to experienced skaters to reduce the risks and making sure she warms up and stretches properly to increase the benefits.

d. Answers may vary, though some students will probably say the benefits outweigh the risks, and therefore say yes to skating. Some students may suggest that the risk to future participation in basketball is too great to decide to go skating.

2. After students have written their own risk-benefit analysis, call on volunteers to share their responses with the class.

Health at Home

L3 A Parent's Perspective

Ask students to sit down with a parent or guardian and work through a risk-benefit analysis of an activity they have always dreamed of doing, such as riding a motorcycle or traveling by train through Europe. Suggest that students write down and rate risks and benefits beforehand so they can teach their parent or guardian how to do a risk-benefit analysis. Through this activity, students might come to better understand the fears of a parent or guardian, and a parent or guardian might come to better understand the dreams of a young person.

Objectives

Before class begins, write the objectives on the board. Have students copy the objectives into their notebooks at the start of class.

1. Focus

Warm-Up Health Stats

After students have completed the writing assignment, call on volunteers to describe the trend the graph reveals to them. Most students will mention that driver fatalities are greatest for the youngest drivers and oldest drivers and least for mature drivers ages 40–59. Call on volunteers to read what they have written to explain that trend. Concentrate on why driver fatalities are so high for younger drivers, and have students describe ways that younger drivers can reduce their risk of being injured or killed in a motor vehicle crash.

Presentation 26-3

⚑ Sensitive Issues

Some students may have been involved in a motor vehicle crash or had family members involved in a crash that resulted in a death or injury. Be careful in the language you use to discuss the blame for crashes.

Motor Vehicle Safety

Objectives

▶ **Identify** the skills you need to be a safe driver.

▶ **List** safety rules you should follow when riding in a school bus.

Vocabulary

• defensive driving
• road rage

Warm-Up

Health Stats What health trend does the graph reveal?

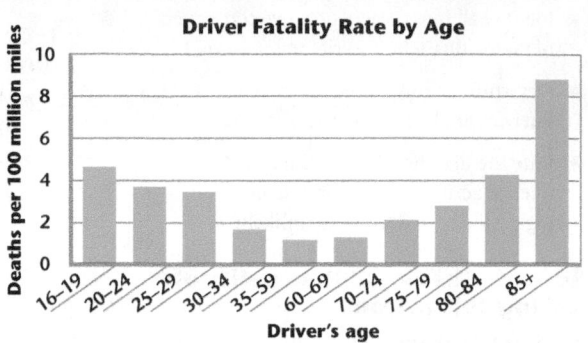

WRITING Describe the trend shown in the graph. Why do you think driver deaths are more common at certain ages than others?

Automobile Safety

Consider these statistics.

▶ Motor vehicle crashes are the number one cause of death for people aged 3 through 33.

▶ Each year, more than 40,000 deaths and millions of injuries occur as a result of motor vehicle crashes.

▶ On average, half of all Americans will be involved in a motor vehicle crash during their lifetimes.

Drivers between the ages of 15 and 24 are involved in more crashes than any other age group. This is due to several factors, including a lack of driving experience and a tendency to take more risks.

The use of alcohol and drugs is another major factor involved in many motor vehicle crashes. Alcohol affects a person's self-control and judgment, slows reaction time, blurs vision, and reduces coordination.

You can be a safe driver, regardless of your age. To be a safe driver, you need to practice good driving skills and know how to respond to risky situations.

TEENS *Are Asking . . .*

Q: I have friends who drink, especially at parties on weekends. I've been in the situation where the person who drove me to a party has been drinking, and I have no other way to get home. What should I do?

A: One thing you should never do is get into a car with a driver who's been drinking. The risk is too great. To protect yourself, call a sober friend or relative to pick you up. Almost no one will resent being called for that purpose when your other choice is riding with a drinker. You should also try to stop your friend from driving by taking and hiding the keys, or even calling the police. Remember, the use of alcohol is a major factor in many motor vehicle crashes.

Factors You Can Control   Whether you are driving or riding as a passenger, certain risk factors are within your control. It is your responsibility to minimize these risks and reduce your chances of being involved in or injured in a motor vehicle crash.

- Take a course in driver education, either at your school or with a paid instructor.
- Never drive if you have been drinking alcohol or using drugs. Never get into a car with someone who has been drinking or using drugs.
- Always wear your seatbelt. When you are driving, insist that your passengers also buckle up, even those in the backseat.
- Minimize your distractions. Stay off your cell phone, do not text, keep your music down, and do not drive with too many passengers.
- Follow the speed limit. Excessive speed is a factor in many crashes.
- Follow the rules of the road.
- Allow enough distance between you and the car in front of you so that you can stop suddenly without hitting it.
- Avoid driving when you are tired, angry, or feeling stressed.
- Always tell a family member or friend where you are going and when you plan to return home.
- Never carry a flammable substance, such as extra gasoline, in the trunk of your car.

Keeping Your Vehicle Safe   The condition of your vehicle can affect your chances of getting into a crash. Take your car in for regular tune-ups and make sure that it is in good repair.

- Make sure that your brakes are working properly.
- Make sure that all of your lights are working, including the brake lights.
- Make sure that your tires are in good shape and appropriate for the climate you live in.
- Make sure that your windshield wipers work properly.

 **How do you minimize your risk when driving or riding in a car?**

Supplies to Keep in Your Vehicle
- Jumper cables
- Flashlight
- First-aid kit
- Extra windshield washer fluid
- Extra motor oil
- Blanket

FIGURE 12 Good preparation is key to being safe on the road.

2. Teach

L3 EL Reading/Note Taking 26-3
L2 Adapted Reading/Note Taking 26-3

Automobile Safety

L3 Class Discussion

After students have read the list of factors you can control, call on a volunteer to read aloud the first factor. Ask: **Why is taking a course in driver education a good idea?** *(Sample answer: You learn how to drive a car properly, and you learn the rules of the road. Your car insurance may cost less after driver education.)* Continue this process with each factor in the list.

L1 Cooperative Learning

Have groups of students create a role-play of a situation in which a designated driver is intoxicated and not in any shape to drive home from a party. The role-play should show how friends try to convince the intoxicated person not to drive, as well as his or her reactions to the friends' arguments. Call on students to present their role-plays to the class.

L3 Building Health Skills

Practicing Healthful Behaviors
Encourage students to work in small groups after school to evaluate a car one of the students has driven to school or a student's family car. They should examine the brakes, head lights and brake lights, tires, and windshield wipers. Have each group report their findings to the class the next day.

Connect to Your Life   *Sample answer:* I never get into a car with someone who has been drinking or using drugs. I always wear a seat belt. I follow the rules of the road. And I always tell a family member or friend where I'm going and when I plan to return home.

Differentiated Instruction

L1 Special Needs

Ask students to remember a time when they were in a car that almost got into a crash or the driver was stopped for a traffic violation. Invite volunteers to share their experiences. Each time students describe a situation, direct their attention to the appropriate item under Factors You Can Control. Read the item aloud, and then call on volunteers to explain how following that suggestion could have affected the situation.

L1 **Visual Learning: Figure 13**

After students have examined the figure, ask: **What is the bad weather condition shown in the photo?** *(The photo shows snow on the road and poor visibility. It may be a snowstorm.)* **Why could this weather condition cause a crash?** *(Drivers may lose control if vehicles slide on the snow and ice on the road.)* **If you were in one of the cars in the photo, would you drive differently than if you were driving on a clear, sunny day? Explain.** *(Sample answer: I'd drive much slower, and I'd constantly monitor the actions of the other vehicles on the road.)* **Caption Answer** *Sample answer:* I would constantly monitor the movement of the truck and make sure that the truck drivers could always see me in their mirrors.

EL **Building Vocabulary**

Make sure that English language learners understand what is meant by the term *defensive driving*. If necessary, review what the term *defense* means. Then relate that to protecting oneself from motor vehicle crashes. Ask students to demonstrate their understanding by giving an example of defensive driving.

L3 **Content Update**  GO ONLINE

Visit Pearson SuccessNet to access more information about motor vehicle safety. Have students complete the Web activity.

School Bus Safety

L3 **Building Health Skills**

Advocacy Have groups of students make a poster that conveys to younger students the rules school bus riders should follow to ensure everyone's safety. Explain that they should include the rules discussed in the text, as well as any other rules they think are appropriate, given their own school bus experiences. Groups should illustrate each rule with a cartoon, sketch, or magazine photo to make the poster interesting and eye-catching. Arrange to display the posters in schools where younger students can see them.

FIGURE 13 Knowing how to drive in bad weather conditions can lower your risk of getting into a motor vehicle crash. **Evaluating** What additional safety precautions would you take when driving near large trucks?

In bad weather, it is important that your tires and windshield wipers be in good shape.

Factors Outside Your Control Some risk factors that come with driving are outside of your control, such as road construction and bad weather. However, you are in control of how you react to such risks. The following guidelines can help you avoid a motor vehicle crash when driving under less-than-ideal conditions.

▶ Slow down. If you are driving through a construction zone, obey the lower posted speed limit.

▶ If visibility is low due to rain, fog, or snow, slow down. Follow the lines painted on the road to make sure you stay in your lane.

▶ Keep a greater distance between you and the car in front of you. It is unpredictable when you may have to stop, so give yourself more room, especially in slippery conditions.

You also have no control over the other drivers on the road. This is why it is important to practice defensive driving. **Defensive driving** means that you constantly monitor other drivers around you, and do not assume that they will do what you think they should do. Defensive driving enables you to actively avoid hazardous situations.

Road Rage You should also be a considerate driver. Allow others to merge, and do not tailgate. Being inconsiderate to other drivers can spark road rage. **Road rage** is dangerous or violent behavior by a person who becomes angry or frustrated while driving. Stay away from drivers you suspect might have road rage. If you have a problem with road rage, seek help.

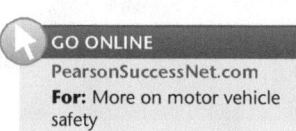

GO ONLINE
PearsonSuccessNet.com
For: More on motor vehicle safety

For Your INFORMATION!

Driving in Bad Weather

These are some tips for driving in rain, snow, or fog.

- Turn on your headlights any time you turn on your windshield wipers.
- When there is ice or snow on the road, bridges and overpasses freeze first. Slow down when approaching a bridge or overpass. Avoid changes of speed or direction.

- When it is snowing, brake with caution. If you slam on the brakes, you may lose control of the car.
- In fog, use your low-beam headlights. If the fog is heavy, roll your windows down so that you can hear other cars.
- Never drive through flooded areas. Your car may float in just two feet of water.

School Bus Safety

You may have spent a lot of time on a school bus during your younger school years. And even though you may not ride the bus regularly anymore, you still might do so occasionally for sports and other activities. **When riding in a school bus, there are rules you should follow to ensure everybody's safety.**

▶ Stay seated at all times.

▶ Do not hang any part of your body out of the windows.

▶ Avoid fighting and arguing. Do not throw things. These behaviors distract the bus driver.

▶ If someone is bullying you, tell the driver.

▶ Know where emergency exits are located.

▶ Watch for cars when getting off the bus and crossing the street.

When you start driving, be sure to look out for school buses. Do not follow a school bus too closely because it makes frequent stops. Always stop when a school bus's stop sign swings out and its red lights are flashing. You must stop whether you are behind the bus or driving in the opposite direction. The stop sign is intended to keep students safe when crossing the street.

FIGURE 14 It is important to follow bus safety rules, whether you ride the bus or not.

Section 3 Review

Key Ideas and Vocabulary

1. List five pieces of safety advice you would give to a new driver.

2. What is **defensive driving?** Why should you practice defensive driving?

3. What is **road rage?** How can you help prevent road rage?

4. List three safety rules you should follow when riding in a school bus. What rules should you observe when driving on the same street as a bus?

Critical Thinking

5. **Evaluating** Some states have a graduated licensing system, which increases young drivers' privileges over time as they gain more experience. Do you think graduated licenses are a good idea? Why or why not? **WRITING**

Health at Home

Good Driving Habits Evaluate your driving habits and the habits of others in your family. Gather a list of good driving habits that you and your family should keep up, and a list of habits you need to improve. Set goals for improving these unsafe behaviors, and reward yourselves when you meet your goals. **WRITING**

6. **Applying Concepts** Suppose you have a friend who you think is an unsafe driver. He drives at high speeds, disobeys traffic rules, and frequently takes his eyes off the road. What would you say to your friend to encourage him to drive more safely? **WRITING**

 GO ONLINE PearsonSuccessNet.com   Audio Summary Section 26.3

Preventing Injuries **715**

Section 3 Review

1. *Sample answer:* Never drive if you've been drinking alcohol. Always wear a seatbelt. Minimize your distractions. Follow the speed limit. Follow the rules of the road.

2. You constantly monitor other drivers around you, and do not assume that they will do what you think they should do. This enables you to actively avoid hazardous situations.

3. Road rage is dangerous or violent behavior by a person who becomes angry or frustrated while driving. Being a considerate driver may help prevent road rage in other drivers.

---

3. Assess

Evaluate
These assignments can help you assess students' mastery of the section content.

Section 3 Review
Answers appear below.

Teaching Resources
• Practice 26-3
• Section 26-2 Quiz

L2 Reteach

Have students rewrite the section objectives as questions and then answer the questions by using material from the section. After students have finished writing, call on one volunteer to read a question and another to read the answer.

L4 Enrich

Teaching Resources
• Enrich 26-3

Health at Home

Good Driving Habits Lead a discussion on driving habits that students have observed. Tell students they should not identify the drivers they are thinking about. Make a list on the board of Poor Driving Habits and Good Driving Habits. Then encourage students to be honest in evaluating their own driving habits as well as the habits of family members. Explain that these evaluations, as well as the goals they set for improving unsafe behaviors, will remain private.

---

4. Students should list three of the safety rules mentioned in the text. They should also mention not following a bus too closely and stopping when the bus stops.

5. Answers will vary. Students should provide logical reasons for the position they take.

6. Answers will vary. Responses might mention the number of deaths and injuries that occur as a result of motor vehicle crashes and, therefore, concern for the friend's safety.

Preventing Injuries **715**

Technology & Health

A Shocking Tool to the Rescue

Teaching Strategies

- Review with students what they learned about the heart in Chapter 12. Ask: **What happens when the ventricles of the heart contract?** *(The contraction of the ventricles pumps blood out into the body or toward the lungs.)* **What regulates the rate at which the heart beats?** *(the pacemaker, a small group of cells in the wall of the right atrium)* Explain that the pacemaker regulates the heartbeat by producing nerve impulses. Impulses cause the atria and then the ventricles to contract.

- After the students read the first paragraph, call on volunteers to read each step aloud. After a student reads Step 1, ask: **Why do you think you should call for medical assistance before beginning to use the AED?** *(Sample answer: Restoring the normal heart rhythm with an AED is only the first step of a patient's treatment. Medical professionals are needed quickly, and once you start the AED process there is no time to call for assistance.)* Continue this process through each of the five steps, questioning the students about the purpose of each instruction.

WRITING Before students begin writing, explain that this letter should be as persuasive as possible. A persuasive letter should include information that motivates the reader to take action. Explain that the letter should contain a description of an AED, an explanation about how it is used, and statements about why the school should have one and why teens should be trained to use AEDs.

Technology & Health

A Shocking Tool to the Rescue

Sudden cardiac arrest is a condition in which the heart beats so erratically that it can no longer pump blood effectively. If a regular rhythm is not restored quickly, the person will die. Over 300,000 people do die from sudden cardiac arrest each year in the United States. A device called an automated external defibrillator, or AED, can save some of those lives. An AED delivers a shock to help restore the heart rhythm. The AED uses visual clues and voice commands that tell even untrained users exactly what to do.

WRITING Write a letter to your school board requesting that they buy an AED for your school. Explain why AEDs are important and why teens should be trained to use them.

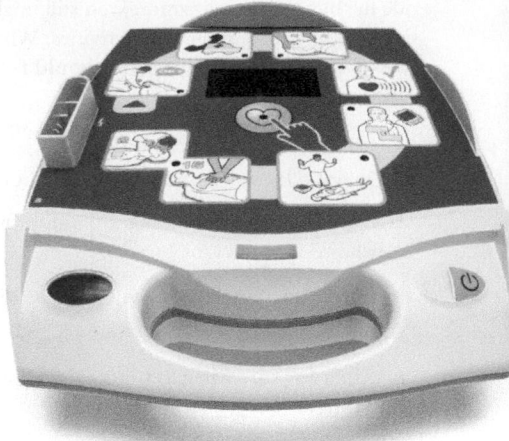

▲ **AED device**
This is one model of AED. It includes shock pads that attach to the victim's chest. Voice prompts tell rescuers what to do.

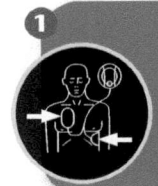
1. • Call for medical assistance.
   • Press pads firmly to patient's bare skin.

2. • Do not touch the patient.
   • Analyzing heart rhythm.
   • Shock advised.

3. • Stand clear of patient.
   • Press the shock button now.

4. • Shock delivered.
   • Assessing heart rhythm.
   • Do not touch the patient.

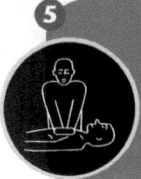
5. • It is safe to touch the patient.
   • Check airway. Check breathing. Check circulation.
   • If needed, begin CPR.

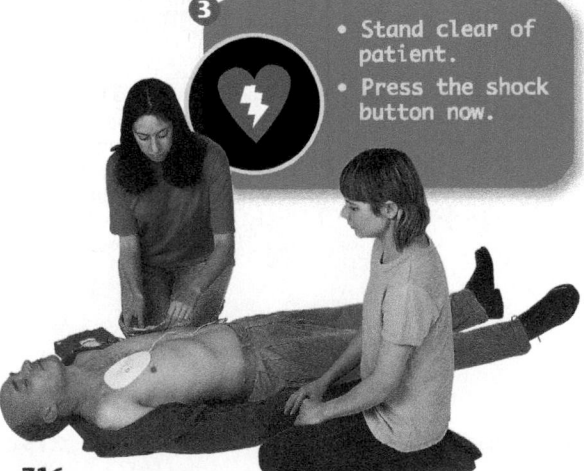

716

For Your INFORMATION!

Automated External Defibrillators

The erratic heartbeat that causes cardiac arrest is called ventricular fibrillation. Restoring the heart to a normal heartbeat is called defibrillation. Once cardiac arrest occurs, the chances of reviving the person diminish minute by minute. After 10 minutes, there is no chance of revival. That is why the development of AEDs has been very important to the treatment of cardiac arrest. An AED contains a tiny computer and electrical circuitry. When an operator places an AED on the chest of a person in cardiac arrest, the computer analyzes the heartbeat. The computer will recommend delivering an electric shock only if it detects ventricular fibrillation.

TEENS Talk

VIDEO

Playing It Safe In what ways did the video influence you to practice safe behaviors in your daily life?

Chapter 26
At a Glance

VIDEO

Playing It Safe Ask for volunteers to share their answers. Use examples from the video to review safe behaviors.

Section 1   Safety at Home and in Your Community

Key Ideas

▶ Five factors that can help prevent unintentional injuries or lessen their damage are awareness, knowledge, ability, state of mind, and environmental conditions.

▶ Common unintentional injuries that occur in the home are due to falls, poisoning, suffocation, fires, electric shock, and firearms.

▶ Earthquakes, tornadoes, hurricanes, floods, blizzards, and many forest fires are examples of natural disasters.

▶ You can prevent assault or reduce the likelihood of injury by following certain safety guidelines. The most basic guideline is to avoid risky situations.

Vocabulary

• unintentional injury (694)
• flammable material (696)
• electrocution (697)
• assault (700)
• rape (700)
• stalker (700)

Key Ideas Review

L1 Help small groups of students incorporate the key ideas on this page into a concept map summarizing chapter content.

L2 Have students write a paragraph in which they summarize how to prevent unintentional injuries in the home, in the community, at work, at play, and while driving motor vehicles.

Vocabulary Review

EL Ask students to write sentences in which they correctly use the vocabulary terms. For each term, call on a student to read his or her sentence. Ask other students whether the term is used correctly. If not, call on a volunteer to read his or her sentence for the term.

Section 2   Safety at Work and Play

Key Ideas

▶ Many occupational injuries and illnesses can be prevented or made less serious by removing potential hazards from the workplace.

▶ Whatever recreational activities you enjoy, you should follow four basic safety guidelines.

Vocabulary

• occupational injury (702)
• occupational illness (702)
• survival floating (705)
• active supervision (705)
• capsizing (706)

L3 Play a quiz game in which you provide the answers and students respond with the correct questions. For answers, use definitions or descriptions of chapter vocabulary terms. For example, you might give the answer, "an unlawful attempt or threat to harm someone," for which the correct question would be, "What is an assault?"

Section 3   Motor Vehicle Safety

Key Ideas

▶ You can be a safe driver, regardless of your age. To be a safe driver, you need to practice good driving skills and know how to respond to risky situations.

▶ When riding in a school bus, there are rules you should follow to ensure everybody's safety.

Vocabulary

• defensive driving (714)
• road rage (714)

Chapter 26 Review

Chapter 26 Review

GO ONLINE

PearsonSuccessNet.com

Students can go online for a review activity on Chapter 26.

Reviewing Key Ideas

Section 1

1. a

2. d

3. The term *unintentional* makes a person aware that it is often possible to prevent injuries.

4. *Sample answer:* Make sure stairways have strong railings. Make sure floors are not slippery. Equip shower stalls with nonskid rubber mats.

5. unloaded and locked in a place where children cannot reach them

6. *Sample answer:* You should because awareness and knowledge can reduce the risk of unintentional injury.

7. Students should respond by citing the safety guidelines for preventing assault discussed in the section.

Section 2

8. b
9. c

10. OSHA

11. Many teens work after school and during the summer.

12. Survival floating can protect a person from drowning.

13. play several different sports to allow different muscle groups to rest

14. *Sample answer:* When biking, I wear a helmet. In the future, I will use hand signals before turning or stopping.

Section 3

15. c

16. three of these four parts: brakes, lights, tires, and windshield wipers

17. slow down and increase my following distance

18. *Sample answer:* When tired, angry, or feeling stressed, a person may have poor judgment and reduced reaction time.

19. Answers will vary but should reflect an understanding that seat belts would probably reduce injuries.

Reviewing Key Ideas

Section 1

1. An example of an unintentional injury is
   a. electric shock.   b. assault.
   c. rape.   d. stalking.

2. A storm with heavy rains and winds over 74 miles per hour is a
   a. tornado.   b. blizzard.
   c. forest fire.   d. hurricane.

3. Why is the term *unintentional injury* usually more appropriate than the term *accident*?

4. List three ways to reduce the risk of injuries from falls in your home.

5. How should firearms be stored?

6. **Critical Thinking** Suppose you have been using electric saws for years. You have just bought a new electric saw. Should you read the instruction manual before you use it? Why or why not?

7. **Critical Thinking** How can you prevent an assault when you are at home? When you are away from home?

Section 2

8. An abnormal condition or disorder caused by exposure to the work environment is called an
   a. occupational injury.   b. occupational illness.
   c. unintentional injury.   d. assault.

9. The overturning of a boat is called
   a. drowning.   b. survival floating.
   c. capsizing.   d. PFD.

10. What federal agency provides information about workplace safety?

11. Explain why it is important for teens to think about their risk of occupational injuries.

12. Why is it important for everyone, even good swimmers, to know the technique of survival floating?

13. How can you prevent overuse injuries?

14. **Critical Thinking** Choose one recreational activity that you enjoy. Describe what you already do to prevent injuries while participating in that activity. In what ways can you better protect yourself from injuries in the future?

Section 3

15. A technique that enables you to actively avoid hazardous situations on the road is
    a. road rage.   b. speeding.
    c. defensive driving.   d. survival floating.

16. List three parts of your car you should have checked regularly.

17. Summarize the actions you should take when driving through a construction zone.

18. **Critical Thinking** It is a bad idea to drive when you are tired, angry, or feeling stressed. Why?

19. **Critical Thinking** There has been much debate about requiring seat belts on school buses. Do you think the extra safety that seat belts might provide justifies the cost of installing them in all school buses? Explain your answer. **WRITING**

Building Health Skills

20. **Accessing Information** Find out what laws and regulations have been established to protect people from stalking. Prepare a written report of your findings. **WRITING**

21. **Making Decisions** Lisa noticed a fire hazard at her after-school job. She reported it to her manager, but he hasn't done anything about it in over a week. What would you do if you were Lisa?

22. **Setting Goals** List three areas of vehicle safety in which your safety skills could be improved, as a driver or as a passenger. Set goals for improving your safety skills. Break your goals down into manageable sub-goals and set deadlines for yourself. **WRITING**

Health and Community

Public Safety Campaign Create a public service poster about one of the safety issues you learned about in this chapter. Think about who your target audience should be. What would be the most effective way to reach that audience? **WRITING**

Building Health Skills

20. Laws and regulations about stalking vary from state to state and community to community. Students may be able to find this information at a local library or by using online resources. If these sources are not adequate, have students inquire at a local police station.

21. Answers will vary. Students might suggest that Lisa report the fire hazard to her manger's boss or to OSHA. Some students might suggest that Lisa quit her job if nothing is done in response to her report.

22. Answers will vary. Students might mention following speed limits, wearing seat belts, and not riding with someone who has been drinking. Students should set a goal for each area mentioned.

Standardized Test Prep

Math Practice

The graph shows the percentage of drivers who were speeding when they were involved in a fatal vehicle crash. Use the graph to answer Questions 23–25.

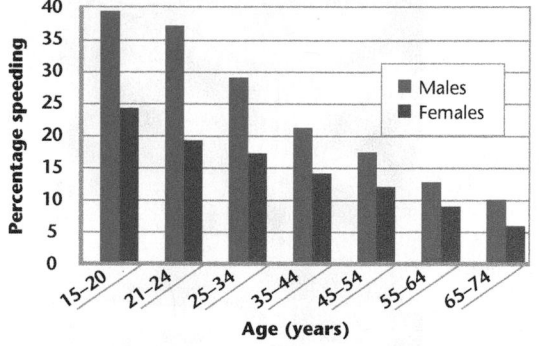

23. What age group has the highest percentage of speeding drivers involved in fatal crashes?
    A Ages 15–20
    B Ages 21–24
    C Ages 25–34
    D Ages 35–44

24. How does speeding compare between males ages 15–20 and females ages 21–24?
    F The males were speeding about 50% less frequently than the females.
    G The males were speeding about 50% more frequently than the females.
    H The males were speeding about 100% more frequently than the females.
    J There was no difference in speeding between the males and the females.

25. Which statement best describes the trend shown in this graph?
    A Speed plays a greater role in fatal crashes involving female drivers than male drivers.
    B Speed plays a greater role in fatal crashes involving male drivers than female drivers.
    C As drivers age, speed plays a greater role in fatal crashes.
    D Speed only plays a role in fatal crashes involving young drivers.

Reading and Writing Practice

Read the passage. Then answer Questions 26–29.

Most young people find paid employment, either during the summer or year-round, before graduating from high school. Young workers ages 14–24 are at risk of workplace injury because of their inexperience at work and their physical, cognitive, and emotional developmental characteristics. They often hesitate to ask questions and may fail to recognize workplace dangers. OSHA's Young Worker Initiative addresses this group's safety and health through an outreach program.

26. Young people
    A always recognize workplace dangers.
    B are at risk for workplace injury.
    C do not usually work until after high school.
    D are fully developed emotionally.

27. In this passage, the word *cognitive* means
    F physical.
    G emotional.
    H mental.
    J muscular.

28. According to the passage, which of these statements is true?
    A Few young people work during the summer.
    B Young people are at no greater risk for workplace injuries than older workers.
    C OSHA does not address the risks that face young workers.
    D Many young workers do not ask questions if they don't understand something.

Constructed Response
29. In a paragraph, summarize the reasons why young workers are at risk for workplace injury.

Test-Taking Tip

Allow yourself plenty of time to get to the test site. You will be more relaxed if you arrive early.

Standardized Test Prep

Math Practice
23. A
24. H
25. B

Reading and Writing Practice
26. B
27. H
28. D
29. Paragraphs will vary, though each paragraph should mention inexperience at work; physical, cognitive, and emotional developmental characteristics; a hesitation to ask questions; and a failure to recognize workplace dangers.

Health and Community

Public Safety Campaign Students might choose any of the situations discussed in the chapter. For home safety, the target audience might be children, and the poster in that case should be child-friendly. By contrast, a poster that focuses on motor vehicle safety might target teens with pictures and words that would appeal to teens.

CAREERS

Community Health and Safety

Teaching Strategies

- Ask students to read about the four careers described on these pages. Discuss with the class how people in each career contribute to community health and safety. Challenge students to think of actual problems that have been prevented or treated by professionals in each career.

- If possible, invite a local professional in one of the careers to speak with the class about the career. Ask the speaker to describe a typical day on the job, the rewards and drawbacks of the career, and how he or she helps protect community health and safety. Encourage students to ask questions.

- Divide the class into groups to brainstorm other careers that help protect community health and safety. Ask each group to compile a list of relevant careers, and then have groups share their lists. Students can select careers from the lists when they research other careers that help make people's lives healthier and safer.

CAREERS

Community Health and Safety

Keeping people in the community healthy and safe is the goal of many health careers. Some workers treat immediate problems, while others deal with long-term health threats.

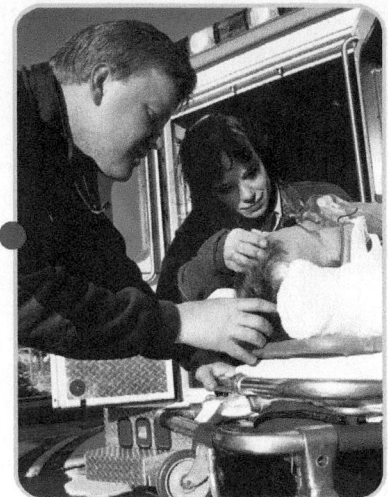

Emergency Medical Technician (EMT)

Emergency medical technicians provide immediate care to ill or injured people in emergency situations. They are trained to evaluate a patient's condition and care for heart and respiratory emergencies. They may even assist with childbirth. A career as an emergency medical technician requires a high school diploma, plus several months of training and certification by the state.

Epidemiologist

Epidemiologists investigate the medical and social aspects of diseases. For example, they may study an outbreak of meningitis to determine why a certain population got the disease. They may also recommend steps for preventing further outbreaks. A career as an epidemiologist usually requires a bachelor's degree in science or health as well as a master's or doctoral degree.

Pharmacy Technician

Pharmacy technicians assist pharmacists by entering prescription orders and patient information into a computer system. They also select and count medicines, keep track of inventory, and order drugs and other supplies. In addition to a high school diploma, pharmacy technicians usually complete a pharmacy technician program at a community college or earn state certification.

GO ONLINE

PearsonSuccessNet.com

Encourage students to go online to find out more about community health and safety careers.

Environmental Engineer

Environmental engineers study environmental problems in order to identify solutions. They may work to improve air quality, protect water supplies, or design safe landfills. To pursue a career in environmental engineering, you must have at least a bachelor's degree in engineering.

Health and Careers

Careers in Public Safety Encourage students to choose a career that interests them. Remind them that they can find careers by searching the *Occupational Outlook Handbook*. Students should learn enough about their selected career to explain how professionals in the career promote community health and safety. For example, if a student chooses the career of community dietitian, he or she might explain that a professional in that career educates people in the community about proper nutrition and its relationship to disease prevention.

Career Focus

Erika Bolden, Environmental Engineer for the EPA

How did you become interested in environmental engineering?

"During college, I interned at an electric power company. The region had poor air quality, due in part to emissions from a coal-fired power plant. From that experience, I became interested in air quality issues in my area."

What do you do?

"I inspect facilities such as chemical plants, automobile dealerships, and steel mills to make sure that they are not releasing too much of any air pollutant into the atmosphere. Federal law sets the limits on pollutant emissions. The air pollutants of most concern to EPA include carbon monoxide, nitrogen oxides, sulfur oxides, lead, and ozone. Any substance can be toxic if a person or the environment is exposed to too much of it."

How does your job affect people's health?

"EPA's job is to protect human health and the environment. My job specifically is to ensure that companies follow the law to minimize pollutant levels in the air. With improved air quality comes lower rates of asthma and cancer. It feels really good to know that people are breathing easier as a result of our efforts."

Health and Careers

Careers in Public Safety Research other careers that help make people's lives healthier and safer. Choose one career and write a paragraph on how you could directly affect your community by pursuing that profession. **WRITING**

721

FirstAid Appendix

Responding to an Emergency

Objectives

Define the term *first aid* and discuss what to do in an emergency situation.

Review universal safety precautions and Good Samaritan laws.

Explain why victims need to be monitored closely for signs of shock.

Emergency Action Plan

- Ask: **What is first aid?** *(immediate care given to a victim before professional medical help arrives)* **What are the three main steps in an emergency action plan?** *(check, call, care)*

- Have students work individually to make a flowchart that describes in detail the steps in an emergency action plan. Ask volunteers to share their completed flowcharts with the class.

- Encourage students to find information about opportunities for first aid training available at school or in their community. Students might contact the American Red Cross, YMCA or YWCA, or American Heart Association for information. Ask students to share their findings with the class.

- Have students write a short newspaper article that summarizes the steps in an emergency action plan and explains the importance of automated external defibrillators. After students have edited their articles and corrected any errors, encourage them to submit the articles to the school or local newspaper for publication. **WRITING**

- Discuss how movies and television shows may give viewers the false impression that first aid efforts always save patients' lives. Make sure students understand that this may not accurately reflect reality. People can die from life-threatening emergencies despite competent first aid efforts.

First-Aid Appendix

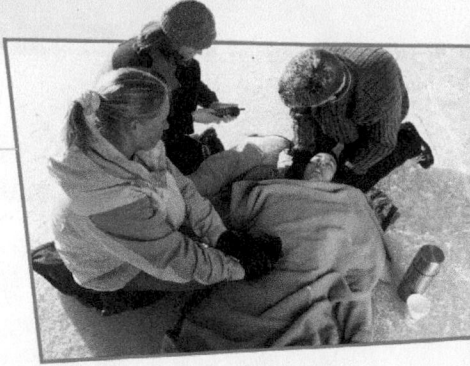

Responding to an Emergency

In the movies, when disaster is about to strike, the music becomes louder and more dramatic. In real life, however, no such warnings alert you to emergency situations. If an emergency occurred, would you be prepared to respond?

Emergency Action Plan

If an emergency occurs, have a clear plan of action to protect yourself and to assist others by providing first aid. First aid is the immediate care given to a victim before professional medical help arrives.

The American Red Cross and the American Heart Association recommend these actions when you encounter an emergency.

1 CHECK Make sure the scene is safe for you, the victim(s), and any bystanders. Check the victim(s) for these life-threatening conditions:

▶ **Severe Bleeding** Signs of severe bleeding include blood pouring from an open wound, blood in vomit, pain or swelling in the abdomen, and weakness or confusion.

▶ **Unconsciousness** Gently tap the victim on the shoulder and ask, "Are you OK?" or say, "Open your eyes." If there is no response, the victim is probably unconscious.

▶ **Breathing Difficulties** Look to see if the person's chest is rising and falling. Listen for normal breathing or feel for escaping air against your cheek. The absence of these signs may indicate that the victim is not breathing normally. Gasping for breath is another sign of breathing difficulties.

2 CALL Call 911 immediately if a victim shows any life-threatening conditions. (If there is another person with you, have that person call 911 while you stay with the victim.) Be prepared to answer the 911 operator's questions and follow directions calmly and completely. If you are unsure about whether to call 911, the safest thing to do is to make the call.

3 CARE Be prepared to act quickly to provide first aid. Always care for victims with life-threatening conditions first. If you suspect a neck or spine injury, do not move the victim unless it is absolutely necessary.

Automated External Defibrillators

One important life-saving tool that you should always check for is an automated external defibrillator (AED). AEDs are found in many public places, including airports, stadiums, health clubs, and malls. By quickly locating, retrieving, and using an AED, you can make the difference between life and death.

An AED uses verbal commands and visual cues to direct even untrained users in exactly what to do. Here's how it works.

▶ Attach the shock pads to the victim's chest.

▶ The AED analyzes the person's heart rhythm.

▶ If an abnormal rhythm is detected, the AED automatically delivers a shock to help restore a normal rhythm.

▶ The AED then instructs you about what to do next.

722

For Your INFORMATION!

In December, 2005, the American Red Cross and the American Heart Association made significant revisions to their guidelines for CPR and other first aid procedures. The guidelines in this First Aid Appendix reflect those revisions. The guidelines on CPR also reflect the call to action on hands-only CPR that the AHA issued in March 2008.

This First Aid Appendix can familiarize students with a number of important first aid procedures. The descriptions provide an overview of the more detailed instructions offered in first aid manuals and courses. This First Aid Appendix should not take the place of formal first aid instruction (including CPR training) by qualified medical personnel.

Universal Safety Precautions

As a provider of first aid, you have a responsibility to yourself and to your victim to guard against the transmission of infectious diseases. When giving first aid, always follow these universal safety precautions.

▶ Wear disposable gloves whenever there is any chance that you will come into contact with body fluids.

▶ Use a plastic face shield or mask with a one-way valve when you perform rescue breathing.

▶ Wash your hands with soap and warm water after providing first aid.

Shock

With any serious injury, you need to monitor the victim closely for signs of shock. Shock is a condition in which the heart fails to circulate blood adequately to the vital organs. The more severe the injury, the more likely that shock will develop. Even if the injury or illness itself is *not* immediately life threatening, shock can lead to death.

Signs of shock include

▶ restlessness or irritability

▶ confusion or disorientation

▶ skin that is pale, ashen, bluish, cool, or moist

▶ rapid breathing

▶ rapid, weak pulse

▶ excessive thirst

▶ nausea or vomiting

Good Samaritan Laws

Even when first aid is applied correctly, there are times when complications can occur. Most states have a Good Samaritan Law for people who administer first aid to victims. These laws prevent the rescuer from being sued if complications arise. Rescuers should use common sense and follow these guidelines.

▶ Call 911.

▶ If someone's life is in danger and you know the correct first aid procedures, you should administer first aid.

▶ If the victim is conscious, you should ask the person's permission first to administer first aid.

▶ Be sure that your help will not further harm the victim.

First Aid for Shock

1 Call 911 immediately if you suspect that someone is in shock.

2 Lay the victim on the floor or ground. If possible, place a blanket or jacket beneath the victim to provide insulation.

3 Raise and support the victim's legs if there is no leg or hip injury. This will improve blood flow to the vital organs.

4 Control any bleeding by applying direct pressure to the wound using a sterile gauze pad or a clean, absorbent cloth.

5 Cover the victim with a blanket or coat to keep him or her warm.

6 Monitor the victim's breathing and pulse. Be prepared to begin rescue breathing (page 725) or CPR (pages 726–727), if needed.

First Aid Appendix **723**

FirstAid Appendix

Choking and Rescue Breathing

Objectives

Identify the universal sign for choking.

Explain how to provide first aid for choking.

Describe how to perform rescue breathing.

Choking

- Point out that choking can result in death unless the object is dislodged within minutes. Explain that waiting for professional help to arrive is usually not an option when a person is choking. For this reason, it is essential that people receive training to learn how to help a choking victim.

- Invite the school nurse or a representative from the American Red Cross to demonstrate the proper first aid procedure for choking. Remind students that abdominal thrusts should *never* be practiced on a person who is not choking.

- Ask students to work in small groups to make a poster that illustrates the universal sign for choking and proper first aid for choking. After checking the accuracy of students' posters, you may want to arrange to display the completed posters in the school cafeteria.

- Make sure students understand that the procedures described on this page apply to adults and children only, and not to infants. Students who care for infants should take a babysitter training course (from a qualified organization such as the American Red Cross) to learn the proper first aid procedures for infants. Ask for volunteers to find out about upcoming babysitter training courses in your area.

Choking and Rescue Breathing

You're at a restaurant when suddenly a person at a nearby table starts gasping for air. What would you do?

Choking

When food or any other object becomes lodged in a person's airway, the person may choke. Choking, also called obstructed airway, is a life-threatening emergency. Unless the object is dislodged within minutes, the person can die because the brain is deprived of oxygen.

A person who is choking may bring one or both hands to the throat, which is the universal sign for choking. The person may also gasp for air or turn blue. A choking person will not be able to speak.

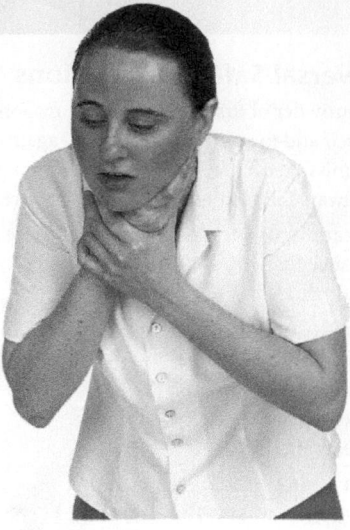

▲ **Universal sign for choking**

First Aid for Choking in an Adult or Child

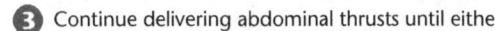

The first aid procedure for choking, sometimes called the Heimlich maneuver, involves delivering abdominal thrusts. Abdominal thrusts push air from the lungs up and out of the victim's airway with enough force to expel the object.

1 Ask the victim, "Are you choking?" If the victim is able to speak or cough, there is no need to deliver first aid. If the victim cannot speak or cough, prepare to perform abdominal thrusts.

2 Stand behind the victim. Wrap both of your arms around the upper part of the victim's abdomen, just below the rib cage. Make a fist with one hand and place it, thumb inward, on the victim's abdomen between the navel and breastbone. Grasp your fist with your other hand and pull sharply inward and upward.

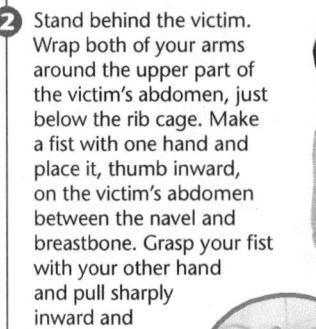

3 Continue delivering abdominal thrusts until either
  - ▶ the object becomes dislodged
  - ▶ the victim begins to cough or breathe
  - ▶ the victim becomes unconscious

4 If the victim becomes unconscious, call 911. Then begin CPR (pages 726–727).

If You Are Alone and You Are Choking

Position your hands on your abdomen (as described in Step 2) and perform abdominal thrusts on yourself. If this is not successful, position yourself over the back of a chair or against another firm object. Push into the chair or object so the force pushes upward and inward against your abdomen.

724

Rescue Breathing

If a person stops breathing, the body's cells quickly run out of oxygen and begin to die. This is especially true of brain cells. If brain cells are deprived of oxygen for more than five or six minutes, some cells will begin to die. This can result in permanent brain damage or death. Rescue breathing is the first aid procedure for someone who stops breathing.

You can recognize that someone has stopped breathing normally by the absence of breathing movements, such as the chest rising and falling, or by a bluish color to the lips, tongue, and fingernails. You can also place your cheek next to the victim's mouth and nose and feel for breath on your skin.

How to Perform Rescue Breathing on an Adult or Child

1 Call 911. Then lay the victim on a firm, flat surface.

2 Place one hand on the victim's forehead. Gently tilt the victim's head back. As you do this, the mouth may fall open.

3 Wearing disposable gloves, use your fingers to pick out obvious obstructions from the victim's mouth.

4 Keep one hand on the victim's forehead to maintain the head tilt. Place the fingertips of your other hand under the victim's chin and lift the chin up. Do not press on the soft tissues of the neck.

5 Keep the head tilted back and chin lifted up so the airway remains open. Look, listen, and feel for normal breathing.

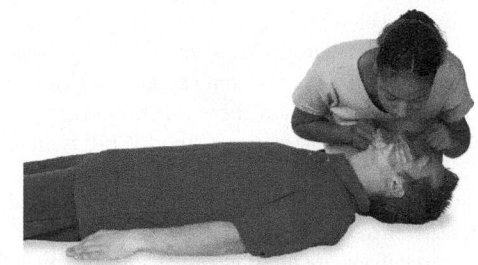

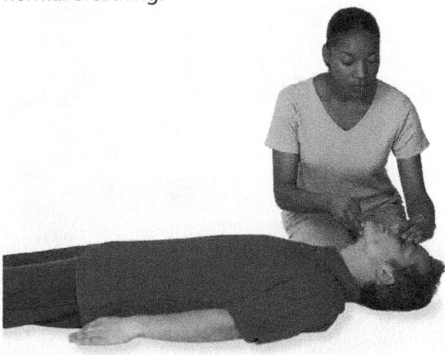

6 If the victim is not breathing normally, pinch the victim's nose closed using your finger and thumb. With your other hand, continue lifting the chin.

7 Place a face shield or mask over the victim's mouth. Take a normal breath, then place your lips on the shield or mask.

8 Blow into the victim's mouth for one second. Then take your mouth off the shield and look to see if the victim's chest moves. If the chest rises, this is a sign that you have given an effective breath.

9 If the victim's chest rises after the first breath, maintain the head tilt and chin lift. Then give a second breath. If the victim is still unresponsive after two breaths, begin CPR (pages 726-727).

10 If the victim's chest does not rise after the first breath, perform the head tilt and chin lift again. Then give a second breath. Whether or not the victim's chest rises, begin CPR.

Rescue Breathing

- Ask: **Why is it important to immediately initiate rescue breathing when someone has stopped breathing?** *(Death or permanent brain damage can occur within minutes if the body's cells do not get oxygen.)* **What universal safety precautions should be carried out when performing rescue breathing?** *(wearing disposable gloves, using a face shield or mask)* **What should you do if you cannot achieve two effective breaths?** *(You should begin CPR.)*

- Divide the class into small groups. Give each group ten unnumbered index cards. On the cards, have students write brief summaries of the steps of rescue breathing. Have a group member mix up the completed set of ten cards. The remaining group members should see how quickly they can arrange the cards in the correct order.

- Have students write a persuasive letter encouraging a friend to learn first aid techniques such as rescue breathing. Challenge students to include several facts to support their opinion. Have students post their completed letters in the classroom. **WRITING**

FirstAid Appendix

Cardiopulmonary Resuscitation (CPR)

Objectives

Identify the signs of cardiac arrest.

Describe when it is appropriate to administer CPR.

List the steps for performing CPR.

Cardiac Arrest

- Before students read about CPR, ask them to identify questions they have about the procedure. Record their questions on the board. As students read the description of CPR in the text, have them note the answers to the recorded questions. If there are still unanswered questions, suggest that students ask the school nurse or use library or Internet resources to find the answers. As students locate answers, have them share the information with the class.

- Make sure students understand that a heart attack and cardiac arrest are not the same thing. Review the warning signs of a heart attack listed on page 604. Contrast that list with the one on this page for cardiac arrest. Clarify that not all heart attack victims go into cardiac arrest, but that all people showing signs of a heart attack need to be monitored closely for any signs that they have gone into cardiac arrest. That way, CPR can begin immediately.

- Ask: **What are the signs of cardiac arrest?** *(unconsciousness, no normal breathing, no circulation)* **What should you check before you administer CPR?** *(You should confirm that the victim is unresponsive.)* **Why should you call 911 before beginning CPR?** *(so that trained professionals will arrive as soon as possible; so that the 911 operator can walk you through the steps for administering CPR)*

Cardiopulmonary Resuscitation (CPR)

If an unconscious victim is not breathing normally, the person might be suffering serious heart complications. Every second is critical for the victim's survival.

Cardiac Arrest

People who suffer heart attacks, severe injuries, drug overdoses, near drownings, or breathing problems may go into cardiac arrest. In cardiac arrest, the heart stops pumping blood throughout the body. When blood does not circulate, the brain and other vital organs do not receive oxygen. Without oxygen, the victim will lose consciousness and die within minutes.

Cardiopulmonary resuscitation (CPR) is the first aid procedure for unconscious victims. If CPR is started immediately after a victim collapses, it can greatly increase the person's chances for survival.

Even if you are not trained in CPR, you can help. If you see an adult collapse from cardiac arrest, call 911. Then do chest compressions, or hands-only CPR, until help arrives.

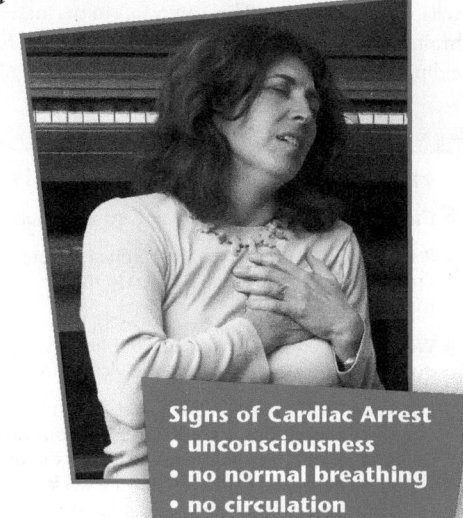

Signs of Cardiac Arrest
- unconsciousness
- no normal breathing
- no circulation

How to Perform Cardiovascular Resuscitation (CPR)

CPR combines rescue breathing (to force oxygen into the lungs) with chest compressions (to pump blood throughout the body). If you have confirmed that the victim is unresponsive and you have been trained in CPR, follow these steps.

1. Call 911. If there is someone with you, have that person call 911 so you can start CPR immediately.

2. Kneel beside the victim and look, listen, and feel for signs of normal breathing.

3. If the victim is not breathing normally, open the airway and give two effective rescue breaths (page 725).

4. To deliver chest compressions, locate the center of the victim's chest, midway between the nipples.

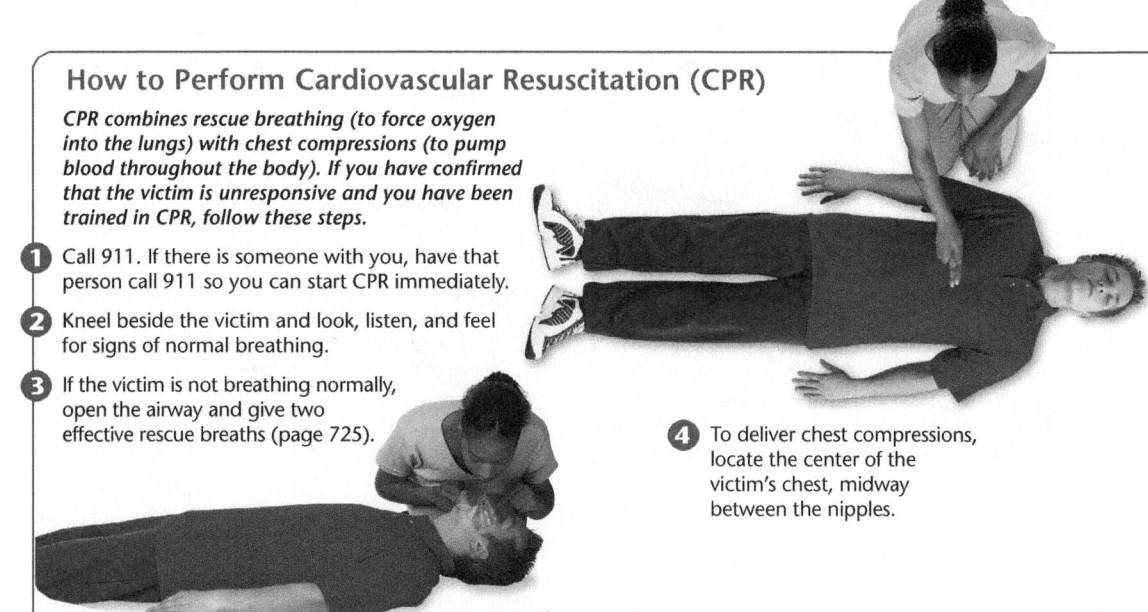

For Your **INFORMATION!**

Guidelines for CPR

In 2008, the American Heart Association amended their 2005 guidelines on CPR to increase the use of CPR. Bystanders who are trained in CPR and confident in their ability to provide rescue breaths with minimal interruption of compressions can use either conventional CPR or hands-only CPR. Those who are not trained or not confident in their ability to combine rescue breaths with compressions should use hands-only CPR. Hands-only CPR should not be used for infants, children, adults who do not collapse suddenly, or adults with a suspected respiratory cause for arrest, e.g., drowning.

⑤ Place the heel of one hand in the center of the victim's chest. Your fingers should be extended and pointing away from you.

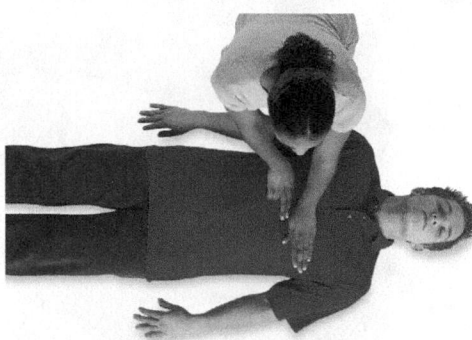

⑥ Place the heel of your second hand on top of the first so that your hands are overlapped and parallel. Interlock your fingers and keep your fingers raised off the victim's chest, as shown in the photo below.

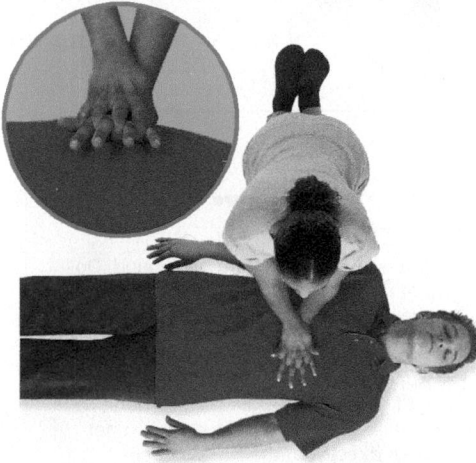

⑦ Lean over the victim so your shoulders are above your hands, and straighten your arms. Press down on the breastbone to compress the chest by 1.5 to 2 inches. Then release the pressure without removing your hands from the victim's chest.

⑧ Compress the victim's chest 30 times at the rate of 100 compressions per minute. Each compression and release should take about the same time.

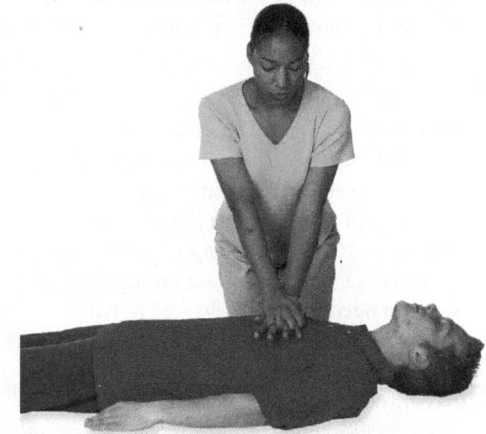

⑨ Establish a cycle of 2 rescue breaths and 30 chest compressions. Five cycles of breaths and compressions should take about two minutes.

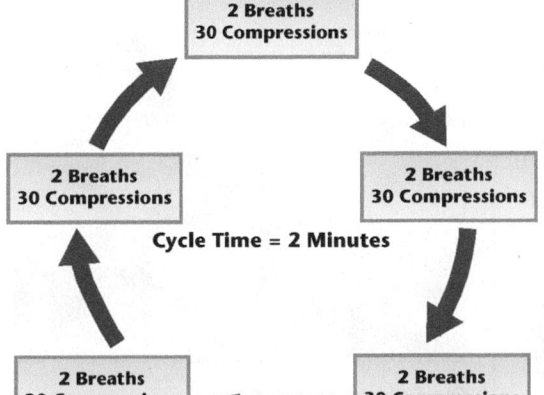

2 Breaths 30 Compressions

2 Breaths 30 Compressions

2 Breaths 30 Compressions

2 Breaths 30 Compressions

2 Breaths 30 Compressions

Cycle Time = 2 Minutes

⑩ Continue CPR until either medical help arrives and takes over, an AED can be located and used, or the victim starts moving on his or her own.

- Ask students to contact the American Red Cross to find out more about CPR training courses offered in your area. Have students investigate the cost of training and the locations where training is offered. Have students make a poster to share information about CPR training opportunities with other students.

- Have students work in small groups to create a multimedia presentation that describes CPR and explains the importance of receiving CPR training. Have each group share its presentation with the class.

- Have students tap 30 times on their desks while a partner times how long it takes. Tell students that it should take about 18 seconds to deliver the 30 "compressions." Both students should practice until they are consistently able to deliver the "compressions" at the proper rate.

- If your school has an automated external defibrillator (AED), review with your students where it is located, when they should retrieve it, and how it works. Students can also find out where else in your community AEDs can be found (for example, malls, health clubs, subway or bus stations, stadiums, town offices). Have students highlight the locations of buildings with AEDs on a town map.

FirstAid Appendix

Bone, Joint, and Muscle Injuries

Objectives

Identify the signs of a possible fracture and explain how to provide first aid for fractures.

Describe the symptoms of strains, sprains, dislocations, and muscle cramps.

Explain how to provide first aid for strains, sprains, dislocations, and muscle cramps.

Fractures

- Ask: **What is the difference between an open fracture and a closed fracture?** *(An open fracture occurs when a piece of the broken bone protrudes through the skin. The skin is not broken in a closed fracture.)* **What is the purpose of a splint?** *(A splint stabilizes the injured limb and prevents further injury.)*

- Remind students that a splint is any object that can be used to stabilize a body part. Have students identify everyday objects that could be used as splints in an emergency situation (for example; cardboard, folded newspaper). Record their responses on the board.

- Have interested students investigate careers in sports medicine. Students can use library or Internet resources or interviews to find information about careers in this field. Ask students to report on specific careers and the training required for those careers.

- Have students interview a family member or friend who has experienced a fracture. During their interviews, have students find out more about first aid for fractures, methods of treating fractures, and the healing process.

Bone, Joint, and Muscle Injuries

Suppose that a friend tripped and fell and his wrist began to swell. Would you know what to do? By providing proper first aid, you can reduce your friend's pain and speed up the healing process.

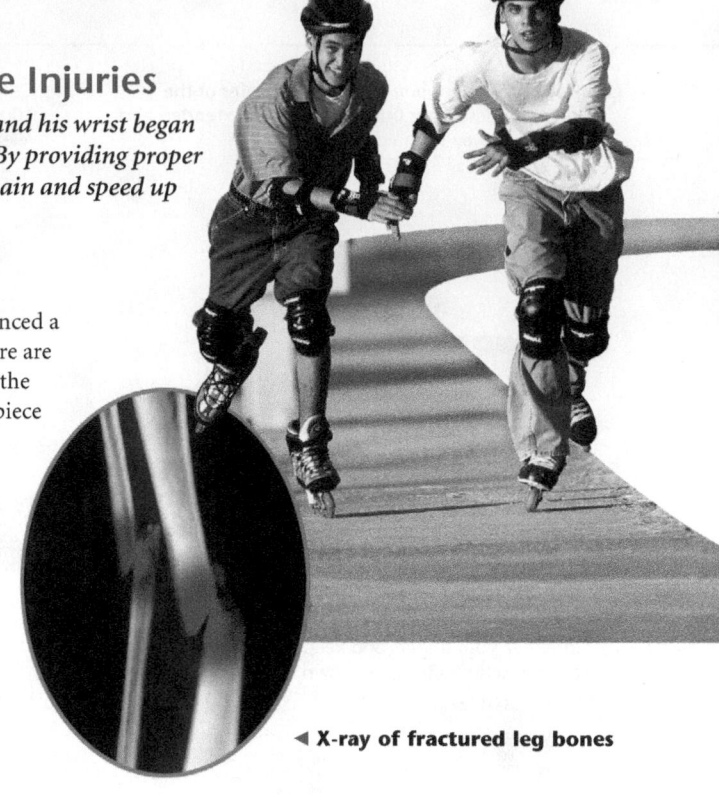

Fractures

You might know someone who has experienced a fracture—a crack or a break in a bone. There are two types of fractures. In a closed fracture, the skin remains intact. In an open fracture, a piece of the broken bone sticks out through the skin. An open fracture may bleed heavily.

The only sure way to identify a fracture is with an X-ray. However, it is important to recognize the signs of a possible fracture. These include

▶ swelling and bruising at the injured area

▶ pain in the injured area

▶ deformity of the injured area, such as a shortened, bent, or twisted limb

▶ difficulty moving the injured area

◀ **X-ray of fractured leg bones**

First Aid for Fractures

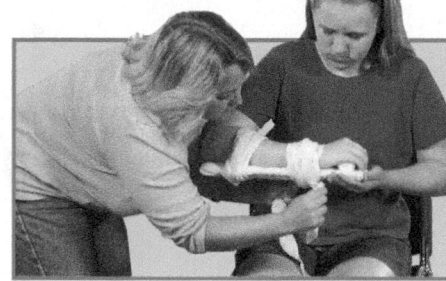

For a Closed Fracture

1. Stabilize the injured area with a sling or a splint. A splint is any material that prevents the injured part from moving. Do not try to straighten a bent bone or limb.

2. Keep the victim still and comfortable. Seek medical attention.

For an Open Fracture

1. Call 911 immediately.

2. Cut away clothing from the wound. Do not try to push the bone back through the skin. Do not try to straighten a bent bone or limb.

3. Apply gentle pressure with a large sterile pad to control bleeding. If you don't have a sterile pad, use a clean cloth. Do not push directly on the exposed bone.

4. Cover the entire wound with a sterile bandage or clean cloth.

5. If the victim needs to be moved before help arrives, first apply a splint to stabilize the injured area.

Strains and Sprains

A muscle strain can result from overexerting or pulling a muscle, such as a back muscle.

Symptoms of a muscle strain include

▶ dull pain that worsens with movement of the injured area

▶ swelling around the injured area

A sprain is an injury to a ligament—the strong, flexible bands of tissue that hold bones together at a joint.

Symptoms of a sprain include

▶ a popping sound or tearing sensation at the time of injury

▶ pain in the injured joint, especially when moving it

▶ swelling of the joint

▶ tenderness when the injured area is touched

▶ discoloration (black and blue) around the injured area

Dislocations

If a joint is twisted or overstressed, one or more of the bones that normally meet at that joint may become displaced, or dislocated.

Symptoms of a dislocation include

▶ swelling and deformity around the injured area

▶ inability to move the joint, or pain when moving the joint

▶ discoloration, tenderness, or numbness

Muscle Cramps

A muscle cramp is the sudden, painful contraction of one or more muscles.

Symptoms of a muscle cramp include

▶ severe pain in the cramping muscle

▶ inability to use the cramping muscle

First Aid for Strains and Sprains

The first aid procedure for strains and sprains can be remembered by the initials R.I.C.E.

R **Rest** the injured area and avoid using it.

I **Ice** the area during the first 24 hours to reduce swelling. After that, periodically apply moist heat to the area.

C **Compress** the area with an elastic wrap.

E **Elevate** the injured area to prevent or limit swelling.

First Aid for Dislocations

The first aid procedure for a dislocated joint is similar to the procedure for a fracture.

1. Do not move the injured limb or try to put a dislocated bone back into its place.

2. Place the victim in a comfortable position.

3. Stabilize the injured body part with a sling or a splint.

4. Seek medical attention promptly.

First Aid for Muscle Cramps

1. Stretch out the cramping muscle to counteract the cramp.

2. Massage the muscle firmly, but gently.

3. Have the victim drink plenty of fluids.

4. Seek medical help if the cramps persist.

Strains and Sprains

● Ask students to work in small groups to develop a short lesson that could be used to teach the R.I.C.E. method of treating strains and sprains to students in grades 3–4. Have each group share its lesson with the class. After students have received feedback on their lessons, arrange for them to teach their lessons to students in grades 3–4.

● Put students into small groups to come up with a list of supplies to include in a first aid kit to take with them on a long hike. Tell students to pay particular attention to supplies needed for potential bone, joint, and muscle injuries. Then bring the class together to create a master list of first aid supplies.

Dislocations

● Invite the school athletic trainer to talk to your class about how dislocations can occur (for example, tackling in football, using the arm to break a fall). Have the trainer discuss how often dislocations and other sports injuries occur during sports activities. Can the trainer suggest some strategies for preventing or treating sports injuries?

Muscle Cramps

● Point out that dehydration is one cause of muscle cramps. Discuss strategies for staying hydrated during exercise, particularly in hot weather.

● Have students work in small groups to create a chart that describes the treatments for fractures, strains and sprains, dislocations, and muscle cramps. Post the completed charts around the classroom.

● Have students write five questions they can use to quiz a partner about fractures, strains and sprains, dislocations, and muscle cramps. Follow up by asking students to identify the questions they found most difficult to answer.

FirstAid Appendix

Outdoor Emergencies

Objectives

Explain how to recognize and treat frostbite and hypothermia.

Distinguish between heat exhaustion and heat stroke and explain how each is treated.

Summarize strategies for water rescue.

Frostbite

- Ask students to write a paragraph that compares and contrasts frostbite and hypothermia. Challenge students to include information about the symptoms and treatments for these conditions. **WRITING**

- Have students identify strategies for preventing frostbite when participating in outdoor activities. List students' suggestions on the board and discuss the merits of each.

Hypothermia

- Write the word *hypothermia* on the board. Discuss the meaning of the word parts *hypo-* (below or less than normal) and *-therm* (temperature).

- Students may think that hypothermia can only occur in very cold weather conditions. Clarify that the risk of hypothermia can be high if a person becomes wet from rain or from immersion in a body of water. Hypothermia is also a serious risk for elderly people whose homes are heated inadequately, homeless people in cool or damp weather, and hikers without adequate clothing to protect themselves when temperatures drop at night.

- Have students write a short, fictional story in which one character develops hypothermia and is given appropriate first aid by another character. Challenge students to provide a detailed description of the steps taken to provide first aid. Ask volunteers to share their stories with the class. **WRITING**

Outdoor Emergencies

Many teens enjoy outdoor activities. But those activities can expose you to extremes in temperatures and other potential dangers that may require first aid.

Frostbite

When extremities, such as hands, feet, arms, and legs, are exposed to very cold temperatures, body tissue can freeze. This is called frostbite. Frostbite is a serious condition that can result in the loss of the affected area.

Signs of frostbite include

▶ lack of feeling in the affected area

▶ skin that appears waxy or discolored and is cold to the touch

First Aid for Frostbite

1. Call 911. Then help move the victim out of the cold.

2. Remove any jewelry and wet or restrictive clothing, if possible.

3. Handle the affected area gently. Avoid rubbing the area, because rubbing could cause further injury.

4. If there is no chance that the affected area will freeze again, begin to rewarm it slowly. Gently soak the area in warm water at 100–105°F. Keep soaking until the area turns red and feels warm.

5. Wrap the affected area with dry blankets or towels.

6. If fingers or toes are frostbitten, place clean cloth between them to keep them separated.

7. Avoid breaking any blisters that may have formed.

Hypothermia

Hypothermia is the overall cooling of the entire body to a body temperature below 95°F. A person suffering from hypothermia may develop an abnormal heart rhythm, and the heart may eventually stop beating. Hypothermia can occur even when the temperature is above freezing, especially in a cold, damp, rainy environment.

Signs of hypothermia include

▶ shivering

▶ numbness or weakness

▶ glassy stare

▶ confusion or impaired consciousness

First Aid for Hypothermia

1. Call 911 immediately. Then help move the victim out of the cold.

2. Carefully remove any wet clothing and dry the victim.

3. Warm the body gradually by wrapping the victim in blankets or dry clothing.

4. Apply hot water bottles or other heat sources, wrapped in a towel, to the victim's body, if available. Do not warm the victim too quickly because this could result in dangerous heart rhythms.

5. If the victim is conscious and alert, give warm liquids, such as warm water or decaffeinated tea or coffee.

6. Monitor breathing and consciousness until medical help arrives. Be prepared to perform rescue breathing or CPR, if necessary.

730

Heat Exhaustion

Working outdoors in the heat or long periods of strenuous exercise can lead to heat exhaustion. With heat exhaustion, a person's body temperature can rise to dangerous levels.

Signs of heat exhaustion include

- ► skin that is cool, moist, pale, ashen, or flushed
- ► headache, nausea, or dizziness
- ► weakness or exhaustion
- ► heavy sweating
- ► muscle cramps

Heat Stroke

If heat exhaustion is not treated and the victim continues to overheat, heat stroke can develop. In heat stroke, body systems become so overheated that they stop functioning. As body fluids become depleted, the person stops sweating and the body can no longer cool itself. Vital organs, such as the brain, heart, and kidneys, can cease to function and death can result.

Signs of heat stroke include

- ► confusion or strange behavior
- ► red, hot, dry skin
- ► inability to drink or vomiting
- ► shallow breathing, seizures, or unconsciousness

Rescuing a Drowning Victim

If someone in the water seems to be having trouble, it is important to assess the situation quickly. Call 911 or send someone for help. Determine how to rescue the person quickly without putting yourself at risk. As soon as the victim is out of the water, perform rescue breathing or CPR, if necessary.

First Aid for Heat Exhaustion

1. Help move the victim to a cool or shady location.
2. Loosen or remove any tight clothing.
3. If the victim is conscious and alert, give fluids to replace fluids lost in sweat.
4. Cool the victim's body by wrapping it in water-soaked towels or by sponging or spraying cool water onto the victim.
5. Monitor the victim for signs of heat stroke or shock. Be prepared to call 911, if necessary.

First Aid for Heat Stroke

1. Call 911 immediately. Then help move the victim to a cool or shady location.
2. Loosen or remove any tight clothing.
3. Cool the victim quickly using whatever means are available. You can soak towels or sheets in cold water and apply them to the victim's body. You can use a hose to spray water on the victim, or wrap cold packs in a cloth and apply them to the victim.
4. Carefully monitor the victim. Be prepared to perform rescue breathing or CPR, if necessary.

Heat Exhaustion

- Have students interview a coach, athletic trainer, or physical education teacher to learn more about preventing heat exhaustion during participation in sports. Ask students to share what they have learned with the class.

Heat Stroke

- Ask students to make a Venn diagram that organizes the similarities and differences between heat exhaustion and heat stroke. Then have students form small groups. Within each group, students should discuss their diagrams. Instruct students to make corrections or additions to their diagrams as they work with their groups.

Rescuing a Drowning Victim

- Have students contact the American Red Cross to learn more about water safety and opportunities for water safety training that are available in the community. Have students make a poster that illustrates one water safety tip.
- Tell students that "Reach or throw, don't go" is a slogan used by the American Red Cross to summarize safe water rescue techniques. Ask students to explain the meaning of the slogan. (Reach a drowning person with a stick, pole, or other object; throw a life preserver or other flotation device to a drowning person; only swim out to a drowning victim if you are properly trained and have the appropriate skills and equipment.) Challenge students to develop a water safety slogan of their own.

Water Rescue Techniques

731

FirstAid Appendix

Bites and Stings

Objectives

Identify the signs of poisonous snakebites and insect stings.

Explain how to provide first aid for poisonous snakebites, insect stings, and animal bites.

Poisonous Snakebites

- Have interested students locate information about the species of poisonous snakes that are found in different regions of the United States. Ask the students to prepare a report that includes pictures of the poisonous snakes. Have students share their reports with the class. **WRITING**

Insect Stings

- Ask: **When does an insect sting become a medical emergency?** *(when an allergic reaction occurs)* **What would you do if a friend had an allergic reaction to an insect sting?** *(Sample answer: I would call 911 and monitor my friend's condition while I waited for help to arrive.)*

- Have a few students interview the school nurse or other medical professional to find out more about recognizing and treating allergic reactions to insect stings. Have the students give a brief oral report that summarizes their findings.

Animal Bites

- Explain that some mammals, including raccoons, bats, dogs, and skunks, can carry rabies, a viral disease. Rabies can be passed to humans if they are bitten. Rabies vaccines are given to pet cats and dogs to prevent rabies. Ask students who are pet owners to find out more about rabies vaccines from their pet's veterinarian and share the information with the class.

Bites and Stings

Poisonous Snakebites

Although about 8,000 people are bitten by poisonous snakes in the United States each year, fewer than five people die. Nevertheless, poisonous snakebites can be dangerous. Medical care needs to be administered quickly.

Signs of a poisonous snakebite include

- ▶ one or two distinct puncture wounds
- ▶ severe pain, redness, and swelling at the bite
- ▶ nausea and vomiting
- ▶ blurred vision
- ▶ increased salivation and sweating
- ▶ labored breathing

Insect Stings

For most people, insect stings can be painful but not life threatening. However, some people are highly allergic to substances in the venom of some insects.

Signs of an insect sting vary with each insect, but generally include

- ▶ pain
- ▶ swelling at the site of the sting
- ▶ hives or a rash
- ▶ nausea and vomiting
- ▶ breathing difficulties
- ▶ swelling of the tongue or face

Animal Bites

Animal bites carry the risk of infection, including the potentially fatal disease rabies. Anyone bitten by a person or by a wild or domestic animal should seek medical help as soon as possible.

First Aid for Poisonous Snakebites

1. Call 911.
2. Gently wash the wound with clean running water.
3. Immobilize the affected area.
4. Minimize the victim's movements.
5. Make sure the victim receives medical assistance within 30 minutes of being bitten.

First Aid for Insect Stings

1. Remove the stinger if it is visible by scraping it off with your fingernail or a credit card. Do not remove the stinger with tweezers.
2. Wash and then cover the wound.
3. Apply a cold pack wrapped in a cloth to the site of the sting.
4. Watch for signs of a severe allergic reaction (blotchy skin, swelling of the tongue or throat, puffiness around the eyes, breathing difficulties, or signs of shock).
5. At the first sign of a severe allergic reaction, call 911 immediately.
6. Monitor the victim's airway and breathing.

First Aid for Animal Bites

1. Wearing disposable gloves, wash the wound thoroughly with clean running water.
2. Control any bleeding with pressure.
3. Apply a clean, dry dressing.
4. Seek medical care.

Poisonings

Swallowed Poisons

A poison is any substance that can cause injury or death when it gets inside the body. Poisons that can be swallowed include cleaning products, pesticides, certain plants, paint thinner, and certain medications.

Signs that a person has swallowed a poisonous substance include

▶ vomiting, sometimes including blood

▶ confusion or impaired consciousness

▶ pain or a burning sensation

▶ empty containers in the vicinity of the victim

Inhaled Poisons

There are many harmful fumes that can poison the body if inhaled. One of the most common is carbon monoxide, a colorless, odorless gas. Carbon monoxide is a component of automobile exhaust, but can also be released by certain fires, defective furnaces or cooking equipment, and kerosene heaters.

Signs of carbon monoxide poisoning include

▶ skin that is pale or bluish in color

▶ headache

▶ noisy, distressed breathing

▶ confusion

▶ loss of consciousness

First Aid for Swallowed Poisons

1 Call 911. (The 911 operator may connect you to a poison control center, where medical professionals will provide specific instructions.)

2 If the victim is conscious, ask what was swallowed so you can relay that information to the medical professionals.

3 Monitor the victim's airway and breathing. Be prepared to perform rescue breathing or CPR, if necessary.

4 Do not induce vomiting. Do not give the victim anything to eat or drink unless the emergency operator tells you to do so.

First Aid for Inhaled Poisons

1 Call 911 and report your observations.

2 Carefully survey the scene to be sure that the poisonous fumes are no longer present and that it is safe for you to approach the victim.

3 If the victim is conscious and it is safe for you to do so, help the victim move into fresh air. Monitor the victim until help arrives. Be prepared to perform rescue breathing or CPR, if needed.

4 If the victim is unconscious, begin CPR immediately.

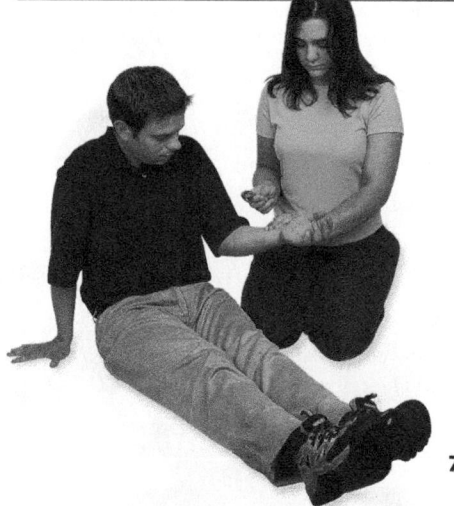

733

Objectives

Identify the signs that a person has swallowed or inhaled a poison.

Describe first aid for swallowed and inhaled poisons.

Swallowed Poisons

● Ask students to locate the telephone number for the poison control center in their area. Have students make cards containing emergency telephone numbers, including the poison control center, to post by their home telephones. Remind students that they should always call 911 first in an emergency.

● Have students use parenting books or Web sites to learn more about how to make a home safe for young children by securing, moving, or removing poisons. Ask students to explain how they could apply this information when caring for a younger sibling or babysitting for others.

Inhaled Poisons

● Explain that carbon monoxide is poisonous because it binds to hemoglobin, the protein in blood that carries oxygen to the cells of the body. When carbon monoxide is bound to hemoglobin, it prevents oxygen from binding and thus from being delivered to the body's cells. Have interested students find out more about the reaction between carbon monoxide and hemoglobin or the mechanisms by which other poisons affect the body.

FirstAid Appendix

Bleeding

Objectives

Explain how to provide first aid for severe bleeding.

Describe first aid for nosebleeds.

Severe Bleeding

- Ask students to imagine the following scenario: You have just witnessed a bicycle crash. When you stop to offer assistance, you observe that the rider has cut her arm and is bleeding severely. Have students write a paragraph explaining what they would do in this situation. Ask volunteers to share their completed paragraphs with the class. **WRITING**

Nosebleeds

- Ask: **What steps would you follow to provide first aid to a friend who has a nosebleed?** *(Sample answer: I would have my friend sit down and lean forward, pinch her nose and breathe though her mouth for 10 minutes. After the 10 minute period I would assess the bleeding and repeat the steps if the bleeding had not stopped. After the bleeding stops, I would have her rest for several hours and avoid blowing her nose or sniffing.)* **What signs would indicate that a nosebleed is a serious medical emergency?** *(A nosebleed that continues for a period of more than a few minutes and results in the loss of a large amount of blood.)*

Bleeding

Severe Bleeding

Bleeding occurs when a blood vessel ruptures. The severity of the bleeding depends on the type of vessel that ruptures. For minor bleeding, applying constant pressure at the site of the wound can usually control the bleeding.

More severe bleeding may occur if an artery ruptures. Blood that is bright red in color may spurt from the wound. If the bleeding is not controlled quickly, the victim can die within a few minutes.

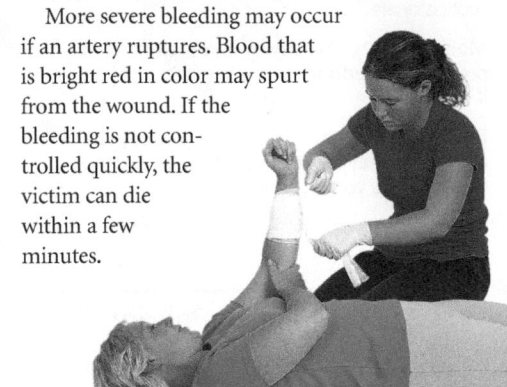

Nosebleeds

Nosebleeds can result from a blow to the nose or from a less obvious situation. Nosebleeds seldom require medical attention. However, if a nosebleed continues for more than a few minutes and results in the loss of a lot of blood, it can become a serious emergency.

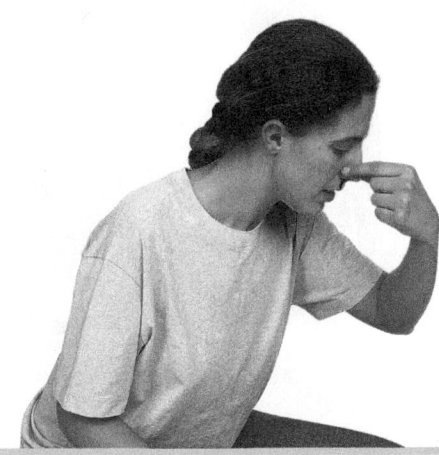

First Aid for Severe Bleeding

1. Call 911.

2. Wearing disposable gloves, apply direct pressure to the wound using a sterile gauze pad or a clean absorbent cloth. If disposable gloves are not available, have the victim apply pressure on the wound.

3. While continuing to apply pressure, elevate the injured area above the level of the heart, unless you suspect a fracture. In that case, follow the guidelines for providing first aid for fractures (page 728).

4. Make a "pressure bandage" by snuggly wrapping an elastic bandage (or another cloth) over the sterile gauze pad. The pressure bandage will apply continuous direct pressure to the wound.

5. If bleeding continues, apply additional bandages on top of the existing ones.

6. Monitor the victim's breathing and consciousness and watch for signs of shock. Be prepared to perform rescue breathing or CPR, if necessary.

First Aid for Nosebleeds

1. Have the victim sit down and lean forward to clear the blood from the nostrils.

2. Tell the victim to breathe through the mouth and to apply pressure by pinching the nostrils closed for 10 minutes.

3. Caution the victim not to cough, spit, or sniff because this could disturb the blood clots that are forming in the nose.

4. After 10 minutes, have the victim release the pressure. If the bleeding has not stopped, have the victim reapply pressure for another 10 minutes.

5. Once the bleeding has stopped, have the victim rest quietly for a few hours. Caution the victim to avoid blowing his or her nose as this could cause the bleeding to start again.

6. If the bleeding will not stop or if the victim is having trouble breathing, call 911.

734

Burns

Severe Burns

Burn injuries are categorized by the depth of the burned tissue. First-degree burns affect only the epidermis, the outer layer of skin. Second-degree burns affect the dermis, the layer of skin below the surface. And third-degree burns affect all the layers of skin and possibly the tissue beneath the skin.

Large or deep burns can be life threatening and require immediate medical attention. Burns that require emergency care include

▶ burns that cover a large surface area of the body or more than one body part

▶ suspected burns to the airway

▶ burns to the head, neck, hands, feet, or genitals

▶ burns to victims under the age of 5 or over 60

▶ burns that result from chemicals, explosions, or electricity

First Aid for Severe Burns

1. Call 911.

2. Remove the victim from the source of the burn if you can do so without causing injury to yourself.

3. Check the victim's breathing and consciousness. Be prepared to perform rescue breathing and CPR, if necessary.

4. Pour cold water over the burn to cool it down and to reduce the pain.

5. Continue cooling the burn until help arrives.

6. If possible, cover the burn with a clean cloth to minimize infection. Do not apply any ointments.

Sunburns

One common first-degree burn is caused by the sun. A sunburn is actually a radiation burn because it is caused by ultraviolet radiation from the sun. The risk of sunburn can be reduced by using sunscreen with an SPF of 15 or more.

Signs of sunburn include

▶ reddened skin

▶ pain in the area of the burn

▶ blisters in the burned area

First Aid for Sunburns

1. Cover the victim's skin with light clothing or a towel.

2. Help the victim move indoors or into the shade.

3. Pour cold water on the cloth covering the burned area to cool the skin and relieve the pain.

4. Encourage the person to take frequent sips of cold water.

5. For a severe sunburn, seek medical help.

Burns

Objectives

Compare first-degree, second-degree, and third-degree burns.

Describe first aid for severe burns.

Explain why sunburns are dangerous.

Severe Burns

- A common misconception about burns is that covering a burn with butter will help it heal. Explain that spreading butter on a burn increases the chance of infection and slows healing. Have students work in small groups to make a pamphlet that describes proper first aid for burns.

- Ask: **What distinguishes first-degree, second-degree, and third-degree burns?** *(First-degree burns affect only the epidermis, or top layer of skin; second-degree burns affect the epidermis and dermis; third-degree burns affect all the layers of skin, as well as the underlying tissue.)* **What indicates that a burn requires immediate medical attention?** *(It covers a large surface area or more than one body part; it affects the airway, head, neck, hands, feet, or genitals; the victim is under 5 or over 60 years of age; or it is the result of chemicals, electricity, or an explosion.)*

Sunburns

- Review the information on pages 349 and 612–614 that describes the long-term dangers of sun exposure. Remind students that tanning beds are *not* a safe alternative to sun exposure. Then have students create a slogan that encourages teens to protect their skin from the sun.

Organ Donation
Appendix

Objectives

List the benefits of organ donation.

Describe the process for becoming a potential organ donor.

Identify local and state resources that support organ donation.

Teaching Strategies

- After discussing the need for organ donation, tell students that many people who say they support organ donation do not become donors. On the board, make a list of reasons why people may be reluctant to become a potential organ donor. For example, some people are afraid that doctors will not work as hard to save a potential organ donor's life. Work with the students to compile a set of responses. Frequently asked questions on organ donation Web sites are an invaluable resource.

- The process for organ donation in a state may change. For example, North Carolina passed the "Heart Prevails" law in 2007, which changed the meaning of the heart symbol on a driver's license from intent to legal consent. Explain the process for organ donation in your state. Then ask students to write simple step-by-step instructions for people who want to be donors. **WRITING**

- Encourage students to make posters to advocate organ donation. Stress that you are looking for a fresh take on the topic, not slogans or images that students have seen before. If possible, make an arrangement with a local library or community center to display some finished posters.

⚑ Sensitive Issues

Some students may know someone who is waiting for a transplant. Others may have known a person who died while on the waiting list. Respect students' decisions to keep this information private or to share their experiences with the class.

Organ Donation Appendix

An organ may become so damaged that it can no longer perform its functions in the body. Sometimes the damaged organ is replaced with an organ that is working. This procedure is called an organ transplant.

As doctors have more success transplanting organs, the list of people waiting for a transplant grows. About 4,000 new patients are added to the waiting list each month. But the number of available organs has not kept pace with the need. So some people die while waiting for "the gift of life."

The Benefits of Organ Donation

More people might become donors if they realized that one donor can save or improve the lives of many people. Organs, such as hearts and lungs, are not the only parts of the body that can be transplanted. Skin grafts can help burn victims heal. Corneas can restore a person's sight. Blood vessels are used in bypass surgeries.

Organ donation can also help a donor's family. As the family grieves the death of a loved one, they can think about all the people who are being helped.

Becoming a Possible Organ Donor

There are no limits on who can donate organs. If you are not yet 18, however, you need the consent of a parent or guardian. People can use one or more of the options listed below to register as a possible organ donor.

- Most states have an organ and tissue donor registry. People can often sign up online.

- People can download a donor card to carry in their wallets. The card must be signed by the donor and two witnesses.

- In many states, people can sign up when they apply for or renew a driver's license. The state will place a symbol on the license. In North Carolina, for example, the symbol is a heart.

People who want to be donors have one more important task. Families are often consulted before organs are accepted for donation. So possible donors need to tell their families about their plan. That way, family members are able to act as advocates for donation.

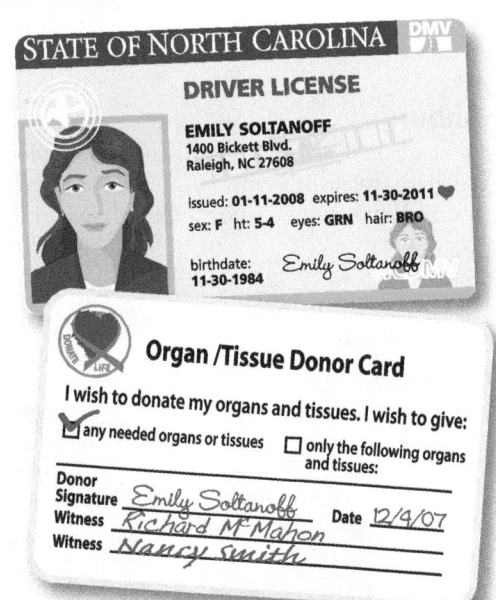

For Your INFORMATION!

Living Donations

Living donors can give part of a liver, lung, or pancreas and one kidney. Live donation increases the number of available organs, and allows time for better tissue matches, which reduces rejection. The operations can be planned, and the organ is outside the body for less time.

The donor faces the risks associated with any surgery, including the risk of infection. He or she may have to deal with postoperative emotional issues, especially if the recipient's outcome is not positive. Some states, such as New York and North Carolina, mandate pre- and postoperative support for live donors.

Becoming a Possible Organ Recipient

A doctor may think that a patient could benefit from a transplant. If so, the doctor will refer the patient to one of about 250 transplant centers in the United States. Each transplant center is qualified to do one or more types of transplants.

The transplant team will decide whether a patient is a good candidate for a transplant. Once patients receive approval, their names are added to a national waiting list. The list is maintained by the United Network for Organ Sharing (UNOS).

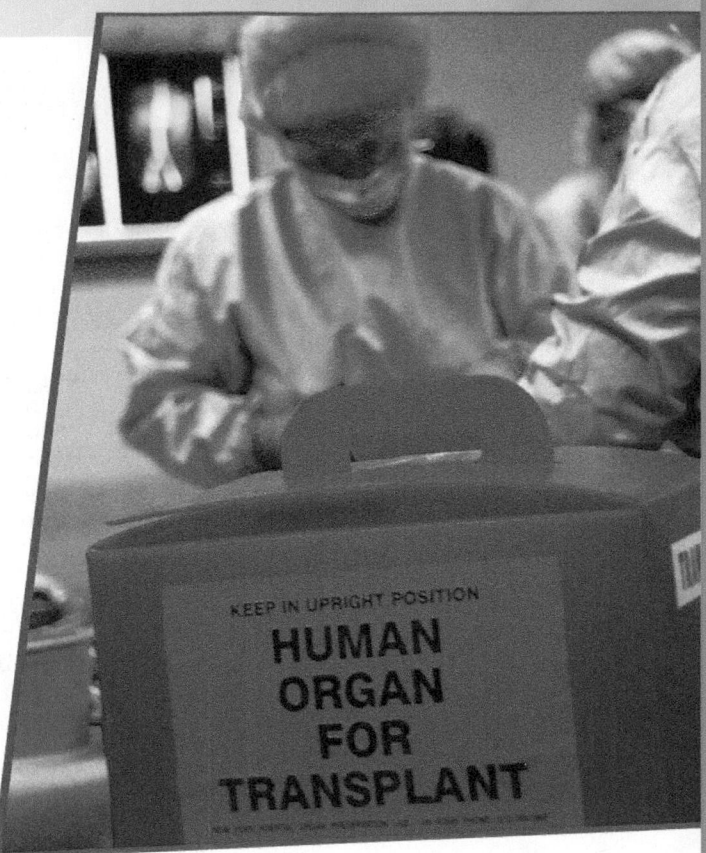

- April is National Donate Life Month. Find out what events will be taking place in your area, and encourage students to get involved.

- Explain that organs such as the heart and lungs can survive outside the body for only 4 to 6 hours. A liver or a pancreas can stay healthy for 12 to 24 hours. A kidney can stay healthy for between 48 and 72 hours. This is one reason why an OPO must consider geography when choosing a recipient for an organ. Then ask students which transplant team has more possible matches: the team doing a heart transplant or the team doing a liver transplant.

- Encourage interested students to identify transplant centers in your region, the types of transplants these centers do, and which OPO they work with. If possible, arrange for someone who works for an OPO to come and talk with your class. Have students prepare questions in advance.

- Students may wonder about the process for tissue testing. Explain that potential organ recipients are tested for tissue compatibility when they are placed on the waiting list. Donors are tested at the time when their organs become available. Also note that the need for a close tissue match depends on the organ. For example, kidneys are more sensitive to a mismatch of antigens than are hearts and lungs, but livers are less sensitive.

Matching Recipients and Donors

When organs become available, a match must be made between patients on the waiting list and the donor. Blood type, tissue type, and organ size are factors. So is a patient's medical condition. Where a patient lives is also a factor. A person who lives nearby is preferred. If no local match is found, an organ is offered within a region, and then nationally.

Recall that the human immune system will attack foreign antigens. This type of attack can cause a donated organ to be so damaged that it can no longer function. This outcome is called rejection. Doctors can reduce the risk of rejection. They use drugs that suppress the immune system. They also try to match donors with recipients who have many of the same antigens. Such matches are most likely between people with similar genetic profiles. So it is important for the donor pool to include people from different ethnic groups.

Organ Procurement

UNOS links transplant centers with organ procurement organizations (OPOs). An OPO is a nonprofit agency. People who work for an OPO do the following tasks.

- They talk with families about organ donation after a person dies.

- They coordinate the recovery of organs.

- They make sure that organs are preserved until the organs are transplanted.

- They arrange to transport organs to transplant centers.

- They educate the public about the need for organ donation.

Glossary

A

absorption The process by which nutrients pass through the lining of the digestive system. (p. 242)
absorción Proceso mediante el cual los nutrientes pasan a través de las paredes del sistema digestivo.

abstinence The act of refraining from, or not having, sex. (p. 154)
abstinencia Acción de privarse de tener relaciones sexuales.

acne A lesion that forms when excess oil and dead cells plug a hair follicle. (p. 350)
acné Lesión que se produce cuando el exceso de grasa y de células muertas obstruyen un folículo piloso.

action plan A series of specific steps you can take to achieve a goal. (p. 15)
plan de acción Serie de pasos determinados que se toman para alcanzar una meta.

active listening Focusing your full attention on what another person is saying and letting that person know you understand and care. (p. 137)
atención activa Concentrar completamente la atención en lo que otra persona dice, haciéndole saber así que se comprende y se siente interés por lo que está diciendo.

active supervision Keeping children in your view at all times when they are in or near the water. (p. 705)
supervisión activa Observar a los niños constantemente cuando están en el agua o cerca de ella.

addiction The state of losing control over the use of a drug; it is accompanied by a strong craving for the drug. (p. 388)
adicción Pérdida del control a causa del uso de una droga; viene acompañada de un intenso deseo de consumir dicha droga.

adolescence The period from about age 12 to 19 during which a child gradually changes into an adult. (p. 514)
adolescencia Período entre los 12 y los 19 años aproximadamente, durante el cual un(a) niño(a) se convierte gradualmente en adulto.

adoption The legal process by which parents take another person's child into their family to be raised as their own. (p. 114)
adopción Procedimiento legal a través del cual los padres reciben en su familia al hijo de otra persona para criarlo como suyo.

advertising The public promotion of a product or service. (p. 21)
publicidad Promoción pública de un producto o servicio.

advocacy The use of communication to influence and support others in making positive health decisions. (p. 15)
propugnación Uso de la comunicación para influir o apoyar a otros para que tomen decisiones positivas relacionadas con la salud.

aerobic exercise An ongoing physical activity that raises your breathing and heart rates. (p. 320)
ejercicio aeróbico Toda actividad física continua que aumenta los ritmos cardíaco y respiratorio.

aggressive A term that describes people who express opinions and feelings in a way that may seem threatening or disrespectful to other people. (p. 138)
agresivo(a) Término que describe a una persona que expresa opiniones y sentimientos de una manera que puede parecer irrespetuosa o amenazante para otras personas.

AIDS Acquired immunodeficiency syndrome, an often fatal disease of the immune system caused by HIV infection. (p. 584)
SIDA Sigla del síndrome de inmunodeficiencia adquirida, una enfermedad del sistema inmunológico, por lo general fatal, causada por el virus de inmunodeficiencia humana (VIH).

alcoholism A disease marked by a person being unable to control their use of alcohol. (p. 388)
alcoholismo Enfermedad que se caracteriza por la incapacidad de una persona para controlar la ingestión de bebidas alcohólicas.

allergen Any substance that causes an allergy. (p. 616)
alergeno Cualquier sustancia que provoca una alergia.

allergy A disorder in which the immune system is overly sensitive to a particular substance not normally found in the body. (p. 616)
alergia Trastorno caracterizado por una reacción excesivamente sensible del sistema inmunológico ante una sustancia particular que no se encuentra normalmente en el cuerpo.

alveoli The sacs in the lungs where gases are exchanged between the air and the blood. (p. 308)
alvéolos Pequeñas bolsas que se hallan en los pulmones, en las cuales ocurre el intercambio de gases entre el aire y la sangre.

Alzheimer's disease A disease that causes brain cells to die, resulting in the gradual loss of mental and physical function. (p. 535)
enfermedad de Alzheimer Enfermedad que causa la muerte de células cerebrales y la pérdida gradual de la facultad mental y la capacidad física.

Americans with Disabilities Act A federal law that guarantees the civil rights of Americans who have physical or mental disabilities. (p. 626)
Ley de los estadounidenses con discapacidades Ley federal que garantiza los derechos civiles de los ciudadanos estadounidenses que sufren discapacidades físicas o mentales.

amino acids Small units that are bound together chemically to form proteins. (p. 198)
aminoácidos Pequeñas unidades que, al formar enlaces químicos entre sí, forman proteínas.

amniocentesis A prenatal test in which a small amount of amniotic fluid is removed and tested for abnormalities. (p. 495)
amniocentesis Examen prenatal que consiste en extraer una pequeña cantidad de líquido amniótico y someterlo a pruebas para detectar anormalidades.

amniotic sac A fluid-filled bag of thin tissue that develops around the embryo. (p. 490)
saco amniótico Bolsa de tejido fino, llena de líquido, que se forma alrededor del feto.

amphetamines Prescription drugs that are sometimes sold illegally as "speed" or "uppers." (p. 442)
anfetaminas Fármaco de prescripción que a veces se vende ilegalmente bajo el nombre de "estimulante".

anabolic steroid An artificial form of the male hormone testosterone that is used to increase muscle size and strength. (p. 274)
esteroide anabólico Presentación artificial de la hormona masculina testosterona que se usa para aumentar el volumen y la fuerza de los músculos.

anaerobic exercise Intense physical activity that lasts for a few seconds to a few minutes. (p. 320)
ejercicio anaeróbico Toda actividad física intensa que dura desde unos segundos hasta unos minutos.

anemia A condition in which the red blood cells do not contain enough hemoglobin. (p. 206)
anemia Trastorno que se presenta cuando los glóbulos rojos no tienen suficiente hemoglobina.

aneurysm A blood-filled weak spot that balloons out from the artery wall. (p. 605)
aneurisma Punto débil en la pared de una arteria, que se llena de sangre y se distiende.

angina pectoris The chest pain that occurs when an area of the heart does not get enough oxygen-rich blood. (p. 603)
angina de pecho Dolor del pecho que se produce cuando el corazón no recibe suficiente sangre rica en oxígeno.

anorexia nervosa An eating disorder in which a person doesn't eat enough food to maintain a healthy body weight. (p. 90)
anorexia nerviosa Trastorno grave de la alimentación en el que el individuo se niega a comer los alimentos necesarios para mantener un peso corporal saludable.

antibiotic A drug that inhibits or kills bacteria. (p. 559)
antibiótico Droga que inhibe el desarrollo de las bacterias o las mata.

antibody A protein that attaches to the surface of pathogens or to the toxins produced by pathogens, keeping the pathogen or toxin from harming the body. (p. 555)
anticuerpo Proteína que se adhiere a la superficie de los patógenos o a las toxinas producidas por éstos, impidiendo que el patógeno o la toxina le haga daño al cuerpo.

antioxidant A vitamin that helps protect healthy cells from the damage caused by the normal aging process as well as from certain types of cancer. (p. 205)
antioxidante Vitamina que ayuda a proteger a las células saludables de los daños causados por el proceso normal de envejecimiento y por ciertos tipos de cáncer.

anxiety Fear caused by a source you cannot identify or a source that doesn't pose as much threat as you think. (p. 84)
ansiedad Miedo que carece de causas identificables o es producido por un peligro mínimo o inexistente.

anxiety disorder A disorder characterized by anxiety that persists for a long time and interferes with daily living. (p. 84)
trastorno de ansiedad Trastorno que se caracteriza por una ansiedad constante que interfiere en las actividades de la vida diaria.

appetite A desire for food based more on emotions and other factors rather than on nutritional need. (p. 220)
apetito Deseo de ingerir alimento cuyo origen se debe más a factores emocionales o de otro tipo que a la necesidad nutricional.

arrhythmia An irregular heartbeat. (p. 301)
arritmia Irregularidad en los latidos del corazón.

artery A thick-walled blood vessel that carries blood away from the heart. (p. 295)
arteria Vaso de paredes gruesas que transporta la sangre desde el corazón.

arthritis Inflammation or irritation of a joint. (p. 618)
artritis Inflamación o irritación de una articulación.

asbestos A fibrous mineral that was once used in fire-proofing and other building materials; asbestos fibers can cause lung disease. (p. 674)
asbesto Mineral fibroso que anteriormente era usado en la fabricación de aislantes y otros materiales de construcción; las fibras de asbestos pueden causar cáncer de pulmón.

assailant A person who attacks another person. (p. 163)
agresor Persona que ataca a otro individuo.

assault An unlawful attempt or threat to harm someone. (p. 700)
asalto Ataque o amenaza ilegal contra otra persona.

assertive A term that describes people who are able to stand up for themselves while expressing their feelings in a way that does not threaten other people. (p. 138)
asertivo Término que describe a una persona que es capaz de resolver sus problemas y expresar sus sentimientos de una manera que no resulte amenazante para otras personas.

asthma A disorder in which respiratory passageways become inflamed and narrow during attacks, leading to difficulty breathing. (p. 309)
asma Trastorno en el que las vías respiratorias se inflaman y se estrechan durante los ataques, dificultando la respiración.

asymptomatic stage The stage of HIV infection in which the infected person shows no symptoms. (p. 585)
etapa asintomática Etapa de la infección del VIH durante la cual la persona infectada no muestra síntomas.

atherosclerosis A condition in which an artery wall hardens and thickens due to plaque buildup. (p. 300)
ateroesclerosis Trastorno caracterizado por el endurecimiento y engrosamiento de las paredes de una arteria debido a la acumulación de placas.

atrium An upper chamber of the heart that receives blood from the rest of the body. (p. 293)
aurícula Cada una de las dos cámaras superiores del corazón que reciben la sangre proveniente del resto del cuerpo.

atrophy A condition in which muscles that cannot contract or are not used often weaken and shrink. (p. 273)
atrofia Condición en la cual se debilitan y se encogen aquellos músculos que no se usan o que han perdido su capacidad de contracción.

audiologist A professional who evaluates hearing and treats hearing loss. (p. 363)
audiólogo Profesional que evalúa la audición y trata la pérdida de la misma.

autonomy An individual's independence from parents and family that strengthens during adolescence. (p. 525)
autonomía Independencia de un individuo respecto a sus padres y familiares, que se acrecienta durante la adolescencia.

B

bacteria Simple, single-celled microorganisms. (p. 548)
bacterias Microorganismos unicelulares simples.

barbiturates A class of depressant drugs; also called sedative-hypnotics. (p. 440)
barbitúrico Tipo de droga depresora; también llamada sedativo o hipnótico.

basal metabolic rate (BMR) The rate at which a person uses energy when the body is at rest. (p. 220)
tasa de metabolismo basal Tasa a la que una persona consume energía en estado de reposo.

B cell A lymphocyte that produces antibodies. (p. 555)
célula B Tipo de linfocito que produce anticuerpos.

bile A substance produced by the liver that aids in digestion by breaking up large fat droplets. (p. 245)
bilis Sustancia producida por el hígado que descompone la grasa, facilitando así la digestión.

binge drinking The consumption of excessive amounts of alcohol at one sitting. (p. 385)
ingestión excesiva de alcohol Consumir cantidades excesivas de alcohol de una vez.

binge eating disorder An eating disorder in which a person regularly has an uncontrollable urge to eat large amounts of food, but without purging. (p. 93)
ingestión excesiva de alimentos Trastorno de la alimentación en el que un individuo siente necesidad de consumir grandes cantidades de alimentos, sin purgarse luego.

biodegradable waste Waste that can be broken down by microorganisms. (p. 677)
desecho biodegradable Desecho que puede ser descompuesto por microorganismos.

biopsy The removal of a small piece of tissue to examine it for signs of cancer. (p. 612)
biopsia Extracción de una pequeña muestra de tejido para examinarla con el fin de determinar la presencia de cáncer.

blackout A period of time that an intoxicated person cannot recall. (p. 381)
pérdida del conocimiento Período que una persona intoxicada no puede recordar.

blastocyst A hollow, spherical structure made up of about 50–100 cells, formed when an embryo divides and grows. (p. 489)
blastocisto Estructura hueca de forma esférica, con aproximadamente 50–100 células, que se forma al crecer y dividirse el embrión.

blended family Consists of a biological parent, a step-parent, and the children of one or both parents. (p. 115)
familia mixta Unidad familiar que consiste en uno de los padres biológicos, un padrastro o una madrastra y el (los) hijo(s) de uno o ambos padres.

blood alcohol concentration (BAC) The amount of alcohol in a person's blood, expressed as a percentage. (p. 382)
concentración de alcohol en la sangre (CAS) Cantidad de alcohol en la sangre de una persona, expresada como porcentaje.

blood pressure The force with which blood pushes against the walls of blood vessels. (p. 296)
presión sanguínea Fuerza ejercida por la sangre contra las paredes de las venas y arterias.

body composition A measure of how much body fat a person has, as compared to muscle and bone. (pp. 227, 318)
composición corporal Proporción de tejido graso en el cuerpo con respecto al tejido muscular y a los huesos.

body language The silent messages people communicate through posture, gestures, facial expressions, and body movements. (p. 139)
lenguaje corporal Forma de comunicación no verbal que las personas realizan a través de las posturas, los gestos, las expresiones faciales y los movimientos del cuerpo.

body mass index (BMI) A ratio of a person's weight to height. BMI = [Weight (in pounds)/Height (in inches)^2] $\times$ 703. (p. 227)
índice de masa corporal (IMC) Relación entre el peso y la altura de una persona. IMC = [Peso (en libras)/Altura (en pulgadas)^2] $\times$ 703.

brain stem The area of the brain between the cerebellum and the spinal cord; it controls automatic functions such as heartbeat and blood pressure. (p. 281)
tallo cerebral Área del cerebro que se encuentra entre el cerebelo y la médula espinal; controla las funciones autónomas, como los latidos del corazón y la presión sanguínea.

bronchitis An infection that causes the mucous membranes lining the bronchi to become inflamed. (p. 310)
bronquitis Infección que causa la inflamación de las membranas mucosas de los bronquios.

bulimia An eating disorder in which a person has uncontrolled eating binges followed by purging. (p. 92)
bulimia Trastorno de la alimentación en el cual una persona ingiere comida en exceso y luego se purga.

bullying The use of threats or physical force to intimidate and control another person. (p. 169)
intimidación Uso de amenazas o de la fuerza física para amedrentar o controlar a otra persona.

calorie Unit for the amount of energy released when nutrients are broken down. (p. 193)
caloría Unidad que expresa la cantidad de energía liberada cuando el cuerpo descompone los nutrientes.

cancer A group of diseases involving the uncontrolled growth and spread of abnormal cells. (p. 609)
cáncer Grupo de enfermedades caracterizadas por el crecimiento y la diseminación rápida y descontrolada de células anormales.

capillary The smallest type of blood vessel in the body. (p. 295)
capilar Vaso sanguíneo más pequeño del cuerpo.

capsizing The overturning of a boat. (p. 706)
zozobra Voltearse o irse a pique una embarcación.

carbohydrate A nutrient made of carbon, hydrogen, and oxygen and that supplies energy. (p. 194)
carbohidrato Nutriente compuesto por carbón, hidrógeno y oxígeno, y que suministra energía.

carbohydrate loading The practice of greatly increasing carbohydrate intake and decreasing exercise on the days immediately before a competition. (p. 236)
carga de carbohidratos Práctica que consiste en ingerir grandes cantidades de carbohidratos y disminuir la cantidad de ejercicio durante los días previos a una competencia atlética.

carbon monoxide A poisonous, colorless, odorless gas produced when substances are burned. (p. 409)
monóxido de carbono Gas venenoso, incoloro e inodoro, que se produce durante la combustión.

carcinogen A substance that is known to cause cancer. (pp. 408, 610)
carcinógeno Sustancia que causa cáncer.

cardiac muscle Involuntary muscle that is found only in the heart. (p. 272)
músculo cardiaco Músculo involuntario que sólo se halla en el corazón.

cardiovascular disease A disease of the heart and blood vessels. (p. 602)
enfermedad cardiovascular Enfermedad del corazón y los vasos sanguíneos.

cartilage A tough, supportive tissue that is softer and more flexible than bone. (p. 268)
cartílago Resistente tejido que sirve de sostén y que es más blando y flexible que el hueso.

catastrophe An unexpected event that threatens lives and may destroy property. (p. 58)
catástrofe Suceso inesperado que pone en peligro o produce pérdidas de vidas y propiedades.

cementum The hard material that covers a tooth's root. (p. 342)
cemento Material duro que cubre la raíz de los dientes.

cerebellum A part of the brain that coordinates movements and balance. (p. 281)
cerebelo Parte del cerebro que coordina los movimientos y el equilibrio.

cerebral hemorrhage A type of stroke that occurs when an artery located in the cerebrum, the main part of the brain, bursts. (p. 605)
hemorragia cerebral Tipo de apoplejía que ocurre por la rotura de una arteria en el cerebro.

cerebrum A part of the brain that contains several specialized regions that receive messages from sense organs, and control movement, memory, communication, and reasoning. (p. 281)
cerebro Parte superior del encéfalo que contiene varias regiones especializadas que reciben mensajes de los órganos sensoriales; además, controla el movimiento, la memoria, la comunicación y el razonamiento.

certified nurse-midwife A nurse who is trained to deliver babies. (p. 498)
enfermera-comadrona certificada Enfermera entrenada para atender partos.

cesarean section A surgical method of birth. (p. 501)
cesárea Parto realizado a través de una intervención quirúrgica.

chancre A painless sore that appears during the first stage of syphilis infection. (p. 582)
chancro Llaga indolora que aparece en la primera etapa de la sífilis.

chewing tobacco A smokeless tobacco product that consists of poor-quality, ground tobacco leaves and is placed between the gum and the cheek. (p. 403)
tabaco de mascar Producto derivado del tabaco, hecho a partir de hojas de tabaco de baja calidad; se coloca entre la encía y la mejilla.

chlamydia A very common sexually transmitted infection caused by bacteria. (p. 579)
linfogranuloma venéreo Infección de transmisión sexual muy común, causada por una bacteria.

cholesterol A waxy, fatlike substance that is found only in animal products. (p. 197)
colesterol Sustancia grasosa y cerosa que se halla sólo en los productos de origen animal.

chorionic villus sampling A prenatal test in which a piece of the developing placenta is removed and tested for inherited disorders. (p. 495)
muestra de vellosidad coriónica Prueba prenatal que consiste en sacar un fragmento de la placenta y examinarlo para detectar trastornos hereditarios.

chromosomes The tiny structures found within cells that carry information about inherited characteristics. (p. 478)
cromosomas Estructuras diminutas que se encuentran en las células y que contienen información sobre las características hereditarias.

chronic bronchitis A condition in which the bronchi in the lungs are constantly swollen and clogged with mucus. (p. 411)
bronquitis crónica Trastorno en el que los bronquios se inflaman y se obstruyen constantemente por mucosidad.

chronic disease A disease that persists for a long period or recurs throughout life; usually caused by behavioral, environmental, or hereditary factors. (p. 602)
enfermedad crónica Enfermedad que persiste por un largo período o que aparece repetidas veces durante la vida; generalmente es causada por factores ambientales, hereditarios o de conducta.

chronic obstructive pulmonary disease (COPD) A disease that results in a gradual loss of lung function. (p. 411)
enfermedad pulmonar obstructiva crónica (EPOC) Enfermedad que causa que los pulmones pierdan gradualmente la capacidad de realizar sus funciones.

chyme A thick mixture of food and gastric juices formed in the stomach. (p. 244)
quimo Mezcla líquida espesa de alimentos y jugo gástrico que se forma en el estómago.

circadian rhythm The body's internal system that regulates behavior patterns during a 24-hour cycle. (p. 366)
ritmo circadiano Sistema interno del cuerpo que regula los patrones de conducta durante un ciclo de 24 horas.

cirrhosis A disease of the liver in which it becomes filled with useless scar tissue; cirrhosis may lead to liver failure. (p. 387)
cirrosis Enfermedad del hígado en la cual éste se llena de tejido cicatrizal; la cirrosis puede conllevar a que el hígado deje de funcionar.

civic engagement The level of involvement that average citizens have in the planning and decision-making that affects their community. (p. 684)
participación cívica Nivel de participación que los ciudadanos comunes tienen en la planificación y la toma de decisiones que afectan a su comunidad.

clinical depression The symptoms of this disorder are feeling sad and hopeless for months, being unable to enjoy activities that were once a source of pleasure, and sometimes being unable to accomplish daily tasks. (p. 94)
depresión clínica Trastorno en el cual una persona experimenta durante meses sentimientos de tristeza y desesperación, que le impiden disfrutar actividades que antes le causaban placer, y que incluso pueden impedirle realizar sus actividades cotidianas.

clinical psychologist A mental health professional who is trained to recognize and treat behavior that is not normal. (p. 103)
psicólogo(a) clínico(a) Profesional en el campo de la salud mental, especializado en identificar y tratar conductas que no son normales.

clique A narrow, exclusive group of people with similar backgrounds or interests. (p. 145)
corrillo Grupo pequeño y exclusivo de personas, con orígenes o intereses similares.

club drugs Drugs that first gained popularity at dance clubs and raves. (p. 446)
drogas de clubes Drogas que inicialmente se vuelven populares en clubes y fiestas.

cluster suicides A series of suicides that occur within a short period of time in the same peer group or community. (p. 97)
suicidio colectivo Serie de suicidios que ocurren en un breve período de tiempo dentro de un mismo grupo de iguales o una misma comunidad.

cocaine A drug that is a powerful but short-acting stimulant. (p. 443)
cocaína Droga que tiene un poderoso, pero breve efecto estimulante.

cochlea A coiled, fluid-filled tube in the inner ear that contains cells that sense sound vibrations. (p. 361)
cóclea Tubo en forma de espiral, lleno de líquido, que se encuentra en el oído interno y que contiene células sensibles a las vibraciones sonoras.

coma A prolonged period of deep unconsciousness. (p. 284)
coma Período prolongado de profunda inconsciencia.

communication The process of sharing information, thoughts, or feelings. (p. 136)
comunicación Proceso mediante el cual se transmite información, ideas o sentimientos.

community service organization An official community group whose members act or unite for a common purpose. (p. 665)
organización de servicio comunitario Grupo comunitario oficial cuyos miembros se unen o trabajan para alcanzar un objetivo común.

compromise The willingness of each person to give up something in order to reach agreement. (p. 140)
concesión Sacrificio que hacen una o varias personas para llegar a un acuerdo.

compulsion An unreasonable need to behave in a certain way to prevent a feared outcome. (p. 85)
compulsión Necesidad irracional de comportarse de determinada manera para evitar que suceda algo que se teme vaya a ocurrir.

concussion A bruiselike injury to the brain caused by brain tissue hitting the skull during a collision. (p. 284)
conmoción cerebral Lesión que sufre el cerebro cuando choca contra el cráneo durante una colisión.

consensus-building The process by which a community arrives at an agreed-upon vision for the future. (p. 685)
búsqueda de consenso Proceso mediante el cual una comunidad se pone de acuerdo sobre una visión en relación con el futuro de la misma.

conservation The protection and preservation of the natural environment by managing natural resources wisely and developing land for new construction responsibly. (p. 682)
conservación Protección y preservación de la naturaleza mediante el uso prudente de los recursos y el desarrollo responsable de nuevas áreas urbanas.

consumer Someone who buys products or services for personal use. (p. 18)
consumidor Persona que compra productos o servicios para su uso personal.

continuum A gradual progression through many stages between one extreme and another. (p. 4)
contínuum Progresión gradual, a través de muchas etapas, de un extremo a otro.

cooperation Working together toward a common goal. (p. 139)
cooperación Acción de trabajar unidos con un objetivo común.

copayment A small fee that a patient with managed care health insurance may have to pay when visiting a doctor. (p. 645)
pago parcial Pequeña suma que en ciertos casos debe pagar el paciente que tiene seguro médico cuando consulta un médico.

coping strategy A way of dealing with an uncomfortable or unbearable feeling or situation. (p. 48)
estrategia de manejo de una situación conflictiva Forma de hacer frente a las situaciones o sentimientos incómodos o insoportables.

cornea Clear tissue that covers the front of the eye. (p. 356)
córnea Tejido transparente que cubre la parte delantera del ojo.

cross-contamination The spread of microorganisms from one food to another food. (p. 251)
contaminación cruzada Propagación de microorganismos de un alimento a otro.

cross-training Participating in a wide variety of activities. (p. 326)
entrenamiento mixto Participación en una gran variedad de actividades.

culture Beliefs and patterns of behavior that are shared by a group of people and passed from generation to generation. (p. 7)
cultura Creencias y patrones de conducta comunes a un grupo de personas, que se transmiten de generación en generación.

cutting The use of a sharp object to intentionally cut or scratch one's body deep enough to bleed. (p. 96)
cortarse/automutilación Usar un objeto afilado para producir intencionalmente una herida sangrante en el cuerpo de uno mismo.

cyber bullying Bullying that takes place by e-mail, instant messaging, text messaging, or at Web sites. (p. 169)
intimidación cibernética Intimidación que se realiza a través del correo electrónico, de los mensajes instantáneos, de los mensajes de texto o en sitios de Internet.

Daily Values Recommendations that specify the amounts of certain nutrients that the average person should obtain each day. (p. 223)
Valores diarios de nutrición Conjunto de recomendaciones que indican la cantidad de ciertos nutrientes que una persona típica necesita consumir a diario.

date rape A rape that occurs during a date. (p. 151)
violación en una cita Violación que ocurre en el transcurso de una cita.

dating violence A pattern of emotional, physical, or sexual abuse that occurs in a dating relationship. (p. 150)
violencia en el noviazgo Patrón de maltrato emocional, físico o sexual que se presenta entre dos personas que son novios.

deductible A fixed amount that must be paid by the patient before traditional health insurance begins paying for covered procedures. (p. 646)
deducible Cantidad fija que debe pagar el paciente para que los seguros médicos tradicionales comiencen a cubrir el costo de algún procedimiento médico.

defense mechanism A coping strategy that helps protect a person from difficult feelings. (p. 48)
mecanismo de defensa Estrategia de manejo de una situación conflictiva con la que una persona se protege de las emociones negativas.

defensive driving A driving technique in which you constantly monitor other drivers around you. (p. 714)
conducir a la defensiva Técnica de manejo que consiste en observar atentamente lo que hacen los conductores de los autos que están alrededor del que uno conduce.

dehydration A serious reduction in the body's water content. (pp. 209, 333)
deshidratación Disminución pronunciada del contenido de agua del cuerpo.

dementia A disorder characterized by loss of mental abilities, abnormal behaviors, and personality changes. (p. 535)
demencia Trastorno caracterizado por comportamientos anormales, cambios en la personalidad y la pérdida de facultades mentales.

dentin The living material beneath enamel and cementum that makes up most of a tooth. (p. 342)
dentina Tejido sensible que se halla debajo del esmalte y el cemento, y que forma la mayor parte del diente.

dependence The condition that results when the brain develops a chemical need for a drug and cannot function normally without it. (p. 388)
dependencia Estado al que llega una persona cuando su cerebro desarrolla la necesidad química por una sustancia sin la cual ya no puede funcionar normalmente.

depressant A drug that slows brain and body reactions. (pp. 374, 440)
sedativo Droga que desacelera las funciones del cerebro y las reacciones corporales.

depression An emotional state in which a person feels extremely sad and hopeless. (p. 86)
depresión Estado emocional en el que una persona siente tristeza intensa y desesperación.

dermatologist A doctor who treats skin problems. (p. 350)
dermatólogo(a) Médico que trata las enfermedades de la piel.

dermis A tough, elastic layer of skin that lies below the epidermis. (p. 348)
dermis Capa de la piel, resistente y elástica, que se halla debajo de la epidermis.

detoxification The process of removing all alcohol or other drugs from a person's body. (p. 391)
desintoxicación Procedimiento para eliminar todo el alcohol u otras drogas del cuerpo de una persona.

developing nation A country with a weak economy and a low standard of living. (p. 656)
país en vías de desarrollo Cualquier país con una economía débil y un bajo nivel de vida.

diabetes A disease in which the body's ability to use glucose (blood sugar) is impaired. (p. 614)
diabetes Enfermedad caracterizada por la disminución de la capacidad del cuerpo para aprovechar la glucosa (azúcar de la sangre).

diagnosis A doctor's opinion of the nature or cause of a medical condition. (p. 634)
diagnóstico Opinión de un médico sobre la naturaleza o causa de un problema de salud.

dialysis A treatment for kidney failure in which a machine is used to filter wastes from blood. (p. 258)
diálisis Tratamiento que se utiliza cuando los riñones dejan de funcionar y en el cual se usa una máquina para filtrar las sustancias nocivas de la sangre.

diaphragm A dome-shaped muscle below the lungs that is involved in the breathing process. (p. 308)
diafragma Músculo en forma de cúpula, ubicado debajo de los pulmones, que interviene en la respiración.

Dietary Guidelines for Americans A document developed by nutrition experts to promote health and to help people reduce their risk for heart disease, cancer, and diabetes through diet and physical activity. (p. 210)
Normas dietéticas para los estadounidenses Documento elaborado por expertos en nutrición para promover la buena salud y ayudar a las personas a reducir el riesgo de sufrir enfermedades del corazón, cáncer y diabetes a través de la dieta y la actividad física.

dietary supplement Any product that contains one or more vitamins, minerals, herbs, or other dietary substances lacking in the diet. (p. 334)
suplemento dietético Cualquier producto que contenga una o más vitaminas, minerales, hierbas u otras sustancias que no se obtienen a través de la dieta.

digestion The process by which the digestive system breaks down food into molecules that the body can use. (p. 242)
digestión Proceso mediante el cual el sistema digestivo descompone los alimentos en moléculas que el cuerpo puede utilizar.

disability Any physical or mental impairment that limits or reduces normal activities. (p. 623)
discapacidad Impedimento físico o mental que limita o reduce la capacidad para realizar actividades normales.

discrimination The unfair treatment of a person or group based on prejudice. (p. 172)
discriminación Trato injusto hacia una persona o un grupo de personas debido a prejuicios que se tienen contra las mismas.

dislocation An injury that occurs when the ends of the bones in a joint are forced out of their normal positions. (p. 271)
dislocación Lesión que sucede cuando los extremos de los huesos dentro de una articulación son desencajados de su posición normal.

distress Stress that produces negative effects. (p. 56)
estrés negativo Estrés que produce efectos dañinos.

divorce A legal agreement to end a marriage. (p. 113)
divorcio Acuerdo legal para poner fin a un matrimonio.

domestic abuse The abuse of one spouse by the other. (p. 121)
violencia doméstica Abuso de uno de los cónyuges por parte del otro.

driving while intoxicated (DWI) The charge given to a driver over age 21 caught driving with a BAC that exceeds 0.08 percent, or to a driver under the age of 21 with any detectable BAC. (p. 384)
manejar en estado de intoxicación Delito del que se acusa a un conductor de un vehículo mayor de 21 años si es sorprendido conduciendo con una CAS superior al 0.08 por ciento, o a un conductor menor de 21 años con cualquier nivel detectable de alcohol en la sangre.

drug A chemical substance that is taken to cause changes in a person's body or behavior. (p. 374)
droga Sustancia química que se toma para alterar el funcionamiento del cuerpo o el comportamiento de una persona.

drug abuse The intentional improper or unsafe use of a drug. (p. 427)
abuso de drogas Uso intencionalmente inapropiado o peligroso de una droga.

drug antagonism A condition that occurs when one drug's effect is canceled out or reduced by another. (p. 430)
antagonismo entre drogas Condición que ocurre cuando el efecto de una droga es cancelado o reducido por el efecto de otra.

drug misuse The improper use of medicines—either prescription or over-the-counter drugs. (p. 427)
abuso de medicamentos Uso inapropiado de medicamentos, ya sean éstos de venta por prescripción o sin ella.

drug synergism A condition that occurs when drugs interact to produce effects greater than those that each drug would produce alone. (p. 430)
sinergismo entre drogas Condición que se presenta cuando distintas drogas interactúan para producir efectos superiores a los que produciría cualquiera de ellas por separado.

eardrum The membrane at the end of the ear canal that passes vibrations to the middle ear. (p. 360)
tímpano Membrana delgada, ubicada al final del canal auricular, que transmite las vibraciones sonoras hasta el oído medio.

eating disorder A mental disorder that reveals itself through abnormal behaviors related to food. (p. 90)
trastorno de la alimentación Trastorno mental que se manifiesta a través de conductas anormales en relación a la comida.

ectopic pregnancy A condition resulting from the implantation of the blastocyst in a location in the abdomen other than the uterus. (p. 496)
embarazo ectópico Condición causada por la implantación del blastocisto en una zona del abdomen que no sea el útero.

eczema A condition in which an area of irritated skin becomes red, swollen, hot, and itchy. (p. 350)
eczema Afección caracterizada por el enrojecimiento, la inflamación, el calentamiento y el escozor de un área de la piel irritada.

ejaculation The ejection of semen from the penis. (p. 466)
eyaculación Eyección del semen por el pene.

electrocution Death from direct contact with electricity. (p. 697)
electrocución Muerte causada por el contacto directo con la corriente eléctrica.

electrolyte A dissolved substance that regulates many processes in cells. (p. 208)
electrolito Sustancia disuelta que regula muchos procesos en las células.

embryo The stage of human development from the two-cell stage until about nine weeks after fertilization. (p. 489)
embrión Etapa del desarrollo humano que tiene lugar a partir de la división del cigoto en dos células hasta aproximadamente la novena semana después de la fecundación.

emerging disease An infectious disease that has become more common within the last 20 years or threatens to become more common in the near future. (p. 566)
enfermedad emergente Enfermedad infecciosa que se ha hecho más común en los últimos 20 años o que amenaza con volverse más común en el futuro inmediato.

emotion A reaction to a situation that involves the mind, body, and behavior. (p. 44)
emoción Reacción ante una situación, en la que intervienen la mente, el cuerpo y la conducta.

emotional abuse The nonphysical mistreatment of a person. (p. 122)
maltrato emocional Todo maltrato que no sea de índole físico.

emotional health The aspect of health that refers to how you react to events in your life. You are emotionally healthy when the feelings you experience are appropriate responses to events. (p. 3)
salud emocional Aspecto de la salud que se refiere a cómo una persona reacciona a los sucesos que ocurren en su vida. Una persona goza de buena salud emocional si los sentimientos que experimenta son respuestas apropiadas a dichos sucesos.

emotional intimacy The openness, sharing, affection, and trust that can develop in a close relationship. (p. 154)
intimidad emocional Franqueza, comunicación intensa, afecto y confianza que se desarrollan en una relación íntima.

emotional maturity The state of being fully developed in the emotional sense. (p. 530)
madurez emocional Estado de desarrollo emocional completo.

empathy The ability to understand another person's thoughts or feelings. (p. 126)
empatía Habilidad para comprender los sentimientos o ideas de otra persona.

emphysema A disorder in which damaged alveoli in the lungs can no longer take in adequate oxygen and eliminate carbon dioxide. (p. 412)
enfisema Trastorno respiratorio en el que los alvéolos del pulmón se dañan y no son capaces de absorber suficiente cantidad de oxígeno ni de expeler suficiente cantidad de dióxido de carbono.

enamel The material, which is harder than bone, that covers a tooth's crown. (p. 342)
esmalte Material más duro que el hueso, que cubre la corona de los dientes.

endocrine gland A gland that produces and releases chemical substances that signal changes in other parts of the body. (p. 460)
glándula endocrina Glándula que produce y segrega sustancias químicas que regulan cambios en otras partes del cuerpo.

endorphins Chemicals that block pain messages from reaching brain cells and produce feelings of pleasure. (p. 317)
endorfinas Sustancias químicas que impiden la llegada de sensaciones de dolor a las células del cerebro y que producen una sensación de placer.

environment All of the physical and social conditions that surround a person and can influence that person's health. (p. 7)
ambiente Conjunto de condiciones físicas y sociales que rodean a una persona y que pueden afectar su salud.

enzyme A chemical that speeds up reactions in the body. (p. 242)
enzima Sustancia química que acelera las reacciones del cuerpo.

epidemic An unusually high occurrence of a disease in a certain place during a certain time period. (p. 566)
epidemia Enfermedad de la que se presenta un número inusualmente alto de casos en determinado lugar durante determinado período.

epidemiology The study of disease among populations. (p. 649)
epidemiología El estudio de las enfermedades en las poblaciones.

epidermis The outermost layer of skin. (p. 348)
epidermis Capa más externa de la piel.

epiglottis A flap of tissue that seals off the trachea when food or liquid is swallowed. (p. 243)
epiglotis Lámina de tejido que ocluye la tráquea cuando se tragan alimentos sólidos o líquidos.

epilepsy A condition in which a person is prone to seizures. (p. 286)
epilepsia Trastorno que causa que la persona sufra convulsiones.

escalate To grow more intense. (p. 175)
intensificar Volverse algo más vigoroso.

estrogen The female sex hormone that signals certain physical changes at puberty and controls the maturation of eggs. (p. 469)
estrógeno Hormona sexual femenina que regula ciertos cambios físicos durante la pubertad, así como la maduración de los óvulos.

eustress Stress that produces positive effects. (p. 56)
estrés positivo Estrés que produce efectos beneficiosos.

excretion The process by which the body collects and removes wastes. (p. 254)
excreción Proceso mediante el cual el cuerpo recoge y elimina desechos.

extended family A group of close relatives living together or near each other. (p. 114)
familia extensa Grupo de parientes cercanos que viven juntos o cerca unos de otros.

eye contact Looking directly into another person's eyes; meeting another person's gaze. (p. 139)
contacto visual Acto de mirar a otra persona directamente a los ojos o de mantener la mirada de otra persona.

F

fad diet A popular diet that may help a person lose or gain weight but without proper regard for nutrition and other health issues. (p. 230)
dieta de moda Régimen alimentario popular que puede ayudar a una persona a perder o ganar peso, pero que no respeta los conceptos de nutrición y otros aspectos relativos a la salud.

fallopian tubes The passageways that carry eggs away from the ovaries. (p. 470)
trompas de Falopio Tubos que conducen los óvulos fuera de los ovarios.

fat A nutrient made of carbon, hydrogen, and oxygen; supplies energy, forms cells, maintains body temperature, and protects nerves. (p. 196)
grasa Nutriente compuesto de carbono, hidrógeno y oxígeno; suministra energía, ayuda a formar las células y mantener la temperatura corporal, y protege los nervios.

fermentation The process that creates alcohol, in which microorganisms called yeast feed on sugars. (p. 374)
fermentación Proceso que produce alcohol, en el cual unos microorganismos llamados levadura se alimentan de azúcares.

fertilization The process of a sperm cell joining with an egg. (p. 464)
fecundación Proceso mediante el cual un espermatozoide se une con un óvulo.

fetal alcohol syndrome A group of birth defects caused by the effects of alcohol on an unborn child.
síndrome alcohólico fetal Conjunto de defectos congénitos causados por los efectos del alcohol sobre el feto. (p. 387)

fetus The stage of human development from the third month after fertilization until birth. (p. 491)
feto Etapa del desarrollo humano que tiene lugar a partir del tercer mes después de la fecundación hasta el nacimiento.

fiber A type of complex carbohydrate that is found in plants and is necessary for the proper functioning of the digestive system. (p. 195)
fibra Tipo de carbohidrato complejo que se halla en las plantas y que es necesario para el buen funcionamiento del sistema digestivo.

fibrillation A life-threatening arrhythmia in which the heart twitches rapidly in an uncoordinated fashion. (p. 604)
fibrilación Tipo de arritmia del corazón que pone en peligro la vida, en la que el corazón se contrae rápida y descoordinadamente.

fight-or-flight response The initial reaction of the body to stress during the alarm stage. (p. 60)
respuesta de lucha o escape Respuesta inicial del cuerpo al estrés durante la reacción de alarma.

FITT formula A fitness plan that depends on four factors of exercise: frequency, intensity, time, and type.
fórmula FIDT Plan de aptitud física que se basa en cuatro factores del régimen de ejercicio: frecuencia, intensidad, duración y tipo. (p. 326)

flammable material Any material that catches fire easily and burns quickly. (p. 696)
material inflamable Cualquier material capaz de incendiarse con facilidad y quemarse rápidamente.

follicle A skin structure in which a strand of hair grows and oil is secreted. (p. 348)
folículo Estructura de la piel en la cual crece un pelo y se segrega grasa.

food allergy The immune system's response to the proteins in certain foods. (p. 235)
alergia alimentaria Respuesta del sistema inmune a las proteínas de ciertos alimentos.

foodborne illness An illness that results from consuming a food or drink that contains either a poison or a disease-causing microorganism. (p. 250)
intoxicación alimentaria Enfermedad causada por el consumo de comidas o bebidas que contienen sustancias dañinas o microorganismos causantes de enfermedades.

food intolerance The inability to digest a particular food or food additive. (p. 235)
intolerancia alimentaria Incapacidad para digerir determinados alimentos o aditivos alimentarios.

fossil fuels Energy-rich substances mined from deep in the earth, including coal, oil, and natural gas. (p. 672)
combustibles fósiles Sustancias ricas en energía, como el carbón, el petróleo y el gas natural, que se extraen del interior de la tierra.

foster family A family in which an adult or a couple cares for children whose biological parents are unable to care for them. (p. 115)
familia adoptiva Familia en la que un adulto o una pareja se encarga de niños cuyos padres biológicos no pueden cuidarlos.

fracture A break in a bone. (p. 270)
fractura Rotura de un hueso.

fraud An illegal act that involves telling lies to obtain money or property. (p. 22)
fraude Acción ilegal en la que se miente para obtener dinero o propiedades.

friendship A relationship based on mutual trust, acceptance, and common interests or values. (p. 141)
amistad Relación basada en la confianza y la aceptación mutua entre personas que comparten intereses o valores semejantes.

fungi Organisms such as yeasts, molds, and mushrooms that grow best in warm, dark, moist areas. (p. 549)
hongos Organismos que incluyen las levaduras, los mohos y los champiñones, que crecen mejor en áreas cálidas, húmedas y con sombra.

gallbladder The organ that stores bile and releases it into the small intestine. (p. 245)
vesícula biliar Órgano que almacena la bilis y la segrega al intestino delgado.

gender A term that refers to whether you are male or female. Gender is part of heredity. (p. 6)
sexo Condición que distingue a las personas como masculinas o femeninas. El sexo es parte de la herencia.

gender roles The behaviors and attitudes that are socially acceptable as either masculine or feminine. (p. 143)
papeles sexuales Conductas y actitudes que son socialmente aceptables como masculinas o femeninas.

gene A section of a chromosome that determines or affects a characteristic, or trait. (p. 479)
gen Sección del cromosoma que determina alguna característica o rasgo.

genetic disorder A disorder caused by the inheritance of an abnormal gene or chromosome. (p. 480)
trastorno genético Trastorno hereditario causado por un gen o cromosoma anormal.

genital herpes A sexually transmitted infection caused by the herpes simplex virus. (p. 581)
herpes genital Infección de transmisión sexual causada por el virus del herpes simple.

gestational diabetes Diabetes that develops during pregnancy. (p. 496)
diabetes gestacional Diabetes que se desarrolla durante el embarazo.

glomerulus A cluster of tiny blood vessels in a nephron. (p. 256)
glomérulo Grupo de pequeños vasos sanguíneos que se encuentra en un nefrón.

goal A result that a person aims for and works hard to reach. (p. 2)
meta Resultado que una persona desea alcanzar y por el cual trabaja con dedicación.

gonorrhea A bacterial sexually transmitted infection that infects the urinary tract of males and females and the reproductive organs of females. (p. 580)
gonorrea Infección bacterial de transmisión sexual que infecta las vías urinarias del hombre y los órganos reproductores de la mujer.

grief A period of deep sorrow. (p. 44)
pesar Período de tristeza profunda.

habit A behavior that is repeated so often that it becomes almost automatic. (p. 9)
hábito Conducta que se repite tan frecuentemente que se vuelve casi automática.

halitosis Bad breath. (p. 344)
halitosis Mal aliento.

hallucinogen A drug that distorts perception, thought, and mood. (p. 443)
alucinógeno Droga que distorsiona la percepción, el pensamiento o el estado de ánimo.

hangover A term used to describe the aftereffects of drinking too much alcohol. (p. 383)
resaca Término usado para describir los efectos posteriores al consumo excesivo de alcohol.

harassment Unwanted remarks or actions that cause a person emotional or physical harm. (p. 168)
acoso Comentarios o acciones indeseables que causan daño emocional o físico a una persona.

hate violence Speech or behavior that is aimed at a person or group based on personal characteristics. (p. 172)
violencia debida al odio Pronunciamientos o conductas contra una persona o un grupo basados en las características personales de esa persona o ese grupo.

hazardous waste Waste that is either flammable, explosive, corrosive, or toxic to humans or other living things. (p. 677)
desecho peligroso Desecho que es inflamable, explosivo, corrosivo o tóxico para los seres humanos u otros seres vivos.

hazing Requiring a person to do degrading, risky, or illegal acts in order to join a group. (p. 170)
novatada El acto de exigirle a una persona que realice actos degradantes, peligrosos o ilegales como condición para formar parte de un grupo.

health The overall well-being of your body, mind, and your relationships with other people. (p. 2)
salud Bienestar general del cuerpo, de la mente y de la relación con otras personas.

healthcare system All available medical services, the ways in which people pay for medical care, and programs aimed at preventing disease and disability. (p. 634)
sistema de salud Conjunto de todos los servicios médicos, métodos de pago por la atención médica y programas dirigidos a prevenir enfermedades y discapacidades.

health code A state standard for factors that affect public health. (p. 652)
código de salud Norma fijada por el estado para regular los factores que afectan la salud.

health literacy The ability to gather, understand, and use health information to improve one's health. (p. 15)
educación sobre la salud Capacidad que tiene una persona de reunir, entender y usar información sobre la salud para mejorar su propia salud.

heart attack The condition that occurs when some of the tissue in the heart doesn't receive its normal blood supply and dies. (p. 604)
ataque de corazón Afección que ocurre cuando parte de los tejidos del corazón no reciben el suministro normal de sangre y mueren.

heredity All the traits that are passed from parent to child; the biological process of passing on, or transmitting, those traits. (pp. 6, 478)
herencia Todas aquellas características transmitidas de padres a hijos; proceso biológico de pasar, o transmitir, esas características.

heroin An illegal opiate made from morphine in a laboratory. (p. 441)
heroína Opiáceo ilegal que se produce a partir de la morfina en un laboratorio.

hierarchy of needs An arrangement of human needs in a pyramid with physical needs at the base and self-actualization at the top. (p. 40)
jerarquía de necesidades Organización de las necesidades humanas en forma de una pirámide, donde las necesidades físicas se encuentran en la base y la autorrealización se encuentra en la cima.

high-density lipoprotein A substance that picks up excess cholesterol from body tissues and artery walls and carries it to the liver. (p. 300)
lipoproteína de alta densidad Sustancia que recoge el exceso de colesterol de los tejidos del cuerpo y las paredes arteriales y lo transporta al hígado.

histamine The chemical responsible for the symptoms of an allergy. (p. 616)
histamina Sustancia química responsable de los síntomas de la alergia.

HIV The human immunodeficiency virus, an incurable sexually transmitted infection that can lead to AIDS. (p. 584)
VIH Virus de inmunodeficiencia humana, una infección de transmisión sexual incurable que puede producir el SIDA.

HIV-positive A person who is diagnosed as being infected with HIV. (p. 594)
VIH-positivo Persona que se diagnostica como infectada con el VIH.

homeostasis The process of maintaining a steady state inside the body. (p. 208)
homeóstasis Proceso que permite mantener la estabilidad en el interior del cuerpo.

homicide The intentional killing of one person by another. (p. 162)
homicidio Acción de matar intencionalmente a otra persona.

hormone A chemical substance produced by an endocrine gland. (p. 461)
hormona Sustancia química producida por una glándula endocrina.

hospice A facility or program that provides physical, emotional, and spiritual care for dying people and support for their families. (p. 537)
hospicio para moribundos Programa o instituto que ofrece cuidados físicos, emocionales y espirituales a las personas moribundas y a sus familiares.

human papilloma virus A very common viral sexually transmitted infection. (p. 579)
virus del papiloma humano Infección viral de transmisión sexual muy común.

hunger A feeling of discomfort caused by the body's need for nutrients. (p. 220)
hambre Sensación de molestia causada por la necesidad del cuerpo de obtener nutrientes.

hypertension Blood pressure that is consistently 140/90 or greater. (p. 296)
hipertensión Presión arterial que se mantiene habitualmente por encima de 140/90.

hypothalamus An endocrine gland in the brain that is part of both the nervous and endocrine systems. (p. 461)
hipotálamo Glándula endocrina, ubicada en el cerebro, que forma parte de los sistemas nervioso y endocrino.

identity A sense of self. (p. 35)
identidad Sentido de individualidad de una persona.

illegal drug A chemical substance that people of any age may not lawfully manufacture, possess, buy, or sell. (p. 427)
droga ilegal Sustancia química cuya manufactura, posesión, compra o venta es ilegal para toda persona, sin importar su edad.

"I" message A statement that expresses your feelings, but does not blame or judge the other person. (p. 136)
mensaje "yo" Afirmación que expresa los sentimientos de una persona, sin culpar ni juzgar a la otra persona.

immune system The body's most sophisticated defense against pathogens. (p. 554)
sistema inmunológico La defensa más sofisticada que tiene el cuerpo contra los patógenos.

immunity The body's ability to destroy a pathogen that it has previously encountered before the pathogen is able to cause disease. (p. 554)
inmunidad Capacidad del cuerpo para destruir patógenos a los que ha sido expuesto previamente, antes de que éstos puedan causar enfermedades.

immunization An injection that causes the body to become immune to an infectious disease; also called a vaccination. (p. 556)
inmunización Inyección que fomenta que el cuerpo de una persona se vuelva inmune a una enfermedad infecciosa; también se la llama vacunación.

implantation The process in which the blastocyst attaches itself to the wall of the uterus. (p. 489)
implantación Proceso mediante el cual el blastocisto se adhiere a la pared del útero.

infatuation Feelings of intense attraction to another person. (p. 148)
enamoramiento Sentimiento de atracción intensa hacia otra persona.

infectious disease A disease caused by an organism or virus that enters and multiplies within the body.
enfermedad infecciosa Enfermedad causada por organismos o virus que entran y se multiplican en el cuerpo humano. (p. 548)

infertility The condition of being unable to reproduce.
infertilidad Incapacidad para reproducirse. (p. 468)

inflammation The body's general response to all kinds of injury. (p. 554)
inflamación Respuesta generalizada del cuerpo ante cualquier lesión.

inhalant A breathable chemical vapor that produces mind-altering effects. (p. 447)
inhalante Vapor químico que se puede aspirar por la nariz y que produce alteraciones psicotrópicas.

inpatient A patient who is required to stay in a hospital overnight or longer. (p. 638)
paciente internado Paciente que debe pasar una o más noches dentro de un hospital.

insomnia A disorder in which a person has trouble falling asleep or staying asleep. (p. 365)
insomnio Trastorno en el cual existe dificultad para conciliar el sueño o para permanecer dormido.

instigator A person who encourages fighting between others while staying out of the fight himself or herself. (p. 176)
instigador Persona que fomenta disputas entre otros sin involucrarse personalmente en las mismas.

insulin A hormone produced by the pancreas that stimulates body cells to take up and use blood sugar. (p. 614)
insulina Hormona producida por el páncreas que estimula las células del cuerpo a utilizar el azúcar en la sangre.

intolerance A lack of acceptance of another person's opinions, beliefs, or actions. (p. 172)
intolerancia Incapacidad para aceptar las opiniones, creencias o acciones de otra persona.

intoxication The state in which a person's mental and physical abilities are impaired by alcohol or another substance. (p. 380)
intoxicación Estado en el cual las habilidades mentales y físicas de una persona se ven afectadas por el alcohol u otra sustancia.

iris The structure that surrounds the pupil and regulates the amount of light that enters the eye. (p. 356)
iris Estructura que rodea la pupila y que regula la cantidad de luz que entra al ojo.

isokinetic exercise Exercise performed with machines that ensure muscles contract at a constant rate. (p. 321)
ejercicio isocinético Ejercicio realizado con la ayuda de máquinas que hacen que los músculos se contraigan a un ritmo constante.

isometric exercise Exercise in which muscles contract but very little body movement occurs. (p. 320)
ejercicio isométrico Ejercicio en el cual los músculos se contraen con muy poco movimiento del cuerpo.

isotonic exercise Exercise that involves contracting and relaxing muscles through the full range of their joint's motion. (p. 321)
ejercicio isotónico Ejercicio en el que se produce la contracción y relajación de los músculos al realizar el movimiento completo de la articulación.

J

joint A place in the body where two or more bones meet. (p. 268)
articulación Lugar del cuerpo en el que convergen dos o más huesos.

K

keratin A protein in dead skin cells of the epidermis that makes skin tough and waterproof. (p. 348)
queratina Proteína que se halla en las células muertas de la epidermis y que otorga a la piel resistencia e impermeabilidad.

kidney A major organ of excretion that filters wastes from the blood and produces urine. (p. 255)
riñón Importante órgano de excreción que filtra las sustancias tóxicas de la sangre y produce orina.

L

labor The work performed by the mother's body to push the fetus out at the end of pregnancy. (p. 499)
trabajo de parto Función realizada por el cuerpo de la madre al final del embrazo para expulsar el feto.

landfill A permanent storage area where garbage and other wastes are deposited and covered with soil. (p. 678)
relleno sanitario Área en la que se depositan basura u otros desechos de manera permanente para después cubrirlos con tierra.

learned emotion An emotion whose expression depends on the social environment in which a person grows up. (p. 46)
emoción adquirida Emoción cuya expresión depende del ambiente social en el que crece una persona.

lens A flexible structure in the eye that focuses light on the retina. (p. 357)
cristalino Estructura flexible del ojo que enfoca la luz sobre la retina.

leukoplakia White patches on the tongue or lining of the mouth that may become cancerous. (p. 414)
leucoplasia Placas blancas que se forman en la lengua o en el interior de la boca y que pueden llegar a ser cancerosas.

life expectancy The number of years a person can expect to live. (p. 2)
esperanza de vida Cantidad de años que una persona puede esperar vivir.

lifelong fitness The ability to stay healthy and fit as you age. (p. 324)
aptitud física vitalicia Capacidad para mantenerse saludable y tener buenas condiciones físicas a medida que se envejece.

ligament A strong, fibrous band that holds bones together at a joint. (p. 269)
ligamento Tejido duro y fibroso, en forma de banda, que mantiene unidos los huesos en las articulaciones.

low birthweight A newborn weight of less than 5.5 pounds. (p. 502)
bajo peso al nacer En el recién nacido, peso inferior a las 5.5 libras.

low-density lipoprotein A substance that carries cholesterol to body tissues for storage; "bad" cholesterol. (p. 300)
lipoproteína de baja densidad Sustancia que transporta colesterol a los tejidos del cuerpo para almacenarlo; también llamada colesterol "malo".

lymphatic system A network of vessels that collects fluid from body tissues and returns it to the bloodstream; contains much of the immune system. (p. 556)
sistema linfático Red de vasos que recoge fluido de los tejidos del cuerpo y lo devuelve al torrente sanguíneo; contiene la mayoría de los componentes del sistema inmunológico.

lymphocyte A type of white blood cell that carries out functions of the immune system. (p. 554)
linfocito Tipo de glóbulo blanco que realiza diversas funciones en el sistema inmunológico.

M

macular degeneration A condition affecting the retina of the eye; the leading cause of vision loss in older Americans. (p. 623)
degeneración macular Afección de la retina del ojo; es la primera causa de pérdida de la visión entre los estadounidenses de la tercera edad.

mainstream smoke Smoke that is exhaled from a smoker's lungs. (p. 414)
humo directo Humo de tabaco que el fumador espira de sus pulmones.

malignant The term used to describe a cancerous tumor. (p. 609)
maligno Término usado para describir los tumores cancerosos.

malocclusion A condition in which the upper and lower teeth do not meet properly. (p. 343)
maloclusión Condición en la que los dientes superiores e inferiores no hacen contacto de forma adecuada.

mammogram An X-ray of the breast that may detect breast cancer. (p. 475)
mamografía Radiografía de la mama que permite detectar el cáncer de mama.

marijuana A drug made from the leaves, stems, and flowering tops of the hemp plant. (p. 445)
marihuana Droga producida a partir de las hojas, los tallos y las ramas del cáñamo.

marrow The soft tissue that fills spaces inside bones. (p. 268)
médula ósea Tejido blando que se encuentra en el interior de los huesos.

media Forms of communication that provide news and entertainment. (p. 8)
medios de comunicación Formas de comunicación que ofrecen noticias y entretenimiento.

mediation A process for resolving conflicts that involves a neutral third party. (p. 183)
mediación Proceso mediante el cual se resuelven conflictos con la ayuda de una tercera persona neutral.

medical history A record of your present and past health as well as the health of members of your family. (p. 643)
historial clínico Archivo de datos sobre el estado de salud actual y pasado de una persona, así como de los miembros de su familia.

medical specialist A doctor who has received additional training in a particular branch of medicine. (p. 635)
médico especialista Médico con entrenamiento adicional en una rama específica de la medicina.

medicine A legal drug that helps the body fight injury, illness, or disease. (p. 426)
medicamento Droga legal que ayuda al cuerpo a combatir lesiones, enfermedades u otros trastornos físicos.

melanin A pigment released in the epidermis that gives skin color and causes skin to tan. (p. 348)
melanina Pigmento liberado en la epidermis, responsable del color de la piel y su capacidad para broncearse.

melanoma A serious form of skin cancer. (p. 349)
melanoma Tipo grave de cáncer de piel.

meningitis An infection that causes inflammation of the membranes surrounding the brain and spinal cord. (p. 285)
meningitis Infección que causa la inflamación de las membranas que rodean el cerebro y la médula espinal.

menopause The time of life during which the ovaries slow down their hormone production and no longer release mature eggs. (p. 471)
menopausia Período de la vida en el que los ovarios disminuyen su producción de hormonas y dejan de liberar óvulos maduros.

menstrual cycle The process during which an ovary releases a mature egg that travels to the uterus; if the egg is not fertilized, the uterine lining is shed and a new cycle begins. (p. 471)
ciclo menstrual Proceso mediante el cual el ovario libera un óvulo maduro que se dirige hacia el útero; si el óvulo no es fecundado, la capa uterina interna es expulsada y comienza un nuevo ciclo.

mental disorder An illness that affects the mind and reduces a person's ability to function, to adjust to change, or to get along with others. (p. 82)
trastorno mental Enfermedad que afecta la mente y limita la capacidad de una persona para desempeñarse, adaptarse a los cambios o relacionarse con los demás.

mental health The state of being comfortable with yourself, with others, and with your surroundings. (p. 3)
salud mental Estado en el cual la persona se siente bien consigo misma, con los demás y con el ambiente que la rodea.

mental rehearsal A technique used to practice an event without actually doing the event. (p. 71)
práctica mental Técnica usada para prepararse para una actividad sin tener que realizarla.

metabolism The chemical process by which the body breaks down food to release energy. (p. 193)
metabolismo Proceso químico mediante el cual el cuerpo descompone los alimentos para liberar energía.

metastasis The spread of cancer from where it first develops to other parts of the body. (p. 609)
metástasis Propagación del cáncer desde el área donde se desarrolló originalmente a otras partes del cuerpo.

methamphetamine A stimulant that is related to amphetamines, but is even more powerful. (p. 442)
metanfetamina Estimulante parecido a la anfetamina, pero de mayor potencia.

microorganism An organism that is so small it can only be seen through a microscope. (p. 548)
microorganismo Organismo de tamaño tan pequeño que sólo puede verse a través de un microscopio.

mineral A nutrient that occurs naturally in rocks or soil; needed by the body in small amounts. (p. 205)
mineral Nutriente que se halla naturalmente en las rocas o el suelo y que el cuerpo necesita sólo en pequeñas cantidades.

miscarriage The death of an embryo or fetus in the first 20 weeks of pregnancy. (p. 496)
aborto espontáneo Muerte de un embrión o feto en las primeras 20 semanas del embarazo.

mixed-use development City or town development in which homes are built close to businesses and schools. (p. 667)
urbanización mixta Desarrollo de pueblos o ciudades en los que las viviendas se construyen cerca de los negocios y las escuelas.

modeling Learning how to behave by copying the behavior of others. (p. 33)
modelar el comportamiento Aprender cierta conducta imitando el comportamiento de otros.

mood disorder A disorder characterized by extreme emotions. (p. 86)
trastorno del estado de ánimo Trastorno en el cual la persona experimenta emociones extremas.

mucous membrane The protective lining that covers any opening into the body. (p. 553)
membrana mucosa Revestimiento protector que cubre el interior de las aberturas del cuerpo.

multiple birth The delivery of more than one baby—for example, twins or triplets. (p. 502)
parto múltiple Parto de más de un bebé; por ejemplo, gemelos o trillizos.

muscle tone Contractions of limited muscle fibers that keep a muscle tense, but do not produce movement. (p. 273)
tono muscular Contracción parcial de las fibras musculares, que mantiene el músculo tenso, pero no produce movimiento.

MyPlate plan A plan that groups foods according to types and indicates how much of each type should be eaten daily for a healthy diet. (p. 213)
plan "Mi plato" Plan en el que se agrupan los alimentos de acuerdo a su tipo y que nos indica qué cantidad de cada grupo alimentario debemos comer diariamente para mantener una dieta saludable.

N

narcolepsy A disorder in which a person experiences severe sleepiness during the day, or falls asleep suddenly. (p. 365)
narcolepsia Trastorno en el cual una persona siente mucho sueño durante el día o se queda dormida de repente.

neglect The failure to provide for the basic needs of children. (p. 122)
abandono Falta del sustento que satisfaga las necesidades básicas de los niños.

nephron A tiny filtering unit in the kidney that removes wastes and produces urine. (p. 256)
nefrón Pequeña unidad de filtración en el riñón que elimina las sustancias tóxicas y produce orina.

neurologist A physician who treats physical disorders of the nervous system. (p. 103)
neurólogo(a) Médico especializado en la identificación y el tratamiento de los trastornos orgánicos del sistema nervioso.

neuron The basic unit of the nervous system that carries nerve impulses. (p. 278)
neurona Unidad básica del sistema nervioso, que transmite los impulsos nerviosos.

nicotine An extremely addictive chemical in tobacco products. (p. 402)
nicotina Sustancia química extremadamente adictiva que se encuentra en los productos derivados del tabaco.

nicotine substitute A product such as a gum, patch, spray, or inhaler, that contains nicotine and is designed to help a person quit tobacco use. (p. 420)
reemplazos de nicotina Productos tales como gomas de mascar, parches, aerosoles o inhaladores, que contienen nicotina y que se producen para ayudar a las personas a dejar de consumir tabaco.

nuclear family A couple and their child or children living together in one household. (p. 114)
familia nuclear Pareja y su(s) hijo(s) que viven juntos en el mismo hogar.

nutrient A substance in foods that the body needs to regulate bodily functions, promote growth, repair body tissues, and obtain energy. (p. 192)
nutriente Sustancia que se halla en los alimentos y que el cuerpo necesita para regular sus funciones, promover el crecimiento, reparar los tejidos y obtener energía.

nutrient-dense food A food that contains lots of vitamins and minerals relative to the number of calories, but is low in saturated fat, trans fat, added sugar, and salt. (p. 211)
alimento rico en nutrientes Alimento que contiene una cantidad de vitaminas y minerales muy elevada en relación con sus calorías, pero que contiene pocas grasas saturadas, grasas trans, azúcares añadidos y sal.

obesity Condition in adults who have a body mass index (BMI) of 30 or higher. (p. 228)
obesidad Trastorno que se presenta cuando un adulto tiene un índice de masa corporal (IMC) igual o mayor que 30.

obsession An unwanted thought or image that takes control of the mind. (p. 85)
obsesión Idea o pensamiento no deseado que ocupa la mente y no puede olvidarse.

obstetrician A doctor who specializes in pregnancy and childbirth. (p. 494)
obstetra Médico que se especializa en el embarazo y el parto.

occupational illness Any abnormal condition or disorder caused by exposure to the work environment. (p. 702)
enfermedad laboral Cualquier condición anormal o desorden causado por exposición al lugar de trabajo.

occupational injury Any wound or damage to the body that results from an event in the work environment. (p. 702)
lesión laboral Cualquier lesión o daño físico que resulta de un accidente en el lugar de trabajo.

oncogene A normal gene that has changed into a cancer-causing gene. (p. 610)
oncogen Gen normal que se ha transformado en un gen causante de cáncer.

opiate Any drug made from psychoactive compounds contained in the seed pods of poppy plants. (p. 441)
opiáceo Toda droga psicoactiva hecha a partir de ciertos compuestos de las cápsulas de amapola.

opportunistic infection An infection that attacks a person with a weakened immune system. (p. 586)
infección oportunista Infección que ataca a una persona que tiene debilitado el sistema inmunológico.

optimism A tendency to focus on the positive aspects of a situation. (p. 66)
optimismo Tendencia a concentrase en los aspectos positivos de una situación.

optometrist A professional trained to provide eye and vision care. (p. 358)
optometrista Profesional capacitado para proporcionar cuidados a los ojos y la visión.

orthodontist A specialist who corrects the position of jaws and teeth. (p. 343)
ortodoncista Dentista especializado en corregir la posición de las mandíbulas y los dientes.

ossification The process during infancy and childhood in which cartilage is replaced by bone. (p. 268)
osificación Proceso que tiene lugar durante la infancia y la niñez, mediante el cual el cartílago se convierte en hueso.

osteoarthritis A common form of arthritis that is caused by wear and tear on a joint or by repeated injuries to a joint. (p. 618)
osteoartritis Forma común de la artritis que es causada por el desgaste progresivo de una articulación o por lesiones frecuentes de la misma.

osteoporosis A condition in which a significant loss of bone mass causes bones to become weak and break easily. (p. 270)
osteoporosis Trastorno caracterizado por una pérdida significativa de masa ósea que hace que los huesos se debiliten y se fracturen fácilmente.

outpatient A person admitted to a clinic for tests or treatments that do not require an overnight stay. (p. 637)
paciente ambulatorio Persona ingresada a una clínica o a un hospital para ser sometida a exámenes o tratamientos que no requieren su permanencia nocturna en la instalación.

ova The reproductive cells in females. (p. 469)
óvulos Células reproductoras femeninas.

ovaries The female reproductive glands. (p. 469)
ovarios Glándulas reproductoras femeninas.

overdose The consequence of taking an excessive amount of a drug that leads to coma or death. (p. 385)
sobredosis Consecuencia de ingerir una cantidad excesiva de una droga que conduce al estado de coma o a la muerte.

over-the-counter drug A medicine that is sold legally in pharmacies and other stores without a doctor's prescription. (p. 426)
fármaco sin receta Medicamento que se vende legalmente en las farmacias u otras tiendas sin prescripción de un médico.

overtraining Exercising too intensely or for too long without allowing enough time for rest. (p. 335)
entrenamiento excesivo La realización de ejercicios demasiado intensos o durante demasiado tiempo sin descansar lo suficiente.

overweight Term used to describe a person who is heavier than the standard for the person's height. (p. 228)
sobrepeso Término que se usa para describir a una persona que tiene un peso superior al adecuado para su estatura.

ovulation The process during which one of the ovaries releases a ripened egg. (p. 469)
ovulación Proceso durante el cual un ovario libera un óvulo maduro.

ozone layer A section of the atmosphere that contains naturally occurring ozone; absorbs ultraviolet light from the sun. (p. 673)
capa de ozono Parte de la atmósfera que contiene ozono natural; esta capa absorbe los rayos ultravioleta del sol.

pacemaker A small group of cells in the wall of the right atrium that controls the rate at which the heart muscles contract. (p. 294)
marcapaso Pequeño grupo de células de la pared de la aurícula derecha, que regula el ritmo de las contracciones de los músculos del corazón.

Pap smear A medical procedure in which a sample of cells is taken from the cervix and examined under a microscope. (p. 475)
Prueba de Papanicolaou Procedimiento médico en que se toma una muestra de células del cuello uterino y se examinan bajo microscopio.

paralysis The loss of the ability to move and feel some part of the body. (p. 284)
parálisis Pérdida de la capacidad de movimiento y sensación en alguna parte del cuerpo.

passive A term that describes people who hold back their true feelings and go along with the other person. (p. 138)
pasivo(a) Término que describe a una persona que reprime los sentimientos propios y cede ante los demás.

pathogen A microorganism or virus that causes disease. (p. 548)
patógeno Microorganismo o virus que causa enfermedades.

peer group A group of people who are about the same age and share similar interests. (p. 33)
grupo de iguales Grupo de personas con edades e intereses semejantes.

peer pressure The need to conform to the expectations of friends. (p. 145)
presión de grupo Necesidad de adaptarse a las expectativas de los amigos.

pelvic inflammatory disease A serious infection of the female reproductive organs that can lead to infertility or an ectopic pregnancy. (p. 579)
enfermedad inflamatoria pélvica Infección grave de los órganos reproductores femeninos, que puede conducir a la infertilidad o al embarazo ectópico.

penis The external male sexual organ through which sperm leave the body. (p. 465)
pene Órgano sexual externo masculino a través del cual el cuerpo libera semen.

perfectionist A person who accepts nothing less than excellence. (p. 66)
perfeccionista Persona que no acepta más que la excelencia en todo.

periodontal disease Gum disease that can lead to tooth loss. (p. 346)
enfermedad periodontal Enfermedad de las encías que puede causar la caída de los dientes.

peristalsis Waves of muscle contractions that push food through the digestive system. (p. 243)
peristaltismo Conjunto de movimientos parecidos a una ola, producidos por las contracciones musculares del sistema digestivo para transportar los alimentos a lo largo del mismo.

personality A set of behaviors, attitudes, feelings, and ways of thinking that are unique to an individual. (p. 30)
personalidad Conjunto de conductas, actitudes, sentimientos y maneras de pensar que caracterizan a un individuo.

personality disorder A mental disorder characterized by rigid patterns of behavior, which make it difficult for a person to get along with others. (p. 88)
trastorno de personalidad Trastorno mental caracterizado por patrones de conducta inflexibles que limitan la capacidad de una persona para relacionarse con los demás.

pessimism A tendency to focus on the negative aspects of a situation and to expect the worst. (p. 66)
pesimismo Tendencia a concentrarse en los aspectos negativos de una situación y esperar que suceda lo peor.

phagocyte A type of white blood cell that engulfs and destroys pathogens. (p. 554)
fagocito Tipo de glóbulo blanco que rodea y destruye a los patógenos.

pharynx The upper portion of the throat; the junction between the digestive and respiratory systems. (p. 243)
faringe Sección superior de la garganta; es el punto de encuentro entre los sistemas digestivo y respiratorio.

phobia Anxiety that is related to a specific situation or object. (p. 84)
fobia Ansiedad relacionada con una situación o un objeto específico.

physical abuse Intentionally causing physical harm to another person. (p. 121)
maltrato físico Daño físico que se causa a otra persona de manera intencional.

physical activity Any movement that requires large muscle groups to work. (p. 316)
actividad física Cualquier movimiento que requiere el uso de un grupo importante de músculos.

physical examination A head-to-toe check of your body to identify any medical problems. (p. 643)
examen físico Revisión de pies a cabeza que se realiza para detectar problemas médicos.

physical fitness Having the energy and strength to participate in a variety of activities. (p. 318)
aptitud física Tener la energía y la fuerza para participar en una amplia variedad de actividades.

physical health The aspect of health that refers to how well your body functions. When you are physically healthy, you have enough energy to carry out everyday tasks. (p. 3)
salud física Capacidad del cuerpo para realizar bien sus funciones. Cuando una persona es físicamente saludable, tiene la energía suficiente para realizar las actividades diarias.

physical maturity The state of being full-grown in the physical sense. (p. 530)
madurez física Estado de desarrollo físico completo.

pituitary gland An endocrine gland in the brain that controls many of the body's functions, including growth, reproduction, and metabolism. (p. 463)
glándula pituitaria Glándula endocrina ubicada en el cerebro, que regula muchas de las funciones del cuerpo, como el crecimiento, la reproducción y el metabolismo.

placenta The structure that holds the embryo to the wall of the uterus. (p. 490)
placenta Estructura que mantiene al embrión unido a la pared del útero.

plaque A substance that builds up in artery walls and contributes to the development of atherosclerosis; a sticky film containing bacteria that adheres to teeth. (pp. 300, 344)
placa Sustancia que se acumula en las paredes de las arterias y que contribuye al desarrollo de la ateroesclerosis; capa pegajosa que contiene bacterias y se adhiere a los dientes.

plasma A liquid that makes up about 55 percent of the blood. (p. 297)
plasma Líquido que forma alrededor del 55 por ciento de la sangre.

platelet A cell fragment that plays an important role in the blood clotting process. (p. 297)
plaqueta Fragmento de célula que juega un importante papel en el proceso de la coagulación de la sangre.

pollution The presence or release of substances into the environment in quantities that are harmful to living organisms. (p. 672)
contaminación Presencia o liberación de sustancias al medio ambiente en cantidades que resultan dañinas para los seres vivos.

pore A tiny opening in the skin through which sweat is secreted. (p. 348)
poro Pequeña abertura de la piel a través de la cual se expulsa el sudor.

postpartum period A period of adjustment for parents and their newborn during the six weeks after birth. (p. 500)
período postparto Período de adaptación para los padres y el recién nacido durante las primeras seis semanas después del nacimiento.

pre-adolescence The stage of development before adolescence. (p. 508)
preadolescencia Etapa de desarrollo que precede a la adolescencia.

preeclampsia A serious condition during pregnancy characterized by high blood pressure, swelling of the wrists and ankles, and high levels of protein in the urine. (p. 496)
preclampsia Trastorno serio del embarazo que se caracteriza por hipertensión arterial, inflamación de las muñecas y los tobillos, y la presencia de niveles elevados de proteína en la orina.

prejudice Negative feelings about a group based on stereotypes. (p. 172)
prejuicio Sentimiento negativo hacia un grupo de personas, basado en estereotipos.

premature birth The delivery of a live baby before the 37th week of pregnancy. (p. 501)
parto prematuro Nacimiento de un bebé vivo antes de la semana 37 del embarazo.

premium A monthly or yearly fee paid for health insurance coverage. (p. 645)
prima Suma mensual o anual que una persona debe pagar por su seguro de salud.

prenatal care Medical care received during pregnancy. (p. 494)
cuidados prenatales Atención médica recibida durante el embarazo.

prescription drug A drug that can be obtained only with a written order from a doctor and can be purchased only at a pharmacy. (p. 427)
fármaco de prescripción Medicamento que se puede obtener únicamente en una farmacia, a partir de una prescripción escrita por un médico.

prevention Taking action to avoid disease, injury, and other negative health outcomes. (p. 12)
prevención Práctica que consiste en tomar medidas para evitar enfermedades, lesiones y otras consecuencias negativas para la salud.

primary care physician A doctor who takes care of people's routine medical needs. (p. 634)
médico de cabecera Médico que atiende las necesidades médicas más básicas o comunes.

primary emotion An emotion that is expressed by people in all cultures. (p. 44)
emoción primaria Emoción que expresan todas las personas, sin importar su origen cultural.

primary healthcare Routine healthcare provided in a doctor's office. (p. 637)
atención médica primaria Atención médica básica que se recibe en el consultorio médico.

progesterone A hormone that signals changes to a woman's reproductive system during the menstrual cycle and pregnancy. (p. 469)
progesterona Hormona que regula los cambios del sistema reproductor de la mujer durante el ciclo menstrual y el embarazo.

protective factor A factor that reduces a person's potential for harmful behavior. (p. 436)
factor protector Factor que reduce la posibilidad de que una persona adopte conductas perjudiciales.

protein A nutrient that contains nitrogen as well as carbon, hydrogen, and oxygen; needed for the growth and repair of body tissues. (p. 198)
proteína Nutriente que contiene nitrógeno así como carbono, hidrógeno y oxígeno; es necesaria para el crecimiento y la reparación de tejidos.

protozoan A large and complex single-celled organism. (p. 549)
protozoo Organismo unicelular grande y complejo.

psychiatric social worker A mental health professional who helps people with mental disorders and their families to accept and adjust to an illness. (p. 103)
trabajador(a) social de psiquiatría Profesional de la salud mental que ayuda a las personas con trastornos mentales y a sus familiares a aceptar una enfermedad y adaptarse a ella.

psychiatrist A physician who can diagnose and treat mental disorders. (p. 103)
psiquiatra Médico especializado en el diagnóstico y tratamiento de los trastornos mentales.

psychoactive drug A chemical that affects brain activity; also known as a "mood-altering" drug. (p. 428)
droga psicoactiva Sustancia química que afecta la actividad del cerebro; también llamada "droga que altera el estado de ánimo".

psychologist A person who studies how people think, feel, and behave. (p. 30)
psicólogo(a) Persona que estudia la manera en que las personas piensan, sienten y se comportan.

puberty The period of sexual development during which a person becomes sexually mature and physically able to reproduce. (p. 463)
pubertad Período de desarrollo sexual durante el cual la persona madura sexualmente y es capaz de reproducirse.

public health The study and practice of protecting and improving the health of people in a group or community. (p. 648)
salud pública El estudio y la aplicación de medidas para proteger y mejorar la salud de las personas de un grupo o una comunidad.

pulp The soft tissue that fills the center of each tooth. (p. 342)
pulpa dentaria Tejido blando que se encuentra en el interior de cada diente.

pupil The opening through which light enters the eye. (p. 356)
pupila Abertura a través de la cual entra la luz al ojo.

quackery The selling of useless medical treatments or products. (p. 22)
charlatanería Venta de productos o tratamientos médicos que carecen de valor o utilidad.

quality of life The degree of total satisfaction that a person gets from life. (p. 2)
calidad de vida Grado de satisfacción total que una persona tiene en su vida.

quarantine A period of isolation imposed on people who may have been exposed to an infectious disease. (p. 648)
cuarentena Período de aislamiento impuesto a aquellas personas que se cree han estado expuestas a una enfermedad infecciosa.

radon A naturally occurring radioactive gas that is a serious indoor air pollutant. (p. 674)
radón Gas natural radioactivo que es uno de los principales contaminantes del aire en el interior de casas y edificios.

rape A type of assault in which one person forces another to have sexual relations. (p. 700)
violación Tipo de asalto en el cual una persona fuerza a otra a tener relaciones sexuales.

recycling The process of reclaiming raw materials from discarded products and using them to create new products. (p. 678)
reciclaje Proceso mediante el cual se recuperan materias primas de los productos de desecho y se vuelven a usar para fabricar nuevos productos.

red blood cell A hemoglobin-containing cell that carries oxygen from the lungs to other parts of the body. (p. 297)
glóbulo rojo Célula que contiene hemoglobina y que lleva oxígeno de los pulmones hacia las otras partes del cuerpo.

reflex An automatic response of the nervous system to the environment. (p. 282)
reflejo Respuesta automática del sistema nervioso al ambiente.

refusal skills The skills needed to say *no* when under pressure. (p. 392)
destrezas de negación Destrezas que necesita una persona para negarse a hacer algo cuando es presionada a hacerlo.

rehabilitation The process of learning to cope with everyday living without drugs. (p. 391)
rehabilitación Proceso mediante el cual se aprende a lidiar con las presiones de la vida cotidiana sin consumir drogas.

reproductive maturity The ability to produce children, signaled by the onset of ovulation in girls, and of sperm production in boys. (p. 515)
madurez reproductiva Capacidad de procrear, indicada por el comienzo de la ovulación en las niñas y la producción de espermatozoides en los niños.

resilience The ability to recover from extreme or prolonged stress. (p. 67)
capacidad de recuperación Capacidad para reponerse del estrés extremo o prolongado.

retina A layer of light-sensing cells that lines the back of the eye. (p. 357)
retina Capa de células sensibles a la luz que recubre la parte posterior del ojo.

reverse tolerance A condition in which less and less alcohol causes intoxication. (p. 389)
tolerancia inversa Condición en la cual la intoxicación es causada cada vez por una menor cantidad de alcohol.

rheumatoid arthritis A form of arthritis in which the membrane surrounding a joint becomes inflamed; the inflammation then spreads to other areas of the joint. (p. 619)
artritis reumatoide Variedad de la artritis caracterizada por la inflamación de la membrana que rodea una articulación; la inflamación se extiende después a otras áreas de la articulación.

risk factor Any action or condition that increases the likelihood of injury, disease, or other negative outcome. (p. 10)
factor de riesgo Cualquier acción o condición que aumenta la posibilidad de sufrir una lesión, contraer una enfermedad o de que se produzcan otras consecuencias negativas para la salud.

road rage Dangerous or violent behavior by a person who becomes angry or frustrated while driving. (p. 714)
violencia vehicular Comportamiento peligroso o violento de una persona que se siente enojada o frustrada mientras conduce.

runaway A child who leaves home without permission and stays away for at least one night, or two nights for teens 15 or older. (p. 123)
niño fugitivo Niño que se va de la casa sin permiso y no regresa por al menos una noche o, en el caso de los mayores de 15 años, por dos noches como mínimo.

runoff Water that drains from land into streams and other water bodies. (p. 680)
escorrentía Agua que fluye sobre la superficie de la tierra hacia los arroyos y otras masas de agua.

S

saturated fat A fat that has all the hydrogen the carbon atoms can hold. (p. 196)
grasa saturada Grasa que tiene el máximo de hidrógeno que los átomos de carbono pueden contener.

schizophrenia A disorder characterized by severe disturbances in thinking, mood, awareness, and behavior. (p. 86)
esquizofrenia Trastorno mental caracterizado por severas alteraciones del pensamiento, el estado de ánimo, la conciencia y la conducta.

scoliosis An abnormal curvature of the spine. (p. 271)
escoliosis Curvatura anormal de la columna vertebral.

scrotum A sac of skin that contains the testes. (p. 464)
escroto Bolsa de piel que contiene los testículos.

sebaceous gland A gland that secretes oil into a hair follicle in the skin; the oil softens and moistens hair and skin. (p. 348)
glándula sebácea Glándula que secreta grasa en el interior de un folículo piloso; la grasa suaviza y humecta el pelo y la piel.

secondary healthcare Healthcare given to a patient in a hospital. (p. 638)
atención médica secundaria Atención médica dada a un paciente en un hospital.

secondary sex characteristics Physical changes during puberty that are not directly involved in reproduction. (p. 515)
caracteres sexuales secundarios Cambios físicos que ocurren durante la pubertad y que no están directamente relacionados con la reproducción.

secondhand smoke A combination of mainstream smoke and sidestream smoke; also known as environmental tobacco smoke. (p. 414)
humo de segunda mano Combinación de humo directo e indirecto; también conocido como humo de tabaco ambiental.

seizure An episode of erratic nerve impulses in the brain that may lead to loss of consciousness, muscle spasms, and other uncontrollable symptoms. (p. 286)
convulsión Serie de impulsos nerviosos irregulares dentro del cerebro que causan pérdida de la consciencia, espasmos musculares y otros síntomas incontrolables.

self-actualization The process by which people achieve their full potential. (p. 40)
autorrealización Proceso mediante el cual una persona alcanza su pleno potencial como individuo.

self-esteem Your opinion of yourself; how much you respect and like yourself. (p. 36)
autoestima Opinión que tiene una persona de sí misma; la medida en que una persona se respeta y se aprecia a sí misma.

semen The mixture of sperm and fluids produced by the glands of the male reproductive system. (p. 466)
semen Mezcla de espermatozoides y fluidos producidos por las glándulas del sistema reproductor masculino.

semicircular canals Structures in the inner ear that help control balance. (p. 361)
conductos semicirculares Estructuras del oído interno que ayudan a controlar el equilibrio.

separation An arrangement in which spouses live apart and try to work out their problems. (p. 120)
separación Arreglo en el que los cónyuges viven aparte mientras tratan de solucionar sus problemas maritales.

sewage Waste material carried from toilets and drains. (p. 679)
aguas negras Desechos que se transportan desde los servicios sanitarios y los desagües.

sexual abuse A criminal offense in which an adult uses a child or adolescent for sexual purposes.
abuso sexual Acto criminal por parte de un adulto que utiliza a un(a) niño(a) o a un(a) adolescente para actividades sexuales. (p. 122)

sexual harassment Any uninvited and unwelcome sexual remark or sexual advance. (p. 171)
acoso sexual Todo comentario o acción de carácter sexual que es mal recibido por una persona.

sexually transmitted infection (STI) An infection caused by any pathogen that spreads from one person to another during sexual contact. (p. 574)
infección de transmisión sexual (ITS) Infección causada por cualquier patógeno que se transmite de una persona a otra por contacto sexual.

sibling A brother or sister. (p. 127)
hermano / hermana Personas que tienen los mismos progenitores.

side effect An unwanted physical or mental effect caused by a drug. (p. 429)
efecto secundario Efecto físico o mental indeseado, causado por drogas o medicamentos.

sidestream smoke Smoke that goes directly into the air from a burning tobacco product. (p. 414)
humo indirecto Humo que se libera directamente al aire por la combustión de productos derivados del tabaco.

single-parent family A family in which only one parent lives with the child or children. (p. 114)
familia monoparental Familia en la que sólo uno de los padres vive con uno o varios hijos.

skeletal muscle Voluntary muscle that is attached to and moves your bones. (p. 272)
músculo esquelético Músculo voluntario que conecta los huesos y los mueve.

sleep apnea A disorder in which a person stops breathing for short periods during sleep. (p. 365)
apnea del sueño Trastorno a causa del cual la persona afectada deja de respirar por breves períodos mientras duerme.

smog A brown haze that forms when air pollutants react in the presence of sunlight. (p. 673)
smog Neblina de color café que se forma cuando los contaminantes del aire reaccionan en presencia de la luz solar.

smokeless tobacco Tobacco products that are chewed, placed between the lower lip and teeth, or sniffed. (p. 403)
tabaco sin humo Cualquier producto derivado del tabaco que es masticado, aspirado por la nariz o colocado entre el labio inferior y los dientes.

smooth muscle Involuntary muscle that causes movements inside your body, such as those involved in breathing and digestion. (p. 272)
músculo liso Músculo involuntario que controla los movimientos internos del cuerpo, como los de la respiración y la digestión.

snuff A smokeless tobacco product that consists of dry or moist powder. It may be placed between the lower lip and teeth or sniffed. (p. 403)
rapé Polvo seco o húmedo, derivado del tabaco, que se consume colocándolo entre el labio inferior y los dientes o aspirándolo por la nariz.

social health The aspect of health that refers to how well you get along with others. (p. 3)
salud social Aspecto de la salud que se refiere a la habilidad de llevarse bien con los demás.

socialization The process by which children are taught to behave in a way that is acceptable to family and society. (p. 116)
socialización Proceso mediante el cual los niños aprenden a comportarse de forma aceptable dentro de su familia y su sociedad.

social network The people with whom you interact and look to for friendship, information, and social support. (p. 664)
red social Conjunto de personas con las que un individuo interactúa y entre las que busca amigos, información y apoyo social.

sperm The reproductive cells in males. (p. 464)
espermatozoides Células reproductoras masculinas.

spinal cord A thick column of nerve tissue in the central nervous system that links the brain to most of the nerves in the peripheral nervous system. (p. 282)
médula espinal Columna gruesa de tejido nervioso, que pertenece al sistema nervioso central y que conecta el cerebro con la mayoría de los nervios del sistema nervioso periférico.

sprain An overstretched or torn ligament. (p. 271)
esguince Lesión producida cuando un ligamento es estirado excesivamente o se desgarra.

stalker Someone who repeatedly makes unwanted contact with a person and may threaten to kill or injure the person. (p. 700)
acosador Persona que constantemente se pone en contacto con otra, sin que ésta lo desee, y que puede llegar a amenazarla con atacarla o matarla.

stereotype An exaggerated belief or overgeneralization about an entire group of people. (p. 172)
estereotipo Creencia excesivamente simplificada o generalizada sobre un grupo de personas.

stillbirth The expulsion of a fetus that has died after the twentieth week of pregnancy. (p. 501)
parto de un mortinato Expulsión de un feto muerto después de la vigésima semana del embarazo.

stimulant A type of drug that increases the activity of the nervous system. (pp. 406, 442)
estimulante Toda droga que acelera la actividad del sistema nervioso.

strain A pulled muscle. (p. 275)
distensión Lesión causada cuando se estira demasiado un músculo.

stress The response of your body and mind to being challenged or threatened. (p. 56)
estrés Respuesta del cuerpo y de la mente al enfrentarse a un desafío o una amenaza.

stressor An event of situation that causes stress. (p. 57)
evento estresante Suceso o situación que causa estrés.

stroke A sudden disruption of blood flow to part of the brain. (p. 605)
apoplejía Interrupción repentina del flujo de sangre a una parte del cerebro.

suicide The intentional killing of oneself. (p. 96)
suicidio Acción que realiza un individuo intencionalmente para matarse a sí mismo.

support group A network of people who help each other cope with a particular problem. (p. 130)
grupo de apoyo Red de personas que se ayudan entre sí para enfrentar un problema específico.

survival floating A technique that allows a person to float in the water and breathe without using much energy. (p. 705)
supervivencia por flotación Técnica que permite a una persona flotar en el agua y respirar sin usar mucha energía.

syphilis A serious bacterial sexually transmitted infection that progresses through three distinct stages. (p. 582)
sífilis Enfermedad bacterial grave de transmisión sexual que se desarrolla en tres etapas distintas.

tar A dark, sticky substance that forms when tobacco burns. (p. 408)
alquitrán Sustancia oscura y pegajosa que se forma al quemarse el tabaco.

target heart rate The heart rate at which your cardiovascular system receives the most benefits from exercise without working too hard. (p. 326)
frecuencia cardíaca ideal Frecuencia a la cual el sistema cardiovascular obtiene la mayor cantidad de beneficios del ejercicio sin tener que realizar un esfuerzo excesivo.

tartar A hardened form of plaque that irritates the gums. (p. 346)
sarro Tipo de placa dental muy dura que irrita las encías.

T cell A type of lymphocyte that helps the immune system destroy pathogens. (p. 555)
célula T Tipo de linfocito que ayuda al sistema inmunológico a destruir a los patógenos.

tendon A think strand of tissue that attaches a muscle to a bone. (p. 272)
tendón Tejido grueso y fibroso que une músculos y huesos.

tendonitis Painful swelling and irritation of a tendon, often caused by overuse. (p. 275)
tendinitis Inflamación e irritación dolorosa de un tendón, habitualmente causada por su uso excesivo.

terminal illness An illness for which there is no chance of recovery. (p. 538)
enfermedad terminal Enfermedad en la cual no hay posibilidad de recuperación.

territorial gang A group that is organized to control a specific neighborhood or "turf." (p. 167)
pandilla territorial Grupo organizado de personas que ejerce control sobre un vecindario o "territorio".

tertiary healthcare Healthcare provided in specialty hospitals and teaching hospitals. (p. 638)
atención médica especializada Atención médica dada a un paciente en un hospital docente o especializado.

testes The male reproductive glands. (p. 464)
testículos Glándulas reproductoras masculinas.

testosterone The sex hormone that affects the production of sperm and signals certain physical changes at puberty. (p. 464)
testosterona Hormona sexual que determina la producción de espermatozoides y regula ciertos cambios físicos durante la pubertad.

therapeutic community A residential treatment center where former drug abusers live together and learn to adjust to drug-free lives. (p. 450)
comunidad terapéutica Centro de tratamiento residencial donde las personas que abusaban de las drogas viven juntas y aprenden a adaptarse a una vida libre de drogas.

therapy A treatment method. (p. 104)
terapia Método de tratamiento.

tinnitus A condition in which ringing is heard in the ears, even when there is no external sound. (p. 624)
tinnitus Trastorno que hace que la persona escuche un zumbido en los oídos, aun cuando no se produce ningún sonido externo.

tolerance The condition that results when repeated use of a drug causes it to have less of an effect on the brain. (p. 388)
tolerancia Condición en la que el uso repetido de una droga hace que ésta tenga cada vez menos efecto sobre el cerebro.

toxin A poison given off by some bacteria that can injure cells. (p. 548)
toxina Sustancia venenosa, producida por algunas bacterias, que puede dañar las células.

trans fat The type of fat produced when manufacturers add hydrogen to the fat molecules in vegetable oils. (p. 197)
grasa trans Tipo de grasa producida por los fabricantes al añadir hidrógeno a las moléculas de grasa de los aceites vegetales.

trichomoniasis A sexually transmitted infection caused by a protozoan that infects the urinary tract or vagina. (p. 578)
tricomoniasis Infección de transmisión sexual causada por un protozoo que infecta las vías urinarias o la vagina.

trimester One of three periods of time that divide a pregnancy. Each trimester is approximately three months long. (p. 494)
trimestre Cada uno de los tres períodos en el que se divide el embarazo. Cada trimestre dura aproximadamente tres meses.

tumor An abnormal mass of tissue. (p. 609)
tumor Masa anormal de tejido.

ultrasound High-frequency sound waves used to create an image of a developing fetus. (p. 495)
ultrasonido Ondas sonoras de alta frecuencia utilizadas para crear una imagen del feto en desarrollo.

umbilical cord The cordlike structure that connects the embryo and the placenta. (p. 491)
cordón umbilical Estructura en forma de cuerda que conecta al embrión con la placenta.

underweight Term used to describe a person who is lighter than the standard for the person's height. (p. 229)
de bajo peso Término que se usa para describir a una persona que tiene un peso inferior al adecuado para su estatura.

unintentional injury An unplanned injury. (p. 694)
lesión accidental Lesión que se produce sin que se planifique o desee.

United Nations Children's Fund (UNICEF) A United Nations agency that aids children in developing nations. (p. 657)
Fondo de las Naciones Unidas para la Infancia (UNICEF) Agencia de las Naciones Unidas dedicada a brindar ayuda a los niños de los países en vías de desarrollo.

universal precautions Actions taken by healthcare providers that reduce their risk of coming into contact with blood and body fluids. (p. 593)
precauciones universales Medidas que toman los profesionales de la salud para reducir el riesgo de entrar en contacto con la sangre y otros fluidos corporales.

unsaturated fat A fat with at least one unsaturated bond in a place where hydrogen can be added to the molecule. (p. 196)
grasa no saturada Grasa que tiene al menos un enlace no saturado en un lugar donde se podría añadir hidrógeno a la molécula.

urban sprawl City or town development in which homes are built in spread-out suburbs that are not near business districts. (p. 667)
expansión urbana Desarrollo urbano de una ciudad o pueblo en el que las viviendas se construyen en suburbios lejanos a las zonas comerciales.

urea A substance formed in the liver from a waste product of protein breakdown. (p. 254)
urea Sustancia de desecho que se forma en el hígado al ser descompuestas las proteínas.

urethritis Inflammation of the lining of the urethra. (p. 578)
uretritis Inflamación del revestimiento interno de la uretra.

urine A watery fluid containing urea and wastes that is excreted from the body. (p. 255)
orina Líquido que contiene urea y otros desechos y que se excreta del cuerpo.

uterus The hollow, muscular, pear-shaped organ in which a fertilized egg develops and grows. (p. 470)
útero Órgano muscular hueco, en forma de pera, en el cual se desarrolla y crece el óvulo fecundado.

vaccine A substance containing small amounts of dead or modified pathogens or their toxins that is injected during an immunization. (p. 556)
vacuna Sustancia que contiene pequeñas cantidades de patógenos muertos o modificados, o sus toxinas, y que se inyecta durante la inmunización.

vagina The hollow, muscular passage leading from the uterus to the outside of the female body. (p. 470)
vagina Canal muscular que comunica el útero con el exterior del cuerpo femenino.

vaginitis A vaginal infection or irritation. (p. 578)
vaginitis Infección o irritación de la vagina.

values The standards and beliefs that are most important to you. (p. 14)
valores Normas y creencias que son muy importantes para una persona.

vandalism Intentionally damaging or destroying another person's property. (p. 173)
vandalismo Daño o destrucción intencional de la(s) propiedad(es) de otra persona.

vegan A person who does not eat food from any animal source. (p. 234)
vegetariano(a) estricto(a) Persona que no come alimentos de procedencia animal.

vegetarian A person who does not eat meat. (p. 234)
vegetariano(a) Persona que no come carne.

vein A large, thin-walled blood vessel that carries blood to the heart. (p. 295)
vena Vaso sanguíneo grande, de paredes delgadas, que lleva la sangre hacia el corazón.

ventricle A lower chamber of the heart that pumps blood out of the heart. (p. 293)
ventrículo Cada una de las dos cámaras inferiores del corazón que bombea sangre desde el corazón al resto del cuerpo.

victim The person who is attacked during a violent act. (p. 163)
víctima Toda persona que es atacada en un acto violento.

villi Tiny fingerlike projections lining the small intestine, through which nutrients are absorbed into the blood. (p. 245)
vellosidades Pequeñas formaciones con aspecto de dedo que cubren la pared interna del intestino delgado; los nutrientes son absorbidos y pasan a la sangre a través de ellas.

violence The threat of or actual use of physical force against oneself or another person. (p. 162)
violencia La amenaza de usar o el uso de la fuerza física contra uno mismo o contra otra persona.

viral load The number of virus particles circulating in the body. (p. 595)
carga viral Cantidad de partículas de un virus que circulan en el cuerpo.

virus The smallest type of pathogen. (p. 549)
virus El tipo más pequeño de patógeno.

vital statistics The numbers of births and deaths and the numbers and kinds of diseases that occur within a population. (p. 652)
estadísticas vitales Número de nacimientos, muertes, y cantidades y tipos de enfermedades que ocurren en determinada población.

vitamin A nutrient that is made by living things, is required in small amounts, and assists in chemical reactions in the body. (p. 203)
vitamina Nutriente producido por los seres vivos, es necesario en pequeñas cantidades, e interviene en las reacciones químicas del cuerpo.

warranty An offer to repair or replace a product if there is a problem with the product. (p. 19)
garantía Acción de asegurar la reparación o el reemplazo de un producto si éste tuviese algún problema.

wellness A state of high-level health. (p. 4)
bienestar Estado en el que se goza de excelente salud.

white blood cell A cell that helps protect the body from diseases and foreign substances. (p. 297)
glóbulo blanco Célula que ayuda a proteger al cuerpo de las enfermedades y los cuerpos ajenos.

withdrawal A group of symptoms that occur when a dependent person stops taking a drug. (p. 391)
síndrome de abstinencia Conjunto de síntomas que se manifiestan cuando una persona adicta a una droga deja de consumirla.

World Health Organization (WHO) A United Nations health organization that provides aid to developing nations and collects worldwide health statistics. (p. 657)
Organización Mundial de la Salud (OMS) Agencia de las Naciones Unidas que brinda ayuda a los países en vías de desarrollo y recopila datos estadísticos sobre la salud a nivel mundial.

zero-tolerance policy A policy that enforces strict consequences for underage drinking. (p. 375)
política de intolerancia total Norma que consiste en imponer castigos estrictos al consumo de alcohol por parte de menores de edad.

zygote The united egg and sperm. (p. 489)
cigoto Óvulo y espermatozoide ya unidos.

Index

Page numbers for key terms are printed in **boldface** type.
Page numbers for illustrations, maps, and charts are printed in *italics*.

Acknowledgments

Acknowledgment for pages 16–17: "DECIDE" adapted from the Stanford DECIDE Drug Education Curriculum.

Acknowledgment for page 397: "My Papa's Waltz," Copyright © 1942 by Hearst Magazines, Inc., from *The Collected Poems of Theodore Roethke* by Theodore Roethke. Used by permission of Doubleday, a division of Random House.

Note: *Every effort has been made to locate the copyright owner of material reprinted in this book. Omissions brought to our attention will be corrected in subsequent editions.*

Staff Credits

The people who made up the **Pearson Health** team—representing design services, editorial, editorial services, education technology, market research, marketing services, planning and budgeting, product planning, production services, publishing processes, and rights and permissions—are listed below. Boldface type denotes the core team members.

Jennifer Angel, Alan Asarch, **Amy C. Austin,** Charlene Barr, **Neil Benjamin,** Peggy Bliss, Stephanie Bradley, **Jim Brady, Diane Braff,** Lisa Brown, Tom Evans, Christian Henry, **Sarah G. Jensen,** Judie Jozokos, Alicia Lankowski, James Lonergan, **Zareh MacPherson Artinian, Dotti Marshall, Lauren McDonough, Maria Milczarek, Natania Mlawer,** Julia F. Osborne, Jennifer Parker, Alice Pihuleac, **Nick Raducanu, Paul M. Ramos, Logan Schmidt,** Malti Sharma, **Aileen Shuman,** Melissa Shustyk, **Nancy Smith,** Cindy Strowman, **Elizabeth Tustian,** Amanda M. Watters, **Berkley Wilson**

Additional Credits AARTPACK, Inc., Dan Breslin, Laura J. Chadwick, Liz Good, Russ Lappa, Ellen Levinger, Brent McKenzie, Laurel Smith, Emily Soltanoff, Linda B. Thornhill.

Illustration

Young Sook Cho: 476; **John Edwards, Inc.:** 61, 243, 267, 268, 269, 273, 279, 280, 293, 294-295, 297, 330, 343, 346, 348, 350, 358, 381, 407, 428, 465, 466, 470, 489, 490, 499, 519, 556, 603, 705; **Phil Guzy:** 307t, 308, 357, 360, 462, 503, 617; **Keith Kasnot:** 255, 256; **Fran Milner:** 245, 307b; **Morgan Cain and Associates:** 282t, 297tr, 555; **Ortelius Design, Inc.:** 566, 588; **Sandra Sevigny:** 283, 294l; **Tyson Smith:** 560-561. **All additional art created by AARTPACK, Inc.**

Photographs

Every effort has been made to secure permission and provide appropriate credit for photographic material. The publisher deeply regrets any omission and pledges to correct errors called to its attention in subsequent editions. Unless otherwise acknowledged, all photographs are the property of Pearson Education, Inc.

Photo locators denoted as follows: Top (T), Center (C), Bottom (B), Left (L), Right (R), Background (Bkgd)

Photo Research AARTPACK, Inc.

Front Cover–Bkgd Ben Welsh/Corbis; **TL** Yellowj/Shutterstock; **BL** Fuse/Thinkstock

Back Cover–T Tim Pannell/Corbis, **BL** siamionau pavel/Shutterstock

vT SW Productions/Photodisc/Getty Images; **viB** Ariel Skelley/cusp/Corbis; **viiB** David Bishop Inc./FoodPix/Getty Images; **viiiB** Markus Moellenberg/Cusp/Corbis; **ixBL** Michael Goldman/Masterfile; **ixBR** MedioImages/Photodisc/Getty Images; **ixT** Pete Saloutos/Cusp/Corbis; **xB** Jeff Greenberg/PhotoEdit; **xiB** IndexStock Imagery/ThinkStock; **xiiB** JonathanNourok/PhotoEdit; **xiv** J&L Images/Photodisc/Getty Images; **xviT** RubberBall Productions/Imagestate; **xviB** Imagestate-Pictor/PictureQuest; **xviiT** Creatix/Fotolia **xviii** Stockbyte/Thinkstock; **3B** Tetra Images/Corbis; **3L** Roy Morsch/Flirt/Corbis; **3T** FANCY/Image Source; **6** Brian Mueller/Shutterstock; **7B** Ryan McVay/Lifesize/Getty Images; **7C** Jeff Greenberg/The Image Works; **7T** Kaz Chiba/Digital Vision/Getty Images; **8L** Andersen Ross/Photodisc/Getty Images; **8R** Reza Estakhrian/Photographer's Choice/Getty Images; **9L** Keith Brofsky/Photodisc/Getty Images; **9R** Illene MacDonald/PhotoEdit; **10** Stephen Simpson/Taxi/Getty Images; **12** Brand X Pictures/PictureQuest; **13** Robert Rathe/Photographer's Choice/Getty Images; **14** CULTURA RF/Image Source; **15** Peter Hvizdak/The Image Works; **16B** ImageState Royalty Free/Alamy; **16TL** Davis Barber/PhotoEdit; **16TR** Comstock Images/Getty Images; **18** Felicia Martinez Photography/PhotoEdit; **19** Bonnie Kamin/PhotoEdit; **20** Michael N. Paras/Corbis; **22** Calvert Litho Co./Corbis; **23C** Stockbyte/Getty Images; **23T** Aaron Haupt/Science Source/Photo Researchers; **24** Comstock Images/Getty Images; **25** Stephen Simpson/Taxi/Getty Images; **28Bkgd** George Shelley/Masterfile; **30** Brand X Pictures/AGE Fotostock; **31L** BananaStock/PictureQuest; **31R** Fotosearch; **32B** Hinata Haga/HAGA/The Image Works; **32T** Thomas Wanstall/The Image Works; **33** Paul Chesley/Stone/Getty Images; **34CR**

Masterfile; **34L** RubberBall Productions/Index Stock Imagery; **34R** Roy Morsch/Corbis; **34TL** Renata Osinska/Fotolia; **35B** Fancy/Image Source; **35L** RubberBall Productions/ImageState; **35TC** Bonninturina/Fotolia; **35TR** Image Source; **37** Timotheos/Shutterstock; **38** Roy Morsch/Flirt/Corbis; **39** Kathy McLaughlin/The Image Works; **40C** Stephen Simpson/The Image Bank/Getty Images; **40L** Masterfile; **40R** Monkey Business/Fotolia; **41C** Ernst Haas/Getty Images; **41L** Larry Kolvoord/The Image Works; **42** PhotoDisc/Getty Images; **44** Matthias Kulka/Corbis; **45BL** Blend Images/Getty Images; **45BR** RubberBall Productions/Index Stock Imagery; **45C** AGE Fotostock/SuperStock; **45T** Cultra RF/Image Source; **46L** Ariel Skelley/Cusp/Corbis; **46R** Rolf Bruderer/Masterfile; **47** Michael S. Yamashita/Terra/Corbis; **48** Exactostock/SuperStock; **49** Rubberball Productions; **50** Comstock RF Images/PictureQuest; **51B** Roy Morsch/Corbis; **51T** Thomas Wanstall/The Image Works; **54** Kaz Mori/The Image Bank/Getty Images; **56** BananaStock/Robertstock; **57** Paul Bradbury/Alamy; **58** Andersen Ross/Photodisc/Getty Images; **59** Jeff Greenberg/PhotoEdit; **61** Rubberball Productions/SuperStock; **62** Viennaphoto/AllOver photography/Alamy; **63** DieKleinert/SuperStock; **64** Tomas del Amo/Stock Connection Blue/Alamy; **65** Rubberball Productions; **66** Comstock RF Images/Getty Images; **67** SW Productions/Photodisc/Getty Images; **68** ImageSource/PictureQuest; **70** Michael Newman/PhotoEdit; **71** Tim Pannell/Corbis; **72** Corbis Super RF/Image Source; **73** Image Source; **74B** Zits Partnership. Reprinted with permission of King Features Syndicate.; **75** Corbis; **76** Blend Images/Alamy; **77B** Blend Images/Alamy; **77T** Paul Bradbury/Alamy; **80** BSIP SA/Alamy; **82** Brandon Sullivan/Masterfile; **83L** Heide Benser/Solus/Corbis; **83R** Nicholas Prior/Stone/Getty Images; **84** Bethlem Art and History Collections Trust; **84L** Josh Westrich/Bridge/Corbis; **84R** Corbis; **85** Shawn Baldwin/AP Images; **86** Bethlem Art and History Collections Trust; **87** Tony French/Alamy; **88** Mark Leibowitz/Masterfile; **89B** Kate Connell/The Image Bank/Getty Images; **89C** Mark Romesser/Alamy; **89T** Christopher A. Record/AP Images; **90B** Tony Freeman/PhotoEdit; **90T** Duncan Smith/Photodisc/Getty Images; **91** Tony Freeman/PhotoEdit; **92** William Sallaz/Duomo/Bridge/Corbis; **93** Donna Day/Stone/Getty Images; **95** SW Productions/Photodisc/Getty Images; **96** Tom Grill/Corbis; **97** Jack Hollingsworth/Corbis; **98** Richard Hutchings/Encyclopedia/Corbis; **99** Dwayne Newton/PhotoEdit; **100** Jim Parkin/Shutterstock; **101** Comstock RF Images/PictureQuest; **102** Comstock RF Images/AGE Fotostock; **103** Lisa F. Young/Fotolia; **104** Zigy Kaluzny/Stone/Getty Images; **105** Dwayne Newton/PhotoEdit; **108B** Simon Punter/Taxi/Getty Images; **108C** Bill Aron/PhotoEdit; **108T** Barros & Barros/The Image Bank/Getty Images; **109B** Courtesy of Kirsten Peterson; **109T** Courtesy of Kirsten Peterson; **110** Chris Robbins/Photodisc/Getty Images; **112** Dasha Petrenko/Shutterstock; **113** Betsie Van der Meer/The Image Bank/Getty Images; **114L** Monkey Business Images/Shutterstock; **114R** George Doyle/Stockbyte/Getty Images; **115L** Eastcott-Momatiuk/The Image Works; **115R** Fancy Collection/SuperStock; **116** Ted Foxx/Alamy; **117** ONOKY/Image Source; **118B** Jeffrey Sylvester/Taxi/Getty Images; **118BL** Maksym Yemelyanov/Alamy; **118CR** Anderson Ross/Photodisc/Getty Images; **118T** Andy Manis/AP Images; **119** Comstock RF Images/PictureQuest; **120** Myrleen Pearson/Alamy; **121** Rachel Epstein/PhotoEdit; **122** Chitose Suzuki/AP Images; **123** Richard Heinzen/SuperStock; **124** Tony Freeman/PhotoEdit; **126** Eastcott/Momatiuk/The Image Works; **127** PhotoDisc/Getty Images; **128** Paul Barton/Cusp/Corbis; **130** Michael Newman/PhotoEdit; **131B** Myrleen Pearson/Alamy; **131T** Monkey Business Images/Shutterstock; **134** Michael Pole/Bridge/Corbis; **136** Big Cheese Photo LLC/Alamy; **137** Ariel Skelley/Cusp/Corbis; **138** Cindy Charles/PhotoEdit; **139** Jeff Greenberg/PhotoEdit; **140** Michael Newman/PhotoEdit; **141** Michael N. Paras/AGE Fotostock; **141** Michael N. Paras/AGE Fotostock; **142** James McLoughlin/AGE Fotostock; **143** Pictorial Press Ltd/Alamy; **144T** Zits Partnership. Reprinted with permission of King Features Syndicate.; **145** Roxana Gonzalez/Shutterstock; **146** Mngostock/Fotolia; **148** Jeff Greenberg/AGE Fotostock; **149** Chuck Savage/Corbis; **150** Brad Wilson/The Image Bank/Getty Images; **153** Jacky Chapman/Janine Wiedel Photolibrary/Alamy; **154** Loretta Ray/Photonica/Getty Images; **155** Claudiu Paizan/Fotolia; **156** SW Productions/PhotoDisc/Getty Images; **157B** Chuck Savage/Flirt/Corbis; **160** Gurinder Osan/AP Images; **162** Comstock RF Images/Alamy; **164** SuperStock; **165** Photononstop/SuperStock; **166** Mario Villafuerte/Stringer/Getty Images; **167** Gilles Mingasson/Liaison/Getty Images; **169** PhotoAlto/Robertstock; **170L** C Squared Studios/Photodisc/Getty Images; **170T** Jim Mahoney/Dallas Morning News/Corbis; **171** Ania Powalowska/Agencja Free/AGE Fotostock; **172** Ariel Skelley/Corbis; **173** Tony Freeman/PhotoEdit; **174** Flying Colours Ltd/Digital Vision/Getty Images; **175** Thinkstock/IndexStock Imagery; **176** Yavuz Arslan/Christoph & Friends/Das Fotoarchiv/Alamy; **177** Bill Aron/PhotoEdit; **178B** Rubberball Productions; **178TL** Rubberball Productions; **178TR** PhotoDisc/Getty Images; **181** Corbis; **182L** Luke Jarvis/Corbis; **182R** BananaStock/Robertstock; **183** SW Productions/Photodisc/Getty Images; **184** Richard Lord/The Image Works; **185** Thinkstock/Comstock Images/Getty Images; **185T** Gilles Mingasson/Liaison/Getty Images; **188** Richard G. Bingham II/Alamy; **189L** Blend Images/Getty Images; **189R** Julia Smith/Taxi/Getty Images; **190Bkgd** G. Biss/Masterfile; **192** SW Productions/Photodisc/Getty Images; **193B** Tom Grill/Corbis; **193C** FoodPix/Jupiter Images; **193TL** Tom Grill/Corbis; **193TR** Comstock Images/Getty Images; **194BL** Photodisc/Getty Images; **194C** John E Kelly/FoodPix/Getty Images; **194R** Judd Pilossof/Getty Images; **195L** Comstock Images/Getty Images; **195R** Pixland/AGE Fotostock; **196BR** Margo555/Fotolia; **196C** Evan Sklar/FoodPix/Getty Images; **196L** Comstock Images/Getty Images; **197** Jiri Hera/Fotolia; **198** Andersen Ross/Photodisc/Getty Images; **199** David Bishop Inc./FoodPix/Getty Images; **202B**

Comstock Images/Getty Images; **202T** Brian Hagiwara/FoodPix/Getty Images; **203B** Burke/Triolo Productions/FoodPix/Getty Images; **203T** Comstock Images/Getty Images; **204B** Africa Studio/Fotolia; **204TL** Comstock Images/Getty Images; **204TR** Clive Streeter/DK Images; **205** Steve Warmowski/Journal-Courier/The Image Works; **206** RubberBall/SuperStock; **207B** Comstock Images/Getty Images; **207C** Jiri Hera/Fotolia; **207TC** Comstock Images/Getty Images; **207TL** Brand X Pictures/Jupiter Images; **207TR** Comstock Images/Getty Images; **208** Matthew Borkoski Photography/Photolibrary/Getty Images; **209** Michael Newman/PhotoEdit; **210** Bob Pardue Signs/Alamy; **211** Pixtal/AGE Fotostock; **212T** U.S. Department of Agriculture; **212BL** Hyrma/Fotolia; **212BR** Cristina Cassinelli/FoodPix/Getty Images; **212CBL** Comstock Images/Getty Images; **212CBR** Elena Schweitzer/Shutterstock; **212CTL** Lew Robertson/FoodPix/Getty Images; **212CTR** Comstock Images/Getty Images; **214** Stockbyte/PictureQuest; **215B** Pixtal/AGE Fotostock; **215T** FoodPix/Jupiter Images; **218** RubberBall/Superstock; **220** Michael Newman/PhotoEdit; **221** Comstock RF Images/PictureQuest; **222BR** Comstock Images/Getty Images; **222C** Jonathan Nourok/PhotoEdit; **222T** Frank Ordo–ez/Syracuse Newspapers/The Image Works; **223** Image100 Food A/Corbis Premium RF/Alamy; **223B** Brand X Pictures/PictureQuest; **224B** John A. Rizzo/Photodisc/Getty Images; **224T** Michael Neelon(misc)/Alamy; **226** Seth Goldfarb/Photonica/Getty Images; **228B** Rubberball Productions; **228L** Michael Pohuski/FoodPix/Getty Images; **228TR** BrandX Pictures/Getty Images; **229** Karan Kapoor/Stone/Getty Images; **230** Peter Dazeley/Photographer's Choice/Getty Images; **231** Mark Harmel/Alamy; **232C** Foodcollection/Getty Images; **232L** Evan Hoffbuhr/Fotolia; **232R** Sergejs Rahunoks/Fotolia; **233** BananaStock/Fotosearch; **234** Foodpix/Jupiter Images; **235B** Comstock Images/Getty Images; **235L** Comstock Images/Getty Images; **235R** Comstock Images/Getty Images; **236** Jeff Greenberg/PhotoEdit; **237B** BananaStock/Fotosearch; **237C** Mark Harmel/Alamy; **237T** Frank Ordo–ez/Syracuse Newspapers/The Image Works; **240** Blend Images/Image Source; **242** Sergey Peterman/Fotolia; **245BR** Prof. P.M. Motta/Dept. of Anatomy/University "La Sapienza", Rome/Science Source/Photo Researchers; **246** CNRI/Science Source/Photo Researchers; **247BL** AJPhoto/Science Source/Photo Researchers; **247BR** David M. Martin, Md/Science Source/Photo Researchers; **247RC** David M. Martin,MD/Science Source/Photo Researchers; **247RT** David M. Martin, Md/Science Source/Photo Researchers; **247T** Andy Crump/Science Source/Photo Researchers; **248** Corbis; **249B** CNRI/Science Source/Photo Researchers; **249C** Comstock Images/Getty Images; **249T** Comstock Images/Getty Images; **250BL** Steve Wisbauer/Getty Images; **250L** Jim Arbogast/Digital Vision/Getty Images; **250TR** Michael Newman/PhotoEdit; **251B** J.L. Carson/Custom Medical Stock Photo; **251T** Jules Frazier/Photodisc/Getty Images; **252** India Images/Dinodia Images/Alamy; **254** Gary Houlder/Bridge/Corbis; **257** Photolibrary/IndexStock Imagery; **258** AJPhoto/Science Source/Photo Researchers; **259** Image Source/Getty Images; **259C** PhotoDisc/Getty Images; **259T** CNRI/Science Source/Photo Researchers; **262B** Tom Carter/PhotoEdit; **262T** Dan Hallman/Photodisc/Getty Images; **263CL** Shioguchi/Taxi/Getty Images; **263R** Inti St. Clair/Photodisc/Getty Images; **264** Aflo Sport/Glow Images; **266** Darrin Henry/Fotolia; **269** RubberBall Productions/Alamy; **270C** BSIP/SuperStock; **270L** David Madison/Getty Images; **270R** BSIP/SuperStock; **271** Ted Horowitz/Cusp/Corbis; **272** Pablo Rivera/SuperStock; **274L** Ron Buskirk/Alamy; **274R** Corbis; **275** Richard Hutchings/PhotoEdit; **281** Stockbyte/SuperStock; **282L** Thomas Del Brase/Stone/Getty Images; **284** Aflo Foto Agency/Alamy; **285L** Steve Krongard/Stone/Getty Images; **285R** Hill Street Studios/Blend Images/Alamy; **286B** Charing Cross Hospital/Science Source; **287B** Steve Krongard/Stone/Getty Images; **287C** Richard Hutchings/PhotoEdit; **287T** BSIP/SuperStock; **290** Richard I'Anson/Lonely Planet Images/Getty Images; **296** Pictor International/ImageState/Alamy; **297B** National Cancer Institute/Science Source/Photo Researchers; **297C** A. Syred/Science Source/Photo Researchers; **297CR** Bill Longcore/Science Source/Photo Researchers; **298** Davies and Starr/Stone/Getty Images; **299** William Whitehurst/Corbis; **300BC** Stewart Cohen/DreamPictures/FoodPix/Getty Images; **300BL** Lew Robertson/Foodpix/Getty Images; **300BR** Repository/Fotolia; **300TL** FoodCollection/SuperStock; **300TR** Mates/Fotolia; **301** Volff/Fotolia; **302** David Stoecklein/Cusp/Corbis; **303** Amber Aiken Photography/Flickr Open/Getty Images; **304** Saxpix/AGE Fotostock; **307L** Daghlian/Phanie/SuperStock; SciMAT/Science Source/Photo Researchers; **309R** Stockbyte/PictureQuest; **310** Andres Rodriguez/Fotolia; **311B** Stewart Cohen/DreamPictures/FoodPix/Getty Images; **314** Nirmalendu Majumdar/AP Images; **316** Rubberball Productions; **317** Howard Grey/Photodisc/Getty Images; **318** Bob Daemmrich/The Image Works; **319B** Alin Dragulin/Alamy; **319BC** Tom Stewart/keepsake RM/Corbis; **319BL** Reed Kaestner/Corbis; **319BR** Michael Newman/PhotoEdit; **319CBL** Scott Markewitz/Taxi/Getty Images; **319CTL** Image Source; **319CTR** Markus Moellenberg/Corbis; **319T** Yoichi Nagata/Getty Images; **320L** Pete Saloutos/Cusp/Corbis; **320R** Alexander Hubrich/Stone/Getty Images; **321C** Tom & Dee Ann McCarthy/Bridge/Corbis; **321L** Inspirestock Inc./Alamy; **321R** Guy Cali/Corbis; **325BL** John Henley/Cusp/Corbis; **325BR** Adam smith/Taxi/Getty Images; **325CR** Andersen Ross/Blend Images/Getty Images; **326** Jeff Greenberg/Alamy; **327B** Bonnie Kamin/PhotoEdit; **330** MichaelSvoboda/E+/Getty Images; **331** PhotoDisc/Getty Images; **332** Peter Cade/Iconica/Getty Images; **333** Belinda Images/SuperStock; **334** Courtesy of The National Institute on Drug Abuse (NIDA); **336B** Jeff Greenberg/PhotoEdit; **336T** Siu Biomed Comm/Custom Medical Stock; **337B** Belinda Images/SuperStock; **337C** John Henley/Cusp/Corbis; **337T** Pete Saloutos/Cusp/Corbis; **340** Ralph A.Clevenger/Bridge/Corbis Images; **342** Sakuoka/Shutterstock; **344BL** Andersen Ross/Stockbyte/Getty images; **344R** Luis Santos/Fotolia; **346** Comstock RF Images/AGE Fotostock; **347** Felicia Martinez Photography/PhotoEdit; **349B** NMSB/Custom Medical Stock; **349T** Jutta Klee/Corbis; **350** Image Source/SuperStock; **351B** Chris Garrett/Stone/Getty Images; **351T** Eye of Science/Science Source/Photo Researchers; **352** Jessie Jean/Taxi/Getty Images; **353** Andreas Kuehn/Stone/Getty Images; **354** Norma Zuniga/Stone+/Getty Images; **356** IndexStock Imagery/ThinkStock; **358** Comstock Images/Fotosearch; **359** Rachel Epstein/The Image Works; **361** EpicStockMedia/Fotolia; **362B** Reed Kaestner/Bridge/Corbis; **362CB** Siede Preis/Photodisc/Getty Images; **362CL** GK Hart/Vicky Hart/The Image Bank/Getty Images; **362CR** DWP/Fotolia; **362TL** Regine Mahaux/The Image Bank/Getty Images; **362TR** Alan Schein/Cusp/CORBIS; **363** Eliseo Fernandez/Reuters/Corbis; **364** MedioImages/Photodisc/Getty Images; **365** Michael Goldman/Masterfile; **366** Zurijeta/Shutterstock; **367** Jessie Jean/Taxi/Getty Images; **370B** Guy Cali/Corbis; **370C** Dynamic Graphics/PIctureQuest; **370T** CULTURA RF/Image Source; **371B** Courtesy of Teodoro Tovar, Jr.; **371T** Courtesy of Teodoro Tovar, Jr; **372** Mike Siluk/The Image Works; **374** Bananastock/Imagestate; **375C** C Squared Studios/Photodisc/Getty Images; **375L** Comstock RF Images/PictureQuest; **375R** David Toase/Stockbyte/Getty Images; **376** Ryan McVay/Photodisc/Getty Images; **377** Ted Foxx/Alamy; **378** Ted Foxx/Alamy; **382** Photos/Index Stock Imagery; **383** Thinkstock/Alamy; **384** Masterfile; **385** Nick Dolding/Stone/Getty Images; **386** Reuters/Corbis; **387B** Martin M. Rotker/Science Source/Photo Researchers; **387C** Southern Illinois University/Science Source/Photo Researchers; **387T** David H. Wells/Corbis; **388L** Dr. Susan Tapert, University of California San Diego and National Institute on Alcohol Abuse and Alcoholism; **388R** Dr. Susan Tapert, University of California San Diego and National Institute on Alcohol Abuse and Alcoholism; **390** Tom & Dee Ann McCarthy/Cusp/Corbis; **391** GARO/PHANIE/AGE Fotostock; **392** WavebreakMediaMicro/Fotolia; **393** SW Productions/Photodisc/Getty Images; **394** Steve Dunwell/Photo Library/Getty Images; **395** Ted Foxx/Alamy; **398** Robert Mora/Staff/Getty Images; **401BL** AGE Fotostock/SuperStock; **401BR** BananaStock/SuperStock; **401TR** Universal/Everett Collection; **402** Photodisc/Fotosearch; **404** Robert Landau/Corbis; **406** PhotoAlto/SuperStock; **408BL** P.Stocklein/Custom Medical Stock Photo; **408BR** 1988 Paul Silverman/Fundamental Photographs, NYC; **408CL** Brand X Pictures/Fotosearch; **408CR** G.DeGrazia/Custom Medical Stock Photo; **408TL** Clayton Sharrard/PhotoEdit; **408TR** Comstock Images/Fotosearch; **409** Courtesy National Institutes of Health; **409** Science Source/Photo Researchers; **410** Luca DiCecco/Alamy; **411** Mel Allen/Imagestate; **413C** Siu Biomed Comm/Custom Medical Stock Photo; **413T** Matt Meadows/Peter Arnold/Getty Images; **414** Sonda Dawes/The Image Works; **415** Scholastic Studio 10 /Photolibrary/Getty Images; **416** Stockbyte Platinum/Alamy; **416B** James Leynse/Corbis News/Corbis; **417** Fotosearch/Corbis; **418B** Rubberball Productions/SuperStock; **418T** Photodisc/Getty Images; **419B** Brian Hagiwara/FoodPix/Getty Images; **419T** RubberBall Productions/IndexStock Imagery; **420B** Martyn Vickery/Alamy; **420T** Doug Martin/Science Source/Photo Researchers; **421B** Photodisc/Fotosearch; **421T** Universal/Everett Collection; **424** Peter Byron/PhotoEdit; **426** Photick/SuperStock; **427** Stephen Mcsweeny/Shutterstock; **429** Mast3r/Fotolia; **430** Brand X Pictures/Getty Images; **431** Brand X Pictures/Imagestate; **432** Steve Warmowski/Journal-Courier/The Image Works; **433B** Science Source/Photo Researchers; **433Bkgd** David De Lossy/Photodisc/Getty Images; **433CB** L. Reneman, J. Habraken, C. Majoie, J. Booij, G. den Heeten, MDMA ("Ecstasy") and Its Association with Cerebrovascular Accidents: Preliminary Findings, American Journal of Nueroradiology, Figure 2, Volume 21, pages 1001-1007, 2000 © by American Journal of Nueroradiology; **433CT** NATIONAL CANCER INSTITUTE/Science Source/Photo Researchers; **433T** Imagestate-Pictor/PictureQuest; **435** Luke Jarvis/Cusp/Corbis; **436** David Grossman/The Image Works; **437** Fotosearch; **438** Thinkstock/Comstock Images/Getty Images; **441** Marga Werner/AGE Fotostock; **442B** Shahn Kermani/Liaison/Getty Images; **442T** Cordelia Molloy/Science Source/Photo Researchers; **443** GeoStock/Photodisc/Getty Images; **444B** Custom Medical Stock Photo; **444C** Bonnie Kamin/PhotoEdit; **444T** Custom Medical Stock Photo; **445** Bartomeu Borrell/AGE Fotostock; **446** Andrew Brookes/Bridge/Corbis; **447** Tony Freeman/PhotoEdit; **448** Michele Cozzolino/Shutterstock; **449** Jeff Greenberg/PhotoEdit; **450L** Michael Newman/PhotoEdit; **450R** Jeff Greenberg/The Image Works; **452** Image Source; **453** Fotosearch; **456B** Banana Stock/Alamy; **456T** Jim Varney/Photo Researchers; **457C** Norma Zuniga/Stone+/Getty Images; **457R** Norma Zuniga/Riser/Getty Images; **458** Stewart Cohen/Taxi/Getty Images; **461C** Stockbyte Silver/Alamy; **461L** Jeremy Maude/Masterfile; **461R** AGE Fotostock/SuperStock; **464** Sartore/Joel/National Geographic/Getty Images; **466B** David M. Phillips/Science Source/Photo Researchers; **467** Suzanne Dunn/Syracuse Newspapers/The Image Works; **468** Aaron Haupt/Science Source/Photo Researchers; **469** Photodisc/Getty Images; **471** RubberBall Productions/Imagestate; **473** Thinkstock/Comstock/JupiterImages; **474** Subbotina Anna/Fotolia; **475B** Robynmac/Fotolia; **475T** Pete Saloutos/Bridge/Corbis; **477** BURGER/PHANIE/AGE Fotostock; **478BL** Tatjana Romanova/Shutterstock; **478BR** Vladimir Voronin/Fotolia; **478TR** Muntz/Getty Images; **479** Thinkstock/Comstock/JupiterImages; **480B** Stockbyte/fotosearch; **480T** Sebastian Kaulitzki/Fotolia; **481** Masterfile; **482** Ted Horowitz/Flirt/Corbis; **483** Stockbyte Silver/Alamy; **486** Martinan/Fotolia; **488** Michael Newman/PhotoEdit; **491B** Petit Format/Science Source/Photo Researchers; **491T** Claude Edelmann/Science Source/Photo Researchers; **492CB** Siede Preis/Photodisc/Getty Images; **493** Brand X Pictures/PictureQuest; **494L** Thinkstock/Getty Images; **494R** BananaStock/PictureQuest; **495R** Gary Bistram/Getty Images; **497CL** ATC Productions/Bridge/CORBIS; **497R** Jeremy Portje/Telegraph Herald/AP Images; **499** Robin Samper/Pearson education; **501** BSIP/Universal Images Group/Getty Images; **502** David J. Green-lifestyle themes/Alamy; **503L** David Schmidt/Masterfile; **503R** Tony Freeman/PhotoEdit; **504** Brand X Pictures/PictureQuest; **506B** Creasource/PictureQuest; **506T** Bananastock/Imagestate; **507C**

Acknowledgments

Fabrizio Cacciatore/Indexstock/PictureQuest; **507L** Brand X Pictures/Robertstock; **507R** Steve Gravano/AGE Fotostock; **508** Wavebreak Media/Thinkstock; **509B** Creasource/PictureQuest; **509T** Claude Edelmann/Science Source/Photo Researchers; **512** Spencer Grant/Science Source/Photo Researchers; **514** Egidia Degrassi/Fotolia; **515R** Comstock RF Images/PictureQuest; **516L** Tim Jones/Digital Vision/Getty Images; **516R** Bill Bachmann/Alamy; **517** Bananastock/Imagestate; **519BL** Rubberball Productions/AGE Fotostock; **519BR** Leland Bobbe/Flirt/Corbis; **519TL** Ariel Skelley/Corbis; **519TR** Gary Conner/Photolibrary/Getty Images; **520** Michael Keller/Flirt/Corbis; **521** Ron Chapple Stock/Alamy; **522** SW Productions/Photodisc/Getty Images; **524** Don Smetzer/PhotoEdit; **525B** Zits Partnership. Reprinted with permission of King Features Syndicate; **526L** Philippe Lissac/Godong/Photononstop/Getty Images; **526R** Jeff Greenberg/PhotoEdit; **527** Ray Guy/Alamy; **528** Eric Raptosh/Hill Street Studios/Blend Images/Getty Images; **530** Brad Wrobleski/Masterfile; **531** Karen Grigoryan/Shutterstock; **532** Reed Kaestner/Corbis; **533** Nick Dolding/Stone/Getty Images; **534** IndexStock Imagery/ThinkStock; **536** Monkey Business/Fotolia; **537** EPF/Alamy; **538** Spencer Grant/PhotoEdit; **539BR** David Samuel Robbins/Encyclopedia/Corbis; **539L** Joe Raedle/Staff/Getty Images; **539T** Andrew Lichtenstein/Corbis News Premium/Corbis; **540** Dynamic Graphics Group/IT Stock Free/Alamy; **541B** Karen Grigoryan/Shutterstock; **541T** Egidia Degrassi/Fotolia; **544B** Hero/Corbis; **544C** Carl Costas/ZUMAPRESS/Newscom; **544T** Romily Lockyer/The Image Bank/Getty Images; **545B** John Robertson/Alamy; **545T** Rebecca Emery/Digital Vision/Getty Images; **546** Center for Disease Control and Prevention; **548** Brand X Pictures/Getty Images; **549CL** Cavallini/Custom Medical Stock Photo; **549CR** Eye of Science/Science Source/Photo Researchers; **549L** Dr. Gary Gaugler/Science Source/Photo Researchers; **549R** Eye of Science/Science Source/Photo Researchers; **550B** Doug Menuez/PhotoDisc/Getty Images; **550C** Siede Preis/Photodisc/Getty Images; **550T** Bartomeu Amengual/AGE Fotostock; **551** Michael Alberstat/Masterfile; **552** Fotosearch; **553L** Eye of Science/Science Source/Photo Researchers; **553R** Wavebreakmedia/Shutterstock; **554** SPL/Science Source/Photo Researchers; **556R** It Stock Free/PictureQuest; **557C** Myrleen Pearson/PhotoEdit; **557L** Purestock/SuperStock; **557R** Randy Faris/Cusp/Corbis; **559L** Larry Mulvehill/Science Source/Photo Researchers; **559R** K. Kjeldsen/Science Source/Photo Researchers; **560** Aaron Haupt/Science Source/Photo Researchers; **562** B. BOISSONNET/BSIP SA/Alamy; **563** Corbis; **564** Exactostock/SuperStock; **567B** CDC/PHIL/CORBIS; **567T** Robert Dowling/Terra/Corbis; **568** Pallava Bagla/Corbis News/Corbis; **569B** CDC/PHIL/CORBIS; **569T** Dr. Gary Gaugler/Science Source/Photo Researchers; **572** Cindy Charles/PhotoEdit; **574** BananaStock/SuperStock; **575** Bob Daemmrich/The Image Works; **576B** Brand X Pictures/Fotosearch; **576T** Will Hart/PhotoEdit; **577** Roy Morsch/Corbis; **578** Marmaduke St. John/Alamy; **579C** NIH/Custom Medical Stock; **579L** Eye of Science/Science Source/Photo Researchers; **579R** Alfred Pasieka/Science Source/Photo Researchers; **580B** Slate River Productions/Alamy; **580L** Meredun Animal Health Ltd/Science Source/Photo Researchers; **581B** Eye of Science/Science Source/Photo Researchers; **581T** David M. Phillips/Science Source/Photo Researchers; **582R** Library of Congress; **582TL** Martin M. Rotker/Science Source/Photo Researchers; **582TR** Dr. Kari Lounatmaa/Science Source/Photo Researchers; **583** ColorBlind Images/Blend Images/Corbis; **584** Hemera Technologies/Alamy; **585T** NIBSC/Science Source/Photo Researchers; **587** Lawrence Manning/Corbis; **588** GlowImages/Alamy; **589** Sean Sprague/The Image Works; **590B** Center for Disease Control and Prevention; **590T** Bartomeu Amengual/Photo Library/Getty Images; **592** E Dygas/Taxi/Getty Images; **593** Guy Cali/Corbis; **594L** Klaus Guldbrandsen/Science Source/Photo Researchers; **594R** Rachel Frank/Fancy/Alamy; **595** Michael Newman/PhotoEdit; **596** Michael Dwyer/AP Images; **597B** Hemera Technologies/Alamy; **597T** Marmaduke St. John/Alamy; **600** Jim West/Alamy; **602** Ocean/Corbis; **603L** Custom Medical Stock Photo; **603R** Custom Medical Stock Photo; **604** Bruce Ayres/Stone/Getty Images; **605** Du Cane Medical Imaging Ltd./Science Source/Photo Researchers; **606BL** Mehau Kulyk/Science Source/Photo Researchers; **606BR** UHB Trust/Stone/Getty Images; **606TC** Bruce Ayres/Stone/Getty Images; **606TL** GJLP/Science Source/Photo Researchers; **606TR** SPL/Science Source/Photo Researchers; **607** Rob Van Petten/Digital Vision/Getty Images; **608** Tom Carter/PhotoEdit; **610** Via Productions/AGE Fotostock; **611** Miles Ertman/Masterfile; **611B** Paul/F1online digitale Bildagentur GmbH/Alamy; **611T** Dr. P. Marazzi/Science Source/Photo Researchers; **614** Jason Hetherington/Getty Images; **615** AGE Fotostock/SuperStock; **616BL** GK Hart/Vikki Hart/Photodisc/Getty Images; **616BR** Blickwinkel/Alamy; **616TL** A. Syred/Science Source/Photo Researchers; **616TR** A. Syred/Science Source/Photo Researchers; **617L** James Cavallini/Science Source/Photo Researchers; **617R** Bill Aron/PhotoEdit; **618** Corbis; **618T** Living Art Enterprises/LLC/Science Source/Photo Researchers; **619** Philippe Sellem/Paul Demri/Olivier Voisin/Science Source/Photo Researchers; **620** Kayte Deioma/PhotoEdit; **622BL** Jiang Jin/SuperStock; **622C** Troels Graugaard/E+/Getty Images; **622CB** Masterfile; **622T** Royal Philips ElectronicsAP Images; **623** Richard Hutchings/PhotoEdit; **624L** Jonathan Nourok/PhotoEdit; **624R** Myrleen Pearson/PhotoEdit; **625** Stephen Simpson/Taxi/Getty Images; **626** Steve Dunwell/Photolibrary/Getty Images; **627B** Productions/AGE Fotostock; **627T** Custom Medical Stock Photo; **630** Tipp Howell/Getty Images; **631C** Stephen Derr/The Image Bank/Getty Images; **631R** Yellow Dog Productions/The Image Bank/Getty Images; **632** Scott Warren/Aurora Photos; **634** Exactostock/SuperStock; **635BL** Bob Daemmrich/The Image Works; **635BR** John Henley/Cusp/Corbis; **635CL** Keith Brofsky/Photodisc/Getty Images; **635CR** Rick Gomez/Corbis; **635TC** AJPhoto/Science Source/Photo Researchers; **635TL** Peter Beck/keepsake RM/Corbis; **635TR** K.Glaser & Associates/Custom Medical Stock Photo; **636BL** Jan Kassay/Photo Library/Getty Images; **636BR** Tim Sharp/AP Images; **636T** Lifesize/Getty Images; **637** Ingram Image/PictureQuest; **638** Edward McCain/Getty Images; **639** Ronnie Kaufman/Bridge/Corbis; **640** Ed Kashi/Corbis; **641** Ragnar Schmuck/zefa/Corbis; **643** Michael A. Keller/AGE Fotostock; **644** William Whitehurst/Corbis; **645** BLEND IMAGES/Image Source; **646** Gary Kazanjian/AP Images; **647B** Big Cheese Photo/SuperStock; **647T** ThinkStock/AGE Fotostock; **648** L.Steinmark/Custom Medical Stock Photo; **649B** Bettmann/Corbis; **649T** Bill Bridges/Time & Life Pictures/Getty Images; **650** A. Ramey/PhotoEdit; **651** Richard T. Nowitz/Terra/Corbis; **652** Syracuse Newspapers/The Image Works; **653** Corbis; **654** Holly Harris/Taxi/Getty Images; **655** Yellow Dog Productions/The Image Bank/Getty Images; **657L** Paula Bronstein/Staff/Getty Images; **657R** Yves Herman/Reuters/Corbis; **658** Super Stock/AGE Fotostock; **659B** Syracuse Newspapers/The Image Works; **659T** Big Cheese Photo/SuperStock; **662** Phil Schermeister/Encyclopedia/Corbis; **664T** Jeff Greenberg/PhotoEdit; **665B** Ryan McVay/Photodisc/Getty Images; **665Bkgd** Brand X Pictures/Jupiter Images; **665C** Donna Day/Imagestate; **665T** Jeff Greenberg/The Image Works; **666B** Myrleen Pearson/PhotoEdit; **666TL** Johnny Crawford/The Image Works; **666TR** Bonnie Kamin/PhotoEdit; **667** Imageshop-zefa visual media uk ltd/Alamy; **668** Tibor Bognár/AGE Fotostock; **669** Jeff Greenberg/PhotoEdit; **670** Jim Craigmyle/Corbis; **671B** Brand X Pictures/AGE Fotostock; **671T** C Squared Studios/Photodisc/Getty Images; **672** StockDisc/PictureQuest; **673** Reed Saxon/AP Images; **674** Brand X Pictures/Alamy; **675** Tomas Abad/Alamy; **676** Photodisc/Getty Images; **677** Somos Images/Alamy; **678L** Masterfile; **678R** Dana White/PhotoEdit; **679B** Jeff Greenberg/PhotoEdit; **680** Philip Wallick/Flirt/Corbis; **681T** BrandX Pictures/Getty Images; **682** Tony Freeman/PhotoEdit; **683** Peter Essick/Aurora Photos; **685Bkgd** Spencer Grant/PhotoEdit; **685L** Jeff Greenberg/PhotoEdit; **685R** Jeff Greenberg/PhotoEdit; **686** Michael Newman/PhotoEdit; **687B** Ariel Skelley/Comet/Corbis; **687T** Tony Freeman/PhotoEdit; **688** Bob Daemmrich/The Image Works; **689B** Ariel Skelley/Comet/Corbis; **689T** Myrleen Pearson/PhotoEdit; **692** Chase Jarvis/Solus/Corbis; **694** Steve Skjold/Alamy; **695** Jiang Jin/SuperStock; **696** Dana White/PhotoEdit; **697** Eric Fowke/PhotoEdit; **698L** NOAA/Handout/ZUMA/Corbis; **698R** Mike Theiss/orbis News/Ultimate Chase/Corbis; **699L** Rob Carr/AP Images; **699R** James Nielsen/Stringer/AFP/Getty Images; **700** Marc Romanelli/Photographer's Choice/Getty Images; **702** Photodisc/Getty Images; **703** Little Blue Wolf Productions/Corbis; **704** Yellow Dog Productions/The Image Bank/Getty Images; **706** Ben Blankenburg/Corbis; **707** Dominic Ebenbichler/Reuters/Corbis; **708B** Glyn Jones/Corbis; **708BR** Rubberball Productions/Imagestate; **708C** Nils-Johan Norenlind/AGE Fotostock; **708TL** Mike Powell/Digital Vision/Getty Images; **708TR** Brian Sytnyk/Masterfile; **710** J&L Images/Photodisc/Getty Images; **711** Comstock Images/Fotosearch; **713** Robert Llewellyn/Corbis; **714** Exactostock/SuperStock; **715** AGE Fotostock/SuperStock; **716B** DK Images; **716T** Nicholas Eveleigh/Alamy; **717B** Robert Llewellyn/Flirt/Corbis; **717C** Nils-Johan Norenlind/AGE Fotostock; **717T** NOAA/Handout/ZUMA/Corbis; **720B** Tyler Olson/Shutterstock; **720C** Zhu Difeng/Fotolia; **720T** Dynamic Graphics/LiquidLibrary/PictureQuest; **721B** Mischa Keijser/Cultura Creative/Alamy; **721T** Will & Deni McIntyre/Science Source/Photo Researchers; **722B** DK Images; **722T** Tom Stewart/Bridge/Corbis; **723** DK Images; **723B** DK Images; **724BC** DK Images; **724BL** DK Images; **724BR** Michael Newman/PhotoEdit; **724T** DK Images; **725B** DK Images; **725T** DK Images; **726C** DK Images; **726T** Michael Newman/PhotoEdit; **727B** DK Images; **727C** DK Images; **727TL** DK Images; **727TR** DK Images; **728B** The American National Red Cross; **728C** Biophoto Associates/Science Source/Photo Researchers; **728T** Bob Daemmrich/The Image Works; **729** Tim Ridley/DK Images; **730B** DK Images; **730T** DK Images; **731BL** The American National Red Cross; **731BR** The American National Red Cross; **731T** DK Images; **732BL** DK Images; **732BR** Brian Kuhlmann/Masterfile; **732C** It Stock Free Royalty Free Photograph/Fotosearch; **732T** J.Patton/Robertstock; **733BL** John Millar/Stone/Getty Images; **733BR** DK Images; **734B** DK Images; **734T** DK Images; **735B** David H. Collier/Workbook Stock/Getty Images; **735T** DK Images; **737** Michelle Del Guercio/Custom Medical Stock Photo/Newscom